Complete Solutions
Manual for Stewart's
SINGLE VARIABLE
SECOND EDITION
CALCULUS
CONCEPTS AND CONTEXTS

Jeffery A. Cole
Anoka-Ramsey Community College

BROOKS/COLE

THOMSON LEARNING

Australia • Canada • Mexico • Singapore • Spain • United Kingdom • United States

BROOKS/COLE

THOMSON LEARNING TM

Cover Design: *Vernon T. Boes*
Cover Photograph: *Erika Ede*

For more information about this or any other Brooks/Cole product, contact:
BROOKS/COLE
511 Forest Lodge Road
Pacific Grove, CA 93950 USA
www.brookscole.com
1-800-423-0563 (Thomson Learning Academic Resource Center)

Printed in Canada

5   4   3   2

ISBN 0-534-37926-5

Preface

This *Complete Solutions Manual* contains solutions to all exercises in the texts *Calculus: Concepts and Contexts, Single Variable, Second Edition,* and Chapters 1–8 of *Calculus: Concepts and Contexts, Second Edition,* by James Stewart. A student version of this manual is also available; it contains solutions to the odd-numbered exercises in each section, the review sections, the True-False Quizzes, and the Problem Solving sections, as well as solutions to all the exercises in the Concept Checks. No solutions to the Projects appear in the student version. It is my hope that by browsing through the solutions, professors will save time in determining appropriate assignments for their particular class.

Some nonstandard use of notation is used in order to save space. If you see a symbol which you don't recognize, refer to the Table of Abbreviations and Symbols on page v.

I appreciate feedback concerning errors, solution correctness or style, and manual style. Any comments may be sent directly to me at the address below, at jcole@an.cc.mn.us, or in care of the publisher: Brooks/Cole Thomson Learning, 511 Forest Lodge Road, Pacific Grove, CA 93950.

I would like to thank Jim Stewart, for his guidance; Dan Clegg, of Palomar College, for his careful assistance with most of the new solutions; Brian Betsill, Stephanie Kuhns, and Kathi Townes, of TECH-arts, for their production services; and Gary Ostedt and Carol Ann Benedict, of Brooks/Cole, for entrusting me with this project as well as for their patience and support.

I dedicate this book to my wife, Joan.

Jeffery A. Cole
Anoka-Ramsey Community College
11200 Mississippi Blvd. NW
Coon Rapids, MN 55433

Abbreviations and Symbols

CD	concave downward
CU	concave upward
D	the domain of f
FDT	First Derivative Test
HA	horizontal asymptote(s)
I	interval of convergence
IP	inflection point(s)
R	radius of convergence
VA	vertical asymptote(s)
$\overset{CAS}{=}$	indicates the use of a computer algebra system.
$\overset{H}{=}$	indicates the use of l'Hospital's Rule.
$\overset{j}{=}$	indicates the use of Formula j in the Table of Integrals in the back endpapers.
$\overset{s}{=}$	indicates the use of the substitution $\{u = \sin x, du = \cos x\, dx\}$.
$\overset{c}{=}$	indicates the use of the substitution $\{u = \cos x, du = -\sin x\, dx\}$.

Contents

1 Functions and Models   1

1.1 Four Ways to Represent a Function   1

1.2 Mathematical Models   9

1.3 New Functions from Old Functions   15

1.4 Graphing Calculators and Computers   26

1.5 Exponential Functions   33

1.6 Inverse Functions and Logarithms   37

1.7 Parametric Curves   44

     Laboratory Project ◻ Running Circles around Circles   53

     Review   56

Principles of Problem Solving   65

2 Limits and Derivatives   71

2.1 The Tangent and Velocity Problems   71

2.2 The Limit of a Function   74

2.3 Calculating Limits Using the Limit Laws   79

2.4 Continuity   86

2.5 Limits Involving Infinity   92

2.6 Tangents, Velocities, and Other Rates of Change   101

2.7 Derivatives   107

2.8 The Derivative as a Function   113

2.9 Linear Approximations   124

2.10 What Does f' Say about f?   128

     Review   133

Focus on Problem Solving   145

3   Differentiation Rules   151

3.1   Derivatives of Polynomials and Exponential Functions   151
    Applied Project □ Building a Better Roller Coaster   159
3.2   The Product and Quotient Rules   162
3.3   Rates of Change in the Natural and Social Sciences   169
3.4   Derivatives of Trigonometric Functions   176
3.5   The Chain Rule   181
    Laboratory Project □ Bézier Curves   191
    Applied Project □ Where Should a Pilot Start Descent?   193
3.6   Implicit Differentiation   194
3.7   Derivatives of Logarithmic Functions   203
    Discovery Project □ Hyperbolic Functions   206
3.8   Linear Approximations and Differentials   209
    Laboratory Project □ Taylor Polynomials   213
    Review   216

Focus on Problem Solving   225

4   Applications of Differentiation   235

4.1   Related Rates   235
4.2   Maximum and Minimum Values   242
    Applied Project □ The Calculus of Rainbows   250
4.3   Derivatives and the Shapes of Curves   251
4.4   Graphing with Calculus *and* Calculators   264
4.5   Indeterminate Forms and l'Hospital's Rule   279
4.6   Optimization Problems   289
    Applied Project □ The Shape of a Can   303
4.7   Applications to Economics   304
4.8   Newton's Method   308
4.9   Antiderivatives   315
    Review   321

Focus on Problem Solving   339

5   Integrals   349

5.1   Areas and Distances   349
5.2   The Definite Integral   357
5.3   Evaluating Definite Integrals   365
    Discovery Project □ Area Functions   371

5.4   The Fundamental Theorem of Calculus   373

5.5   The Substitution Rule   378

5.6   Integration by Parts   384

5.7   Additional Techniques of Integration   391

5.8   Integration Using Tables and Computer Algebra Systems   398

        Discovery Project □ Patterns in Integrals   406

5.9   Approximate Integration   409

5.10   Improper Integrals   419

        Review   430

Focus on Problem Solving   443

6 Applications of Integration   451

6.1   More about Areas   451

6.2   Volumes   461

        Discovery Project □ Rotating on a Slant   475

6.3   Arc Length   476

        Discovery Project □ Arc Length Contest   483

6.4   Average Value of a Function   483

        Applied Project □ Where to Sit at the Movies   486

6.5   Applications to Physics and Engineering   487

6.6   Applications to Economics and Biology   494

6.7   Probability   496

        Review   500

Focus on Problem Solving   507

7 Differential Equations   519

7.1   Modeling with Differential Equations   519

7.2   Direction Fields and Euler's Method   522

7.3   Separable Equations   528

        Applied Project □ Which Is Faster, Going Up
                        or Coming Down?   538

7.4   Exponential Growth and Decay   539

        Applied Project □ Calculus and Baseball   543

7.5   The Logistic Equation   545

7.6   Predator-Prey Systems   552

        Review   556

Focus on Problem Solving   563

8 Infinite Sequences and Series   569

8.1	Sequences 569	
	Laboratory Project □ Logistic Sequences 576	
8.2	Series 580	
8.3	The Integral and Comparison Tests; Estimating Sums 591	
8.4	Other Convergence Tests 596	
8.5	Power Series 601	
8.6	Representations of Functions as Power Series 606	
8.7	Taylor and Maclaurin Series 614	
8.8	The Binomial Series 625	
8.9	Applications of Taylor Polynomials 630	
	Applied Project □ Radiation from the Stars 639	
8.10	Using Series to Solve Differential Equations 641	
	Review 645	

Focus on Problem Solving   657

Appendixes   665

A	Intervals, Inequalities, and Absolute Values 665	
B	Coordinate Geometry 668	
C	Trigonometry 674	
D	Precise Definitions of Limits 679	
F	Sigma Notation 684	
G	Integration of Rational Functions by Partial Fractions 688	
H	Polar Coordinates 695	
	H.1 Curves in Polar Coordinates 695	
	H.2 Areas and Lengths in Polar Coordinates 708	
	Discovery Project □ Conic Sections in Polar Coordinates 716	
I	Complex Numbers 718	

1 ▸ Functions and Models

◂1.1▸ Four Ways to Represent a Function · · · · · · · · · ·

1. (a) The point $(-1, -2)$ is on the graph of f, so $f(-1) = -2$.

   (b) When $x = 2$, y is about 2.8, so $f(2) \approx 2.8$.

   (c) $f(x) = 2$ is equivalent to $y = 2$. When $y = 2$, we have $x = -3$ and $x = 1$.

   (d) Reasonable estimates for x when $y = 0$ are $x = -2.5$ and $x = 0.3$.

   (e) The domain of f consists of all x-values on the graph of f. For this function, the domain is $-3 \le x \le 3$, or $[-3, 3]$. The range of f consists of all y-values on the graph of f. For this function, the range is $-2 \le y \le 3$, or $[-2, 3]$.

   (f) As x increases from -1 to 3, y increases from -2 to 3. Thus, f is increasing on the interval $[-1, 3]$.

2. (a) The point $(-4, -2)$ is on the graph of f, so $f(-4) = -2$. The point $(3, 4)$ is on the graph of g, so $g(3) = 4$.

   (b) We are looking for the values of x for which the y-values are equal. The y-values for f and g are equal at the points $(-2, 1)$ and $(2, 2)$, so the desired values of x are -2 and 2.

   (c) $f(x) = -1$ is equivalent to $y = -1$. When $y = -1$, we have $x = -3$ and $x = 4$.

   (d) As x increases from 0 to 4, y decreases from 3 to -1. Thus, f is decreasing on the interval $[0, 4]$.

   (e) The domain of f consists of all x-values on the graph of f. For this function, the domain is $-4 \le x \le 4$, or $[-4, 4]$. The range of f consists of all y-values on the graph of f. For this function, the range is $-2 \le y \le 3$, or $[-2, 3]$.

   (f) The domain is $[-4, 3]$ and the range is $[0.5, 4]$.

3. From Figure 1 in the text, the lowest point occurs at about $(t, a) = (12, -85)$. The highest point occurs at about $(17, 115)$. Thus, the range of the vertical ground acceleration is $-85 \le a \le 115$. In Figure 11, the range of the north-south acceleration is approximately $-325 \le a \le 485$. In Figure 12, the range of the east-west acceleration is approximately $-210 \le a \le 200$.

4. *Example 1:* A car is driven at 60 mi/h for 2 hours. The distance d traveled by the car is a function of the time t. The domain of the function is $\{t \mid 0 \le t \le 2\}$, where t is measured in hours. The range of the function is $\{d \mid 0 \le d \le 120\}$, where d is measured in miles.

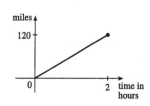

Example 2: At a certain university, the number of students N on campus at any time on a particular day is a function of the time t after midnight. The domain of the function is $\{t \mid 0 \le t \le 24\}$, where t is measured in hours. The range of the function is $\{N \mid 0 \le N \le k\}$, where N is an integer and k is the largest number of students on campus at once.

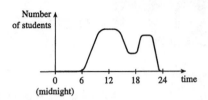

Example 3: A certain employee is paid $8.00 per hour and works a maximum of 30 hours per week. The number of hours worked is rounded down to the nearest quarter of an hour. This employee's gross weekly pay P is a function of the number of hours worked h. The domain of the function is $\{0, 0.25, 0.5, \ldots, 29.75, 30\}$ and the range of the function is $\{0, 2.00, 4.00, \ldots, 238.00, 240.00\}$.

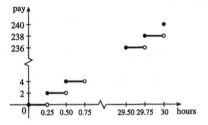

5. Yes, the curve is the graph of a function because it passes the Vertical Line Test. The domain is $[-3, 2]$ and the range is $[-2, 2]$.

6. No, the curve is not the graph of a function because a vertical line intersects the curve more than once and hence, the curve fails the Vertical Line Test.

7. No, the curve is not the graph of a function since for $x = -1$ there are infinitely many points on the curve.

8. Yes, the curve is the graph of a function with domain $[-3, 2]$ and range $\{-2\} \cup (0, 3]$.

9. The person's weight increased to about 160 pounds at age 20 and stayed fairly steady for 10 years. The person's weight dropped to about 120 pounds for the next 5 years, then increased rapidly to about 170 pounds. The next 30 years saw a gradual increase to 190 pounds. Possible reasons for the drop in weight at 30 years of age: diet, exercise, health problems.

10. The salesman travels away from home from 8 to 9 A.M. and is then stationary until 10:00. The salesman travels farther away from 10 until noon. There is no change in his distance from home until 1:00, at which time the distance from home decreases until 3:00. Then the distance starts increasing again, reaching the maximum distance away from home at 5:00. There is no change from 5 until 6, and then the distance decreases rapidly until 7:00 P.M., at which time the salesman reaches home.

11. The water will cool down almost to freezing as the ice melts. Then, when the ice has melted, the water will slowly warm up to room temperature.

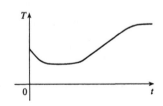

12. The summer solstice (the longest day of the year) is around June 21, and the winter solstice (the shortest day) is around December 22.

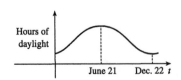

13. Of course, this graph depends strongly on the geographical location!

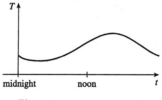

14. The temperature of the pie would increase rapidly, level off to oven temperature, decrease rapidly, and then level off to room temperature.

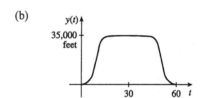

15.

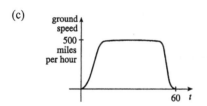

16. (a)

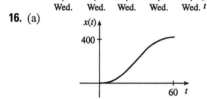

(b)

(c)

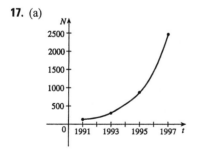

(d)

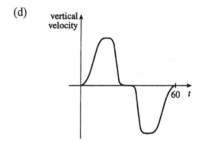

17. (a)

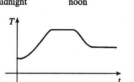

(b) From the graph, we estimate the number of cell-phone subscribers in Malaysia to be about 540 in 1994 and 1450 in 1996.

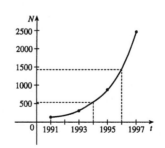

18. (a)

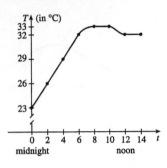

(b) From the graph in part (a), we estimate the temperature at 5:00 A.M. to be about 30.5 °C (halfway from 29 to 32).

19. $f(x) = 3x^2 - x + 2$.

$f(2) = 3(2)^2 - 2 + 2 = 12 - 2 + 2 = 12$.

$f(-2) = 3(-2)^2 - (-2) + 2 = 12 + 2 + 2 = 16$.

$f(a) = 3a^2 - a + 2$.

$f(-a) = 3(-a)^2 - (-a) + 2 = 3a^2 + a + 2$.

$f(a+1) = 3(a+1)^2 - (a+1) + 2 = 3(a^2 + 2a + 1) - a - 1 + 2 = 3a^2 + 6a + 3 - a + 1 = 3a^2 + 5a + 4$.

$2f(a) = 2 \cdot f(a) = 2(3a^2 - a + 2) = 6a^2 - 2a + 4$.

$f(2a) = 3(2a)^2 - (2a) + 2 = 3(4a^2) - 2a + 2 = 12a^2 - 2a + 2$.

$f(a^2) = 3(a^2)^2 - (a^2) + 2 = 3(a^4) - a^2 + 2 = 3a^4 - a^2 + 2$.

$\left[f(a)^2\right] = \left[3a^2 - a + 2\right]^2 = (3a^2 - a + 2)(3a^2 - a + 2)$

$\qquad = 9a^4 - 3a^3 + 6a^2 - 3a^3 + a^2 - 2a + 6a^2 - 2a + 4 = 9a^4 - 6a^3 + 13a^2 - 4a + 4$.

$f(a+h) = 3(a+h)^2 - (a+h) + 2 = 3(a^2 + 2ah + h^2) - a - h + 2 = 3a^2 + 6ah + 3h^2 - a - h + 2$.

20. A spherical balloon with radius $r + 1$ has volume $V(r+1) = \frac{4}{3}\pi(r+1)^3 = \frac{4}{3}\pi(r^3 + 3r^2 + 3r + 1)$. We wish to find the amount of air needed to inflate the balloon from a radius of r to $r + 1$. Hence, we need to find the difference $V(r+1) - V(r) = \frac{4}{3}\pi(r^3 + 3r^2 + 3r + 1) - \frac{4}{3}\pi r^3 = \frac{4}{3}\pi(3r^2 + 3r + 1)$.

21. $f(x) = x - x^2$, so

$f(2+h) = 2 + h - (2+h)^2 = 2 + h - (4 + 4h + h^2) = 2 + h - 4 - 4h - h^2 = -(h^2 + 3h + 2)$,

$f(x+h) = x + h - (x+h)^2 = x + h - x^2 - 2xh - h^2$, and

$\dfrac{f(x+h) - f(x)}{h} = \dfrac{x + h - x^2 - 2xh - h^2 - x + x^2}{h} = \dfrac{h - 2xh - h^2}{h} = \dfrac{h(1 - 2x - h)}{h} = 1 - 2x - h$.

22. $f(x) = \dfrac{x}{x+1}$, so $f(2+h) = \dfrac{2+h}{2+h+1} = \dfrac{2+h}{3+h}$, $f(x+h) = \dfrac{x+h}{x+h+1}$, and

$\dfrac{f(x+h) - f(x)}{h} = \dfrac{\frac{x+h}{x+h+1} - \frac{x}{x+1}}{h} = \dfrac{(x+h)(x+1) - x(x+h+1)}{h(x+h+1)(x+1)} = \dfrac{1}{(x+h+1)(x+1)}$.

23. $f(x) = x/(3x - 1)$ is defined for all x except when $0 = 3x - 1 \quad \Leftrightarrow \quad x = \frac{1}{3}$, so the domain is $\left\{x \in \mathbb{R} \mid x \neq \frac{1}{3}\right\} = \left(-\infty, \frac{1}{3}\right) \cup \left(\frac{1}{3}, \infty\right)$.

24. $f(x) = (5x + 4)/(x^2 + 3x + 2)$ is defined for all x except when $0 = x^2 + 3x + 2 \quad \Leftrightarrow$
$0 = (x+2)(x+1) \quad \Leftrightarrow \quad x = -2$ or -1, so the domain is
$\{x \in \mathbb{R} \mid x \neq -2, -1\} = (-\infty, -2) \cup (-2, -1) \cup (-1, \infty)$.

25. $f(t) = \sqrt{t} + \sqrt[3]{t}$ is defined when $t \geq 0$. These values of t give real number results for $\sqrt{t}$, whereas any value of t gives a real number result for $\sqrt[3]{t}$. The domain is $[0, \infty)$.

26. $g(u) = \sqrt{u} + \sqrt{4-u}$ is defined when $u \geq 0$ and $4 - u \geq 0$ $\Leftrightarrow$ $u \leq 4$. Thus, the domain is $0 \leq u \leq 4 = [0, 4]$.

27. $h(x) = 1 / \sqrt[4]{x^2 - 5x}$ is defined when $x^2 - 5x > 0$ $\Leftrightarrow$ $x(x - 5) > 0$. Note that $x^2 - 5x \neq 0$ since that would result in division by zero. The expression $x(x - 5)$ is positive if $x < 0$ or $x > 5$. (See Appendix A for methods for solving inequalities.) Thus, the domain is $(-\infty, 0) \cup (5, \infty)$.

28. $h(x) = \sqrt{4 - x^2}$. Now $y = \sqrt{4 - x^2}$ $\Rightarrow$ $y^2 = 4 - x^2$ $\Leftrightarrow$ $x^2 + y^2 = 4$, so the graph is the top half of a circle of radius 2 with center at the origin. The domain is $\{x \mid 4 - x^2 \geq 0\} = \{x \mid 4 \geq x^2\} = \{x \mid 2 \geq |x|\} = [-2, 2]$. From the graph, the range is $0 \leq y \leq 2$, or $[0, 2]$.

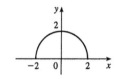

29. $y = \frac{1}{2}t - 1$ is the equation of a line with slope $\frac{1}{2}$ and y-intercept -1. The domain of the function $f(t) = \frac{1}{2}t - 1$ is $\mathbb{R}$, or $(-\infty, \infty)$.

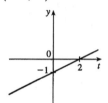

30. $F(x) = |2x + 1| = \begin{cases} 2x + 1 & \text{if } 2x + 1 \geq 0 \\ -(2x + 1) & \text{if } 2x + 1 < 1 \end{cases}$

$= \begin{cases} 2x + 1 & \text{if } x \geq -\frac{1}{2} \\ -2x - 1 & \text{if } x < -\frac{1}{2} \end{cases}$

The domain is $\mathbb{R}$, or $(-\infty, \infty)$.

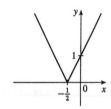

31. $G(x) = \dfrac{3x + |x|}{x}$. Since $|x| = \begin{cases} x & \text{if } x \geq 0 \\ -x & \text{if } x < 0 \end{cases}$, we have

$G(x) = \begin{cases} \dfrac{3x + x}{x} & \text{if } x > 0 \\ \dfrac{3x - x}{x} & \text{if } x < 0 \end{cases} = \begin{cases} \dfrac{4x}{x} & \text{if } x > 0 \\ \dfrac{2x}{x} & \text{if } x < 0 \end{cases} = \begin{cases} 4 & \text{if } x > 0 \\ 2 & \text{if } x < 0 \end{cases}$

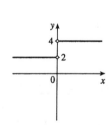

Note that G is not defined for $x = 0$. The domain is $(-\infty, 0) \cup (0, \infty)$.

32. $H(t) = \dfrac{4 - t^2}{2 - t} = \dfrac{(2 + t)(2 - t)}{2 - t}$, so for $t \neq 2$, $H(t) = 2 + t$.

The domain is $\{t \mid t \neq 2\}$. So the graph of H is the same as the graph of the function $f(t) = t + 2$ (a line) except for the hole at $(2, 4)$.

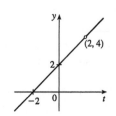

33. $f(x) = \begin{cases} x & \text{if } x \le 0 \\ x+1 & \text{if } x > 0 \end{cases}$

Domain is $\mathbb{R}$, or $(-\infty, \infty)$.

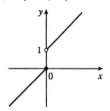

34. $f(x) = \begin{cases} 2x+3 & \text{if } x < -1 \\ 3-x & \text{if } x \ge -1 \end{cases}$

Domain is $\mathbb{R}$, or $(-\infty, \infty)$.

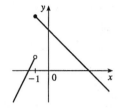

35. $f(x) = \begin{cases} x+2 & \text{if } x \le -1 \\ x^2 & \text{if } x > -1 \end{cases}$

Note that for $x = -1$, both $x + 2$ and x^2 are equal to 1. Domain is $\mathbb{R}$.

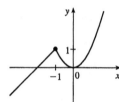

36. $f(x) = \begin{cases} -1 & \text{if } x \le -1 \\ 3x+2 & \text{if } -1 < x < 1 \\ 7-2x & \text{if } x \ge 1 \end{cases}$

Domain is $\mathbb{R}$.

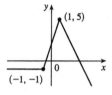

37. Recall that the slope m of a line between the two points (x_1, y_1) and (x_2, y_2) is $m = \dfrac{y_2 - y_1}{x_2 - x_1}$ and an equation of the line connecting those two points is $y - y_1 = m(x - x_1)$. The slope of this line segment is $\dfrac{-6 - 1}{4 - (-2)} = -\dfrac{7}{6}$, so an equation is $y - 1 = -\frac{7}{6}(x + 2)$. The function is $f(x) = -\frac{7}{6}x - \frac{4}{3}, -2 \le x \le 4$.

38. The slope of this line segment is $\dfrac{3 - (-2)}{6 - (-3)} = \dfrac{5}{9}$, so an equation is $y + 2 = \frac{5}{9}(x + 3)$. The function is $f(x) = \frac{5}{9}x - \frac{1}{3}, -3 \le x \le 6$.

39. We need to solve the given equation for y. $x + (y - 1)^2 = 0 \Leftrightarrow (y - 1)^2 = -x \Leftrightarrow y - 1 = \pm\sqrt{-x} \Leftrightarrow$ $y = 1 \pm \sqrt{-x}$. The expression with the positive radical represents the top half of the parabola, and the one with the negative radical represents the bottom half. Hence, we want $f(x) = 1 - \sqrt{-x}$. Note that the domain is $x \le 0$.

40. $(x - 1)^2 + y^2 = 1 \Leftrightarrow y = \pm\sqrt{1 - (x - 1)^2} = \pm\sqrt{2x - x^2}$. The top half is given by the function $f(x) = \sqrt{2x - x^2}, 0 \le x \le 2$.

41. For $-1 \le x \le 2$, the graph is the line with slope 1 and y-intercept 1, that is, the line $y = x + 1$. For $2 < x \le 4$, the graph is the line with slope $-\frac{3}{2}$ and x-intercept 4 [which corresponds to the point $(4, 0)$], so

$y - 0 = -\frac{3}{2}(x - 4) = -\frac{3}{2}x + 6$. So the function is $f(x) = \begin{cases} x+1 & \text{if } -1 \le x \le 2 \\ -\frac{3}{2}x + 6 & \text{if } 2 < x \le 4 \end{cases}$

42. For $x \leq 0$, the graph is the line $y = 2$. For $0 < x \leq 1$, the graph is the line with slope -2 and y-intercept 2, that is, the line $y = -2x + 2$. For $x > 1$, the graph is the line with slope 1 and x-intercept 1, that is, the line $y = 1\,(x - 1) = x - 1$. So the function is $f(x) = \begin{cases} 2 & \text{if } x \leq 0 \\ -2x + 2 & \text{if } 0 < x \leq 1. \\ x - 1 & \text{if } 1 < x \end{cases}$

43. Let the length and width of the rectangle be L and W. Then the perimeter is $2L + 2W = 20$ and the area is $A = LW$. Solving the first equation for W in terms of L gives $W = \dfrac{20 - 2L}{2} = 10 - L$. Thus, $A(L) = L(10 - L) = 10L - L^2$. Since lengths are positive, the domain of A is $0 < L < 10$. If we further restrict L to be larger than W, then $5 < L < 10$ would be the domain.

44. Let the length and width of the rectangle be L and W. Then the area is $LW = 16$, so that $W = 16/L$. The perimeter is $P = 2L + 2W$, so $P(L) = 2L + 2(16/L) = 2L + 32/L$, and the domain of P is $L > 0$, since lengths must be positive quantities. If we further restrict L to be larger than W, then $L > 4$ would be the domain.

45. Let the length of a side of the equilateral triangle be x. Then by the Pythagorean Theorem, the height y of the triangle satisfies $y^2 + \left(\frac{1}{2}x\right)^2 = x^2$, so that $y^2 = x^2 - \frac{1}{4}x^2 = \frac{3}{4}x^2$ and $y = \frac{\sqrt{3}}{2}x$. Using the formula for the area A of a triangle, $A = \frac{1}{2}(\text{base})(\text{height})$, we obtain $A(x) = \frac{1}{2}(x)\left(\frac{\sqrt{3}}{2}x\right) = \frac{\sqrt{3}}{4}x^2$, with domain $x > 0$.

46. Let the volume of the cube be V and the length of an edge be L. Then $V = L^3$ so $L = \sqrt[3]{V}$, and the surface area is $S(V) = 6\left(\sqrt[3]{V}\right)^2 = 6V^{2/3}$, with domain $V > 0$.

47. Let each side of the base of the box have length x, and let the height of the box be h. Since the volume is 2, we know that $2 = hx^2$, so that $h = 2/x^2$, and the surface area is $S = x^2 + 4xh$. Thus, $S(x) = x^2 + 4x(2/x^2) = x^2 + (8/x)$, with domain $x > 0$.

48. The area of the window is $A = xh + \frac{1}{2}\pi\left(\frac{1}{2}x\right)^2 = xh + \dfrac{\pi x^2}{8}$, where h is the height of the rectangular portion of the window. The perimeter is $P = 2h + x + \frac{1}{2}\pi x = 30 \iff 2h = 30 - x - \frac{1}{2}\pi x \iff h = \frac{1}{4}(60 - 2x - \pi x)$. Thus,

$$A(x) = x\,\frac{60 - 2x - \pi x}{4} + \frac{\pi x^2}{8} = 15x - \tfrac{1}{2}x^2 - \tfrac{\pi}{4}x^2 + \tfrac{\pi}{8}x^2 = 15x - \tfrac{4}{8}x^2 - \tfrac{\pi}{8}x^2 = 15x - x^2\left(\tfrac{\pi + 4}{8}\right)$$

Since the lengths x and h must be positive quantities, we have $x > 0$ and $h > 0$. For $h > 0$, we have $2h > 0 \iff 30 - x - \frac{1}{2}\pi x > 0 \iff 60 > 2x + \pi x \iff x < \dfrac{60}{2 + \pi}$. Hence, the domain of A is $0 < x < \dfrac{60}{2 + \pi}$.

49. The height of the box is x and the length and width are $L = 20 - 2x$, $W = 12 - 2x$. Then $V = LWx$ and so $V(x) = (20 - 2x)(12 - 2x)(x) = 4(10 - x)(6 - x)(x) = 4x\left(60 - 16x + x^2\right) = 4x^3 - 64x^2 + 240x$. The sides L, W, and x must be positive. Thus, $L > 0 \iff 20 - 2x > 0 \iff x < 10$; $W > 0 \iff 12 - 2x > 0 \iff x < 6$; and $x > 0$. Combining these restrictions gives us the domain $0 < x < 6$.

50.

$$C(x) = \begin{cases} \$2.00 & \text{if } 0.0 < x \le 1.0 \\ 2.20 & \text{if } 1.0 < x \le 1.1 \\ 2.40 & \text{if } 1.1 < x \le 1.2 \\ 2.60 & \text{if } 1.2 < x \le 1.3 \\ 2.80 & \text{if } 1.3 < x \le 1.4 \\ 3.00 & \text{if } 1.4 < x \le 1.5 \\ 3.20 & \text{if } 1.5 < x \le 1.6 \\ 3.40 & \text{if } 1.6 < x \le 1.7 \\ 3.60 & \text{if } 1.7 < x \le 1.8 \\ 3.80 & \text{if } 1.8 < x \le 1.9 \\ 4.00 & \text{if } 1.9 < x < 2.0 \end{cases}$$

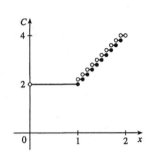

51. (a)

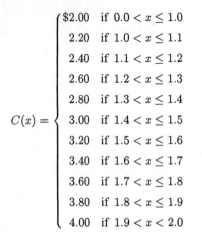

(b) On \$14,000, tax is assessed on \$4000, and $10\%(\$4000) = \$400$.
On \$26,000, tax is assessed on \$16,000, and
$10\%(\$10,000) + 15\%(\$6000) = \$1000 + \$900 = \$1900$.

(c) As in part (b), there is \$1000 tax assessed on \$20,000 of
income, so the graph of T is a line segment from $(10,000, 0)$
to $(20,000, 1000)$. The tax on \$30,000 is \$2500, so the graph
of T for $x > 20,000$ is the ray with initial point
$(20,000, 1000)$ that passes through $(30,000, 2500)$.

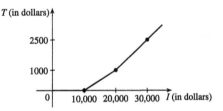

52. One example is the amount paid for cable or telephone system repair in the home, usually measured to the nearest
quarter hour. Another example is the amount paid by a student in tuition fees, if the fees vary according to the
number of credits for which the student has registered.

53. (a) Because an even function is symmetric with respect to the y-axis, and the point $(5, 3)$ is on the graph of this
even function, the point $(-5, 3)$ must also be on its graph.

(b) Because an odd function is symmetric with respect to the origin, and the point $(5, 3)$ is on the graph of this odd
function, the point $(-5, -3)$ must also be on its graph.

54. (a) If f is even, we get the rest of the graph by
reflecting about the y-axis.

(b) If f is odd, we get the rest of the graph by
rotating $180°$ about the origin.

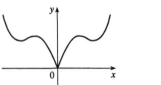
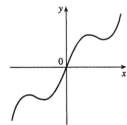

55. $f(x) = x^{-2}$.

$$f(-x) = (-x)^{-2} = \frac{1}{(-x)^2} = \frac{1}{x^2}$$

$$= x^{-2} = f(x)$$

So f is an even function.

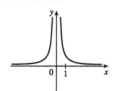

56. $f(x) = x^{-3}$.

$$f(-x) = (-x)^{-3} = \frac{1}{(-x)^3} = \frac{1}{-x^3}$$

$$= -\frac{1}{x^3} = -\left(x^{-3}\right) = -f(x)$$

So f is odd.

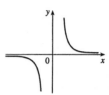

57. $f(x) = x^2 + x$, so $(-x) = (-x)^2 + (-x) = x^2 - x$. Since this is neither $f(x)$ nor $-f(x)$, the function f is neither even nor odd.

58. $f(x) = x^4 - 4x^2$.

$$f(-x) = (-x)^4 - 4(-x)^2$$

$$= x^4 - 4x^2 = f(x)$$

So f is even.

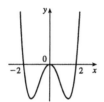

59. $f(x) = x^3 - x$.

$$f(-x) = (-x)^3 - (-x) = -x^3 + x$$

$$= -\left(x^3 - x\right) = -f(x)$$

So f is odd.

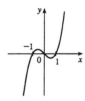

60. $f(x) = 3x^3 + 2x^2 + 1$, so $f(-x) = 3(-x)^3 + 2(-x)^2 + 1 = -3x^3 + 2x^2 + 1$. Since this is neither $f(x)$ nor $-f(x)$, the function f is neither even nor odd.

◆ 1.2 Mathematical Models · · · · · · · · · · · · · · · · · ·

1. (a) $f(x) = \sqrt[5]{x}$ is a root function with $n = 5$.

(b) $g(x) = \sqrt{1 - x^2}$ is an algebraic function because it is a root of a polynomial.

(c) $h(x) = x^9 + x^4$ is a polynomial of degree 9.

(d) $r(x) = \dfrac{x^2 + 1}{x^3 + x}$ is a rational function because it is a ratio of polynomials.

(e) $s(x) = \tan 2x$ is a trigonometric function.

(f) $t(x) = \log_{10} x$ is a logarithmic function.

2. (a) $y = (x - 6)/(x + 6)$ is a rational function because it is a ratio of polynomials.

(b) $y = x + x^2/\sqrt{x - 1}$ is an algebraic function because it involves polynomials and roots of polynomials.

(c) $y = 10^x$ is an exponential function (notice that x is the *exponent*).

(d) $y = x^{10}$ is a power function (notice that x is the *base*).

(e) $y = 2t^6 + t^4 - \pi$ is a polynomial of degree 6.

(f) $y = \cos\theta + \sin\theta$ is a trigonometric function.

3. We notice from the figure that g and h are even functions (symmetric with respect to the y-axis) and that f is an odd function (symmetric with respect to the origin). So (b) $\left[y = x^5\right]$ must be f. Since g is flatter than h near the origin, we must have (c) $\left[y = x^8\right]$ matched with g and (a) $\left[y = x^2\right]$ matched with h.

4. (a) The graph of $y = 3x$ is a line (choice G).

(b) $y = 3^x$ is an exponential function (choice f).

(c) $y = x^3$ is an odd polynomial function or power function (choice F).

(d) $y = \sqrt[3]{x} = x^{1/3}$ is a root function (choice g).

5. (a) An equation for the family of linear functions with slope 2 is $y = f(x) = 2x + b$, where b is the y-intercept.

(b) $f(2) = 1$ means that the point $(2, 1)$ is on the graph of f. We can use the point-slope form of a line to obtain an equation for the family of linear functions through the point $(2, 1)$. $y - 1 = m(x - 2)$, which is equivalent to $y = mx + (1 - 2m)$ in slope-intercept form.

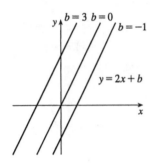

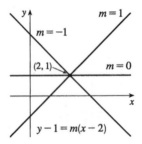

(c) To belong to both families, an equation must have slope $m = 2$, so the equation in part (b), $y = mx + (1 - 2m)$, becomes $y = 2x - 3$. It is the *only* function that belongs to both families.

6. (a)

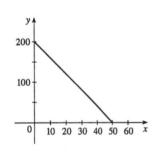

(b) The slope of -4 means that for each increase of 1 dollar for a rental space, the number of spaces rented *decreases* by 4. The y-intercept of 200 is the number of spaces that would be occupied if there were no charge for each space. The x-intercept of 50 is the smallest rental fee that results in no spaces rented.

7. (a)

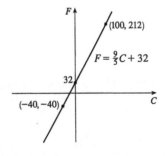

(b) The slope of $\frac{9}{5}$ means that F increases $\frac{9}{5}$ degrees for each increase of $1°C$. (Equivalently, F increases by 9 when C increases by 5 and F decreases by 9 when C decreases by 5.) The F-intercept of 32 is the Fahrenheit temperature corresponding to a Celsius temperature of 0.

8. (a) Let d = distance traveled (in miles) and t = time elapsed (in hours). At $t = 0$, $d = 0$ and at $t = 50$ minutes $= 50 \cdot \frac{1}{60} = \frac{5}{6}$ h, $d = 40$. Thus we have two points: $(0, 0)$ and $\left(\frac{5}{6}, 40\right)$, so

$$m = \frac{40 - 0}{\frac{5}{6} - 0} = 48 \text{ and so } d = 48t.$$

(b)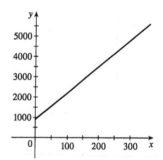

(c) The slope is 48 and represents the car's speed in mi/h.

9. (a) Using N in place of x and T in place of y, we find the slope to be $\dfrac{T_2 - T_1}{N_2 - N_1} = \dfrac{80 - 70}{173 - 113} = \dfrac{10}{60} = \dfrac{1}{6}$. So a linear equation is $T - 80 = \frac{1}{6}(N - 173) \iff T - 80 = \frac{1}{6}N - \frac{173}{6} \iff T = \frac{1}{6}N + \frac{307}{6}$ $\left[\frac{307}{6} = 51.1\overline{6}\right]$.

(b) The slope of $\frac{1}{6}$ means that the temperature in Fahrenheit degrees increases one-sixth as rapidly as the number of cricket chirps per minute. Said differently, each increase of 6 cricket chirps per minute corresponds to an increase of $1°F$.

(c) When $N = 150$, the temperature is given approximately by $T = \frac{1}{6}(150) + \frac{307}{6} = 76.1\overline{6}°F \approx 76°F$.

10. (a) Let x denote the number of chairs produced in one day and y the associated cost. Using the points $(100, 2200)$ and $(300, 4800)$ we get the slope $\frac{4800 - 2200}{300 - 100} = \frac{2600}{200} = 13$. So $y - 2200 = 13(x - 100) \iff y = 13x + 900$.

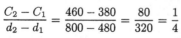

(b) The slope of the line in part (a) is 13 and it represents the cost (in dollars) of producing each additional chair.

(c) The y-intercept is 900 and it represents the fixed daily costs of operating the factory.

11. (a) We are given $\dfrac{\text{change in pressure}}{10 \text{ feet change in depth}} = \dfrac{4.34}{10} = 0.434$. Using P for pressure and d for depth with the point $(d, P) = (0, 15)$, we have the slope-intercept form of the line, $P = 0.434d + 15$.

(b) When $P = 100$, then $100 = 0.434d + 15 \iff 0.434d = 85 \iff d = \frac{85}{0.434} \approx 195.85$ feet. Thus, the pressure is 100 lb/in^2 at a depth of approximately 196 feet.

12. (a) Using d in place of x and C in place of y, we find the slope to be

$$\frac{C_2 - C_1}{d_2 - d_1} = \frac{460 - 380}{800 - 480} = \frac{80}{320} = \frac{1}{4}$$

So a linear equation is $C - 460 = \frac{1}{4}(d - 800) \iff C - 460 = \frac{1}{4}d - 200 \iff C = \frac{1}{4}d + 260$.

(b) Letting $d = 1500$ we get $C = \frac{1}{4}(1500) + 260 = 635$. The cost of driving 1500 miles is \$635.

(c)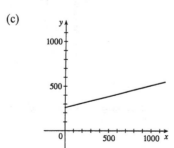

The slope of the line represents the cost per mile, \$0.25.

(d) The y-intercept represents the fixed cost, $260.

(e) A linear function gives a suitable model in this situation because you have fixed monthly costs such as insurance and car payments, as well as costs that increase as you drive, such as gasoline, oil, and tires, and the cost of these for each additional mile driven is a constant.

13. (a) The data appear to be periodic and a sine or cosine function would make the best model. A model of the form $f(x) = a\cos(bx) + c$ seems appropriate.

(b) The data appear to be decreasing in a linear fashion. A model of the form $f(x) = mx + b$ seems appropriate.

14. (a) The data appear to be increasing exponentially. A model of the form $f(x) = a \cdot b^x$ or $f(x) = a \cdot b^x + c$ seems appropriate.

(b) The data appear to be decreasing similarly to the values of the reciprocal function. A model of the form $f(x) = a/x$ seems appropriate.

Some values are given to many decimal places. These are the results given by several computer algebra systems — rounding is left to the reader.

15. (a)

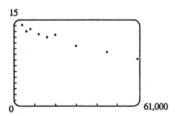

A linear model does seem appropriate.

(b) Using the points $(4000, 14.1)$ and $(60,000, 8.2)$, we obtain

$$y - 14.1 = \frac{8.2 - 14.1}{60,000 - 4000}(x - 4000) \text{ or, equivalently,}$$

$$y \approx -0.000105357x + 14.521429.$$

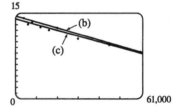

(c) Using a computing device, we obtain the least squares regression line $y = -0.0000997855x + 13.950764$. The following commands and screens illustrate how to find the least squares regression line on a TI-83 Plus. Enter the data into list one (L1) and list two (L2). Press STAT 1 to enter the editor.

Find the regession line and store it in Y_1. Press 2nd QUIT STAT ▶ 4 VARS ▶ 1 1 ENTER.

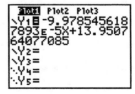

Note from the last figure that the regression line has been stored in Y_1 and that Plot1 has been turned on (Plot1 is highlighted). You can turn on Plot1 from the Y= menu by placing the cursor on Plot1 and pressing $\boxed{\text{ENTER}}$ or by pressing $\boxed{\text{2nd}}\boxed{\text{STAT PLOT}}\boxed{1}\boxed{\text{ENTER}}$.

 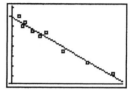

Now press $\boxed{\text{ZOOM}}\boxed{9}$ to produce a graph of the data and the regression line. Note that choice 9 of the ZOOM menu automatically selects a window that displays all of the data.

(d) When $x = 25{,}000$, $y \approx 11.456$; or about 11.5 per 100 population.

(e) When $x = 80{,}000$, $y \approx 5.968$; or about a 6% chance.

(f) When $x = 200{,}000$, y is negative, so the model does not apply.

16. (a)

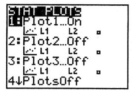

(b)

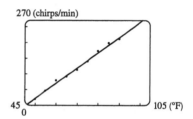

Using a computing device, we obtain the least squares regression line $y = 4.85\overline{6}x - 220.9\overline{6}$.

(c) When $x = 100°$F, $y = 264.7 \approx 265$ chirps/min.

17. (a)

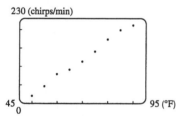

A linear model does seem appropriate.

(b)

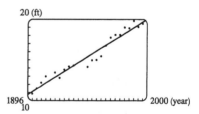

Using a computing device, we obtain the least squares regression line $y = 0.089119747x - 158.2403249$, where x is the year and y is the height in feet.

(c) When $x = 2000$, the model gives $y \approx 20.00$ ft. Note that the actual winning height for the 2000 Olympics is *less than* the winning height for 1996 — so much for that prediction.

(d) When $x = 2100$, $y \approx 28.91$ ft. This would be an increase of 9.49 ft from 1996 to 2100. Even though there was an increase of 8.59 ft from 1900 to 1996, it is unlikely that a similar increase will occur over the next 100 years.

18. By looking at the scatter plot of the data, we rule out the linear and logarithmic models.

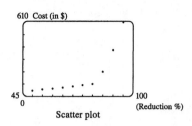

Scatter plot

We try various models:

Quadratic: $y = 0.49\overline{6}x^2 - 62.28\overline{93}x + 1970.6\overline{39}$

Cubic: $y = 0.0201243201x^3 - 3.88037296x^2 + 247.6754468x - 5163.935198$

Quartic: $y = 0.0002951049x^4 - 0.0654560995x^3 + 5.27525641x^2 - 180.2266511x + 2203.210956$

Exponential: $y = 2.41422994\,(1.054516914)^x$

Power: $y = 0.000022854971x^{3.616078251}$

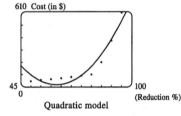

Quadratic model

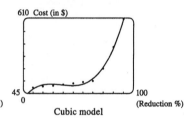

Cubic model

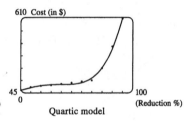

Quartic model

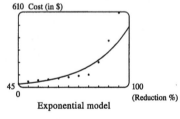

Exponential model

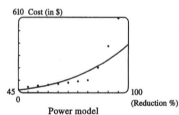

Power model

After examining the graphs of these models, we see that the cubic and quartic models are clearly the best.

19.

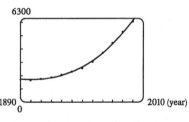

Using a computing device, we obtain the cubic function $y = ax^3 + bx^2 + cx + d$ with $a = 0.0012354312$, $b = -6.722261072$, $c = 12{,}165.08275$, and $d = -7{,}318{,}428.648$. When $x = 1925$, $y \approx 1913$ (million).

20. (a) $T = 1.000396048d^{1.499661718}$

(b) The power model in part (a) is approximately $T = d^{1.5}$. Squaring both sides gives us $T^2 = d^3$, so the model matches Kepler's Third Law, $T^2 = kd^3$.

1.3 **New Functions from Old Functions** • • • • • • • •

1. (a) If the graph of f is shifted 3 units upward, its equation becomes $y = f(x) + 3$.

(b) If the graph of f is shifted 3 units downward, its equation becomes $y = f(x) - 3$.

(c) If the graph of f is shifted 3 units to the right, its equation becomes $y = f(x - 3)$.

(d) If the graph of f is shifted 3 units to the left, its equation becomes $y = f(x + 3)$.

(e) If the graph of f is reflected about the x-axis, its equation becomes $y = -f(x)$.

(f) If the graph of f is reflected about the y-axis, its equation becomes $y = f(-x)$.

(g) If the graph of f is stretched vertically by a factor of 3, its equation becomes $y = 3f(x)$.

(h) If the graph of f is shrunk vertically by a factor of 3, its equation becomes $y = \frac{1}{3}f(x)$.

2. (a) To obtain the graph of $y = 5f(x)$ from the graph of $y = f(x)$, stretch the graph vertically by a factor of 5.

(b) To obtain the graph of $y = f(x - 5)$ from the graph of $y = f(x)$, shift the graph 5 units to the right.

(c) To obtain the graph of $y = -f(x)$ from the graph of $y = f(x)$, reflect the graph about the x-axis.

(d) To obtain the graph of $y = -5f(x)$ from the graph of $y = f(x)$, stretch the graph vertically by a factor of 5 and reflect it about the x-axis.

(e) To obtain the graph of $y = f(5x)$ from the graph of $y = f(x)$, shrink the graph horizontally by a factor of 5.

(f) To obtain the graph of $y = 5f(x) - 3$ from the graph of $y = f(x)$, stretch the graph vertically by a factor of 5 and shift it 3 units downward.

3. (a) (graph 3) The graph of f is shifted 4 units to the right and has equation $y = f(x - 4)$.

(b) (graph 1) The graph of f is shifted 3 units upward and has equation $y = f(x) + 3$.

(c) (graph 4) The graph of f is shrunk vertically by a factor of 3 and has equation $y = \frac{1}{3}f(x)$.

(d) (graph 5) The graph of f is shifted 4 units to the left and reflected about the x-axis. Its equation is $y = -f(x + 4)$.

(e) (graph 2) The graph of f is shifted 6 units to the left and stretched vertically by a factor of 2. Its equation is $y = 2f(x + 6)$.

4. (a) To graph $y = f(x + 4)$ we shift the graph of f, 4 units to the left.

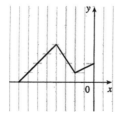

The point $(2, 1)$ on the graph of f corresponds to the point $(2 - 4, 1) = (-2, 1)$.

(b) To graph $y = f(x) + 4$ we shift the graph of f, 4 units upward.

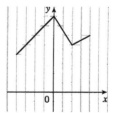

The point $(2, 1)$ on the graph of f corresponds to the point $(2, 1 + 4) = (2, 5)$.

(c) To graph $y = 2f(x)$ we stretch the graph of f vertically by a factor of 2.

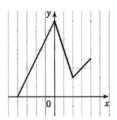

The point $(2, 1)$ on the graph of f corresponds to the point $(2, 2 \cdot 1) = (2, 2)$.

5. (a) To graph $y = f(2x)$ we shrink the graph of f horizontally by a factor of 2.

The point $(4, -1)$ on the graph of f corresponds to the point $\left(\frac{1}{2} \cdot 4, -1\right) = (2, -1)$.

(c) To graph $y = f(-x)$ we reflect the graph of f about the y-axis.

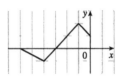

The point $(4, -1)$ on the graph of f corresponds to the point $(-1 \cdot 4, -1) = (-4, -1)$.

(d) To graph $y = -\frac{1}{2}f(x) + 3$, we shrink the graph of f vertically by a factor of 2, then reflect the resulting graph about the x-axis, then shift the resulting graph 3 units upward.

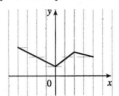

The point $(2, 1)$ on the graph of f corresponds to the point $\left(2, -\frac{1}{2} \cdot 1 + 3\right) = (2, 2.5)$.

(b) To graph $y = f\left(\frac{1}{2}x\right)$ we stretch the graph of f horizontally by a factor of 2.

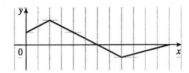

The point $(4, -1)$ on the graph of f corresponds to the point $(2 \cdot 4, -1) = (8, -1)$.

(d) To graph $y = -f(-x)$ we reflect the graph of f about the y-axis, then about the x-axis.

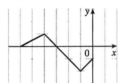

The point $(4, -1)$ on the graph of f corresponds to the point $(-1 \cdot 4, -1 \cdot -1) = (-4, 1)$.

6. The graph of $y = f(x) = \sqrt{3x - x^2}$ has been shifted 2 units to the right and stretched vertically by a factor of 2. Thus, a function describing the graph is

$$y = 2f(x - 2) = 2\sqrt{3(x - 2) - (x - 2)^2} = 2\sqrt{3x - 6 - (x^2 - 4x + 4)} = 2\sqrt{-x^2 + 7x - 10}$$

7. The graph of $y = f(x) = \sqrt{3x - x^2}$ has been shifted 4 units to the left, reflected about the x-axis, and shifted downward 1 unit. Thus, a function describing the graph is

$$y = \underbrace{-1 \cdot}_{\substack{\text{reflect} \\ \text{about} \\ x\text{-axis}}} \underbrace{f(x + 4)}_{\substack{\text{shift} \\ \text{4 units} \\ \text{left}}} \underbrace{-1}_{\substack{\text{shift} \\ \text{1 unit} \\ \text{down}}}$$

This function can be written as

$$y = -f(x+4) - 1 = -\sqrt{3(x+4) - (x+4)^2} - 1 = -\sqrt{3x + 12 - (x^2 + 8x + 16)} - 1$$
$$= -\sqrt{-x^2 - 5x - 4} - 1$$

8. (a) The graph of $y = 2\sin x$ can be obtained from the graph of $y = \sin x$ by stretching it vertically by a factor of 2.

(b) The graph of $y = 1 + \sqrt{x}$ can be obtained from the graph of $y = \sqrt{x}$ by shifting it upward 1 unit.

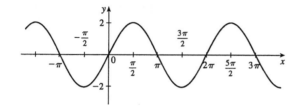

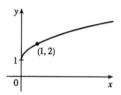

9. $y = -1/x$: Start with the graph of $y = 1/x$ and reflect about the x-axis.

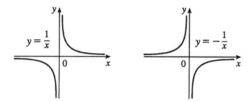

10. $y = 2 - \cos x$: Start with the graph of $y = \cos x$, reflect about the x-axis, and then shift 2 units upward.

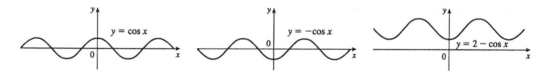

11. $y = \tan 2x$: Start with the graph of $y = \tan x$ and compress horizontally by a factor of 2.

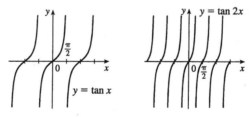

12. $y = \sqrt[3]{x+2}$: Start with the graph of $y = \sqrt[3]{x}$ and shift 2 units to the left.

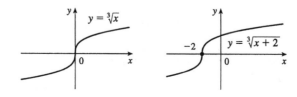

13. $y = \cos(x/2)$: Start with the graph of $y = \cos x$ and stretch horizontally by a factor of 2.

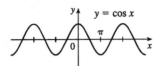
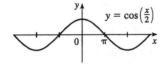

14. $y = x^2 + 2x + 3 = (x^2 + 2x + 1) + 2 = (x + 1)^2 + 2$: Start with the graph of $y = x^2$, shift 1 unit left, and then shift 2 units upward.

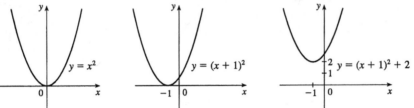
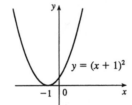

15. $y = \dfrac{1}{x - 3}$: Start with the graph of $y = 1/x$ and shift 3 units to the right.

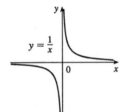
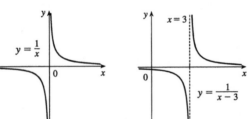

16. $y = -2 \sin \pi x$: Start with the graph of $y = \sin x$, compress horizontally by a factor of π, stretch vertically by a factor of 2, and then reflect about the x-axis.

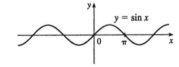
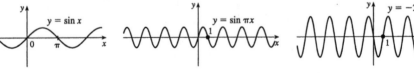

17. $y = \frac{1}{3} \sin\left(x - \frac{\pi}{6}\right)$: Start with the graph of $y = \sin x$, shift $\frac{\pi}{6}$ units to the right, and then compress vertically by a factor of 3.

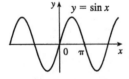
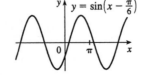
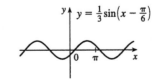

18. $y = 2 + \dfrac{1}{x+1}$: Start with the graph of $y = 1/x$, shift 1 unit left, and then shift 2 units upward.

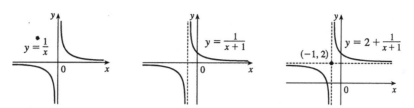

19. $y = 1 + 2x - x^2 = -x^2 + 2x + 1 = -(x^2 - 2x + 1) + 1 + 1 = -(x-1)^2 + 2$: Start with the graph of $y = x^2$, shift 1 unit right, reflect about the x-axis, and then shift 2 units upward.

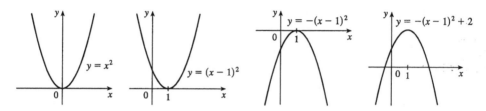

20. $y = \frac{1}{2}\sqrt{x+4} - 3$: Start with the graph of $y = \sqrt{x}$, shift 4 units to the left and compress vertically by a factor of 2, and then shift 3 units downward.

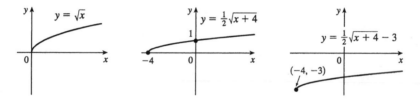

21. $y = 2 - \sqrt{x+1}$: Start with the graph of $y = \sqrt{x}$, reflect about the x-axis, shift 1 unit to the left, and then shift 2 units upward.

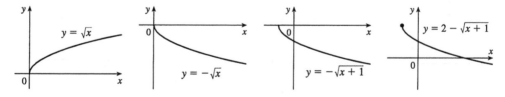

22. $y = (x-1)^3 + 2$: Start with the graph of $y = x^3$, shift 1 unit to the right, and then shift 2 units upward.

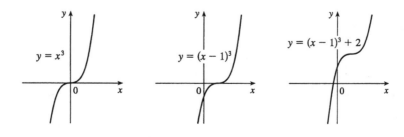

23. $y = |\sin x|$: Start with the graph of $y = \sin x$ and reflect all the parts of the graph below the x-axis about the x-axis.

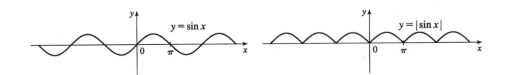

24. $y = |x^2 - 2x| = |x^2 - 2x + 1 - 1| = |(x-1)^2 - 1|$: Start with the graph of $y = x^2$, shift 1 unit right, shift 1 unit downward, and reflect the portion of the graph below the x-axis about the x-axis.

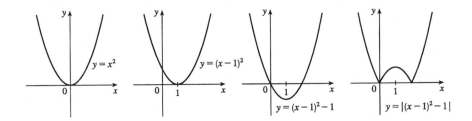

25. This is just like the solution to Example 4 except the amplitude of the curve is $14 - 12 = 2$. So the function is $L(t) = 12 + 2 \sin\left[\frac{2\pi}{365}(t - 80)\right]$. March 31 is the 90th day of the year, so the model gives $L(90) \approx 12.34$ h. The daylight time (5:51 A.M. to 6:18 P.M.) is 12 hours and 27 minutes, or 12.45 h. The model value differs from the actual value by $\frac{12.45 - 12.34}{12.45} \approx 0.009$, less than 1%.

26. Using a sine function to model the brightness of Delta Cephei as a function of time, we take its period to be 5.4 days, its amplitude to be 0.35 (on the scale of magnitude), and its average magnitude to be 4.0. If we take $t = 0$ at a time of average brightness, then the magnitude (brightness) as a function of time t in days can be modeled by the formula $M(t) = 4.0 + 0.35 \sin\left(\frac{2\pi}{5.4} t\right)$.

27. (a) To obtain $y = f(|x|)$, the portion of the graph of $y = f(x)$ to the right of the y-axis is reflected about the y-axis.

(b) $y = \sin|x|$

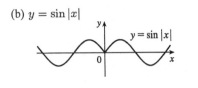

(c) $y = \sqrt{|x|}$

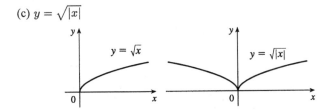

28. The most important features of the given graph are the x-intercepts and the maximum and minimum points. The graph of $y = 1/f(x)$ has vertical asymptotes at the x-values where there are x-intercepts on the graph of $y = f(x)$. The maximum of 1 on the graph of $y = f(x)$ corresponds to a minimum of $1/1 = 1$ on $y = 1/f(x)$. Similarly, the minimum on the graph of $y = f(x)$ corresponds to a maximum on the graph of $y = 1/f(x)$. As the values of y get large (positively or negatively) on the graph of $y = f(x)$, the values of y get close to zero on the graph of $y = 1/f(x)$.

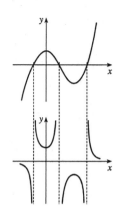

29. Assuming that successive horizontal and vertical gridlines are a unit apart, we can make a table of approximate values as follows.

x	0	1	2	3	4	5	6
$f(x)$	2	1.7	1.3	1.0	0.7	0.3	0
$g(x)$	2	2.7	3	2.8	2.4	1.7	0
$f(x) + g(x)$	4	4.4	4.3	3.8	3.1	2.0	0

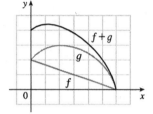

Connecting the points $(x, f(x) + g(x))$ with a smooth curve gives an approximation to the graph of $f + g$. Extra points can be plotted between those listed above if necessary.

30. First note that the domain of $f + g$ is the intersection of the domains of f and g; that is, $f + g$ is only defined where both f and g are defined. Taking the horizontal and vertical units of length to be the distances between successive vertical and horizontal gridlines, we can make a table of approximate values as follows:

x	-2	-1	0	1	2	2.5	3
$f(x)$	-1	2.2	2.0	2.4	2.7	2.7	2.3
$g(x)$	1	-1.3	-1.2	-0.6	0.3	0.5	0.7
$f(x) + g(x)$	0	0.9	0.8	1.8	3.0	3.2	3.0

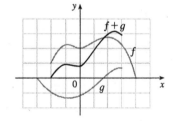

Extra values of x (like the value 2.5 in the table above) can be added as needed.

31. $f(x) = x^3 + 2x^2$; $g(x) = 3x^2 - 1$. $D = \mathbb{R}$ for both f and g.

$(f + g)(x) = (x^3 + 2x^2) + (3x^2 - 1) = x^3 + 5x^2 - 1$, $D = \mathbb{R}$.

$(f - g)(x) = (x^3 + 2x^2) - (3x^2 - 1) = x^3 - x^2 + 1$, $D = \mathbb{R}$.

$(fg)(x) = (x^3 + 2x^2)(3x^2 - 1) = 3x^5 + 6x^4 - x^3 - 2x^2$, $D = \mathbb{R}$.

$\left(\dfrac{f}{g}\right)(x) = \dfrac{x^3 + 2x^2}{3x^2 - 1}$, $D = \left\{ x \mid x \neq \pm \dfrac{1}{\sqrt{3}} \right\}$ since $3x^2 - 1 \neq 0$.

32. $f(x) = \sqrt{1+x}$, $D = [-1, \infty)$; $g(x) = \sqrt{1-x}$, $D = (-\infty, 1]$.

$(f+g)(x) = \sqrt{1+x} + \sqrt{1-x}$, $D = (-\infty, 1] \cap [-1, \infty) = [-1, 1]$.

$(f-g)(x) = \sqrt{1+x} - \sqrt{1-x}$, $D = [-1, 1]$.

$(fg)(x) = \sqrt{1+x} \cdot \sqrt{1-x} = \sqrt{1-x^2}$, $D = [-1, 1]$.

$\left(\dfrac{f}{g}\right)(x) = \dfrac{\sqrt{1+x}}{\sqrt{1-x}}$, $D = [-1, 1)$. We must exclude $x = 1$ since it would make $\dfrac{f}{g}$ undefined.

33. $f(x) = x$, $g(x) = 1/x$

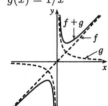

34. $f(x) = x^3$, $g(x) = -x^2$

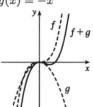

35. $f(x) = \sin x$, $D = \mathbb{R}$; $g(x) = 1 - \sqrt{x}$, $D = [0, \infty)$.

$(f \circ g)(x) = f(g(x)) = f\left(1 - \sqrt{x}\right) = \sin(1 - \sqrt{x})$, $D = [0, \infty)$.

$(g \circ f)(x) = g(f(x)) = g(\sin x) = 1 - \sqrt{\sin x}$. For $\sqrt{\sin x}$ to be defined, we must have

$\sin x \geq 0 \iff x \in [0, \pi], [2\pi, 3\pi], [-2\pi, -\pi], [4\pi, 5\pi], [-4\pi, -3\pi], \ldots$, so

$D = \{x \mid x \in [2n\pi, \pi + 2n\pi]$, where n is an integer$\}$.

$(f \circ f)(x) = f(f(x)) = f(\sin x) = \sin(\sin x)$, $D = \mathbb{R}$.

$(g \circ g)(x) = g(g(x)) = g(1 - \sqrt{x}) = 1 - \sqrt{1 - \sqrt{x}}$, $D = \{x \geq 0 \mid 1 - \sqrt{x} \geq 0\} = [0, 1]$.

36. $f(x) = 1 - 3x$, $D = \mathbb{R}$; $g(x) = 5x^2 + 3x + 2$, $D = \mathbb{R}$.

$(f \circ g)(x) = f(g(x)) = f(5x^2 + 3x + 2) = 1 - 3(5x^2 + 3x + 2)$

$\qquad = 1 - 15x^2 - 9x - 6 = -15x^2 - 9x - 5$, $D = \mathbb{R}$.

$(g \circ f)(x) = g(f(x)) = g(1 - 3x) = 5(1 - 3x)^2 + 3(1 - 3x) + 2 = 5(1 - 6x + 9x^2) + 3 - 9x + 2$

$\qquad = 5 - 30x + 45x^2 - 9x + 5 = 45x^2 - 39x + 10$, $D = \mathbb{R}$.

$(f \circ f)(x) = f(f(x)) = f(1 - 3x) = 1 - 3(1 - 3x) = 1 - 3 + 9x = 9x - 2$, $D = \mathbb{R}$.

$(g \circ g)(x) = g(g(x)) = g(5x^2 + 3x + 2) = 5(5x^2 + 3x + 2)^2 + 3(5x^2 + 3x + 2) + 2$

$\qquad = 5(25x^4 + 30x^3 + 29x^2 + 12x + 4) + 15x^2 + 9x + 6 + 2$

$\qquad = 125x^4 + 150x^3 + 145x^2 + 60x + 20 + 15x^2 + 9x + 8$

$\qquad = 125x^4 + 150x^3 + 160x^2 + 69x + 28$, $D = \mathbb{R}$.

37. $f(x) = x + \dfrac{1}{x}$, $D = \{x \mid x \neq 0\}$; $g(x) = \dfrac{x+1}{x+2}$, $D = \{x \mid x \neq -2\}$.

$(f \circ g)(x) = f(g(x)) = f\left(\dfrac{x+1}{x+2}\right) = \dfrac{x+1}{x+2} + \dfrac{1}{\frac{x+1}{x+2}} = \dfrac{x+1}{x+2} + \dfrac{x+2}{x+1}$

$\qquad = \dfrac{(x+1)(x+1) + (x+2)(x+2)}{(x+2)(x+1)} = \dfrac{(x^2 + 2x + 1) + (x^2 + 4x + 4)}{(x+2)(x+1)} = \dfrac{2x^2 + 6x + 5}{(x+2)(x+1)}$

Since $g(x)$ is not defined for $x = -2$ and $f(g(x))$ is not defined for $x = -2$ and $x = -1$, the domain of $(f \circ g)(x)$ is $D = \{x \mid x \neq -2, -1\}$.

$$(g \circ f)(x) = g(f(x)) = g\left(x + \frac{1}{x}\right) = \frac{\left(x + \frac{1}{x}\right) + 1}{\left(x + \frac{1}{x}\right) + 2} = \frac{\frac{x^2 + 1 + x}{x}}{\frac{x^2 + 1 + 2x}{x}} = \frac{x^2 + x + 1}{x^2 + 2x + 1} = \frac{x^2 + x + 1}{(x+1)^2}.$$

Since $f(x)$ is not defined for $x = 0$ and $g(f(x))$ is not defined for $x = -1$, the domain of $(g \circ f)(x)$ is $D = \{x \mid x \neq -1, 0\}$.

$$(f \circ f)(x) = f(f(x)) = f\left(x + \frac{1}{x}\right) = \left(x + \frac{1}{x}\right) + \frac{1}{x + \frac{1}{x}} = x + \frac{1}{x} + \frac{1}{\frac{x^2 + 1}{x}} = x + \frac{1}{x} + \frac{x}{x^2 + 1}$$

$$= \frac{x(x)\left(x^2 + 1\right) + 1\left(x^2 + 1\right) + x(x)}{x\left(x^2 + 1\right)} = \frac{x^4 + x^2 + x^2 + 1 + x^2}{x\left(x^2 + 1\right)}$$

$$= \frac{x^4 + 3x^2 + 1}{x\left(x^2 + 1\right)}, \quad D = \{x \mid x \neq 0\}.$$

$$(g \circ g)(x) = g(g(x)) = g\left(\frac{x + 1}{x + 2}\right) = \frac{\frac{x+1}{x+2} + 1}{\frac{x+1}{x+2} + 2} = \frac{\frac{x+1+1(x+2)}{x+2}}{\frac{x+1+2(x+2)}{x+2}} = \frac{x + 1 + x + 2}{x + 1 + 2x + 4} = \frac{2x + 3}{3x + 5}.$$

Since $g(x)$ is not defined for $x = -2$ and $g(g(x))$ is not defined for $x = -\frac{5}{3}$, the domain of $(g \circ g)(x)$ is $D = \{x \mid x \neq -2, -\frac{5}{3}\}$.

38. $f(x) = \sqrt{2x + 3}, \quad D = \{x \mid x \geq -\frac{3}{2}\}; \quad g(x) = x^2 + 1, \quad D = \mathbb{R}.$

$(f \circ g)(x) = f(x^2 + 1) = \sqrt{2(x^2 + 1) + 3} = \sqrt{2x^2 + 5}, \quad D = \mathbb{R}.$

$(g \circ f)(x) = g(\sqrt{2x + 3}) = (\sqrt{2x + 3})^2 + 1 = (2x + 3) + 1 = 2x + 4, \quad D = \{x \mid x \geq -\frac{3}{2}\}.$

$(f \circ f)(x) = f(\sqrt{2x + 3}) = \sqrt{2(\sqrt{2x + 3}) + 3} = \sqrt{2\sqrt{2x + 3} + 3}, \quad D = \{x \mid x \geq -\frac{3}{2}\}.$

$(g \circ g)(x) = g(x^2 + 1) = (x^2 + 1)^2 + 1 = (x^4 + 2x^2 + 1) + 1 = x^4 + 2x^2 + 2, \quad D = \mathbb{R}.$

39. $(f \circ g \circ h)(x) = f(g(h(x))) = f(g(x + 3)) = f((x + 3)^2 + 2)$

$\qquad = f(x^2 + 6x + 11) = \sqrt{(x^2 + 6x + 11) - 1} = \sqrt{x^2 + 6x + 10}$

40. $(f \circ g \circ h)(x) = f(g(h(x))) = f(g(\sqrt{x + 3})) = f(\cos\sqrt{x + 3}) = \dfrac{2}{\cos\sqrt{x + 3} + 1}$

41. Let $g(x) = x^2 + 1$ and $f(x) = x^{10}$. Then $(f \circ g)(x) = (x^2 + 1)^{10} = F(x)$.

42. Let $g(x) = \sqrt{x}$ and $f(x) = \sin x$. Then $(f \circ g)(x) = \sin(\sqrt{x}) = F(x)$.

43. Let $g(t) = \cos t$ and $f(t) = \sqrt{t}$. Then $(f \circ g)(t) = \sqrt{\cos t} = u(t)$.

44. Let $g(t) = \tan t$ and $f(t) = \dfrac{t}{1 + t}$. Then $(f \circ g)(t) = \dfrac{\tan t}{1 + \tan t} = u(t)$.

45. Let $h(x) = x^2$, $g(x) = 3^x$, and $f(x) = 1 - x$. Then $(f \circ g \circ h)(x) = 1 - 3^{x^2} = H(x)$.

46. Let $h(x) = \sqrt{x}$, $g(x) = x - 1$, and $f(x) = \sqrt[3]{x}$. Then $(f \circ g \circ h)(x) = \sqrt[3]{\sqrt{x} - 1} = H(x)$.

47. Let $h(x) = \sqrt{x}$, $g(x) = \sec x$, and $f(x) = x^4$. Then $(f \circ g \circ h)(x) = (\sec\sqrt{x})^4 = \sec^4(\sqrt{x}) = H(x)$.

48. (a) $f(g(1)) = f(6) = 5$ \qquad\qquad (b) $g(f(1)) = g(3) = 2$

(c) $f(f(1)) = f(3) = 4$ \qquad\qquad (d) $g(g(1)) = g(6) = 3$

(e) $(g \circ f)(3) = g(f(3)) = g(4) = 1$ \qquad (f) $(f \circ g)(6) = f(g(6)) = f(3) = 4$

49. (a) $g(2) = 5$, because the point $(2, 5)$ is on the graph of g. Thus, $f(g(2)) = f(5) = 4$, because the point $(5, 4)$ is on the graph of f.

(b) $g(f(0)) = g(0) = 3$

(c) $(f \circ g)(0) = f(g(0)) = f(3) = 0$

(d) $(g \circ f)(6) = g(f(6)) = g(6)$. This value is not defined, because there is no point on the graph of g that has x-coordinate 6.

(e) $(g \circ g)(-2) = g(g(-2)) = g(1) = 4$

(f) $(f \circ f)(4) = f(f(4)) = f(2) = -2$

50. To find a particular value of $f(g(x))$, say for $x = 0$, we note from the graph that $g(0) \approx 2.8$ and $f(2.8) \approx -0.5$. Thus, $f(g(0)) \approx f(2.8) \approx -0.5$. The other values listed in the table were obtained in a similar fashion.

x	$g(x)$	$f(g(x))$
-5	-0.2	-4
-4	1.2	-3.3
-3	2.2	-1.7
-2	2.8	-0.5
-1	3	-0.2

x	$g(x)$	$f(g(x))$
0	2.8	-0.5
1	2.2	-1.7
2	1.2	-3.3
3	-0.2	-4
4	-1.9	-2.2
5	-4.1	1.9

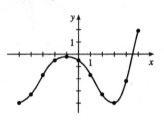

51. (a) Using the relationship *distance* = *rate · time* with the radius r as the distance, we have $r(t) = 60t$.

(b) $A = \pi r^2 \;\Rightarrow\; (A \circ r)(t) = A(r(t)) = \pi(60t)^2 = 3600\pi t^2$. This formula gives us the extent of the rippled area (in cm^2) at any time t.

52. (a) $d = rt \;\Rightarrow\; d(t) = 350t$

(b) There is a Pythagorean relationship involving the legs with lengths d and 1 and the hypotenuse with length s: $d^2 + 1^2 = s^2$. Thus, $s(d) = \sqrt{d^2 + 1}$.

(c) $(s \circ d)(t) = s(d(t)) = s(350t) = \sqrt{(350t)^2 + 1}$

53. (a)

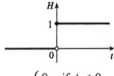

$$H(t) = \begin{cases} 0 & \text{if } t < 0 \\ 1 & \text{if } t \geq 0 \end{cases}$$

(b)

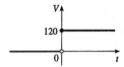

$$V(t) = \begin{cases} 0 & \text{if } t < 0 \\ 120 & \text{if } t \geq 0 \end{cases} \quad \text{so } V(t) = 120H(t).$$

(c)

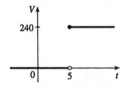

Starting with the formula in part (b), we replace 120 with 240 to reflect the different voltage. Also, because we are starting 5 units to the right of $t = 0$, we replace t with $t - 5$. Thus, the formula is $V(t) = 240H(t - 5)$.

54. (a) $R(t) = tH(t)$

$$= \begin{cases} 0 & \text{if } t < 0 \\ t & \text{if } t \geq 0 \end{cases}$$

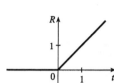

(b) $V(t) = \begin{cases} 0 & \text{if } t < 0 \\ 2t & \text{if } 0 \leq t \leq 60 \end{cases}$

so $V(t) = 2tH(t), t \leq 60$.

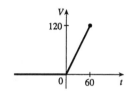

(c) $V(t) = \begin{cases} 0 & \text{if } t < 7 \\ 4(t - 7) & \text{if } 7 \leq t \leq 32 \end{cases}$

so $V(t) = 4(t - 7)H(t - 7), t \leq 32$.

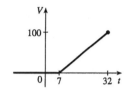

55. (a) By examining the variable terms in g and h, we deduce that we must square g to get the terms $4x^2$ and $4x$ in h. If we let $f(x) = x^2 + c$, then $(f \circ g)(x) = f(g(x)) = f(2x + 1) = (2x + 1)^2 + c = 4x^2 + 4x + (1 + c)$. Since $h(x) = 4x^2 + 4x + 7$, we must have $1 + c = 7$. So $c = 6$ and $f(x) = x^2 + 6$.

(b) We need a function g so that

$f(g(x)) = 3(g(x)) + 5 = h(x) = 3x^2 + 3x + 2 = 3(x^2 + x) + 2 = 3(x^2 + x - 1) + 5$. So we see that $g(x) = x^2 + x - 1$.

56. We need a function g so that $g(f(x)) = g(x + 4) = h(x) = 4x - 1 = 4(x + 4) - 17$. So we see that the function g must be $g(x) = 4x - 17$.

57. We need to examine $h(-x)$.

$$h(-x) = (f \circ g)(-x) = f(g(-x)) = f(g(x)) \quad \text{[because } g \text{ is even]} \quad = h(x)$$

Because $h(-x) = h(x)$, h is an even function.

58. $h(-x) = f(g(-x)) = f(-g(x))$. At this point, we can't simplify the expression, so we might try to find a counterexample to show that h is not an odd function. Let $g(x) = x$, an odd function, and $f(x) = x^2 + x$. Then $h(x) = x^2 + x$, which is neither even nor odd.

Now suppose f is an odd function. Then $f(-g(x)) = -f(g(x)) = -h(x)$. Hence, $h(-x) = -h(x)$, and so h is odd if both f and g are odd.

Now suppose f is an even function. Then $f(-g(x)) = f(g(x)) = h(x)$. Hence, $h(-x) = h(x)$, and so h is even if g is odd and f is even.

59. (a) $P = (a, g(a))$ and $Q = (g(a), g(a))$ because Q has the same y-value as P and it is on the line $y = x$.

(b) The x-value of Q is $g(a)$; this is also the x-value of R. The y-value of R is therefore $f(x$-value), that is, $f(g(a))$. Hence, $R = (g(a), f(g(a)))$.

(c) The coordinates of S are $(a, f(g(a)))$ or, equivalently, $(a, h(a))$.

(d)

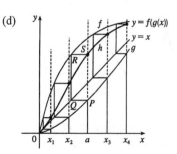

60. We only need to plot points for the first quadrant since we can see that f is an odd function, and by Exercise 58, we then know that $f \circ f$ is an odd function, and hence, symmetric with respect to the origin.

x	0	0.5	1	1.5	2
$f(x)$	0	1	1.5	1.4	0
$f(f(x))$	0	1.5	1.4	1.5	0

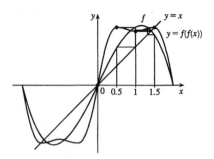

1.4 Graphing Calculators and Computers · · · · · · · ·

1. $f(x) = 10 + 25x - x^3$

(a) $[-4, 4]$ by $[-4, 4]$

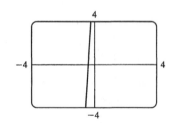

(b) $[-10, 10]$ by $[-10, 10]$

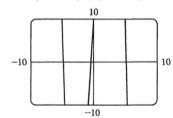

(c) $[-20, 20]$ by $[-100, 100]$

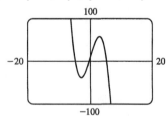

(d) $[-100, 100]$ by $[-200, 200]$

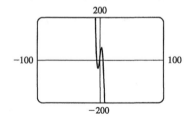

The most appropriate graph is produced in viewing rectangle (c) because the maximum and minimum points are fairly easy to see and estimate.

2. $f(x) = \sqrt{8x - x^2}$

(a) $[-4, 4]$ by $[-4, 4]$

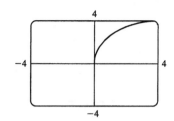

(b) $[-5, 5]$ by $[0, 100]$

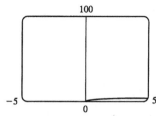

(c) $[-10, 10]$ by $[-10, 40]$

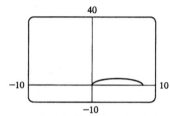

(d) $[-2, 10]$ by $[-2, 6]$

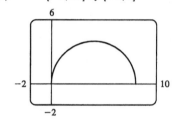

The most appropriate graph is produced in viewing rectangle (d).

3. Since the graph of $f(x) = 5 + 20x - x^2$ is a parabola opening downward, an appropriate viewing rectangle should include the maximum point.

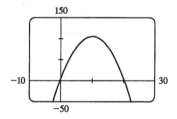

4. An appropriate viewing rectangle for $f(x) = x^3 + 30x^2 + 200x$ should include the high and low points.

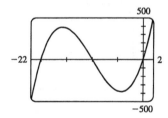

5. $f(x) = \sqrt[4]{81 - x^4}$ is defined when

$81 - x^4 \geq 0 \iff x^4 \leq 81 \iff |x| \leq 3$, so the domain of f is $[-3, 3]$. Also

$0 \leq \sqrt[4]{81 - x^4} \leq \sqrt[4]{81} = 3$, so the range is $[0, 3]$.

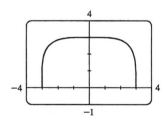

6. $f(x) = \sqrt{0.1x + 20}$ is defined when

$0.1x + 20 \geq 0 \iff x \geq -200$, so the domain of f is $[-200, \infty)$.

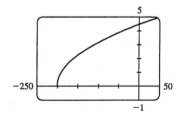

7. The graph of $f(x) = x^2 + (100/x)$ has a vertical asymptote of $x = 0$. As you zoom out, the graph of f looks more and more like that of $y = x^2$.

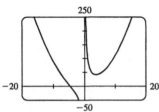

8. The graph of $f(x) = x/(x^2 + 100)$ is symmetric with respect to the origin.

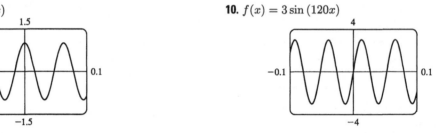

9. $f(x) = \cos{(100x)}$

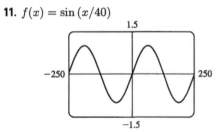

10. $f(x) = 3\sin{(120x)}$

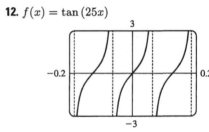

11. $f(x) = \sin{(x/40)}$

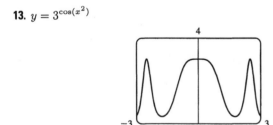

12. $f(x) = \tan{(25x)}$

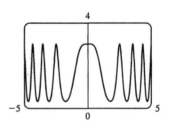

13. $y = 3^{\cos(x^2)}$

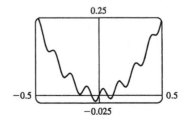

14. $y = x^2 + 0.02\sin{(50x)}$

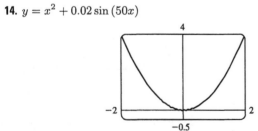

15. We must solve the given equation for y to obtain equations for the upper and lower halves of the ellipse.

$$4x^2 + 2y^2 = 1 \iff 2y^2 = 1 - 4x^2 \iff y^2 = \frac{1 - 4x^2}{2}$$

$$\iff y = \pm\sqrt{\frac{1 - 4x^2}{2}}$$

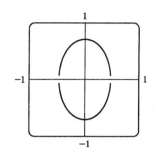

16. $y^2 - 9x^2 = 1 \iff y^2 = 1 + 9x^2 \iff y = \pm\sqrt{1 + 9x^2}$

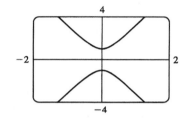

17. From the graph of $f(x) = x^3 - 9x^2 - 4$, we see that there is one solution of the equation $f(x) = 0$ and it is slightly larger than 9. By zooming in or using a root or zero feature, we obtain $x \approx 9.05$.

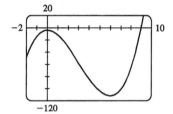

18. We see that the graphs of $f(x) = x^3$ and $g(x) = 4x - 1$ intersect three times. The x-coordinates of these points (which are the solutions of the equation) are approximately $-2.11, 0.25,$ and 1.86. Alternatively, we could find these values by finding the zeros of $h(x) = x^3 - 4x + 1$.

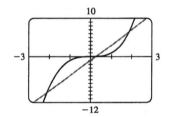

19. We see that the graphs of $f(x) = x^2$ and $g(x) = \sin x$ intersect twice. One solution is $x = 0$. The other solution of $f = g$ is the x-coordinate of the point of intersection in the first quadrant. Using an intersect feature or zooming in, we find this value to be approximately 0.88. Alternatively, we could find that value by finding the positive zero of $h(x) = x^2 - \sin x$.

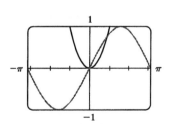

Note: After producing the graph on a TI-83 Plus, we can find the approximate value 0.88 by using the following keystrokes: 2nd CALC 5 ENTER ENTER 1 ENTER . The "1" is just a guess for 0.88.

20. (a)

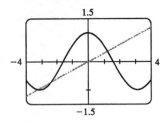

The x-coordinates of the three points of intersection are $x \approx -3.29$, -2.36 and 1.20.

(b) Using trial and error, we find that $m \approx 0.3365$. Note that m could also be negative.

21. $g(x) = x^3/10$ is larger than $f(x) = 10x^2$ whenever $x > 100$.

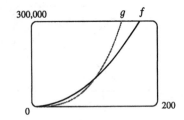

22. $f(x) = x^4 - 100x^3$ is larger than $g(x) = x^3$ whenever $x > 101$.

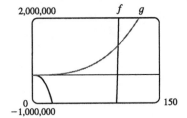

23.

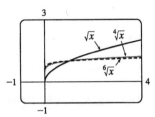

We see from the graphs of $y = |\sin x - x|$ and $y = 0.1$ that there are two solutions to the equation $|\sin x - x| = 0.1$: $x \approx -0.85$ and $x \approx 0.85$. The condition $|\sin x - x| < 0.1$ holds for any x lying between these two values.

24.

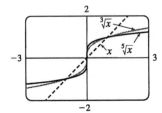

$P(x) = 3x^5 - 5x^3 + 2x$,
$Q(x) = 3x^5$. These graphs are significantly different only in the region close to the origin. The larger a viewing rectangle one chooses, the more similar the two graphs look.

25. (a) The root functions $y = \sqrt{x}$, $y = \sqrt[4]{x}$ and $y = \sqrt[6]{x}$

(b) The root functions $y = x$, $y = \sqrt[3]{x}$ and $y = \sqrt[5]{x}$

(c) The root functions $y = \sqrt{x}$, $y = \sqrt[3]{x}$, $y = \sqrt[4]{x}$ and $y = \sqrt[5]{x}$

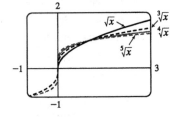

(d) ● For any n, the nth root of 0 is 0 and the nth root of 1 is 1; that is, all nth root functions pass through the points $(0, 0)$ and $(1, 1)$.

● For odd n, the domain of the nth root function is $\mathbb{R}$, while for even n, it is $\{x \in \mathbb{R} \mid x \geq 0\}$.

● Graphs of even root functions look similar to that of $\sqrt{x}$, while those of odd root functions resemble that of $\sqrt[3]{x}$.

● As n increases, the graph of $\sqrt[n]{x}$ becomes steeper near 0 and flatter for $x > 1$.

26. (a) The functions $y = 1/x$ and $y = 1/x^3$

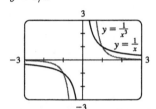

(b) The functions $y = 1/x^2$ and $y = 1/x^4$

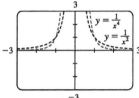

(c) The functions $y = 1/x$, $y = 1/x^2$, $y = 1/x^3$ and $y = 1/x^4$

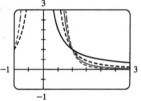

(d) ● The graphs of all functions of the form $y = 1/x^n$ pass through the point $(1, 1)$.

● If n is even, the graph of the function is entirely above the x-axis. The graphs of $1/x^n$ for n even are similar to one another.

● If n is odd, the function is positive for positive x and negative for negative x. The graphs of $1/x^n$ for n odd are similar to one another.

● As n increases, the graphs of $1/x^n$ approach 0 faster as $x \to \infty$.

27. $f(x) = x^4 + cx^2 + x$. If $c < 0$, there are three humps: two minimum points and a maximum point. These humps get flatter as c increases, until at $c = 0$ two of the humps disappear and there is only one minimum point. This single hump then moves to the right and approaches the origin as c increases.

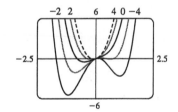

28. $f(x) = \sqrt{1 + cx^2}$. If $c < 0$, the function is only defined on $\left[-1/\sqrt{-c}, 1/\sqrt{-c} \right]$, and its graph is the top half of an ellipse. If $c = 0$, the graph is the line $y = 1$. If $c > 0$, the graph is the top half of a hyperbola. As c approaches 0, these curves become flatter and approach the line $y = 1$.

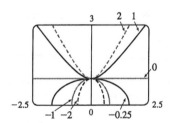

29. $y = x^n 2^{-x}$. As n increases, the maximum of the function moves further from the origin, and gets larger. Note, however, that regardless of n, the function approaches 0 as $x \to \infty$.

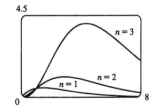

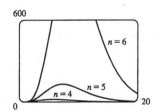

30. $y = \dfrac{|x|}{\sqrt{c - x^2}}$. The "bullet" becomes broader as c increases.

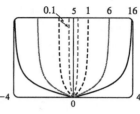

31. $y^2 = cx^3 + x^2$

If $c < 0$, the loop is to the right of the origin, and if c is positive, it is to the left. In both cases, the closer c is to 0, the larger the loop is. (In the limiting case, $c = 0$, the loop is "infinite", that is, it doesn't close.) Also, the larger $|c|$ is, the steeper the slope is on the loopless side of the origin.

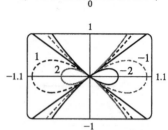

32. (a) $y = \sin(\sqrt{x})$

This function is not periodic; it oscillates less frequently as x increases.

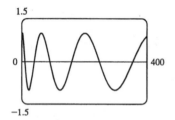

(b) $y = \sin(x^2)$

This function oscillates more frequently as $|x|$ increases. Note also that this function is even, whereas $\sin x$ is odd.

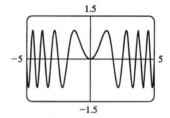

33. The graphing window is 95 pixels wide and we want to start with $x = 0$ and end with $x = 2\pi$. Since there are 94 "gaps" between pixels, the distance between pixels is $\frac{2\pi - 0}{94}$. Thus, the x-values that the calculator actually plots are $x = 0 + \frac{2\pi}{94} \cdot n$, where $n = 0, 1, 2, \ldots, 93, 94$. For $y = \sin 2x$, the actual points plotted by the calculator are $\left(\frac{2\pi}{94} \cdot n, \sin\left(2 \cdot \frac{2\pi}{94} \cdot n\right)\right)$ for $n = 0, 1, \ldots, 94$. For $y = \sin 96x$, the points plotted are $\left(\frac{2\pi}{94} \cdot n, \sin\left(96 \cdot \frac{2\pi}{94} \cdot n\right)\right)$ for $n = 0, 1, \ldots, 94$. But

$$\begin{aligned} \sin\left(96 \cdot \tfrac{2\pi}{94} \cdot n\right) &= \sin\left(94 \cdot \tfrac{2\pi}{94} \cdot n + 2 \cdot \tfrac{2\pi}{94} \cdot n\right) = \sin\left(2\pi n + 2 \cdot \tfrac{2\pi}{94} \cdot n\right) \\ &= \sin(2\pi n)\cos\left(2 \cdot \tfrac{2\pi}{94} \cdot n\right) + \cos(2\pi n)\sin\left(2 \cdot \tfrac{2\pi}{94} \cdot n\right) \quad \text{[Addition formula for the sine]} \\ &= 0 \cdot \cos\left(2 \cdot \tfrac{2\pi}{94} \cdot n\right) + 1 \cdot \sin\left(2 \cdot \tfrac{2\pi}{94} \cdot n\right) = \sin\left(2 \cdot \tfrac{2\pi}{94} \cdot n\right), \quad n = 0, 1, \ldots, 94 \end{aligned}$$

So the y-values, and hence the points, plotted for $y = \sin 96x$ are identical to those plotted for $y = \sin 2x$.

Note: Try graphing $y = \sin 94x$. Can you see why all the y-values are zero?

34. As in Exercise 33, we know that the points being plotted for $y = \sin 45x$ are $\left(\frac{2\pi}{94} \cdot n, \sin\left(45 \cdot \frac{2\pi}{94} \cdot n\right)\right)$ for $n = 0, 1, \ldots, 94$. But

$$\begin{aligned} \sin\left(45 \cdot \tfrac{2\pi}{94} \cdot n\right) &= \sin\left(47 \cdot \tfrac{2\pi}{94} \cdot n - 2 \cdot \tfrac{2\pi}{94} \cdot n\right) = \sin\left(n\pi - 2 \cdot \tfrac{2\pi}{94} \cdot n\right) \\ &= \sin(n\pi)\cos\left(2 \cdot \tfrac{2\pi}{94} \cdot n\right) - \cos(n\pi)\sin\left(2 \cdot \tfrac{2\pi}{94} \cdot n\right) \quad \text{[Subtraction formula for the sine]} \\ &= 0 \cdot \cos\left(2 \cdot \tfrac{2\pi}{94} \cdot n\right) - (\pm 1)\sin\left(2 \cdot \tfrac{2\pi}{94} \cdot n\right) = \pm\sin\left(2 \cdot \tfrac{2\pi}{94} \cdot n\right), \quad n = 0, 1, \ldots, 94 \end{aligned}$$

So the y-values, and hence the points, plotted for $y = \sin 45x$ lie on either $y = \sin 2x$ or $y = -\sin 2x$.

1.5 Exponential Functions · · · · · · · · · · ·

1. (a) $f(x) = a^x, a > 0$ (b) $\mathbb{R}$

(c) $(0, \infty)$ (d) See Figures 4(c), 4(b), and 4(a), respectively.

2. (a) The number e is the value of a such that the slope of the tangent line at $x = 0$ on the graph of $y = a^x$ is exactly 1.

(b) $e \approx 2.71828$ (c) $f(x) = e^x$

3. All of these graphs approach 0 as $x \to -\infty$, all of them pass through the point $(0, 1)$, and all of them are increasing and approach ∞ as $x \to \infty$. The larger the base, the faster the function increases for $x > 0$, and the faster it approaches 0 as $x \to -\infty$.

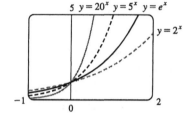

4. The graph of e^{-x} is the reflection of the graph of e^x about the y-axis, and the graph of 8^{-x} is the reflection of that of 8^x about the y-axis. The graph of 8^x increases more quickly than that of e^x for $x > 0$, and approaches 0 faster as $x \to -\infty$.

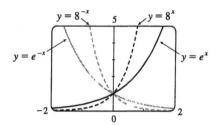

5. The functions with bases greater than 1 (3^x and 10^x) are increasing, while those with bases less than 1 $[\left(\frac{1}{3}\right)^x$ and $\left(\frac{1}{10}\right)^x]$ are decreasing. The graph of $\left(\frac{1}{3}\right)^x$ is the reflection of that of 3^x about the y-axis, and the graph of $\left(\frac{1}{10}\right)^x$ is the reflection of that of 10^x about the y-axis. The graph of 10^x increases more quickly than that of 3^x for $x > 0$, and approaches 0 faster as $x \to -\infty$.

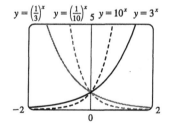

6. Each of the graphs approaches ∞ as $x \to -\infty$, and each approaches 0 as $x \to \infty$. The smaller the base, the faster the function grows as $x \to -\infty$, and the faster it approaches 0 as $x \to \infty$.

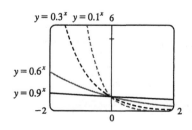

7. We start with the graph of $y = 4^x$ (Figure 3) and then shift 3 units downward. This shift doesn't affect the domain, but the range of $y = 4^x - 3$ is $(-3, \infty)$. There is a horizontal asymptote of $y = -3$.

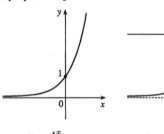

$y = 4^x$

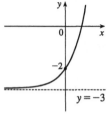

$y = 4^x - 3$

8. We start with the graph of $y = 4^x$ (Figure 3) and then shift 3 units to the right. There is a horizontal asymptote of $y = 0$.

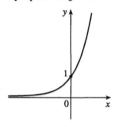

$y = 4^x$

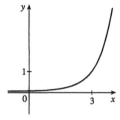

$y = 4^{x-3}$

9. We start with the graph of $y = 2^x$ (Figure 3), reflect it about the y-axis, and then about the x-axis (or just rotate $180°$ to handle both reflections) to obtain the graph of $y = -2^{-x}$. In each graph, $y = 0$ is the horizontal asymptote.

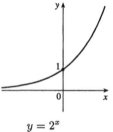

$y = 2^x$

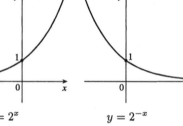

$y = 2^{-x}$

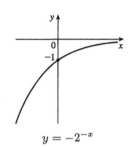

$y = -2^{-x}$

10. We start with the graph of $y = e^x$ (Figure 13), vertically stretch by a factor of 2, and then shift 1 unit upward. There is a horizontal asymptote of $y = 1$.

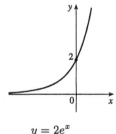

$y = 2e^x$

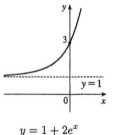

$y = 1 + 2e^x$

11. We start with the graph of $y = e^x$ (Figure 13), reflect it about the x-axis, and then shift 3 units upward. Note the horizontal asymptote of $y = 3$.

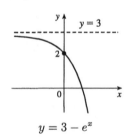

$y = -e^x$

$y = 3 - e^x$

12. We start with the graph of $y = e^x$ (Figure 13), reflect it about the y-axis, and then about the x-axis (or just rotate $180°$ to handle both reflections) to obtain the graph of $y = -e^{-x}$. Now shift this graph 1 unit upward, vertically stretch by a factor of 5, and then shift 2 units upward.

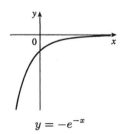

$y = -e^{-x}$

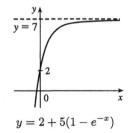

$y = 2 + 5(1 - e^{-x})$

13. (a) To find the equation of the graph that results from shifting the graph of $y = e^x$ 2 units downward, we subtract 2 from the original function to get $y = e^x - 2$.

(b) To find the equation of the graph that results from shifting the graph of $y = e^x$ 2 units to the right, we replace x with $x - 2$ in the original function to get $y = e^{(x-2)}$.

(c) To find the equation of the graph that results from reflecting the graph of $y = e^x$ about the x-axis, we multiply the original function by -1 to get $y = -e^x$.

(d) To find the equation of the graph that results from reflecting the graph of $y = e^x$ about the y-axis, we replace x with $-x$ in the original function to get $y = e^{-x}$.

(e) To find the equation of the graph that results from reflecting the graph of $y = e^x$ about the x-axis and then about the y-axis, we first multiply the original function by -1 (to get $y = -e^x$) and then replace x with $-x$ in this equation to get $y = -e^{-x}$.

14. (a) This reflection consists of first reflecting the graph about the x-axis (giving the graph with equation $y = -e^x$) and then shifting this graph $2 \cdot 4 = 8$ units upward. So the equation is $y = -e^x + 8$.

(b) This reflection consists of first reflecting the graph about the y-axis (giving the graph with equation $y = e^{-x}$) and then shifting this graph $2 \cdot 2 = 4$ units to the right. So the equation is $y = e^{-(x-4)}$.

15. Use $y = Ca^x$ with the points $(1, 6)$ and $(3, 24)$. $6 = Ca^1$ $\left(C = \frac{6}{a} \right)$ and $24 = Ca^3$ $\Rightarrow$ $24 = \left(\dfrac{6}{a} \right) a^3$ $\Rightarrow$

$4 = a^2$ $\Rightarrow$ $a = 2$ (since $a > 0$) and $C = 3$. The function is $f(x) = 3 \cdot 2^x$.

16. Given the y-intercept $(0, 2)$, we have $y = Ca^x = 2a^x$. Using the point $\left(2, \frac{2}{9} \right)$ gives us $\frac{2}{9} = 2a^2$ $\Rightarrow$ $\frac{1}{9} = a^2$ $\Rightarrow$ $a = \frac{1}{3}$ (since $a > 0$). The function is $f(x) = 2 \left(\frac{1}{3} \right)^x$ or $f(x) = 2 (3)^{-x}$.

17. If $f(x) = 5^x$, then $\dfrac{f(x+h) - f(x)}{h} = \dfrac{5^{x+h} - 5^x}{h} = \dfrac{5^x 5^h - 5^x}{h} = \dfrac{5^x (5^h - 1)}{h} = 5^x \left(\dfrac{5^h - 1}{h} \right)$.

18. Suppose the month is February. Your payment on the 28th day would be $2^{28-1} = 2^{27} = 134{,}217{,}728$ cents, or $\$1{,}342{,}177.28$. Clearly, the second method of payment results in a larger amount for any month.

19. 2 ft $= 24$ in, $f(24) = 24^2$ in $= 576$ in $= 48$ ft. $g(24) = 2^{24}$ in $= 2^{24} / (12 \cdot 5280)$ mi ≈ 265 mi

20. We see from the graphs that for x less than about 1.8, $g(x) = 5^x > f(x) = x^5$, and then near the point $(1.8, 17.1)$ the curves intersect. Then $f(x) > g(x)$ from $x \approx 1.8$ until $x = 5$. At $(5, 3125)$ there is another point of intersection, and for $x > 5$ we see that $g(x) > f(x)$. In fact, g increases much more rapidly than f beyond that point.

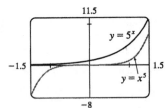

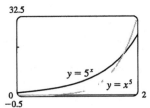

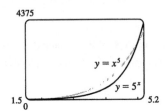

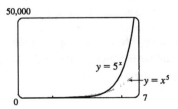

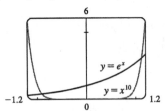

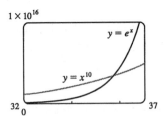

21. The graph of g finally surpasses that of f at $x \approx 35.8$.

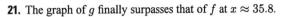

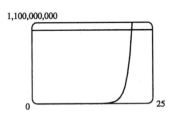

22. We graph $y = e^x$ and $y = 1{,}000{,}000{,}000$ and determine where $e^x = 1 \times 10^9$. This seems to be true at $x \approx 20.723$, so $e^x > 1 \times 10^9$ for $x > 20.723$.

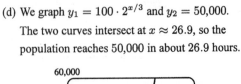

23. (a) Fifteen hours represents 5 doubling periods (one doubling period is three hours).

$100 \cdot 2^5 = 3200$

(b) In t hours, there will be $t/3$ doubling periods. The initial population is 100, so the population y at time t is $y = 100 \cdot 2^{t/3}$.

(c) $t = 20 \implies y = 100 \cdot 2^{20/3} \approx 10{,}159$

(d) We graph $y_1 = 100 \cdot 2^{x/3}$ and $y_2 = 50{,}000$. The two curves intersect at $x \approx 26.9$, so the population reaches 50,000 in about 26.9 hours.

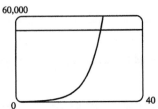

24. (a) Sixty hours represents 4 half-life periods.

$2 \cdot \left(\frac{1}{2}\right)^4 = \frac{1}{8}$ g

(b) In t hours, there will be $t/15$ half-life periods.
The initial mass is 2 g, so the mass y at time t
is $y = 2 \cdot \left(\frac{1}{2}\right)^{t/15}$.

(c) 4 days $= 4 \cdot 24 = 96$ hours. $t = 96 \Rightarrow$
$y = 2 \cdot \left(\frac{1}{2}\right)^{96/15} \approx 0.024$ g

(d) $y = 0.01 \Rightarrow t \approx 114.7$ hours

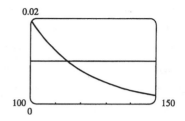

25. An exponential model is $y = ab^t$, where
$a = 3.3039025371408 \times 10^{-12}$ and $b = 1.0177407727104$.
This model gives $y(1993) \approx 5494$ million and
$y(2010) \approx 7409$ million.

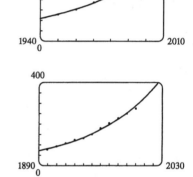

26. An exponential model is $y = ab^t$, where
$a = 2.4141114809373 \times 10^{-9}$ and $b = 1.0128340610383$.
This model gives $y(1925) \approx 111$ million,
$y(2010) \approx 327$ million, and $y(2020) \approx 372$ million.

1.6 Inverse Functions and Logarithms · · · · · · · · · ·

1. (a) See Definition 1.

(b) It must pass the Horizontal Line Test.

2. (a) $f^{-1}(y) = x \Leftrightarrow f(x) = y$ for any y in B. The domain of f^{-1} is B and the range of f^{-1} is A.

(b) See the steps in (5).

(c) Reflect the graph of f about the line $y = x$.

3. f is not one-to-one because $2 \neq 6$, but $f(2) = f(6)$.

4. f is one-to-one since for any two different domain values, there are different range values.

5. No horizontal line intersects the graph of f more than once. Thus, by the Horizontal Line Test, f is one-to-one.

6. The horizontal line $y = 0$ (the x-axis) intersects the graph of f in more than one point. Thus, by the Horizontal Line Test, f is not one-to-one.

7. The horizontal line $y = 0$ (the x-axis) intersects the graph of f in more than one point. Thus, by the Horizontal Line Test, f is not one-to-one.

8. No horizontal line intersects the graph of f more than once. Thus, by the Horizontal Line Test, f is one-to-one.

9. The graph of $f(x) = \frac{1}{2}(x+5)$ is a line with slope $\frac{1}{2}$. It passes the Horizontal Line Test, so f is one-to-one.
Algebraic soution: If $x_1 \neq x_2$, then $x_1 + 5 \neq x_2 + 5$ $\Rightarrow$ $\frac{1}{2}(x_1 + 5) \neq \frac{1}{2}(x_2 + 5)$ $\Rightarrow$ $f(x_1) \neq f(x_2)$, so f is one-to-one.

10. The graph of $f(x) = 1 + 4x - x^2$ is a parabola with axis of symmetry $x = -\frac{b}{2a} = -\frac{4}{2(-1)} = 2$. Pick any x-values equidistant from 2 to find two equal function values. For example, $f(1) = 4$ and $f(3) = 4$, so f is not 1-1.

11. $g(x) = |x|$ $\Rightarrow$ $g(-1) = 1 = g(1)$, so g is not one-to-one.

12. $x_1 \neq x_2$ $\Rightarrow$ $\sqrt{x_1} \neq \sqrt{x_2}$ $\Rightarrow$ $g(x_1) \neq g(x_2)$, so g is 1-1.

13. A football will attain every height h up to its maximum height twice: once on the way up, and again on the way down. Thus, even if t_1 does not equal t_2, $f(t_1)$ may equal $f(t_2)$, so f is not 1-1.

14. f is not 1-1 because eventually we all stop growing and therefore, there are two times at which we have the same height.

15. f does not pass the Horizontal Line Test, so f is not 1-1.

16. f passes the Horizontal Line Test, so f is 1-1.

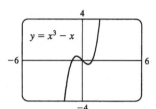

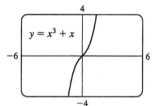

17. Since $f(2) = 9$ and f is 1-1, we know that $f^{-1}(9) = 2$. Remember, if the point $(2, 9)$ is on the graph of f, then the point $(9, 2)$ is on the graph of f^{-1}.

18. (a) First, we must determine x such that $f(x) = 3$. By inspection, we see that if $x = 0$, then $f(x) = 3$. Since f is 1-1 (f is an increasing function), it has an inverse, and $f^{-1}(3) = 0$.

(b) By the second cancellation equation in (4), we have $f(f^{-1}(5)) = 5$.

19. First, we must determine x such that $g(x) = 4$. By inspection, we see that if $x = 0$, then $g(x) = 4$. Since g is 1-1 (g is an increasing function), it has an inverse, and $g^{-1}(4) = 0$.

20. (a) f is 1-1 because it passes the Horizontal Line Test.

(b) Domain of $f = [-3, 3]$ = Range of f^{-1}. Range of $f = [-2, 2]$ = Domain of f^{-1}.

(c) Since $f(-2) = 1$, $f^{-1}(1) = -2$.

21. We solve $C = \frac{5}{9}(F - 32)$ for F: $\frac{9}{5}C = F - 32$ $\Rightarrow$ $F = \frac{9}{5}C + 32$. This gives us the Fahrenheit temperature F as a function of the Celsius temperature C. $F \geq -459.67$ $\Rightarrow$ $\frac{9}{5}C + 32 \geq -459.67$ $\Rightarrow$ $\frac{9}{5}C \geq -491.67$ $\Rightarrow$ $C \geq -273.15$, the domain of the inverse function.

22. $m = \dfrac{m_0}{\sqrt{1 - v^2/c^2}}$ $\Rightarrow$ $1 - \dfrac{v^2}{c^2} = \dfrac{m_0^2}{m^2}$ $\Rightarrow$ $\dfrac{v^2}{c^2} = 1 - \dfrac{m_0^2}{m^2}$ $\Rightarrow$ $v^2 = c^2\left(1 - \dfrac{m_0^2}{m^2}\right)$ $\Rightarrow$

$v = c\sqrt{1 - \dfrac{m_0^2}{m^2}}$. This formula gives us the velocity v of the particle in terms of its mass m, that is, $v = f^{-1}(m)$.

23. $f(x) = \sqrt{10 - 3x}$ $\Rightarrow$ $y = \sqrt{10 - 3x}$; $y \geq 0$ $\Rightarrow$ $y^2 = 10 - 3x$ $\Rightarrow$ $3x = 10 - y^2$ $\Rightarrow$
$x = -\frac{1}{3}y^2 + \frac{10}{3}$. Interchange x and y: $y = -\frac{1}{3}x^2 + \frac{10}{3}$. So $f^{-1}(x) = -\frac{1}{3}x^2 + \frac{10}{3}$. Note that the domain of f^{-1} is $x \geq 0$.

24. $f(x) = \dfrac{4x-1}{2x+3}$ ⇒ $y = \dfrac{4x-1}{2x+3}$ ⇒ $y(2x+3) = 4x-1$ ⇒ $2xy + 3y = 4x - 1$ ⇒

$3y + 1 = 4x - 2xy$ ⇒ $3y + 1 = (4-2y)x$ ⇒ $x = \dfrac{3y+1}{4-2y}$. Interchange x and y: $y = \dfrac{3x+1}{4-2x}$.

So $f^{-1}(x) = \dfrac{3x+1}{4-2x}$.

25. $f(x) = e^{x^3}$ ⇒ $y = e^{x^3}$ ⇒ $\ln y = x^3$ ⇒ $x = \sqrt[3]{\ln y}$. Interchange x and y: $y = \sqrt[3]{\ln x}$.
So $f^{-1}(x) = \sqrt[3]{\ln x}$.

26. $y = 2x^3 + 3$ ⇒ $y - 3 = 2x^3$ ⇒ $\dfrac{y-3}{2} = x^3$ ⇒ $x = \sqrt[3]{\dfrac{y-3}{2}}$.

Interchange x and y: $y = \sqrt[3]{\dfrac{x-3}{2}}$. So $f^{-1}(x) = \sqrt[3]{\dfrac{x-3}{2}}$.

27. $y = \ln(x+3)$ ⇒ $x + 3 = e^y$ ⇒ $x = e^y - 3$. Interchange x and y: $y = e^x - 3$. So $f^{-1}(x) = e^x - 3$.

28. $y = \dfrac{1+e^x}{1-e^x}$ ⇒ $y - ye^x = 1 + e^x$ ⇒ $y - 1 = ye^x + e^x$ ⇒ $y - 1 = e^x(y+1)$ ⇒

$e^x = \dfrac{y-1}{y+1}$ ⇒ $x = \ln\left(\dfrac{y-1}{y+1}\right)$. Interchange x and y: $y = \ln\left(\dfrac{x-1}{x+1}\right)$. So $f^{-1}(x) = \ln\left(\dfrac{x-1}{x+1}\right)$.

Note that the domain of f^{-1} is $|x| > 1$.

29. $y = f(x) = 1 - \dfrac{2}{x^2}$ ⇒ $1 - y = \dfrac{2}{x^2}$ ⇒ $x^2 = \dfrac{2}{1-y}$ ⇒

$x = \sqrt{\dfrac{2}{1-y}}$, since $x > 0$. Interchange x and y: $y = \sqrt{\dfrac{2}{1-x}}$.

So $f^{-1}(x) = \sqrt{\dfrac{2}{1-x}}$.

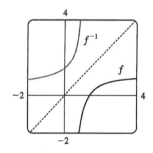

30. $y = f(x) = \sqrt{x^2 + 2x}$, $x > 0$ ⇒ $y > 0$ and $y^2 = x^2 + 2x$ ⇒

$x^2 + 2x - y^2 = 0$. Now we use the quadratic formula:

$x = \dfrac{-2 \pm \sqrt{2^2 - 4 \cdot 1 \cdot (-y^2)}}{2 \cdot 1} = -1 \pm \sqrt{1 + y^2}$. But $x > 0$, so the

negative root is inadmissible. Interchange x and y: $y = -1 + \sqrt{1 + x^2}$.
So $f^{-1}(x) = -1 + \sqrt{1 + x^2}$, $x > 0$.

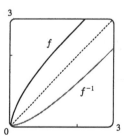

31. The function f is one-to-one, so its inverse exists and the graph of its inverse
can be obtained by reflecting the graph of f about the line $y = x$.

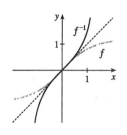

32. The function f is one-to-one, so its inverse exists and the graph of its inverse can be obtained by reflecting the graph of f about the line $y = x$. For the graph of $1/f$, the y-coordinates are simply the reciprocals of f. For example, if $f(5) = 9$, then $1/f(5) = \frac{1}{9}$. If we draw the horizontal line $y = 1$, we see that the only place where the graphs intersect is on that line.

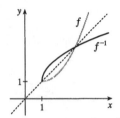 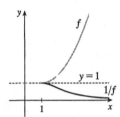

33. (a) It is defined as the inverse of the exponential function with base a, that is, $\log_a x = y \Leftrightarrow a^y = x$.

(b) $(0, \infty)$ (c) $\mathbb{R}$ (d) See Figure 1.

34. (a) The natural logarithm is the logarithm with base e, denoted $\ln x$.

(b) The common logarithm is the logarithm with base 10, denoted $\log x$.

(c) See Figure 3.

35. (a) $\log_2 64 = 6$ since $2^6 = 64$. (b) $\log_6 \frac{1}{36} = -2$ since $6^{-2} = \frac{1}{36}$.

36. (a) $\log_8 2 = \frac{1}{3}$ since $8^{1/3} = 2$. (b) $\ln e^{\sqrt{2}} = \sqrt{2}$

37. (a) $\log_{10} 1.25 + \log_{10} 80 = \log_{10}(1.25 \cdot 80) = \log_{10} 100 = \log_{10} 10^2 = 2$

(b) $\log_5 10 + \log_5 20 - 3\log_5 2 = \log_5 (10 \cdot 20) - \log_5 2^3 = \log_5 \frac{200}{8} = \log_5 25 = \log_5 5^2 = 2$

38. (a) $2^{(\log_2 3 + \log_2 5)} = 2^{\log_2 15} = 15$ [*Or:* $2^{(\log_2 3 + \log_2 5)} = 2^{\log_2 3} \cdot 2^{\log_2 5} = 3 \cdot 5 = 15$]

(b) $e^{3\ln 2} = e^{\ln(2^3)} = e^{\ln 8} = 8$ [*Or:* $e^{3\ln 2} = (e^{\ln 2})^3 = 2^3 = 8$]

39. $2\ln 4 - \ln 2 = \ln 4^2 - \ln 2 = \ln 16 - \ln 2 = \ln \frac{16}{2} = \ln 8$

40. $\ln x + a\ln y - b\ln z = \ln x + \ln y^a - \ln z^b = \ln \left(xy^a / z^b\right)$

41. (a) $\log_2 5 = \dfrac{\ln 5}{\ln 2} \approx 2.321928$ (b) $\log_5 26.05 = \dfrac{\ln 26.05}{\ln 5} \approx 2.025563$

42. The domain of $\ln$ is $(0, \infty)$, so the domain of $g(x) = \ln(4 - x^2)$ is found by solving the inequality $4 - x^2 > 0 \Leftrightarrow x^2 < 4 \Leftrightarrow |x| < 2$. Thus, the domain of g is $(-2, 2)$. As x gets close to 2 from the left (or -2 from the right), $4 - x^2$ gets close to 0, and $\ln(4 - x^2)$ decreases without bound. The maximum value occurs when $x = 0$. Hence, the range is $(-\infty, \ln 4]$.

43. To graph these functions, we use $\log_{1.5} x = \dfrac{\ln x}{\ln 1.5}$ and

$\log_{50} x = \dfrac{\ln x}{\ln 50}$. These graphs all approach $-\infty$ as $x \to 0^+$, and they all pass through the point $(1, 0)$. Also, they are all increasing, and all approach ∞ as $x \to \infty$. The functions with larger bases increase extremely slowly, and the ones with smaller bases do so somewhat more quickly. The functions with large bases approach the y-axis more closely as $x \to 0^+$.

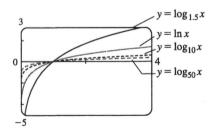

44. We see that the graph of $\ln x$ is the reflection of the graph of e^x about the line $y = x$, and that the graph of $\log_{10} x$ is the reflection of the graph of 10^x about the same line. The graph of 10^x increases more quickly than that of e^x. Also note that $\log_{10} x \to \infty$ as $x \to \infty$ more slowly than $\ln x$.

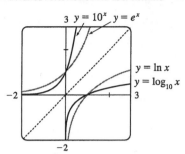

45. 3 ft $= 36$ in, so we need x such that $\log_2 x = 36$ $\Leftrightarrow$ $x = 2^{36} = 68{,}719{,}476{,}736$. In miles, this is
$$68{,}719{,}476{,}736 \text{ in} \cdot \frac{1 \text{ ft}}{12 \text{ in}} \cdot \frac{1 \text{ mi}}{5280 \text{ ft}} \approx 1{,}084{,}587.7 \text{ mi}.$$

46.

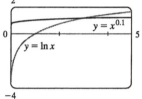 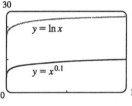 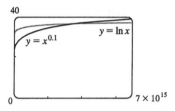

From the graphs, we see that $f(x) = x^{0.1} > g(x) = \ln x$ for approximately $0 < x < 3.06$, and then $g(x) > f(x)$ for $3.06 < x < 3.43 \times 10^{15}$ (approximately). At that point, the graph of f finally surpasses the graph of g for good.

47. (a) Shift the graph of $y = \log_{10} x$ five units to the left to obtain the graph of $y = \log_{10}(x + 5)$. Note the vertical asymptote of $x = -5$.

$$y = \log_{10} x \qquad\qquad y = \log_{10}(x + 5)$$

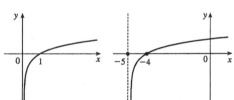

(b) Reflect the graph of $y = \ln x$ about the x-axis to obtain the graph of $y = -\ln x$.

$$y = \ln x \qquad\qquad y = -\ln x$$

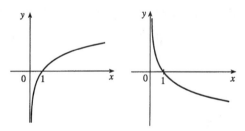

48. (a) Reflect the graph of $y = \ln x$ about the y-axis to obtain the graph of $y = \ln(-x)$.

$$y = \ln x \qquad\qquad y = \ln(-x)$$

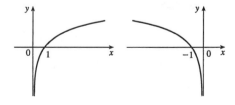

(b) Reflect the portion of the graph of $y = \ln x$ to the right of the y-axis about the y-axis. The graph of $y = \ln |x|$ is that reflection in addition to the original portion.

$$y = \ln x \qquad\qquad y = \ln |x|$$

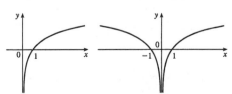

49. (a) $2\ln x = 1 \;\Rightarrow\; \ln x = \frac{1}{2} \;\Rightarrow\; x = e^{1/2} = \sqrt{e}$

(b) $e^{-x} = 5 \;\Rightarrow\; -x = \ln 5 \;\Rightarrow\; x = -\ln 5$

50. (a) $e^{2x+3} - 7 = 0 \;\Rightarrow\; e^{2x+3} = 7 \;\Rightarrow\; 2x + 3 = \ln 7 \;\Rightarrow\; 2x = \ln 7 - 3 \;\Rightarrow\; x = \frac{1}{2}(\ln 7 - 3)$

(b) $\ln(5 - 2x) = -3 \;\Rightarrow\; 5 - 2x = e^{-3} \;\Rightarrow\; 2x = 5 - e^{-3} \;\Rightarrow\; x = \frac{1}{2}(5 - e^{-3})$

51. (a) $2^{x-5} = 3 \;\Leftrightarrow\; \log_2 3 = x - 5 \;\Leftrightarrow\; x = 5 + \log_2 3. \;\Leftrightarrow\;$

$\quad$ Or: $2^{x-5} = 3 \;\Leftrightarrow\; \ln(2^{x-5}) = \ln 3 \;\Leftrightarrow\; (x - 5)\ln 2 = \ln 3 \;\Leftrightarrow\; x - 5 = \dfrac{\ln 3}{\ln 2} \;\Leftrightarrow\; x = 5 + \dfrac{\ln 3}{\ln 2}$

(b) $\ln x + \ln(x - 1) = \ln(x(x - 1)) = 1 \;\Leftrightarrow\; x(x - 1) = e^1 \;\Leftrightarrow\; x^2 - x - e = 0.$ The quadratic formula
$\quad$ (with $a = 1$, $b = -1$, and $c = -e$) gives $x = \frac{1}{2}(1 \pm \sqrt{1 + 4e})$, but we reject the negative root since the natural
$\quad$ logarithm is not defined for $x < 0$. So $x = \frac{1}{2}(1 + \sqrt{1 + 4e})$.

52. (a) $\ln(\ln x) = 1 \;\Leftrightarrow\; e^{\ln(\ln x)} = e^1 \;\Leftrightarrow\; \ln x = e^1 = e \;\Leftrightarrow\; e^{\ln x} = e^e \;\Leftrightarrow\; x = e^e$

(b) $e^{ax} = Ce^{bx} \;\Leftrightarrow\; \ln e^{ax} = \ln C\,(e^{bx}) \;\Leftrightarrow\; ax = \ln C + bx \;\Leftrightarrow\; (a - b)x = \ln C \;\Leftrightarrow\;$

$\quad x = \dfrac{\ln C}{a - b}$

53. (a) $e^x < 10 \;\Rightarrow\; \ln e^x < \ln 10 \;\Rightarrow\; x < \ln 10 \;\Rightarrow\; x \in (-\infty, \ln 10)$

(b) $\ln x > -1 \;\Rightarrow\; e^{\ln x} > e^{-1} \;\Rightarrow\; x > e^{-1} \;\Rightarrow\; x \in (1/e, \infty)$

54. (a) $2 < \ln x < 9 \;\Rightarrow\; e^2 < e^{\ln x} < e^9 \;\Rightarrow\; e^2 < x < e^9 \;\Rightarrow\; x \in (e^2, e^9)$

(b) $e^{2-3x} > 4 \;\Rightarrow\; \ln e^{2-3x} > \ln 4 \;\Rightarrow\; 2 - 3x > \ln 4 \;\Rightarrow\; -3x > \ln 4 - 2 \;\Rightarrow\;$
$\quad x < -\frac{1}{3}(\ln 4 - 2) \;\Rightarrow\; x \in (-\infty, \frac{1}{3}(2 - \ln 4))$

55. We see that the graph of $y = f(x) = \sqrt{x^3 + x^2 + x + 1}$ is increasing, so
f is 1-1. Enter $x = \sqrt{y^3 + y^2 + y + 1}$ and use your CAS to solve the
equation for y. Using Derive, we get two (irrelevant) solutions involving
imaginary expressions, as well as one which can be simplified to the
following:

$$y = f^{-1}(x) = -\tfrac{\sqrt[3]{4}}{6}\left(\sqrt[3]{D - 27x^2 + 20} - \sqrt[3]{D + 27x^2 - 20} + \sqrt[3]{2}\right)$$

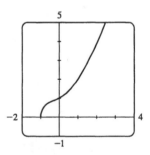

where $D = 3\sqrt{3}\sqrt{27x^4 - 40x^2 + 16}$. Maple and Mathematica each give two complex expressions and one real
expression, and the real expression is equivalent to that given by Derive. For example, Maple's expression simplifies
to $\dfrac{1}{6}\,\dfrac{M^{2/3} - 8 - 2M^{1/3}}{2M^{1/3}}$, where $M = 108x^2 + 12\sqrt{48 - 120x^2 + 81x^4} - 80$.

56. (a) If we use Derive, then solving $x = y^6 + y^4$ for y gives us six solutions of the form $y = \pm\frac{\sqrt{3}}{3}\sqrt{B - 1}$, where

$$B \in \left\{-2\sin\frac{A}{3},\, 2\sin\left(\frac{A}{3} + \frac{\pi}{3}\right),\, -2\cos\left(\frac{A}{3} + \frac{\pi}{6}\right)\right\} \text{ and } A = \sin^{-1}\left(\frac{27x - 2}{2}\right). \text{ The inverse for}$$

$y = x^6 + x^4$ $(x \geq 0)$ is $y = \frac{\sqrt{3}}{3}\sqrt{B - 1}$ with $B = 2\sin\left(\dfrac{A}{3} + \dfrac{\pi}{3}\right)$, but because the domain of A is $[0, \frac{4}{27}]$,

this expression is only valid for $x \in [0, \frac{4}{27}]$.

Happily, Maple gives us the rest of the solution! We solve $x = y^6 + y^4$ for y to get the two real solutions

$$\pm \frac{\sqrt{6}}{6} \frac{\sqrt{C^{1/3} \left(C^{2/3} - 2C^{1/3} + 4\right)}}{C^{1/3}}, \text{ where } C = 108x + 12\sqrt{3}\sqrt{x\,(27x - 4)}, \text{ and the inverse for } y = x^6 + x^4$$

($x \geq 0$) is the positive solution, whose domain is $\left[\frac{4}{27}, \infty\right)$.

Mathematica also gives two real solutions, equivalent to those of

Maple. The positive one is $\dfrac{\sqrt{6}}{6}\left(\sqrt[3]{4}D^{1/3} + 2\sqrt[3]{2}D^{-1/3} - 2\right)$, where

$D = -2 + 27x + 3\sqrt{3}\sqrt{x}\sqrt{27x - 4}$. Although this expression also has

domain $\left[\frac{4}{27}, \infty\right)$, Mathematica is mysteriously able to plot the solution

for all $x \geq 0$.

(b)

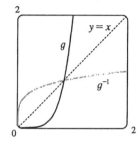

57. (a) $n = 100 \cdot 2^{t/3}$ $\Rightarrow$ $\dfrac{n}{100} = 2^{t/3}$ $\Rightarrow$ $\log_2\left(\dfrac{n}{100}\right) = \dfrac{t}{3}$ $\Rightarrow$ $t = 3\log_2\left(\dfrac{n}{100}\right)$. Using formula (10), we

can write this as $t = 3 \cdot \dfrac{\ln(n/100)}{\ln 2}$. This function tells us how long it will take to obtain n bacteria (given the

number n).

(b) $n = 50,000$ $\Rightarrow$ $t = 3\log_2\dfrac{50,000}{100} = 3\log_2 500 = 3\left(\dfrac{\ln 500}{\ln 2}\right) \approx 26.9$ hours

58. (a) $Q = Q_0\left(1 - e^{-t/a}\right)$ $\Rightarrow$ $\dfrac{Q}{Q_0} = 1 - e^{-t/a}$ $\Rightarrow$ $e^{-t/a} = 1 - \dfrac{Q}{Q_0}$ $\Rightarrow$ $-\dfrac{t}{a} = \ln\left(1 - \dfrac{Q}{Q_0}\right)$ $\Rightarrow$

$t = -a\ln(1 - Q/Q_0)$. This gives us the time t necessary to obtain a given charge Q.

(b) $Q = 0.9Q_0$ and $a = 2$ $\Rightarrow$ $t = -2\ln\left(1 - 0.9\left(Q_0/Q_0\right)\right) = -2\ln 0.1 \approx 4.6$ seconds.

59. (a) To find the equation of the graph that results from shifting the graph of $y = \ln x$ 3 units upward, we add 3 to the original function to get $y = \ln x + 3$.

(b) To find the equation of the graph that results from shifting the graph of $y = \ln x$ 3 units to the left, we replace x with $x + 3$ in the original function to get $y = \ln(x + 3)$.

(c) To find the equation of the graph that results from reflecting the graph of $y = \ln x$ about the x-axis, we multiply the original equation by -1 to get $y = -\ln x$.

(d) To find the equation of the graph that results from reflecting the graph of $y = \ln x$ about the y-axis, we replace x with $-x$ in the original equation to get $y = \ln(-x)$.

(e) To find the equation of the graph that results from reflecting the graph of $y = \ln x$ about the line $y = x$, we interchange x and y in the original equation to get $x = \ln y$ $\Leftrightarrow$ $y = e^x$.

(f) To find the equation of the graph that results from reflecting the graph of $y = \ln x$ about the x-axis and then about the line $y = x$, we first multiply the original equation by -1 [to get $y = -\ln x$] and then interchange x and y in this equation to get $x = -\ln y$ $\Leftrightarrow$ $\ln y = -x$ $\Leftrightarrow$ $y = e^{-x}$.

(g) To find the equation of the graph that results from reflecting the graph of $y = \ln x$ about the y-axis and then about the line $y = x$, we first replace x with $-x$ in the original equation [to get $y = \ln(-x)$] and then interchange x and y to get $x = \ln(-y)$ $\Leftrightarrow$ $-y = e^x$ $\Leftrightarrow$ $y = -e^x$.

(h) To find the equation of the graph that results from shifting the graph of $y = \ln x$ 3 units to the left and then reflecting it about the line $y = x$, we first replace x with $x + 3$ in the original equation [to get $y = \ln(x + 3)$] and then interchange x and y in this equation to get $x = \ln(y + 3)$ $\Leftrightarrow$ $y + 3 = e^x$ $\Leftrightarrow$ $y = e^x - 3$.

60. (a) If the point (x, y) is on the graph of $y = f(x)$, then the point $(x - c, y)$ is that point shifted c units to the left. Since f is 1-1, the point (y, x) is on the graph of $y = f^{-1}(x)$ and the point corresponding to $(x - c, y)$ on the graph of f is $(y, x - c)$ on the graph of f^{-1}. Thus, the curve's reflection is shifted *down* the same number of units as the curve itself is shifted to the left. So an expression for the inverse function is $g^{-1}(x) = f^{-1}(x) - c$.

(b) If we compress (or stretch) a curve horizontally, the curve's reflection in the line $y = x$ is compressed (or stretched) *vertically* by the same factor. Using this geometric principle, we see that the inverse of $h(x) = f(cx)$ can be expressed as $h^{-1}(x) = (1/c) f^{-1}(x)$.

 1.7 Parametric Curves • • • • • • • • • • • • •

1.

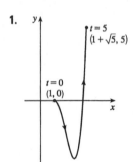

$x = 1 + \sqrt{t}, \quad y = t^2 - 4t, \quad 0 \le t \le 5$

t	0	1	2	3	4	5
x	1	2	$1 + \sqrt{2}$	$1 + \sqrt{3}$	3	$1 + \sqrt{5}$
			2.41	2.73		3.24
y	0	-3	-4	-3	0	5

2.

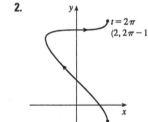

$x = 2 \cos t, \quad y = t - \cos t, \quad 0 \le t \le 2\pi$

t	0	$\pi/2$	π	$3\pi/2$	2π
x	2	0	-2	0	2
y	-1	$\pi/2$	$\pi + 1$	$3\pi/2$	$2\pi - 1$
		1.57	4.14	4.71	5.28

3.

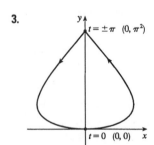

$x = 5 \sin t, \quad y = t^2, \quad -\pi \le t \le \pi$

t	$-\pi$	$-\pi/2$	0	$\pi/2$	π
x	0	-5	0	5	0
y	π^2	$\pi^2/4$	0	$\pi^2/4$	π^2
	9.87	2.47		2.47	9.87

4.

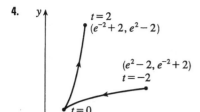

$x = e^{-t} + t, \quad y = e^t - t, \quad -2 \le t \le 2$

t	-2	-1	0	1	2
x	$e^2 - 2$	$e - 1$	1	$e^{-1} + 1$	$e^{-2} + 2$
	5.39	1.72		1.37	2.14
y	$e^{-2} + 2$	$e^{-1} + 1$	1	$e - 1$	$e^2 - 2$
	2.14	1.37		1.72	5.39

5. (a) $x = 2t + 4, y = t - 1$

t	-3	-2	-1	0	1	2
x	-2	0	2	4	6	8
y	-4	-3	-2	-1	0	1

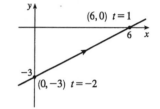

(b) $x = 2t + 4, y = t - 1 \Rightarrow x = 2(y+1) + 4 = 2y + 6$ or

$y = \frac{1}{2}x - 3$

6. (a) $x = t^2, y = 6 - 3t$

t	-3	-2	-1	0	1	2	3
x	9	4	1	0	1	4	9
y	15	12	9	6	3	0	-3

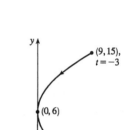

(b) $y = 6 - 3t \Rightarrow 3t = 6 - y \Rightarrow t = \dfrac{6 - y}{3} \Rightarrow$

$x = t^2 = \left(\dfrac{6 - y}{3}\right)^2 = \frac{1}{9}(y - 6)^2$

7. (a) $x = \sqrt{t}, y = 1 - t$

t	0	1	2	3	4
x	0	1	1.414	1.732	2
y	1	0	-1	-2	-3

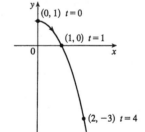

(b) $x = \sqrt{t} \Rightarrow t = x^2.$ $y = 1 - t = 1 - x^2.$ Since $t \ge 0, x \ge 0.$

8. (a) $x = t^2, y = t^3$

t	-2	-1	0	1	2
x	4	1	0	1	4
y	-8	-1	0	1	8

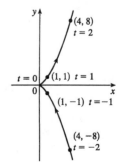

(b) $y = t^3 \Rightarrow t = \sqrt[3]{y}.$ $x = t^2 = \left(\sqrt[3]{y}\right)^2 = y^{2/3}.$

$t \in \mathbb{R}, y \in \mathbb{R}, x \ge 0.$

9. (a) $x = \sin\theta$, $y = \cos\theta$, $0 \le \theta \le \pi$.

$x^2 + y^2 = \sin^2\theta + \cos^2\theta = 1$.

Since $0 \le \theta \le \pi$, we have $\sin\theta \ge 0$,

so $x \ge 0$.

(b)

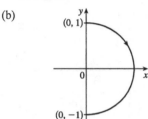

10. (a) $x = 4\cos\theta$, $y = 5\sin\theta$, $-\pi/2 \le \theta \le \pi/2$.

$\left(\frac{x}{4}\right)^2 + \left(\frac{y}{5}\right)^2 = \cos^2\theta + \sin^2\theta = 1$, which is an

ellipse with x-intercepts $(\pm 4, 0)$ and y-intercepts

$(0, \pm 5)$. We obtain the portion of the ellipse with

$x \ge 0$ since $4\cos\theta \ge 0$ for $-\pi/2 \le \theta \le \pi/2$.

(b)

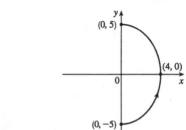

11. (a) $x = e^t$, $y = e^{-t}$.

$y = 1/e^t = 1/x$, $x > 0$

(b)

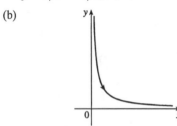

12. (a) $x = \ln t$, $y = \sqrt{t}$, $t \ge 1$.

$x = \ln t \implies t = e^x \implies y = \sqrt{t} = e^{x/2}$,

$x \ge 0$.

(b)

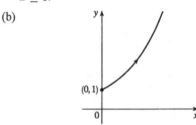

13. (a) $x = \sin^2\theta$, $y = \cos^2\theta$.

$x + y = \sin^2\theta + \cos^2\theta = 1$, $0 \le x \le 1$.

Note that the curve is at $(0, 1)$ whenever

$\theta = \pi n$ and is at $(1, 0)$ whenever $\theta = \frac{\pi}{2}n$ for

every integer n.

(b)

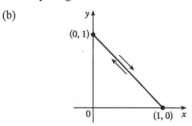

14. (a) $x = \sec\theta$, $y = \tan\theta$, $-\frac{\pi}{2} < \theta < \frac{\pi}{2}$.

$x^2 - y^2 = \sec^2\theta - \tan^2\theta = 1$, $x \ge 1$,

or $x = \sqrt{y^2 + 1}$.

(b)

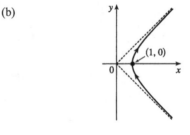

15. $x^2 + y^2 = \cos^2\pi t + \sin^2\pi t = 1$, $1 \le t \le 2$, so the particle moves counterclockwise along the circle $x^2 + y^2 = 1$ from $(-1, 0)$ to $(1, 0)$, along the lower half of the circle.

16. $(x - 2)^2 + (y - 3)^2 = \cos^2 t + \sin^2 t = 1$, so the motion takes place on a unit circle centered at $(2, 3)$. As t goes from 0 to 2π, the particle makes one complete counterclockwise rotation around the circle, starting and ending at $(3, 3)$.

17. $\left(\frac{1}{2}x\right)^2 + \left(\frac{1}{3}y\right)^2 = \sin^2 t + \cos^2 t = 1$, so the particle moves once clockwise along the ellipse $\frac{1}{4}x^2 + \frac{1}{9}y^2 = 1$, starting and ending at $(0, 3)$.

18. $x = \cos^2 t = y^2$, so the particle moves along the parabola $x = y^2$. As t goes from 0 to 4π, the particle moves from $(1, 1)$ down to $(1, -1)$ (at $t = \pi$), back up to $(1, 1)$ again (at $t = 2\pi$), and then repeats this entire cycle between $t = 2\pi$ and $t = 4\pi$.

19. We must have $1 \le x \le 4$ and $2 \le y \le 3$. So the graph of the curve must be contained in the rectangle $[1, 4]$ by $[2, 3]$.

20. (a) From the first graph, we have $1 \le x \le 2$. From the second graph, we have $-1 \le y \le 1$. The only choice that satisfies either of those conditions is III.

(b) From the first graph, the values of x cycle through the values from -2 to 2 four times. From the second graph, the values of y cycle through the values from -2 to 2 six times. Choice I satisfies these conditions.

(c) From the first graph, the values of x cycle through the values from -2 to 2 three times. From the second graph, we have $0 \le y \le 2$. Choice IV satisfies these conditions.

(d) From the first graph, the values of x cycle through the values from -2 to 2 two times. From the second graph, the values of y do the same thing. Choice II satisfies these conditions.

21. When $t = 0$ we see that $x = 0$ and $y = 0$, so the curve starts at the origin. As t increases from 0 to $\frac{1}{2}$, the graphs show that y increases from 0 to 1 while x increases from 0 to 1, decreases to 0 and to -1, then increases back to 0, so we arrive at the point $(0, 1)$. Similarly, as t increases from $\frac{1}{2}$ to 1, y decreases from 1 to 0 while x repeats its pattern, and we arrive back at the origin. We could achieve greater accuracy by estimating x- and y-values for selected values of t from the given graphs and plotting the corresponding points.

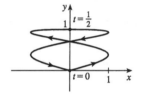

22. When $t = -1$, $(x, y) = (0, 0)$ and, as t increases from -1 to 0, x becomes negative and y increases from 0 to 1. At $t = 0$, $(x, y) = (0, 1)$ and, as t increases from 0 to 1, y decreases from 1 to 0 and x is positive. At $t = 1$, $(x, y) = (0, 0)$ again, so the loop is completed. For $t > 1$, x and y both become large negative. This enables us to draw a rough sketch. We could achieve greater accuracy by estimating x- and y-values for selected values of t from the given graphs and plotting the corresponding points.

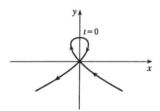

23. (a) $x = x_1 + (x_2 - x_1)t$, $y = y_1 + (y_2 - y_1)t$, $0 \le t \le 1$. Clearly the curve passes through $P_1(x_1, y_1)$ when $t = 0$ and through $P_2(x_2, y_2)$ when $t = 1$. For $0 < t < 1$, x is strictly between x_1 and x_2 and y is strictly between y_1 and y_2. For every value of t, x and y satisfy the relation $y - y_1 = \dfrac{y_2 - y_1}{x_2 - x_1}(x - x_1)$, which is the equation of the line through $P_1(x_1, y_1)$ and $P_2(x_2, y_2)$.

Finally, any point (x, y) on that line satisfies $\dfrac{y - y_1}{y_2 - y_1} = \dfrac{x - x_1}{x_2 - x_1}$; if we call that common value t, then the given parametric equations yield the point (x, y); and any (x, y) on the line between $P_1(x_1, y_1)$ and $P_2(x_2, y_2)$ yields a value of t in $[0, 1]$. So the given parametric equations exactly specify the line segment from $P_1(x_1, y_1)$ to $P_2(x_2, y_2)$.

(b) $x = -2 + [3 - (-2)]t = -2 + 5t$ and $y = 7 + (-1 - 7)t = 7 - 8t$ for $0 \le t \le 1$.

24. For the side of the triangle from A to B, use $(x_1, y_1) = (1, 1)$ and

$(x_2, y_2) = (4, 2)$. Hence, the equations are

$x = x_1 + (x_2 - x_1) t = 1 + (4 - 1) t = 1 + 3t$,

$y = y_1 + (y_2 - y_1) t = 1 + (2 - 1) t = 1 + t$. Graphing $x = 1 + 3t$ and

$y = 1 + t$ with $0 \le t \le 1$ gives us the side of the triangle from A to B.

Similarly, for the side BC we use $x = 4 - 3t$ and $y = 2 + 3t$, and for

the side AC we use $x = 1$ and $y = 1 + 4t$.

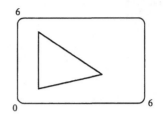

25. As in Example 5, we let $y = t$ and $x = t - 3t^3 + t^5$ and use a t-interval

of $[-2\pi, 2\pi]$.

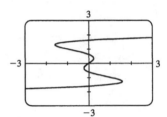

26. We use $x_1 = t$, $y_1 = t^5$ and $x_2 = t (t - 1)^2$, $y_2 = t$ with $-2\pi \le t \le 2\pi$.

There are 3 points of intersection; $(0, 0)$ is fairly obvious. The point in

quadrant III is approximately $(-0.8, -0.4)$ and the point in quadrant I is

approximately $(1.1, 1.8)$.

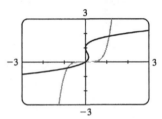

27. The circle $x^2 + y^2 = 4$ can be represented parametrically by $x = 2 \cos t$, $y = 2 \sin t$; $0 \le t \le 2\pi$. The circle

$x^2 + (y - 1)^2 = 4$ can be represented by $x = 2 \cos t$, $y = 1 + 2 \sin t$; $0 \le t \le 2\pi$. This representation gives us the

circle with a counterclockwise orientation starting at $(2, 1)$.

(a) To get a clockwise orientation, we could change the equations to $x = 2 \cos t$, $y = 1 - 2 \sin t$, $0 \le t \le 2\pi$.

(b) To get three times around in the counterclockwise direction, we use the original equations $x = 2 \cos t$,
   $y = 1 + 2 \sin t$ with the domain expanded to $0 \le t \le 6\pi$.

(c) To start at $(0, 3)$ using the original equations, we must have $x_1 = 0$; that is, $2 \cos t = 0$. Hence, $t = \frac{\pi}{2}$. So we
   use $x = 2 \cos t$, $y = 1 + 2 \sin t$; $\frac{\pi}{2} \le t \le \frac{3\pi}{2}$.
   Alternatively, if we want t to start at 0, we could change the equations of the curve. For example, we could use
   $x = -2 \sin t$, $y = 1 + 2 \cos t$, $0 \le t \le \pi$.

28.

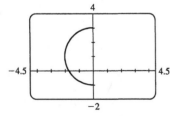

29. (a) Let $x^2/a^2 = \sin^2 t$ and $y^2/b^2 = \cos^2 t$ to obtain
$x = a \sin t$ and $y = b \cos t$ with $0 \le t \le 2\pi$ as possible
parametric equations for the ellipse
$x^2/a^2 + y^2/b^2 = 1$.

(c) As b increases, the ellipse stretches vertically.

(b) The equations are $x = 3 \sin t$ and
$y = b \cos t$ for $b \in \{1, 2, 4, 8\}$.

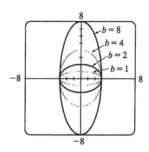

30. (a) If $\alpha = 30°$ and $v_0 = 500$ m/s, then the equations become $x = (500 \cos 30°) t = 250\sqrt{3}t$ and
$y = (500 \sin 30°) t - \frac{1}{2}(9.8) t^2 = 250t - 4.9t^2$. $y = 0$ when $t = 0$ (when the gun is fired) and again when
$t = \frac{250}{4.9} \approx 51$ s. Then $x = \left(250\sqrt{3}\right)\left(\frac{250}{4.9}\right) \approx 22,092$ m, so the bullet hits the ground about 22 km from
the gun.

The formula for y is quadratic in t. To find the maximum y-value, we will complete the square:
$$y = -4.9\left(t^2 - \frac{250}{4.9}t\right) = -4.9\left[t^2 - \frac{250}{4.9}t + \left(\frac{125}{4.9}\right)^2\right] + \frac{125^2}{4.9} = -4.9\left(t - \frac{125}{4.9}\right)^2 + \frac{125^2}{4.9} \le \frac{125^2}{4.9}$$
with equality when $t = \frac{125}{4.9}$ s, so the maximum height attained is $\frac{125^2}{4.9} \approx 3189$ m.

(b)

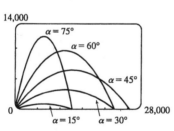

As α $(0° < \alpha < 90°)$ increases up to $45°$, the projectile
attains a greater height and a greater range. As α increases
past $45°$, the projectile attains a greater height, but its range
decreases.

(c) $x = (v_0 \cos \alpha) t \implies t = \dfrac{x}{v_0 \cos \alpha}$.

$$y = (v_0 \sin \alpha) t - \tfrac{1}{2}gt^2 \implies y = (v_0 \sin \alpha)\frac{x}{v_0 \cos \alpha} - \frac{g}{2}\left(\frac{x}{v_0 \cos \alpha}\right)^2 = (\tan \alpha) x - \left(\frac{g}{2v_0^2 \cos^2 \alpha}\right) x^2,$$
which is the equation of a parabola (quadratic in x).

31. The case $\frac{\pi}{2} < \theta < \pi$ is illustrated. C has coordinates $(r\theta, r)$ as in Example 7,
and Q has coordinates $(r\theta, r + r \cos(\pi - \theta)) = (r\theta, r(1 - \cos \theta))$ [since
$\cos(\pi - \alpha) = \cos \pi \cos \alpha + \sin \pi \sin \alpha = -\cos \alpha$], so P has coordinates
$(r\theta - r \sin(\pi - \theta), r(1 - \cos \theta)) = (r(\theta - \sin \theta), r(1 - \cos \theta))$ [since
$\sin(\pi - \alpha) = \sin \pi \cos \alpha - \cos \pi \sin \alpha = \sin \alpha$]. Again we have the
parametric equations $x = r(\theta - \sin \theta)$, $y = r(1 - \cos \theta)$.

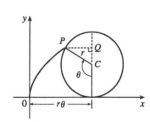

32. The first two diagrams depict the case $\pi < \theta < \frac{3\pi}{2}$, $d < r$. As in Example 7, C has coordinates $(r\theta, r)$.

Now Q (in the second diagram) has coordinates $(r\theta, r + d\cos(\theta - \pi)) = (r\theta, r - d\cos\theta)$, so a typical point P of

the trochoid has coordinates $(r\theta + d\sin(\theta - \pi), r - d\cos\theta)$. That is, P has coordinates (x, y), where

$x = r\theta - d\sin\theta$ and $y = r - d\cos\theta$. When $d = r$, these equations agree with those of the cycloid.

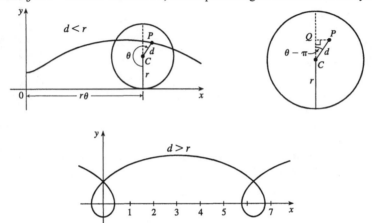

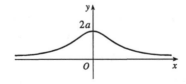

33. It is apparent that $x = |OQ|$ and $y = |QP| = |ST|$. From the
diagram, $x = |OQ| = a\cos\theta$ and $y = |ST| = b\sin\theta$. Thus, the
parametric equations are $x = a\cos\theta$ and $y = b\sin\theta$. To eliminate θ
we rearrange: $\sin\theta = y/b \implies \sin^2\theta = (y/b)^2$ and
$\cos\theta = x/a \implies \cos^2\theta = (x/a)^2$. Adding the two equations:
$\sin^2\theta + \cos^2\theta = 1 = x^2/a^2 + y^2/b^2$. Thus, we have an ellipse.

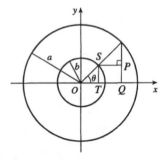

34. A has coordinates $(a\cos\theta, a\sin\theta)$. Since OA is perpendicular to AB, $\triangle OAB$ is a right triangle and B has

coordinates $(a\sec\theta, 0)$. It follows that P has coordinates $(a\sec\theta, b\sin\theta)$. Thus, the parametric equations are

$x = a\sec\theta$, $y = b\sin\theta$.

35. $C = (2a\cot\theta, 2a)$, so the x-coordinate of P is $x = 2a\cot\theta$. Let $B = (0, 2a)$. Then $\angle OAB$ is a right angle and

$\angle OBA = \theta$, so $|OA| = 2a\sin\theta$ and $A = ((2a\sin\theta)\cos\theta, (2a\sin\theta)\sin\theta)$. Thus, the y-coordinate of P is

$y = 2a\sin^2\theta$.

36. (a)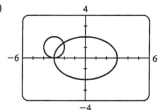

There are 2 points of intersection:

$(-3, 0)$ and approximately $(-2.1, 1.4)$.

(b) As an aid in finding collision points, set your graphing utility to graph both curves simultaneously and closely observe the drawing of the graphs. In this case, we have one collision point: both particles are at $(-3, 0)$ when $t = \frac{3\pi}{2}$. [Notice that the first curve passes through $(-2.1, 1.4)$ when $t \approx 5.5$, but the second curve passes through $(-2.1, 1.4)$ when $t \approx 0.4$.]

(c) The circle is centered at $(3, 1)$ instead of $(-3, 1)$. There are still 2 intersection points: $(3, 0)$ and $(2.1, 1.4)$, but there are no collision points.

37. $x = t^2$, $y = t^3 - ct$. We use a graphing device to produce the graphs for various values of c with $-\pi \le t \le \pi$. Note that all the members of the family are symmetric about the x-axis. For $c < 0$, the graph does not cross itself, but for $c = 0$ it has a cusp at $(0, 0)$ and for $c > 0$ the graph crosses itself at $x = c$, so the loop grows larger as c increases.

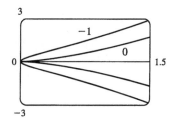 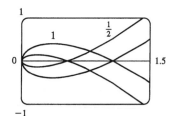

38. $x = 2ct - 4t^3$, $y = -ct^2 + 3t^4$. We use a graphing device to produce the graphs for various values of c with $-\pi \le t \le \pi$. Note that all the members of the family are symmetric about the y-axis. When $c < 0$, the graph resembles that of a polynomial of even degree, but when $c = 0$ there is a corner at the origin, and when $c > 0$, the graph crosses itself at the origin, and has two cusps below the x-axis. The size of the "swallowtail" increases as c increases.

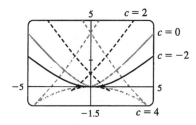

39. Note that all the Lissajous figures are symmetric about the x-axis. The parameters a and b simply stretch the graph in the x- and y-directions respectively. For $a = b = n = 1$ the graph is simply a circle with radius 1. For $n = 2$ the graph crosses itself at the origin and there are loops above and below the x-axis. In general, the figures have $n - 1$ points of intersection, all of which are on the y-axis, and a total of n closed loops.

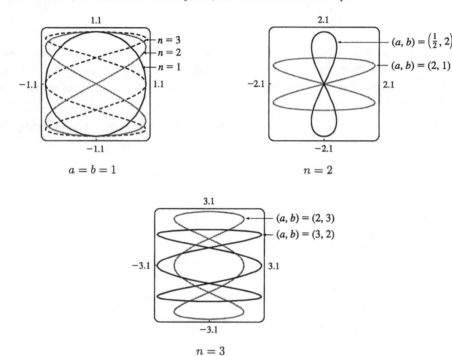

40. We use $-\pi \leq t \leq \pi$ in the viewing rectangle $[-4, 2] \times [-3, 3]$. We first observe that for $c = 0$, we obtain a circle with center $\left(-\frac{1}{2}, 0\right)$ and radius $\frac{1}{2}$. As the value of c increases, there is a larger outer loop and a smaller inner loop until $c = 1$, when we obtain a curve with a dent (called a **cardioid**). As c increases, we get curve with a dimple (called a **limaçon**) until $c = 2$. For $c > 2$, we have convex limaçons. For negative values of c, we obtain the same graphs as for positive c, but with different values of t corresponding to the points on the curve.

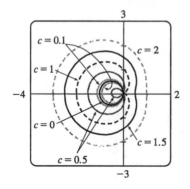

| Discovery Project | **Running Circles around Circles** |

1. The center Q of the smaller circle has coordinates

$((a-b)\cos\theta, (a-b)\sin\theta)$. Arc PS on circle C has length $a\theta$ since it is
equal in length to arc AS (the smaller circle rolls without slipping against the
larger.) Thus, $\angle PQS = \dfrac{a}{b}\theta$ and $\angle PQT = \dfrac{a}{b}\theta - \theta$, so P has coordinates

$$x = (a-b)\cos\theta + b\cos(\angle PQT) = (a-b)\cos\theta + b\cos\left(\frac{a-b}{b}\theta\right)$$

and

$$y = (a-b)\sin\theta - b\sin(\angle PQT) = (a-b)\sin\theta - b\sin\left(\frac{a-b}{b}\theta\right)$$

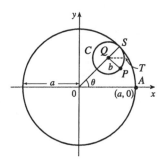

2. With $b=1$ and a a positive integer greater than 2, we obtain a hypocycloid of a
cusps. Shown in the figure is the graph for $a=4$. Let $a=4$ and $b=1$. Using
the sum identities to expand $\cos 3\theta$ and $\sin 3\theta$, we obtain

$$x = 3\cos\theta + \cos 3\theta = 3\cos\theta + \left(4\cos^3\theta - 3\cos\theta\right) = 4\cos^3\theta$$

and

$$y = 3\sin\theta - \sin 3\theta = 3\sin\theta - \left(3\sin\theta - 4\sin^3\theta\right) = 4\sin^3\theta$$

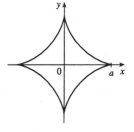

3. The following graphs are obtained with $b=1$ and $a=\frac{1}{2}, \frac{1}{3}, \frac{1}{4}$, and $\frac{1}{10}$ with $-2\pi \le \theta \le 2\pi$. We conclude that as
the denominator d increases, the graph gets smaller, but maintains the basic shape shown.

Letting $d=2$ and $n=3, 5$, and 7 with $-2\pi \le \theta \le 2\pi$ gives us the following:

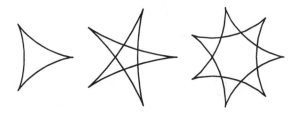

So if d is held constant and n varies, we get a graph with n cusps (assuming n/d is in lowest form). When $n = d + 1$, we obtain a hypocycloid of n cusps. As n increases, we must expand the range of θ in order to get a closed curve. The following graphs have $a = \frac{3}{2}$, $\frac{5}{4}$, and $\frac{11}{10}$.

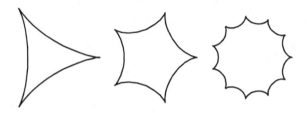

4. If $b = 1$, the equations for the hypocycloid are

$$x = (a - 1) \cos \theta + \cos ((a - 1) \theta)$$

$$y = (a - 1) \sin \theta - \sin ((a - 1) \theta)$$

which is a hypocycloid of a cusps (from Problem 2). In general, if $a > 1$, we get a figure with cusps on the "outside ring" and if $a < 1$, the cusps are on the "inside ring". In any case, as the values of θ get larger, we get a figure that looks more and more like a washer. If we were to graph the hypocycloid for all values of θ, every point on the washer would eventually be arbitrarily close to a point on the curve.

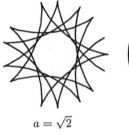

$a = \sqrt{2}$

$-10\pi \le \theta \le 10\pi$

$a = e - 2$

$0 \le \theta \le 446$

5. The center Q of the smaller circle has coordinates $((a + b) \cos \theta, (a + b) \sin \theta)$. Arc PS has length $a\theta$ (as in Problem 1), so that $\angle PQS = \dfrac{a\theta}{b}$, $\angle PQR = \pi - \dfrac{a\theta}{b}$, and

$$\angle PQT = \pi - \frac{a\theta}{b} - \theta = \pi - \left(\frac{a + b}{b}\right) \theta \text{ since } \angle RQT = \theta.$$

Thus, the coordinates of P are

$$x = (a + b) \cos \theta + b \cos \left(\pi - \frac{a + b}{b} \theta\right) = (a + b) \cos \theta - b \cos \left(\frac{a + b}{b} \theta\right)$$

and

$$y = (a + b) \sin \theta - b \sin \left(\pi - \frac{a + b}{b} \theta\right) = (a + b) \sin \theta - b \sin \left(\frac{a + b}{b} \theta\right).$$

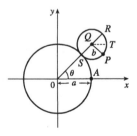

6. Let $b = 1$ and the equations become

$$x = (a + 1) \cos \theta - \cos((a + 1)\theta) \qquad y = (a + 1) \sin \theta - \sin((a + 1)\theta)$$

If $a = 1$, we have a cardioid. If a is a positive integer greater than 1, we get the graph of an "a-leafed clover", with cusps that are a units from the origin. (Some of the pairs of figures are not to scale.)

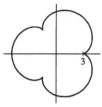

$a = 3, -2\pi \le \theta \le 2\pi$

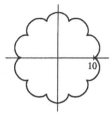

$a = 10, -2\pi \le \theta \le 2\pi$

If $a = n/d$ with $n = 1$, we obtain a figure that does not increase in size and requires $-d\pi \le \theta \le d\pi$ to be a closed curve traced exactly once.

$a = \frac{1}{4}, -4\pi \le \theta \le 4\pi$

$a = \frac{1}{7}, -7\pi \le \theta \le 7\pi$

Next, we keep d constant and let n vary. As n increases, so does the size of the figure. There is an n-pointed star in the middle.

$a = \frac{2}{5}, -5\pi \le \theta \le 5\pi$

$a = \frac{7}{5}, -5\pi \le \theta \le 5\pi$

Now if $n = d + 1$ we obtain figures similar to the previous ones, but the size of the figure does not increase.

$a = \frac{4}{3}, -3\pi \le \theta \le 3\pi$

$a = \frac{7}{6}, -6\pi \le \theta \le 6\pi$

If a is irrational, we get washers that increase in size as a increases.

$a = \sqrt{2}, 0 \le \theta \le 200$

$a = e - 2, 0 \le \theta \le 446$

1 Review

─────────────── • CONCEPT CHECK • ───────────────

1. (a) A **function** f is a rule that assigns to each element x in a set A exactly one element, called $f(x)$, in a set B. The set A is called the **domain** of the function. The **range** of f is the set of all possible values of $f(x)$ as x varies throughout the domain.

   (b) If f is a function with domain A, then its **graph** is the set of ordered pairs $\{(x, f(x)) \mid x \in A\}$.

   (c) Use the Vertical Line Test on page 17.

2. The four ways to represent a function are: verbally, numerically, visually, and algebraically. An example of each is given below.
   Verbally: An assignment of students to chairs in a classroom (a description in words)
   Numerically: A tax table that assigns an amount of tax to an income (a table of values)
   Visually: A graphical history of the Dow Jones average (a graph)
   Algebraically: A relationship between distance, rate, and time: $d = rt$ (an explicit formula)

3. (a) An **even function** f satisfies $f(-x) = f(x)$ for every number x in its domain. It is symmetric with respect to the y-axis.

   (b) An **odd function** g satisfies $g(-x) = -g(x)$ for every number x in its domain. It is symmetric with respect to the origin.

4. A function f is called **increasing** on an interval I if $f(x_1) < f(x_2)$ whenever $x_1 < x_2$ in I.

5. A **mathematical model** is a mathematical description (often by means of a function or an equation) of a real-world phenomenon.

6. (a) Linear function: $f(x) = 2x + 1$, $f(x) = ax + b$

   (b) Power function: $f(x) = x^2$, $f(x) = x^a$

   (c) Exponential function: $f(x) = 2^x$, $f(x) = a^x$

   (d) Quadratic function: $f(x) = x^2 + x + 1$,
   $f(x) = ax^2 + bx + c$

   (e) Polynomial of degree 5: $f(x) = x^5 + 2$

   (f) Rational function: $f(x) = \dfrac{x}{x+2}$, $f(x) = \dfrac{P(x)}{Q(x)}$ where
   $P(x)$ and $Q(x)$ are polynomials

7.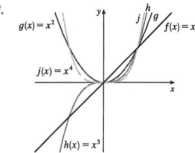

8. (a)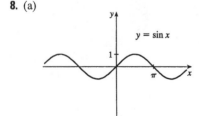

   (b)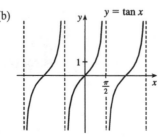

   (c)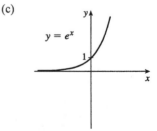

(d)

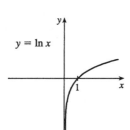

$y = \ln x$

(e)

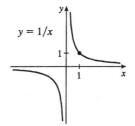

$y = 1/x$

(f)

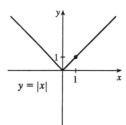

$y = |x|$

(g)

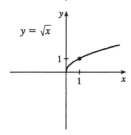

$y = \sqrt{x}$

9. (a) The domain of $f + g$ is the intersection of the domain of f and the domain of g; that is, $A \cap B$.

(b) The domain of fg is also $A \cap B$.

(c) The domain of f/g must exclude values of x that make g equal to 0; that is, $\{x \in A \cap B \mid g(x) \neq 0\}$.

10. Given two functions f and g, the **composite** function $f \circ g$ is defined by $(f \circ g)(x) = f(g(x))$. The domain of $f \circ g$ is the set of all x in the domain of g such that $g(x)$ is in the domain of f.

11. (a) If the graph of f is shifted 2 units upward, its equation becomes $y = f(x) + 2$.

(b) If the graph of f is shifted 2 units downward, its equation becomes $y = f(x) - 2$.

(c) If the graph of f is shifted 2 units to the right, its equation becomes $y = f(x - 2)$.

(d) If the graph of f is shifted 2 units to the left, its equation becomes $y = f(x + 2)$.

(e) If the graph of f is reflected about the x-axis, its equation becomes $y = -f(x)$.

(f) If the graph of f is reflected about the y-axis, its equation becomes $y = f(-x)$.

(g) If the graph of f is stretched vertically by a factor of 2, its equation becomes $y = 2f(x)$.

(h) If the graph of f is shrunk vertically by a factor of 2, its equation becomes $y = \frac{1}{2}f(x)$.

(i) If the graph of f is stretched horizontally by a factor of 2, its equation becomes $y = f\left(\frac{1}{2}x\right)$.

(j) If the graph of f is shrunk horizontally by a factor of 2, its equation becomes $y = f(2x)$.

12. (a) A function f is called a *one-to-one function* if it never takes on the same value twice; that is, if $f(x_1) \neq f(x_2)$ whenever $x_1 \neq x_2$. (Or, f is 1-1 if each output corresponds to only one input.)

Use the Horizontal Line Test: A function is one-to-one if and only if no horizontal line intersects its graph more than once.

(b) If f is a one-to-one function with domain A and range B, then its *inverse function* f^{-1} has domain B and range A and is defined by

$$f^{-1}(y) = x \quad \Leftrightarrow \quad f(x) = y$$

for any y in B. The graph of f^{-1} is obtained by reflecting the graph of f about the line $y = x$.

13. (a) A **parametric curve** C is the set of points $(x, y) = (f(t), g(t))$ that is traced out as t varies through an interval.

(b) There are several ways to sketch a parametric curve, including creating a table and plotting points, creating an equation in x and y by eliminating the parameter, observing general trends of the equations for x and y, and using a graphing device.

▲ **TRUE–FALSE QUIZ** ▲

---

1. False. Let $f(x) = x^2$, $s = -1$, and $t = 1$. Then $f(s+t) = (-1+1)^2 = 0^2 = 0$, but
$f(s) + f(t) = (-1)^2 + 1^2 = 2 \neq 0 = f(s+t)$.

2. False. Let $f(x) = x^2$. Then $f(-2) = 4 = f(2)$, but $-2 \neq 2$.

3. False. Let $f(x) = x^2$. Then $f(3x) = (3x)^2 = 9x^2$ and $3f(x) = 3x^2$. So $f(3x) \neq 3f(x)$.

4. True. If $x_1 < x_2$ and f is a decreasing function, then the y-values get smaller as we move from left to right. Thus, $f(x_1) > f(x_2)$.

5. True. See the Vertical Line Test.

6. False. Let $f(x) = x^2$ and $g(x) = 2x$. Then $(f \circ g)(x) = f(g(x)) = f(2x) = (2x)^2 = 4x^2$ and
$(g \circ f)(x) = g(f(x)) = g(x^2) = 2x^2$. So $f \circ g \neq g \circ f$.

7. False. Let $f(x) = x^3$. Then f is one-to-one and $f^{-1}(x) = \sqrt[3]{x}$. But $1/f(x) = 1/x^3$, which is not equal to $f^{-1}(x)$.

8. True. We can divide by e^x since $e^x \neq 0$ for every x.

9. True. The function $\ln x$ is an increasing function on $(0, \infty)$.

10. False. Let $x = e$. Then $(\ln x)^6 = (\ln e)^6 = 1^6 = 1$, but $6\ln x = 6\ln e = 6 \cdot 1 = 6 \neq 1 = (\ln x)^6$.

11. False. Let $x = e^2$ and $a = e$. Then $\dfrac{\ln x}{\ln a} = \dfrac{\ln e^2}{\ln e} = \dfrac{2\ln e}{\ln e} = 2$ and $\ln \dfrac{x}{a} = \ln \dfrac{e^2}{e} = \ln e = 1$, so in general the statement is false. What *is* true, however, is that $\ln \dfrac{x}{a} = \ln x - \ln a$.

◆ **EXERCISES** ◆

---

1. (a) When $x = 2$, $y \approx 2.7$. Thus, $f(2) \approx 2.7$.

(b) $f(x) = 3 \;\Rightarrow\; x \approx 2.3, 5.6$

(c) The domain of f is $-6 \leq x \leq 6$, or $[-6, 6]$.

(d) The range of f is $-4 \leq y \leq 4$, or $[-4, 4]$.

(e) f is increasing on $[-4, 4]$.

(f) f is not one-to-one since it fails the Horizontal Line Test.

(g) f is odd since its graph is symmetric about the origin.

2. (a) When $x = 2$, $y = 3$. Thus, $g(2) = 3$.

(b) g is one-to-one because it passes the Horizontal Line Test.

(c) When $y = 2$, $x \approx 0.2$. So $g^{-1}(2) \approx 0.2$.

(d) The range of g is $[-1, 3.5]$, which is the same as the domain of g^{-1}.

(e) We reflect the graph of g through the line $y = x$ to obtain the graph of g^{-1}.

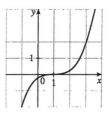

3. (a)

(b) From the graph, we see that the distance is slightly less than 150 feet.

4.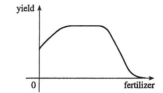

There will be some yield with no fertilizer, increasing yields with increasing fertilizer use, a leveling-off of yields at some point, and disaster with too much fertilizer use.

5. $f(x) = \sqrt{4 - 3x^2}$. Domain: $4 - 3x^2 \geq 0 \;\Rightarrow\; 3x^2 \leq 4 \;\Rightarrow\; x^2 \leq \frac{4}{3} \;\Rightarrow\; |x| \leq \frac{2}{\sqrt{3}}$. Range: $y \geq 0$ and $y \leq \sqrt{4} \;\Rightarrow\; 0 \leq y \leq 2$.

6. $g(x) = \dfrac{1}{x + 1}$. Domain: $x + 1 \neq 0 \;\Rightarrow\; x \neq -1$. Range: all reals except 0 ($y = 0$ is the horizontal asymptote for g.)

7. $y = 1 + \sin x$. Domain: $\mathbb{R}$. Range: $-1 \leq \sin x \leq 1 \;\Rightarrow\; 0 \leq 1 + \sin x \leq 2 \;\Rightarrow\; 0 \leq y \leq 2$.

8. $y = \ln \ln x$. Domain: We must have $\ln x > 0 \;\Rightarrow\; x > e^0 \;\Rightarrow\; x > 1$. Range: $\ln x > 0$, so $\ln(\ln x)$ takes on all real numbers and, hence, the range is $\mathbb{R}$.

9. (a) To obtain the graph of $y = f(x) + 8$, we shift the graph of $y = f(x)$ up 8 units.

(b) To obtain the graph of $y = f(x + 8)$, we shift the graph of $y = f(x)$ left 8 units.

(c) To obtain the graph of $y = 1 + 2f(x)$, we stretch the graph of $y = f(x)$ vertically by a factor of 2, and then shift the resulting graph 1 unit upward.

(d) To obtain the graph of $y = f(x - 2) - 2$, we shift the graph of $y = f(x)$ right 2 units (for the "-2" inside the parentheses), and then shift the resulting graph 2 units downward.

(e) To obtain the graph of $y = -f(x)$, we reflect the graph of $y = f(x)$ about the x-axis.

(f) To obtain the graph of $y = f^{-1}(x)$, we reflect the graph of $y = f(x)$ about the line $y = x$ (assuming f is one–to-one).

10. (a) To obtain the graph of $y = f(x - 8)$, we
shift the graph of $y = f(x)$ right 8 units.

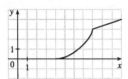

(b) To obtain the graph of $y = -f(x)$, we reflect the
graph of $y = f(x)$ about the x-axis.

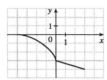

(c) To obtain the graph of $y = 2 - f(x)$, we
reflect the graph of $y = f(x)$ about the
x-axis, and then shift the resulting graph 2
units upward.

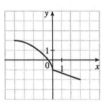

(d) To obtain the graph of $y = \frac{1}{2}f(x) - 1$, we shrink
the graph of $y = f(x)$ by a factor of 2, and then
shift the resulting graph 1 unit downward.

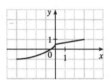

(e) To obtain the graph of $y = f^{-1}(x)$, we
reflect the graph of $y = f(x)$ about the line
$y = x$.

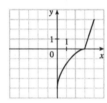

(f) To obtain the graph of $y = f^{-1}(x + 3)$, we reflect
the graph of $y = f(x)$ about the line $y = x$ [see
part (e)], and then shift the resulting graph left
3 units.

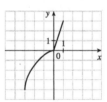

11. $y = -\sin 2x$: Start with the graph of $y = \sin x$, compress horizontally by a factor of 2, and reflect about the x-axis.

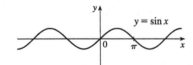 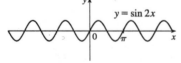 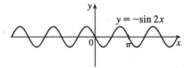

12. $y = 3\ln(x - 2)$: Start with the graph of $y = \ln x$, shift 2 units to the right, and stretch vertically by a factor of 3.

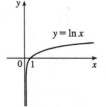 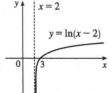 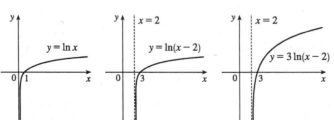

13. $y = (1 + e^x)/2$: Start with the graph of $y = e^x$, shift 1 unit upward, and compress vertically by a factor of 2.

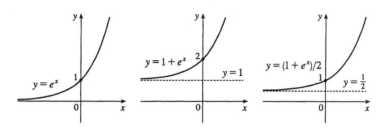

14. $y = 2 - \sqrt{x}$: Start with the graph of $y = \sqrt{x}$, reflect about the x-axis, and shift 2 units upward.

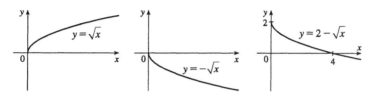

15. $f(x) = \dfrac{1}{x + 2}$: Start with the graph of

$f(x) = 1/x$ and shift 2 units to the left.

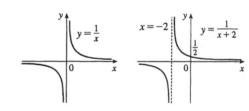

16. $f(x) = \begin{cases} 1 + x & \text{if } x < 0 \\ e^x & \text{if } x \geq 0 \end{cases}$

On $(-\infty, 0)$, graph $y = 1 + x$ (the line with slope 1 and
y-intercept 1) with open endpoint $(0, 1)$.

On $[0, \infty)$, graph $y = e^x$ with closed endpoint $(0, 1)$.

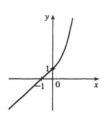

17. (a) The terms of f are a mixture of odd and even powers of x, so f is neither even nor odd.

(b) The terms of f are all odd powers of x, so f is odd.

(c) $f(-x) = e^{-(-x)^2} = e^{-x^2} = f(x)$, so f is even.

(d) $f(-x) = 1 + \sin(-x) = 1 - \sin x$. Now $f(-x) \neq f(x)$ and $f(-x) \neq -f(x)$, so f is neither even nor odd.

18. For the line segment from $(-2, 2)$ to $(-1, 0)$, the slope is $\dfrac{0 - 2}{-1 + 2} = -2$, and an equation is $y - 0 = -2(x + 1)$

or, equivalently, $y = -2x - 2$. The circle has equation $x^2 + y^2 = 1$; the top half has equation $y = \sqrt{1 - x^2}$ (we

have solved for positive y.) Thus, $f(x) = \begin{cases} -2x - 2 & \text{if } -2 \leq x \leq -1 \\ \sqrt{1 - x^2} & \text{if } -1 < x \leq 1 \end{cases}$

19. $f(x) = \ln x, \quad D = (0, \infty); \quad g(x) = x^2 - 9, \quad D = \mathbb{R}.$

$(f \circ g)(x) = f(g(x)) = f(x^2 - 9) = \ln(x^2 - 9).$

Domain: $x^2 - 9 > 0 \quad \Rightarrow \quad x^2 > 9 \quad \Rightarrow \quad |x| > 3 \quad \Rightarrow \quad x \in (-\infty, -3) \cup (3, \infty)$

$(g \circ f)(x) = g(f(x)) = g(\ln x) = (\ln x)^2 - 9.$ Domain: $x > 0$, or $(0, \infty)$

$(f \circ f)(x) = f(f(x)) = f(\ln x) = \ln(\ln x).$ Domain: $\ln x > 0 \quad \Rightarrow \quad x > e^0 = 1$, or $(1, \infty)$

$(g \circ g)(x) = g(g(x)) = g(x^2 - 9) = (x^2 - 9)^2 - 9.$ Domain: $x \in \mathbb{R}$, or $(-\infty, \infty)$

20. Let $h(x) = x + \sqrt{x}, g(x) = \sqrt{x}$, and $f(x) = 1/x$. Then $(f \circ g \circ h)(x) = \dfrac{1}{\sqrt{x + \sqrt{x}}} = F(x).$

21.

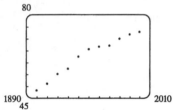

Many models appear to be plausible. Your choice depends on whether you think medical advances will keep increasing life expectancy, or if there is bound to be a natural leveling-off of life expectancy. A linear model, $y = 0.2493x - 423.4818$ gives us an estimate of 77.6 years for the year 2010.

22. (a) Let x denote the number of toaster ovens produced in one week and y the associated cost. Using the points $(1000, 9000)$ and $(1500, 12,000)$, we get an equation of a line: $y - 9000 = \dfrac{12,000 - 9000}{1500 - 1000}(x - 1000) \quad \Rightarrow$

$y = 6(x - 1000) + 9000 \quad \Rightarrow \quad y = 6x + 3000.$

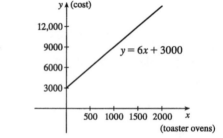

(b) The slope of 6 means that each additional toaster oven produced adds \$6 to the weekly production cost.

(c) The y-intercept of 3000 represents the overhead cost—the cost incurred without producing anything.

23. We need to know the value of x such that $f(x) = 2x + \ln x = 2$. Since $x = 1$ gives us $y = 2$, $f^{-1}(2) = 1.$

24. $y = \dfrac{x + 1}{2x + 1}$. Interchanging x and y gives us $x = \dfrac{y + 1}{2y + 1} \quad \Rightarrow \quad 2xy + x = y + 1 \quad \Rightarrow \quad 2xy - y = 1 - x \quad \Rightarrow$

$y(2x - 1) = 1 - x \quad \Rightarrow \quad y = \dfrac{1 - x}{2x - 1} = f^{-1}(x).$

25. (a) $e^{2\ln 3} = (e^{\ln 3})^2 = 3^2 = 9$

(b) $\log_{10} 25 + \log_{10} 4 = \log_{10}(25 \cdot 4) = \log_{10} 100 = \log_{10} 10^2 = 2$

26. (a) $e^x = 5 \quad \Rightarrow \quad x = \ln 5$

(b) $\ln x = 2 \quad \Rightarrow \quad x = e^2$

(c) $e^{e^x} = 2 \quad \Rightarrow \quad e^x = \ln 2 \quad \Rightarrow \quad x = \ln(\ln 2)$

27. (a) After 4 days, $\frac{1}{2}$ gram remains; after 8 days, $\frac{1}{4}$ g; after 12 days, $\frac{1}{8}$ g; after 16 days, $\frac{1}{16}$ g.

(b) $m(4) = \dfrac{1}{2}, m(8) = \dfrac{1}{2^2}, m(12) = \dfrac{1}{2^3}, m(16) = \dfrac{1}{2^4}.$ From the pattern, we see that $m(t) = \dfrac{1}{2^{t/4}}$, or $2^{-t/4}.$

(c) $m = 2^{-t/4} \quad \Rightarrow \quad \log_2 m = -t/4 \quad \Rightarrow \quad t = -4\log_2 m$; this is the time elapsed when there are m grams of ^{100}Pd.

(d) $m = 0.01 \quad\Rightarrow\quad t = -4\log_2 0.01 = -4\left(\dfrac{\ln 0.01}{\ln 2}\right) \approx 26.6$ days

28. (a)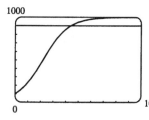

The population would reach 900 in about 4.4 years.

(b) $P = \dfrac{100{,}000}{100 + 900e^{-t}} \quad\Rightarrow\quad 100P + 900Pe^{-t} = 100{,}000 \Rightarrow$

$900Pe^{-t} = 100{,}000 - 100P \quad\Rightarrow\quad e^{-t} = \dfrac{100{,}000 - 100P}{900P} \Rightarrow$

$-t = \ln\left(\dfrac{1000 - P}{9P}\right) \quad\Rightarrow\quad t = -\ln\left(\dfrac{1000 - P}{9P}\right)$, or

$\ln\left(\dfrac{9P}{1000 - P}\right)$; this is the time required for the population to reach a given number P.

(c) $P = 900 \quad\Rightarrow\quad t = \ln\left(\dfrac{9 \cdot 900}{1000 - 900}\right) = \ln 81 \approx 4.4$ years, as in part (a).

29. $f(x) = \ln(x^2 - c)$. If $c < 0$, the domain of f is $\mathbb{R}$. If $c = 0$, the domain of f is $(-\infty, 0) \cup (0, \infty)$. If $c > 0$, the domain of f is $(-\infty, -\sqrt{c}) \cup (\sqrt{c}, \infty)$. As c increases, the dip at $x = 0$ becomes deeper. For $c \geq 0$, the graph has asymptotes at $x = \pm\sqrt{c}$.

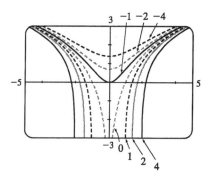

30.

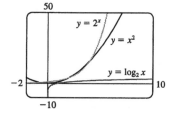

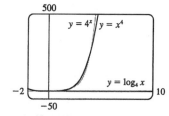

For large values of x, $y = a^x$ has the largest y-values and $y = \log_a x$ has the smallest y-values. This makes sense because they are inverses of each other.

31. (a)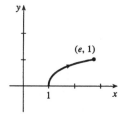

(e, 1)

$0 \leq t \leq 1 \quad\Rightarrow\quad 0 \leq y \leq 1$ and $1 \leq x \leq e$.

(b) $x = e^t \quad\Rightarrow\quad t = \ln x; \; y = \sqrt{t}$ so $y = \sqrt{\ln x}$.

32. (a) $(x-2)^2 + y^2 = 4 \Rightarrow \dfrac{(x-2)^2}{4} + \dfrac{y^2}{4} = 1$. Let $\dfrac{(x-2)^2}{4} = \sin^2 t$

and $\dfrac{y^2}{4} = \cos^2 t$ (since $\sin^2 t + \cos^2 t = 1$). Solving for x and y gives

$x = 2 \pm 2\sin t$ and $y = \pm 2\cos t$. We want to move from $(2, 2)$ to

$(2, -2)$ and pass through $(0, 0)$. When $t = 0$, we want $y = 2$, so

choose $y = 2\cos t$. When $t = \frac{\pi}{2}$, we want $x = 0$, so choose

$x = 2 - 2\sin t$. Thus, parametric equations are $x = 2 - 2\sin t$,

$y = 2\cos t$, $0 \le t \le \pi$. Another possibility is $x = 2 + 2\cos t$,

$y = 2\sin t$, $\frac{\pi}{2} \le t \le \frac{3\pi}{2}$.

(b)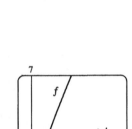

33. We sketch $x = t$, $y = 2t + \ln t$ (the function) and $x = 2t + \ln t$,
$y = t$ (its inverse) for $t > 0$.

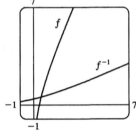

34. (a) In $\triangle OCB$, $\cos\theta = \dfrac{2a}{|OB|}$. In $\triangle OAC$, $\cos\theta = \dfrac{|OA|}{2a}$.

$$|OP| = |AB| = |OB| - |OA| = \dfrac{2a}{\cos\theta} - 2a\cos\theta$$

$$= 2a\left(\dfrac{1 - \cos^2\theta}{\cos\theta}\right) = 2a\dfrac{\sin^2\theta}{\cos\theta}$$

The coordinates of $P(x, y)$ can be found by the relationships

$\cos\theta = \dfrac{x}{|OP|}$ and $\sin\theta = \dfrac{y}{|OP|}$.

Thus, $x = (\cos\theta)\left(2a\dfrac{\sin^2\theta}{\cos\theta}\right) = 2a\sin^2\theta$ and

$y = (\sin\theta)\left(2a\dfrac{\sin^2\theta}{\cos\theta}\right) = 2a\sin^2\theta\tan\theta$.

(b)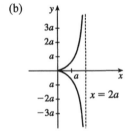

1.

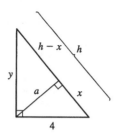

By using the area formula for a triangle, $\frac{1}{2}$ (base) (height), in two ways,

we see that $\frac{1}{2}(4)(y) = \frac{1}{2}(h)(a)$, so $a = \frac{4y}{h}$. Since $4^2 + y^2 = h^2$,

$$y = \sqrt{h^2 - 16}, \text{ and } a = \frac{4\sqrt{h^2 - 16}}{h}.$$

2.

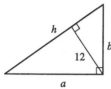

Refer to Example 1, where we obtained $h = \dfrac{P^2 - 100}{2P}$. The 100 came from 4 times the area of the triangle.

In this case, the area of the triangle is $\frac{1}{2}(h)(12) = 6h$. Thus, $h = \dfrac{P^2 - 4\,(6h)}{2P} \quad\Rightarrow\quad 2Ph = P^2 - 24h \quad\Rightarrow$

$2Ph + 24h = P^2 \quad\Rightarrow\quad h\,(2P + 24) = P^2 \quad\Rightarrow\quad h = \dfrac{P^2}{2P + 24}.$

3. $|2x - 1| = \begin{cases} 1 - 2x & \text{if } x < \frac{1}{2} \\ 2x - 1 & \text{if } x \geq \frac{1}{2} \end{cases}$ and $|x + 5| = \begin{cases} -x - 5 & \text{if } x < -5 \\ x + 5 & \text{if } x \geq -5 \end{cases}$

Therefore, we consider the three cases $x < -5$, $-5 \leq x < \frac{1}{2}$, and $x \geq \frac{1}{2}$.

If $x < -5$, we must have $1 - 2x - (-x - 5) = 3 \quad\Leftrightarrow\quad x = 3$, which is false, since we are considering $x < -5$.

If $-5 \leq x < \frac{1}{2}$, we must have $1 - 2x - (x + 5) = 3 \quad\Leftrightarrow\quad x = -\frac{7}{3}$.

If $x \geq \frac{1}{2}$, we must have $2x - 1 - (x + 5) = 3 \quad\Leftrightarrow\quad x = 9$.

So the two solutions of the equation are $x = -\frac{7}{3}$ and $x = 9$.

4. $|x - 1| = \begin{cases} 1 - x & \text{if } x < 1 \\ x - 1 & \text{if } x \geq 1 \end{cases}$ and $|x - 3| = \begin{cases} 3 - x & \text{if } x < 3 \\ x - 3 & \text{if } x \geq 3 \end{cases}$

Therefore, we consider the three cases $x < 1$, $1 \leq x < 3$, and $x \geq 3$.

If $x < 1$, we must have $1 - x - (3 - x) \geq 5 \quad\Leftrightarrow\quad 0 \geq 7$, which is false.

If $1 \leq x < 3$, we must have $x - 1 - (3 - x) \geq 5 \quad\Leftrightarrow\quad x \geq \frac{9}{2}$, which is false because $x < 3$.

If $x \geq 3$, we must have $x - 1 - (x - 3) \geq 5 \quad\Leftrightarrow\quad 2 \geq 5$, which is false.

All three cases lead to falsehoods, so the inequality has no solution.

5. $f(x) = |x^2 - 4|x| + 3|$. If $x \geq 0$, then $f(x) = |x^2 - 4x + 3| = |(x-1)(x-3)|$.

       Case (i):   If $0 < x \leq 1$, then $f(x) = x^2 - 4x + 3$.

       Case (ii):   If $1 < x \leq 3$, then $f(x) = -(x^2 - 4x + 3) = -x^2 + 4x - 3$.

       Case (iii):   If $x > 3$, then $f(x) = x^2 - 4x + 3$.

This enables us to sketch the graph for $x \geq 0$. Then we use the fact that f is an even function to reflect this part of the graph about the y-axis to obtain the entire graph. Or, we could consider also the cases $x < -3$, $-3 \leq x < -1$, and $-1 \leq x < 0$.

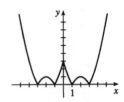

6. $g(x) = |x^2 - 1| - |x^2 - 4|$.

$$|x^2 - 1| = \begin{cases} x^2 - 1 & \text{if } |x| \geq 1 \\ 1 - x^2 & \text{if } |x| < 1 \end{cases} \text{ and } |x^2 - 4| = \begin{cases} x^2 - 4 & \text{if } |x| \geq 2 \\ 4 - x^2 & \text{if } |x| < 2 \end{cases}$$

So for $0 \leq |x| < 1$, $g(x) = 1 - x^2 - (4 - x^2) = -3$, for

$1 \leq |x| < 2$, $g(x) = x^2 - 1 - (4 - x^2) = 2x^2 - 5$, and for

$|x| \geq 2$, $g(x) = x^2 - 1 - (x^2 - 4) = 3$.

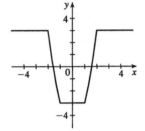

7. $|x| + |y| = 1 + |xy| \Leftrightarrow |xy| - |x| - |y| + 1 = 0 \Leftrightarrow$

$|x||y| - |x| - |y| + 1 = 0 \Leftrightarrow (|x| - 1)(|y| - 1) = 0 \Leftrightarrow x = \pm 1$ or

$y = \pm 1$.

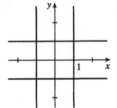

8. $x^2 y - y^3 - 5x^2 + 5y^2 = 0 \Leftrightarrow x^2(y-5) - y^2(y-5) = 0 \Leftrightarrow$

$(x^2 - y^2)(y-5) = 0 \Leftrightarrow x = \pm y$ or $y = 5$

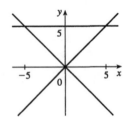

9. $|x| + |y| \leq 1$. The boundary of the region has equation $|x| + |y| = 1$.

In quadrants I, II, III, and IV, this becomes the lines $x + y = 1$,

$-x + y = 1$, $-x - y = 1$, and $x - y = 1$ respectively.

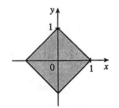

10. $|x - y| + |x| - |y| \le 2$

Case (i):	$x > y > 0$	$\Leftrightarrow$	$x - y + x - y \le 2$	$\Leftrightarrow$	$x - y \le 1$	$\Leftrightarrow$ $y \ge x - 1$
Case (ii):	$y > x > 0$	$\Leftrightarrow$	$y - x + x - y \le 2$	$\Leftrightarrow$	$0 \le 2$ (true)	
Case (iii):	$x > 0$ and $y < 0$	$\Leftrightarrow$	$x - y + x + y \le 2$	$\Leftrightarrow$	$2x \le 2$	$\Leftrightarrow$ $x \le 1$
Case (iv):	$x < 0$ and $y > 0$	$\Leftrightarrow$	$y - x - x - y \le 2$	$\Leftrightarrow$	$-2x \le 2$	$\Leftrightarrow$ $x \ge -1$
Case (v):	$y < x < 0$	$\Leftrightarrow$	$x - y - x + y \le 2$	$\Leftrightarrow$	$0 \le 2$ (true)	
Case (vi):	$x < y < 0$	$\Leftrightarrow$	$y - x - x + y \le 2$	$\Leftrightarrow$	$y - x \le 1$	$\Leftrightarrow$ $y \le x + 1$

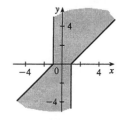

Note: Instead of considering cases (iv), (v), and (vi), we could have noted that the region is unchanged if x and y are replaced by $-x$ and $-y$, so the region is symmetric about the origin. Therefore, we need only draw cases (i), (ii), and (iii), and rotate through $180°$ about the origin.

11. $(\log_2 3)(\log_3 4)(\log_4 5) \cdots (\log_{31} 32) = \left(\dfrac{\ln 3}{\ln 2}\right)\left(\dfrac{\ln 4}{\ln 3}\right)\left(\dfrac{\ln 5}{\ln 4}\right) \cdots \left(\dfrac{\ln 32}{\ln 31}\right) = \dfrac{\ln 32}{\ln 2} = \dfrac{\ln 2^5}{\ln 2} = \dfrac{5\ln 2}{\ln 2} = 5$

12. (a) $f(-x) = \ln\left(-x + \sqrt{(-x)^2 + 1}\right) = \ln\left(-x + \sqrt{x^2 + 1} \cdot \dfrac{-x - \sqrt{x^2 + 1}}{-x - \sqrt{x^2 + 1}}\right)$

$= \ln\left(\dfrac{x^2 - (x^2 + 1)}{-x - \sqrt{x^2 + 1}}\right) = \ln\left(\dfrac{-1}{-x - \sqrt{x^2 + 1}}\right) = \ln\left(\dfrac{1}{x + \sqrt{x^2 + 1}}\right)$

$= \ln 1 - \ln\left(x + \sqrt{x^2 + 1}\right) = -\ln\left(x + \sqrt{x^2 - 1}\right) = -f(x)$

(b) $y = \ln\left(x + \sqrt{x^2 + 1}\right)$. Interchanging x and y, we get $x = \ln\left(y + \sqrt{y^2 + 1}\right)$ $\Rightarrow$ $e^x = y + \sqrt{y^2 + 1}$ $\Rightarrow$

$e^x - y = \sqrt{y^2 + 1}$ $\Rightarrow$ $e^{2x} - 2ye^x + y^2 = y^2 + 1$ $\Rightarrow$ $e^{2x} - 1 = 2ye^x$ $\Rightarrow$

$y = \dfrac{e^{2x} - 1}{2e^x} = f^{-1}(-x)$

13. $\ln(x^2 - 2x - 2) \le 0$ $\Rightarrow$ $x^2 - 2x - 2 \le e^0 = 1$ $\Rightarrow$ $x^2 - 2x - 3 \le 0$ $\Rightarrow$ $(x - 3)(x + 1) \le 0$ $\Rightarrow$

$x \in [-1, 3]$. Since the argument must be positive, $x^2 - 2x - 2 > 0$ $\Rightarrow$ $\left[x - (1 - \sqrt{3})\right]\left[x - (1 + \sqrt{3})\right] > 0$

$\Rightarrow$ $x \in (-\infty, 1 - \sqrt{3}) \cup (1 + \sqrt{3}, \infty)$. The intersection of these intervals is $[-1, 1 - \sqrt{3}) \cup (1 + \sqrt{3}, 3]$.

14. Assume that $\log_2 5$ is rational. Then $\log_2 5 = m/n$ for natural numbers m and n. Changing to exponential form gives us $2^{m/n} = 5$ and then raising both sides to the nth power gives $2^m = 5^n$. But 2^m is even and 5^n is odd. We have arrived at a contradiction, so we conclude that our hypothesis, that $\log_2 5$ is rational, is false. Thus, $\log_2 5$ is irrational.

15. Let d be the distance traveled on each half of the trip. Let t_1 and t_2 be the times taken for the first and second halves of the trip.

For the first half of the trip we have $t_1 = d/30$ and for the second half we have $t_2 = d/60$. Thus, the average speed for the entire trip is $\dfrac{\text{total distance}}{\text{total time}} = \dfrac{2d}{t_1 + t_2} = \dfrac{2d}{\dfrac{d}{30} + \dfrac{d}{60}} \cdot \dfrac{60}{60} = \dfrac{120d}{2d + d} = \dfrac{120d}{3d} = 40$. The average speed for

the entire trip is 40 mi/h.

16. Let $f = \sin$, $g = x$, and $h = x$. Then the left-hand side of the equation is

$f \circ (g + h) = \sin(x + x) = \sin 2x = 2 \sin x \cos x$; and the right-hand side is

$f \circ g + f \circ h = \sin x + \sin x = 2 \sin x$. The two sides are not equal, so the given statement is false.

17. Let S_n be the statement that $7^n - 1$ is divisible by 6.

- S_1 is true because $7^1 - 1 = 6$ is divisible by 6.

- Assume S_k is true, that is, $7^k - 1$ is divisible by 6. In other words, $7^k - 1 = 6m$ for some positive integer m. Then $7^{k+1} - 1 = 7^k \cdot 7 - 1 = (6m + 1) \cdot 7 - 1 = 42m + 6 = 6(7m + 1)$, which is divisible by 6, so S_{k+1} is true.

- Therefore, by mathematical induction, $7^n - 1$ is divisible by 6 for every positive integer n.

18. Let S_n be the statement that $1 + 3 + 5 + \cdots + (2n - 1) = n^2$.

- S_1 is true because $[2(1) - 1] = 1 = 1^2$.

- Assume S_k is true, that is, $1 + 3 + 5 + \cdots + (2k - 1) = k^2$. Then

$$1 + 3 + 5 + \cdots + (2k - 1) + [(2k + 1) - 1] = 1 + 3 + 5 + \cdots + (2k - 1) + (2k + 1)$$
$$= k^2 + (2k + 1) = (k + 1)^2$$

which shows that S_{k+1} is true.

- Therefore, by mathematical induction, $1 + 3 + 5 + \cdots + (2n - 1) = n^2$ for every positive integer n.

19. $f_0(x) = x^2$ and $f_{n+1}(x) = f_0(f_n(x))$ for $n = 0, 1, 2, \ldots$.

$f_1(x) = f_0(f_0(x)) = f_0(x^2) = (x^2)^2 = x^4$, $f_2(x) = f_0(f_1(x)) = f_0(x^4) = (x^4)^2 = x^8$,

$f_3(x) = f_0(f_2(x)) = f_0(x^8) = (x^8)^2 = x^{16}, \ldots$. Thus, a general formula is $f_n(x) = x^{2^{n+1}}$.

20. (a) $f_0(x) = 1/(2 - x)$ and $f_{n+1} = f_0 \circ f_n$ for $n = 0, 1, 2, \ldots$.

$$f_1(x) = f_0\left(\frac{1}{2 - x}\right) = \frac{1}{2 - \dfrac{1}{2 - x}} = \frac{2 - x}{2(2 - x) - 1} = \frac{2 - x}{3 - 2x},$$

$$f_2(x) = f_0\left(\frac{2 - x}{3 - 2x}\right) = \frac{1}{2 - \dfrac{2 - x}{3 - 2x}} = \frac{3 - 2x}{2(3 - 2x) - (2 - x)} = \frac{3 - 2x}{4 - 3x},$$

$$f_3(x) = f_0\left(\frac{3 - 2x}{4 - 3x}\right) = \frac{1}{2 - \dfrac{3 - 2x}{4 - 3x}} = \frac{4 - 3x}{2(4 - 3x) - (3 - 2x)} = \frac{4 - 3x}{5 - 4x}, \ldots$$

Thus, we conjecture that the general formula is $f_n(x) = \dfrac{n + 1 - nx}{n + 2 - (n + 1)x}$.

To prove this, we use the Principle of Mathematical Induction. We have already verified that f_n is true for $n = 1$. Assume that the formula is true for $n = k$; that is, $f_k(x) = \dfrac{k+1-kx}{k+2-(k+1)x}$. Then

$$f_{k+1}(x) = (f_0 \circ f_k)(x) = f_0(f_k(x)) = f_0\left(\frac{k+1-kx}{k+2-(k+1)x}\right) = \frac{1}{2 - \dfrac{k+1-kx}{k+2-(k+1)x}}$$

$$= \frac{k+2-(k+1)x}{2\left[k+2-(k+1)x\right]-(k+1-kx)} = \frac{k+2-(k+1)x}{k+3-(k+2)x}$$

This shows that the formula for f_n is true for $n = k + 1$. Therefore, by mathematical induction, the formula is true for all positive integers n.

(b)

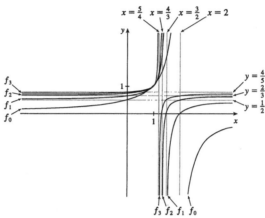

From the graph, we can make several observations:

- The values at $x = a$ keep increasing as k increases.

- The vertical asymptote gets closer to $x = 1$ as k increases.

- The horizontal asymptote gets closer to $y = 1$ as k increases.

- The x-intercept for f_{k+1} is the value of the vertical asymptote for f_k.

- The y-intercept for f_k is the value of the horizontal asymptote for f_{k+1}.

2 Limits and Derivatives

2.1 The Tangent and Velocity Problems • • • • • • • • •

1. (a) Using $P(15, 250)$, we construct the following table:

t	Q	slope $= m_{PQ}$
5	$(5, 694)$	$\frac{694-250}{5-15} = -\frac{444}{10} = -44.4$
10	$(10, 444)$	$\frac{444-250}{10-15} = -\frac{194}{5} = -38.8$
20	$(20, 111)$	$\frac{111-250}{20-15} = -\frac{139}{5} = -27.8$
25	$(25, 28)$	$\frac{28-250}{25-15} = -\frac{222}{10} = -22.2$
30	$(30, 0)$	$\frac{0-250}{30-15} = -\frac{250}{15} = -16.\overline{6}$

(b) Using the values of t that correspond to the points closest to P ($t = 10$ and $t = 20$), we have

$$\frac{-38.8 + (-27.8)}{2} = -33.3$$

(c) From the graph, we can estimate the slope of the tangent line at P to be $\frac{-300}{9} = -33.\overline{3}$.

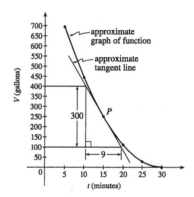

2. (a) Slope $= \frac{2948 - 2530}{42 - 36} = \frac{418}{6} \approx 69.67$ (b) Slope $= \frac{2948 - 2661}{42 - 38} = \frac{287}{4} = 71.75$

(c) Slope $= \frac{2948 - 2806}{42 - 40} = \frac{142}{2} = 71$ (d) Slope $= \frac{3080 - 2948}{44 - 42} = \frac{132}{2} = 66$

From the data, we see that the patient's heart rate is decreasing from 71 to 66 heartbeats/minute after 42 minutes. After being stable for a while, the patient's heart rate is dropping.

3. For the curve $y = x/(1 + x)$ and the point $P\left(1, \frac{1}{2}\right)$:

(a)

	x	Q	m_{PQ}
(i)	0.5	$(0.5, 0.333333)$	0.333333
(ii)	0.9	$(0.9, 0.473684)$	0.263158
(iii)	0.99	$(0.99, 0.497487)$	0.251256
(iv)	0.999	$(0.999, 0.499750)$	0.250125
(v)	1.5	$(1.5, 0.6)$	0.2
(vi)	1.1	$(1.1, 0.523810)$	0.238095
(vii)	1.01	$(1.01, 0.502488)$	0.248756
(viii)	1.001	$(1.001, 0.500250)$	0.249875

(b) The slope appears to be $\frac{1}{4}$.

(c) $y - \frac{1}{2} = \frac{1}{4}(x - 1)$ or $y = \frac{1}{4}x + \frac{1}{4}$.

4. For the curve $y = \ln x$ and the point $P(2, \ln 2)$:

(a)

	x	Q	m_{PQ}
(i)	1.5	$(1.5, 0.405465)$	0.575364
(ii)	1.9	$(1.9, 0.641854)$	0.512933
(iii)	1.99	$(1.99, 0.688135)$	0.501254
(iv)	1.999	$(1.999, 0.692647)$	0.500125
(v)	2.5	$(2.5, 0.916291)$	0.446287
(vi)	2.1	$(2.1, 0.741937)$	0.487902
(vii)	2.01	$(2.01, 0.698135)$	0.498754
(viii)	2.001	$(2.001, 0.693647)$	0.499875

(b) The slope appears to be $\frac{1}{2}$.

(c) $y - \ln 2 = \frac{1}{2}(x - 2)$ or

$y = \frac{1}{2}x - 1 + \ln 2$

(d)

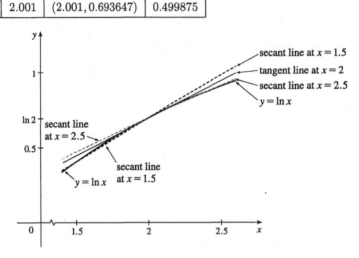

5. (a) At $t = 2$, $y = 40(2) - 16(2)^2 = 16$. The average velocity between times 2 and $2 + h$ is

$$\frac{40(2+h) - 16(2+h)^2 - 16}{h} = \frac{-24h - 16h^2}{h} = -24 - 16h, \text{ if } h \neq 0.$$

(i) $h = 0.5$, -32 ft/s

(ii) $h = 0.1$, -25.6 ft/s

(iii) $h = 0.05$, -24.8 ft/s

(iv) $h = 0.01$, -24.16 ft/s

(b) The instantaneous velocity when $t = 2$ (h approaches 0) is -24 ft/s.

6. The average velocity between t and $t + h$ seconds is

$$\frac{58(t+h) - 0.83(t+h)^2 - (58t - 0.83t^2)}{h} = \frac{58h - 1.66th - 0.83h^2}{h} = 58 - 1.66t - 0.83h \text{ if } h \neq 0.$$

(a) Here $t = 1$, so the average velocity is $58 - 1.66 - 0.83h = 56.34 - 0.83h$.

(i) $[1, 2]$: $h = 1$, 55.51 m/s

(ii) $[1, 1.5]$: $h = 0.5$, 55.925 m/s

(iii) $[1, 1.1]$: $h = 0.1$, 56.257 m/s

(iv) $[1, 1.01]$: $h = 0.01$, 56.3317 m/s

(v) $[1, 1.001]$: $h = 0.001$, 56.33917 m/s

(b) The instantaneous velocity after 1 second is 56.34 m/s.

7. Average velocity between times 1 and $1 + h$ is

$$\frac{s(1+h) - s(1)}{h} = \frac{(1+h)^3/6 - 1/6}{h} = \frac{h^3 + 3h^2 + 3h}{6h} = \frac{h^2 + 3h + 3}{6} \text{ if } h \neq 0.$$

(a) (i) $[1,3]$: $h = 2$, $\frac{13}{6}$ ft/s

(ii) $[1,2]$: $h = 1$, $\frac{7}{6}$ ft/s

(iii) $[1,1.5]$: $h = 0.5$, $\frac{19}{24}$ ft/s

(iv) $[1,1.1]$: $h = 0.1$, $\frac{331}{600}$ ft/s

(b) As h approaches 0, the velocity approaches $\frac{3}{6} = \frac{1}{2}$ ft/s.

(c)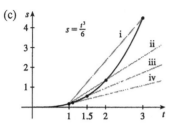

(d)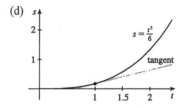

8. Average velocity between times $t = 2$ and $t = 2 + h$ is given by $\dfrac{s(2+h) - s(2)}{h}$.

(a) (i) $h = 3 \Rightarrow v_{av} = \dfrac{s(5) - s(2)}{5 - 2} = \dfrac{178 - 32}{3} = \dfrac{146}{3} \approx 48.7$ ft/s

(ii) $h = 2 \Rightarrow v_{av} = \dfrac{s(4) - s(2)}{4 - 2} = \dfrac{119 - 32}{2} = \dfrac{87}{2} = 43.5$ ft/s

(iii) $h = 1 \Rightarrow v_{av} = \dfrac{s(3) - s(2)}{3 - 2} = \dfrac{70 - 32}{1} = 38$ ft/s

(b) Using the points $(0.8, 0)$ and $(5, 118)$ from the approximate tangent line, the instantaneous velocity at $t = 2$ is about $\frac{118 - 0}{5 - 0.8} \approx 28$ ft/s.

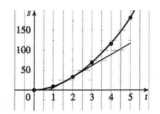

9. For the curve $y = \sin(10\pi/x)$ and the point $P(1, 0)$:

(a)

x	Q	m_{PQ}
2	$(2, 0)$	0
1.5	$(1.5, 0.8660)$	1.7321
1.4	$(1.4, -0.4339)$	-1.0847
1.3	$(1.3, -0.8230)$	-2.7433
1.2	$(1.2, 0.8660)$	4.3301
1.1	$(1.1, -0.2817)$	-2.8173

x	Q	m_{PQ}
0.5	$(0.5, 0)$	0
0.6	$(0.6, 0.8660)$	-2.1651
0.7	$(0.7, 0.7818)$	-2.6061
0.8	$(0.8, 1)$	-5
0.9	$(0.9, -0.3420)$	3.4202

As x approaches 1, the slopes do not appear to be approaching any particular value.

(b)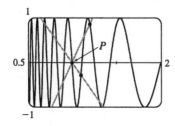

We see that problems with estimation are caused by the frequent oscillations of the graph. The tangent is so steep at P that we need to take x-values much closer to 1 in order to get accurate estimates of its slope.

(c) If we choose $x = 1.001$, then the point Q is $(1.001, -0.0314)$ and $m_{PQ} \approx -31.3794$. If $x = 0.999$, then Q is $(0.999, 0.0314)$ and $m_{PQ} = -31.4422$. The average of these slopes is -31.4108. So we estimate that the slope of the tangent line at P is about -31.4.

2.2 The Limit of a Function • • • • • • • • • • • • •

1. As x approaches 2, $f(x)$ approaches 5. [Or, the values of $f(x)$ can be made as close to 5 as we like by taking x sufficiently close to 2 (but $x \neq 2$).] Yes, the graph could have a hole at $(2, 5)$ and be defined such that $f(2) = 3$.

2. As x approaches 1 from the left, $f(x)$ approaches 3; and as x approaches 1 from the right, $f(x)$ approaches 7. No, the limit does not exist because the left- and right-hand limits are different.

3. (a) $f(x)$ approaches 2 as x approaches 1 from the left, so $\lim\limits_{x \to 1^-} f(x) = 2$.

   (b) $f(x)$ approaches 3 as x approaches 1 from the right, so $\lim\limits_{x \to 1^+} f(x) = 3$.

   (c) $\lim\limits_{x \to 1} f(x)$ does not exist because the limits in part (a) and part (b) are not equal.

   (d) $f(x)$ approaches 4 as x approaches 5 from the left and from the right, so $\lim\limits_{x \to 5} f(x) = 4$.

   (e) $f(5)$ is not defined, so it doesn't exist.

4. (a) $\lim\limits_{x \to 0} f(x) = 3$ (b) $\lim\limits_{x \to 3^-} f(x) = 4$ (c) $\lim\limits_{x \to 3^+} f(x) = 2$

   (d) $\lim\limits_{x \to 3} f(x)$ does not exist because the limits in part (b) and part (c) are not equal.

   (e) $f(3) = 3$

5. (a) $\lim\limits_{t \to 0^-} g(t) = -1$ (b) $\lim\limits_{t \to 0^+} g(t) = -2$

   (c) $\lim\limits_{t \to 0} g(t)$ does not exist because the limits in part (a) and part (b) are not equal.

   (d) $\lim\limits_{t \to 2^-} g(t) = 2$ (e) $\lim\limits_{t \to 2^+} g(t) = 0$

   (f) $\lim\limits_{t \to 2} g(t)$ does not exist because the limits in part (d) and part (e) are not equal.

   (g) $g(2) = 1$ (h) $\lim\limits_{t \to 4} g(t) = 3$

6. $\lim\limits_{x \to a} f(x)$ exists for all a except $a = \pm 1$.

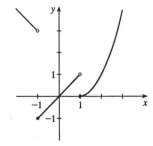

7.

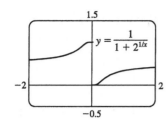

(a) $\lim\limits_{x \to 0^-} f(x) = 1$

(b) $\lim\limits_{x \to 0^+} f(x) = 0$

(c) $\lim\limits_{x \to 0} f(x)$ does not exist because the limits in part (a) and part (b) are not equal.

8. $\lim\limits_{t \to 12^-} f(t) = 150$ mg and $\lim\limits_{t \to 12^+} f(t) = 300$ mg. These limits show that there is an abrupt change in the amount of drug in the patient's bloodstream at $t = 12$ h. The left-hand limit represents the amount of the drug just before the fourth injection. The right-hand limit represents the amount of the drug just after the fourth injection.

9. $\lim\limits_{x \to 3^+} f(x) = 4, \quad \lim\limits_{x \to 3^-} f(x) = 2,$

$\lim\limits_{x \to -2} f(x) = 2, \quad f(3) = 3, \quad f(-2) = 1$

10. $\lim\limits_{x \to 0^-} f(x) = 1, \quad \lim\limits_{x \to 0^+} f(x) = -1,$

$\lim\limits_{x \to 2^-} f(x) = 0, \quad \lim\limits_{x \to 2^+} f(x) = 1, \quad f(2) = 1,$

$f(0)$ is undefined

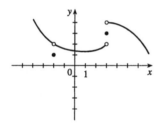

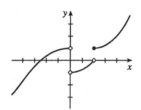

11. For $g(x) = \dfrac{x-1}{x^3-1}$:

x	$g(x)$	x	$g(x)$
0.2	0.806452	1.8	0.165563
0.4	0.641026	1.6	0.193798
0.6	0.510204	1.4	0.229358
0.8	0.409836	1.2	0.274725
0.9	0.369004	1.1	0.302115
0.99	0.336689	1.01	0.330022

It appears that $\lim\limits_{x \to 1} \dfrac{x-1}{x^3-1} = 0.\overline{3} = \frac{1}{3}$.

12. For $F(t) = \dfrac{\sqrt[3]{t}-1}{\sqrt{t}-1}$:

t	$F(t)$
1.5	0.643905
1.2	0.656488
1.1	0.661358
1.01	0.666114
1.001	0.666611

It appears that $\lim\limits_{t \to 1} \dfrac{\sqrt[3]{t}-1}{\sqrt{t}-1} = 0.\overline{6} = \frac{2}{3}$.

13. For $f(x) = \dfrac{e^x - 1 - x}{x^2}$:

x	$f(x)$	x	$f(x)$
1	0.718282	-1	0.367879
0.5	0.594885	-0.5	0.426123
0.1	0.517092	-0.1	0.483742
0.05	0.508439	-0.05	0.491770
0.01	0.501671	-0.01	0.498337

It appears that $\lim\limits_{x \to 0} \dfrac{e^x - 1 - x}{x^2} = 0.5 = \frac{1}{2}$.

14. For $g(x) = x \ln(x + x^2)$:

x	$g(x)$
1	-0.693147
0.5	-0.143841
0.1	-0.220727
0.05	-0.147347
0.01	-0.045952
0.005	-0.026467
0.001	-0.006907

It appears that $\lim\limits_{x \to 0^+} x \ln(x + x^2) = 0$.

15. (a) From the graphs, it seems that $\lim\limits_{x \to 0} \dfrac{\tan 4x}{x} = 4$.

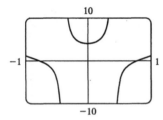
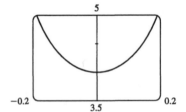

(b)

x	$f(x)$
± 0.1	4.227932
± 0.01	4.002135
± 0.001	4.000021
± 0.0001	4.000000

16. (a) From the following graphs, it seems that $\lim\limits_{x \to 0} \dfrac{6^x - 2^x}{x} \approx 1.10$.

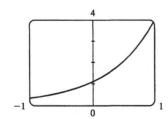
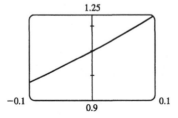

(b)

x	$f(x)$
-0.01	1.085052
-0.001	1.097248
-0.0001	1.098476
0.0001	1.098749
0.001	1.099978
0.01	1.112353

17. (a) Let $h(x) = (1+x)^{1/x}$.

x	$h(x)$
-0.001	2.71964
-0.0001	2.71842
-0.00001	2.71830
-0.000001	2.71828
0.000001	2.71828
0.00001	2.71827
0.0001	2.71815
0.001	2.71692

It appears that $\lim_{x \to 0} (1+x)^{1/x} \approx 2.71828$, which is approximately e.

In Section 3.7 we'll see that the value of the limit is exactly e.

(b)

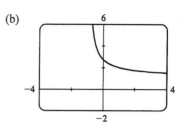

18. For the curve $y = 2^x$ and the points $P(0, 1)$ and $Q(x, 2^x)$:

x	Q	m_{PQ}
0.1	$(0.1, 1.0717735)$	0.71773
0.01	$(0.01, 1.0069556)$	0.69556
0.001	$(0.001, 1.0006934)$	0.69339
0.0001	$(0.0001, 1.0000693)$	0.69317

The slope appears to be about 0.693.

19. For $f(x) = x^2 - (2^x/1000)$:

(a)

x	$f(x)$
1	0.998000
0.8	0.638259
0.6	0.358484
0.4	0.158680
0.2	0.038851
0.1	0.008928
0.05	0.001465

It appears that $\lim_{x \to 0} f(x) = 0$.

(b)

x	$f(x)$
0.04	0.000572
0.02	-0.000614
0.01	-0.000907
0.005	-0.000978
0.003	-0.000993
0.001	-0.001000

It appears that $\lim_{x \to 0} f(x) = -0.001$.

20. $h(x) = \dfrac{\tan x - x}{x^3}$

(a)

x	$h(x)$
1.0	0.55740773
0.5	0.37041992
0.1	0.33467209
0.05	0.33366700
0.01	0.33334667
0.005	0.33333667

(c)

x	$h(x)$
0.001	0.33333350
0.0005	0.33333344
0.0001	0.33333000
0.00005	0.33333600
0.00001	0.33300000
0.000001	0.00000000

(b) It seems that $\lim\limits_{x \to 0} h(x) = \frac{1}{3}$.

Here the values will vary from one calculator to another. Every calculator will eventually give *false values*.

(d) As in part (c), when we take a small enough viewing rectangle we get incorrect output.

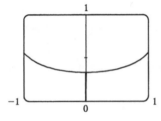

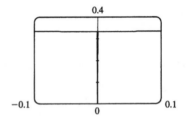

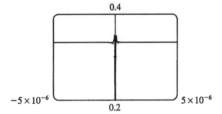

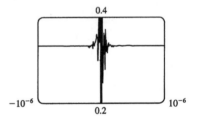

21.

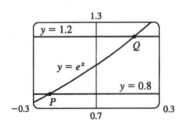

We need to have $0.8 < e^x < 1.2$. From the graph we obtain the approximate points of intersection $P(-0.2231436, 0.8)$ and $Q(0.18232156, 1.2)$. So if x is within 0.182 of 0, then y will be within 0.2 of 1. If we must have e^x within 0.1 of 1, we get $P(-0.1053605, 0.9)$ and $Q(0.09531018, 1.1)$. We would then need x to be within 0.095 of 0.

22. (a) Let $y = (x^3 - 1)/(\sqrt{x} - 1)$.

x	y
0.99	5.92531
0.999	5.99250
0.9999	5.99925
1.01	6.07531
1.001	6.00750
1.0001	6.00075

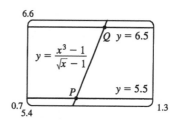

From the table and the graph, we guess that the limit of y as x approaches 1 is 6.

(b) We need to have $5.5 < \dfrac{x^3 - 1}{\sqrt{x} - 1} < 6.5$. From the graph we obtain the approximate points of intersection

$P(0.9313853, 5.5)$ and $Q(1.0649004, 6.5)$. Now $1 - 0.9313853 \approx 0.0686$ and $1.0649004 - 1 \approx 0.0649$, so by requiring that x be within 0.0649 of 1, we ensure that y is within 0.5 of 6.

2.3   Calculating Limits Using the Limit Laws   •   •   •   •   •   •   •

1. (a) $\lim\limits_{x \to a} [f(x) + h(x)] = \lim\limits_{x \to a} f(x) + \lim\limits_{x \to a} h(x)$

$= -3 + 8 = 5$

(b) $\lim\limits_{x \to a} [f(x)]^2 = \left[\lim\limits_{x \to a} f(x)\right]^2 = (-3)^2 = 9$

(c) $\lim\limits_{x \to a} \sqrt[3]{h(x)} = \sqrt[3]{\lim\limits_{x \to a} h(x)} = \sqrt[3]{8} = 2$

(d) $\lim\limits_{x \to a} \dfrac{1}{f(x)} = \dfrac{1}{\lim\limits_{x \to a} f(x)} = \dfrac{1}{-3} = -\dfrac{1}{3}$

(e) $\lim\limits_{x \to a} \dfrac{f(x)}{h(x)} = \dfrac{\lim\limits_{x \to a} f(x)}{\lim\limits_{x \to a} h(x)} = \dfrac{-3}{8} = -\dfrac{3}{8}$

(f) $\lim\limits_{x \to a} \dfrac{g(x)}{f(x)} = \dfrac{\lim\limits_{x \to a} g(x)}{\lim\limits_{x \to a} f(x)} = \dfrac{0}{-3} = 0$

(g) The limit does not exist, since $\lim\limits_{x \to a} g(x) = 0$ but $\lim\limits_{x \to a} f(x) \neq 0$.

(h) $\lim\limits_{x \to a} \dfrac{2f(x)}{h(x) - f(x)} = \dfrac{2\lim\limits_{x \to a} f(x)}{\lim\limits_{x \to a} h(x) - \lim\limits_{x \to a} f(x)} = \dfrac{2(-3)}{8 - (-3)} = -\dfrac{6}{11}$

2. (a) $\lim\limits_{x \to 2} [f(x) + g(x)] = \lim\limits_{x \to 2} f(x) + \lim\limits_{x \to 2} g(x) = 2 + 0 = 2$

(b) $\lim\limits_{x \to 1} g(x)$ does not exist since its left- and right-hand limits are not equal, so the given limit does not exist.

(c) $\lim\limits_{x \to 0} [f(x)g(x)] = \lim\limits_{x \to 0} f(x) \cdot \lim\limits_{x \to 0} g(x) = 0 \cdot 1.3 = 0$

(d) Since $\lim\limits_{x \to -1} g(x) = 0$ and g is in the denominator, the given limit does not exist.

(e) $\lim\limits_{x \to 2} x^3 f(x) = \left[\lim\limits_{x \to 2} x^3\right]\left[\lim\limits_{x \to 2} f(x)\right] = 2^3 \cdot 2 = 16$

(f) $\lim\limits_{x \to 1} \sqrt{3 + f(x)} = \sqrt{3 + \lim\limits_{x \to 1} f(x)} = \sqrt{3 + 1} = 2$

3. $\lim\limits_{x\to 4} \left(5x^2 - 2x + 3\right) = \lim\limits_{x\to 4} 5x^2 - \lim\limits_{x\to 4} 2x + \lim\limits_{x\to 4} 3$ (Limit Laws 2 & 1)

$$= 5 \lim\limits_{x\to 4} x^2 - 2 \lim\limits_{x\to 4} x + 3$$ (3 & 7)

$$= 5\,(4)^2 - 2\,(4) + 3 = 75$$ (9 & 8)

4. $\lim\limits_{x\to 2} \dfrac{2x^2 + 1}{x^2 + 6x - 4} = \dfrac{\lim\limits_{x\to 2} \left(2x^2 + 1\right)}{\lim\limits_{x\to 2} \left(x^2 + 6x - 4\right)}$ (Limit Law 5)

$$= \dfrac{2 \lim\limits_{x\to 2} x^2 + \lim\limits_{x\to 2} 1}{\lim\limits_{x\to 2} x^2 + 6 \lim\limits_{x\to 2} x - \lim\limits_{x\to 2} 4}$$ (2, 1, & 3)

$$= \dfrac{2(2)^2 + 1}{(2)^2 + 6(2) - 4} = \dfrac{9}{12} = \dfrac{3}{4}$$ (9, 7, & 8)

5. $\lim\limits_{t\to -2} (t+1)^9 \left(t^2 - 1\right) = \lim\limits_{t\to -2} (t+1)^9 \lim\limits_{t\to -2} \left(t^2 - 1\right)$ (4)

$$= \left[\lim\limits_{t\to -2} (t+1) \right]^9 \lim\limits_{t\to -2} \left(t^2 - 1\right)$$ (6)

$$= \left[\lim\limits_{t\to -2} t + \lim\limits_{t\to -2} 1 \right]^9 \left[\lim\limits_{t\to -2} t^2 - \lim\limits_{t\to -2} 1 \right]$$ (1 & 2)

$$= [(-2) + 1]^9 \left[(-2)^2 - 1 \right] = -3$$ (8, 7 & 9)

6. $\lim\limits_{u\to -2} \sqrt{u^4 + 3u + 6} = \sqrt{\lim\limits_{u\to -2} \left(u^4 + 3u + 6\right)}$ (11)

$$= \sqrt{\lim\limits_{u\to -2} u^4 + 3 \lim\limits_{u\to -2} u + \lim\limits_{u\to -2} 6}$$ (1, 2 & 3)

$$= \sqrt{(-2)^4 + 3\,(-2) + 6}$$ (9, 8 & 7)

$$= \sqrt{16 - 6 + 6} = \sqrt{16} = 4$$

7. $\lim\limits_{x\to 1} \left(\dfrac{1 + 3x}{1 + 4x^2 + 3x^4}\right)^3 = \left(\lim\limits_{x\to 1} \dfrac{1 + 3x}{1 + 4x^2 + 3x^4}\right)^3$ (6)

$$= \left[\dfrac{\lim\limits_{x\to 1} (1 + 3x)}{\lim\limits_{x\to 1} \left(1 + 4x^2 + 3x^4\right)} \right]^3$$ (5)

$$= \left[\dfrac{\lim\limits_{x\to 1} 1 + 3 \lim\limits_{x\to 1} x}{\lim\limits_{x\to 1} 1 + 4 \lim\limits_{x\to 1} x^2 + 3 \lim\limits_{x\to 1} x^4} \right]^3$$ (2, 1, & 3)

$$= \left[\dfrac{1 + 3(1)}{1 + 4(1)^2 + 3\,(1)^4} \right]^3 = \left[\dfrac{4}{8} \right]^3 = \left(\dfrac{1}{2} \right)^3 = \dfrac{1}{8}$$ (7, 8, & 9)

8. (a) The left-hand side of the equation is not defined for $x = 2$, but the right-hand side is.

(b) Since the equation holds for all $x \neq 2$, it follows that both sides of the equation approach the same limit as $x \to 2$, just as in Example 3. Remember that in finding $\lim\limits_{x\to a} f(x)$, we never consider $x = a$.

9. $\lim\limits_{x\to 2} \dfrac{x^2 + x - 6}{x - 2} = \lim\limits_{x\to 2} \dfrac{(x+3)(x-2)}{x-2} = \lim\limits_{x\to 2}(x + 3) = 2 + 3 = 5$

10. $\lim\limits_{x\to -4} \dfrac{x^2 + 5x + 4}{x^2 + 3x - 4} = \lim\limits_{x\to -4} \dfrac{(x+4)(x+1)}{(x+4)(x-1)} = \lim\limits_{x\to -4} \dfrac{x+1}{x-1} = \dfrac{-4+1}{-4-1} = \dfrac{-3}{-5} = \dfrac{3}{5}$

11. $\lim\limits_{x\to 2} \dfrac{x^2 - x + 6}{x - 2}$ does not exist since $x - 2 \to 0$ but $x^2 - x + 6 \to 8$ as $x \to 2$.

12. $\lim\limits_{x \to 1} \dfrac{x^3 - 1}{x^2 - 1} = \lim\limits_{x \to 1} \dfrac{(x-1)(x^2 + x + 1)}{(x-1)(x+1)} = \lim\limits_{x \to 1} \dfrac{x^2 + x + 1}{x+1} = \dfrac{1^2 + 1 + 1}{1+1} = \dfrac{3}{2}$

13. $\lim\limits_{t \to -3} \dfrac{t^2 - 9}{2t^2 + 7t + 3} = \lim\limits_{t \to -3} \dfrac{(t+3)(t-3)}{(2t+1)(t+3)} = \lim\limits_{t \to -3} \dfrac{t-3}{2t+1} = \dfrac{-3-3}{2(-3)+1} = \dfrac{-6}{-5} = \dfrac{6}{5}$

14. $\lim\limits_{h \to 0} \dfrac{\sqrt{1+h} - 1}{h} = \lim\limits_{h \to 0} \dfrac{\sqrt{1+h} - 1}{h} \cdot \dfrac{\sqrt{1+h} + 1}{\sqrt{1+h} + 1} = \lim\limits_{h \to 0} \dfrac{(1+h) - 1}{h\left(\sqrt{1+h} + 1\right)} = \lim\limits_{h \to 0} \dfrac{h}{h\left(\sqrt{1+h} + 1\right)}$

$\qquad = \lim\limits_{h \to 0} \dfrac{1}{\sqrt{1+h} + 1} = \dfrac{1}{\sqrt{1} + 1} = \dfrac{1}{2}$

15. $\lim\limits_{h \to 0} \dfrac{(2+h)^3 - 8}{h} = \lim\limits_{h \to 0} \dfrac{\left(8 + 12h + 6h^2 + h^3\right) - 8}{h} = \lim\limits_{h \to 0} \dfrac{12h + 6h^2 + h^3}{h}$

$\qquad = \lim\limits_{h \to 0} \left(12 + 6h + h^2\right) = 12 + 0 + 0 = 12$

16. $\lim\limits_{x \to 2} \dfrac{x^4 - 16}{x - 2} = \lim\limits_{x \to 2} \dfrac{(x+2)(x-2)(x^2 + 4)}{x - 2} = \lim\limits_{x \to 2} (x+2)(x^2 + 4) = \lim\limits_{x \to 2} (x+2) \lim\limits_{x \to 2} (x^2 + 4)$

$\qquad = (2+2)(2^2 + 4) = 32$

17. $\lim\limits_{x \to 7} \dfrac{\sqrt{x+2} - 3}{x - 7} = \lim\limits_{x \to 7} \dfrac{\sqrt{x+2} - 3}{x - 7} \cdot \dfrac{\sqrt{x+2} + 3}{\sqrt{x+2} + 3} = \lim\limits_{x \to 7} \dfrac{(x+2) - 9}{(x - 7)\left(\sqrt{x+2} + 3\right)}$

$\qquad = \lim\limits_{x \to 7} \dfrac{x - 7}{(x - 7)\left(\sqrt{x+2} + 3\right)} = \lim\limits_{x \to 7} \dfrac{1}{\sqrt{x+2} + 3} = \dfrac{1}{\sqrt{9} + 3} = \dfrac{1}{6}$

18. $\lim\limits_{h \to 0} \dfrac{(3+h)^{-1} - 3^{-1}}{h} = \lim\limits_{h \to 0} \dfrac{\dfrac{1}{3+h} - \dfrac{1}{3}}{h} = \lim\limits_{h \to 0} \dfrac{3 - (3+h)}{h(3+h)3} = \lim\limits_{h \to 0} \dfrac{-h}{h(3+h)3}$

$\qquad = \lim\limits_{h \to 0} \left[-\dfrac{1}{3(3+h)}\right] = -\dfrac{1}{\lim\limits_{h \to 0} [3(3+h)]} = -\dfrac{1}{3(3+0)} = -\dfrac{1}{9}$

19. $\lim\limits_{x \to -4} \dfrac{\dfrac{1}{4} + \dfrac{1}{x}}{4 + x} = \lim\limits_{x \to -4} \dfrac{\dfrac{x + 4}{4x}}{4 + x} = \lim\limits_{x \to -4} \dfrac{x + 4}{4x(4 + x)} = \lim\limits_{x \to -4} \dfrac{1}{4x} = \dfrac{1}{4(-4)} = -\dfrac{1}{16}$

20. $\lim\limits_{t \to 0} \left[\dfrac{1}{t} - \dfrac{1}{t^2 + t}\right] = \lim\limits_{t \to 0} \dfrac{(t^2 + t) - t}{t(t^2 + t)} = \lim\limits_{t \to 0} \dfrac{t^2}{t \cdot t(t + 1)} = \lim\limits_{t \to 0} \dfrac{1}{t + 1} = \dfrac{1}{0 + 1} = 1$

21. (a)

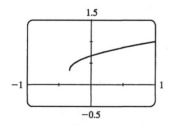

$\lim\limits_{x \to 0} \dfrac{x}{\sqrt{1 + 3x} - 1} \approx \dfrac{2}{3}$

(b)

x	$f(x)$
-0.001	0.6661663
-0.0001	0.6666167
-0.00001	0.6666617
-0.000001	0.6666662
0.000001	0.6666672
0.00001	0.6666717
0.0001	0.6667167
0.001	0.6671663

The limit appears to be $\frac{2}{3}$.

(c) $\lim\limits_{x\to 0}\left(\dfrac{x}{\sqrt{1+3x}-1}\cdot\dfrac{\sqrt{1+3x}+1}{\sqrt{1+3x}+1}\right)=\lim\limits_{x\to 0}\dfrac{x\left(\sqrt{1+3x}+1\right)}{(1+3x)-1}=\lim\limits_{x\to 0}\dfrac{x\left(\sqrt{1+3x}+1\right)}{3x}$

$=\tfrac{1}{3}\lim\limits_{x\to 0}\left(\sqrt{1+3x}+1\right)$ (Limit Law 3)

$=\tfrac{1}{3}\left[\sqrt{\lim\limits_{x\to 0}(1+3x)}+\lim\limits_{x\to 0}1\right]$ (1 & 11)

$=\tfrac{1}{3}\left(\sqrt{\lim\limits_{x\to 0}1+3\lim\limits_{x\to 0}x}+1\right)$ (1, 3 & 7)

$=\tfrac{1}{3}\left(\sqrt{1+3\cdot 0}+1\right)$ (7 & 8)

$=\tfrac{1}{3}(1+1)=\tfrac{2}{3}$

22. (a)

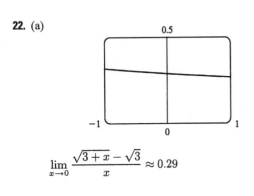

0.5

−1   0   1

$\lim\limits_{x\to 0}\dfrac{\sqrt{3+x}-\sqrt{3}}{x}\approx 0.29$

(b)

x	$f(x)$
−0.001	0.2886992
−0.0001	0.2886775
−0.00001	0.2886754
−0.000001	0.2886752
0.000001	0.2886751
0.00001	0.2886749
0.0001	0.2886727
0.001	0.2886511

The limit appears to be approximately 0.2887.

(c) $\lim\limits_{x\to 0}\left(\dfrac{\sqrt{3+x}-\sqrt{3}}{x}\cdot\dfrac{\sqrt{3+x}+\sqrt{3}}{\sqrt{3+x}+\sqrt{3}}\right)=\lim\limits_{x\to 0}\dfrac{(3+x)-3}{x\left(\sqrt{3+x}+\sqrt{3}\right)}=\lim\limits_{x\to 0}\dfrac{1}{\sqrt{3+x}+\sqrt{3}}$

$=\dfrac{\lim\limits_{x\to 0}1}{\lim\limits_{x\to 0}\sqrt{3+x}+\lim\limits_{x\to 0}\sqrt{3}}$ (Limit Laws 5 & 1)

$=\dfrac{1}{\sqrt{\lim\limits_{x\to 0}(3+x)}+\sqrt{3}}$ (7 & 11)

$=\dfrac{1}{\sqrt{3+0}+\sqrt{3}}$ (1, 7 & 8)

$=\dfrac{1}{2\sqrt{3}}$

23. Let $f(x)=-x^2$, $g(x)=x^2\cos 20\pi x$ and $h(x)=x^2$. Then

$-1\le \cos 20\pi x\le 1\ \Rightarrow\ -x^2\le x^2\cos 20\pi x\le x^2\ \Rightarrow$

$f(x)\le g(x)\le h(x)$. So since $\lim\limits_{x\to 0}f(x)=\lim\limits_{x\to 0}h(x)=0$, by the

Squeeze Theorem we have $\lim\limits_{x\to 0}g(x)=0$.

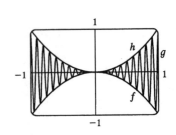

24. Let $f(x) = -\sqrt{x^3 + x^2}$, $g(x) = \sqrt{x^3 + x^2} \sin(\pi/x)$, and

$h(x) = \sqrt{x^3 + x^2}$. Then $-1 \le \sin(\pi/x) \le 1 \Rightarrow$

$-\sqrt{x^3 + x^2} \le \sqrt{x^3 + x^2} \sin(\pi/x) \le \sqrt{x^3 + x^2} \Rightarrow$

$f(x) \le g(x) \le h(x)$. So since $\lim\limits_{x \to 0} f(x) = \lim\limits_{x \to 0} h(x) = 0$, by the

Squeeze Theorem we have $\lim\limits_{x \to 0} g(x) = 0$.

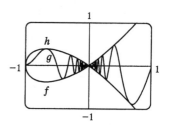

25. $1 \le f(x) \le x^2 + 2x + 2$ for all x. Now $\lim\limits_{x \to -1} 1 = 1$ and

$\lim\limits_{x \to -1} (x^2 + 2x + 2) = \lim\limits_{x \to -1} x^2 + 2 \lim\limits_{x \to -1} x + \lim\limits_{x \to -1} 2 = (-1)^2 + 2(-1) + 2 = 1$. Therefore, by the Squeeze

Theorem, $\lim\limits_{x \to -1} f(x) = 1$.

26. $3x \le f(x) \le x^3 + 2$ for $0 \le x \le 2$. Now $\lim\limits_{x \to 1} 3x = 3$ and $\lim\limits_{x \to 1} (x^3 + 2) = \lim\limits_{x \to 1} x^3 + \lim\limits_{x \to 1} 2 = 1^3 + 2 = 3$.

Therefore, by the Squeeze Theorem, $\lim\limits_{x \to 1} f(x) = 3$.

27. $-1 \le \cos(2/x) \le 1 \Rightarrow -x^4 \le x^4 \cos(2/x) \le x^4$. Since $\lim\limits_{x \to 0} (-x^4) = 0$ and $\lim\limits_{x \to 0} x^4 = 0$, we have

$\lim\limits_{x \to 0} \left[x^4 \cos(2/x) \right] = 0$ by the Squeeze Theorem.

28. $-1 \le \sin(\pi/x) \le 1 \Rightarrow e^{-1} \le e^{\sin(\pi/x)} \le e^1 \Rightarrow \sqrt{x}/e \le \sqrt{x} \, e^{\sin(\pi/x)} \le \sqrt{x} \, e$. Since

$\lim\limits_{x \to 0^+} (\sqrt{x}/e) = 0$ and $\lim\limits_{x \to 0^+} (\sqrt{x} \, e) = 0$, we have $\lim\limits_{x \to 0^+} \left[\sqrt{x} \, e^{\sin(\pi/x)} \right] = 0$ by the Squeeze Theorem.

29. If $x > -4$, then $|x + 4| = x + 4$, so $\lim\limits_{x \to -4^+} |x + 4| = \lim\limits_{x \to -4^+} (x + 4) = -4 + 4 = 0$.

If $x < -4$, then $|x + 4| = -(x + 4)$, so $\lim\limits_{x \to -4^-} |x + 4| = \lim\limits_{x \to -4^-} -(x + 4) = -(-4 + 4) = 0$.

Since the right and left limits are equal, $\lim\limits_{x \to -4} |x + 4| = 0$.

30. If $x > 2$, then $|x - 2| = x - 2$, so $\lim\limits_{x \to 2^+} \dfrac{|x - 2|}{x - 2} = \lim\limits_{x \to 2^+} \dfrac{x - 2}{x - 2} = \lim\limits_{x \to 2^+} 1 = 1$. If $x < 2$, then

$|x - 2| = -(x - 2)$, so $\lim\limits_{x \to 2^-} \dfrac{|x - 2|}{x - 2} = \lim\limits_{x \to 2^-} \dfrac{-(x - 2)}{x - 2} = \lim\limits_{x \to 2^-} -1 = -1$. The right and left limits are

different, so $\lim\limits_{x \to 2} \dfrac{|x - 2|}{x - 2}$ does not exist.

31. Since $|x| = -x$ for $x < 0$, we have $\lim\limits_{x \to 0^-} \left(\dfrac{1}{x} - \dfrac{1}{|x|} \right) = \lim\limits_{x \to 0^-} \left(\dfrac{1}{x} - \dfrac{1}{-x} \right) = \lim\limits_{x \to 0^-} \dfrac{2}{x}$, which does not exist

since the denominator approaches 0 and the numerator does not.

32. Since $|x| = x$ for $x > 0$, we have $\lim\limits_{x \to 0^+} \left(\dfrac{1}{x} - \dfrac{1}{|x|} \right) = \lim\limits_{x \to 0^+} \left(\dfrac{1}{x} - \dfrac{1}{x} \right) = \lim\limits_{x \to 0^+} 0 = 0$.

33. (a) (i) If $x \to 1^+$, then $x > 1$ and $g(x) = x - 1$. Thus, $\lim\limits_{x \to 1^+} g(x) = \lim\limits_{x \to 1^+} (x - 1) = 1 - 1 = 0$.

    (ii) If $x \to 1^-$, then $x < 1$ and $g(x) = 1 - x^2$. Thus, $\lim\limits_{x \to 1^-} g(x) = \lim\limits_{x \to 1^-} (1 - x^2) = 1 - 1^2 = 0$.

    Since the left- and right-hand limits of g at 1 are equal, $\lim\limits_{x \to 1} g(x) = 0$.

    (iii) If $x \to 0$, then $-1 < x < 1$ and $g(x) = 1 - x^2$. Thus, $\lim\limits_{x \to 0} g(x) = \lim\limits_{x \to 0} (1 - x^2) = 1 - 0^2 = 1$.

    (iv) If $x \to -1^-$, then $x < -1$ and $g(x) = -x$. Thus, $\lim\limits_{x \to -1^-} g(x) = \lim\limits_{x \to -1^-} (-x) = -(-1) = 1$.

(v) If $x \to -1^+$, then $-1 < x < 1$ and $g(x) = 1 - x^2$. Thus,

$$\lim_{x \to -1^+} g(x) = \lim_{x \to -1^+} (1 - x^2) = 1 - (-1)^2 = 1 - 1 = 0$$

(vi) $\lim\limits_{x \to -1} g(x)$ does not exist because the limits in part (iv) and part (v) are not equal.

(b)

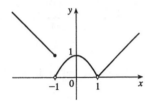

34. (a) (i) $\lim\limits_{x \to 1^+} \dfrac{x^2 - 1}{|x - 1|} = \lim\limits_{x \to 1^+} \dfrac{x^2 - 1}{x - 1} = \lim\limits_{x \to 1^+} (x + 1) = 2$

(c)

(ii) $\lim\limits_{x \to 1^-} \dfrac{x^2 - 1}{|x - 1|} = \lim\limits_{x \to 1^-} \dfrac{x^2 - 1}{-(x - 1)} = \lim\limits_{x \to 1^-} -(x + 1) = -2$

(b) No, $\lim\limits_{x \to 1} F(x)$ does not exist since $\lim\limits_{x \to 1^+} F(x) \neq \lim\limits_{x \to 1^-} F(x)$.

35. (a) (i) $[\![x]\!] = -2$ for $-2 \leq x < -1$, so $\lim\limits_{x \to -2^+} [\![x]\!] = \lim\limits_{x \to -2^+} (-2) = -2$

(ii) $[\![x]\!] = -3$ for $-3 \leq x < -2$, so $\lim\limits_{x \to -2^-} [\![x]\!] = \lim\limits_{x \to -2^-} (-3) = -3$. The right and left limits are different,

so $\lim\limits_{x \to -2} [\![x]\!]$ does not exist.

(iii) $[\![x]\!] = -3$ for $-3 \leq x < -2$, so $\lim\limits_{x \to -2.4} [\![x]\!] = \lim\limits_{x \to -2.4} (-3) = -3$.

(b) (i) $[\![x]\!] = n - 1$ for $n - 1 \leq x < n$, so $\lim\limits_{x \to n^-} [\![x]\!] = \lim\limits_{x \to n^-} (n - 1) = n - 1$.

(ii) $[\![x]\!] = n$ for $n \leq x < n + 1$, so $\lim\limits_{x \to n^+} [\![x]\!] = \lim\limits_{x \to n^+} n = n$.

(c) $\lim\limits_{x \to a} [\![x]\!]$ exists $\Leftrightarrow$ a is not an integer.

36. (a)

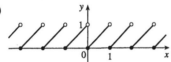

(b) (i) $\lim\limits_{x \to n^-} f(x) = \lim\limits_{x \to n^-} (x - [\![x]\!]) = \lim\limits_{x \to n^-} [x - (n - 1)] = n - (n - 1) = 1$

(ii) $\lim\limits_{x \to n^+} f(x) = \lim\limits_{x \to n^+} (x - [\![x]\!]) = \lim\limits_{x \to n^+} (x - n) = n - n = 0$

(c) $\lim\limits_{x \to a} f(x)$ exists $\Leftrightarrow$ a is not an integer.

37. The graph of $f(x) = [\![x]\!] + [\![-x]\!]$ is the same as the graph of $g(x) = -1$ with holes at each integer, since $f(a) = 0$ for any integer a. Thus, $\lim\limits_{x \to 2^-} f(x) = -1$ and $\lim\limits_{x \to 2^+} f(x) = -1$, so $\lim\limits_{x \to 2} f(x) = -1$.

$f(2) = [\![2]\!] + [\![-2]\!] = 2 + (-2) = 0$.

38. $\lim\limits_{v \to c^-} \left(L_0 \sqrt{1 - \dfrac{v^2}{c^2}} \right) = L_0 \sqrt{1 - 1} = 0$. As the velocity approaches the speed of light, the length approaches 0.

A left-hand limit is necessary since L is not defined for $v > c$.

39. Since $p(x)$ is a polynomial, $p(x) = a_0 + a_1 x + a_2 x^2 + \cdots + a_n x^n$. Thus, by the Limit Laws,

$$\lim_{x \to a} p(x) = \lim_{x \to a} \left(a_0 + a_1 x + a_2 x^2 + \cdots + a_n x^n \right)$$

$$= a_0 + a_1 \lim_{x \to a} x + a_2 \lim_{x \to a} x^2 + \cdots + a_n \lim_{x \to a} x^n$$

$$= a_0 + a_1 a + a_2 a^2 + \cdots + a_n a^n = p(a)$$

Thus, for any polynomial p, $\lim_{x \to a} p(x) = p(a)$.

40. Let $r(x) = \dfrac{p(x)}{q(x)}$ where $p(x)$ and $q(x)$ are any polynomials, and suppose that $q(a) \neq 0$. Thus,

$$\lim_{x \to a} r(x) = \lim_{x \to a} \frac{p(x)}{q(x)} = \frac{\lim_{x \to a} p(x)}{\lim_{x \to a} q(x)} \quad \text{(Limit Law 5)} \quad = \frac{p(a)}{q(a)} \quad \text{(Exercise 39)} \quad = r(a).$$

41. Let $f(x) = [\![x]\!]$ and $g(x) = -[\![x]\!]$. Then $\lim_{x \to 3} f(x)$ and $\lim_{x \to 3} g(x)$ do not exist (Example 9) but

$$\lim_{x \to 3} [f(x) + g(x)] = \lim_{x \to 3} ([\![x]\!] - [\![x]\!]) = \lim_{x \to 3} 0 = 0.$$

42. Let $f(x) = H(x)$ and $g(x) = 1 - H(x)$, where H is the Heaviside function defined in Exercise 1.3.53.
Thus, either f or g is 0 for any value of x. Then $\lim_{x \to 0} f(x)$ and $\lim_{x \to 0} g(x)$ do not exist, but

$$\lim_{x \to 0} [f(x)g(x)] = \lim_{x \to 0} 0 = 0.$$

43. Since the denominator approaches 0 as $x \to -2$, the limit will exist only if the numerator also approaches 0 as
$x \to -2$. In order for this to happen, we need $\lim_{x \to -2} \left(3x^2 + ax + a + 3 \right) = 0 \iff$

$3(-2)^2 + a(-2) + a + 3 = 0 \iff 12 - 2a + a + 3 = 0 \iff a = 15$. With $a = 15$, the limit becomes

$$\lim_{x \to -2} \frac{3x^2 + 15x + 18}{x^2 + x - 2} = \lim_{x \to -2} \frac{3(x + 2)(x + 3)}{(x - 1)(x + 2)} = \frac{3(-2 + 3)}{-2 - 1} = -1.$$

44. *Solution 1:* First, we find the coordinates of P and Q as functions of r. Then we can find the equation of the line
determined by these two points, and thus find the x-intercept (the point R), and take the limit as $r \to 0$.
The coordinates of P are $(0, r)$. The point Q is the point of intersection of the two circles $x^2 + y^2 = r^2$ and
$(x - 1)^2 + y^2 = 1$. Eliminating y from these equations, we get $r^2 - x^2 = 1 - (x - 1)^2 \iff r^2 = 1 + 2x - 1$
$\iff x = \frac{1}{2} r^2$. Substituting back into the equation of the shrinking circle to find the y-coordinate, we get

$\left(\frac{1}{2} r^2 \right)^2 + y^2 = r^2 \iff y^2 = r^2 \left(1 - \frac{1}{4} r^2 \right) \iff y = r\sqrt{1 - \frac{1}{4} r^2}$ (the positive y-value). So the coordinates

of Q are $\left(\frac{1}{2} r^2, r\sqrt{1 - \frac{1}{4} r^2} \right)$. The equation of the line joining P and Q is thus

$$y - r = \frac{r\sqrt{1 - \frac{1}{4} r^2} - r}{\frac{1}{2} r^2 - 0} (x - 0). \text{ We set } y = 0 \text{ in order to find the } x\text{-intercept, and get}$$

$$x = -r \frac{\frac{1}{2} r^2}{r \left(\sqrt{1 - \frac{1}{4} r^2} - 1 \right)} = \frac{-\frac{1}{2} r^2 \left(\sqrt{1 - \frac{1}{4} r^2} + 1 \right)}{1 - \frac{1}{4} r^2 - 1} = 2 \left(\sqrt{1 - \frac{1}{4} r^2} + 1 \right).$$

Now we take the limit as $r \to 0^+$: $\lim_{r \to 0^+} x = \lim_{r \to 0^+} 2 \left(\sqrt{1 - \frac{1}{4} r^2} + 1 \right) = \lim_{r \to 0^+} 2 \left(\sqrt{1} + 1 \right) = 4$.

So the limiting position of R is the point $(4, 0)$.

Solution 2: We add a few lines to the diagram, as shown. Note that $\angle PQS = 90°$ (subtended by diameter PS). So $\angle SQR = 90° = \angle OQT$ (subtended by diameter OT). It follows that $\angle OQS = \angle TQR$. Also $\angle PSQ = 90° - \angle SPQ = \angle ORP$. Since $\triangle QOS$ is isosceles, so is $\triangle QTR$, implying that $QT = TR$. As the circle C_2 shrinks, the point Q plainly approaches the origin, so the point R must approach a point twice as far from the origin as T, that is, the point $(4, 0)$, as above.

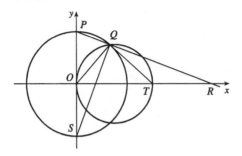

2.4 Continuity • • • • • • • • • • • • • • • • • •

1. From Equation 1, $\lim\limits_{x \to 4} f(x) = f(4)$.

2. The graph of f has no hole, jump, or vertical asymptote.

3. (a) The following are the numbers at which f is discontinuous and the type of discontinuity at that number:
    -4 (removable), -2 (jump), 2 (jump), 4 (infinite).

  (b) f is continuous from the left at -2, and continuous from the right at 2 and 4. It is continuous from neither side at -4.

4. g is continuous on $[-4, -2), (-2, 2), [2, 4), (4, 6),$ and $(6, 8)$.

5.

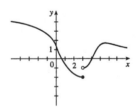

6.

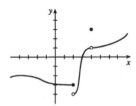

7. (a)

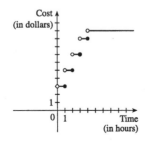

(b) There are discontinuities at $t = 1, 2, 3,$ and 4. A person parking in the lot would want to keep in mind that the charge will jump at the beginning of each hour.

8. (a) Continuous; at the location in question, the temperature changes smoothly as time passes, without any instantaneous jumps from one temperature to another.

(b) Continuous; the temperature at a specific time changes smoothly as the distance due west from New York City increases, without any instantaneous jumps.

(c) Discontinuous; as the distance due west from New York City increases, the altitude above sea level may jump from one height to another without going through all of the intermediate values — at a cliff, for example.

(d) Discontinuous; as the distance traveled increases, the cost of the ride jumps in small increments.

(e) Discontinuous; when the lights are switched on (or off), the current suddenly changes between 0 and some nonzero value, without passing through all of the intermediate values. This is debatable, though, depending on your definition of current.

9. Since f and g are continuous functions,

$$\lim_{x \to 3} [2f(x) - g(x)] = 2 \lim_{x \to 3} f(x) - \lim_{x \to 3} g(x) \quad \text{(by Limit Laws 2 \& 3)}$$

$$= 2f(3) - g(3) \quad \text{(by continuity of } f \text{ and } g \text{ at } x = 3)$$

$$= 2 \cdot 5 - g(3) = 10 - g(3)$$

Since it is given that $\lim_{x \to 3} [2f(x) - g(x)] = 4$, we have $10 - g(3) = 4$, or $g(3) = 6$.

10. $\lim_{x \to 4} f(x) = \lim_{x \to 4} \left(x^2 + \sqrt{7 - x}\right) = \lim_{x \to 4} x^2 + \sqrt{\lim_{x \to 4} 7 - \lim_{x \to 4} x} = 4^2 + \sqrt{7 - 4} = 16 + \sqrt{3} = f(4)$.

By the definition of continuity, f is continuous at $a = 4$.

11. $\lim_{x \to -1} f(x) = \lim_{x \to -1} \left(x + 2x^3\right)^4 = \left(\lim_{x \to -1} x + 2 \lim_{x \to -1} x^3\right)^4 = \left[-1 + 2(-1)^3\right]^4 = (-3)^4 = 81 = f(-1)$.

By the definition of continuity, f is continuous at $a = -1$.

12. For $-4 < a < 4$ we have $\lim_{x \to a} f(x) = \lim_{x \to a} x\sqrt{16 - x^2} = \lim_{x \to a} x \sqrt{\lim_{x \to a} 16 - \lim_{x \to a} x^2} = a\sqrt{16 - a^2} = f(a)$,

so f is continuous on $(-4, 4)$. Similarly, we get $\lim_{x \to 4^-} f(x) = 0 = f(4)$ and $\lim_{x \to -4^+} f(x) = 0 = f(-4)$,

so f is continuous from the left at 4 and from the right at -4. Thus, f is continuous on $[-4, 4]$.

13. $f(x) = \ln|x - 2|$ is discontinuous at 2 since $f(2) = \ln 0$ is not defined.

14. $f(x) = \begin{cases} 1/(x - 1) & \text{if } x \neq 1 \\ 2 & \text{if } x = 1 \end{cases}$ is discontinuous at 1 because $\lim_{x \to 1} f(x)$ does not exist.

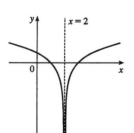

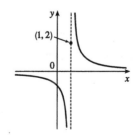

15. $f(x) = \begin{cases} \dfrac{x^2 - x - 12}{x + 3} & \text{if } x \neq -3 \\ -5 & \text{if } x = -3 \end{cases} = \begin{cases} x - 4 & \text{if } x \neq -3 \\ -5 & \text{if } x = -3 \end{cases}$

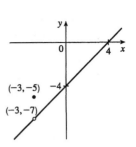

So $\lim\limits_{x \to -3} f(x) = \lim\limits_{x \to -3} (x - 4) = -7$ and $f(-3) = -5$.

Since $\lim\limits_{x \to -3} f(x) \neq f(-3)$, f is discontinuous at -3.

16. $f(x) = \begin{cases} 1 + x^2 & \text{if } x < 1 \\ 4 - x & \text{if } x \geq 1 \end{cases}$

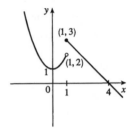

$\lim\limits_{x \to 1^-} f(x) = \lim\limits_{x \to 1^-} (1 + x^2) = 1 + 1^2 = 2$ and

$\lim\limits_{x \to 1^+} f(x) = \lim\limits_{x \to 1^+} (4 - x) = 4 - 1 = 3.$

Thus, f is discontinuous at 1 because $\lim\limits_{x \to 1} f(x)$ does not exist.

17. $F(x) = \dfrac{x}{x^2 + 5x + 6}$ is a rational function. So by Theorem 5 (or Theorem 7), F is continuous at every number in

its domain, $\{x \mid x^2 + 5x + 6 \neq 0\} = \{x \mid (x + 3)(x + 2) \neq 0\} = \{x \mid x \neq -3, \, -2\}$ or

$(-\infty, -3) \cup (-3, -2) \cup (-2, \infty).$

18. $G(t) = 25 - t^2$ is a polynomial, so it is continuous (Theorem 5). $F(x) = \sqrt{x}$ is continuous by Theorem 7.

So, by Theorem 9, $F(G(t)) = \sqrt{25 - t^2}$ is continuous on its domain, which is

$\{t \mid 25 - t^2 \geq 0\} = \{t \mid |t| \leq 5\} = [-5, 5]$. Also, $2t$ is continuous on $\mathbb{R}$, so by Theorem 4 #1,

$f(t) = 2t + \sqrt{25 - t^2}$ is continuous on its domain, which is $[-5, 5]$.

19. By Theorem 5, the polynomial $5x$ is continuous on $(-\infty, \infty)$. By Theorems 9 and 7, $\sin 5x$ is continuous on

$(-\infty, \infty)$. By Theorem 7, e^x is continuous on $(-\infty, \infty)$. By Theorem 4 #4, the product of e^x and $\sin 5x$ is

continuous at all numbers which are in both of their domains, that is, on $(-\infty, \infty)$.

20. By Theorem 5, the polynomial $x^2 - 1$ is continuous on $(-\infty, \infty)$. By Theorem 7, $\sin^{-1}$ is continuous on its

domain, $[-1, 1]$. By Theorem 9, $\sin^{-1}(x^2 - 1)$ is continuous on its domain, which is

$\{x \mid -1 \leq x^2 - 1 \leq 1\} = \{x \mid 0 \leq x^2 \leq 2\} = \{x \mid |x| \leq \sqrt{2}\} = [-\sqrt{2}, \sqrt{2}].$

21. By Theorem 5, the polynomial $t^4 - 1$ is continuous $(-\infty, \infty)$. By Theorem 7, $\ln x$ is continuous on its

domain, $(0, \infty)$. By Theorem 9, $\ln(t^4 - 1)$ is continuous on its domain, which is

$\{t \mid t^4 - 1 > 0\} = \{t \mid t^4 > 1\} = \{t \mid |t| > 1\} = (-\infty, -1) \cup (1, \infty).$

22. By Theorem 7, $\sqrt{x}$ is continuous on $[0, \infty)$. By Theorems 7 and 9, $e^{\sqrt{x}}$ is continuous on $[0, \infty)$. Also by

Theorems 7 and 9, $\cos\left(e^{\sqrt{x}}\right)$ is continuous on $[0, \infty)$.

23. The function $y = 1 \Big/ \left(1 + e^{1/x}\right)$ is discontinuous at $x = 0$ because
the left- and right-hand limits at $x = 0$ are different.

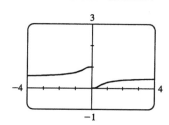

24. The function $y = \tan^2 x$ is discontinuous at $x = \frac{\pi}{2} + \pi k$, where k is
any integer. The function $y = \ln\left(\tan^2 x\right)$ is also discontinuous where
$\tan^2 x$ is 0, that is, at $x = \pi k$. So $y = \ln\left(\tan^2 x\right)$ is discontinuous at
$x = \frac{\pi}{2}n$, n any integer.

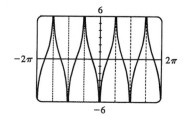

25. Because we are dealing with root functions, $5 + \sqrt{x}$ is continuous on $[0, \infty)$, $\sqrt{x+5}$ is continuous on $[-5, \infty)$, so
the quotient $f(x) = \dfrac{5 + \sqrt{x}}{\sqrt{5+x}}$ is continuous on $[0, \infty)$. Since f is continuous at $x = 4$, $\displaystyle\lim_{x \to 4} f(x) = f(4) = \frac{7}{3}$.

26. Because x is continuous on $\mathbb{R}$, $\sin x$ is continuous on $\mathbb{R}$, and $x + \sin x$ is continuous on $\mathbb{R}$, the composite function
$f(x) = \sin(x + \sin x)$ is continuous on $\mathbb{R}$, so $\displaystyle\lim_{x \to \pi} f(x) = f(\pi) = \sin(\pi + \sin \pi) = \sin \pi = 0$.

27. Because $x^2 - x$ is continuous on $\mathbb{R}$, the composite function $f(x) = e^{x^2 - x}$ is continuous on $\mathbb{R}$, so
$\displaystyle\lim_{x \to 1} f(x) = f(1) = e^{1-1} = e^0 = 1$.

28. Because arctan is a continuous function, we can apply Theorem 8.

$$\lim_{x \to 2} \arctan\left(\frac{x^2 - 4}{3x^2 - 6x}\right) = \arctan\left(\lim_{x \to 2} \frac{(x+2)(x-2)}{3x(x-2)}\right) = \arctan\left(\lim_{x \to 2} \frac{x+2}{3x}\right) = \arctan\frac{2}{3} \approx 0.588$$

29. $f(x) = \begin{cases} x + 2 & \text{if } x < 0 \\ e^x & \text{if } 0 \le x \le 1 \\ 2 - x & \text{if } x > 1 \end{cases}$

f is continuous on $(-\infty, 0)$ and $(1, \infty)$ since on each of these intervals it is
a polynomial; it is continuous on $(0, 1)$ since it is an exponential. Now
$\displaystyle\lim_{x \to 0^-} f(x) = \lim_{x \to 0^-} (x + 2) = 2$ and $\displaystyle\lim_{x \to 0^+} f(x) = \lim_{x \to 0^+} e^x = 1$, so f is
discontinuous at 0. Since $f(0) = 1$, f is continuous from the right at 0.
Also $\displaystyle\lim_{x \to 1^-} f(x) = \lim_{x \to 1^-} e^x = e$ and $\displaystyle\lim_{x \to 1^+} f(x) = \lim_{x \to 1^+} (2 - x) = 1$, so
f is discontinuous at 1. Since $f(1) = e$, f is continuous from the left at 1.

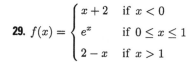

30. By Theorem 5, each piece of F is continuous on its domain. We need to check for continuity at $r = R$.

$$\lim_{r \to R^-} F(r) = \lim_{r \to R^-} \frac{GMr}{R^3} = \frac{GM}{R^2} \text{ and } \lim_{r \to R^+} F(r) = \lim_{r \to R^+} \frac{GM}{r^2} = \frac{GM}{R^2}, \text{ so } \lim_{r \to R} F(r) = \frac{GM}{R^2}. \text{ Since}$$

$F(R) = \dfrac{GM}{R^2}$, F is continuous at R. Therefore, F is a continuous function of r.

31. f is continuous on $(-\infty, 3)$ and $(3, \infty)$. Now $\lim\limits_{x \to 3^-} f(x) = \lim\limits_{x \to 3^-} (cx + 1) = 3c + 1$ and

$\lim\limits_{x \to 3^+} f(x) = \lim\limits_{x \to 3^+} (cx^2 - 1) = 9c - 1$. So f is continuous $\Leftrightarrow$ $3c + 1 = 9c - 1$ $\Leftrightarrow$ $6c = 2$ $\Leftrightarrow$ $c = \frac{1}{3}$.

Thus, for f to be continuous on $(-\infty, \infty)$, $c = \frac{1}{3}$.

32.

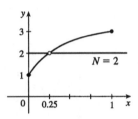

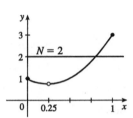

f does not satisfy the conclusion of the f does satisfy the conclusion of the

Intermediate Value Theorem.   Intermediate Value Theorem.

33. $f(x) = x^3 - x^2 + x$ is continuous on the interval $[2, 3]$, $f(2) = 6$, and $f(3) = 21$. Since $6 < 10 < 21$, there is a number c in $(2, 3)$ such that $f(c) = 10$ by the Intermediate Value Theorem.

34. $f(x) = x^2$ is continuous on the interval $[1, 2]$, $f(1) = 1$, and $f(2) = 4$. Since $1 < 2 < 4$, there is a number c in $(1, 2)$ such that $f(c) = c^2 = 2$ by the Intermediate Value Theorem.

35. $f(x) = x^3 - 3x + 1$ is continuous on the interval $[0, 1]$, $f(0) = 1$, and $f(1) = -1$. Since $-1 < 0 < 1$, there is a number c in $(0, 1)$ such that $f(c) = 0$ by the Intermediate Value Theorem. Thus, there is a root of the equation $x^3 - 3x + 1 = 0$ in the interval $(0, 1)$.

36. $f(x) = x^2 - \sqrt{x + 1}$ is continuous on the interval $[1, 2]$, $f(1) = 1 - \sqrt{2}$, and $f(2) = 4 - \sqrt{3}$. Since $1 - \sqrt{2} < 0 < 4 - \sqrt{3}$, there is a number c in $(1, 2)$ such that $f(c) = 0$ by the Intermediate Value Theorem. Thus, there is a root of the equation $x^2 - \sqrt{x + 1} = 0$, or $x^2 = \sqrt{x + 1}$, in the interval $(1, 2)$.

37. $f(x) = \cos x - x$ is continuous on the interval $[0, 1]$, $f(0) = 1$, and $f(1) = \cos 1 - 1 \approx -0.46$. Since $-0.46 < 0 < 1$, there is a number c in $(0, 1)$ such that $f(c) = 0$ by the Intermediate Value Theorem. Thus, there is a root of the equation $\cos x - x = 0$, or $\cos x = x$, in the interval $(0, 1)$.

38. $f(x) = \ln x - e^{-x}$ is continuous on the interval $[1, 2]$, $f(1) = -e^{-1} \approx -0.37$, and $f(2) = \ln 2 - e^{-2} \approx 0.56$. Since $-0.37 < 0 < 0.56$, there is a number c in $(1, 2)$ such that $f(c) = 0$ by the Intermediate Value Theorem. Thus, there is a root of the equation $\ln x - e^{-x} = 0$, or $\ln x = e^{-x}$, in the interval $(1, 2)$.

39. (a) $f(x) = e^x + x - 2$ is continuous on the interval $[0, 1]$, $f(0) = -1 < 0$, and $f(1) = e - 1 \approx 1.72 > 0$. Since $-1 < 0 < 1.72$, there is a number c in $(0, 1)$ such that $f(c) = 0$ by the Intermediate Value Theorem. Thus, there is a root of the equation $e^x + x - 2 = 0$, or $e^x = 2 - x$, in the interval $(0, 1)$.

(b) $f(0.44) \approx -0.007 < 0$ and $f(0.45) \approx 0.018 > 0$, so there is a root between 0.44 and 0.45.

40. (a) $f(x) = x^5 - x^2 + 2x + 3$ is continuous on $[-1, 0]$, $f(-1) = -1 < 0$, and $f(0) = 3 > 0$. Since $-1 < 0 < 3$, there is a number c in $(-1, 0)$ such that $f(c) = 0$ by the Intermediate Value Theorem. Thus, there is a root of the equation $x^5 - x^2 + 2x + 3 = 0$ in the interval $(-1, 0)$.

(b) $f(-0.88) \approx -0.062 < 0$ and $f(-0.87) \approx 0.0047 > 0$, so there is a root between -0.88 and -0.87.

41. (a) Let $f(x) = 100e^{-x/100} - 0.01x^2$.

Then $f(0) = 100 > 0$ and

$f(100) = 100e^{-1} - 100 \approx -63.2 < 0$.

So by the Intermediate Value Theorem, there is a

number c in $(0, 100)$ such that $f(c) = 0$. This

implies that $100e^{-c/100} = 0.01c^2$.

(b) Using the intersect feature of the graphing device,

we find that the root of the equation is

$x = 70.347$, correct to three decimal places.

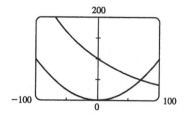

42. (a) Let $f(x) = \arctan x + x - 1$.

Then $f(0) = -1 < 0$ and $f(1) = \frac{\pi}{4} > 0$.

So by the Intermediate Value Theorem, there is a

number c in $(0, 1)$ such that $f(c) = 0$. This implies

that $\arctan c = 1 - c$.

(b) Using the intersect feature of the graphing device,

we find that the root of the equation is $x = 0.520$,

correct to three decimal places.

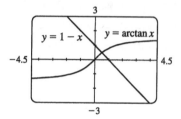

43. $\displaystyle\lim_{h \to 0} \sin(a + h) = \lim_{h \to 0} (\sin a \cos h + \cos a \sin h)$

$\qquad = \displaystyle\lim_{h \to 0} (\sin a \cos h) + \lim_{h \to 0} (\cos a \sin h)$

$\qquad = \left(\displaystyle\lim_{h \to 0} \sin a\right)\left(\lim_{h \to 0} \cos h\right) + \left(\lim_{h \to 0} \cos a\right)\left(\lim_{h \to 0} \sin h\right)$

$\qquad = (\sin a)(1) + (\cos a)(0) = \sin a$

44. As in the previous exercise, we must show that $\displaystyle\lim_{h \to 0} \cos(a + h) = \cos a$ to prove that the cosine function is

continuous.

$\displaystyle\lim_{h \to 0} \cos(a + h) = \lim_{h \to 0} (\cos a \cos h - \sin a \sin h)$

$\qquad = \displaystyle\lim_{h \to 0} (\cos a \cos h) - \lim_{h \to 0} (\sin a \sin h)$

$\qquad = \left(\displaystyle\lim_{h \to 0} \cos a\right)\left(\lim_{h \to 0} \cos h\right) - \left(\lim_{h \to 0} \sin a\right)\left(\lim_{h \to 0} \sin h\right)$

$\qquad = (\cos a)(1) - (\sin a)(0) = \cos a$

45. If there is such a number, it satisfies the equation $x^3 + 1 = x \iff x^3 - x + 1 = 0$. Let the LHS of this equation

be called $f(x)$. Now $f(-2) = -5 < 0$, and $f(-1) = 1 > 0$. Note also that $f(x)$ is a polynomial, and thus

continuous. So by the Intermediate Value Theorem, there is a number c between -2 and -1 such that $f(c) = 0$, so

that $c = c^3 + 1$.

46. (a) $\lim\limits_{x\to 0+} F(x) = 0$ and $\lim\limits_{x\to 0-} F(x) = 0$, so $\lim\limits_{x\to 0} F(x) = 0$, which is $F(0)$, and hence F is continuous at $x = a$ if

$a = 0$. For $a > 0$, $\lim\limits_{x\to a} F(x) = \lim\limits_{x\to a} x = a = F(a)$. For $a < 0$, $\lim\limits_{x\to a} F(x) = \lim\limits_{x\to a}(-x) = -a = F(a)$. Thus,

F is continuous at $x = a$; that is, continuous everywhere.

(b) Assume that f is continuous on the interval I. Then for $a \in I$, $\lim\limits_{x\to a}|f(x)| = \left|\lim\limits_{x\to a} f(x)\right| = |f(a)|$ by

Theorem 7. (If a is an endpoint of I, use the appropriate one-sided limit.) So $|f|$ is continuous on I.

(c) No, the converse is false. For example, the function $f(x) = \begin{cases} 1 & \text{if } x \geq 0 \\ -1 & \text{if } x < 0 \end{cases}$ is not continuous at $x = 0$, but

$|f(x)| = 1$ is continuous on $\mathbb{R}$.

47. Define $u(t)$ to be the monk's distance from the monastery, as a function of time, on the first day, and define $d(t)$ to be his distance from the monastery, as a function of time, on the second day. Let D be the distance from the monastery to the top of the mountain. From the given information we know that $u(0) = 0$, $u(12) = D$, $d(0) = D$ and $d(12) = 0$. Now consider the function $u - d$, which is clearly continuous. We calculate that $(u - d)(0) = -D$ and $(u - d)(12) = D$. So by the Intermediate Value Theorem, there must be some time t_0 between 0 and 12 such that $(u - d)(t_0) = 0 \iff u(t_0) = d(t_0)$. So at time t_0 after 7:00 A.M., the monk will be at the same place on both days.

2.5 Limits Involving Infinity

1. (a) As x approaches 2 (from the right or the left), the values of $f(x)$ become large.

(b) As x approaches 1 from the right, the values of $f(x)$ become large negative.

(c) As x becomes large, the values of $f(x)$ approach 5.

(d) As x becomes large negative, the values of $f(x)$ approach 3.

2. (a) The graph of a function can intersect a vertical asymptote in the sense that it can meet but not cross it.

The graph of a function can intersect a horizontal asymptote. It can even intersect its horizontal asymptote an infinite number of times.

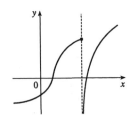

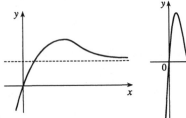

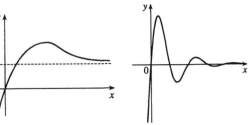

(b) The graph of a function can have 0, 1, or 2 horizontal asymptotes. Representative examples are shown.

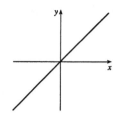

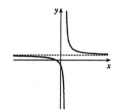

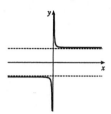

No horizontal asymptote   One horizontal asymptote   Two horizontal asymptotes

3. (a) $\lim\limits_{x \to 2} f(x) = \infty$

   (c) $\lim\limits_{x \to -1+} f(x) = -\infty$

   (e) $\lim\limits_{x \to -\infty} f(x) = 2$

   (b) $\lim\limits_{x \to -1^-} f(x) = \infty$

   (d) $\lim\limits_{x \to \infty} f(x) = 1$

   (f) Vertical: $x = -1$, $x = 2$; Horizontal: $y = 1$, $y = 2$

4. (a) $\lim\limits_{x \to \infty} g(x) = 2$

   (c) $\lim\limits_{x \to 3} g(x) = \infty$

   (e) $\lim\limits_{x \to -2+} g(x) = -\infty$

   (b) $\lim\limits_{x \to -\infty} g(x) = -2$

   (d) $\lim\limits_{x \to 0} g(x) = -\infty$

   (f) Vertical: $x = -2$, $x = 0$, $x = 3$; Horizontal: $y = -2$, $y = 2$

5. $f(0) = 0$, $f(1) = 1$, $\lim\limits_{x \to \infty} f(x) = 0$,

    f is odd

6. $\lim\limits_{x \to 0+} f(x) = \infty$, $\lim\limits_{x \to 0^-} f(x) = -\infty$,

      $\lim\limits_{x \to \infty} f(x) = 1$, $\lim\limits_{x \to -\infty} f(x) = 1$

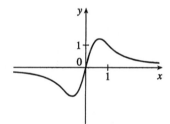

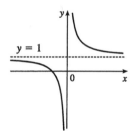

7. $\lim\limits_{x \to 2} f(x) = -\infty$, $\lim\limits_{x \to \infty} f(x) = \infty$,

    $\lim\limits_{x \to -\infty} f(x) = 0$, $\lim\limits_{x \to 0+} f(x) = \infty$,

    $\lim\limits_{x \to 0^-} f(x) = -\infty$

8. $\lim\limits_{x \to -2} f(x) = \infty$, $\lim\limits_{x \to -\infty} f(x) = 3$,

    $\lim\limits_{x \to \infty} f(x) = -3$

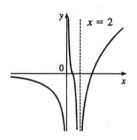

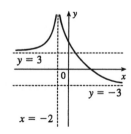

9. If $f(x) = x^2/2^x$, then a calculator gives $f(0) = 0$, $f(1) = 0.5$, $f(2) = 1$, $f(3) = 1.125$, $f(4) = 1$, $f(5) = 0.78125$, $f(6) = 0.5625$, $f(7) = 0.3828125$, $f(8) = 0.25$, $f(9) = 0.158203125$, $f(10) = 0.09765625$, $f(20) \approx 0.00038147$, $f(50) \approx 2.2204 \times 10^{-12}$, $f(100) \approx 7.8886 \times 10^{-27}$.

It appears that $\lim_{x \to \infty} (x^2/2^x) = 0$.

10. (a)

x	$f(x)$
0.5	−1.14
0.9	−3.69
0.99	−33.7
0.999	−333.7
0.9999	−3333.7
0.99999	−33,333.7

x	$f(x)$
1.5	0.42
1.1	3.02
1.01	33.0
1.001	333.0
1.0001	3333.0
1.00001	33,333.3

From these calculations, it seems that $\lim_{x \to 1^-} f(x) = -\infty$ and $\lim_{x \to 1^+} f(x) = \infty$.

(b) If x is slightly smaller than 1, then $x^3 - 1$ will be a negative number close to 0, and the reciprocal of $x^3 - 1$, that is, $f(x)$, will be a negative number with large absolute value. So $\lim_{x \to 1^-} f(x) = -\infty$.

If x is slightly larger than 1, then $x^3 - 1$ will be a small positive number, and its reciprocal, $f(x)$, will be a large positive number. So $\lim_{x \to 1^+} f(x) = \infty$.

(c) It appears from the graph of f that $\lim_{x \to 1^-} f(x) = -\infty$

and $\lim_{x \to 1^+} f(x) = \infty$.

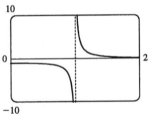

11. Vertical: $x \approx -1.62$, $x \approx 0.62$, $x = 1$;

Horizontal: $y = 1$

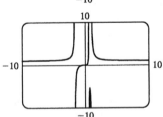

12. (a) From a graph of $f(x) = (1 - 2/x)^x$ in a window of $[0, 10,000]$ by $[0, 0.2]$, we estimate that $\lim_{x \to \infty} f(x) = 0.14$

(to two decimal places.)

(b)

x	$f(x)$
10,000	0.135308
100,000	0.135333
1,000,000	0.135335

From the table, we estimate that $\lim_{x \to \infty} f(x) = 0.1353$

(to four decimal places.)

13. $\lim_{x \to -3^+} \dfrac{x + 2}{x + 3} = -\infty$ since the numerator is negative and the denominator approaches 0 from the positive side

as $x \to -3^+$.

14. $\displaystyle\lim_{x\to 5^-}\frac{e^x}{(x-5)^3}=-\infty$ since the numerator is positive and the denominator approaches 0 from the negative side

as $x\to 5^-$.

15. $\displaystyle\lim_{x\to 1}\frac{2-x}{(x-1)^2}=\infty$ since the numerator is positive and the denominator approaches 0 through positive values

as $x\to 1$.

16. $\displaystyle\lim_{x\to 5^+}\ln(x-5)=-\infty$ since $x-5\to 0^+$ as $x\to 5^+$.

17. $\displaystyle\lim_{x\to(-\pi/2)^-}\sec x=\lim_{x\to(-\pi/2)^-}(1/\cos x)=-\infty$ since $\cos x\to 0^-$ as $x\to(-\pi/2)^-$.

18. $\displaystyle\lim_{x\to\infty}\frac{3x+5}{x-4}=\lim_{x\to\infty}\frac{(3x+5)/x}{(x-4)/x}=\lim_{x\to\infty}\frac{3+5/x}{1-4/x}=\frac{\displaystyle\lim_{x\to\infty}3+5\lim_{x\to\infty}\frac{1}{x}}{\displaystyle\lim_{x\to\infty}1-4\lim_{x\to\infty}\frac{1}{x}}=\frac{3+5(0)}{1-4(0)}=3$

19. Divide both the numerator and denominator by x^3 (the highest power of x that occurs in the denominator).

$$\lim_{x\to\infty}\frac{x^3+5x}{2x^3-x^2+4}=\lim_{x\to\infty}\frac{\dfrac{x^3+5x}{x^3}}{\dfrac{2x^3-x^2+4}{x^3}}=\lim_{x\to\infty}\frac{1+\dfrac{5}{x^2}}{2-\dfrac{1}{x}+\dfrac{4}{x^3}}=\frac{\displaystyle\lim_{x\to\infty}\left(1+\dfrac{5}{x^2}\right)}{\displaystyle\lim_{x\to\infty}\left(2-\dfrac{1}{x}+\dfrac{4}{x^3}\right)}$$

$$=\frac{\displaystyle\lim_{x\to\infty}1+5\lim_{x\to\infty}\frac{1}{x^2}}{\displaystyle\lim_{x\to\infty}2-\lim_{x\to\infty}\frac{1}{x}+4\lim_{x\to\infty}\frac{1}{x^3}}=\frac{1+5(0)}{2-0+4(0)}=\frac{1}{2}$$

20. $\displaystyle\lim_{t\to-\infty}\frac{t^2+2}{t^3+t^2-1}=\lim_{t\to-\infty}\frac{(t^2+2)/t^3}{(t^3+t^2-1)/t^3}=\lim_{t\to-\infty}\frac{1/t+2/t^3}{1+1/t-1/t^3}=\frac{0+0}{1+0-0}=0$

21. First, multiply the factors in the denominator. Then divide both the numerator and denominator by u^4.

$$\lim_{u\to\infty}\frac{4u^4+5}{(u^2-2)(2u^2-1)}=\lim_{u\to\infty}\frac{4u^4+5}{2u^4-5u^2+2}=\lim_{u\to\infty}\frac{\dfrac{4u^4+5}{u^4}}{\dfrac{2u^4-5u^2+2}{u^4}}=\lim_{u\to\infty}\frac{4+\dfrac{5}{u^4}}{2-\dfrac{5}{u^2}+\dfrac{2}{u^4}}$$

$$=\frac{\displaystyle\lim_{u\to\infty}\left(4+\dfrac{5}{u^4}\right)}{\displaystyle\lim_{u\to\infty}\left(2-\dfrac{5}{u^2}+\dfrac{2}{u^4}\right)}=\frac{\displaystyle\lim_{u\to\infty}4+5\lim_{u\to\infty}\frac{1}{u^4}}{\displaystyle\lim_{u\to\infty}2-5\lim_{u\to\infty}\frac{1}{u^2}+2\lim_{u\to\infty}\frac{1}{u^4}}=\frac{4+5(0)}{2-5(0)+2(0)}$$

$$=\frac{4}{2}=2$$

22. $\displaystyle\lim_{x\to\infty}\frac{x+2}{\sqrt{9x^2+1}}=\lim_{x\to\infty}\frac{(x+2)/x}{\sqrt{9x^2+1}/\sqrt{x^2}}=\lim_{x\to\infty}\frac{1+2/x}{\sqrt{9+1/x^2}}=\frac{1+0}{\sqrt{9+0}}=\frac{1}{3}$

23. $\displaystyle\lim_{x\to\infty}\left(\sqrt{9x^2+x}-3x\right)=\lim_{x\to\infty}\frac{\left(\sqrt{9x^2+x}-3x\right)\left(\sqrt{9x^2+x}+3x\right)}{\sqrt{9x^2+x}+3x}=\lim_{x\to\infty}\frac{\left(\sqrt{9x^2+x}\right)^2-(3x)^2}{\sqrt{9x^2+x}+3x}$

$$=\lim_{x\to\infty}\frac{(9x^2+x)-9x^2}{\sqrt{9x^2+x}+3x}=\lim_{x\to\infty}\frac{x/x}{\left(\sqrt{9x^2+x}+3x\right)/x}=\lim_{x\to\infty}\frac{1}{\sqrt{9+1/x}+3}$$

$$=\frac{1}{\sqrt{9}+3}=\frac{1}{3+3}=\frac{1}{6}$$

24. Since $0 \le \sin^2 x \le 1$, we have $0 \le \dfrac{\sin^2 x}{x^2} \le \dfrac{1}{x^2}$. Now $\lim\limits_{x\to\infty} 0 = 0$ and $\lim\limits_{x\to\infty} \dfrac{1}{x^2} = 0$, so by the Squeeze

Theorem, $\lim\limits_{x\to\infty} \dfrac{\sin^2 x}{x^2} = 0$.

25. $\lim\limits_{x\to\infty} \cos x$ does not exist because, as x increases, $\cos x$ does not approach any one value, but oscillates between 1 and -1.

26. If $z = x^4 - x^2$, then $\lim\limits_{x\to\infty} z = \infty$. Thus, $\lim\limits_{x\to\infty} \tan^{-1}\left(x^4 - x^2\right) = \lim\limits_{z\to\infty} \tan^{-1} z = \frac{\pi}{2}$.

27. $\lim\limits_{x\to\infty} \dfrac{x^7 - 1}{x^6 + 1} = \lim\limits_{x\to\infty} \dfrac{1 - 1/x^7}{(1/x) + (1/x^7)} = \infty$ since $1 - \dfrac{1}{x^7} \to 1$ while $\dfrac{1}{x} + \dfrac{1}{x^7} \to 0^+$ as $x \to \infty$.

Or: Divide numerator and denominator by x^6 instead of x^7.

28. As $x \to \infty$, $x^2 \to \infty$ and $-x^2 \to -\infty$. Thus, $\lim\limits_{x\to\infty} e^{-x^2} = \lim\limits_{t\to-\infty} e^t = 0$.

29. $\lim\limits_{x\to-\infty} \left(x^3 - 5x^2\right) = -\infty$ since $x^3 \to -\infty$ and $-5x^2 \to -\infty$ as $x \to -\infty$.

Or: $\lim\limits_{x\to-\infty} \left(x^3 - 5x^2\right) = \lim\limits_{x\to-\infty} x^2(x - 5) = -\infty$ since $x^2 \to \infty$ and $x - 5 \to -\infty$.

30. (a)

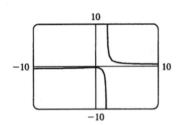
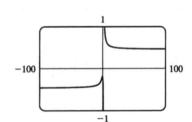

From the graph, it appears at first that there is only one horizontal asymptote, at $y \approx 0$, and a vertical asymptote at $x \approx 1.7$. However, if we graph the function with a wider viewing rectangle, we see that in fact there seem to be two horizontal asymptotes: one at $y \approx 0.5$ and one at $y \approx -0.5$. So we estimate that

$$\lim_{x\to\infty} \frac{\sqrt{2x^2 + 1}}{3x - 5} \approx 0.5 \qquad \text{and} \qquad \lim_{x\to-\infty} \frac{\sqrt{2x^2 + 1}}{3x - 5} \approx -0.5$$

(b) $f(1000) \approx 0.4722$ and $f(10{,}000) \approx 0.4715$, so we estimate that $\lim\limits_{x\to\infty} \dfrac{\sqrt{2x^2 + 1}}{3x - 5} \approx 0.47$.

$f(-1000) \approx -0.4706$ and $f(-10{,}000) \approx -0.4713$, so we estimate that $\lim\limits_{x\to-\infty} \dfrac{\sqrt{2x^2 + 1}}{3x - 5} \approx -0.47$.

(c) $\lim\limits_{x\to\infty} \dfrac{\sqrt{2x^2 + 1}}{3x - 5} = \lim\limits_{x\to\infty} \dfrac{\sqrt{2 + 1/x^2}}{3 - 5/x}$ [since $\sqrt{x^2} = x$ for $x > 0$] $= \dfrac{\sqrt{2}}{3} \approx 0.471404$.

For $x < 0$, we have $\sqrt{x^2} = |x| = -x$, so when we divide the numerator by x, with

$x < 0$, we get $\dfrac{1}{x}\sqrt{2x^2 + 1} = -\dfrac{1}{\sqrt{x^2}}\sqrt{2x^2 + 1} = -\sqrt{2 + 1/x^2}$. Therefore,

$$\lim_{x\to-\infty} \frac{\sqrt{2x^2 + 1}}{3x - 5} = \lim_{x\to-\infty} \frac{-\sqrt{2 + 1/x^2}}{3 - 5/x} = -\frac{\sqrt{2}}{3} \approx -0.471404.$$

31. $\lim\limits_{x\to\infty} \dfrac{2x^2+x-1}{x^2+x-2} = \lim\limits_{x\to\infty} \dfrac{\dfrac{2x^2+x-1}{x^2}}{\dfrac{x^2+x-2}{x^2}} = \lim\limits_{x\to\infty} \dfrac{2+\dfrac{1}{x}-\dfrac{1}{x^2}}{1+\dfrac{1}{x}-\dfrac{2}{x^2}} = \dfrac{\lim\limits_{x\to\infty}\left(2+\dfrac{1}{x}-\dfrac{1}{x^2}\right)}{\lim\limits_{x\to\infty}\left(1+\dfrac{1}{x}-\dfrac{2}{x^2}\right)}$

$= \dfrac{\lim\limits_{x\to\infty}2 + \lim\limits_{x\to\infty}\dfrac{1}{x} - \lim\limits_{x\to\infty}\dfrac{1}{x^2}}{\lim\limits_{x\to\infty}1 + \lim\limits_{x\to\infty}\dfrac{1}{x} - 2\lim\limits_{x\to\infty}\dfrac{1}{x^2}} = \dfrac{2+0-0}{1+0-2(0)} = 2$, so $y=2$ is a horizontal asymptote.

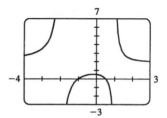

$y=f(x) = \dfrac{2x^2+x-1}{x^2+x-2} = \dfrac{(2x-1)(x+1)}{(x+2)(x-1)}$, so

$\lim\limits_{x\to-2^-} f(x) = \infty$, $\lim\limits_{x\to-2^+} f(x) = -\infty$,

$\lim\limits_{x\to1^-} f(x) = -\infty$, and $\lim\limits_{x\to1^+} f(x) = \infty$. Thus,

$x=-2$ and $x=1$ are vertical asymptotes. The

graph confirms our work.

32. $\lim\limits_{x\to\infty} \dfrac{x-9}{\sqrt{4x^2+3x+2}} = \lim\limits_{x\to\infty} \dfrac{1-9/x}{\sqrt{4+(3/x)+(2/x^2)}} = \dfrac{1-0}{\sqrt{4+0+0}} = \dfrac{1}{2}$.

Using the fact that $\sqrt{x^2} = |x| = -x$ for $x<0$, we divide the numerator by $-x$ and the denominator by $\sqrt{x^2}$.

Thus, $\lim\limits_{x\to-\infty} \dfrac{x-9}{\sqrt{4x^2+3x+2}} = \lim\limits_{x\to-\infty} \dfrac{-1+9/x}{\sqrt{4+(3/x)+(2/x^2)}} = \dfrac{-1+0}{\sqrt{4+0+0}} = -\dfrac{1}{2}$.

The horizontal asymptotes are $y=\pm\dfrac{1}{2}$. The

polynomial $4x^2+3x+2$ is positive for all x,

so the denominator never approaches zero,

and thus there is no vertical asymptote.

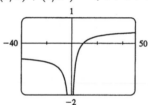 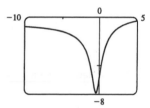

33. (a)

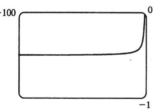

From the graph of $f(x) = \sqrt{x^2+x+1}+x$, we

estimate the value of $\lim\limits_{x\to-\infty} f(x)$ to be -0.5.

(b)

x	$f(x)$
$-10{,}000$	-0.4999625
$-100{,}000$	-0.4999962
$-1{,}000{,}000$	-0.4999996

From the table, we estimate the limit to be -0.5.

(c) $\lim\limits_{x\to-\infty}\left(\sqrt{x^2+x+1}+x\right) = \lim\limits_{x\to-\infty}\left(\sqrt{x^2+x+1}+x\right)\left[\dfrac{\sqrt{x^2+x+1}-x}{\sqrt{x^2+x+1}-x}\right]$

$= \lim\limits_{x\to-\infty} \dfrac{\left(x^2+x+1\right)-x^2}{\sqrt{x^2+x+1}-x} = \lim\limits_{x\to-\infty} \dfrac{(x+1)\,(1/x)}{\left(\sqrt{x^2+x+1}-x\right)(1/x)}$

$= \lim\limits_{x\to-\infty} \dfrac{1+(1/x)}{-\sqrt{1+(1/x)+(1/x^2)}-1} = \dfrac{1+0}{-\sqrt{1+0+0}-1} = -\dfrac{1}{2}$

Note that for $x<0$, we have $\sqrt{x^2}=|x|=-x$, so when we divide the radical by x, with $x<0$, we get

$\dfrac{1}{x}\sqrt{x^2+x+1} = -\dfrac{1}{\sqrt{x^2}}\sqrt{x^2+x+1} = -\sqrt{1+(1/x)+(1/x^2)}$.

34. (a)

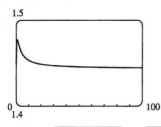

From the graph of $f(x) = \sqrt{3x^2 + 8x + 6} - \sqrt{3x^2 + 3x + 1}$, we estimate (to one decimal place) the value of $\lim\limits_{x \to \infty} f(x)$ to be 1.4.

(b)

x	$f(x)$
10,000	1.44339
100,000	1.44338
1,000,000	1.44338

From the table, we estimate (to four decimal places) the limit to be 1.4434.

(c) $\lim\limits_{x \to \infty} f(x) = \lim\limits_{x \to \infty} \dfrac{\left(\sqrt{3x^2 + 8x + 6} - \sqrt{3x^2 + 3x + 1}\right)\left(\sqrt{3x^2 + 8x + 6} + \sqrt{3x^2 + 3x + 1}\right)}{\sqrt{3x^2 + 8x + 6} + \sqrt{3x^2 + 3x + 1}}$

$= \lim\limits_{x \to \infty} \dfrac{(3x^2 + 8x + 6) - (3x^2 + 3x + 1)}{\sqrt{3x^2 + 8x + 6} + \sqrt{3x^2 + 3x + 1}}$

$= \lim\limits_{x \to \infty} \dfrac{(5x + 5)(1/x)}{\left(\sqrt{3x^2 + 8x + 6} + \sqrt{3x^2 + 3x + 1}\right)(1/x)}$

$= \lim\limits_{x \to \infty} \dfrac{5 + 5/x}{\sqrt{3 + 8/x + 6/x^2} + \sqrt{3 + 3/x + 1/x^2}} = \dfrac{5}{\sqrt{3} + \sqrt{3}} = \dfrac{5}{2\sqrt{3}} = \dfrac{5\sqrt{3}}{6} \approx 1.443376$

35. (a) This must be graph IV, the only graph that is always negative to the left of $x = 1$ and positive to the right of $x = 1$.

(b) This is graph III, the only graph with a horizontal asymptote of $y = 1$.

(c) This must be graph II, since it's the only graph that is positive everywhere. [$(x - 1)^2 > 0$ for $x \neq 1$.]

(d) $x^2 - 1 < 0$ if $|x| < 1$. Since the function is the reciprocal of $x^2 - 1$, the graph must be negative for $|x| < 1$ and positive elsewhere. The only graph fitting this description is VI.

(e) $(x - 1)^2 > 0$ if $x \neq 1$, so the sign of y is determined by the sign of the numerator, x. Thus, $y < 0$ if $x < 0$ and $y > 0$ if $x > 0$, as is only the case with graph I.

(f) The graph must have vertical asymptotes at $x = \pm 1$ and an x-intercept at $x = 0$. The only graph fitting this description is V.

36. Since the function has vertical asymptotes $x = 1$ and $x = 3$, the denominator of the rational function we are looking for must have factors $(x - 1)$ and $(x - 3)$. Because the horizontal asymptote is $y = 1$, the degree of the numerator must equal the degree of the denominator, and the ratio of the leading coefficients must be 1. One possibility is

$f(x) = \dfrac{x^2}{(x - 1)(x - 3)}.$

37. Let's look for a rational function.

(1) $\lim\limits_{x \to \pm\infty} f(x) = 0 \;\Rightarrow\;$ degree of numerator < degree of denominator

(2) $\lim\limits_{x \to 0} f(x) = -\infty \;\Rightarrow\;$ there is a factor of x^2 in the denominator (not just x, since that would produce a

sign change at $x = 0$), and the function is negative near $x = 0$.

(3) $\lim\limits_{x \to 3^-} f(x) = \infty$ and $\lim\limits_{x \to 3^+} f(x) = -\infty \;\Rightarrow\;$ vertical asymptote at $x = 3$; there is a factor of $(x - 3)$ in

the denominator.

(4) $f(2) = 0 \;\Rightarrow\;$ 2 is an x-intercept; there is at least one factor of $(x - 2)$ in the numerator.

Combining all of this information, and putting in a negative sign to give us the desired left- and right-hand limits,

gives us $f(x) = \dfrac{2 - x}{x^2(x - 3)}$ as one possibility.

38. (a) In both viewing rectangles, $\lim\limits_{x \to \infty} P(x) = \lim\limits_{x \to \infty} Q(x) = \infty$ and $\lim\limits_{x \to -\infty} P(x) = \lim\limits_{x \to -\infty} Q(x) = -\infty$. In the

larger viewing rectangle, P and Q become less distinguishable.

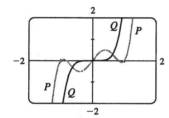 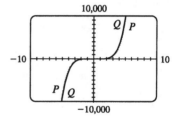

(b) $\lim\limits_{x \to \infty} \dfrac{P(x)}{Q(x)} = \lim\limits_{x \to \infty} \dfrac{3x^5 - 5x^3 + 2x}{3x^5} = \lim\limits_{x \to \infty} \left(1 - \dfrac{5}{3} \cdot \dfrac{1}{x^2} + \dfrac{2}{3} \cdot \dfrac{1}{x^4} \right) = 1 - \tfrac{5}{3}(0) + \tfrac{2}{3}(0) = 1 \;\Rightarrow\;$

P and Q have the same end behavior.

39. Divide numerator and denominator by the highest power of x in $Q(x)$.

(a) If $\deg P < \deg Q$, then numerator $\to 0$ but denominator doesn't. So $\lim\limits_{x \to \infty} [P(x)/Q(x)] = 0$.

(b) If $\deg P > \deg Q$, then numerator $\to \pm\infty$ but denominator doesn't, so $\lim\limits_{x \to \infty} [P(x)/Q(x)] = \pm\infty$ (depending

on the ratio of the leading coefficients of P and Q).

40.

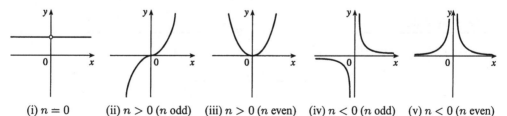

(i) $n = 0$ (ii) $n > 0$ (n odd)   (iii) $n > 0$ (n even)   (iv) $n < 0$ (n odd)   (v) $n < 0$ (n even)

From these sketches we see that

(a) $\lim\limits_{x \to 0^+} x^n = \begin{cases} 1 & \text{if } n = 0 \\ 0 & \text{if } n > 0 \\ \infty & \text{if } n < 0 \end{cases}$

(b) $\lim\limits_{x \to 0^-} x^n = \begin{cases} 1 & \text{if } n = 0 \\ 0 & \text{if } n > 0 \\ -\infty & \text{if } n < 0,\ n \text{ odd} \\ \infty & \text{if } n < 0,\ n \text{ even} \end{cases}$

(c) $\lim\limits_{x\to\infty} x^n = \begin{cases} 1 & \text{if } n = 0 \\ \infty & \text{if } n > 0 \\ 0 & \text{if } n < 0 \end{cases}$

(d) $\lim\limits_{x\to-\infty} x^n = \begin{cases} 1 & \text{if } n = 0 \\ -\infty & \text{if } n > 0,\ n \text{ odd} \\ \infty & \text{if } n > 0,\ n \text{ even} \\ 0 & \text{if } n < 0 \end{cases}$

41. $\lim\limits_{x\to\infty} \dfrac{4x - 1}{x} = \lim\limits_{x\to\infty} \left(4 - \dfrac{1}{x}\right) = 4$, and $\lim\limits_{x\to\infty} \dfrac{4x^2 + 3x}{x^2} = \lim\limits_{x\to\infty} \left(4 + \dfrac{3}{x}\right) = 4$. Therefore, by the Squeeze

Theorem, $\lim\limits_{x\to\infty} f(x) = 4$.

42. $\lim\limits_{v\to c^-} m = \lim\limits_{v\to c^-} \dfrac{m_0}{\sqrt{1 - v^2/c^2}}$. As $v \to c^-$, $\sqrt{1 - v^2/c^2} \to 0^+$, and $m \to \infty$.

43. (a) After t minutes, $25t$ liters of brine with 30 g of salt per liter has been pumped into the tank, so it contains
$(5000 + 25t)$ liters of water and $25t \cdot 30 = 750t$ grams of salt. Therefore, the salt concentration at time t will
be $C(t) = \dfrac{750t}{5000 + 25t} = \dfrac{30t}{200 + t} \ \dfrac{\text{g}}{\text{L}}$.

(b) $\lim\limits_{t\to\infty} C(t) = \lim\limits_{t\to\infty} \dfrac{30t}{200 + t} = \lim\limits_{t\to\infty} \dfrac{30t/t}{200/t + t/t} = \dfrac{30}{0 + 1} = 30$. So the salt concentration approaches that of
the brine being pumped into the tank.

44. (a) $\lim\limits_{t\to\infty} v(t) = \lim\limits_{t\to\infty} v^*\left(1 - e^{-gt/v^*}\right) = v^*(1 - 0) = v^*$

(b) We graph $v(t) = 1 - e^{-9.8t}$ and $v(t) = 0.99v^*$, or in this case,
$v(t) = 0.99$. Using an intersect feature or zooming in on the point
of intersection, we find that $t \approx 0.47$ s.

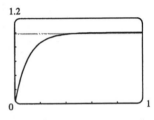

45. (a) If $t = -x/10$, then $x = -10t$ and as $x \to \infty$, $t \to -\infty$. Thus,
$\lim\limits_{x\to\infty} e^{-x/10} = \lim\limits_{t\to-\infty} e^t = 0$ by Equation 8.

(b) $y = e^{-x/10}$ and $y = 0.1$ intersect at $x_1 \approx 23.03$.
If $x > x_1$, then $e^{-x/10} < 0.1$.

(c) $e^{-x/10} < 0.1 \ \Rightarrow \ -x/10 < \ln 0.1 \ \Rightarrow$
$x > -10\ln\frac{1}{10} = -10\ln 10^{-1} = 10\ln 10$

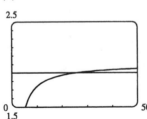

46. (a) $\lim\limits_{x\to\infty} f(x) = \lim\limits_{x\to\infty} \dfrac{4x^2 - 5x}{2x^2 + 1} = \lim\limits_{x\to\infty} \dfrac{4 - 5/x}{2 + 1/x^2} = \dfrac{4}{2} = 2$

(b) $f(x) = 1.9 \Longrightarrow x \approx 25.3744$, so $f(x) > 1.9$ when $x > N = 25.4$.

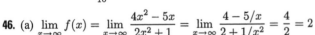

$f(x) = 1.99 \Longrightarrow x \approx 250.3974$, so $f(x) > 1.99$ when $x > N = 250.4$.

2.6 Tangents, Velocities, and Other Rates of Change · · · · · ·

1. (a) This is just the slope of the line through two points: $m_{PQ} = \dfrac{\Delta y}{\Delta x} = \dfrac{f(x) - f(3)}{x - 3}$.

(b) This is the limit of the slope of the secant line PQ as Q approaches P: $m = \lim\limits_{x \to 3} \dfrac{f(x) - f(3)}{x - 3}$.

2. (a) Average velocity $= \dfrac{\Delta s}{\Delta t} = \dfrac{f(a + h) - f(a)}{(a + h) - a} = \dfrac{f(a + h) - f(a)}{h}$

(b) Instantaneous velocity $= \lim\limits_{h \to 0} \dfrac{f(a + h) - f(a)}{h}$

3. The slope at D is the largest positive slope, followed by the positive slope at E. The slope at C is zero. The slope at B is steeper than at A (both are negative). In decreasing order, we have the slopes at: D, E, C, A, B.

4. The curve looks more like a line as the viewing rectangle gets smaller.

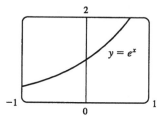

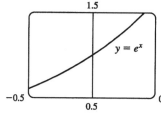

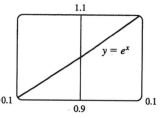

5. (a) (i) Using Definition 1,

$$m = \lim\limits_{x \to a} \frac{f(x) - f(a)}{x - a} \quad \lim\limits_{x \to -3} \frac{f(x) - f(-3)}{x - (-3)} = \lim\limits_{x \to -3} \frac{(x^2 + 2x) - (3)}{x - (-3)} = \lim\limits_{x \to -3} \frac{(x + 3)(x - 1)}{x + 3}$$

$$= \lim\limits_{x \to -3} (x - 1) = -4$$

(ii) Using Equation 2,

$$m = \lim\limits_{h \to 0} \frac{f(a + h) - f(a)}{h} = \lim\limits_{h \to 0} \frac{f(-3 + h) - f(-3)}{h} = \lim\limits_{h \to 0} \frac{\left[(-3 + h)^2 + 2(-3 + h)\right] - (3)}{h}$$

$$= \lim\limits_{h \to 0} \frac{9 - 6h + h^2 - 6 + 2h - 3}{h} = \lim\limits_{h \to 0} \frac{h(h - 4)}{h} = \lim\limits_{h \to 0} (h - 4) = -4$$

(b) Using the point-slope form of the equation of a line, an equation of the tangent line is $y - 3 = -4(x + 3)$. Solving for y gives us $y = -4x - 9$, which is the slope-intercept form of the equation of the tangent line.

(c)

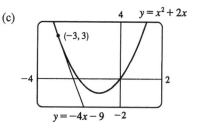

6. (a) (i) $m = \lim\limits_{x \to -1} \dfrac{f(x) - f(-1)}{x - (-1)} = \lim\limits_{x \to -1} \dfrac{x^3 - (-1)}{x + 1} = \lim\limits_{x \to -1} \dfrac{(x + 1)(x^2 - x + 1)}{x + 1}$

$= \lim\limits_{x \to -1} (x^2 - x + 1) = 3$

(ii) $m = \lim\limits_{h \to 0} \dfrac{f(-1 + h) - f(-1)}{h} = \lim\limits_{h \to 0} \dfrac{(-1 + h)^3 - (-1)}{h} = \lim\limits_{h \to 0} \dfrac{h^3 - 3h^2 + 3h - 1 + 1}{h}$

$= \lim\limits_{h \to 0} (h^2 - 3h + 3) = 3$

(b) $y - (-1) = 3\left[x - (-1)\right]$ $\Leftrightarrow$ $y + 1 = 3x + 3$ $\Leftrightarrow$ $y = 3x + 2$

(c)

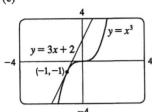

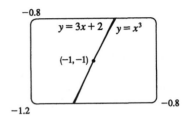

7. Using (1) with $f(x) = \dfrac{x-1}{x-2}$ and $P(3, 2)$,

$$m = \lim_{x \to a} \frac{f(x) - f(a)}{x - a} = \lim_{x \to 3} \frac{\dfrac{x-1}{x-2} - 2}{x - 3} = \lim_{x \to 3} \frac{\dfrac{x - 1 - 2(x-2)}{x - 2}}{x - 3} = \lim_{x \to 3} \frac{3 - x}{(x-2)(x-3)}$$

$$= \lim_{x \to 3} \frac{-1}{x - 2} = \frac{-1}{1} = -1.$$

Tangent line: $y - 2 = -1(x - 3)$ $\Leftrightarrow$ $y - 2 = -x + 3$ $\Leftrightarrow$ $y = -x + 5$

8. Using (1),

$$m = \lim_{x \to -1} \frac{(2x^3 - 5x) - 3}{x - (-1)} = \lim_{x \to -1} \frac{2x^3 - 5x - 3}{x + 1} = \lim_{x \to -1} \frac{(2x^2 - 2x - 3)(x + 1)}{x + 1}$$

$$= \lim_{x \to -1} (2x^2 - 2x - 3) = 1.$$

Tangent line: $y - 3 = 1\left[x - (-1)\right]$ $\Leftrightarrow$ $y = x + 4$

9. Using (1), $m = \lim_{x \to 1} \dfrac{\sqrt{x} - \sqrt{1}}{x - 1} = \lim_{x \to 1} \dfrac{(\sqrt{x} - 1)(\sqrt{x} + 1)}{(x - 1)(\sqrt{x} + 1)} = \lim_{x \to 1} \dfrac{x - 1}{(x - 1)(\sqrt{x} + 1)} = \lim_{x \to 1} \dfrac{1}{\sqrt{x} + 1} = \dfrac{1}{2}.$

Tangent line: $y - 1 = \frac{1}{2}(x - 1)$ $\Leftrightarrow$ $y = \frac{1}{2}x + \frac{1}{2}.$

10. Using (1), $m = \lim_{x \to 0} \dfrac{\dfrac{2x}{(x+1)^2} - 0}{x - 0} = \lim_{x \to 0} \dfrac{2x}{x(x+1)^2} = \lim_{x \to 0} \dfrac{2}{(x+1)^2} = \dfrac{2}{1^2} = 2.$

Tangent line: $y - 0 = 2(x - 0)$ $\Leftrightarrow$ $y = 2x$

11. (a) Using (1),

$$m = \lim_{x \to a} \frac{(x^3 - 4x + 1) - (a^3 - 4a + 1)}{x - a} = \lim_{x \to a} \frac{(x^3 - a^3) - 4(x - a)}{x - a}$$

$$= \lim_{x \to a} \frac{(x - a)(x^2 + ax + a^2) - 4(x - a)}{x - a} = \lim_{x \to a} (x^2 + ax + a^2 - 4) = 3a^2 - 4$$

(b) At $(1, -2)$: $m = 3(1)^2 - 4 = -1$, so an equation of the

tangent line is $y - (-2) = -1(x - 1)$ $\Leftrightarrow$ $y = -x - 1.$

At $(2, 1)$: $m = 3(2)^2 - 4 = 8$, so an equation of the

tangent line is $y - 1 = 8(x - 2)$ $\Leftrightarrow$ $y = 8x - 15.$

(c)

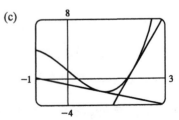

12. (a) Using (1),

$$m = \lim_{x \to a} \frac{\dfrac{1}{\sqrt{x}} - \dfrac{1}{\sqrt{a}}}{x - a} = \lim_{x \to a} \frac{\dfrac{\sqrt{a} - \sqrt{x}}{\sqrt{ax}}}{x - a} = \lim_{x \to a} \frac{(\sqrt{a} - \sqrt{x})(\sqrt{a} + \sqrt{x})}{\sqrt{ax}\,(x - a)\,(\sqrt{a} + \sqrt{x})}$$

$$= \lim_{x \to a} \frac{a - x}{\sqrt{ax}\,(x - a)\,(\sqrt{a} + \sqrt{x})} = \lim_{x \to a} \frac{-1}{\sqrt{ax}\,(\sqrt{a} + \sqrt{x})} = \frac{-1}{\sqrt{a^2}\,(2\sqrt{a}\,)} = -\frac{1}{2a^{3/2}} \text{ or } -\tfrac{1}{2}a^{-3/2}$$

(b) At $(1, 1)$: $m = -\tfrac{1}{2}$, so an equation of the tangent line is

$$y - 1 = -\tfrac{1}{2}(x - 1) \iff y = -\tfrac{1}{2}x + \tfrac{3}{2}.$$

At $\left(4, \tfrac{1}{2}\right)$: $m = -\tfrac{1}{16}$, so an equation of the tangent line is

$$y - \tfrac{1}{2} = -\tfrac{1}{16}(x - 4) \iff y = -\tfrac{1}{16}x + \tfrac{3}{4}.$$

(c)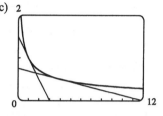

13. (a) Since the slope of the tangent at $t = 0$ is 0, the car's initial velocity was 0.

(b) The slope of the tangent is greater at C than at B, so the car was going faster at C.

(c) Near A, the tangent lines are becoming steeper as x increases, so the velocity was increasing, so the car was speeding up. Near B, the tangent lines are becoming less steep, so the car was slowing down. The steepest tangent near C is the one at C, so at C the car had just finished speeding up, and was about to start slowing down.

(d) Between D and E, the slope of the tangent is 0, so the car did not move during that time.

14. Let a denote the distance traveled from 1:00 to 1:02, b from 1:28 to 1:30, and c from 3:30 to 3:33, where all the times are relative to $t = 0$ at the beginning of the trip.

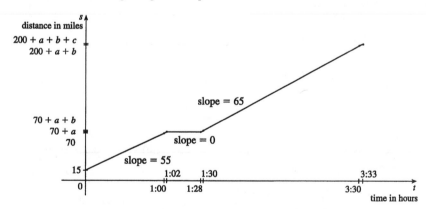

15. Let $s(t) = 40t - 16t^2$.

$$v(2) = \lim_{t \to 2} \frac{s(t) - s(2)}{t - 2} = \lim_{t \to 2} \frac{(40t - 16t^2) - 16}{t - 2} = \lim_{t \to 2} \frac{-16t^2 + 40t - 16}{t - 2} = \lim_{t \to 2} \frac{-8(2t^2 - 5t + 2)}{t - 2}$$

$$= \lim_{t \to 2} \frac{-8(t - 2)(2t - 1)}{t - 2} = -8 \lim_{t \to 2}(2t - 1) = -8(3) = -24$$

Thus, the instantaneous velocity when $t = 2$ is -24 ft/s.

16. (a) $v(1) = \lim\limits_{h \to 0} \dfrac{H(1+h) - H(1)}{h}$

$$= \lim\limits_{h \to 0} \dfrac{(58 + 58h - 0.83 - 1.66h - 0.83h^2) - 57.17}{h} = \lim\limits_{h \to 0} (56.34 - 0.83h) = 56.34 \text{ m/s}$$

(b) $v(a) = \lim\limits_{h \to 0} \dfrac{H(a+h) - H(a)}{h}$

$$= \lim\limits_{h \to 0} \dfrac{(58a + 58h - 0.83a^2 - 1.66ah - 0.83h^2) - (58a - 0.83a^2)}{h}$$

$$= \lim\limits_{h \to 0} (58 - 1.66a - 0.83h) = 58 - 1.66a \text{ m/s}$$

(c) The arrow strikes the moon when the height is 0, that is, $58t - 0.83t^2 = 0 \iff t(58 - 0.83t) = 0 \iff$
$t = \frac{58}{0.83} \approx 69.9$ s (since t can't be 0).

(d) Using the time from part (c), $v\left(\frac{58}{0.83}\right) = 58 - 1.66\left(\frac{58}{0.83}\right) = -58$ m/s. Thus, the arrow will have a velocity
of -58 m/s.

17. $v(a) = \lim\limits_{h \to 0} \dfrac{s(a+h) - s(a)}{h} = \lim\limits_{h \to 0} \dfrac{4(a+h)^3 + 6(a+h) + 2 - (4a^3 + 6a + 2)}{h}$

$$= \lim\limits_{h \to 0} \dfrac{4a^3 + 12a^2 h + 12ah^2 + 4h^3 + 6a + 6h + 2 - 4a^3 - 6a - 2}{h}$$

$$= \lim\limits_{h \to 0} \dfrac{12a^2 h + 12ah^2 + 4h^3 + 6h}{h} = \lim\limits_{h \to 0} (12a^2 + 12ah + 4h^2 + 6) = (12a^2 + 6) \text{ m/s}$$

So $v(1) = 12(1)^2 + 6 = 18$ m/s, $v(2) = 12(2)^2 + 6 = 54$ m/s, and $v(3) = 12(3)^2 + 6 = 114$ m/s.

18. (a) The average velocity between times t and $t + h$ is

$$\dfrac{s(t+h) - s(t)}{(t+h) - t} = \dfrac{(t+h)^2 - 8(t+h) + 18 - (t^2 - 8t + 18)}{h}$$

$$= \dfrac{t^2 + 2th + h^2 - 8t - 8h + 18 - t^2 + 8t - 18}{h} = \dfrac{2th + h^2 - 8h}{h}$$

$$= (2t + h - 8) \text{ m/s}$$

(i) $[3, 4]$: $t = 3$, $h = 4 - 3 = 1$, so the average
velocity is $2(3) + 1 - 8 = -1$ m/s.

(ii) $[3.5, 4]$: $t = 3.5$, $h = 0.5$, so the average velocity
is $2(3.5) + 0.5 - 8 = -0.5$ m/s.

(iii) $[4, 5]$: $t = 4$, $h = 1$, so the average velocity is
$2(4) + 1 - 8 = 1$ m/s.

(iv) $[4, 4.5]$: $t = 4$, $h = 0.5$, so the average velocity is
$2(4) + 0.5 - 8 = 0.5$ m/s.

(b) $v(t) = \lim\limits_{h \to 0} \dfrac{s(t+h) - s(t)}{h}$

$= \lim\limits_{h \to 0} (2t + h - 8) = 2t - 8,$

so $v(4) = 0$.

(c)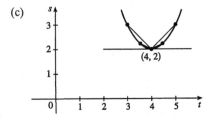

19. The sketch shows the graph for a room temperature of $72°$ and a refrigerator temperature of $38°$. The initial rate of change is greater in magnitude than the rate of change after an hour.

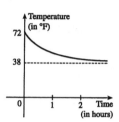

20. The slope of the tangent (that is, the rate of change of temperature with respect to time) at $t = 1$ h seems to be about
$$\frac{75 - 168}{132 - 0} \approx -0.7\,°\text{F/min}.$$

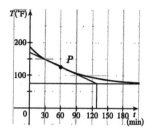

21. (a) (i) $[20, 23]$: $\dfrac{7.9 - 11.5}{3} = -1.2\,°\text{C/h}$

(ii) $[20, 22]$: $\dfrac{9.0 - 11.5}{2} = -1.25\,°\text{C/h}$

(iii) $[20, 21]$: $\dfrac{10.2 - 11.5}{1} = -1.3\,°\text{C/h}$

(b) In the figure, we estimate A to be $(18, 15.5)$ and B as $(23, 6)$. So the slope is
$$\frac{6 - 15.5}{23 - 18} = -1.9\,°\text{C/h at 8:00 P.M.}$$

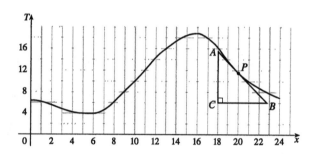

22. (a) (i) $[1992, 1996]$: $\dfrac{P(1996) - P(1992)}{1996 - 1992} = \dfrac{10{,}152 - 10{,}036}{4} = \dfrac{116}{4} = 29$ thousand/year

(ii) $[1994, 1996]$: $\dfrac{P(1996) - P(1994)}{1996 - 1994} = \dfrac{10{,}152 - 10{,}109}{2} = \dfrac{43}{2} = 21.5$ thousand/year

(iii) $[1996, 1998]$: $\dfrac{P(1998) - P(1996)}{1998 - 1996} = \dfrac{10{,}175 - 10{,}152}{2} = \dfrac{23}{2} = 11.5$ thousand/year

(b) Using the values from (ii) and (iii), we have $\dfrac{21.5 + 11.5}{2} = 16.5$ thousand/year.

(c) Estimating A as $(1994, 10{,}125)$ and B as $(1998, 10{,}182)$, the slope at 1996 is
$$\frac{10{,}182 - 10{,}125}{1998 - 1994} = \frac{57}{4} = 14.25 \text{ thousand/year.}$$

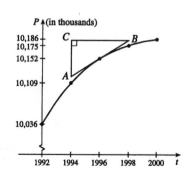

23. (a) (i) [1995, 1997]: $\dfrac{N(1997) - N(1995)}{1997 - 1995} = \dfrac{2461 - 873}{2} = \dfrac{1588}{2} = 794$ thousand/year

(ii) [1995, 1996]: $\dfrac{N(1996) - N(1995)}{1996 - 1995} = \dfrac{1513 - 873}{1} = 640$ thousand/year

(iii) [1994, 1995]: $\dfrac{N(1995) - N(1994)}{1995 - 1994} = \dfrac{873 - 572}{1} = 301$ thousand/year

(b) Using the values from (ii) and (iii), we have $\dfrac{640 + 301}{2} = \dfrac{941}{2} = 470.5$ thousand/year.

(c) Estimating A as $(1994, 420)$ and B as $(1996, 1275)$, the slope

at 1995 is $\dfrac{1275 - 420}{1996 - 1994} = \dfrac{855}{2} = 427.5$ thousand/year

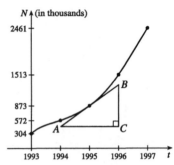

24. (a) (i) [1996, 1998]: $\dfrac{N(1998) - N(1996)}{1998 - 1996} = \dfrac{1886 - 1015}{2} = \dfrac{871}{2} = 435.5$ locations/year

(ii) [1996, 1997]: $\dfrac{N(1997) - N(1996)}{1997 - 1996} = \dfrac{1412 - 1015}{1} = 397$ locations/year

(iii) [1995, 1996]: $\dfrac{N(1996) - N(1995)}{1996 - 1995} = \dfrac{1015 - 676}{1} = 339$ locations/year

(b) Using the values from (ii) and (iii), we have $\dfrac{397 + 339}{2} = \dfrac{736}{2} = 368$ locations/year.

(c) Estimating A as $(1995, 660)$ and B as $(1997, 1350)$, the slope

at 1996 is $\dfrac{1350 - 660}{1997 - 1995} = \dfrac{690}{2} = 345$ locations/year.

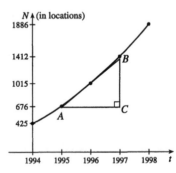

25. (a) (i) $\dfrac{\Delta C}{\Delta x} = \dfrac{C(105) - C(100)}{105 - 100} = \dfrac{6601.25 - 6500}{5} = \$20.25$/unit.

(ii) $\dfrac{\Delta C}{\Delta x} = \dfrac{C(101) - C(100)}{101 - 100} = \dfrac{6520.05 - 6500}{1} = \$20.05$/unit.

(b) $\dfrac{C(100 + h) - C(100)}{h} = \dfrac{\left[5000 + 10(100 + h) + 0.05(100 + h)^2\right] - 6500}{h} = \dfrac{20h + 0.05h^2}{h}$

$= 20 + 0.05h, \; h \neq 0$

So the instantaneous rate of change is $\displaystyle\lim_{h \to 0} \dfrac{C(100 + h) - C(100)}{h} = \lim_{h \to 0} (20 + 0.05h) = \$20$/unit.

26. $\Delta V = V(t+h) - V(t) = 100{,}000 \left(1 - \dfrac{t+h}{60}\right)^2 - 100{,}000 \left(1 - \dfrac{t}{60}\right)^2$

$$= 100{,}000 \left[\left(1 - \dfrac{t+h}{30} + \dfrac{(t+h)^2}{3600}\right) - \left(1 - \dfrac{t}{30} + \dfrac{t^2}{3600}\right)\right] = 100{,}000 \left(-\dfrac{h}{30} + \dfrac{2th}{3600} + \dfrac{h^2}{3600}\right)$$

$$= \dfrac{100{,}000}{3600} h \left(-120 + 2t + h\right) = \dfrac{250}{9} h \left(-120 + 2t + h\right)$$

Dividing ΔV by h and then letting $h \to 0$, we see that the instantaneous rate of change is $\dfrac{500}{9} (t - 60)$ gal/min.

t	Flow rate (gal/min)	Water remaining $V(t)$ (gal)
0	$-3333.\overline{3}$	$100{,}000$
10	$-2777.\overline{7}$	$69{,}444.\overline{4}$
20	$-2222.\overline{2}$	$44{,}444.\overline{4}$
30	$-1666.\overline{6}$	$25{,}000$
40	$-1111.\overline{1}$	$11{,}111.\overline{1}$
50	$-555.\overline{5}$	$2{,}777.\overline{7}$
60	0	0

The magnitude of the flow rate is greatest at the beginning and gradually decreases to 0.

2.7 Derivatives

1.

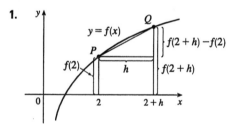

The line from $P(2, f(2))$ to $Q(2 + h, f(2 + h))$

is the line that has slope $\dfrac{f(2+h) - f(2)}{h}$.

2. As h decreases, the line PQ becomes steeper, so its slope increases. So

$$0 < \dfrac{f(4) - f(2)}{4 - 2} < \dfrac{f(3) - f(2)}{3 - 2} < \lim_{x \to 2} \dfrac{f(x) - f(2)}{x - 2}. \text{ Thus, } 0 < \tfrac{1}{2}\left[f(4) - f(2)\right] < f(3) - f(2) < f'(2).$$

3. $g'(0)$ is the only negative value. The slope at $x = 4$ is smaller than the slope at $x = 2$ and both are smaller than the slope at $x = -2$. Thus, $g'(0) < 0 < g'(4) < g'(2) < g'(-2)$.

4. Since $(4, 3)$ is on $y = f(x)$, $f(4) = 3$. The slope of the tangent line between $(0, 2)$ and $(4, 3)$ is $\tfrac{1}{4}$, so $f'(4) = \tfrac{1}{4}$.

5. We begin by drawing a curve through the origin at a slope of 3 to satisfy $f(0) = 0$ and $f'(0) = 3$. Since $f'(1) = 0$, we will round off our figure so that there is a horizontal tangent directly over $x = 1$. Lastly, we make sure that the curve has a slope of -1 as we pass over $x = 2$. Two of the many possibilities are shown.

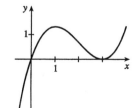

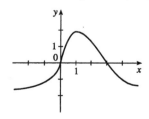

6.

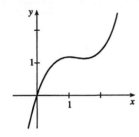

7. Using Definition 2 with $f(x) = 3x^2 - 5x$ and the point $(2, 2)$, we have

$$f'(2) = \lim_{h \to 0} \frac{f(2+h) - f(2)}{h} = \lim_{h \to 0} \frac{[3(2+h)^2 - 5(2+h)] - 2}{h}$$

$$= \lim_{h \to 0} \frac{(12 + 12h + 3h^2 - 10 - 5h) - 2}{h} = \lim_{h \to 0} \frac{3h^2 + 7h}{h} = \lim_{h \to 0} (3h + 7) = 7.$$

So an equation of the tangent line at $(2, 2)$ is $y - 2 = 7(x - 2)$ or $y = 7x - 12$.

8. Using Definition 2 with $g(x) = 1 - x^3$ and the point $(0, 1)$, we have

$$g'(0) = \lim_{h \to 0} \frac{g(0+h) - g(0)}{h} = \lim_{h \to 0} \frac{[1 - (0+h)^3] - 1}{h} = \lim_{h \to 0} \frac{(1 - h^3) - 1}{h} = \lim_{h \to 0} (-h^2) = 0.$$

So an equation of the tangent line is $y - 1 = 0(x - 0)$ or $y = 1$.

9. (a) Using Equation 3 with $F(x) = x^3 - 5x + 1$ and the point $(1, -3)$, we have

$$F'(1) = \lim_{x \to 1} \frac{F(x) - F(1)}{x - 1} = \lim_{x \to 1} \frac{(x^3 - 5x + 1) - (-3)}{x - 1} = \lim_{x \to 1} \frac{x^3 - 5x + 4}{x - 1}$$

$$= \lim_{x \to 1} \frac{(x - 1)(x^2 + x - 4)}{x - 1} = \lim_{x \to 1} (x^2 + x - 4) = -2.$$

So an equation of the tangent line at $(1, -3)$ is

$y - (-3) = -2(x - 1)$ $\Leftrightarrow$ $y = -2x - 1$.

Note: Instead of using Equation 3 to compute $F'(1)$, we
could have used Definition 2.

(b)

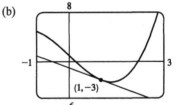

10. (a) $G'(a) = \lim_{h \to 0} \dfrac{G(a+h) - G(a)}{h} = \lim_{h \to 0} \dfrac{\dfrac{a+h}{1 + 2(a+h)} - \dfrac{a}{1 + 2a}}{h}$

$$= \lim_{h \to 0} \frac{a + 2a^2 + h + 2ah - a - 2a^2 - 2ah}{h(1 + 2a + 2h)(1 + 2a)} = \lim_{h \to 0} \frac{1}{(1 + 2a + 2h)(1 + 2a)} = (1 + 2a)^{-2}$$

So the slope of the tangent at the point $\left(-\frac{1}{4}, -\frac{1}{2}\right)$ is

$m = \left[1 + 2\left(-\frac{1}{4}\right)\right]^{-2} = 4$, and thus an equation is

$y + \frac{1}{2} = 4\left(x + \frac{1}{4}\right)$ or $y = 4x + \frac{1}{2}$.

(b)

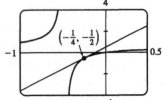

11. (a) $f'(1) = \lim_{h \to 0} \dfrac{f(1+h) - f(1)}{h} = \lim_{h \to 0} \dfrac{3^{1+h} - 3^1}{h}$.

So let $F(h) = \dfrac{3^{1+h} - 3}{h}$. We calculate:

h	$F(h)$
0.1	3.484
0.01	3.314
0.001	3.298
0.0001	3.296
−0.1	3.121
−0.01	3.278
−0.001	3.294
−0.0001	3.296

We estimate that $f'(1) \approx 3.296$.

(b)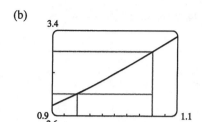

From the graph, we estimate that the slope of the tangent is about

$$\frac{3.2 - 2.8}{1.06 - 0.94} = \frac{0.4}{0.12} \approx 3.3.$$

12. (a) $g'\left(\frac{\pi}{4}\right) = \lim_{h \to 0} \dfrac{g\left(\frac{\pi}{4} + h\right) - g\left(\frac{\pi}{4}\right)}{h} = \lim_{h \to 0} \dfrac{\tan\left(\frac{\pi}{4} + h\right) - \tan\left(\frac{\pi}{4}\right)}{h}$.

So let $G(h) = \dfrac{\tan\left(\frac{\pi}{4} + h\right) - 1}{h}$. We calculate:

h	$G(h)$
0.1	2.2305
0.01	2.0203
0.001	2.0020
0.0001	2.0002
−0.1	1.8237
−0.01	1.9803
−0.001	1.9980
−0.0001	1.9998

We estimate that $g'\left(\frac{\pi}{4}\right) = 2$.

(b)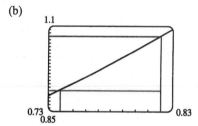

From the graph, we estimate that the slope of the tangent is about

$$\frac{1.07 - 0.91}{0.82 - 0.74} = \frac{0.16}{0.08} = 2.$$

13. Use Definition 2 with $f(x) = 3 - 2x + 4x^2$.

$$f'(a) = \lim_{h \to 0} \frac{f(a+h) - f(a)}{h} = \lim_{h \to 0} \frac{\left[3 - 2(a+h) + 4(a+h)^2\right] - \left(3 - 2a + 4a^2\right)}{h}$$

$$= \lim_{h \to 0} \frac{\left(3 - 2a - 2h + 4a^2 + 8ah + 4h^2\right) - \left(3 - 2a + 4a^2\right)}{h}$$

$$= \lim_{h \to 0} \frac{-2h + 8ah + 4h^2}{h} = \lim_{h \to 0} \frac{h(-2 + 8a + 4h)}{h} = \lim_{h \to 0} (-2 + 8a + 4h) = -2 + 8a$$

14. $f'(a) = \lim\limits_{h \to 0} \dfrac{f(a+h) - f(a)}{h} = \lim\limits_{h \to 0} \dfrac{\left[(a+h)^4 - 5(a+h)\right] - \left(a^4 - 5a\right)}{h}$

$= \lim\limits_{h \to 0} \dfrac{\left(a^4 + 4a^3h + 6a^2h^2 + 4ah^3 + h^4 - 5a - 5h\right) - \left(a^4 - 5a\right)}{h}$

$= \lim\limits_{h \to 0} \dfrac{4a^3h + 6a^2h^2 + 4ah^3 + h^4 - 5h}{h} = \lim\limits_{h \to 0} \dfrac{h\left(4a^3 + 6a^2h + 4ah^2 + h^3 - 5\right)}{h}$

$= \lim\limits_{h \to 0} \left(4a^3 + 6a^2h + 4ah^2 + h^3 - 5\right) = 4a^3 - 5$

15. $f'(a) = \lim\limits_{h \to 0} \dfrac{f(a+h) - f(a)}{h} = \lim\limits_{h \to 0} \dfrac{\dfrac{2(a+h)+1}{(a+h)+3} - \dfrac{2a+1}{a+3}}{h}$

$= \lim\limits_{h \to 0} \dfrac{(2a+2h+1)(a+3) - (2a+1)(a+h+3)}{h(a+h+3)(a+3)}$

$= \lim\limits_{h \to 0} \dfrac{\left(2a^2 + 6a + 2ah + 6h + a + 3\right) - \left(2a^2 + 2ah + 6a + a + h + 3\right)}{h(a+h+3)(a+3)}$

$= \lim\limits_{h \to 0} \dfrac{5h}{h(a+h+3)(a+3)} = \lim\limits_{h \to 0} \dfrac{5}{(a+h+3)(a+3)} = \dfrac{5}{(a+3)^2}$

16. $f'(a) = \lim\limits_{h \to 0} \dfrac{f(a+h) - f(a)}{h} = \lim\limits_{h \to 0} \dfrac{\dfrac{(a+h)^2 + 1}{(a+h) - 2} - \dfrac{a^2 + 1}{a - 2}}{h}$

$= \lim\limits_{h \to 0} \dfrac{\left(a^2 + 2ah + h^2 + 1\right)(a-2) - \left(a^2 + 1\right)(a+h-2)}{h(a+h-2)(a-2)}$

$= \lim\limits_{h \to 0} \dfrac{\left(a^3 - 2a^2 + 2a^2h - 4ah + ah^2 - 2h^2 + a - 2\right) - \left(a^3 + a^2h - 2a^2 + a + h - 2\right)}{h(a+h-2)(a-2)}$

$= \lim\limits_{h \to 0} \dfrac{a^2h - 4ah + ah^2 - 2h^2 - h}{h(a+h-2)(a-2)} = \lim\limits_{h \to 0} \dfrac{h\left(a^2 - 4a + ah - 2h - 1\right)}{h(a+h-2)(a-2)}$

$= \lim\limits_{h \to 0} \dfrac{a^2 - 4a + ah - 2h - 1}{(a+h-2)(a-2)} = \dfrac{a^2 - 4a - 1}{(a-2)^2}$

17. $f'(a) = \lim\limits_{h \to 0} \dfrac{f(a+h) - f(a)}{h} = \lim\limits_{h \to 0} \dfrac{\dfrac{1}{\sqrt{(a+h)+2}} - \dfrac{1}{\sqrt{a+2}}}{h}$

$= \lim\limits_{h \to 0} \dfrac{\dfrac{\sqrt{a+2} - \sqrt{a+h+2}}{\sqrt{a+h+2}\sqrt{a+2}}}{h} = \lim\limits_{h \to 0} \left[\dfrac{\sqrt{a+2} - \sqrt{a+h+2}}{h\sqrt{a+h+2}\sqrt{a+2}} \cdot \dfrac{\sqrt{a+2} + \sqrt{a+h+2}}{\sqrt{a+2} + \sqrt{a+h+2}}\right]$

$= \lim\limits_{h \to 0} \dfrac{(a+2) - (a+h+2)}{h\sqrt{a+h+2}\sqrt{a+2}\left(\sqrt{a+2} + \sqrt{a+h+2}\right)}$

$= \lim\limits_{h \to 0} \dfrac{-h}{h\sqrt{a+h+2}\sqrt{a+2}\left(\sqrt{a+2} + \sqrt{a+h+2}\right)}$

$= \lim\limits_{h \to 0} \dfrac{-1}{\sqrt{a+h+2}\sqrt{a+2}\left(\sqrt{a+2} + \sqrt{a+h+2}\right)}$

$= \dfrac{-1}{\left(\sqrt{a+2}\right)^2\left(2\sqrt{a+2}\right)} = -\dfrac{1}{2\left(a+2\right)^{3/2}}$

18. $f'(a) = \lim\limits_{h \to 0} \dfrac{f(a+h) - f(a)}{h} = \lim\limits_{h \to 0} \dfrac{\sqrt{3(a+h)+1} - \sqrt{3a+1}}{h}$

$= \lim\limits_{h \to 0} \dfrac{\left(\sqrt{3a+3h+1} - \sqrt{3a+1}\right)\left(\sqrt{3a+3h+1} + \sqrt{3a+1}\right)}{h\left(\sqrt{3a+3h+1} + \sqrt{3a+1}\right)}$

$= \lim\limits_{h \to 0} \dfrac{(3a+3h+1) - (3a+1)}{h\left(\sqrt{3a+3h+1} + \sqrt{3a+1}\right)} = \lim\limits_{h \to 0} \dfrac{3h}{h\left(\sqrt{3a+3h+1} + \sqrt{3a+1}\right)}$

$= \lim\limits_{h \to 0} \dfrac{3}{\sqrt{3a+3h+1} + \sqrt{3a+1}} = \dfrac{3}{2\sqrt{3a+1}}$

Note that the answers to Exercises 19–24 are not unique.

19. By Definition 2, $\lim\limits_{h \to 0} \dfrac{(1+h)^{10} - 1}{h} = f'(1)$, where $f(x) = x^{10}$.

20. By Definition 2, $\lim\limits_{h \to 0} \dfrac{\sqrt[4]{16+h} - 2}{h} = f'(16)$, where $f(x) = \sqrt[4]{x}$.

21. By Equation 3, $\lim\limits_{x \to 5} \dfrac{2^x - 32}{x - 5} = f'(5)$, where $f(x) = 2^x$.

22. By Equation 3, $\lim\limits_{x \to \pi/4} \dfrac{\tan x - 1}{x - \pi/4} = f'(\pi/4)$, where $f(x) = \tan x$.

23. By Definition 2, $\lim\limits_{h \to 0} \dfrac{\cos(\pi + h) + 1}{h} = f'(\pi)$, where $f(x) = \cos x$.

24. By Equation 3, $\lim\limits_{t \to 1} \dfrac{t^4 + t - 2}{t - 1} = f'(1)$, where $f(t) = t^4 + t$.

25. $v(2) = f'(2) = \lim\limits_{h \to 0} \dfrac{f(2+h) - f(2)}{h} = \lim\limits_{h \to 0} \dfrac{\left[(2+h)^2 - 6(2+h) - 5\right] - \left[2^2 - 6(2) - 5\right]}{h}$

$= \lim\limits_{h \to 0} \dfrac{\left(4 + 4h + h^2 - 12 - 6h - 5\right) - (-13)}{h} = \lim\limits_{h \to 0} \dfrac{h^2 - 2h}{h} = \lim\limits_{h \to 0} (h - 2) = -2 \text{ m/s}$

26. $v(2) = f'(2) = \lim\limits_{h \to 0} \dfrac{f(2+h) - f(2)}{h} = \lim\limits_{h \to 0} \dfrac{\left[2(2+h)^3 - (2+h) + 1\right] - \left[2(2)^3 - 2 + 1\right]}{h}$

$= \lim\limits_{h \to 0} \dfrac{\left(2h^3 + 12h^2 + 24h + 16 - 2 - h + 1\right) - 15}{h} = \lim\limits_{h \to 0} \dfrac{2h^3 + 12h^2 + 23h}{h}$

$= \lim\limits_{h \to 0} \left(2h^2 + 12h + 23\right) = 23 \text{ m/s}$

27. (a) $f'(x)$ is the rate of change of the production cost with respect to the number of ounces of gold produced. Its units are dollars per ounce.

(b) After 800 ounces of gold have been produced, the rate at which the production cost is increasing is \$17/ounce. So the cost of producing the 800th (or 801st) ounce is about \$17.

(c) In the short term, the values of $f'(x)$ will decrease because more efficient use is made of start-up costs as x increases. But eventually $f'(x)$ might increase due to large-scale operations.

28. (a) $f'(5)$ is the rate of growth of the bacteria population when $t = 5$ hours. Its units are bacteria per hour.

(b) With unlimited space and nutrients, f' should increase as t increases; so $f'(5) < f'(10)$. If the supply of nutrients is limited, the growth rate slows down at some point in time, and the opposite may be true.

29. (a) $f'(v)$ is the rate at which the fuel consumption is changing with respect to the speed. Its units are $(\text{gal/h})/(\text{mi/h})$.

(b) The fuel consumption is decreasing by 0.05 $(\text{gal/h})/(\text{mi/h})$ as the car's speed reaches 20 mi/h. So if you increase your speed to 21 mi/h, you could expect to decrease your fuel consumption by about 0.05 $(\text{gal/h})/(\text{mi/h})$.

30. (a) $f'(8)$ is the rate of change of the quantity of coffee sold with respect to the price per pound when the price is \$8 per pound. The units for $f'(8)$ are pounds/(dollars/pound).

(b) $f'(8)$ is negative since the quantity of coffee sold will decrease as the price charged for it increases. People are generally less willing to buy a product when its price increases.

31. $T'(6)$ is the rate of change of the temperature with respect to time when $t = 6$. Its units are °C/h. To estimate the value of $T'(6)$, we will average the difference quotients obtained using the times $t = 4$ and $t = 8$.

Let $A = \dfrac{T(4) - T(6)}{4 - 6} = \dfrac{29 - 32}{-2} = 1.5$ and $B = \dfrac{T(8) - T(6)}{8 - 6} = \dfrac{33 - 32}{2} = 0.5$. Then

$T'(6) = \lim\limits_{t \to 6} \dfrac{T(t) - T(6)}{t - 6} \approx \dfrac{A + B}{2} = 1\,°\text{C/h}.$

32. (a) $S'(T)$ is the rate of change of the maximum sustainable speed of Coho salmon with respect to the temperature. Its units are $(\text{cm/s})/°\text{C}$.

(b) For $T = 15\,°\text{C}$, it appears the tangent line to the curve goes through the points $(10, 25)$ and $(20, 32)$. So

$S'(15) \approx \dfrac{32 - 25}{20 - 10} = 0.7\ (\text{cm/s})/°\text{C}$. This tells us that at $T = 15\,°\text{C}$, the maximum sustainable speed of Coho salmon is changing at a rate of 0.7 $(\text{cm/s})/°\text{C}$. In a similar fashion for $T = 25\,°\text{C}$, we can use the points $(20, 35)$ and $(25, 25)$ to obtain $S'(25) \approx \dfrac{25 - 35}{25 - 20} = -2\ (\text{cm/s})/°\text{C}$. As it gets warmer than 20 °C, the maximum sustainable speed decreases rapidly.

33. $C'(1980)$ is the rate of change of U.S. cash per capita in circulation with respect to time. To estimate the value of $C'(1980)$, we will average the difference quotients obtained using the years 1970 and 1990.

Let $A = \dfrac{C(1970) - C(1980)}{1970 - 1980} = \dfrac{265 - 571}{-10} = 30.6$ and $B = \dfrac{C(1990) - C(1980)}{1990 - 1980} = \dfrac{1063 - 571}{10} = 49.2$.

Then $C'(1980) = \lim\limits_{t \to 1980} \dfrac{C(t) - C(1980)}{t - 1980} \approx \dfrac{A + B}{2} = 39.9$ dollars per year.

34. For 1910: We will average the difference quotients obtained using the years 1900 and 1920.

Let $A = \dfrac{E(1900) - E(1910)}{1900 - 1910} = \dfrac{48.3 - 51.1}{-10} = 0.28$ and

$B = \dfrac{E(1920) - E(1910)}{1920 - 1910} = \dfrac{55.2 - 51.1}{10} = 0.41$. Then

$E'(1910) = \lim\limits_{t \to 1910} \dfrac{E(t) - E(1910)}{t - 1910} \approx \dfrac{A + B}{2} = 0.345$. This means that life expectancy at birth was increasing at about 0.345 year/year in 1910.

For 1950: Using data for 1940 and 1960 in a similar fashion, we obtain $E'(1950) \approx [0.31 + 0.10]\,/2 = 0.205$. So life expectancy at birth was increasing at about 0.205 year/year in 1950.

35. Since $f(x) = x\sin(1/x)$ when $x \neq 0$ and $f(0) = 0$, we have

$$f'(0) = \lim_{h\to 0} \frac{f(0+h) - f(0)}{h} = \lim_{h\to 0} \frac{h\sin(1/h) - 0}{h} = \lim_{h\to 0} \sin(1/h). \text{ This limit does not exist since } \sin(1/h)$$

takes the values -1 and 1 on any interval containing 0. (Compare with Example 4 in Section 2.2.)

36. Since $f(x) = x^2\sin(1/x)$ when $x \neq 0$ and $f(0) = 0$, we have

$$f'(0) = \lim_{h\to 0} \frac{f(0+h) - f(0)}{h} = \lim_{h\to 0} \frac{h^2\sin(1/h) - 0}{h} = \lim_{h\to 0} h\sin(1/h). \text{ Since } -1 \leq \sin\frac{1}{h} \leq 1, \text{ we have}$$

$$-|h| \leq |h|\sin\frac{1}{h} \leq |h| \quad\Rightarrow\quad -|h| \leq h\sin\frac{1}{h} \leq |h|. \text{ Because } \lim_{h\to 0}(-|h|) = 0 \text{ and } \lim_{h\to 0}|h| = 0, \text{ we know that}$$

$$\lim_{h\to 0}\left(h\sin\frac{1}{h}\right) = 0 \text{ by the Squeeze Theorem. Thus, } f'(0) = 0.$$

2.8 The Derivative as a Function • • • • • • • • • • •

1. It appears that f is an odd function, so f' will be an even function—that is, $f'(-a) = f'(a)$.

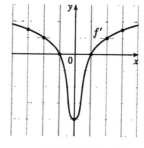

(a) $f'(-3) \approx 1.5$ (b) $f'(-2) \approx 1$

(c) $f'(-1) \approx 0$ (d) $f'(0) \approx -4$

(e) $f'(1) \approx 0$ (f) $f'(2) \approx 1$

(g) $f'(3) \approx 1.5$

2. From the graph of f, it appears that

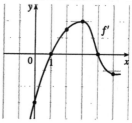

(a) $f'(0) \approx -3$ (b) $f'(1) \approx 0$

(c) $f'(2) \approx 1.5$ (d) $f'(3) \approx 2$

(e) $f'(4) \approx 0$ (f) $f'(5) \approx -1.2$

3. (a)$'$ = II, since from left to right, the slopes of the tangents to graph (a) start out negative, become 0, then positive, then 0, then negative again. The actual function values in graph II follow the same pattern.

(b)$'$ = IV, since from left to right, the slopes of the tangents to graph (b) start out at a fixed positive quantity, then suddenly become negative, then positive again. The discontinuities in graph IV indicate sudden changes in the slopes of the tangents.

(c)$'$ = I, since the slopes of the tangents to graph (c) are negative for $x < 0$ and positive for $x > 0$, as are the function values of graph I.

(d)$'$ = III, since from left to right, the slopes of the tangents to graph (d) are positive, then 0, then negative, then 0, then positive, then 0, then negative again, and the function values in graph III follow the same pattern.

Hints for Exercises 4–11: First plot x-intercepts on the graph of f' for any horizontal tangents on the graph of f. Look for any corners on the graph of f—there will be a discontinuity on the graph of f'. On any interval where f has a tangent with positive (or negative) slope, the graph of f' will be positive (or negative). If the graph of the function is linear, the graph of f' will be a horizontal line.

4.

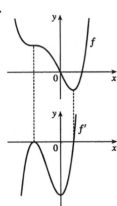

5.

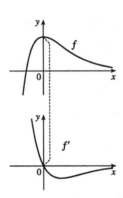

6.

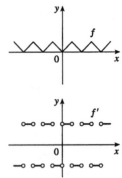

7.

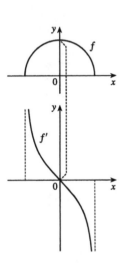

8.

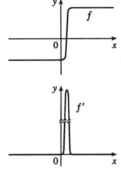

9.

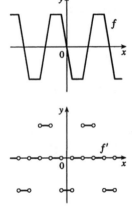

10.

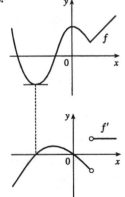

11.

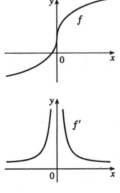

12. The slopes of the tangent lines on the graph of $y = P(t)$ are always
positive, so the y-values of $y = P'(t)$ are always positive. These
values start out relatively small and keep increasing, reaching a
maximum at about $t = 6$. Then the y-values of $y = P'(t)$ decrease
and get close to zero. The graph of P' tells us that the yeast culture
grows most rapidly after 6 hours and then the growth rate declines.

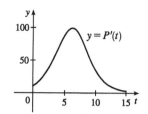

13. It appears that there are horizontal tangents on the graph of M for
$t = 1963$ and $t = 1971$. Thus, there are zeros for those values of t
on the graph of M'. The derivative is negative for the years 1963
to 1971.

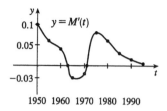

14. See Figure 1 in Section 3.4.

15.

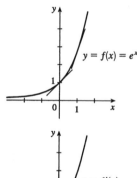

16.

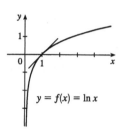

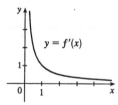

The slope at 0 appears to be 1 and the slope at 1
appears to be 2.7. As x decreases, the slope gets
closer to 0. Since the graphs are so similar, we
might guess that $f'(x) = e^x$.

As x increases toward 1, $f'(x)$ decreases from
very large numbers to 1. As x becomes large,
$f'(x)$ gets closer to 0. As a guess, $f'(x) = 1/x^2$
or $f'(x) = 1/x$ make sense.

17. (a) By zooming in, we estimate that $f'(0) = 0$, $f'\left(\frac{1}{2}\right) = 1$, $f'(1) = 2$,
and $f'(2) = 4$.

(b) By symmetry, $f'(-x) = -f'(x)$. So $f'\left(-\frac{1}{2}\right) = -1$,
$f'(-1) = -2$, and $f'(-2) = -4$.

(c) It appears that $f'(x)$ is twice the value of x, so we guess that
$f'(x) = 2x$.

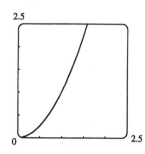

(d) $f'(x) = \lim\limits_{h \to 0} \dfrac{f(x+h) - f(x)}{h} = \lim\limits_{h \to 0} \dfrac{(x+h)^2 - x^2}{h} = \lim\limits_{h \to 0} \dfrac{(x^2 + 2hx + h^2) - x^2}{h}$

$\qquad = \lim\limits_{h \to 0} \dfrac{2hx + h^2}{h} = \lim\limits_{h \to 0} \dfrac{h(2x + h)}{h} = \lim\limits_{h \to 0} (2x + h) = 2x$

18. (a) By zooming in, we estimate that $f'(0) = 0$, $f'\left(\frac{1}{2}\right) \approx 0.75$, $f'(1) \approx 3$, (c)

$\qquad f'(2) \approx 12$, and $f'(3) \approx 27$.

(b) By symmetry, $f'(-x) = f'(x)$. So $f'\left(-\frac{1}{2}\right) \approx 0.75$, $f'(-1) \approx 3$,

$\qquad f'(-2) \approx 12$, and $f'(-3) \approx 27$.

(d) Since $f'(0) = 0$, it appears that f' may have the form $f'(x) = ax^2$.

$\qquad$ Using $f'(1) = 3$, we have $a = 3$, so $f'(x) = 3x^2$.

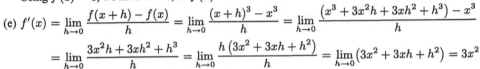

(e) $f'(x) = \lim\limits_{h \to 0} \dfrac{f(x+h) - f(x)}{h} = \lim\limits_{h \to 0} \dfrac{(x+h)^3 - x^3}{h} = \lim\limits_{h \to 0} \dfrac{(x^3 + 3x^2h + 3xh^2 + h^3) - x^3}{h}$

$\qquad = \lim\limits_{h \to 0} \dfrac{3x^2h + 3xh^2 + h^3}{h} = \lim\limits_{h \to 0} \dfrac{h\left(3x^2 + 3xh + h^2\right)}{h} = \lim\limits_{h \to 0} \left(3x^2 + 3xh + h^2\right) = 3x^2$

19. $f'(x) = \lim\limits_{h \to 0} \dfrac{f(x+h) - f(x)}{h} = \lim\limits_{h \to 0} \dfrac{[4 - 7(x+h)] - (4 - 7x)}{h} = \lim\limits_{h \to 0} \dfrac{(4 - 7x - 7h) - (4 - 7x)}{h}$

$\qquad = \lim\limits_{h \to 0} \dfrac{-7h}{h} = \lim\limits_{h \to 0} (-7) = -7$

Domain of f = domain of f' = $\mathbb{R}$.

20. $f'(x) = \lim\limits_{h \to 0} \dfrac{f(x+h) - f(x)}{h} = \lim\limits_{h \to 0} \dfrac{\left[5 - 4(x+h) + 3(x+h)^2\right] - \left[5 - 4x + 3x^2\right]}{h}$

$\qquad = \lim\limits_{h \to 0} \dfrac{\left[5 - 4x - 4h + 3x^2 + 6xh + 3h^2\right] - \left[5 - 4x + 3x^2\right]}{h}$

$\qquad = \lim\limits_{h \to 0} \dfrac{-4h + 6xh + 3h^2}{h} = \lim\limits_{h \to 0} (-4 + 6x + 3h) = -4 + 6x$

Domain of f = domain of f' = $\mathbb{R}$.

21. $f'(x) = \lim\limits_{h \to 0} \dfrac{f(x+h) - f(x)}{h} = \lim\limits_{h \to 0} \dfrac{\left[(x+h)^3 - 3(x+h) + 5\right] - (x^3 - 3x + 5)}{h}$

$\qquad = \lim\limits_{h \to 0} \dfrac{(x^3 + 3x^2h + 3xh^2 + h^3 - 3x - 3h + 5) - (x^3 - 3x + 5)}{h}$

$\qquad = \lim\limits_{h \to 0} \dfrac{3x^2h + 3xh^2 + h^3 - 3h}{h} = \lim\limits_{h \to 0} \dfrac{h\left(3x^2 + 3xh + h^2 - 3\right)}{h}$

$\qquad = \lim\limits_{h \to 0} \left(3x^2 + 3xh + h^2 - 3\right) = 3x^2 - 3$

Domain of f = domain of f' = $\mathbb{R}$.

22. $f'(x) = \lim\limits_{h \to 0} \dfrac{f(x+h) - f(x)}{h} = \lim\limits_{h \to 0} \dfrac{(x + h + \sqrt{x+h}) - (x + \sqrt{x})}{h}$

$\qquad = \lim\limits_{h \to 0} \left(\dfrac{h}{h} + \dfrac{\sqrt{x+h} - \sqrt{x}}{h} \cdot \dfrac{\sqrt{x+h} + \sqrt{x}}{\sqrt{x+h} + \sqrt{x}}\right) = \lim\limits_{h \to 0} \left[1 + \dfrac{(x+h) - x}{h\left(\sqrt{x+h} + \sqrt{x}\right)}\right]$

$\qquad = \lim\limits_{h \to 0} \left(1 + \dfrac{1}{\sqrt{x+h} + \sqrt{x}}\right) = 1 + \dfrac{1}{\sqrt{x} + \sqrt{x}} = 1 + \dfrac{1}{2\sqrt{x}}$

Domain of f = $[0, \infty)$, domain of f' = $(0, \infty)$.

23. $g'(x) = \lim\limits_{h \to 0} \dfrac{g(x+h) - g(x)}{h} = \lim\limits_{h \to 0} \dfrac{\sqrt{1 + 2(x+h)} - \sqrt{1 + 2x}}{h} \left[\dfrac{\sqrt{1 + 2(x+h)} + \sqrt{1 + 2x}}{\sqrt{1 + 2(x+h)} + \sqrt{1 + 2x}} \right]$

$= \lim\limits_{h \to 0} \dfrac{(1 + 2x + 2h) - (1 + 2x)}{h \left[\sqrt{1 + 2(x+h)} + \sqrt{1 + 2x} \right]} = \lim\limits_{h \to 0} \dfrac{2}{\sqrt{1 + 2x + 2h} + \sqrt{1 + 2x}} = \dfrac{2}{2\sqrt{1 + 2x}} = \dfrac{1}{\sqrt{1 + 2x}}$

Domain of $g = \left[-\frac{1}{2}, \infty \right)$, domain of $g' = \left(-\frac{1}{2}, \infty \right)$.

24. $f'(x) = \lim\limits_{h \to 0} \dfrac{f(x+h) - f(x)}{h} = \lim\limits_{h \to 0} \dfrac{\dfrac{3 + (x+h)}{1 - 3(x+h)} - \dfrac{3 + x}{1 - 3x}}{h}$

$= \lim\limits_{h \to 0} \dfrac{(3 + x + h)(1 - 3x) - (3 + x)(1 - 3x - 3h)}{h(1 - 3x - 3h)(1 - 3x)}$

$= \lim\limits_{h \to 0} \dfrac{\left(3 - 9x + x - 3x^2 + h - 3hx\right) - \left(3 - 9x - 9h + x - 3x^2 - 3hx\right)}{h(1 - 3x - 3h)(1 - 3x)}$

$= \lim\limits_{h \to 0} \dfrac{10h}{h(1 - 3x - 3h)(1 - 3x)} = \lim\limits_{h \to 0} \dfrac{10}{(1 - 3x - 3h)(1 - 3x)} = \dfrac{10}{(1 - 3x)^2}$

Domain of $f =$ domain of $f' = \left(-\infty, \frac{1}{3} \right) \cup \left(\frac{1}{3}, \infty \right)$.

25. $G'(t) = \lim\limits_{h \to 0} \dfrac{G(t+h) - G(t)}{h} = \lim\limits_{h \to 0} \dfrac{\dfrac{4(t+h)}{(t+h) + 1} - \dfrac{4t}{t + 1}}{h} = \lim\limits_{h \to 0} \dfrac{\dfrac{4(t+h)(t+1) - 4t(t+h+1)}{(t+h+1)(t+1)}}{h}$

$= \lim\limits_{h \to 0} \dfrac{\left(4t^2 + 4ht + 4t + 4h\right) - \left(4t^2 + 4ht + 4t\right)}{h(t+h+1)(t+1)}$

$= \lim\limits_{h \to 0} \dfrac{4h}{h(t+h+1)(t+1)} = \lim\limits_{h \to 0} \dfrac{4}{(t+h+1)(t+1)} = \dfrac{4}{(t+1)^2}$

Domain of $G =$ domain of $G' = (-\infty, -1) \cup (-1, \infty)$.

26. (a)

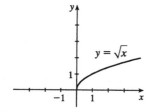
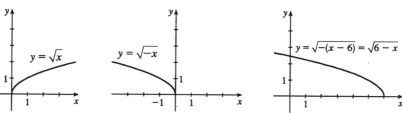

(b) Note that the third graph in part (a) has small negative values for its slope, f'; but as $x \to 6^-$, $f' \to -\infty$.
See the graph in part (d).

(c) $f'(x) = \lim\limits_{h \to 0} \dfrac{f(x+h) - f(x)}{h} = \lim\limits_{h \to 0} \dfrac{\sqrt{6 - (x+h)} - \sqrt{6 - x}}{h} \left[\dfrac{\sqrt{6 - (x+h)} + \sqrt{6 - x}}{\sqrt{6 - (x+h)} + \sqrt{6 - x}} \right]$

$= \lim\limits_{h \to 0} \dfrac{[6 - (x+h)] - (6 - x)}{h \left[\sqrt{6 - (x+h)} + \sqrt{6 - x} \right]} = \lim\limits_{h \to 0} \dfrac{-h}{h \left(\sqrt{6 - x - h} + \sqrt{6 - x} \right)}$

$= \lim\limits_{h \to 0} \dfrac{-1}{\sqrt{6 - x - h} + \sqrt{6 - x}} = \dfrac{-1}{2\sqrt{6 - x}}$

Domain of $f = (-\infty, 6]$, domain of $f' = (-\infty, 6)$.

(d)

$$f'(x) = \lim_{h \to 0} \frac{f(x+h) - f(x)}{h} = \lim_{h \to 0} \frac{\left[x+h - \left(\dfrac{2}{x+h}\right)\right] - \left[x - \left(\dfrac{2}{x}\right)\right]}{h}$$

$$= \lim_{h \to 0} \frac{\left[h - \dfrac{2}{(x+h)} + \dfrac{2}{x}\right]}{h} = \lim_{h \to 0} \left[1 + \frac{-2x + 2(x+h)}{h(x)(x+h)}\right] = \lim_{h \to 0} \left[1 + \frac{2h}{h(x)(x+h)}\right]$$

$$= \lim_{h \to 0} \left[1 + \frac{2}{x(x+h)}\right] = 1 + \frac{2}{x^2}$$

(b) Notice that when f has steep tangent lines, $f'(x)$ is very large. When f is flatter, $f'(x)$ is smaller.

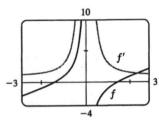

28. (a) $f'(t) = \lim_{h \to 0} \dfrac{f(t+h) - f(t)}{h} = \lim_{h \to 0} \dfrac{\dfrac{6}{1 + (t+h)^2} - \dfrac{6}{1+t^2}}{h} = \lim_{h \to 0} \dfrac{6 + 6t^2 - 6 - 6(t+h)^2}{h\left[1 + (t+h)^2\right](1+t^2)}$

$$= \lim_{h \to 0} \frac{-12th - 6h^2}{h\left[1 + (t+h)^2\right](1+t^2)} = \lim_{h \to 0} \frac{-12t - 6h}{\left[1 + (t+h)^2\right](1+t^2)} = \frac{-12t}{(1+t^2)^2}$$

(b) Notice that f has a horizontal tangent when $t = 0$. This corresponds to $f'(0) = 0$. f' is positive when f is increasing and negative when f is decreasing.

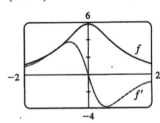

29. (a) $U'(t)$ is the rate at which the unemployment rate is changing with respect to time. Its units are percent per year.

(b) To find $U'(t)$, we use $\lim_{h \to 0} \dfrac{U(t+h) - U(t)}{h} \approx \dfrac{U(t+h) - U(t)}{h}$ for small values of h.

For 1989: $U'(1989) = \dfrac{U(1990) - U(1989)}{1990 - 1989} = \dfrac{5.6 - 5.3}{1} = 0.30$

For 1990: We estimate $U'(1990)$ by using $h = -1$ and $h = 1$, and then averaging the two results to obtain a final estimate.

$h = -1 \quad \Rightarrow \quad U'(1990) \approx \dfrac{U(1989) - U(1990)}{1989 - 1990} = \dfrac{5.3 - 5.6}{-1} = 0.30;$

$$h = 1 \quad \Rightarrow \quad U'(1990) \approx \frac{U(1991) - U(1990)}{1991 - 1990} = \frac{6.8 - 5.6}{1} = 1.20.$$

So we estimate that $U'(1990) \approx \frac{1}{2}(0.30 + 1.20) = 0.75$.

t	1989	1990	1991	1992	1993	1994	1995	1996	1997	1998
$U'(t)$	0.30	0.75	0.95	0.05	-0.70	-0.65	-0.35	-0.35	-0.45	-0.40

30. (a) $S'(t)$ is the rate at which the smoking rate is changing with respect to time. Its units are percent per year.

(b) To find $S'(t)$, we use $\lim\limits_{h \to 0} \dfrac{S(t+h) - S(t)}{h} \approx \dfrac{S(t+h) - S(t)}{h}$ for small values of h.

For 1980: $S'(1980) \approx \dfrac{S(1982) - S(1980)}{1982 - 1980} = \dfrac{21.0 - 21.4}{2} = \dfrac{-0.4}{2} = -0.20$

For 1982: We estimate $S'(1982)$ by using $h = -2$ and $h = 2$, and then averaging the two results to obtain a final estimate.

$$h = -2 \quad \Rightarrow \quad S'(1982) = \frac{S(1980) - S(1982)}{1980 - 1982} = \frac{21.4 - 21.0}{-2} = -0.20$$

$$h = 2 \quad \Rightarrow \quad S'(1982) = \frac{S(1984) - S(1982)}{1984 - 1982} = \frac{18.7 - 21.0}{2} = -1.15$$

So we estimate that $S'(1982) \approx \frac{1}{2}(-0.20 - 1.15) = -0.675$.

t	1980	1982	1984	1986	1988	1990	1992	1994	1996	1998
$S'(t)$	-0.20	-0.675	-0.575	-0.15	0.10	-0.225	0.075	1.25	0.75	0.10

(c)

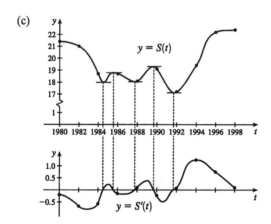

(d) We could get more accurate values for $S'(t)$ by obtaining data for the odd-numbered years.

31. f is not differentiable at $x = -1$ or at $x = 11$ because the graph has vertical tangents at those points; at $x = 4$, because there is a discontinuity there; and at $x = 8$, because the graph has a corner there.

32. (a) g is discontinuous at $x = -2$ (a removable discontinuity), at $x = 0$ (g is not defined there), and at $x = 5$ (a jump discontinuity).

(b) g is not differentiable at the above points (by Theorem 4), and also at $x = -1$ (corner), at $x = 2$ (vertical tangent), and at $x = 4$ (vertical tangent).

33. As we zoom in toward $(-1, 0)$, the curve appears more and more like a straight line, so f is differentiable at $x = -1$. But no matter how much we zoom in toward the origin, the curve doesn't straighten out—we can't eliminate the sharp point (a cusp). So f is not differentiable at $x = 0$.

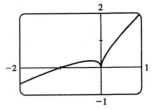

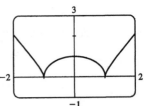

34. As we zoom in toward $(0, 1)$, the curve appears more and more like a straight line, so f is differentiable at $x = 0$. But no matter how much we zoom in toward $(1, 0)$ or $(-1, 0)$, the curve doesn't straighten out—we can't eliminate the sharp point (a cusp). So f is not differentiable at $x = \pm 1$.

35. $a = f$, $b = f'$, $c = f''$. We can see this because where a has a horizontal tangent, $b = 0$, and where b has a horizontal tangent, $c = 0$. We can immediately see that c can be neither f nor f', since at the points where c has a horizontal tangent, neither a nor b is equal to 0.

36. Where d has horizontal tangents, only c is 0, so $d' = c$. c has negative tangents for $x < 0$ and b is the only graph that is negative for $x < 0$, so $c' = b$. b has positive tangents on $\mathbb{R}$ (except at $x = 0$), and the only graph that is positive on the same domain is a, so $b' = a$. We conclude that $d = f$, $c = f'$, $b = f''$, and $a = f'''$.

37. We can immediately see that a is the graph of the acceleration function, since at the points where a has a horizontal tangent, neither c nor b is equal to 0. Next, we note that $a = 0$ at the point where b has a horizontal tangent, so b must be the graph of the velocity function, and hence, $b' = a$. We conclude that c is the graph of the position function.

38. a must be the jerk since none of the graphs are 0 at its high and low points. a is 0 where b has a maximum, so $b' = a$. b is 0 where c has a maximum, so $c' = b$. We conclude that d is the position function, c is the velocity, b is the acceleration, and a is the jerk.

39. $f'(x) = \lim\limits_{h \to 0} \dfrac{f(x+h) - f(x)}{h} = \lim\limits_{h \to 0} \dfrac{\left[1 + 4(x+h) - (x+h)^2\right] - \left(1 + 4x - x^2\right)}{h}$

$= \lim\limits_{h \to 0} \dfrac{\left(1 + 4x + 4h - x^2 - 2xh - h^2\right) - \left(1 + 4x - x^2\right)}{h} = \lim\limits_{h \to 0} \dfrac{4h - 2xh - h^2}{h}$

$= \lim\limits_{h \to 0} (4 - 2x - h) = 4 - 2x$

$f''(x) = \lim\limits_{h \to 0} \dfrac{f'(x+h) - f'(x)}{h} = \lim\limits_{h \to 0} \dfrac{[4 - 2(x+h)] - (4 - 2x)}{h} = \lim\limits_{h \to 0} \dfrac{-2h}{h} = \lim\limits_{h \to 0} (-2) = -2$

We see from the graph that our answers are reasonable because the graph of f' is that of a linear function and the graph of f'' is that of a constant function.

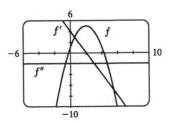

40. $f'(x) = \lim\limits_{h \to 0} \dfrac{f(x+h) - f(x)}{h} = \lim\limits_{h \to 0} \dfrac{\dfrac{1}{x+h} - \dfrac{1}{x}}{h} = \lim\limits_{h \to 0} \dfrac{x - (x+h)}{hx(x+h)}$

$= \lim\limits_{h \to 0} \dfrac{-h}{hx(x+h)} = \lim\limits_{h \to 0} \dfrac{-1}{x(x+h)} = -\dfrac{1}{x^2}$

$f''(x) = \lim\limits_{h \to 0} \dfrac{f'(x+h) - f'(x)}{h} = \lim\limits_{h \to 0} \dfrac{-\dfrac{1}{(x+h)^2} - \left(-\dfrac{1}{x^2}\right)}{h} = \lim\limits_{h \to 0} \dfrac{-x^2 + (x+h)^2}{hx^2(x+h)^2}$

$= \lim\limits_{h \to 0} \dfrac{2hx + h^2}{hx^2(x+h)^2} = \lim\limits_{h \to 0} \dfrac{2x + h}{x^2(x+h)^2} = \dfrac{2x}{x^4} = \dfrac{2}{x^3}$

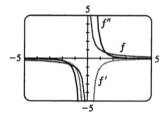

We see from the graph that our answers are reasonable because the graph of f' is that of an even function and is negative for all $x \neq 0$, and the graph of f'' is that of an odd function (negative for $x < 0$ and positive for $x > 0$).

41. $f'(x) = \lim\limits_{h \to 0} \dfrac{f(x+h) - f(x)}{h} = \lim\limits_{h \to 0} \dfrac{[2(x+h)^2 - (x+h)^3] - (2x^2 - x^3)}{h}$

$= \lim\limits_{h \to 0} \dfrac{h(4x + 2h - 3x^2 - 3xh - h^2)}{h} = \lim\limits_{h \to 0} (4x + 2h - 3x^2 - 3xh - h^2) = 4x - 3x^2$

$f''(x) = \lim\limits_{h \to 0} \dfrac{f'(x+h) - f'(x)}{h} = \lim\limits_{h \to 0} \dfrac{[4(x+h) - 3(x+h)^2] - (4x - 3x^2)}{h}$

$= \lim\limits_{h \to 0} \dfrac{h(4 - 6x - 3h)}{h} = \lim\limits_{h \to 0} (4 - 6x - 3h) = 4 - 6x$

$f'''(x) = \lim\limits_{h \to 0} \dfrac{f''(x+h) - f''(x)}{h} = \lim\limits_{h \to 0} \dfrac{[4 - 6(x+h)] - (4 - 6x)}{h} = \lim\limits_{h \to 0} \dfrac{-6h}{h} = \lim\limits_{h \to 0} (-6) = -6$

$f^{(4)}(x) = \lim\limits_{h \to 0} \dfrac{f'''(x+h) - f'''(x)}{h} = \lim\limits_{h \to 0} \dfrac{-6 - (-6)}{h} = \lim\limits_{h \to 0} \dfrac{0}{h} = \lim\limits_{h \to 0} (0) = 0$

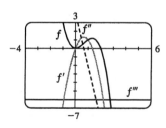

The graphs are consistent with the geometric interpretations of the derivatives because f' has zeros where f has a local minimum and a local maximum, f'' has a zero where f' has a local maximum, and f''' is a constant function equal to the slope of f''.

42. (a) Since we estimate the velocity to be a maximum at $t = 10$, the acceleration is 0 at $t = 10$.

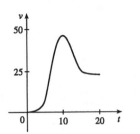
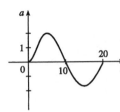

(b) Drawing a tangent line at $t = 10$ on the graph of a, a appears to decrease by $10\,\text{ft/s}^2$ over a period of 20 s. So at
$t = 10$ s, the jerk is approximately $-10/20 = -0.5 \;\; (\text{ft/s}^2)/\text{s}$ or ft/s^3.

43. (a) Note that we have factored $x - a$ as the difference of two cubes in the third step.

$$f'(a) = \lim_{x \to a} \frac{f(x) - f(a)}{x - a} = \lim_{x \to a} \frac{x^{1/3} - a^{1/3}}{x - a} = \lim_{x \to a} \frac{x^{1/3} - a^{1/3}}{(x^{1/3} - a^{1/3})(x^{2/3} + x^{1/3}a^{1/3} + a^{2/3})}$$

$$= \lim_{x \to a} \frac{1}{x^{2/3} + x^{1/3}a^{1/3} + a^{2/3}} = \lim_{x \to a} \frac{1}{3x^{2/3}} = \frac{1}{3a^{2/3}} \text{ or } \tfrac{1}{3}a^{-2/3}$$

(b) $f'(0) = \lim\limits_{h \to 0} \dfrac{f(0 + h) - f(0)}{h} = \lim\limits_{h \to 0} \dfrac{\sqrt[3]{h} - 0}{h} = \lim\limits_{h \to 0} \dfrac{1}{h^{2/3}}$. This function increases without bound, so the

limit does not exist, and therefore $f'(0)$ does not exist.

(c) $\lim\limits_{x \to 0} |f'(x)| = \lim\limits_{x \to 0} \dfrac{1}{3x^{2/3}} = \infty$ and f is continuous at $x = 0$ (root function), so f has a vertical tangent

at $x = 0$.

44. (a) $g'(0) = \lim\limits_{x \to 0} \dfrac{g(x) - g(0)}{x - 0} = \lim\limits_{x \to 0} \dfrac{x^{2/3} - 0}{x} = \lim\limits_{x \to 0} \dfrac{1}{x^{1/3}}$, which does not exist.

(b) $g'(a) = \lim\limits_{x \to a} \dfrac{g(x) - g(a)}{x - a} = \lim\limits_{x \to a} \dfrac{x^{2/3} - a^{2/3}}{x - a} = \lim\limits_{x \to a} \dfrac{\left(x^{1/3} - a^{1/3}\right)\left(x^{1/3} + a^{1/3}\right)}{(x^{1/3} - a^{1/3})\left(x^{2/3} + x^{1/3}a^{1/3} + a^{2/3}\right)}$

$$= \lim_{x \to a} \frac{x^{1/3} + a^{1/3}}{x^{2/3} + x^{1/3}a^{1/3} + a^{2/3}} = \frac{2a^{1/3}}{3a^{2/3}} = \frac{2}{3a^{1/3}}$$

(c) $g(x) = x^{2/3}$ is continuous at $x = 0$ and

(d)

$\lim\limits_{x \to 0} |g'(x)| = \lim\limits_{x \to 0} \dfrac{2}{3\,|x|^{1/3}} = \infty$. This shows that

g has a vertical tangent line at $x = 0$.

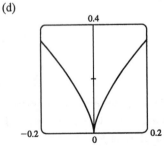

45. $f(x) = |x - 6| = \begin{cases} -(x-6) & \text{if } x < 6 \\ x - 6 & \text{if } x \geq 6 \end{cases} = \begin{cases} 6 - x & \text{if } x < 6 \\ x - 6 & \text{if } x \geq 6 \end{cases}$

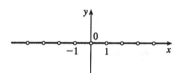

$y = f'(x)$

$$\lim_{x \to 6^+} \frac{f(x) - f(6)}{x - 6} = \lim_{x \to 6^+} \frac{|x - 6| - 0}{x - 6} = \lim_{x \to 6^+} \frac{x - 6}{x - 6} = \lim_{x \to 6^+} 1 = 1.$$

$$\text{But } \lim_{x \to 6^-} \frac{f(x) - f(6)}{x - 6} = \lim_{x \to 6^-} \frac{|x - 6| - 0}{x - 6} = \lim_{x \to 6^-} \frac{6 - x}{x - 6}$$

$$= \lim_{x \to 6^-} (-1) = -1$$

So $f'(6) = \lim_{x \to 6} \dfrac{f(x) - f(6)}{x - 6}$ does not exist. However, $f'(x) = \begin{cases} -1 & \text{if } x < 6 \\ 1 & \text{if } x > 6 \end{cases}$

Another way of writing the answer is $f'(x) = \dfrac{x - 6}{|x - 6|}$.

46. $f(x) = \llbracket x \rrbracket$ is not continuous at any integer n, so f is not differentiable at n by the contrapositive of Theorem 4. If a is not an integer, then f is constant on an open interval containing a, so $f'(a) = 0$. Thus, $f'(x) = 0$, x not an integer.

47. (a) If f is even, then

$$f'(-x) = \lim_{h \to 0} \frac{f(-x + h) - f(-x)}{h} = \lim_{h \to 0} \frac{f(x - h) - f(x)}{h}$$

$$= -\lim_{h \to 0} \frac{f(x - h) - f(x)}{-h} \quad [\text{let } \Delta x = -h] \quad = -\lim_{\Delta x \to 0} \frac{f(x + \Delta x) - f(x)}{\Delta x} = -f'(x)$$

Therefore, f' is odd.

(b) If f is odd, then

$$f'(-x) = \lim_{h \to 0} \frac{f(-x + h) - f(-x)}{h} = \lim_{h \to 0} \frac{-f(x - h) + f(x)}{h}$$

$$= \lim_{h \to 0} \frac{f(x - h) - f(x)}{-h} \quad [\text{let } \Delta x = -h] \quad = \lim_{\Delta x \to 0} \frac{f(x + \Delta x) - f(x)}{\Delta x} = f'(x)$$

Therefore, f' is even.

48. (a)

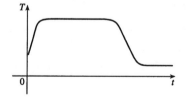

(c)

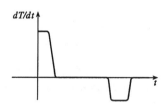

(b) The initial temperature of the water is close to room temperature because of the water that was in the pipes. When the water from the hot water tank starts coming out, dT/dt is large and positive as T increases to the temperature of the water in the tank. In the next phase, $dT/dt = 0$ as the water comes out at a constant, high temperature. After some time, dT/dt becomes small and negative as the contents of the hot water tank are exhausted. Finally, when the hot water has run out, dT/dt is once again 0 as the water maintains its (cold) temperature.

49.

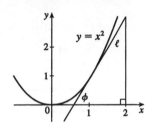

In the right triangle in the diagram, let Δy be the side opposite angle ϕ and Δx the side adjacent angle ϕ. Then the slope of the tangent line ℓ is $m = \Delta y/\Delta x = \tan\phi$. Note that $0 < \phi < \frac{\pi}{2}$. We know (see Exercise 17) that the derivative of $f(x) = x^2$ is $f'(x) = 2x$. So the slope of the tangent to the curve at the point $(1,1)$ is 2. Thus, ϕ is the angle between 0 and $\frac{\pi}{2}$ whose tangent is 2; that is, $\phi = \tan^{-1}2 \approx 63°$.

2.9 Linear Approximations · · · · · · · · · · · · ·

1. (a) If $f(x) = 3^x$, then

$$f'(0) = \lim_{h\to 0}\frac{f(h)-f(0)}{h} = \lim_{h\to 0}\frac{3^h-1}{h}.$$

Let $y = \dfrac{3^h-1}{h}$.

From the table, we conclude that $f'(0) \approx 1.0986$.

x	y		x	y
0.01	1.1047		-0.01	1.0926
0.001	1.0992		-0.001	1.0980
0.0001	1.0987		-0.0001	1.0986

(b) An approximate equation of the tangent line is

$y - 1 = 1.0986(x - 0)$, or $y = 1.0986x + 1$.

Thus, the linearization of f at 0 is

$L(x) = 1.0986x + 1$.

$L(0.05) = 1.0986(0.05) + 1 = 1.05493$ and

$L(0.1) = 1.0986(0.1) + 1 = 1.10986$. So we

estimate that $3^{0.05} \approx 1.0549$ and $3^{0.1} \approx 1.1099$.

(c)

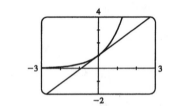

The approximations are y-values on the tangent line. Since the tangent line lies *below* the curve, the approximations are *less* than the true values.

2. (a)

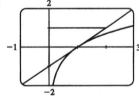

Consider the triangle in the graph. The vertices that lie on the tangent line are $(0, -1)$ and $(2, 1)$. Check these points with the linearization in part (b). Thus, $f'(1) \approx \Delta y/\Delta x = [1 - (-1)]/(2 - 0) = 1$.

(b) Using $f(x) = \ln x$ and $a = 1$, we have $L(x) = f(1) + f'(1)(x - 1) = 0 + 1(x - 1) = x - 1$.

$L(0.9) = 0.9 - 1 = -0.1$ and $L(1.3) = 0.3$. So we estimate that $\ln 0.9 \approx -0.1$ and $\ln 1.3 \approx 0.3$.

(c) From the graph, we see that the tangent line lies *above* the curve, so the estimates are *greater* than the values.

3. (a)

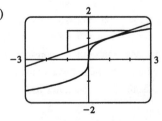

Consider the triangle in the graph. The vertices that lie on the tangent line are $\left(2, \frac{4}{3}\right)$ and $\left(-1, \frac{1}{3}\right)$. Check these points with the linearization in part (b). Thus,

$$f'(1) \approx \frac{\Delta y}{\Delta x} = \frac{\frac{4}{3} - \frac{1}{3}}{2 - (-1)} = \frac{1}{3}$$

(b) Using $f(x) = \sqrt[3]{x}$ and $a = 1$, we have $L(x) = f(1) + f'(1)(x-1) = 1 + \frac{1}{3}(x-1) = \frac{1}{3}x + \frac{2}{3}$.

(c)

x	$L(x)$	Calculator
0.5	$0.8\overline{33}$	0.793701
0.9	$0.96\overline{6}$	0.965489
0.99	$0.99\overline{6}$	0.996655
1.01	$1.00\overline{3}$	1.003322
1.1	$1.03\overline{3}$	1.032280
1.5	$1.16\overline{6}$	1.144714
2	$1.33\overline{3}$	1.259921

We see from the table that all of the estimates are overestimates. The most accurate estimates are for $x = 0.99$ and $x = 1.01$, which are the closest values to $x = 1$.

(d) The graph in part (a) shows that the tangent line lies above the curve. That explains why the estimates are overestimates.

4. (a)

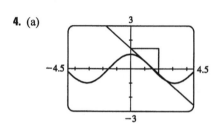

From the triangle in the graph, $\dfrac{\Delta y}{\Delta x} \approx \dfrac{-0.3 - 1.4}{2 - 0} = -0.85$.

(b) $L(x) = f\left(\frac{\pi}{3}\right) + f'\left(\frac{\pi}{3}\right)\left(x - \frac{\pi}{3}\right) \approx \frac{1}{2} - 0.85\left(x - \frac{\pi}{3}\right) \approx -0.85x + 1.39$.
Remember that this estimate is dependent on the estimates made in part (a).

(c) $\cos 1 \approx L(1) = 0.54$, $\cos 1.1 \approx L(1.1) = 0.455$, $\cos 1.5 \approx L(1.5) = 0.115$, and $\cos 2 \approx L(2) = -0.31$.
Compare those values with the following calculator values: $\cos 1 \approx 0.5403$, $\cos 1.1 \approx 0.4536$,
$\cos 1.5 \approx 0.0707$, and $\cos 2 \approx -0.4161$. [It turns out that $L(1) < f(1)$, but only because of the "eyeball" estimates in part (a).] The estimates that are most accurate are those at $x = 1$ and $x = 1.1$, since they are closest to $x = \frac{\pi}{3} \approx 1.047$.

(d) The graph in part (a) shows that the tangent line lies above the curve for $1 \le x \le 2$. That explains why the estimates are overestimate

5. (a) From Exercise 2.8.17(d) for $f(x) = x^2$, $f'(x) = 2x$, so $f'(1) = 2$.

(b) $L(x) = f(1) + f'(1)(x-1)$
$L(x) = 1 + 2(x-1) = 2x - 1$

The estimates using L are all underestimates of the actual function values.

x	$L(x) = 2x - 1$	$f(x) = x^2$
0.9	0.8	0.81
0.95	0.9	0.9025
0.99	0.98	0.9801
1.01	1.02	1.0201
1.05	1.1	1.1025
1.1	1.2	1.21

(c)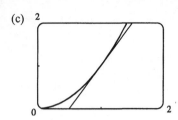

Since the tangent line lies under the graph, our underestimate claim in part (b) is supported.

6. (a) From Exercise 2.8.18(e) for $f(x) = x^3$, $f'(x) = 3x^2$, so $f'(1) = 3$.

(b) $L(x) = f(1) + f'(1)(x - 1)$
$= 1 + 3(x - 1) = 3x - 2$

x	$L(x) = 3x - 2$	$f(x) = x^3$
0.9	0.7	0.729
0.95	0.85	0.857375
0.99	0.97	0.970299
1.01	1.03	1.030301
1.05	1.15	1.157625
1.1	1.3	1.331

The estimates using L are all underestimates of the actual function values.

(c)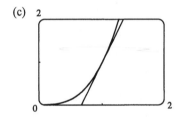

Since the tangent line lies under the graph, our underestimate claim in part (b) is supported.

7. As in Example 3, $T(0) = 185$, $T(10) = 172$, $T(20) = 160$, and

$$T'(20) \approx \frac{T(10) - T(20)}{10 - 20} = \frac{172 - 160}{-10} = -1.2 \,°\text{F/min}.$$

$T(30) \approx T(20) + T'(20)(30 - 20) \approx 160 - 1.2(10) = 148\,°\text{F}.$
We would expect the temperature of the turkey to get closer to $75\,°\text{F}$
as time increases. Since the temperature decreased $13\,°\text{F}$ in the first
10 minutes and $12\,°\text{F}$ in the second 10 minutes, we can assume that the
slopes of the tangent line are increasing through negative values:

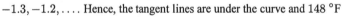

$-1.3, -1.2, \ldots$. Hence, the tangent lines are under the curve and $148\,°\text{F}$
is an underestimate. From the figure, we estimate the slope of the tangent line at $t = 20$ to be $\frac{184 - 147}{0 - 30} = -\frac{37}{30}$.
Then the linear approximation becomes $T(30) \approx T(20) + T'(20) \cdot 10 \approx 160 - \frac{37}{30}(10) = 147\frac{2}{3} \approx 147.7$.

8. $P'(2) \approx \dfrac{P(1) - P(2)}{1 - 2} = \dfrac{87.1 - 74.9}{-1} = -12.2$ kilopascals/km.

$P(3) \approx P(2) + P'(2)(3 - 2) \approx 74.9 - 12.2(1) = 62.7$ kPa.

From the figure, we estimate the slope of the tangent line at $h = 2$ to be

$\frac{98 - 63}{0 - 3} = -\frac{35}{3}$. Then the linear approximation becomes

$P(3) \approx P(2) + P'(2) \cdot 1 \approx 74.9 - \frac{35}{3} \approx 63.23$ kPa.

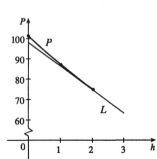

9. If $C(t)$ represents the cash per capita in circulation in year t, then we estimate $C(2000)$ using a linear approximation based on the tangent line to the graph of C at $(1990, C(1990)) = (1990, 1063)$.

$$C'(1990) \approx \frac{C(1980) - C(1990)}{1980 - 1990} = \frac{571 - 1063}{-10} = 49.2 \frac{\text{dollars}}{\text{year}}.$$

$$C(2000) \approx C(1990) + C'(1990)(2000 - 1990) \approx 1063 + 49.2(10) = 1555.$$

So our estimate of cash per capita in circulation in the year 2000 is $1555. For the given data, C' is increasing, so the tangent line approximations are below the curve, indicating that our prediction is an underestimate.

10. Let $A = \dfrac{N(1980) - N(1985)}{1980 - 1985} = \dfrac{15.0 - 17.0}{-5} = 0.4$ and $B = \dfrac{N(1990) - N(1985)}{1990 - 1985} = \dfrac{19.3 - 17.0}{5} = 0.46$.

Then $N'(1985) = \lim\limits_{t \to 1985} \dfrac{N(t) - N(1985)}{t - 1985} \approx \dfrac{A + B}{2} = 0.43$ million/year. So

$$N(1984) \approx N(1985) + N'(1985)(1984 - 1985) \approx 17.0 + 0.43(-1) = 16.57 \text{ million.}$$

$$N'(2000) \approx \frac{N(1995) - N(2000)}{1995 - 2000} = \frac{22.0 - 24.9}{-5} = 0.58 \text{ million/year.}$$

$$N(2006) \approx N(2000) + N'(2000)(2006 - 2000) \approx 24.9 + 0.58(6) = 28.38 \text{ million.}$$

11. Extend the tangent line at the point $(2030, 21)$ to the t-axis. Answers will vary based on this approximation—we'll use $t = 1900$ as our t-intercept. The linearization is then

$$P(t) \approx P(2030) + P'(2030)(t - 2030)$$

$$\approx 21 + \tfrac{21}{130}(t - 2030)$$

$$P(2040) = 21 + \tfrac{21}{130}(2040 - 2030) \approx 22.6\%$$

$$P(2050) = 21 + \tfrac{21}{130}(2050 - 2030) \approx 24.2\%$$

These predictions are probably too high since the tangent line lies above the graph at $t = 2030$.

12. (a)

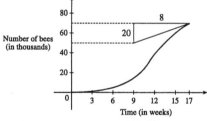

From the figure,

$$P'(17) \approx \frac{20}{8} = 2.5 \text{ thousand bees/week.}$$

$$P(18) \approx P(17) + P'(17)(18 - 17)$$

$$\approx 70 + 2.5(1) = 72.5 \text{ or } 72,500 \text{ bees.}$$

$$P(20) \approx P(17) + P'(17)(20 - 17)$$

$$\approx 70 + 2.5(3) = 77.5 \text{ or } 77,500 \text{ bees.}$$

(b) Since the tangent line at $t = 17$ is above the graph, our predictions are overestimates.

(c) $P(18)$ is more accurate than $P(20)$ since it is closer to the given data.

13. (a) The graph shows that $f'(1) = 2$, so $L(x) = f(1) + f'(1)(x - 1) = 5 + 2(x - 1) = 2x + 3$.

$f(0.9) \approx L(0.9) = 4.8$ and $f(1.1) \approx L(1.1) = 5.2$.

(b) From the graph, we see that $f'(x)$ is positive and decreasing. This means that the slopes of the tangent lines are positive, but the tangents are becoming less steep. So the tangent lines lie *above* the curve. Thus, the estimates in part (a) are too large.

14. (a) $g'(x) = \sqrt{x^2 + 5} \quad \Rightarrow \quad g'(2) = \sqrt{9} = 3$. $g(1.95) \approx g(2) + g'(2)(1.95 - 2) = -4 + 3(-0.05) = -4.15$.

$g(2.05) \approx g(2) + g'(2)(2.05 - 2) = -4 + 3(0.05) = -3.85$.

(b) The formula $g'(x) = \sqrt{x^2 + 5}$ shows that $g'(x)$ is positive and increasing. This means that the slopes of the tangent lines are positive and the tangents are getting steeper. So the tangent lines lie *below* the graph of g. Hence, the estimates in part (a) are too small.

 2.10 What Does f' Say about f? • • • • • • • • • • •

1. (a) Since $f'(x) > 0$ on $(1, 5)$, f is increasing on this interval. Since $f'(x) < 0$ on $(0, 1)$ and $(5, 6)$, f is decreasing on these intervals.

(b) Since $f'(x) = 0$ at $x = 1$ and f' changes from negative to positive there, f changes from decreasing to increasing and has a local minimum at $x = 1$. Since $f'(x) = 0$ at $x = 5$ and f' changes from positive to negative there, f changes from increasing to decreasing and has a local maximum at $x = 5$.

(c) Since $f(0) = 0$, start at the origin. Draw a decreasing function on $(0, 1)$ with a local minimum at $x = 1$. Now draw an increasing function on $(1, 5)$ and the steepest slope should occur at $x = 3$ since that's where the largest value of f' occurs. Lastly, draw a decreasing function on $(5, 6)$ making sure you have a local maximum at $x = 5$.

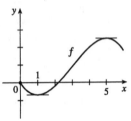

2. (a) $f'(x) > 0$ and f is increasing on $(0, 1)$ and $(3, 5)$. $f'(x) < 0$ and f is decreasing on $(1, 3)$ and $(5, 6)$.

(b) Since $f'(x) = 0$ at $x = 1$ and $x = 5$ and f' changes from positive to negative at both values, f changes from increasing to decreasing and has local maxima at $x = 1$ and $x = 5$. Since $f'(x) = 0$ at $x = 3$ and f' changes from negative to positive there, f changes from decreasing to increasing and has a local minimum at $x = 3$.

(c)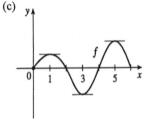

3. The derivative f' is increasing when the slopes of the tangent lines of f are becoming larger as x increases. This seems to be the case on the interval $(2, 5)$. The derivative is decreasing when the slopes of the tangent lines of f are becoming smaller as x increases, and this seems to be the case on $(-\infty, 2)$ and $(5, \infty)$. So f' is increasing on $(2, 5)$ and decreasing on $(-\infty, 2)$ and $(5, \infty)$.

4. (a)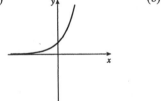

(b)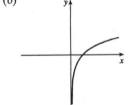

(c) In part (a), the graph of $y = e^x$ is a curve whose slope is always positive and increasing. In part (b), the graph of $y = \ln x$ is a curve whose slope is always positive and decreasing.

5. If $D(t)$ is the size of the deficit as a function of time, then at the time of the speech $D'(t) > 0$, but $D''(t) < 0$ because $D''(t) = (D')'(t)$ is the rate of change of $D'(t)$.

6. (a) The rate of increase of the population is initially very small, then gets larger until it reaches a maximum at about $t = 8$ hours, and decreases toward 0 as the population begins to level off.

(b) The rate of increase has its maximum value at $t = 8$ hours.

(c) The population function is concave upward on $(0, 8)$ and concave downward on $(8, 18)$.

(d) At $t = 8$, the population is about 350, so the inflection point is about $(8, 350)$.

7. (a) The rate of increase of the population is initially very small, then increases rapidly until about 1932 when it starts decreasing. The rate becomes negative by 1936, peaks in magnitude in 1937, and approaches 0 in 1940.

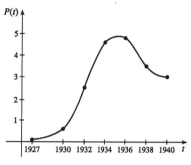

(b) Inflection points (IP) appear to be at $(1932, 2.5)$ and $(1937, 4.3)$. The rate of change of population density starts to decrease in 1932 and starts to increase in 1937. The rates of population increase and decrease have their maximum values at those points.

8. (a) If the position function is increasing, then the particle is moving toward the right. This occurs on t-intervals $(0, 2)$ and $(4, 6)$. If the function is decreasing, then the particle is moving toward the left—that is, on $(2, 4)$.

(b) The acceleration is the second derivative and is positive where the curve is concave upward. This occurs on $(3, 6)$. The acceleration is negative where the curve is concave downward—that is, on $(0, 3)$.

9. Most students learn more in the third hour of studying than in the eighth hour, so $K(3) - K(2)$ is larger than $K(8) - K(7)$. In other words, as you begin studying for a test, the rate of knowledge gain is large and then starts to taper off, so $K'(t)$ decreases and the graph of K is concave downward.

10. At first the depth increases slowly because the base of the mug is wide. But as the mug narrows, the coffee rises more quickly. Thus, the depth d increases at an increasing rate and its graph is concave upward. The rate of increase of d has a maximum where the mug is narrowest; that is, when the mug is half full. It is there that the inflection point (IP) occurs. Then the rate of increase of d starts to decrease as the mug widens and the graph becomes concave down.

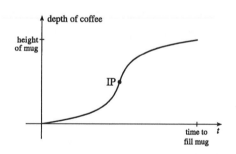

11. (a) f is increasing where f' is positive, that is, on $(0, 2)$, $(4, 6)$, and $(8, \infty)$; and decreasing where f' is negative, that is, on $(2, 4)$ and $(6, 8)$.

(b) f has local maxima where f' changes from positive to negative, at $x = 2$ and at $x = 6$, and local minima where f' changes from negative to positive, at $x = 4$ and at $x = 8$.

(c) f is concave upward (CU) where f' is increasing, that is, on $(3, 6)$ and $(6, \infty)$, and concave downward (CD) where f' is decreasing, that is, on $(0, 3)$.

(e)

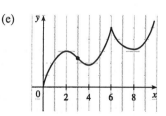

(d) There is a point of inflection where f changes from being CD to being CU, that is, at $x = 3$.

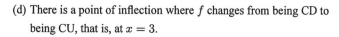

12. (a) f is increasing where f' is positive, on $(1, 6)$ and $(8, \infty)$, and decreasing where f' is negative, on $(0, 1)$ and $(6, 8)$.

(b) f has a local maximum where f' changes from positive to negative, at $x = 6$, and local minima where f' changes from negative to positive, at $x = 1$ and at $x = 8$.

(c) f is concave upward where f' is increasing, that is, on $(0, 2)$, $(3, 5)$, and $(7, \infty)$, and concave downward where f' is decreasing, that is, on $(2, 3)$ and $(5, 7)$.

(e)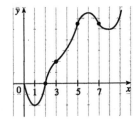

(d) There are points of inflection where f changes its direction of concavity, at $x = 2$, $x = 3$, $x = 5$ and $x = 7$.

13. The function must be always decreasing and concave downward.

14. The function must be always decreasing and concave upward.

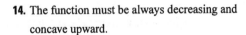

15. Since $f'(x) > 0$ if $x < 2$ and if $x > 2$, f is increasing on $(-\infty, 2)$ and $(2, \infty)$. The graph of f must level off and have a horizontal tangent at $x = 2$ because $f'(2) = 0$.

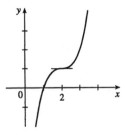

16. $f''(x) < 0$ on $(-\infty, 2)$ and $(2, \infty)$, so the graph of f is CD on these intervals. Since f is not differentiable at 2, f could be discontinuous at 2 or have a cusp or corner at 2.

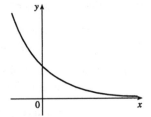

17. $f(-1) = 4$ and $f(1) = 0$ gives us two points to start with. $f'(-1) = f'(1) = 0 \Rightarrow$ horizontal tangents at $x = \pm 1$. $f'(x) < 0$ if $|x| < 1 \Rightarrow f$ is decreasing on $(-1, 1)$. $f'(x) > 0$ if $|x| > 1 \Rightarrow f$ is increasing on $(-\infty, -1)$ and $(1, \infty)$. $f''(x) < 0$ if $x < 0 \Rightarrow f$ is concave downward on $(-\infty, 0)$. $f''(x) > 0$ if $x > 0 \Rightarrow f$ is concave upward on $(0, \infty)$ and there is an inflection point at $x = 0$.

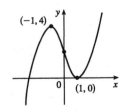

18. Since $f'(-1) = 0$ and $f'(1)$ does not exist, we have a horizontal tangent at

$x = -1$ and a vertical tangent at $x = 1$. $f'(x) < 0$ if $|x| < 1$ ⇒ f is

decreasing on $(-1, 1)$, and $f'(x) > 0$ if $|x| > 1$ ⇒ f is increasing on

$(-\infty, -1)$ and $(1, \infty)$. $f''(x) < 0$ if $x \neq 1$ ⇒ f is concave downward on

$(-\infty, 1)$ and $(1, \infty)$.

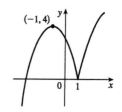

19. First we plot the points which are known to be on the graph: $(2, -1)$ and

$(0, 0)$. We can also draw a short line segment of slope 0 at $x = 2$, since

we are given that $f'(2) = 0$. Now we know that $f'(x) < 0$ (that is, the

function is decreasing) on $(0, 2)$, and that $f''(x) < 0$ on $(0, 1)$ and

$f''(x) > 0$ on $(1, 2)$. So we must join the points $(0, 0)$ and $(2, -1)$ in

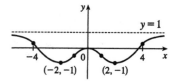

such a way that the curve is concave down on $(0, 1)$ and concave up on $(1, 2)$. The curve must be concave up and

increasing on $(2, 4)$ and concave down and increasing toward $y = 1$ on $(4, \infty)$. Now we just need to reflect the

curve in the y-axis, since we are given that f is an even function [the condition that $f(-x) = f(x)$ for all x].

20. $\lim\limits_{x \to 3} f(x) = -\infty$ ⇒ there is a vertical asymptote at $x = 3$. $f'(0) = 0$

means that there is a horizontal tangent at $x = 0$. $f'(x) > 0$ if $x < 0$ or

$x > 3$ and $f'(x) < 0$ if $0 < x < 3$ indicates that there is a local

maximum at $x = 0$, since f is increasing on $(-\infty, 0)$ and decreasing on

$(0, 3)$, and then increasing on $(3, \infty)$. $f''(x) < 0$ if $x \neq 3$ ⇒ f is

concave downward on $(-\infty, 3)$ and $(3, \infty)$.

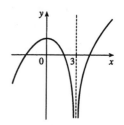

21. (a) Since e^{-x^2} is positive for all x, $f'(x) = xe^{-x^2}$ is positive where $x > 0$ and negative where $x < 0$. Thus, f is

increasing on $(0, \infty)$ and decreasing on $(-\infty, 0)$.

(b) Since f changes from decreasing to increasing at $x = 0$, f has a minimum value there.

22. Since $f'(x) = e^{-x^2} > 0$ on $\mathbb{R}$, f is increasing on $\mathbb{R}$.

23. (a) To find the intervals on which f is increasing, we need to find the intervals on which $f'(x) = 3x^2 - 1$ is

positive. $3x^2 - 1 > 0$ ⇔ $3x^2 > 1$ ⇔ $x^2 > \frac{1}{3}$ ⇔ $|x| > \sqrt{\frac{1}{3}}$, so

$x \in \left(-\infty, -\sqrt{\frac{1}{3}}\right) \cup \left(\sqrt{\frac{1}{3}}, \infty\right)$. Thus, f is increasing on $\left(-\infty, -\sqrt{\frac{1}{3}}\right)$ and on $\left(\sqrt{\frac{1}{3}}, \infty\right)$. In a similar

fashion, f is decreasing on $\left(-\sqrt{\frac{1}{3}}, \sqrt{\frac{1}{3}}\right)$.

(b) To find the intervals on which f is concave upward, we need to find the intervals on which $f''(x) = 6x$ is

positive. $6x > 0$ ⇔ $x > 0$. So f is concave upward on $(0, \infty)$ and f is concave downward on $(-\infty, 0)$.

(c) There is an inflection point at $(0, 0)$ since f changes its direction of concavity at $x = 0$.

24. (a) $f'(x) = \lim\limits_{h \to 0} \dfrac{f(x+h) - f(x)}{h} = \lim\limits_{h \to 0} \dfrac{[(x+h)^4 - 2(x+h)^2] - (x^4 - 2x^2)}{h}$

$\qquad = \lim\limits_{h \to 0} \dfrac{(x^4 + 4x^3h + 6x^2h^2 + 4xh^3 + h^4 - 2x^2 - 4xh - 2h^2) - (x^4 - 2x^2)}{h}$

$\qquad = \lim\limits_{h \to 0} \dfrac{4x^3h + 6x^2h^2 + 4xh^3 + h^4 - 4xh - 2h^2}{h}$

$\qquad = \lim\limits_{h \to 0} \left(4x^3 + 6x^2h + 4xh^2 + h^3 - 4x - 2h\right) = 4x^3 - 4x$

$f''(x) = \lim\limits_{h \to 0} \dfrac{f'(x+h) - f'(x)}{h} = \lim\limits_{h \to 0} \dfrac{[4(x+h)^3 - 4(x+h)] - (4x^3 - 4x)}{h}$

$\qquad = \lim\limits_{h \to 0} \dfrac{(4x^3 + 12x^2h + 12xh^2 + 4h^3 - 4x - 4h) - (4x^3 - 4x)}{h}$

$\qquad = \lim\limits_{h \to 0} \dfrac{12x^2h + 12xh^2 + 4h^3 - 4h}{h}$

$\qquad = \lim\limits_{h \to 0} \left(12x^2 + 12xh + 4h^2 - 4\right) = 12x^2 - 4$

(b) $f'(x) > 0 \iff 4x^3 - 4x > 0 \iff 4x(x^2 - 1) > 0 \iff 4x(x+1)(x-1) > 0$, so f is increasing on $(-1, 0)$ and $(1, \infty)$ and f is decreasing on $(-\infty, -1)$ and $(0, 1)$.

(c) $f''(x) > 0 \iff 12x^2 - 4 > 0 \iff 12x^2 > 4 \iff x^2 > \frac{1}{3} \iff |x| > \sqrt{\frac{1}{3}}$, so f is CU on $\left(-\infty, -\sqrt{\frac{1}{3}}\right)$ and $\left(\sqrt{\frac{1}{3}}, \infty\right)$ and f is CD on $\left(-\sqrt{\frac{1}{3}}, \sqrt{\frac{1}{3}}\right)$.

25. b is the antiderivative of f. For small x, f is negative, so the graph of its antiderivative must be decreasing. But both a and c are increasing for small x, so only b can be f's antiderivative. Also, f is positive where b is increasing, which supports our conclusion.

26. We know right away that c cannot be f's antiderivative, since the slope of c is not zero at the x-value where $f = 0$. Now f is positive when a is increasing and negative when a is decreasing, so a is the antiderivative of f.

27. The graph of F will have a minimum at 0 and a maximum at 2, since $f = F'$ goes from negative to positive at $x = 0$, and from positive to negative at $x = 2$.

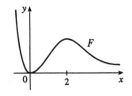

28. The position function is the antiderivative of the velocity function, so its graph will have be horizontal where the velocity function is equal to 0.

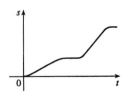

29.

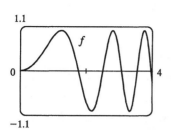

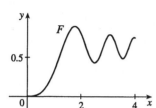

30.

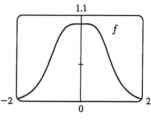

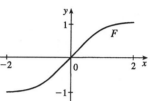

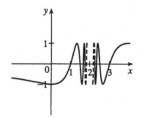

2 Review

━━━━━━━━━━━━━━━━━━ • **CONCEPT CHECK** • ━━━━━━━━━━━━━━━━━━

1. (a) $\lim_{x \to a} f(x) = L$: See Definition 2.2.1 and Figures 1 and 2 in Section 2.2.

(b) $\lim_{x \to a^+} f(x) = L$: See the paragraph after Definition 2.2.2 and Figure 9(b) in Section 2.2.

(c) $\lim_{x \to a^-} f(x) = L$: See Definition 2.2.2 and Figure 9(a) in Section 2.2.

(d) $\lim_{x \to a} f(x) = \infty$: See Definition 2.5.1 and Figure 2 in Section 2.5.

(e) $\lim_{x \to \infty} f(x) = L$: See Definition 2.5.4 and Figure 9 in Section 2.5.

2. In general, the limit of a function fails to exist when the function does not approach a fixed number. For each of the following functions, the limit fails to exist at $x = 2$.

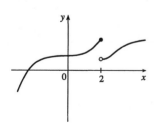

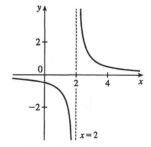

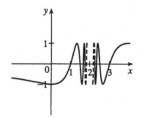

The left- and right-hand limits are not equal.

There is an infinite discontinuity.

There are an infinite number of oscillations.

3. (a)–(g) See the statements of Limit Laws 1–6 and 11 in Section 2.3.

4. See Theorem 3 in Section 2.3.

5. (a) See Definition 2.5.2 and Figures 2–4 in Section 2.5.

(b) See Definition 2.5.5 and Figures 9 and 10 in Section 2.5.

6. (a) $y = x^4$: No asymptote

(b) $y = \sin x$: No asymptote

(c) $y = \tan x$: Vertical asymptotes $x = \frac{\pi}{2} + \pi n$, n an integer

(d) $y = \tan^{-1} x$: Horizontal asymptotes $y = \pm\frac{\pi}{2}$

(e) $y = e^x$: Horizontal asymptote $y = 0$
($\lim_{x \to -\infty} e^x = 0$)

(f) $y = \ln x$: Vertical asymptote $x = 0$
($\lim_{x \to 0+} \ln x = -\infty$)

(g) $y = 1/x$: Vertical asymptote $x = 0$, horizontal asymptote $y = 0$

(h) $y = \sqrt{x}$: No asymptote

7. (a) A function f is continuous at a number a if $f(x)$ gets closer to $f(a)$ as x gets close to a; that is,
$$\lim_{x \to a} f(x) = f(a).$$

(b) A function f is continuous on the interval $(-\infty, \infty)$ if f is continuous at every real number a. The graph of such a function has no breaks and every vertical line crosses it.

8. See Theorem 2.4.10.

9. See Definition 2.6.1.

10. See the paragraph containing Formula 3 in Section 2.6.

11. (a) The average rate of change of y with respect to x over the interval $[x_1, x_2]$ is $\dfrac{f(x_2) - f(x_1)}{x_2 - x_1}$.

(b) The instantaneous rate of change of y with respect to x at $x = x_1$ is $\displaystyle\lim_{x_2 \to x_1} \dfrac{f(x_2) - f(x_1)}{x_2 - x_1}$.

12. See Definition 2.7.2. The pages following the definition discuss interpretations of $f'(a)$ as the slope of a tangent line to the graph of f at $x = a$ and as an instantaneous rate of change of $f(x)$ with respect to x when $x = a$.

13. See the paragraphs before and after Example 7 in Section 2.8.

14. (a) A function f is differentiable at a number a if its derivative f' exists at $x = a$; that is, if $f'(a)$ exists.

(b) See Theorem 2.8.4. This theorem also tells us that if f is *not* continuous at a, then f is *not* differentiable at a.

15. (a) See the first box in Section 2.10.

(b) See the second box in Section 2.10.

16. (a) When x is near a, the linear approximation to f at a is the approximation $f(x) \approx f(a) + f'(a)(x - a)$.

(b) An antiderivative of a function f is a function F such that $F' = f$.

▲ TRUE–FALSE QUIZ ▲

1. False.   Limit Law 2 applies only if the individual limits exist (these don't).

2. False.   Limit Law 5 cannot be applied if the limit of the denominator is 0 (it is).

3. True.   Limit Law 5 applies.

4. True.   The limit doesn't exist since $f(x)/g(x)$ doesn't approach any real number as x approaches 5.
(The denominator approaches 0 and the numerator doesn't.)

5. False. Consider $\lim\limits_{x\to 5} \dfrac{x^2 - 5x}{x - 5}$ or $\lim\limits_{x\to 5} \dfrac{\sin{(x-5)}}{x-5}$. The first limit exists and is equal to 5. By Example 3 in Section 2.2, we know that the latter limit exists (and it is equal to 1).

6. False. Consider $\lim\limits_{x\to 6} [f(x)g(x)] = \lim\limits_{x\to 6}\left[(x-6)\dfrac{1}{x-6}\right]$. It exists (its value is 1) but $f(6) = 0$ and $g(6)$ does not exist, so $f(6)g(6) \neq 1$.

7. True. A polynomial is continuous everywhere, so $\lim\limits_{x\to b} p(x)$ exists and is equal to $p(b)$.

8. False. Consider $\lim\limits_{x\to 0} [f(x) - g(x)] = \lim\limits_{x\to 0}\left(\dfrac{1}{x^2} - \dfrac{1}{x^4}\right)$. This limit is $-\infty$ (not 0), but each of the individual functions approaches ∞.

9. True. See Figure 11 in Section 2.5.

10. False. Consider $f(x) = \sin x$ for $x \geq 0$. $\lim\limits_{x\to\infty} f(x) \neq \pm\infty$ and f has no horizontal asymptote.

11. False. Consider $f(x) = \begin{cases} 1/(x-1) & \text{if } x \neq 1 \\ 2 & \text{if } x = 1 \end{cases}$

12. False. The function f must be *continuous* in order to use the Intermediate Value Theorem. For example, let
$$f(x) = \begin{cases} 1 & \text{if } 0 \leq x < 3 \\ -1 & \text{if } x = 3 \end{cases}$$
There is no number $c \in [0, 3]$ with $f(c) = 0$.

13. True. Use Theorem 2.4.8 with $a = 2$, $b = 5$, and $g(x) = 4x^2 - 11$. Note that $f(4) = 3$ is not needed.

14. True. Use the Intermediate Value Theorem with $a = -1$, $b = 1$, and $N = \pi$, since $3 < \pi < 4$.

15. False. See the note after Theorem 4 in Section 2.8.

16. True. $f'(r)$ exists $\Rightarrow$ f is differentiable at r $\Rightarrow$ f is continuous at r $\Rightarrow$ $\lim\limits_{x\to r} f(x) = f(r)$.

17. False. $\dfrac{d^2y}{dx^2}$ is the second derivative while $\left(\dfrac{dy}{dx}\right)^2$ is the first derivative squared. For example, if $y = x$, then $\dfrac{d^2y}{dx^2} = 0$, but $\left(\dfrac{dy}{dx}\right)^2 = 1$.

18. False. For example, let $f(x) = \begin{cases} x^2 + 1 & \text{if } x \neq 0 \\ 2 & \text{if } x = 0 \end{cases}$
Then $f(x) > 1$ for all x, but $\lim\limits_{x\to 0} f(x) = \lim\limits_{x\to 0} (x^2 + 1) = 1$.

◆ **EXERCISES** ◆

1. (a) (i) $\lim\limits_{x\to 2^+} f(x) = 3$

(ii) $\lim\limits_{x\to -3^+} f(x) = 0$

(iii) $\lim\limits_{x\to -3} f(x)$ does not exist since the left and right limits are not equal. (The left limit is -2.)

(iv) $\lim\limits_{x\to 4} f(x) = 2$

(v) $\lim\limits_{x\to 0} f(x) = \infty$

(vi) $\lim\limits_{x\to 2^-} f(x) = -\infty$

(vii) $\lim\limits_{x\to\infty} f(x) = 4$

(viii) $\lim\limits_{x\to -\infty} f(x) = -1$

(b) The horizontal asymptotes are $y = 4$ and $y = -1$.

(c) The vertical asymptotes are $x = 0$ and $x = 2$.

(d) f is discontinuous at $x = -3, 0, 2$, and 4. The discontinuities are jump, infinite, infinite, and removable, respectively.

2.

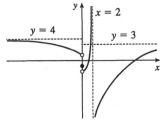

3. Since the exponential function is continuous,

$$\lim_{x \to 1} e^{x^3 - x} = e^{1-1} = e^0 = 1.$$

4. Since rational functions are continuous, $\displaystyle\lim_{x \to 3} \frac{x^2 - 9}{x^2 + 2x - 3} = \frac{3^2 - 9}{3^2 + 2(3) - 3} = \frac{0}{12} = 0.$

5. $\displaystyle\lim_{x \to -3} \frac{x^2 - 9}{x^2 + 2x - 3} = \lim_{x \to -3} \frac{(x+3)(x-3)}{(x+3)(x-1)} = \lim_{x \to -3} \frac{x-3}{x-1} = \frac{-3-3}{-3-1} = \frac{-6}{-4} = \frac{3}{2}$

6. $\displaystyle\lim_{x \to 1^+} \frac{x^2 - 9}{x^2 + 2x - 3} = -\infty$ since $x^2 + 2x - 3 \to 0$ as $x \to 1^+$ and $\dfrac{x^2 - 9}{x^2 + 2x - 3} < 0$ for $1 < x < 3$.

7. $\displaystyle\lim_{h \to 0} \frac{(h-1)^3 + 1}{h} = \lim_{h \to 0} \frac{(h^3 - 3h^2 + 3h - 1) + 1}{h} = \lim_{h \to 0} \frac{h^3 - 3h^2 + 3h}{h} = \lim_{h \to 0} (h^2 - 3h + 3) = 3$

Another solution: Factor the numerator as a sum of two cubes and then simplify.

$$\lim_{h \to 0} \frac{(h-1)^3 + 1}{h} = \lim_{h \to 0} \frac{(h-1)^3 + 1^3}{h} = \lim_{h \to 0} \frac{[(h-1) + 1]\left[(h-1)^2 - 1(h-1) + 1^2\right]}{h}$$
$$= \lim_{h \to 0} \left[(h-1)^2 - h + 2\right] = 1 - 0 + 2 = 3$$

8. $\displaystyle\lim_{t \to 2} \frac{t^2 - 4}{t^3 - 8} = \lim_{t \to 2} \frac{(t+2)(t-2)}{(t-2)(t^2 + 2t + 4)} = \lim_{t \to 2} \frac{t+2}{t^2 + 2t + 4} = \frac{2+2}{4+4+4} = \frac{4}{12} = \frac{1}{3}$

9. $\displaystyle\lim_{r \to 9} \frac{\sqrt{r}}{(r-9)^4} = \infty$ since $(r-9)^4 \to 0$ as $r \to 9$ and $\dfrac{\sqrt{r}}{(r-9)^4} > 0$ for $r \neq 9$.

10. $\displaystyle\lim_{v \to 4^+} \frac{4-v}{|4-v|} = \lim_{v \to 4^+} \frac{4-v}{-(4-v)} = \lim_{v \to 4^+} \frac{1}{-1} = -1$

11. $\displaystyle\lim_{x \to \infty} e^{-3x} = 0$ since $-3x \to -\infty$ as $x \to \infty$ and $\displaystyle\lim_{t \to -\infty} e^t = 0.$

12. $\displaystyle\lim_{x \to 10^-} \ln(100 - x^2) = -\infty$ since as $x \to 10^-$, $(100 - x^2) \to 0^+$.

13. $\displaystyle\lim_{x \to 0} \frac{1 - \sqrt{1 - x^2}}{x} \cdot \frac{1 + \sqrt{1 - x^2}}{1 + \sqrt{1 - x^2}} = \lim_{x \to 0} \frac{1 - (1 - x^2)}{x(1 + \sqrt{1 - x^2})} = \lim_{x \to 0} \frac{x^2}{x(1 + \sqrt{1 - x^2})} = \lim_{x \to 0} \frac{x}{1 + \sqrt{1 - x^2}} = 0$

14. $\displaystyle\lim_{x \to -\infty} \frac{5x^3 - x^2 + 2}{2x^3 + x - 3} = \lim_{x \to -\infty} \frac{(5x^3 - x^2 + 2)/x^3}{(2x^3 + x - 3)/x^3} = \lim_{x \to -\infty} \frac{5 - 1/x + 2/x^3}{2 + 1/x^2 - 3/x^3} = \frac{5 - 0 + 0}{2 + 0 - 0} = \frac{5}{2}$

15. $\displaystyle\lim_{x \to \infty} \frac{\sqrt{3x^2 - 1}}{x - 1} = \lim_{x \to \infty} \frac{\sqrt{3x^2 - 1}/\sqrt{x^2}}{(x-1)/x} = \lim_{x \to \infty} \frac{\sqrt{3 - 1/x^2}}{1 - 1/x} = \frac{\sqrt{3}}{1} = \sqrt{3}$

16. If $y = x^3 - x = x(x^2 - 1)$, then as $x \to \infty$, $y \to \infty$. $\displaystyle\lim_{x \to \infty} \arctan(x^3 - x) = \lim_{y \to \infty} \arctan y = \frac{\pi}{2}$ by (2.5.6).

17. From the graph of $y = (\cos^2 x)/x^2$, it appears that $y = 0$ is the horizontal

asymptote and $x = 0$ is the vertical asymptote. Now $0 \le (\cos x)^2 \le 1$

$$\Rightarrow \quad \frac{0}{x^2} \le \frac{\cos^2 x}{x^2} \le \frac{1}{x^2} \quad \Rightarrow \quad 0 \le \frac{\cos^2 x}{x^2} \le \frac{1}{x^2}. \text{ But } \lim_{x \to \pm\infty} 0 = 0 \text{ and}$$

$$\lim_{x \to \pm\infty} \frac{1}{x^2} = 0, \text{ so by the Squeeze Theorem,}$$

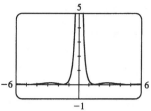

$$\lim_{x \to \pm\infty} \frac{\cos^2 x}{x^2} = 0. \text{ Thus, } y = 0 \text{ is the horizontal asymptote. } \lim_{x \to 0} \frac{\cos^2 x}{x^2} = \infty \text{ because } \cos^2 x \to 1 \text{ and } x^2 \to 0 \text{ as}$$

$x \to 0$, so $x = 0$ is the vertical asymptote.

18. From the graph of $y = f(x) = \sqrt{x^2 + x + 1} - \sqrt{x^2 - x}$, it appears that there are 2 horizontal asymptotes and

possibly 2 vertical asymptotes. To obtain a different form for f, let's multiply and divide it by its conjugate.

$$f_1(x) = \left(\sqrt{x^2 + x + 1} - \sqrt{x^2 - x} \right) \frac{\sqrt{x^2 + x + 1} + \sqrt{x^2 - x}}{\sqrt{x^2 + x + 1} + \sqrt{x^2 - x}}$$

$$= \frac{(x^2 + x + 1) - (x^2 - x)}{\sqrt{x^2 + x + 1} + \sqrt{x^2 - x}} = \frac{2x + 1}{\sqrt{x^2 + x + 1} + \sqrt{x^2 - x}}$$

Now

$$\lim_{x \to \infty} f_1(x) = \lim_{x \to \infty} \frac{2x + 1}{\sqrt{x^2 + x + 1} + \sqrt{x^2 - x}}$$

$$= \lim_{x \to \infty} \frac{2 + (1/x)}{\sqrt{1 + (1/x) + (1/x^2)} + \sqrt{1 - (1/x)}} \qquad (\text{since } \sqrt{x^2} = x \text{ for } x > 0)$$

$$= \frac{2}{1 + 1} = 1,$$

so $y = 1$ is a horizontal asymptote. For $x < 0$, we have $\sqrt{x^2} = |x| = -x$, so when we divide the denominator by

x, with $x < 0$, we get

$$\frac{\sqrt{x^2 + x + 1} + \sqrt{x^2 - x}}{x} = -\frac{\sqrt{x^2 + x + 1} + \sqrt{x^2 - x}}{\sqrt{x^2}} = -\left[\sqrt{1 + \frac{1}{x} + \frac{1}{x^2}} + \sqrt{1 - \frac{1}{x}} \right]$$

Therefore,

$$\lim_{x \to -\infty} f_1(x) = \lim_{x \to -\infty} \frac{2x + 1}{\sqrt{x^2 + x + 1} + \sqrt{x^2 - x}}$$

$$= \lim_{x \to \infty} \frac{2 + (1/x)}{-\left[\sqrt{1 + (1/x) + (1/x^2)} + \sqrt{1 - (1/x)} \right]} = \frac{2}{-(1 + 1)} = -1,$$

so $y = -1$ is a horizontal asymptote. As $x \to 0^-$, $f(x) \to 1$, so $x = 0$ is *not* a vertical asymptote. As $x \to 1^+$,

$f(x) \to \sqrt{3}$, so $x = 1$ is *not* a vertical asymptote and hence there are no vertical asymptotes.

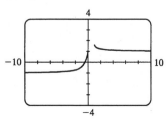

19. Since $2x - 1 \le f(x) \le x^2$ for $0 < x < 3$ and $\lim\limits_{x \to 1} (2x - 1) = 1 = \lim\limits_{x \to 1} x^2$, we have $\lim\limits_{x \to 1} f(x) = 1$ by the Squeeze Theorem.

20. Let $f(x) = -x^2$, $g(x) = x^2 \cos(1/x^2)$ and $h(x) = x^2$. Then since $\left|\cos(1/x^2)\right| \le 1$ for $x \ne 0$, we have $f(x) \le g(x) \le h(x)$ for $x \ne 0$, and so $\lim\limits_{x \to 0} f(x) = \lim\limits_{x \to 0} h(x) = 0 \Rightarrow \lim\limits_{x \to 0} g(x) = 0$ by the Squeeze Theorem.

21. (a) $f(x) = \sqrt{-x}$ if $x < 0$, $f(x) = 3 - x$ if $0 \le x < 3$, $f(x) = (x-3)^2$ if $x > 3$.

(i) $\lim\limits_{x \to 0^+} f(x) = \lim\limits_{x \to 0^+} (3 - x) = 3$

(ii) $\lim\limits_{x \to 0^-} f(x) = \lim\limits_{x \to 0^-} \sqrt{-x} = 0$

(iii) Because of (i) and (ii), $\lim\limits_{x \to 0} f(x)$ does not exist.

(iv) $\lim\limits_{x \to 3^-} f(x) = \lim\limits_{x \to 3^-} (3 - x) = 0$

(v) $\lim\limits_{x \to 3^+} f(x) = \lim\limits_{x \to 3^+} (x - 3)^2 = 0$

(vi) Because of (iv) and (v), $\lim\limits_{x \to 3} f(x) = 0$.

(b) f is discontinuous at 0 since $\lim\limits_{x \to 0} f(x)$ does not exist.

f is discontinuous at 3 since $f(3)$ does not exist.

(c)

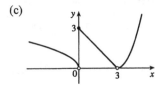

22. (a) $x^2 - 9$ is continuous on $\mathbb{R}$ since it is a polynomial and $\sqrt{x}$ is continuous on $[0, \infty)$, so the composition $\sqrt{x^2 - 9}$ is continuous on $\left\{x \mid x^2 - 9 \ge 0\right\} = (-\infty, -3] \cup [3, \infty)$. Note that $x^2 - 2 \ne 0$ on this set and so the quotient function $g(x) = \dfrac{\sqrt{x^2 - 9}}{x^2 - 2}$ is continuous on its domain, $(-\infty, -3] \cup [3, \infty)$.

(b) $\sin x$ is continuous on $\mathbb{R}$ by Theorem 7 in Section 2.4. Since e^x is continuous on $\mathbb{R}$, $e^{\sin x}$ is continuous on $\mathbb{R}$ by Theorem 9 in Section 2.4. Lastly, x is continuous on $\mathbb{R}$ since it's a polynomial and the product $xe^{\sin x}$ is continuous on its domain $\mathbb{R}$ by Theorem 4 in Section 2.4.

23. $f(x) = 2x^3 + x^2 + 2$ is a polynomial, so it is continuous on $[-2, -1]$ and $f(-2) = -10 < 0 < 1 = f(-1)$. So by the Intermediate Value Theorem there is a number c in $(-2, -1)$ such that $f(c) = 0$, that is, the equation $2x^3 + x^2 + 2 = 0$ has a root in $(-2, -1)$.

24. $f(x) = e^{-x^2} - x$ is continuous on $\mathbb{R}$ so it is continuous on $[0, 1]$. $f(0) = 1 > 0 > 1/e - 1 = f(1)$. So by the Intermediate Value Theorem, there is a number c in $(0, 1)$ such that $f(c) = 0$. Thus, $e^{-x^2} - x = 0$, or $e^{-x^2} = x$, has a root in $(0, 1)$.

25. (a) $s = 1 + 2t + t^2/4$. The average velocity over the time interval $[1, 1 + h]$ is

$$\frac{s(1 + h) - s(1)}{h} = \frac{1 + 2(1 + h) + (1 + h)^2/4 - 13/4}{h} = \frac{10h + h^2}{4h} = \frac{10 + h}{4}. \text{ So for the following}$$

intervals the average velocities are:

(i) $[1, 3]$: $(10 + 2)/4 = 3$ m/s

(ii) $[1, 2]$: $(10 + 1)/4 = 2.75$ m/s

(iii) $[1, 1.5]$: $(10 + 0.5)/4 = 2.625$ m/s

(iv) $[1, 1.1]$: $(10 + 0.1)/4 = 2.525$ m/s

(b) When $t = 1$ the velocity is $\lim\limits_{h \to 0} \dfrac{s(1 + h) - s(1)}{h} = \lim\limits_{h \to 0} \dfrac{10 + h}{4} = 2.5$ m/s.

26. (a) When V increases from 200 in^3 to 250 in^3, we have $\Delta V = 250 - 200 = 50$ in^3, and since $P = 800/V$,

$$\Delta P = P(250) - P(200) = \frac{800}{250} - \frac{800}{200} = 3.2 - 4 = -0.8 \text{ lb/in}^2. \text{ So the average rate of change is}$$

$$\frac{\Delta P}{\Delta V} = \frac{-0.8}{50} = -0.016 \ \frac{\text{lb/in}^2}{\text{in}^3}.$$

(b) Since $V = 800/P$, the instantaneous rate of change of V with respect to P is

$$\lim_{h \to 0} \frac{\Delta V}{\Delta P} = \lim_{h \to 0} \frac{V(P + h) - V(P)}{h} = \lim_{h \to 0} \frac{800/(P + h) - 800/P}{h}$$

$$= \lim_{h \to 0} \frac{800 \left[P - (P + h) \right]}{h(P + h)P} = \lim_{h \to 0} \frac{-800}{(P + h)P} = -\frac{800}{P^2}$$

which is inversely proportional to the square of P.

27. Estimating the slopes of the tangent lines at $x = 2$, 3, and 5, we obtain approximate values 0.4, 2, and 0.1. Since the graph is concave downward at $x = 5$, $f''(5)$ is negative. Arranging the numbers in increasing order, we have: $f''(5) < 0 < f'(5) < f'(2) < 1 < f'(3)$.

28. (a) $f'(2) = \lim\limits_{x \to 2} \dfrac{f(x) - f(2)}{x - 2} = \lim\limits_{x \to 2} \dfrac{x^3 - 2x - 4}{x - 2}$

$\qquad = \lim\limits_{x \to 2} \dfrac{(x - 2)(x^2 + 2x + 2)}{x - 2} = \lim\limits_{x \to 2} (x^2 + 2x + 2) = 10$

(c)

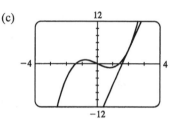

(b) $y - 4 = 10(x - 2)$ or $y = 10x - 16$

29. (a) Estimating $f'(1)$ from the triangle in the graph,

we get $\dfrac{\Delta y}{\Delta x} \approx \dfrac{-0.37}{0.50} = -0.74$.

To estimate $f'(1)$ numerically, we have

$$f'(1) = \lim_{h \to 0} \frac{f(1 + h) - f(1)}{h}$$

$$= \lim_{h \to 0} \frac{e^{-(1+h)^2} - e^{-1}}{h} = y$$

From the table, we have $f'(1) \approx -0.736$.

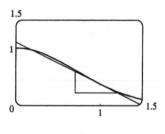

h	y
0.01	−0.732
0.001	−0.735
0.0001	−0.736
−0.01	−0.739
−0.001	−0.736
−0.0001	−0.736

(b) $y - e^{-1} \approx -0.736(x - 1)$ or $y \approx -0.736x + 1.104$

(c) See the graph in part (a).

30. $2^6 = 64$, so $f(x) = x^6$ and $a = 2$.

31. (a) $f'(r)$ is the rate at which the total cost changes with respect to the interest rate. Its units are dollars/(percent per year).

(b) The total cost of paying off the loan is increasing by 1200/(percent per year) as the interest rate reaches 10%. So if the interest rate goes up from 10% to 11%, the cost goes up approximately 1200.

(c) As r increases, C increases. So $f'(r)$ will always be positive.

For Exercises 32–34, see the hints before Exercise 4 in Section 2.8.

32.

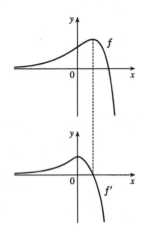

33.

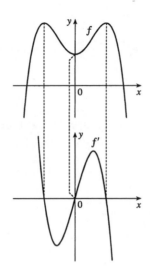

34.

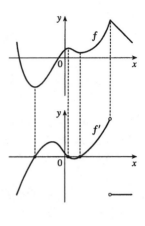

35. (a) $f'(x) = \lim\limits_{h \to 0} \dfrac{f(x+h) - f(x)}{h} = \lim\limits_{h \to 0} \dfrac{\sqrt{3 - 5(x+h)} - \sqrt{3 - 5x}}{h} \cdot \dfrac{\sqrt{3 - 5(x+h)} + \sqrt{3 - 5x}}{\sqrt{3 - 5(x+h)} + \sqrt{3 - 5x}}$

$\quad = \lim\limits_{h \to 0} \dfrac{[3 - 5(x+h)] - (3 - 5x)}{h\left(\sqrt{3 - 5(x+h)} + \sqrt{3 - 5x}\right)} = \lim\limits_{h \to 0} \dfrac{-5}{\sqrt{3 - 5(x+h)} + \sqrt{3 - 5x}} = \dfrac{-5}{2\sqrt{3 - 5x}}$

(b) Domain of f: (the radicand must be nonnegative) $3 - 5x \geq 0 \;\Rightarrow\; 5x \leq 3 \;\Rightarrow\; x \in \left(-\infty, \frac{3}{5}\right]$

Domain of f': exclude $\frac{3}{5}$ because it makes the denominator zero; $x \in \left(-\infty, \frac{3}{5}\right)$

(c) Our answer to part (a) is reasonable because $f'(x)$ is always
negative and f is always decreasing.

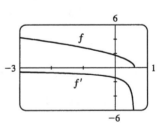

36. (a) As $x \to \pm\infty$, $f(x) = (4 - x)/(3 + x) \to -1$, so there is a
horizontal asymptote at $y = -1$. As $x \to -3^{+}$, $f(x) \to \infty$,
and as $x \to -3^{-}$, $f(x) \to -\infty$. Thus, there is a vertical
asymptote at $x = -3$.

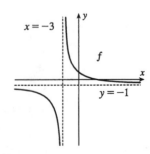

(b) Note that f is decreasing on $(-\infty, -3)$ and $(-3, \infty)$, so f' is negative on those intervals. As $x \to \pm\infty$, $f' \to 0$. As $x \to -3^-$ and as $x \to -3^+$, $f' \to -\infty$.

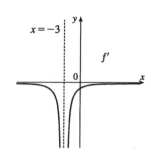

(c) $f'(x) = \lim\limits_{h \to 0} \dfrac{f(x+h) - f(x)}{h} = \lim\limits_{h \to 0} \dfrac{\dfrac{4 - (x+h)}{3 + (x+h)} - \dfrac{4 - x}{3 + x}}{h}$

$= \lim\limits_{h \to 0} \dfrac{(3+x)\left[4 - (x+h)\right] - (4 - x)\left[3 + (x+h)\right]}{h\left[3 + (x+h)\right](3+x)}$

$= \lim\limits_{h \to 0} \dfrac{-7h}{h\left[3 + (x+h)\right](3+x)} = \lim\limits_{h \to 0} \dfrac{-7}{\left[3 + (x+h)\right](3+x)} = -\dfrac{7}{(3+x)^2}$

(d) The graphing device confirms our graph in part (b).

37. f is not differentiable: at $x = -4$ because f is not continuous, at $x = -1$ because f has a corner, at $x = 2$ because f is not continuous, and at $x = 5$ because f has a vertical tangent.

38. The graph of a has tangent lines with positive slope for $x < 0$ and negative slope for $x > 0$, and the values of c fit this pattern, so c must be the graph of the derivative of the function for a. The graph of c has horizontal tangent lines to the left and right of the x-axis and b has zeros at these points. Hence, b is the graph of the derivative of the function for c. Therefore, a is the graph of f, c is the graph of f', and b is the graph of f''.

39. (a) Remember that the slope of the tangent for $f(x) = e^x$ at $x = 0$ is 1 (by definition of the number e).

(b) $L(x) = f(0) + f'(0)(x - 0) = 1 + 1(x) = x + 1$

(c)

x	-0.2	-0.1	-0.01	0.01	0.1	0.2
$e^x \approx L(x)$	0.8	0.9	0.99	1.01	1.1	1.2

(d) The graph of $f(x) = e^x$ is concave upward, so its tangent lines are below the graph and thus, the approximations are underestimates. The most accurate estimates are for those closest to $x = 0$, namely, for $e^{-0.01}$ and for $e^{0.01}$.

40. Let $C(t)$ be the function that denotes the cost of living in terms of time t. $C(t)$ is an increasing function, so $C'(t) > 0$. Since the cost of living is rising at a slower rate, the slopes of the tangent lines are positive but decreasing as t increases. Hence, $C''(t) < 0$.

41. (a) $f'(x) > 0$ on $(-2, 0)$ and $(2, \infty)$ $\Rightarrow$ f is increasing on those intervals. $f'(x) < 0$ on $(-\infty, -2)$ and $(0, 2)$ $\Rightarrow$ f is decreasing on those intervals.

(b) $f'(x) = 0$ at $x = -2$, 0, and 2, so these are where local maxima or minima will occur. At $x = \pm 2$, f' changes from negative to positive, so f has local minima at those values. At $x = 0$, f' changes from positive to negative, so f has a local maximum there.

(c) f' is increasing on $(-\infty, -1)$ and $(1, \infty)$ $\Rightarrow$
$f'' > 0$ and f is concave upward on those intervals.
f' is decreasing on $(-1, 1)$ $\Rightarrow$ $f'' < 0$ and
f is concave downward on this interval.

(d)

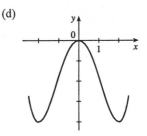

42. (a) We sketch the graph of $f'' = (f')'$ by
estimating slopes.

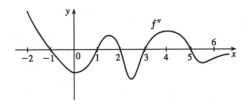

(b) Since $f' > 0$ on $(-2, 0)$ and $(4, \infty)$, we know that f is increasing on those intervals. Because $f' < 0$ on
$(-\infty, -2)$, $(0, 2)$, and $(2, 4)$, f is decreasing on those intervals. We know that f has a local maximum at $x = 0$
because f' changes from positive to negative at $x = 0$; and f has local minima at $x = 2$ and at $x = 4$ because f'
changes from negative to positive at these points.

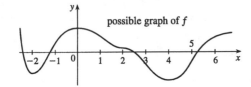

possible graph of f

43. $f(0) = 0$, $f'(-2) = f'(1) = f'(9) = 0$,
$\lim\limits_{x \to \infty} f(x) = 0$, $\lim\limits_{x \to 6} f(x) = -\infty$,
$f'(x) < 0$ on $(-\infty, -2)$, $(1, 6)$, and $(9, \infty)$,
$f'(x) > 0$ on $(-2, 1)$ and $(6, 9)$,
$f''(x) > 0$ on $(-\infty, 0)$ and $(12, \infty)$,
$f''(x) < 0$ on $(0, 6)$ and $(6, 12)$

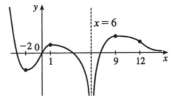

44. (a) Drawing slope triangles, we obtain the following estimates: $F'(1950) \approx \frac{1.1}{10} = 0.11$,
$F'(1965) \approx \frac{-1.6}{10} = -0.16$, and $F'(1987) \approx \frac{0.2}{10} = 0.02$.

(b) The rate of change of the average number of children born to each woman was increasing by 0.11 in 1950,
decreasing by 0.16 in 1965, and increasing by 0.02 in 1987.

(c) There are many possible reasons:
- In the baby-boom era (post-WWII), there was optimism about the economy and family size was rising.
- In the baby-bust era, there was less economic optimism, and it was considered less socially responsible to have a large family.
- In the baby-boomlet era, there was increased economic optimism and a return to more conservative attitudes.

45. (a) Using the data closest to $t = 6$, we have $\dfrac{s(8) - s(6)}{8 - 6} = \dfrac{180 - 95}{2} = 42.5$ and

$\dfrac{s(4) - s(6)}{4 - 6} = \dfrac{40 - 95}{-2} = 27.5$. Averaging these two values gives us $\dfrac{42.5 + 27.5}{2} = 35$ ft/s as an estimate for the speed of the car after 6 seconds.

(b)

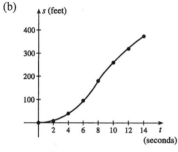

From the graph, it appears that the inflection point is at $(8, 180)$.

(c) The velocity of the car is at a maximum at the inflection point.

46. Let f be the function shown. Since f is negative for $x < 0$ and positive for $x > 0$, F is decreasing for $x < 0$ and increasing for $x > 0$. f is increasing on $(-a, a)$ (from the low point to the high point) so its derivative f' (the second derivative of F) is positive, making F concave upward on $(-a, a)$. f is decreasing elsewhere, so its derivative f' is negative and F is concave downward on $(-\infty, -a)$ and (a, ∞).

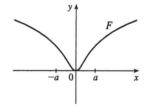

Focus on Problem Solving

1. Let $t = \sqrt[6]{x}$, so $x = t^6$. Then $t \to 1$ as $x \to 1$, so

$$\lim_{x \to 1} \frac{\sqrt[3]{x} - 1}{\sqrt{x} - 1} = \lim_{t \to 1} \frac{t^2 - 1}{t^3 - 1} = \lim_{t \to 1} \frac{(t-1)(t+1)}{(t-1)(t^2 + t + 1)} = \lim_{t \to 1} \frac{t+1}{t^2 + t + 1} = \frac{1+1}{1^2 + 1 + 1} = \frac{2}{3}.$$

Another method: Multiply both numerator and denominator by $(\sqrt{x} + 1)\left(\sqrt[3]{x^2} + \sqrt[3]{x} + 1\right)$.

2. First rationalize the numerator: $\lim_{x \to 0} \frac{\sqrt{ax+b} - 2}{x} \cdot \frac{\sqrt{ax+b} + 2}{\sqrt{ax+b} + 2} = \lim_{x \to 0} \frac{ax+b-4}{x\left(\sqrt{ax+b} + 2\right)}$. Now since the

denominator approaches 0 as $x \to 0$, the limit will exist only if the numerator also approaches 0 as $x \to 0$. So we

require that $a(0) + b - 4 = 0 \Rightarrow b = 4$. So the equation becomes $\lim_{x \to 0} \frac{a}{\sqrt{ax+4} + 2} = 1 \Rightarrow \frac{a}{\sqrt{4} + 2} = 1$

$\Rightarrow a = 4$. Therefore, $a = b = 4$.

3. For $-\frac{1}{2} < x < \frac{1}{2}$, we have $2x - 1 < 0$ and $2x + 1 > 0$, so $|2x - 1| = -(2x-1)$ and $|2x+1| = 2x+1$.

Therefore, $\lim_{x \to 0} \frac{|2x-1| - |2x+1|}{x} = \lim_{x \to 0} \frac{-(2x-1) - (2x+1)}{x} = \lim_{x \to 0} \frac{-4x}{x} = \lim_{x \to 0} (-4) = -4.$

4. Let R be the midpoint of OP, so the coordinates of R are $\left(\frac{1}{2}x, \frac{1}{2}x^2\right)$ since the coordinates of P are $\left(x, x^2\right)$. Let

$Q = (0, a)$. Since the slope $m_{OP} = \dfrac{x^2}{x} = x$, $m_{QR} = -\dfrac{1}{x}$ (negative reciprocal). But

$m_{QR} = \dfrac{\frac{1}{2}x^2 - a}{\frac{1}{2}x - 0} = \dfrac{x^2 - 2a}{x}$, so we conclude that $-1 = x^2 - 2a \Rightarrow 2a = x^2 + 1 \Rightarrow a = \frac{1}{2}x^2 + \frac{1}{2}$. As

$x \to 0$, $a \to \frac{1}{2}$, and the limiting position of Q is $\left(0, \frac{1}{2}\right)$.

5. Since $[\![x]\!] \le x < [\![x]\!] + 1$, we have $1 \le \dfrac{x}{[\![x]\!]} \le 1 + \dfrac{1}{[\![x]\!]}$ for $x > 0$. As $x \to \infty$, $[\![x]\!] \to \infty$, so $\dfrac{1}{[\![x]\!]} \to 0$ and

$1 + \dfrac{1}{[\![x]\!]} \to 1$. Thus, $\lim_{x \to \infty} \dfrac{x}{[\![x]\!]} = 1$ by the Squeeze Theorem.

6. (a) $[\![x]\!]^2 + [\![y]\!]^2 = 1$. Since $[\![x]\!]^2$ and $[\![y]\!]^2$ are positive integers or 0, there are only 4 cases:

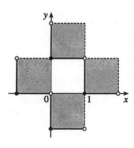

Case (i):	$[\![x]\!] = 1, [\![y]\!] = 0$	$\Rightarrow$	$1 \le x < 2$ and $0 \le y < 1$
Case (ii):	$[\![x]\!] = -1, [\![y]\!] = 0$	$\Rightarrow$	$-1 \le x < 0$ and $0 \le y < 1$
Case (iii):	$[\![x]\!] = 0, [\![y]\!] = 1$	$\Rightarrow$	$0 \le x < 1$ and $1 \le y < 2$
Case (iv):	$[\![x]\!] = 0, [\![y]\!] = -1$	$\Rightarrow$	$0 \le x < 1$ and $-1 \le y < 0$

(b) $[\![x]\!]^2 - [\![y]\!]^2 = 3$. The only integral solution of $n^2 - m^2 = 3$ is $n = \pm 2$ and
$m = \pm 1$. So the graph is
$\{(x,y) \mid [\![x]\!] = \pm 2,\ [\![y]\!] = \pm 1\} =$
$\left\{ (x,y) \; \middle| \; \begin{array}{l} 2 \le x \le 3 \text{ or } -2 \le x < 1, \\ 1 \le y < 2 \text{ or } -1 \le y < 0 \end{array} \right\}.$

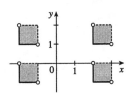

(c) $[\![x+y]\!]^2 = 1 \;\Rightarrow\; [\![x+y]\!] = \pm 1$
$\Rightarrow\; 1 \le x+y < 2$ or
$-1 \le x+y < 0$

(d) For $n \le x < n+1$, $[\![x]\!] = n$. Then $[\![x]\!] + [\![y]\!] = 1 \;\Rightarrow$
$[\![y]\!] = 1 - n \;\Rightarrow\; 1 - n \le y < 2 - n$. Choosing integer
values for n produces the graph.

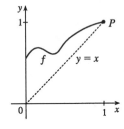

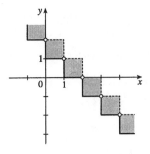

7. f is continuous on $(-\infty, a)$ and (a, ∞). To make f continuous on $\mathbb{R}$, we must have continuity at a. Thus,
$$\lim_{x \to a^+} f(x) = \lim_{x \to a^-} f(x) \;\Rightarrow\; \lim_{x \to a^+} x^2 = \lim_{x \to a^-} (x+1) \;\Rightarrow\; a^2 = a+1 \;\Rightarrow\; a = \left(1 \pm \sqrt{5}\right)/2 \approx 1.618$$
or -0.618.

8. (a) Here are a few possibilities:

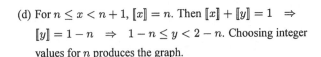

(b) The "obstacle" is the line $x = y$ (see diagram). Any intersection of the graph of f with the line $y = x$ constitutes a fixed point, and if the graph of the function does not cross the line somewhere in $(0, 1)$, then it must either start at $(0, 0)$ (in which case 0 is a fixed point) or finish at $(1, 1)$ (in which case 1 is a fixed point).

(c) Consider the function $F(x) = f(x) - x$, where f is any continuous function with domain $[0, 1]$ and range in $[0, 1]$. We shall prove that f has a fixed point.
Now if $f(0) = 0$ then we are done: f has a fixed point (the number 0), which is what we are trying to prove. So assume $f(0) \ne 0$. For the same reason we can assume that $f(1) \ne 1$. Then $F(0) = f(0) > 0$ and $F(1) = f(1) - 1 < 0$. So by the Intermediate Value Theorem, there exists some number c in the interval $(0, 1)$ such that $F(c) = f(c) - c = 0$. So $f(c) = c$, and therefore f has a fixed point.

9. (a) Consider $G(x) = T(x + 180°) - T(x)$. Fix any number a. If $G(a) = 0$, we are done:
Temperature at a = Temperature at $a + 180°$. If $G(a) > 0$, then $G(a + 180°) = T(a + 360°) - T(a + 180°)$
$= T(a) - T(a + 180°) = -G(a) < 0$. Also, G is continuous since temperature varies continuously. So, by the
Intermediate Value Theorem, G has a zero on the interval $[a, a + 180°]$. If $G(a) < 0$, then a similar argument
applies.

(b) Yes. The same argument applies.

(c) The same argument applies for quantities that vary continuously, such as barometric pressure. But one could
argue that altitude above sea level is sometimes discontinuous, so the result might not always hold for that
quantity.

10. (a) *Solution 1:* We introduce a coordinate system and drop a perpendicular
from P, as shown. We see from $\angle NCP$ that $\tan 2\theta = \dfrac{y}{1 - x}$, and
from $\angle NBP$ that $\tan \theta = y/x$. Using the double-angle formula for
tangents, we get $\dfrac{y}{1 - x} = \tan 2\theta = \dfrac{2\tan\theta}{1 - \tan^2\theta} = \dfrac{2(y/x)}{1 - (y/x)^2}$.

After a bit of simplification, this becomes $\dfrac{1}{1 - x} = \dfrac{2x}{x^2 - y^2}$ ⇔

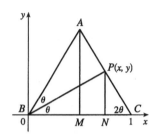

$y^2 = x(3x - 2)$. As the altitude AM decreases in length, the point P will approach the x-axis, that is, $y \to 0$,
so the limiting location of P must be one of the roots of the equation $x(3x - 2) = 0$. Obviously it is not $x = 0$
(the point P can never be to the left of the altitude AM, which it would have to be in order to approach 0) so it
must be $3x - 2 = 0$, that is, $x = \frac{2}{3}$.

Solution 2: We add a few lines to the original diagram, as shown. Now
note that $\angle BPQ = \angle PBC$ (alternate angles; $QP \parallel BC$ by
symmetry) and similarly $\angle CQP = \angle QCB$. So $\triangle BPQ$ and $\triangle CQP$
are isosceles, and the line segments BQ, QP and PC are all of equal
length. As $|AM| \to 0$, P and Q approach points on the base, and the
point P is seen to approach a position two-thirds of the way between B
and C, as above.

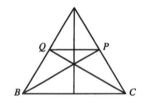

(b) The equation $y^2 = x(3x - 2)$ calculated in part (a) is the equation of
the curve traced out by P. Now as $|AM| \to \infty$, $2\theta \to \frac{\pi}{2}$, $\theta \to \frac{\pi}{4}$,
$x \to 1$, and since $\tan \theta = y/x$, $y \to 1$. Thus, P only traces out the
part of the curve with $0 \le y < 1$.

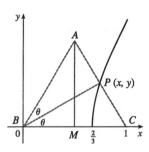

11. Let a be the x-coordinate of Q. Since the derivative of $y = 1 - x^2$ is $y' = -2x$, the slope at Q is $-2a$. But since
the triangle is equilateral, $\overline{AO}/\overline{OC} = \sqrt{3}/1$, so the slope at Q is $-\sqrt{3}$. Therefore, we must have that $-2a = -\sqrt{3}$
⇒ $a = \frac{\sqrt{3}}{2}$. Thus, the point Q has coordinates $\left(\frac{\sqrt{3}}{2}, 1 - \left(\frac{\sqrt{3}}{2}\right)^2\right) = \left(\frac{\sqrt{3}}{2}, \frac{1}{4}\right)$ and by symmetry, P has
coordinates $\left(-\frac{\sqrt{3}}{2}, \frac{1}{4}\right)$.

12. (a) $V'(t)$ is the rate of change of the volume of the water with respect to time. $H'(t)$ is the rate of change of the height of the water with respect to time. Since the volume and the height are increasing, $V'(t)$ and $H'(t)$ are positive.

(b) $V'(t)$ is constant, so $V''(t)$ is zero (the slope of a constant function is 0).

(c) At first, the height H of the water increases quickly because the tank is narrow. But as the sphere widens, the rate of increase of the height slows down, reaching a minimum at $t = t_2$. Thus, the height is increasing at a decreasing rate on $(0, t_2)$, so its graph is concave downward and $H''(t_1) < 0$. As the sphere narrows for $t > t_2$, the rate of increase of the height begins to increase, and the graph of H is concave upward. Therefore, $H''(t_2) = 0$ and $H''(t_3) > 0$.

13. (a) Put $x = 0$ and $y = 0$ in the equation: $f(0) = f(0+0) = f(0) + f(0) + 0^2 \cdot 0 + 0 \cdot 0^2 = 2f(0)$. Subtracting $f(0)$ from each side of this equation gives $f(0) = 0$.

(b) $f'(0) = \lim_{h \to 0} \dfrac{f(0+h) - f(0)}{h} = \lim_{h \to 0} \dfrac{\left[f(0) + f(h) + 0^2 h + 0h^2\right] - f(0)}{h}$

$= \lim_{h \to 0} \dfrac{f(h)}{h} = \lim_{x \to 0} \dfrac{f(x)}{x} = 1$

(c) $f'(x) = \lim_{h \to 0} \dfrac{f(x+h) - f(x)}{h} = \lim_{h \to 0} \dfrac{\left[f(x) + f(h) + x^2 h + xh^2\right] - f(x)}{h}$

$= \lim_{h \to 0} \dfrac{f(h) + x^2 h + xh^2}{h} = \lim_{h \to 0} \left[\dfrac{f(h)}{h} + x^2 + xh\right] = 1 + x^2$

14. We find the equation of the parabola by substituting the point $(-100, 100)$, at which the car is situated, into the general equation $y = ax^2$: $100 = a(-100)^2 \Rightarrow a = \frac{1}{100}$. Now we find the equation of a tangent to the parabola at the point (x_0, y_0). We can show that $y' = a(2x) = \frac{1}{100}(2x) = \frac{1}{50}x$, so an equation of the tangent is $y - y_0 = \frac{1}{50}x_0(x - x_0)$. Since the point (x_0, y_0) is on the parabola, we must have $y_0 = \frac{1}{100}x_0^2$, so our equation of the tangent can be simplified to $y = \frac{1}{100}x_0^2 + \frac{1}{50}x_0(x - x_0)$. We want the statue to be located on the tangent line, so we substitute its coordinates $(100, 50)$ into this equation: $50 = \frac{1}{100}x_0^2 + \frac{1}{50}x_0(100 - x_0) \Rightarrow$

$x_0^2 - 200x_0 + 5000 = 0 \Rightarrow x_0 = \frac{1}{2}\left[200 \pm \sqrt{200^2 - 4(5000)}\right] \Rightarrow x_0 = 100 \pm 50\sqrt{2}$. But $x_0 < 100$, so the car's headlights illuminate the statue when it is located at the point $\left(100 - 50\sqrt{2}, 150 - 100\sqrt{2}\right) \approx (29.3, 8.6)$, that is, about 29.3 m east and 8.6 m north of the origin.

15. $\lim\limits_{x \to a} f(x) = \lim\limits_{x \to a} \left(\frac{1}{2} \left[f(x) + g(x) \right] + \frac{1}{2} \left[f(x) - g(x) \right] \right)$

$\qquad\qquad = \frac{1}{2} \lim\limits_{x \to a} \left[f(x) + g(x) \right] + \frac{1}{2} \lim\limits_{x \to a} \left[f(x) - g(x) \right]$

$\qquad\qquad = \frac{1}{2} \cdot 2 + \frac{1}{2} \cdot 1 = \frac{3}{2}$, and

$\lim\limits_{x \to a} g(x) = \lim\limits_{x \to a} \left(\left[f(x) + g(x) \right] - f(x) \right) = \lim\limits_{x \to a} \left[f(x) + g(x) \right] - \lim\limits_{x \to a} f(x) = 2 - \frac{3}{2} = \frac{1}{2}$.

So $\lim\limits_{x \to a} \left[f(x) g(x) \right] = \left[\lim\limits_{x \to a} f(x) \right] \left[\lim\limits_{x \to a} g(x) \right] = \frac{3}{2} \cdot \frac{1}{2} = \frac{3}{4}$.

Another solution: Since $\lim\limits_{x \to a} \left[f(x) + g(x) \right]$ and $\lim\limits_{x \to a} \left[f(x) - g(x) \right]$ exist, we must have

$\lim\limits_{x \to a} \left[f(x) + g(x) \right]^2 = \left(\lim\limits_{x \to a} \left[f(x) + g(x) \right] \right)^2$ and $\lim\limits_{x \to a} \left[f(x) - g(x) \right]^2 = \left(\lim\limits_{x \to a} \left[f(x) - g(x) \right] \right)^2$, so

$\lim\limits_{x \to a} \left[f(x) \, g(x) \right] = \lim\limits_{x \to a} \frac{1}{4} \left(\left[f(x) + g(x) \right]^2 - \left[f(x) - g(x) \right]^2 \right)$ (because all of the f^2 and g^2 cancel)

$\qquad\qquad = \frac{1}{4} \left(\lim\limits_{x \to a} \left[f(x) + g(x) \right]^2 - \lim\limits_{x \to a} \left[f(x) - g(x) \right]^2 \right) = \frac{1}{4} \left(2^2 - 1^2 \right) = \frac{3}{4}$.

16. $g'(x) = \lim\limits_{h \to 0} \dfrac{g(x+h) - g(x)}{h} = \lim\limits_{h \to 0} \dfrac{(x+h) f(x+h) - x f(x)}{h}$

$\qquad = \lim\limits_{h \to 0} \left[\dfrac{x f(x+h) - x f(x)}{h} + \dfrac{h f(x+h)}{h} \right] = x \lim\limits_{h \to 0} \dfrac{f(x+h) - f(x)}{h} + \lim\limits_{h \to 0} f(x+h)$

$\qquad = x f'(x) + f(x)$ because f is differentiable and therefore continuous.

17. We are given that $|f(x)| \le x^2$ for all x. In particular, $|f(0)| \le 0$, but $|a| \ge 0$ for all a. The only conclusion is that

$f(0) = 0$. Now $\left| \dfrac{f(x) - f(0)}{x - 0} \right| = \left| \dfrac{f(x)}{x} \right| = \dfrac{|f(x)|}{|x|} \le \dfrac{x^2}{|x|} = \dfrac{|x^2|}{|x|} = |x| \;\Rightarrow\; -|x| \le \dfrac{f(x) - f(0)}{x - 0} \le |x|$. But

$\lim\limits_{x \to 0} \left(-|x| \right) = 0 = \lim\limits_{x \to 0} |x|$, so by the Squeeze Theorem, $\lim\limits_{x \to 0} \dfrac{f(x) - f(0)}{x - 0} = 0$. So by the definition of a

derivative, f is differentiable at 0 and, furthermore, $f'(0) = 0$.

3 ◆ Differentiation Rules

3.1 Derivatives of Polynomials and Exponential Functions • • •

1. (a) e is the number such that $\lim\limits_{h \to 0} \dfrac{e^h - 1}{h} = 1$.

(b)

x	$(2.7^x - 1)/x$
-0.001	0.9928
-0.0001	0.9932
0.001	0.9937
0.0001	0.9933

x	$(2.8^x - 1)/x$
-0.001	1.0291
-0.0001	1.0296
0.001	1.0301
0.0001	1.0297

From the tables (to two decimal places), $\lim\limits_{h \to 0} \dfrac{2.7^h - 1}{h} = 0.99$ and $\lim\limits_{h \to 0} \dfrac{2.8^h - 1}{h} = 1.03$. Since $0.99 < 1 < 1.03$, $2.7 < e < 2.8$.

2. (a)

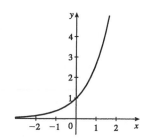

The function value at $x = 0$ is 1 and the slope at $x = 0$ is 1.

(b) $f(x) = e^x$ is an exponential function and $g(x) = x^e$ is a power function. $\dfrac{d}{dx}(e^x) = e^x$ and $\dfrac{d}{dx}(x^e) = ex^{e-1}$.

(c) $f(x) = e^x$ grows more rapidly than $g(x) = x^e$ when x is large.

3. $f(x) = 5x - 1 \;\Rightarrow\; f'(x) = 5 - 0 = 5$

4. $F(x) = -4x^{10} \;\Rightarrow\; F'(x) = -4(10x^{10-1}) = -40x^9$

5. $f(x) = 9x^4 - 3x^2 + 8 \;\Rightarrow\; f'(x) = 9(4x^{4-1}) - 3(2x^{2-1}) + 0 = 36x^3 - 6x$

6. $g(x) = 5x^8 - 2x^5 + 6 \;\Rightarrow\; g'(x) = 5(8x^{8-1}) - 2(5x^{5-1}) + 0 = 40x^7 - 10x^4$

7. $y = x^{-2/5} \;\Rightarrow\; y' = -\frac{2}{5}x^{(-2/5)-1} = -\frac{2}{5}x^{-7/5} = -\dfrac{2}{5x^{7/5}}$

8. $y = 5e^x + 3 \;\Rightarrow\; y' = 5(e^x) + 0 = 5e^x$

9. $G(x) = \sqrt{x} - 2e^x = x^{1/2} - 2e^x \;\Rightarrow\; G'(x) = \frac{1}{2}x^{-1/2} - 2e^x = \dfrac{1}{2\sqrt{x}} - 2e^x$

10. $R(t) = 5t^{-3/5} \;\Rightarrow\; R'(t) = 5\left[-\frac{3}{5}t^{(-3/5)-1}\right] = -3t^{-8/5}$

11. $V(r) = \frac{4}{3}\pi r^3 \;\Rightarrow\; V'(r) = \frac{4}{3}\pi(3r^2) = 4\pi r^2$

12. $R(x) = \dfrac{\sqrt{10}}{x^7} = \sqrt{10}\,x^{-7} \;\Rightarrow\; R'(x) = -7\sqrt{10}\,x^{-8} = -\dfrac{7\sqrt{10}}{x^8}$

13. $F(x) = (16x)^3 = 4096x^3 \;\Rightarrow\; F'(x) = 4096(3x^2) = 12{,}288x^2$

14. $y = \sqrt{x}\,(x - 1) = x^{3/2} - x^{1/2} \;\Rightarrow\; y' = \frac{3}{2}x^{1/2} - \frac{1}{2}x^{-1/2} = \frac{1}{2}x^{-1/2}(3x - 1)$ (factor out $\frac{1}{2}x^{-1/2}$)

   or $y' = \dfrac{3x - 1}{2\sqrt{x}}$.

15. $y = 4\pi^2 \;\Rightarrow\; y' = 0$ since $4\pi^2$ is a constant.

16. $H(s) = (s/2)^5 = s^5/2^5 = \frac{1}{32}s^5 \;\Rightarrow\; H'(s) = \frac{1}{32}(5s^{5-1}) = \frac{5}{32}s^4$

17. $y = \dfrac{x^2 + 4x + 3}{\sqrt{x}} = x^{3/2} + 4x^{1/2} + 3x^{-1/2} \;\Rightarrow\;$

   $y' = \frac{3}{2}x^{1/2} + 4\left(\frac{1}{2}\right)x^{-1/2} + 3\left(-\frac{1}{2}\right)x^{-3/2} = \frac{3}{2}\sqrt{x} + \dfrac{2}{\sqrt{x}} - \dfrac{3}{2x\sqrt{x}}$

18. $y = \dfrac{x^2 - 2\sqrt{x}}{x} = x - 2x^{-1/2} \;\Rightarrow\; y' = 1 - 2\left(-\frac{1}{2}\right)x^{-3/2} = 1 + 1/(x\sqrt{x})$

19. $v = t^2 - \dfrac{1}{\sqrt[4]{t^3}} = t^2 - t^{-3/4} \;\Rightarrow\; v' = 2t - \left(-\frac{3}{4}\right)t^{-7/4} = 2t + \dfrac{3}{4t^{7/4}} = 2t + \dfrac{3}{4t\sqrt[4]{t^3}}$

20. $y = ae^v + \dfrac{b}{v} + \dfrac{c}{v^2} = ae^v + bv^{-1} + cv^{-2} \;\Rightarrow\; y' = ae^v - bv^{-2} - 2cv^{-3} = ae^v - \dfrac{b}{v^2} - \dfrac{2c}{v^3}$

21. $z = \dfrac{A}{y^{10}} + Be^y = Ay^{-10} + Be^y \;\Rightarrow\; z' = -10Ay^{-11} + Be^y = -\dfrac{10A}{y^{11}} + Be^y$

22. $u = \sqrt[3]{t^2} + 2\sqrt{t^3} = t^{2/3} + 2t^{3/2} \;\Rightarrow\; u' = \frac{2}{3}t^{-1/3} + 2\left(\frac{3}{2}\right)t^{1/2} = \dfrac{2}{3\sqrt[3]{t}} + 3\sqrt{t}$

23. $f(x) = 2x^2 - x^4 \;\Rightarrow\; f'(x) = 4x - 4x^3$.

24. $f(x) = 3x^5 - 20x^3 + 50x \;\Rightarrow$
   $f'(x) = 15x^4 - 60x^2 + 50$.

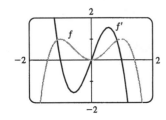

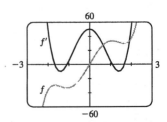

Notice that $f'(x) = 0$ when f has a horizontal tangent and that f' is an odd function while f is an even function.

Notice that $f'(x) = 0$ when f has a horizontal tangent and that f' is an even function while f is an odd function.

25. $f(x) = 3x^{15} - 5x^3 + 3 \implies$
$f'(x) = 45x^{14} - 15x^2.$

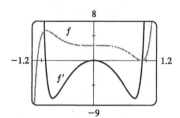

Notice that $f'(x) = 0$ when f has a horizontal
tangent, f' is positive when f is increasing, and f'
is negative when f is decreasing.

26. $f(x) = x + 1/x = x + x^{-1} \implies$
$f'(x) = 1 - x^{-2} = 1 - 1/x^2.$

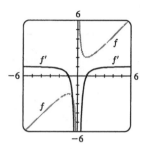

Notice that $f'(x) = 0$ when f has a horizontal
tangent, f' is positive when f is increasing, and f'
is negative when f is decreasing.

27. $f(x) = x - 3x^{1/3} \implies$
$f'(x) = 1 - x^{-2/3} = 1 - 1/x^{2/3}.$

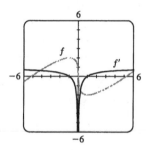

Note that $f'(x) = 0$ when f has a horizontal
tangent, f' is positive when f is increasing, and f'
is negative when f is decreasing.

28. $f(x) = x^2 + 2e^x \implies f'(x) = 2x + 2e^x.$

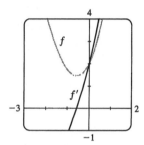

Note that $f'(x) = 0$ when f has a horizontal
tangent, f' is positive when f is increasing, and f'
is negative when f is decreasing.

29. (a)

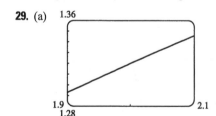

The endpoints of f in this graph are about $(1.9, 1.2927)$ and
$(2.1, 1.3455)$. An estimate of $f'(2)$ is
$\frac{1.3455 - 1.2927}{2.1 - 1.9} = \frac{0.0528}{0.2} = 0.264.$

(b) $f(x) = x^{2/5} \implies f'(x) = \frac{2}{5}x^{-3/5} = 2/\left(5x^{3/5}\right).$
$f'(2) = 2/\left(5 \cdot 2^{3/5}\right) = 2^{2/5}/5 \approx 0.263902.$

30. (a)

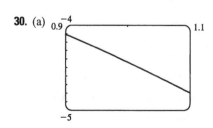

The endpoints of f in this graph are about $(0.9, -4.1092)$ and
$(1.1, -4.7983)$. An estimate of $f'(1)$ is
$\frac{-4.7983 - (-4.1092)}{1.1 - 0.9} = \frac{-0.6891}{0.2} = -3.4455.$

(b) $f(x) = x^2 - 2e^x \implies f'(x) = 2x - 2e^x.$
$f'(1) = 2 - 2e \approx -3.436564.$

31. $y = f(x) = x + \dfrac{4}{x}$ $\Rightarrow$ $f'(x) = 1 - \dfrac{4}{x^2}$. So the

slope of the tangent line at $(2, 4)$ is $f'(2) = 0$ and

its equation is $y - 4 = 0(x - 2)$ or $y = 4$.

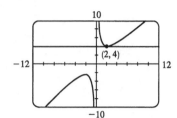

32. $y = f(x) = x^{5/2}$ $\Rightarrow$ $f'(x) = \frac{5}{2}x^{3/2}$. So the

slope of the tangent line at $(4, 32)$ is $f'(4) = 20$

and its equation is $y - 32 = 20(x - 4)$ or

$y = 20x - 48$.

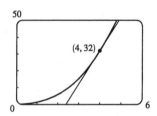

33. $y = f(x) = x + \sqrt{x}$ $\Rightarrow$ $f'(x) = 1 + \frac{1}{2}x^{-1/2}$.

So the slope of the tangent line at $(1, 2)$ is

$f'(1) = 1 + \frac{1}{2}(1) = \frac{3}{2}$ and its equation is

$y - 2 = \frac{3}{2}(x - 1)$ or $y = \frac{3}{2}x + \frac{1}{2}$.

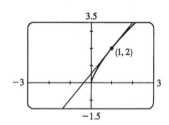

34. $y = f(x) = x^2 + 2e^x$ $\Rightarrow$ $f'(x) = 2x + 2e^x$.

So the slope of the tangent line at $(0, 2)$ is

$f'(0) = 2e^0 = 2$ and its equation is

$y - 2 = 2(x - 0)$ or $y = 2x + 2$.

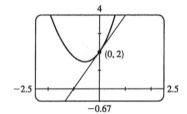

35. (a)

50

−3   5

−10

(b)

From the graph in part (a), it appears that f' is zero at

$x_1 \approx -1.25$, $x_2 \approx 0.5$, and $x_3 \approx 3$. The slopes are negative (so

f' is negative) on $(-\infty, x_1)$ and (x_2, x_3). The slopes are positive

(so f' is positive) on (x_1, x_2) and (x_3, ∞).

(c) $f(x) = x^4 - 3x^3 - 6x^2 + 7x + 30 \Rightarrow$

$f'(x) = 4x^3 - 9x^2 - 12x + 7$

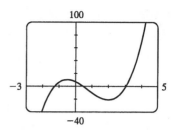

36. (a)

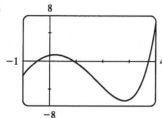

(b)

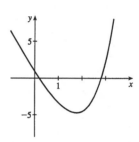

From the graph in part (a), it appears that f' is zero at $x_1 \approx 0.2$ and $x_2 \approx 2.8$. The slopes are positive (so f' is positive) on $(-\infty, x_1)$ and (x_2, ∞). The slopes are negative (so f' is negative) on (x_1, x_2).

(c) $g(x) = e^x - 3x^2 \Rightarrow g'(x) = e^x - 6x$

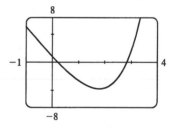

37. $f(x) = x^4 - 3x^3 + 16x \Rightarrow f'(x) = 4x^3 - 9x^2 + 16 \Rightarrow f''(x) = 12x^2 - 18x$

38. $G(r) = \sqrt{r} + \sqrt[3]{r} \Rightarrow G'(r) = \frac{1}{2}r^{-1/2} + \frac{1}{3}r^{-2/3} \Rightarrow G''(r) = -\frac{1}{4}r^{-3/2} - \frac{2}{9}r^{-5/3}$

39. $f(x) = 2x - 5x^{3/4} \Rightarrow f'(x) = 2 - \frac{15}{4}x^{-1/4} \Rightarrow f''(x) = \frac{15}{16}x^{-5/4}$

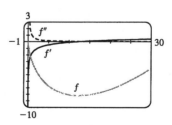

Note that f' is negative when f is decreasing and positive when f is increasing. f'' is always positive since f' is always increasing.

40. $f(x) = e^x - x^3 \Rightarrow f'(x) = e^x - 3x^2 \Rightarrow f''(x) = e^x - 6x.$

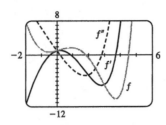

Note that $f'(x) = 0$ when f has a horizontal tangent and that $f''(x) = 0$ when f' has a horizontal tangent.

41. (a) $s = t^3 - 3t \Rightarrow v(t) = s'(t) = 3t^2 - 3 \Rightarrow a(t) = v'(t) = 6t$

(b) $a(2) = 6(2) = 12$ m/s^2

(c) $v(t) = 3t^2 - 3 = 0$ when $t^2 = 1$, that is, $t = 1$ and $a(1) = 6$ m/s^2.

42. (a) $s = 2t^3 - 7t^2 + 4t + 1 \Rightarrow v(t) = s'(t) = 6t^2 - 14t + 4 \Rightarrow a(t) = v'(t) = 12t - 14$

(b) $a(1) = 12 - 14 = -2$ m/s^2

(c)

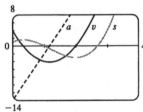

43. $f(x) = 1 + 2e^x - 3x \Rightarrow f'(x) = 2e^x - 3.$ $f'(x) > 0 \Rightarrow 2e^x - 3 > 0 \Rightarrow 2e^x > 3 \Rightarrow$
$e^x > 1.5 \Rightarrow x > \ln 1.5 \approx 0.41.$ f is increasing when f' is positive; that is, on $(\ln 1.5, \infty)$.

44. $f(x) = x^3 - 4x^2 + 5x \Rightarrow f'(x) = 3x^2 - 8x + 5 \Rightarrow f''(x) = 6x - 8.$
$f''(x) > 0 \Rightarrow 6x - 8 > 0 \Rightarrow x > \frac{4}{3}.$ f is concave upward when $f''(x) > 0$; that is, on $\left(\frac{4}{3}, \infty\right)$.

45. $y = x^3 - x^2 - x + 1$ has a horizontal tangent when $y' = 3x^2 - 2x - 1 = 0.$ $(3x + 1)(x - 1) = 0 \Leftrightarrow$
$x = 1$ or $-\frac{1}{3}.$ Therefore, the points are $(1, 0)$ and $\left(-\frac{1}{3}, \frac{32}{27}\right).$

46. $f(x) = 2x^3 - 3x^2 - 6x + 87$ has a horizontal tangent when $f'(x) = 6x^2 - 6x - 6 = 0 \Leftrightarrow$
$x^2 - x - 1 = 0 \Leftrightarrow x = \frac{1 \pm \sqrt{5}}{2}.$

47. $y = 6x^3 + 5x - 3 \Rightarrow m = y' = 18x^2 + 5,$ but $x^2 \geq 0$ for all x, so $m \geq 5$ for all x.

48. The slope of $y = 1 + 2e^x - 3x$ is given by $m = y' = 2e^x - 3.$
The slope of $3x - y = 5 \Leftrightarrow y = 3x - 5$ is 3.
$m = 3 \Rightarrow 2e^x - 3 = 3 \Rightarrow e^x = 3 \Rightarrow x = \ln 3.$ This
occurs at the point $(\ln 3, 7 - 3\ln 3) \approx (1.1, 3.7).$

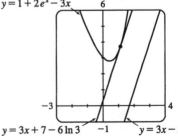

49.

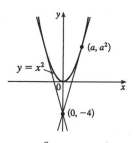

Let (a, a^2) be a point on the parabola at which the tangent line passes through the point $(0, -4)$. The tangent line has slope $2a$ and equation $y - (-4) = 2a(x - 0) \iff y = 2ax - 4$. Since (a, a^2) also lies on the line, $a^2 = 2a(a) - 4$, or $a^2 = 4$. So $a = \pm 2$ and the points are $(2, 4)$ and $(-2, 4)$.

50. If $y = x^2 + x$, then $y' = 2x + 1$. If the point at which a tangent meets the parabola is $(a, a^2 + a)$, then the slope of the tangent is $2a + 1$. But since it passes through $(2, -3)$, the slope must also be $\dfrac{\Delta y}{\Delta x} = \dfrac{a^2 + a + 3}{a - 2}$.

Therefore, $2a + 1 = \dfrac{a^2 + a + 3}{a - 2}$. Solving this equation for a we get $a^2 + a + 3 = 2a^2 - 3a - 2 \iff$
$a^2 - 4a - 5 = (a - 5)(a + 1) = 0 \iff a = 5$ or -1. If $a = -1$, the point is $(-1, 0)$ and the slope is -1, so the equation is $y - 0 = (-1)(x + 1)$ or $y = -x - 1$. If $a = 5$, the point is $(5, 30)$ and the slope is 11, so the equation is $y - 30 = 11(x - 5)$ or $y = 11x - 25$.

51. $y = f(x) = 1 - x^2 \implies f'(x) = -2x$, so the tangent line at $(2, -3)$ has slope $f'(2) = -4$. The normal line has slope $-\dfrac{1}{-4} = \dfrac{1}{4}$ and equation $y + 3 = \frac{1}{4}(x - 2)$ or $y = \frac{1}{4}x - \frac{7}{2}$.

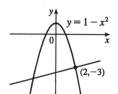

52. $y = f(x) = x - x^2 \implies f'(x) = 1 - 2x$. So $f'(1) = -1$, and the slope of the normal line is the negative reciprocal of that of the tangent line, that is, $-1/(-1) = 1$. So the equation of the normal line at $(1, 0)$ is $y - 0 = 1(x - 1)$ $\iff y = x - 1$. Substituting this into the equation of the parabola, we obtain $x - 1 = x - x^2 \iff x = \pm 1$. The solution $x = -1$ is the one we require. Substituting $x = -1$ into the equation of the parabola to find the y-coordinate, we have $y = -2$. So the point of intersection is $(-1, -2)$, as shown in the sketch.

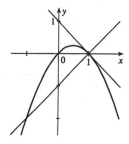

53. $f'(x) = \lim\limits_{h \to 0} \dfrac{f(x + h) - f(x)}{h} = \lim\limits_{h \to 0} \dfrac{\dfrac{1}{x + h} - \dfrac{1}{x}}{h} = \lim\limits_{h \to 0} \dfrac{x - (x + h)}{hx(x + h)}$

$= \lim\limits_{h \to 0} \dfrac{-h}{hx(x + h)} = \lim\limits_{h \to 0} \dfrac{-1}{x(x + h)} = -\dfrac{1}{x^2}$

54. (a) $f(x) = x^n \implies f'(x) = nx^{n-1} \implies f''(x) = n(n - 1)x^{n-2} \implies \cdots \implies$
$f^{(n)}(x) = n(n - 1)(n - 2) \cdots 2 \cdot 1x^{n-n} = n!$

(b) $f(x) = x^{-1} \implies f'(x) = (-1)x^{-2} \implies f''(x) = (-1)(-2)x^{-3} \implies \cdots \implies$
$f^{(n)}(x) = (-1)(-2)(-3) \cdots (-n)x^{-(n+1)} = (-1)^n n! x^{-(n+1)}$ or $\dfrac{(-1)^n n!}{x^{n+1}}$

55. Let $P(x) = ax^2 + bx + c$. Then $P'(x) = 2ax + b$ and $P''(x) = 2a$. $P''(2) = 2 \implies 2a = 2 \implies a = 1$.
$P'(2) = 3 \implies 2(1)(2) + b = 3 \implies 4 + b = 3 \implies b = -1$.
$P(2) = 5 \implies 1(2)^2 + (-1)(2) + c = 5 \implies 2 + c = 5 \implies c = 3$. So $P(x) = x^2 - x + 3$.

56. $y = Ax^2 + Bx + C \Rightarrow y' = 2Ax + B \Rightarrow y'' = 2A$. We substitute these expressions into the equation $y'' + y' - 2y = x^2$ to get

$$(2A) + (2Ax + B) - 2(Ax^2 + Bx + C) = x^2$$
$$2A + 2Ax + B - 2Ax^2 - 2Bx - 2C = x^2$$
$$(-2A)x^2 + (2A - 2B)x + (2A + B - 2C) = (1)x^2 + (0)x + (0)$$

The coefficients of x^2 on each side must be equal, so $-2A = 1 \Rightarrow A = -\frac{1}{2}$. Similarly, $2A - 2B = 0 \Rightarrow A = B = -\frac{1}{2}$ and $2A + B - 2C = 0 \Rightarrow -1 - \frac{1}{2} - 2C = 0 \Rightarrow C = -\frac{3}{4}$.

57. (a) At this stage, we would guess that an antiderivative of x^2 must have x^3 in it. Differentiating x^3 gives us $3x^2$, so we know that we must divide x^3 by 3. That gives us $F(x) = \frac{1}{3}x^3$. Checking, we have $F'(x) = \frac{1}{3}(3x^2) = x^2 = f(x)$. Because we can add an arbitrary constant C to F without changing its derivative, we have an infinite number of antiderivatives of the form $F(x) = \frac{1}{3}x^3 + C$.

(b) As in part (a), antiderivatives of $f(x) = x^3$ and $f(x) = x^4$ are $F(x) = \frac{1}{4}x^4 + C$ and $F(x) = \frac{1}{5}x^5 + C$.

(c) Similarly, an antiderivative for $f(x) = x^n$ is $F(x) = \frac{1}{n+1}x^{n+1} + C$, since then

$$F'(x) = \frac{1}{n+1}[(n+1)x^n] = x^n = f(x) \text{ for } n \neq -1.$$

58. (a) $f(x) = \sqrt{x} = x^{1/2} \Rightarrow F(x) = \frac{1}{(1/2)+1}x^{(1/2)+1} + C = \frac{2}{3}x^{3/2} + C$

(b) $f(x) = e^x + 8x^3 \Rightarrow F(x) = e^x + 8 \cdot \frac{1}{3+1}x^{3+1} + C = e^x + 2x^4 + C$

59. $y = f(x) = ax^2 \Rightarrow f'(x) = 2ax$. So the slope of the tangent to the parabola at $x = 2$ is $m = 2a(2) = 4a$. The slope of the given line, $2x + y = b \Leftrightarrow y = -2x + b$, is seen to be -2, so we must have $4a = -2 \Leftrightarrow a = -\frac{1}{2}$. So when $x = 2$, the point in question has y-coordinate $-\frac{1}{2} \cdot 2^2 = -2$. Now we simply require that the given line, whose equation is $2x + y = b$, pass through the point $(2, -2)$: $2(2) + (-2) = b \Leftrightarrow b = 2$. So we must have $a = -\frac{1}{2}$ and $b = 2$.

60. $y = ax^2 + bx + c \Rightarrow y'(x) = 2ax + b$. The parabola has slope 4 at $x = 1$ and slope -8 at $x = -1$, so $y'(1) = 4 \Rightarrow 2a + b = 4$ **(1)** and $y'(-1) = -8 \Rightarrow -2a + b = -8$ **(2)**. Adding **(1)** and **(2)** gives us $2b = -4 \Leftrightarrow b = -2$. From **(1)**, $2a - 2 = 4 \Leftrightarrow a = 3$. Thus, the equation of the parabola is $y = 3x^2 - 2x + c$. Since it passes through the point $(2, 15)$, we have $15 = 3(2)^2 - 2(2) + c \Rightarrow c = 7$, so the equation is $y = 3x^2 - 2x + 7$.

61. $y = f(x) = ax^3 + bx^2 + cx + d \Rightarrow f'(x) = 3ax^2 + 2bx + c$. The point $(-2, 6)$ is on f, so $f(-2) = 6 \Rightarrow -8a + 4b - 2c + d = 6$ **(1)**. The point $(2, 0)$ is on f, so $f(2) = 0 \Rightarrow 8a + 4b + 2c + d = 0$ **(2)**. Since there are horizontal tangents at $(-2, 6)$ and $(2, 0)$, $f'(\pm 2) = 0$. $f'(-2) = 0 \Rightarrow 12a - 4b + c = 0$ **(3)** and $f'(2) = 0 \Rightarrow 12a + 4b + c = 0$ **(4)**. Subtracting equation **(3)** from **(4)** gives $8b = 0 \Rightarrow b = 0$. Adding **(1)** and **(2)** gives $8b + 2d = 6$, so $d = 3$ since $b = 0$. From **(3)** we have $c = -12a$, so **(2)** becomes $8a + 4(0) + 2(-12a) + 3 = 0 \Rightarrow 3 = 16a \Rightarrow a = \frac{3}{16}$. Now $c = -12a = -12(\frac{3}{16}) = -\frac{9}{4}$ and the desired cubic function is $y = \frac{3}{16}x^3 - \frac{9}{4}x + 3$.

62. (a) $xy = c \Rightarrow y = \frac{c}{x}$. Let $P = \left(a, \frac{c}{a}\right)$. The slope of the tangent line at $x = a$ is $y'(a) = -\frac{c}{a^2}$. Its equation is $y - \frac{c}{a} = -\frac{c}{a^2}(x - a)$ or $y = -\frac{c}{a^2}x + \frac{2c}{a}$, so its y-intercept is $\frac{2c}{a}$. Setting $y = 0$ gives $x = 2a$, so the x-intercept is $2a$. The midpoint of the line segment joining $\left(0, \frac{2c}{a}\right)$ and $(2a, 0)$ is $\left(a, \frac{c}{a}\right) = P$.

(b) We know the x- and y-intercepts of the tangent line from part (a), so the area of the triangle bounded by the axes and the tangent is $\frac{1}{2}(\text{base})(\text{height}) = \frac{1}{2}xy = \frac{1}{2}(2a)(2c/a) = 2c$, a constant.

63. *Solution 1:* Let $f(x) = x^{1000}$. Then, by the definition of derivative,

$$f'(1) = \lim_{x \to 1} \frac{f(x) - f(1)}{x - 1} = \lim_{x \to 1} \frac{x^{1000} - 1}{x - 1}.$$ But this is just the limit we want to find, and we know (from the

Power Rule) that $f'(x) = 1000x^{999}$, so $f'(1) = 1000(1)^{999} = 1000$. So $\displaystyle\lim_{x \to 1} \frac{x^{1000} - 1}{x - 1} = 1000$.

Solution 2: Note that $\left(x^{1000} - 1\right) = (x - 1)\left(x^{999} + x^{998} + x^{997} + \cdots + x^2 + x + 1\right)$. So

$$\lim_{x \to 1} \frac{x^{1000} - 1}{x - 1} = \lim_{x \to 1} \frac{(x - 1)\left(x^{999} + x^{998} + x^{997} + \cdots + x^2 + x + 1\right)}{x - 1}$$

$$= \lim_{x \to 1} \left(x^{999} + x^{998} + x^{997} + \cdots + x^2 + x + 1\right) = \underbrace{1 + 1 + 1 + \cdots + 1 + 1 + 1}_{1000 \text{ ones}}$$

$$= 1000, \text{ as above.}$$

64.

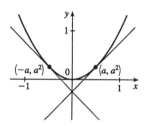

In order for the two tangents to intersect on the y-axis, the points of tangency must be at equal distances from the y-axis, since the parabola $y = x^2$ is symmetric about the y-axis. Say the points of tangency are $\left(a, a^2\right)$ and $\left(-a, a^2\right)$, for some $a > 0$. Then since the derivative of $y = x^2$ is $dy/dx = 2x$, the left-hand tangent has slope $-2a$ and equation $y - a^2 = -2a(x + a)$, or $y = -2ax - a^2$, and similarly the right-hand tangent line has equation $y - a^2 = 2a(x - a)$, or $y = 2ax - a^2$. So the two lines intersect at $\left(0, -a^2\right)$. Now if the lines are perpendicular, then the product of their slopes is -1, so $(-2a)(2a) = -1 \iff a^2 = \frac{1}{4} \iff a = \frac{1}{2}$. So the lines intersect at $\left(0, -\frac{1}{4}\right)$.

Applied Project	**Building a Better Roller Coaster**

1. (a) $f(x) = ax^2 + bx + c \implies f'(x) = 2ax + b$.

The origin is at P : $f(0) = 0 \implies c = 0$

The slope of the ascent is 0.8: $f'(0) = 0.8 \implies b = 0.8$

The slope of the drop is -1.6: $f'(100) = -1.6 \implies 200a + b = -1.6$

(b) $b = 0.8$, so $200a + b = -1.6 \implies 200a + 0.8 = -1.6 \implies 200a = -2.4 \implies a = -\dfrac{2.4}{200} = -0.012$.

Thus, $f(x) = -0.012x^2 + 0.8x$.

(c) Since L_1 passes through the origin with slope 0.8, it has equation $y = 0.8x$. The horizontal distance between P and Q is 100, so the y-coordinate at Q is $f(100) = -0.012(100)^2 + 0.8(100) = -40$. Since L_2 passes through the point $(100, -40)$ and has slope -1.6, it has equation $y + 40 = -1.6(x - 100)$ or $y = -1.6x + 120$.

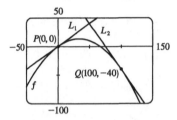

(d) The difference in elevation between $P(0,0)$ and $Q(100, -40)$ is $0 - (-40) = 40$ feet.

2. (a)

Interval	Function	First Derivative	Second Derivative
$(-\infty, 0)$	$L_1(x) = 0.8x$	$L_1'(x) = 0.8$	$L_1''(x) = 0$
$[0, 10)$	$g(x) = kx^3 + lx^2 + mx + n$	$g'(x) = 3kx^2 + 2lx + m$	$g''(x) = 6kx + 2l$
$[10, 90]$	$q(x) = ax^2 + bx + c$	$q'(x) = 2ax + b$	$q''(x) = 2a$
$(90, 100]$	$h(x) = px^3 + qx^2 + rx + s$	$h'(x) = 3px^2 + 2qx + r$	$h''(x) = 6px + 2q$
$(100, \infty)$	$L_2(x) = -1.6x + 120$	$L_2'(x) = -1.6$	$L_2''(x) = 0$

There are 4 values of x $(0, 10, 90,$ and $100)$ for which we must make sure the function values are equal, the first derivative values are equal, and the second derivative values are equal. The third column in the following table contains the value of each side of the condition—these are found after solving the system in part (b).

At $x =$	Condition	Value	Resulting Equation
0	$g(0) = L_1(0)$	0	$n = 0$
	$g'(0) = L_1'(0)$	$\frac{4}{5}$	$m = 0.8$
	$g''(0) = L_1''(0)$	0	$2l = 0$
10	$g(10) = q(10)$	$\frac{68}{9}$	$1000k + 100l + 10m + n = 100a + 10b + c$
	$g'(10) = q'(10)$	$\frac{2}{3}$	$300k + 20l + m = 20a + b$
	$g''(10) = q''(10)$	$-\frac{2}{75}$	$60k + 2l = 2a$
90	$h(90) = q(90)$	$-\frac{220}{9}$	$729,000p + 8100q + 90r + s = 8100a + 90b + c$
	$h'(90) = q'(90)$	$-\frac{22}{15}$	$24,300p + 180q + r = 180a + b$
	$h''(90) = q''(90)$	$-\frac{2}{75}$	$540p + 2q = 2a$
100	$h(100) = L_2(100)$	-40	$1,000,000p + 10,000q + 100r + s = -40$
	$h'(100) = L_2'(100)$	$-\frac{8}{5}$	$30,000p + 200q + r = -1.6$
	$h''(100) = L_2''(100)$	0	$600p + 2q = 0$

(b) We can arrange our work in a 12×12 matrix as follows.

a	b	c	k	l	m	n	p	q	r	s	constant
0	0	0	0	0	0	1	0	0	0	0	0
0	0	0	0	0	1	0	0	0	0	0	0.8
0	0	0	0	2	0	0	0	0	0	0	0
−100	−10	−1	1000	100	10	1	0	0	0	0	0
−20	−1	0	300	20	1	0	0	0	0	0	0
−2	0	0	60	2	0	0	0	0	0	0	0
−8100	−90	−1	0	0	0	0	729,000	8100	90	1	0
−180	−1	0	0	0	0	0	24,300	180	1	0	0
−2	0	0	0	0	0	0	540	2	0	0	0
0	0	0	0	0	0	0	1,000,000	10,000	100	1	−40
0	0	0	0	0	0	0	30,000	200	1	0	−1.6
0	0	0	0	0	0	0	600	2	0	0	0

Solving the system gives us the formulas for q, g, and h.

$$\left.\begin{array}{l} a = -0.01\overline{3} = -\frac{1}{75} \\ b = 0.9\overline{3} = \frac{14}{15} \\ c = -0.\overline{4} = -\frac{4}{9} \end{array}\right\} q(x) = -\frac{1}{75}x^2 + \frac{14}{15}x - \frac{4}{9}$$

$$\left.\begin{array}{l} k = -0.000\overline{4} = -\frac{1}{2250} \\ l = 0 \\ m = 0.8 = \frac{4}{5} \\ n = 0 \end{array}\right\} g(x) = -\frac{1}{2250}x^3 + \frac{4}{5}x$$

$$\left.\begin{array}{l} p = 0.000\overline{4} = \frac{1}{2250} \\ q = -0.1\overline{3} = -\frac{2}{15} \\ r = 11.7\overline{3} = \frac{176}{15} \\ s = -324.\overline{4} = -\frac{2920}{9} \end{array}\right\} h(x) = \frac{1}{2250}x^3 - \frac{2}{15}x^2 + \frac{176}{15}x - \frac{2920}{9}$$

(c) Graph of L_1, q, g, h, and L_2:

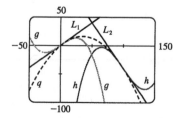

The graph of the five functions as a piecewise-defined function:

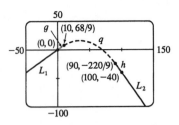

This is the piecewise-defined function assignment on a TI-83 Plus calculator, where $Y_2 = L_1$, $Y_6 = g$, $Y_5 = q$, $Y_7 = h$, and $Y_3 = L_2$.

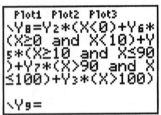

A comparison of the graphs in part 1(c) and part 2(c):

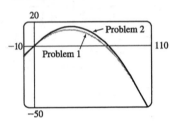

◆ 3.2 The Product and Quotient Rules · · · · · · · · · · ·

1. Product Rule: $y = (x^2 + 1)(x^3 + 1)$ ⇒

$$y' = (x^2 + 1)(3x^2) + (x^3 + 1)(2x) = 3x^4 + 3x^2 + 2x^4 + 2x = 5x^4 + 3x^2 + 2x.$$

Multiplying first: $y = (x^2 + 1)(x^3 + 1) = x^5 + x^3 + x^2 + 1$ ⇒ $y' = 5x^4 + 3x^2 + 2x$ (equivalent)

2. Quotient Rule: $F(x) = \dfrac{x - 3x\sqrt{x}}{\sqrt{x}} = \dfrac{x - 3x^{3/2}}{x^{1/2}}$ ⇒

$$F'(x) = \frac{x^{1/2}\left(1 - \frac{9}{2}x^{1/2}\right) - \left(x - 3x^{3/2}\right)\left(\frac{1}{2}x^{-1/2}\right)}{\left(x^{1/2}\right)^2}$$

$$= \frac{x^{1/2} - \frac{9}{2}x - \frac{1}{2}x^{1/2} + \frac{3}{2}x}{x} = \frac{\frac{1}{2}x^{1/2} - 3x}{x} = \frac{1}{2}x^{-1/2} - 3$$

Simplifying first: $F(x) = \dfrac{x - 3x\sqrt{x}}{\sqrt{x}} = \sqrt{x} - 3x = x^{1/2} - 3x$ ⇒ $F'(x) = \frac{1}{2}x^{-1/2} - 3$ (equivalent)

For this problem, simplifying first seems to be the better method.

3. By the Product Rule, $f(x) = x^2 e^x$ ⇒ $f'(x) = x^2 \dfrac{d}{dx}(e^x) + e^x \dfrac{d}{dx}(x^2) = x^2 e^x + e^x(2x) = xe^x(x + 2)$.

4. By the Product Rule, $g(x) = \sqrt{x}\, e^x = x^{1/2} e^x$ ⇒ $g'(x) = x^{1/2}(e^x) + e^x\left(\frac{1}{2}x^{-1/2}\right) = \frac{1}{2}x^{-1/2} e^x(2x + 1)$.

5. By the Quotient Rule, $y = \dfrac{e^x}{x^2}$ $\Rightarrow$

$$y' = \frac{x^2 \dfrac{d}{dx}(e^x) - e^x \dfrac{d}{dx}(x^2)}{(x^2)^2} = \frac{x^2 (e^x) - e^x (2x)}{x^4} = \frac{xe^x (x-2)}{x^4} = \frac{e^x (x-2)}{x^3}$$

6. By the Quotient Rule, $y = \dfrac{e^x}{1+x}$ $\Rightarrow$ $y' = \dfrac{(1+x)\,e^x - e^x(1)}{(1+x)^2} = \dfrac{e^x + xe^x - e^x}{(x+1)^2} = \dfrac{xe^x}{(x+1)^2}$.

7. $h(x) = \dfrac{x+2}{x-1}$ $\Rightarrow$ $h'(x) = \dfrac{(x-1)(1) - (x+2)(1)}{(x-1)^2} = \dfrac{x-1-x-2}{(x-1)^2} = -\dfrac{3}{(x-1)^2}$

8. $f(u) = \dfrac{1-u^2}{1+u^2}$ $\Rightarrow$ $f'(u) = \dfrac{(1+u^2)(-2u) - (1-u^2)(2u)}{(1+u^2)^2} = \dfrac{-2u - 2u^3 - 2u + 2u^3}{(1+u^2)^2} = -\dfrac{4u}{(1+u^2)^2}$

9. $H(x) = (x^3 - x + 1)(x^{-2} + 2x^{-3}) = (x^3 - x + 1)(x^{-2}) + (x^3 - x + 1)(2x^{-3})$

$= x - x^{-1} + x^{-2} + 2 - 2x^{-2} + 2x^{-3} = 2 + x - x^{-1} - x^{-2} + 2x^{-3}$ $\Rightarrow$

$H'(x) = 0 + 1 - (-1)x^{-2} - (-2)\,x^{-3} + 2(-3)x^{-4} = 1 + x^{-2} + 2x^{-3} - 6x^{-4}$.

Another method: Use the Product Rule.

10. $H(t) = e^t(1 + 3t^2 + 5t^4)$ $\Rightarrow$

$H'(t) = e^t(6t + 20t^3) + (1 + 3t^2 + 5t^4)e^t = e^t(5t^4 + 20t^3 + 3t^2 + 6t + 1)$

11. $y = \dfrac{t^2}{3t^2 - 2t + 1}$ $\Rightarrow$

$y' = \dfrac{(3t^2 - 2t + 1)(2t) - t^2(6t - 2)}{(3t^2 - 2t + 1)^2} = \dfrac{2t\left[3t^2 - 2t + 1 - t(3t - 1)\right]}{(3t^2 - 2t + 1)^2}$

$= \dfrac{2t(3t^2 - 2t + 1 - 3t^2 + t)}{(3t^2 - 2t + 1)^2} = \dfrac{2t(1 - t)}{(3t^2 - 2t + 1)^2}$

12. $y = \dfrac{t^3 + t}{t^4 - 2}$ $\Rightarrow$ $y' = \dfrac{(t^4 - 2)(3t^2 + 1) - (t^3 + t)(4t^3)}{(t^4 - 2)^2} = \dfrac{(3t^6 + t^4 - 6t^2 - 2) - (4t^6 + 4t^4)}{(t^4 - 2)^2}$

$= \dfrac{-t^6 - 3t^4 - 6t^2 - 2}{(t^4 - 2)^2} = -\dfrac{t^6 + 3t^4 + 6t^2 + 2}{(t^4 - 2)^2}$

13. $y = (r^2 - 2r)e^r$ $\Rightarrow$ $y' = (r^2 - 2r)(e^r) + e^r(2r - 2) = e^r(r^2 - 2r + 2r - 2) = e^r(r^2 - 2)$

14. $y = \dfrac{1}{s + ke^s}$ $\Rightarrow$ $y' = \dfrac{(s + ke^s)(0) - (1)(1 + ke^s)}{(s + ke^s)^2} = -\dfrac{1 + ke^s}{(s + ke^s)^2}$

15. $y = \dfrac{v^3 - 2v\sqrt{v}}{v} = v^2 - 2\sqrt{v} = v^2 - 2v^{1/2}$ $\Rightarrow$ $y' = 2v - 2\left(\tfrac{1}{2}\right)v^{-1/2} = 2v - v^{-1/2}$.

We can change the form of the answer as follows: $2v - v^{-1/2} = 2v - \dfrac{1}{\sqrt{v}} = \dfrac{2v\sqrt{v} - 1}{\sqrt{v}} = \dfrac{2v^{3/2} - 1}{\sqrt{v}}$

16. $z = w^{3/2}(w + ce^w) = w^{5/2} + cw^{3/2}e^w$ $\Rightarrow$

$z' = \tfrac{5}{2}w^{3/2} + c\left(w^{3/2} \cdot e^w + e^w \cdot \tfrac{3}{2}w^{1/2}\right) = \tfrac{5}{2}w^{3/2} + \tfrac{1}{2}cw^{1/2}e^w(2w + 3)$

17. $f(x) = \dfrac{x}{x + c/x}$ $\Rightarrow$

$f'(x) = \dfrac{(x + c/x)(1) - x\left(1 - c/x^2\right)}{\left(x + \dfrac{c}{x}\right)^2} = \dfrac{x + c/x - x + c/x}{\left(\dfrac{x^2 + c}{x}\right)^2} = \dfrac{2c/x}{\dfrac{(x^2 + c)^2}{x^2}} \cdot \dfrac{x^2}{x^2} = \dfrac{2cx}{(x^2 + c)^2}$

18. $f(x) = \dfrac{ax+b}{cx+d}$ $\Rightarrow$ $f'(x) = \dfrac{(cx+d)(a) - (ax+b)(c)}{(cx+d)^2} = \dfrac{acx + ad - acx - bc}{(cx+d)^2} = \dfrac{ad - bc}{(cx+d)^2}$

19. $y = 2xe^x$ $\Rightarrow$ $y' = 2(x \cdot e^x + e^x \cdot 1) = 2e^x(x+1)$. At $(0,0)$, $y' = 2e^0(0+1) = 2 \cdot 1 \cdot 1 = 2$, and an equation of the tangent line is $y - 0 = 2(x-0)$, or $y = 2x$.

20. $y = \dfrac{\sqrt{x}}{x+1}$ $\Rightarrow$ $y' = \dfrac{(x+1)\left(\dfrac{1}{2\sqrt{x}}\right) - \sqrt{x}\,(1)}{(x+1)^2} = \dfrac{(x+1) - (2x)}{2\sqrt{x}\,(x+1)^2} = \dfrac{1-x}{2\sqrt{x}\,(x+1)^2}$. At $(4, 0.4)$,

$y' = \frac{-3}{100} = -0.03$, and an equation of the tangent line is $y - 0.4 = -0.03(x-4)$, or $y = -0.03x + 0.52$.

21. (a) $y = f(x) = \dfrac{1}{1+x^2}$ $\Rightarrow$

(b)
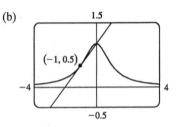

$f'(x) = \dfrac{(1+x^2)(0) - 1(2x)}{(1+x^2)^2} = \dfrac{-2x}{(1+x^2)^2}$. So the slope of the

tangent line at the point $\left(-1, \frac{1}{2}\right)$ is $f'(-1) = \dfrac{2}{2^2} = \frac{1}{2}$ and its

equation is $y - \frac{1}{2} = \frac{1}{2}(x+1)$ or $y = \frac{1}{2}x + 1$.

22. (a) $y = f(x) = \dfrac{x}{1+x^2}$ $\Rightarrow$

(b)
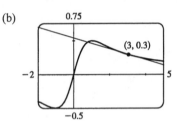

$f'(x) = \dfrac{(1+x^2)1 - x(2x)}{(1+x^2)^2} = \dfrac{1-x^2}{(1+x^2)^2}$. So the slope of the

tangent line at the point $(3, 0.3)$ is $f'(3) = \frac{-8}{100}$ and its equation is

$y - 0.3 = -0.08(x-3)$ or $y = -0.08x + 0.54$.

23. (a) $f(x) = \dfrac{e^x}{x^3}$ $\Rightarrow$ $f'(x) = \dfrac{x^3(e^x) - e^x(3x^2)}{(x^3)^2} = \dfrac{x^2 e^x (x-3)}{x^6} = \dfrac{e^x(x-3)}{x^4}$

(b)
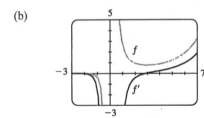

$f' = 0$ when f has a horizontal tangent line, f' is negative when f is decreasing, and f' is positive when f is increasing.

24. (a) $f(x) = \dfrac{x}{x^2 - 1}$ $\Rightarrow$ $f'(x) = \dfrac{(x^2 - 1)1 - x(2x)}{(x^2 - 1)^2} = \dfrac{-x^2 - 1}{(x^2 - 1)^2}$

(b)
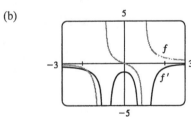

Notice that the slopes of all tangents to f are negative and $f'(x) < 0$ always.

25. (a) $f(x) = (x-1)e^x$ $\Rightarrow$ $f'(x) = (x-1)e^x + e^x(1) = e^x(x - 1 + 1) = xe^x$.

$f''(x) = x(e^x) + e^x(1) = e^x(x+1)$

(b)

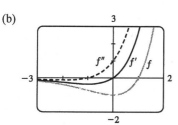

$f' = 0$ when f has a horizontal tangent and $f'' = 0$ when f' has a horizontal tangent. f' is negative when f is decreasing and positive when f is increasing. f'' is negative when f' is decreasing and positive when f' is increasing. f'' is negative when f is concave down and positive when f is concave up.

26. (a) $f(x) = \dfrac{x}{x^2 + 1}$ $\Rightarrow$ $f'(x) = \dfrac{(x^2 + 1)(1) - x(2x)}{(x^2 + 1)^2} = \dfrac{1 - x^2}{(x^2 + 1)^2} = \dfrac{1 - x^2}{x^4 + 2x^2 + 1}$ $\Rightarrow$ $f''(x) =$

$\dfrac{(x^2 + 1)^2 (-2x) - (1 - x^2)(4x^3 + 4x)}{(x^2 + 1)^4} = \dfrac{(2x)(x^2 + 1)\left[-(x^2 + 1) - (1 - x^2)(2)\right]}{(x^2 + 1)^4} = \dfrac{2x(x^2 - 3)}{(x^2 + 1)^3}$

(b)

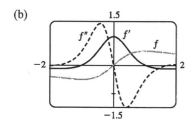

We can see that our answers are plausible, since f has horizontal tangents where $f'(x) = 0$, and f' has horizontal tangents where $f''(x) = 0$.

27. We are given that $f(5) = 1$, $f'(5) = 6$, $g(5) = -3$, and $g'(5) = 2$.

(a) $(fg)'(5) = f(5)g'(5) + g(5)f'(5) = (1)(2) + (-3)(6) = 2 - 18 = -16$

(b) $\left(\dfrac{f}{g}\right)'(5) = \dfrac{g(5)f'(5) - f(5)g'(5)}{[g(5)]^2} = \dfrac{(-3)(6) - (1)(2)}{(-3)^2} = -\dfrac{20}{9}$

(c) $\left(\dfrac{g}{f}\right)'(5) = \dfrac{f(5)g'(5) - g(5)f'(5)}{[f(5)]^2} = \dfrac{(1)(2) - (-3)(6)}{(1)^2} = 20$

28. We are given that $f(3) = 4$, $g(3) = 2$, $f'(3) = -6$, and $g'(3) = 5$.

(a) $(f + g)'(3) = f'(3) + g'(3) = -6 + 5 = -1$

(b) $(fg)'(3) = f(3)g'(3) + g(3)f'(3) = (4)(5) + (2)(-6) = 20 - 12 = 8$

(c) $\left(\dfrac{f}{g}\right)'(3) = \dfrac{g(3)f'(3) - f(3)g'(3)}{[g(3)]^2} = \dfrac{(2)(-6) - (4)(5)}{(2)^2} = \dfrac{-32}{4} = -8$

(d) $\left(\dfrac{f}{f - g}\right)'(3) = \dfrac{[f(3) - g(3)]\,f'(3) - f(3)\,[f'(3) - g'(3)]}{[f(3) - g(3)]^2}$

$\qquad = \dfrac{(4 - 2)(-6) - 4(-6 - 5)}{(4 - 2)^2} = \dfrac{-12 + 44}{2^2} = 8$

29. $f(x) = e^x g(x)$ $\Rightarrow$ $f'(x) = e^x g'(x) + g(x)e^x = e^x\left[g'(x) + g(x)\right]$.

$f'(0) = e^0\left[g'(0) + g(0)\right] = 1(5 + 2) = 7$

30. $\dfrac{d}{dx}\left[\dfrac{h(x)}{x}\right] = \dfrac{xh'(x) - h(x) \cdot 1}{x^2}$ $\Rightarrow$ $\dfrac{d}{dx}\left[\dfrac{h(x)}{x}\right]_{x=2} = \dfrac{2h'(2) - h(2)}{2^2} = \dfrac{2(-3) - (4)}{4} = \dfrac{-10}{4} = -2.5$

31. (a) From the graphs of f and g, we obtain the following values: $f(1) = 2$ since the point $(1,2)$ is on the graph
of f; $g(1) = 1$ since the point $(1,1)$ is on the graph of g; $f'(1) = 2$ since the slope of the line segment between
$(0,0)$ and $(2,4)$ is $\dfrac{4-0}{2-0} = 2$; $g'(1) = -1$ since the slope of the line segment between $(-2,4)$ and $(2,0)$

is $\dfrac{0-4}{2-(-2)} = -1$. Now $u(x) = f(x)g(x)$, so $u'(1) = f(1)g'(1) + g(1)\,f'(1) = 2\cdot(-1) + 1\cdot 2 = 0$.

(b) $v(x) = f(x)/g(x)$, so $v'(5) = \dfrac{g(5)f'(5) - f(5)g'(5)}{[g(5)]^2} = \dfrac{2\left(-\frac{1}{3}\right) - 3\cdot\frac{2}{3}}{2^2} = \dfrac{-\frac{8}{3}}{4} - \dfrac{2}{3}$

32. (a) $y = x^2 f(x) \quad\Rightarrow\quad y' = x^2 f'(x) + f(x)(2x)$

(b) $y = \dfrac{f(x)}{x^2} \quad\Rightarrow\quad y' = \dfrac{x^2 f'(x) - f(x)(2x)}{(x^2)^2} = \dfrac{x f'(x) - 2f(x)}{x^3}$

(c) $y = \dfrac{x^2}{f(x)} \quad\Rightarrow\quad y' = \dfrac{f(x)(2x) - x^2 f'(x)}{[f(x)]^2}$

(d) $y = \dfrac{1 + x f(x)}{\sqrt{x}} \quad\Rightarrow$

$y' = \dfrac{\sqrt{x}\,[x f'(x) + f(x)] - [1 + x f(x)]\dfrac{1}{2\sqrt{x}}}{\left(\sqrt{x}\right)^2}$

$= \dfrac{x^{3/2} f'(x) + x^{1/2} f(x) - \frac{1}{2}x^{-1/2} - \frac{1}{2}x^{1/2} f(x)}{x} \cdot \dfrac{2x^{1/2}}{2x^{1/2}} = \dfrac{x f(x) + 2x^2 f'(x) - 1}{2x^{3/2}}$

33. Let $P(t)$ be the population and let $A(t)$ be the average annual income at time t, where t is measured in years and
$t = 0$ corresponds to July 1993. Then the total personal income is given by $T(t) = P(t)A(t)$. We wish to find
$T'(0)$. $T'(t) = P(t)A'(t) + A(t)P'(t)$. The term $P(t)A'(t)$ represents the portion of the rate of change of total
income due to the existing population's increasing income. The term $A(t)P'(t)$ represents the
portion of the rate of change of total income due to the increasing population.
$T'(0) = P(0)A'(0) + A(0)P'(0) \approx (3{,}354{,}000)(1900) + (21{,}107)(45{,}000) = 7{,}322{,}415{,}000$. So the total
personal income was rising at a rate of about \$7.322 billion per year.

34. (a) $f(20) = 10{,}000$ means that when the price of the fabric is \$20/yard, 10,000 yards will be sold. $f'(20) = -350$
means that as the price of the fabric increases past \$20/yard, the amount of fabric which will be sold is
decreasing at a rate of 350 yards per (dollar per yard).

(b) $R(p) = p f(p) \quad\Rightarrow\quad R'(p) = p f'(p) + f(p)\cdot 1 \quad\Rightarrow$
$R'(20) = 20 f'(20) + f(20)\cdot 1 = 20(-350) + 10{,}000 = 3000$. This means that as the price of the fabric
increases past \$20/yard, the total revenue is increasing at \$3000/(\$/yard). Note that the Product Rule indicates
that we will lose \$7000/(\$/yard) due to selling less fabric, but that that loss is more than made up for by the
additional revenue due to the increase in price.

35. f is increasing when f' is positive. $f(x) = x^3 e^x \quad\Rightarrow\quad f'(x) = x^3 e^x + e^x(3x^2) = x^2 e^x(x+3)$. Now $x^2 \geq 0$
and $e^x > 0$ for all x, so $f'(x) > 0$ when $x + 3 > 0$ and $x \neq 0$; that is, when $x \in (-3,0)\cup(0,\infty)$. So f is
increasing on $(-3,\infty)$.

36. f is concave downward when f'' is negative. $f(x) = x^2 e^x \quad\Rightarrow\quad f'(x) = x^2 e^x + e^x(2x) \quad\Rightarrow$
$f''(x) = x^2 e^x + e^x(2x) + e^x(2) + (2x)e^x = e^x(x^2 + 2x + 2 + 2x) = e^x(x^2 + 4x + 2)$. Note that $e^x > 0$ for
all x and $f''(x) = 0 \quad\Leftrightarrow\quad x = -2 \pm \sqrt{2}$. $f''(x) < 0$ when $x \in (-2-\sqrt{2}, -2+\sqrt{2})$.

37. If $y = f(x) = \dfrac{x}{x+1}$, then $f'(x) = \dfrac{(x+1)(1) - x(1)}{(x+1)^2} = \dfrac{1}{(x+1)^2}$. When $x = a$, the equation of the tangent

line is $y - \dfrac{a}{a+1} = \dfrac{1}{(a+1)^2}(x - a)$. This line passes through $(1, 2)$ when $2 - \dfrac{a}{a+1} = \dfrac{1}{(a+1)^2}(1 - a)$ $\Leftrightarrow$

$2(a+1)^2 - a(a+1) = 1 - a$ $\Leftrightarrow$ $2a^2 + 4a + 2 - a^2 - a - 1 + a = 0$ $\Leftrightarrow$ $a^2 + 4a + 1 = 0$.

The quadratic formula gives the roots of this equation as $a = \dfrac{-4 \pm \sqrt{4^2 - 4(1)(1)}}{2(1)} = \dfrac{-4 \pm \sqrt{12}}{2} = -2 \pm \sqrt{3}$,

so there are two such tangent lines. Since

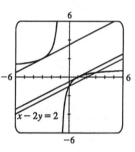

$$f\left(-2 \pm \sqrt{3}\right) = \frac{-2 \pm \sqrt{3}}{-2 \pm \sqrt{3} + 1} = \frac{-2 \pm \sqrt{3}}{-1 \pm \sqrt{3}} \cdot \frac{-1 \mp \sqrt{3}}{-1 \mp \sqrt{3}}$$

$$= \frac{2 \pm 2\sqrt{3} \mp \sqrt{3} - 3}{1 - 3} = \frac{-1 \pm \sqrt{3}}{-2} = \frac{1 \mp \sqrt{3}}{2},$$

the lines touch the curve at $A\left(-2 + \sqrt{3}, \frac{1 - \sqrt{3}}{2}\right) \approx (-0.27, -0.37)$ and

$B\left(-2 - \sqrt{3}, \frac{1 + \sqrt{3}}{2}\right) \approx (-3.73, 1.37)$.

38. $y = \dfrac{x-1}{x+1}$ $\Rightarrow$ $y' = \dfrac{(x+1)(1) - (x-1)(1)}{(x+1)^2} = \dfrac{2}{(x+1)^2}$. If the tangent intersects the curve when $x = a$,

then its slope is $2/(a+1)^2$. But if the tangent is parallel to $x - 2y = 2$,

that is, $y = \frac{1}{2}x - 1$, then its slope is $\frac{1}{2}$. Thus, $\dfrac{2}{(a+1)^2} = \dfrac{1}{2}$ $\Rightarrow$

$(a+1)^2 = 4$ $\Rightarrow$ $a + 1 = \pm 2$ $\Rightarrow$ $a = 1$ or -3. When $a = 1$, $y = 0$

and the equation of the tangent is $y - 0 = \frac{1}{2}(x - 1)$ or $y = \frac{1}{2}x - \frac{1}{2}$.

When $a = -3$, $y = 2$ and the equation of the tangent is $y - 2 = \frac{1}{2}(x + 3)$

or $y = \frac{1}{2}x + \frac{7}{2}$.

We will sometimes use the form $f'g + fg'$ rather than the form $fg' + gf'$ for the Product Rule.

39. (a) $(fgh)' = [(fg)h]' = (fg)'h + (fg)h' = (f'g + fg')h + (fg)h' = f'gh + fg'h + fgh'$

(b) Putting $f = g = h$ in part (a), we have

$$\frac{d}{dx}[f(x)]^3 = (fff)' = f'ff + ff'f + fff' = 3fff' = 3[f(x)]^2 f'(x).$$

(c) $\dfrac{d}{dx}\left(e^{3x}\right) = \dfrac{d}{dx}\left(e^x\right)^3 = 3(e^x)^2 e^x = 3e^{2x}e^x = 3e^{3x}$

40. (a) We use the Product Rule repeatedly: $F = fg$ $\Rightarrow$ $F' = f'g + fg'$ $\Rightarrow$

$F'' = (f''g + f'g') + (f'g' + fg'') = f''g + 2f'g' + fg''$.

(b) $F''' = f'''g + f''g' + 2(f''g' + f'g'') + f'g'' + fg''' = f'''g + 3f''g' + 3f'g'' + fg'''$ $\Rightarrow$

$F^{(4)} = f^{(4)}g + f'''g' + 3(f'''g' + f''g'') + 3(f''g'' + f'g''') + f'g''' + fg^{(4)}$

$= f^{(4)}g + 4f'''g' + 6f''g'' + 4f'g''' + fg^{(4)}$

(c) By analogy with the Binomial Theorem, we make the guess:

$$F^{(n)} = f^{(n)}g + nf^{(n-1)}g' + \binom{n}{2}f^{(n-2)}g'' + \cdots + \binom{n}{k}f^{(n-k)}g^{(k)} + \cdots + nf'g^{(n-1)} + fg^{(n)}, \text{ where}$$

$$\binom{n}{k} = \frac{n!}{k!\,(n-k)!} = \frac{n(n-1)(n-2)\cdots(n-k+1)}{k!}.$$

41. For $f(x) = x^2 e^x$, $f'(x) = x^2 e^x + e^x(2x) = e^x(x^2 + 2x)$. Similarly, we have

$$f''(x) = e^x(x^2 + 4x + 2)$$

$$f'''(x) = e^x(x^2 + 6x + 6)$$

$$f^{(4)}(x) = e^x(x^2 + 8x + 12)$$

$$f^{(5)}(x) = e^x(x^2 + 10x + 20)$$

It appears that the coefficient of x in the quadratic term increases by 2 with each differentiation. The pattern for the constant terms seems to be $0 = 1 \cdot 0, 2 = 2 \cdot 1, 6 = 3 \cdot 2, 12 = 4 \cdot 3, 20 = 5 \cdot 4$. So a reasonable guess is that $f^{(n)}(x) = e^x[x^2 + 2nx + n(n-1)]$.

Proof: Let S_n be the statement that $f^{(n)}(x) = e^x[x^2 + 2nx + n(n-1)]$.

1. S_1 is true because $f'(x) = e^x(x^2 + 2x)$.

2. Assume that S_k is true; that is, $f^{(k)}(x) = e^x[x^2 + 2kx + k(k-1)]$. Then

$$f^{(k+1)}(x) = \frac{d}{dx}\left[f^{(k)}(x)\right] = e^x(2x + 2k) + [x^2 + 2kx + k(k-1)]e^x$$

$$= e^x[x^2 + (2k+2)x + (k^2+k)] = e^x[x^2 + 2(k+1)x + (k+1)k]$$

This shows that S_{k+1} is true.

3. Therefore, by mathematical induction, S_n is true for all n; that is, $f^{(n)}(x) = e^x[x^2 + 2nx + n(n-1)]$

   for every positive integer n.

42. (a) Let $f(x) = 1/g(x)$. By the definition of derivative,

$$f'(x) = \lim_{h \to 0} \frac{f(x+h) - f(x)}{h} = \lim_{h \to 0} \frac{1/g(x+h) - 1/g(x)}{h} = \lim_{h \to 0} \frac{g(x) - g(x+h)}{hg(x)g(x+h)}$$

$$= -\lim_{h \to 0} \frac{g(x+h) - g(x)}{h} \cdot \lim_{h \to 0} \frac{1}{g(x)g(x+h)} = -g'(x) \cdot \frac{1}{[g(x)]^2}$$

Thus, $\dfrac{d}{dx}\left[\dfrac{1}{g(x)}\right] = -\dfrac{g'(x)}{[g(x)]^2}$.

(b) $y = \dfrac{1}{s + ke^s} \quad \Rightarrow \quad y' = -\dfrac{1 + ke^s}{(s + ke^s)^2}$

43. $\dfrac{d}{dx}(x^{-n}) = \dfrac{d}{dx}\left(\dfrac{1}{x^n}\right) = -\dfrac{nx^{n-1}}{(x^n)^2} = -n \cdot \dfrac{x^{n-1}}{x^{2n}} - nx^{n-1-2n} = -nx^{-n-1}$

44. $\dfrac{d}{dx}\left[\dfrac{f(x)}{g(x)}\right] = \dfrac{d}{dx}\left[f(x) \cdot \dfrac{1}{g(x)}\right] = f(x)\dfrac{d}{dx}\left[\dfrac{1}{g(x)}\right] + \dfrac{1}{g(x)}\dfrac{d}{dx}[f(x)]$

$$= f(x)\left[-\dfrac{g'(x)}{[g(x)]^2}\right] + \dfrac{1}{g(x)}f'(x) = \dfrac{-f(x)g'(x) + g(x)f'(x)}{[g(x)]^2} = \dfrac{gf' - fg'}{g^2}$$

3.3 Rates of Change in the Natural and Social Sciences · · ·

1. (a) $s = f(t) = t^3 - 12t^2 + 36t \implies v(t) = f'(t) = 3t^2 - 24t + 36$

(b) $v(3) = 27 - 72 + 36 = -9 \text{ m/s}$

(c) The particle is at rest when $v(t) = 0$. $3t^2 - 24t + 36 = 0 \implies 3(t-2)(t-6) = 0 \implies t = 2, 6$.

(d) The particle is moving in the positive direction when $v(t) > 0$. $3(t-2)(t-6) > 0 \iff 0 \le t < 2$ or $t > 6$.

(e) Since the particle is moving forward and backward, we need to calculate the distance traveled in the intervals $[0, 2]$, $[2, 6]$, and $[6, 8]$ separately.

$|f(2) - f(0)| = |32 - 0| = 32$.

$|f(6) - f(2)| = |0 - 32| = 32$.

$|f(8) - f(6)| = |32 - 0| = 32$.

The total distance is $32 + 32 + 32 = 96$ m.

(f)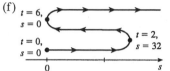

(g) $a(t) = v'(t) = 6t - 24$. $a(3) = 6(3) - 24 = -6 \text{ (m/s)/s or m/s}^2$.

(h)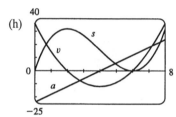

(i) The particle is speeding up when v and a have the same sign. This occurs when $2 < t < 4$ and when $t > 6$. It is slowing down when v and a have opposite signs; that is, when $0 \le t < 2$ and when $4 < t < 6$.

2. (a) $x(t) = \dfrac{t}{1+t^2} \implies v(t) = x'(t) = \dfrac{(1+t^2)(1) - t(2t)}{(1+t^2)^2} = \dfrac{1-t^2}{(1+t^2)^2}$

(b) Right: $v(t) > 0 \implies 1 - t^2 > 0 \implies t^2 < 1 \implies |t| < 1 \implies 0 \le t < 1$

Left: $v(t) < 0 \implies 1 - t^2 < 0 \implies t > 1$

(c) $|x(1) - x(0)| + |x(4) - x(1)| = \left|\frac{1}{2} - 0\right| + \left|\frac{4}{17} - \frac{1}{2}\right| = \frac{1}{2} + \frac{9}{34} = \frac{13}{17}$

(d) $a(t) = v'(t) = \dfrac{2t(t^2 - 3)}{(1+t^2)^3}$. $a(t) = 0 \implies 2t(t^2 - 3) = 0 \implies t = 0 \text{ or } \sqrt{3}$

(e)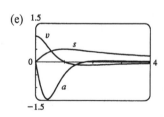

(f) v and a have the same sign and the particle is speeding up when $1 < t < \sqrt{3}$. The particle is slowing down and v and a have opposite signs when $0 < t < 1$ and when $t > \sqrt{3}$.

3. (a) $s(t) = t^3 - 4.5t^2 - 7t \implies v(t) = s'(t) = 3t^2 - 9t - 7 = 5 \iff 3t^2 - 9t - 12 = 0 \iff 3(t-4)(t+1) = 0 \iff t = 4$ or -1. Since $t \ge 0$, the particle reaches a velocity of 5 m/s at $t = 4$ s.

(b) $a(t) = v'(t) = 6t - 9 = 0 \iff t = 1.5$. The acceleration changes from negative to positive, so the velocity changes from decreasing to increasing. Thus, at $t = 1.5$ s, the velocity has its minimum value.

4. (a) At maximum height the velocity of the ball is 0 ft/s. $v(t) = s'(t) = 80 - 32t = 0 \iff 32t = 80 \iff$
$t = \frac{5}{2}$. So the maximum height is $s\left(\frac{5}{2}\right) = 80\left(\frac{5}{2}\right) - 16\left(\frac{5}{2}\right)^2 = 200 - 100 = 100$ ft.

(b) $s(t) = 80t - 16t^2 = 96 \iff 16t^2 - 80t + 96 = 0 \iff 16(t^2 - 5t + 6) = 0 \iff 16(t-3)(t-2) = 0.$
So the ball has a height of 96 ft on the way up at $t = 2$ and on the way down at $t = 3$. At these times the
velocities are $v(2) = 80 - 32(2) = 16$ ft/s and $v(3) = 80 - 32(3) = -16$ ft/s, respectively.

5. (a) $A(x) = x^2 \implies A'(x) = 2x$. $A'(15) = 30$ mm²/mm is the rate at which the area is increasing with respect
to the side length as x reaches 15 mm.

(b) The perimeter is $P(x) = 4x$, so
$A'(x) = 2x = \frac{1}{2}(4x) = \frac{1}{2}P(x)$. The figure suggests that if
Δx is small, then the change in the area of the square is
approximately half of its perimeter (2 of the 4 sides) times
Δx. From the figure, $\Delta A = 2x(\Delta x) + (\Delta x)^2$. If Δx is
small, then $\Delta A \approx 2x(\Delta x)$ and so $\Delta A/\Delta x \approx 2x$.

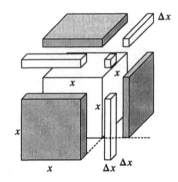

6. (a) $V(x) = x^3 \implies \dfrac{dV}{dx} = 3x^2$. $\dfrac{dV}{dx}\bigg|_{x=3} = 3(3)^2 = 27$ mm³/mm is

the rate at which the volume is increasing as x increases past 15 mm.

(b) The surface area is $S(x) = 6x^2$, so
$V'(x) = 3x^2 = \frac{1}{2}(6x^2) = \frac{1}{2}S(x)$. The figure suggests that if Δx is
small, then the change in the volume of the cube is approximately half
of its surface area (the area of 3 of the 6 faces) times Δx. From the
figure, $\Delta V = 3x^2(\Delta x) + 3x(\Delta x)^2 + (\Delta x)^3$. If Δx is small, then
$\Delta V \approx 3x^2(\Delta x)$ and so $\Delta V/\Delta x \approx 3x^2$.

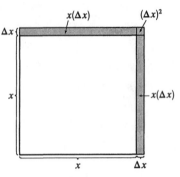

7. (a) Using $A(r) = \pi r^2$, we find that the average rate of change is:

(i) $\dfrac{A(3) - A(2)}{3 - 2} = \dfrac{9\pi - 4\pi}{1} = 5\pi$

(ii) $\dfrac{A(2.5) - A(2)}{2.5 - 2} = \dfrac{6.25\pi - 4\pi}{0.5} = 4.5\pi$

(iii) $\dfrac{A(2.1) - A(2)}{2.1 - 2} = \dfrac{4.41\pi - 4\pi}{0.1} = 4.1\pi$

(b) $A(r) = \pi r^2 \implies A'(r) = 2\pi r$, so $A'(2) = 4\pi$.

(c) The circumference is $C(r) = 2\pi r = A'(r)$. The figure suggests that if Δr is
small, then the change in the area of the circle (a ring around the outside) is
approximately equal to its circumference times Δr. Straightening out this ring
gives us a shape that is approximately rectangular with length $2\pi r$ and width
Δr, so $\Delta A \approx 2\pi r(\Delta r)$. Algebraically,
$\Delta A = A(r + \Delta r) - A(r) = \pi(r + \Delta r)^2 - \pi r^2 = 2\pi r(\Delta r) + \pi(\Delta r)^2$. So
we see that if Δr is small, then $\Delta A \approx 2\pi r(\Delta r)$ and therefore,
$\Delta A/\Delta r \approx 2\pi r$.

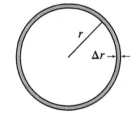

8. After t seconds the radius is $r = 60t$, so the area is $A(t) = \pi(60t)^2 = 3600\pi t^2$ $\Rightarrow$ $A'(t) = 7200\pi t$ $\Rightarrow$

(a) $A'(1) = 7200\pi$ cm^2/s

(b) $A'(3) = 21{,}600\pi$ cm^2/s

(c) $A'(5) = 36{,}000\pi$ cm^2/s

As time goes by, the area grows at an increasing rate. In fact, the rate of change is linear with respect to time.

9. $S(r) = 4\pi r^2$ $\Rightarrow$ $S'(r) = 8\pi r$ $\Rightarrow$

(a) $S'(1) = 8\pi$ ft^2/ft

(b) $S'(2) = 16\pi$ ft^2/ft

(c) $S'(3) = 24\pi$ ft^2/ft

As the radius increases, the surface area grows at an increasing rate. In fact, the rate of change is linear with respect to the radius.

10. (a) Using $V(r) = \frac{4}{3}\pi r^3$, we find that the average rate of change is:

(i) $\dfrac{V(8) - V(5)}{8 - 5} = \dfrac{\frac{4}{3}\pi(512) - \frac{4}{3}\pi(125)}{3} = 172\pi \ \mu\text{m}^3/\mu\text{m}$

(ii) $\dfrac{V(6) - V(5)}{6 - 5} = \dfrac{\frac{4}{3}\pi(216) - \frac{4}{3}\pi(125)}{1} = 121.\overline{3}\pi \ \mu\text{m}^3/\mu\text{m}$

(iii) $\dfrac{V(5.1) - V(5)}{5.1 - 5} = \dfrac{\frac{4}{3}\pi(5.1)^3 - \frac{4}{3}\pi(5)^3}{0.1} = 102.01\overline{3}\pi \ \mu\text{m}^3/\mu\text{m}$

(b) $V'(r) = 4\pi r^2$, so $V'(5) = 100\pi \ \mu\text{m}^3/\mu\text{m}$.

(c) $V(r) = \frac{4}{3}\pi r^3$ $\Rightarrow$ $V'(r) = 4\pi r^2 = S(r)$. By analogy with Exercise 7(c), we can say that the change in the volume of the spherical shell, ΔV, is approximately equal to its thickness, Δr, times the surface area of the inner sphere. Thus, $\Delta V \approx 4\pi r^2(\Delta r)$ and so $\Delta V/\Delta r \approx 4\pi r^2$.

11. The mass is $f(x) = 3x^2$, so the linear density at x is $\rho(x) = f'(x) = 6x$.

(a) $\rho(1) = 6$ kg/m

(b) $\rho(2) = 12$ kg/m

(c) $\rho(3) = 18$ kg/m

Since ρ is an increasing function, the density will be the highest at the right end of the rod and lowest at the left end.

12. $V(t) = 5000\left(1 - \frac{1}{40}t\right)^2 = 5000\left(1 - \frac{1}{20}t + \frac{1}{1600}t^2\right)$ $\Rightarrow$ $V'(t) = 5000\left(-\frac{1}{20} + \frac{1}{800}t\right) = -250\left(1 - \frac{1}{40}t\right)$

(a) $V'(5) = -250\left(1 - \frac{5}{40}\right) = -218.75$ gal/min

(b) $V'(10) = -250\left(1 - \frac{10}{40}\right) = -187.5$ gal/min

(c) $V'(20) = -250\left(1 - \frac{20}{40}\right) = -125$ gal/min

(d) $V'(40) = -250\left(1 - \frac{40}{40}\right) = 0$ gal/min

The water is flowing out the fastest at the beginning — when $t = 0$, $V'(t) = -250$ gal/min. The water is flowing out the slowest at the end — when $t = 40$, $V'(t) = 0$. As the tank empties, the water flows out more slowly.

13. The quantity of charge is $Q(t) = t^3 - 2t^2 + 6t + 2$, so the current is $Q'(t) = 3t^2 - 4t + 6$.

(a) $Q'(0.5) = 3(0.5)^2 - 4(0.5) + 6 = 4.75$ A

(b) $Q'(1) = 3(1)^2 - 4(1) + 6 = 5$ A

The current is lowest when Q' has a minimum. $Q''(t) = 6t - 4 < 0$ when $t < \frac{2}{3}$. So the current decreases when $t < \frac{2}{3}$ and increases when $t > \frac{2}{3}$. Thus, the current is lowest at $t = \frac{2}{3}$ s.

14. (a) $F = \dfrac{GmM}{r^2} = (GmM)r^{-2} \Rightarrow \dfrac{dF}{dr} = -2(GmM)r^{-3} = -\dfrac{2GmM}{r^3}$, which is the rate of change of the

force with respect to the distance between the bodies. The minus sign indicates that as the distance r between the bodies increases, the magnitude of the force F exerted by the body of mass m on the body of mass M is decreasing.

(b) Given $F'(20,000) = -2$, find $F'(10,000)$. $-2 = -\dfrac{2GmM}{20,000^3} \Rightarrow GmM = 20,000^3$.

$$F'(10,000) = -\dfrac{2\left(20,000^3\right)}{10,000^3} = -2 \cdot 2^3 = -16 \text{ N/km}$$

15. (a) To find the rate of change of volume with respect to pressure, we first solve for V in terms of P.

$$PV = C \Rightarrow V = \dfrac{C}{P} \Rightarrow \dfrac{dV}{dP} = -\dfrac{C}{P^2}.$$

(b) From the formula for dV/dP in part (a), we see that as P increases, the absolute value of dV/dP decreases. Thus, the volume is decreasing more rapidly at the beginning.

(c) $\beta = -\dfrac{1}{V}\dfrac{dV}{dP} = -\dfrac{1}{V}\left(-\dfrac{C}{P^2}\right) = \dfrac{C}{(PV)P} = \dfrac{C}{CP} = \dfrac{1}{P}$

16. (a) (i) $\dfrac{C(6) - C(2)}{6 - 2} = \dfrac{0.0295 - 0.0570}{4}$

$= -0.006875 \text{ (moles/L)/min}$

(ii) $\dfrac{C(4) - C(2)}{4 - 2} = \dfrac{0.0408 - 0.0570}{2}$

$= -0.008 \text{ (moles/L)/min}$

(iii) $\dfrac{C(2) - C(0)}{2 - 0} = \dfrac{0.0570 - 0.0800}{2}$

$= -0.0115 \text{ (moles/L)/min}$

(b) Slope $= \dfrac{\Delta C}{\Delta t} \approx -\dfrac{0.077}{7.8} \approx -0.01 \text{ (moles/L)/min}$

(c) From the graph in part (b), we see that the reaction is slowing down, because the magnitude of the slope is getting smaller.

17. (a) 1920: $m_1 = \dfrac{1860 - 1750}{1920 - 1910} = \dfrac{110}{10} = 11$, $m_2 = \dfrac{2070 - 1860}{1930 - 1920} = \dfrac{210}{10} = 21$,

$(m_1 + m_2)/2 = (11 + 21)/2 = 16 \text{ million/year}$

1980: $m_1 = \dfrac{4450 - 3710}{1980 - 1970} = \dfrac{740}{10} = 74$, $m_2 = \dfrac{5280 - 4450}{1990 - 1980} = \dfrac{830}{10} = 83$,

$(m_1 + m_2)/2 = (74 + 83)/2 = 78.5 \text{ million/year}$

(b) $P(t) = at^3 + bt^2 + ct + d$, where $a = 0.0012354312$, $b = -6.722261072$, $c = 12,165.08275$, and $d = -7,318,428.648$.

(c) $P(t) = at^3 + bt^2 + ct + d \Rightarrow P'(t) = 3at^2 + 2bt + c$

(d) $P'(1920) = 3(0.0012354312)(1920)^2 + 2(-6.722261072)(1920) + 12,165.08275$

$= 14,481,352/\text{year}$ [smaller than the answer in part (a), but close to it]

$P'(1980) = 75,082,751/\text{year}$ (smaller, but close)

(e) $P'(1985) = 81,337,413/\text{year}$, so the rate of growth in 1985 was about 81.3 million/year.

18. (a) $A(t) = at^4 + bt^3 + ct^2 + dt + e$, where $a = -5.8275058275396 \times 10^{-6}$, $b = 0.0460458430461$, $c = -136.43277039706$, $d = 179,661.02676871$, and $e = -88,717,597.060767$.

(b) $A(t) = at^4 + bt^3 + ct^2 + dt + e \Rightarrow A'(t) = 4at^3 + 3bt^2 + 2ct + d$

(c) $A'(1990) \approx 0.0833$ years of age per year

(d)

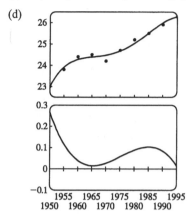

19. (a) $[C] = \dfrac{a^2 kt}{akt + 1}$ $\Rightarrow$

$\text{rate of reaction} = \dfrac{d\,[C]}{dt} = \dfrac{(akt + 1)\left(a^2 k\right) - \left(a^2 kt\right)(ak)}{(akt + 1)^2} = \dfrac{a^2 k(akt + 1 - akt)}{(akt + 1)^2} = \dfrac{a^2 k}{(akt + 1)^2}$

(b) If $x = [C]$, then $a - x = a - \dfrac{a^2 kt}{akt + 1} = \dfrac{a^2 kt + a - a^2 kt}{akt + 1} = \dfrac{a}{akt + 1}.$

So $k(a - x)^2 = k\left(\dfrac{a}{akt + 1}\right)^2 = \dfrac{a^2 k}{(akt + 1)^2} = \dfrac{d\,[C]}{dt}$ [from part (a)] $= \dfrac{dx}{dt}.$

(c) As $t \to \infty$, $[C] = \dfrac{a^2 kt}{akt + 1} = \dfrac{\left(a^2 kt\right)/t}{(akt + 1)/t} = \dfrac{a^2 k}{ak + (1/t)} \to \dfrac{a^2 k}{ak} = a$ moles/L.

(d) As $t \to \infty$, $\dfrac{d[C]}{dt} = \dfrac{a^2 k}{(akt + 1)^2} \to 0.$

(e) As t increases, nearly all of the reactants A and B are converted into product C. In practical terms, the reaction virtually stops.

20. (a) After an hour the population is $n(1) = 3 \cdot 500$; after two hours it is $n(2) = 3(3 \cdot 500) = 3^2 \cdot 500$; after three hours, $n(3) = 3\left(3^2 \cdot 500\right) = 3^3 \cdot 500$; after four hours, $n(4) = 3^4 \cdot 500$. From this pattern, we see that the population after t hours is $n(t) = 3^t \cdot 500 = 500 \cdot 3^t$.

(b) From (5) in Section 3.1, we have $\dfrac{d}{dx}(3^x) \approx (1.10)3^x$. Thus, for $n(t) = 500 \cdot 3^t$,

$\dfrac{dn}{dt} = 500\,\dfrac{d}{dt}(3^t) \approx 500(1.10)3^t$ $\Rightarrow$ $\dfrac{dn}{dt}\bigg|_{t=6} \approx 500(1.10)3^6 \approx 400{,}950$ bacteria/hour.

21. (a) Using $v = \dfrac{P}{4\eta l}\left(R^2 - r^2\right)$ with $R = 0.01$, $l = 3$, $P = 3000$, and $\eta = 0.027$, we have v as a function of r:

$v(r) = \dfrac{3000}{4(0.027)3}\left(0.01^2 - r^2\right)$. $v(0) = 0.\overline{925}$ cm/s, $v(0.005) = 0.69\overline{4}$ cm/s, $v(0.01) = 0$.

(b) $v(r) = \dfrac{P}{4\eta l}\left(R^2 - r^2\right)$ $\Rightarrow$ $v'(r) = \dfrac{P}{4\eta l}(-2r) = -\dfrac{Pr}{2\eta l}$. When $l = 3$, $P = 3000$, and $\eta = 0.027$, we have

$v'(r) = -\dfrac{3000r}{2(0.027)3}$. $v'(0) = 0$, $v'(0.005) = -92.\overline{592}$ (cm/s) /cm, and $v'(0.01) = -185.\overline{185}$ (cm/s)/cm.

(c) The velocity is greatest where $r = 0$ (at the center) and the velocity is changing most where $r = R = 0.01$ cm (at the edge).

22. (a) (i) $f = \dfrac{1}{2L}\sqrt{\dfrac{T}{\rho}} = \left(\dfrac{1}{2}\sqrt{\dfrac{T}{\rho}}\right)L^{-1}$ $\Rightarrow$ $\dfrac{df}{dL} = -\left(\dfrac{1}{2}\sqrt{\dfrac{T}{\rho}}\right)L^{-2} = -\dfrac{1}{2L^2}\sqrt{\dfrac{T}{\rho}}$

(ii) $f = \dfrac{1}{2L}\sqrt{\dfrac{T}{\rho}} = \left(\dfrac{1}{2L\sqrt{\rho}}\right)T^{1/2}$ $\Rightarrow$ $\dfrac{df}{dT} = \dfrac{1}{2}\left(\dfrac{1}{2L\sqrt{\rho}}\right)T^{-1/2} = \dfrac{1}{4L\sqrt{T\rho}}$

(iii) $f = \dfrac{1}{2L}\sqrt{\dfrac{T}{\rho}} = \left(\dfrac{\sqrt{T}}{2L}\right)\rho^{-1/2}$ $\Rightarrow$ $\dfrac{df}{d\rho} = -\dfrac{1}{2}\left(\dfrac{\sqrt{T}}{2L}\right)\rho^{-3/2} = -\dfrac{\sqrt{T}}{4L\rho^{3/2}}$

(b) *Note:* Illustrating tangent lines on the generic figures may help to explain the results.

(i) $\dfrac{df}{dL} < 0$ and L is decreasing $\Rightarrow$ f is increasing $\Rightarrow$ higher note

(ii) $\dfrac{df}{dT} > 0$ and T is increasing $\Rightarrow$ f is increasing $\Rightarrow$ higher note

(iii) $\dfrac{df}{d\rho} < 0$ and ρ is increasing $\Rightarrow$ f is decreasing $\Rightarrow$ lower note

(i)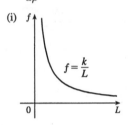

(ii)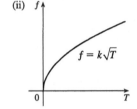

(iii)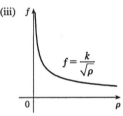

23. (a) $C(x) = 2000 + 3x + 0.01x^2 + 0.0002x^3$ $\Rightarrow$ $C'(x) = 3 + 0.02x + 0.0006x^2$

(b) $C'(100) = 3 + 0.02(100) + 0.0006(10{,}000) = 3 + 2 + 6 = \$11/\text{pair}$. $C'(100)$ is the rate at which the cost is increasing as the 100th pair of jeans is produced. It predicts the cost of the 101st pair.

(c) The cost of manufacturing the 101st pair of jeans is

$$C(101) - C(100) = (2000 + 303 + 102.01 + 206.0602) - (2000 + 300 + 100 + 200)$$
$$= 11.0702 \approx \$11.07$$

24. (a) $C(x) = 84 + 0.16x - 0.0006x^2 + 0.000003x^3$ $\Rightarrow$ $C'(x) = 0.16 - 0.0012x + 0.000009x^2$ $\Rightarrow$ $C'(100) = 0.13$. This is the rate at which the cost is increasing as the 100th item is produced.

(b) $C(101) - C(100) = 97.13030299 - 97 \approx \$0.13$.

(c)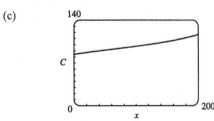

From the graph, we can estimate the x-coordinate of the point of inflection to be between 60 and 80.

(d) $C''(x) = -0.0012 + 0.000018x = 0$ $\Rightarrow$ $x = 66\frac{2}{3}$ and $C''(x)$ changes from negative to positive at this value of x. This is where the *marginal cost* changes from decreasing to increasing and so has its minimum value.

25. (a) $A(x) = \dfrac{p(x)}{x} \;\Rightarrow\; A'(x) = \dfrac{xp'(x) - p(x) \cdot 1}{x^2} = \dfrac{xp'(x) - p(x)}{x^2}$. $A'(x) > 0 \;\Rightarrow\; A(x)$ is increasing; that

is, the average productivity increases as the size of the work force increases.

(b) $p'(x)$ is greater than the average productivity $\;\Rightarrow\; p'(x) > A(x) \;\Rightarrow\; p'(x) > \dfrac{p(x)}{x} \;\Rightarrow$

$xp'(x) > p(x) \;\Rightarrow\; xp'(x) - p(x) > 0 \;\Rightarrow\; \dfrac{xp'(x) - p(x)}{x^2} > 0 \;\Rightarrow\; A'(x) > 0$.

26. (a) $S = \dfrac{dR}{dx} = \dfrac{\left(1 + 4x^{0.4}\right)\left(9.6x^{-0.6}\right) - \left(40 + 24x^{0.4}\right)\left(1.6x^{-0.6}\right)}{\left(1 + 4x^{0.4}\right)^2}$

$= \dfrac{9.6x^{-0.6} + 38.4x^{-0.2} - 64x^{-0.6} - 38.4x^{-0.2}}{\left(1 + 4x^{0.4}\right)^2} = -\dfrac{54.4x^{-0.6}}{\left(1 + 4x^{0.4}\right)^2}$

(b)

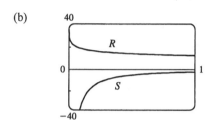

At low levels of brightness, R is quite large $[R(0) = 40]$ and is quickly decreasing, that is, S is negative with large absolute value. This is to be expected: at low levels of brightness, the eye is more sensitive to slight changes than it is at higher levels of brightness.

27. $PV = nRT \;\Rightarrow\; T = \dfrac{PV}{nR} = \dfrac{PV}{(10)(0.0821)} = \dfrac{1}{0.821}(PV)$. Using the Product Rule, we have

$\dfrac{dT}{dt} = \dfrac{1}{0.821}\left[P(t)V'(t) + V(t)P'(t)\right] = \dfrac{1}{0.821}\left[(8)(-0.15) + (10)(0.10)\right] \approx -0.2436 \text{ K/min}$.

28. (a) If $dP/dt = 0$, the population is stable (it is constant).

(b) $\dfrac{dP}{dt} = 0 \;\Rightarrow\; \beta P = r_0\left(1 - \dfrac{P}{P_c}\right)P \;\Rightarrow\; \dfrac{\beta}{r_0} = 1 - \dfrac{P}{P_c} \;\Rightarrow\; \dfrac{P}{P_c} = 1 - \dfrac{\beta}{r_0} \;\Rightarrow\; P = P_c\left(1 - \dfrac{\beta}{r_0}\right)$.

If $P_c = 10{,}000$, $r_0 = 5\% = 0.05$, and $\beta = 4\% = 0.04$, then $P = 10{,}000\left(1 - \frac{4}{5}\right) = 2000$.

(c) If $\beta = 0.05$, then $P = 10{,}000\left(1 - \frac{5}{5}\right) = 0$. There is no stable population.

29. (a) If the populations are stable, then the growth rates are neither positive nor negative; that is,

$\dfrac{dC}{dt} = 0$ and $\dfrac{dW}{dt} = 0$.

(b) "The caribou go extinct" means that the population is zero, or mathematically, $C = 0$.

(c) We have the equations $\dfrac{dC}{dt} = aC - bCW$ and $\dfrac{dW}{dt} = -cW + dCW$. Let $dC/dt = dW/dt = 0$, $a = 0.05$,

$b = 0.001$, $c = 0.05$, and $d = 0.0001$ to obtain **(1)** $0.05C - 0.001CW = 0$ and

(2) $-0.05W + 0.0001CW = 0$. Adding 10 times **(2)** to **(1)** eliminates the CW-terms and gives us

$0.05C - 0.5W = 0 \;\Rightarrow\; C = 10W$. Substituting $C = 10W$ into **(1)** results in

$0.05(10W) - 0.001(10W)W = 0 \;\Leftrightarrow\; 0.5W - 0.01W^2 = 0 \;\Leftrightarrow\; 50W - W^2 = 0 \;\Leftrightarrow$

$W(50 - W) = 0 \;\Leftrightarrow\; W = 0$ or 50. Since $C = 10W$, $C = 0$ or 500. Thus, the population pairs (C, W)

that lead to stable populations are $(0, 0)$ and $(500, 50)$. So it is possible for the two species to live in harmony.

3.4 Derivatives of Trigonometric Functions • • • • • • •

1. $f(x) = x - 3\sin x \implies f'(x) = 1 - 3\cos x$

2. $f(x) = x\sin x \implies f'(x) = x \cdot \cos x + (\sin x) \cdot 1 = x\cos x + \sin x$

3. $g(t) = t^3 \cos t \implies g'(t) = t^3(-\sin t) + (\cos t) \cdot 3t^2 = 3t^2 \cos t - t^3 \sin t$ or $t^2(3\cos t - t\sin t)$

4. $g(t) = 4\sec t + \tan t \implies g'(t) = 4\sec t \tan t + \sec^2 t$

5. $h(\theta) = \csc\theta + e^\theta \cot\theta \implies$
$h'(\theta) = -\csc\theta\cot\theta + e^\theta\left(-\csc^2\theta\right) + (\cot\theta)e^\theta = -\csc\theta\cot\theta + e^\theta\left(\cot\theta - \csc^2\theta\right)$

6. $y = e^u(\cos u + cu) \implies y' = e^u(-\sin u + c) + (\cos u + cu)e^u = e^u(\cos u - \sin u + cu + c)$

7. $y = \dfrac{\tan x}{x} \implies \dfrac{dy}{dx} = \dfrac{x\sec^2 x - \tan x}{x^2}$

8. $y = \dfrac{\sin x}{1 + \cos x} \implies$
$\dfrac{dy}{dx} = \dfrac{(1 + \cos x)\cos x - \sin x\,(-\sin x)}{(1 + \cos x)^2} = \dfrac{\cos x + \cos^2 x + \sin^2 x}{(1 + \cos x)^2} = \dfrac{\cos x + 1}{(1 + \cos x)^2} = \dfrac{1}{1 + \cos x}$

9. $y = \dfrac{x}{\sin x + \cos x} \implies$
$\dfrac{dy}{dx} = \dfrac{(\sin x + \cos x) - x(\cos x - \sin x)}{(\sin x + \cos x)^2} = \dfrac{\sin x + \cos x - x\cos x + x\sin x}{\sin^2 x + \cos^2 x + 2\sin x\cos x}$
$= \dfrac{\sin x + \cos x + x\sin x - x\cos x}{1 + \sin 2x}$ or $\dfrac{(1 + x)\sin x + (1 - x)\cos x}{1 + \sin 2x}$

10. $y = \dfrac{\tan x - 1}{\sec x} \implies$
$\dfrac{dy}{dx} = \dfrac{\sec x\sec^2 x - (\tan x - 1)\sec x\tan x}{\sec^2 x} = \dfrac{\sec x\left(\sec^2 x - \tan^2 x + \tan x\right)}{\sec^2 x} = \dfrac{1 + \tan x}{\sec x}$
Another method: Simplify y first: $y = \sin x - \cos x \implies y' = \cos x + \sin x$.

11. $y = \sec\theta\tan\theta \implies y' = \sec\theta\left(\sec^2\theta\right) + \tan\theta\left(\sec\theta\tan\theta\right) = \sec\theta\left(\sec^2\theta + \tan^2\theta\right)$
Using the identity $1 + \tan^2\theta = \sec^2\theta$, we can write alternative forms of the answer as
$$\sec\theta\left(1 + 2\tan^2\theta\right) \quad \text{or} \quad \sec\theta\left(2\sec^2\theta - 1\right)$$

12. $y = \csc\theta\,(\theta + \cot\theta) \implies$
$y' = \csc\theta\left(1 - \csc^2\theta\right) + (\theta + \cot\theta)(-\csc\theta\cot\theta) = \csc\theta\left(1 - \csc^2\theta - \theta\cot\theta - \cot^2\theta\right)$
$= \csc\theta\left(-\cot^2\theta - \theta\cot\theta - \cot^2\theta\right) \qquad \left[1 + \cot^2\theta = \csc^2\theta\right]$
$= \csc\theta\left(-\theta\cot\theta - 2\cot^2\theta\right) = -\csc\theta\cot\theta\,(\theta + 2\cot\theta)$

13. $\dfrac{d}{dx}(\csc x) = \dfrac{d}{dx}\left(\dfrac{1}{\sin x}\right) = \dfrac{(\sin x)(0) - 1(\cos x)}{\sin^2 x} = \dfrac{-\cos x}{\sin^2 x} = -\dfrac{1}{\sin x} \cdot \dfrac{\cos x}{\sin x} = -\csc x\cot x$

14. $\dfrac{d}{dx}(\sec x) = \dfrac{d}{dx}\left(\dfrac{1}{\cos x}\right) = \dfrac{(\cos x)(0) - 1(-\sin x)}{\cos^2 x} = \dfrac{\sin x}{\cos^2 x} = \dfrac{1}{\cos x} \cdot \dfrac{\sin x}{\cos x} = \sec x\tan x$

15. $\dfrac{d}{dx}(\cot x) = \dfrac{d}{dx}\left(\dfrac{\cos x}{\sin x}\right) = \dfrac{(\sin x)(-\sin x)-(\cos x)(\cos x)}{\sin^2 x} = -\dfrac{\sin^2 x+\cos^2 x}{\sin^2 x} = -\dfrac{1}{\sin^2 x} = -\csc^2 x$

16. $f(x) = \cos x \ \Rightarrow$

$$f'(x) = \lim_{h\to 0}\frac{f(x+h)-f(x)}{h} = \lim_{h\to 0}\frac{\cos(x+h)-\cos x}{h} = \lim_{h\to 0}\frac{\cos x\cos h - \sin x\sin h - \cos x}{h}$$

$$= \lim_{h\to 0}\left(\cos x\,\frac{\cos h - 1}{h}-\sin x\,\frac{\sin h}{h}\right) = \cos x\lim_{h\to 0}\frac{\cos h - 1}{h}-\sin x\lim_{h\to 0}\frac{\sin h}{h}$$

$$= (\cos x)(0)-(\sin x)(1) = -\sin x$$

17. $y = \tan x \ \Rightarrow \ y' = \sec^2 x \Rightarrow$ the slope of the tangent line at $\left(\frac{\pi}{4},1\right)$ is $\sec^2 \frac{\pi}{4} = \left(\sqrt{2}\right)^2 = 2$ and an equation is

$y - 1 = 2\left(x-\frac{\pi}{4}\right)$ or $y = 2x+1-\frac{\pi}{2}$.

18. $y = e^x\cos x \ \Rightarrow \ y' = e^x(-\sin x)+(\cos x)e^x = e^x(\cos x - \sin x) \ \Rightarrow$ the slope of the tangent line at

$(0,1)$ is $e^0(\cos 0 - \sin 0) = 1(1-0) = 1$ and an equation is $y - 1 = 1(x-0)$ or $y = x+1$.

19. (a) $y = x\cos x \ \Rightarrow \ y' = x(-\sin x)+\cos x(1) = \cos x - x\sin x$.   (b)

So the slope of the tangent at the point $(\pi,-\pi)$ is

$\cos\pi - \pi\sin\pi = -1 - \pi(0) = -1$, and an equation is

$y+\pi = -(x-\pi)$ or $y = -x$.

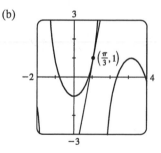

20. (a) $y = \sec x - 2\cos x \ \Rightarrow \ y' = \sec x\tan x + 2\sin x \ \Rightarrow$ (b)

the slope of the tangent line at $\left(\frac{\pi}{3},1\right)$ is

$\sec\frac{\pi}{3}\tan\frac{\pi}{3}+2\sin\frac{\pi}{3} = 2\cdot\sqrt{3}+2\cdot\frac{\sqrt{3}}{2} = 3\sqrt{3}$ and an equation is

$y - 1 = 3\sqrt{3}\left(x-\frac{\pi}{3}\right)$ or $y = 3\sqrt{3}\,x+1-\pi\sqrt{3}$.

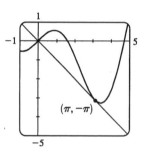

21. (a) $f(x) = 2x+\cot x \ \Rightarrow \ f'(x) = 2 - \csc^2 x$

(b)

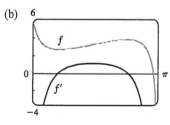

Notice that $f'(x) = 0$ when f has a horizontal tangent.

Also, $f'(x)$ is large negative when the graph of f is

steep.

22. (a) $f(x) = e^x\cos x \ \Rightarrow \ f'(x) = e^x(-\sin x)+(\cos x)e^x = e^x(\cos x - \sin x) \ \Rightarrow$

$f''(x) = e^x(-\sin x - \cos x)+(\cos x - \sin x)e^x = e^x(-\sin x - \cos x + \cos x - \sin x) = -2e^x\sin x$

(b)

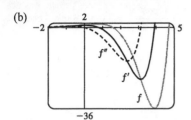

Note that $f' = 0$ where f has a minimum and $f'' = 0$ where f' has a minimum. Also note that f' is negative when f is decreasing and f'' is negative when f' is decreasing.

23. $H(\theta) = \theta \sin \theta \Rightarrow H'(\theta) = \theta (\cos \theta) + (\sin \theta) \cdot 1 = \theta \cos \theta + \sin \theta \Rightarrow$
$H''(\theta) = \theta (- \sin \theta) + (\cos \theta) \cdot 1 + \cos \theta = -\theta \sin \theta + 2 \cos \theta$

24. $f(x) = \sec x \Rightarrow f'(x) = \sec x \tan x \Rightarrow$
$f''(x) = \sec x (\sec^2 x) + \tan x (\sec x \tan x) = \sec x (\sec^2 x + \tan^2 x).$
$f'' \left(\frac{\pi}{4}\right) = \sqrt{2} \left[\left(\sqrt{2}\right)^2 + 1^2\right] = \sqrt{2}(2+1) = 3\sqrt{2}$

25. $f(x) = x + 2 \sin x$ has a horizontal tangent when $f'(x) = 0 \Leftrightarrow 1 + 2 \cos x = 0 \Leftrightarrow \cos x = -\frac{1}{2} \Leftrightarrow$
$x = \frac{2\pi}{3} + 2\pi n$ or $\frac{4\pi}{3} + 2\pi n$, where n is an integer. Note that $\frac{4\pi}{3}$ and $\frac{2\pi}{3}$ are $\pm \frac{\pi}{3}$ units from π. This allows us to write the solutions in the more compact equivalent form $(2n+1)\pi \pm \frac{\pi}{3}$, n an integer.

26. $y = \dfrac{\cos x}{2 + \sin x} \Rightarrow$

$y' = \dfrac{(2 + \sin x)(- \sin x) - \cos x \cos x}{(2 + \sin x)^2} = \dfrac{-2 \sin x - \sin^2 x - \cos^2 x}{(2 + \sin x)^2} = \dfrac{-2 \sin x - 1}{(2 + \sin x)^2} = 0$ when

$-2 \sin x - 1 = 0 \Leftrightarrow \sin x = -\frac{1}{2} \Leftrightarrow x = \frac{11\pi}{6} + 2\pi n$ or $x = \frac{7\pi}{6} + 2\pi n$, n an integer. So $y = -\frac{1}{\sqrt{3}}$ or

$y = -\frac{1}{\sqrt{3}}$ and the points on the curve with horizontal tangents are: $\left(\frac{11\pi}{6} + 2\pi n, \frac{1}{\sqrt{3}}\right)$, $\left(\frac{7\pi}{6} + 2\pi n, -\frac{1}{\sqrt{3}}\right)$,

n an integer.

27. $f(x) = x - 2 \sin x$, $0 \le x \le 2\pi$. $f'(x) = 1 - 2 \cos x$. So $f'(x) > 0 \Leftrightarrow 1 - 2 \cos x > 0 \Leftrightarrow$
$-2 \cos x > -1 \Leftrightarrow \cos x < \frac{1}{2} \Leftrightarrow \frac{\pi}{3} < x < \frac{5\pi}{3} \Rightarrow f$ is increasing on $\left(\frac{\pi}{3}, \frac{5\pi}{3}\right)$.

28. $f(x) = x - \sin x$, $0 \le x \le 2\pi$. $f'(x) = 1 - \cos x \Rightarrow f''(x) = \sin x$. Since $\sin x > 0$ on $(0, \pi)$, f is concave upward on $(0, \pi)$.

29. (a) $x(t) = 8 \sin t \Rightarrow v(t) = x'(t) = 8 \cos t \Rightarrow a(t) = x''(t) = -8 \sin t$

(b) The mass at time $t = \frac{2\pi}{3}$ has position $x\left(\frac{2\pi}{3}\right) = 8 \sin \frac{2\pi}{3} = 8\left(\frac{\sqrt{3}}{2}\right) = 4\sqrt{3}$, velocity

$v\left(\frac{2\pi}{3}\right) = 8 \cos \frac{2\pi}{3} = 8\left(-\frac{1}{2}\right) = -4$, and acceleration $a\left(\frac{2\pi}{3}\right) = -8 \sin \frac{2\pi}{3} = -8\left(\frac{\sqrt{3}}{2}\right) = -4\sqrt{3}$. Since

$v\left(\frac{2\pi}{3}\right) < 0$, the particle is moving to the left. Because v and a have the same sign, the particle is speeding up.

30. (a) $s(t) = 2 \cos t + 3 \sin t \Rightarrow v(t) = -2 \sin t + 3 \cos t \Rightarrow a(t) = -2 \cos t - 3 \sin t$

(b)

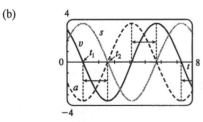

(c) $s = 0 \Rightarrow t_2 \approx 2.55$. So the mass passes through the equilibrium position for the first time when $t \approx 2.55$ s.

(d) $v = 0 \Rightarrow t_1 \approx 0.98$, $s(t_1) \approx 3.61$ cm. So the mass travels a maximum of about 3.6 cm (upward and downward) from its equilibrium position.

(e) The speed $|v|$ is greatest when $s = 0$; that is, when $t = t_2 + n\pi$, n a positive integer. The mass is speeding up when v and a have the same sign. From the figure, we see that this is the case on the intervals $(t_1 + n\pi, t_2 + n\pi)$ where n is a whole number.

31.

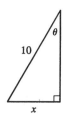

From the diagram we can see that $\sin \theta = x/10 \iff x = 10 \sin \theta$. We want to find the rate of change of x with respect to θ; that is, $dx/d\theta$. Taking the derivative of the above expression, $dx/d\theta = 10(\cos \theta)$. So when $\theta = \frac{\pi}{3}$,

$$dx/d\theta = 10 \cos \frac{\pi}{3} = 10\left(\tfrac{1}{2}\right) = 5 \text{ ft/rad}$$

32. (a) $F = \dfrac{\mu W}{\mu \sin \theta + \cos \theta} \quad \Rightarrow \quad \dfrac{dF}{d\theta} = \dfrac{(\mu \sin \theta + \cos \theta)(0) - \mu W(\mu \cos \theta - \sin \theta)}{(\mu \sin \theta + \cos \theta)^2} = \dfrac{\mu W(\sin \theta - \mu \cos \theta)}{(\mu \sin \theta + \cos \theta)^2}$

(b) $\dfrac{dF}{d\theta} = 0 \quad \Rightarrow \quad \mu W(\sin \theta - \mu \cos \theta) = 0 \quad \Rightarrow \quad \sin \theta = \mu \cos \theta \quad \Rightarrow \quad \tan \theta = \mu \quad \Rightarrow \quad \theta = \tan^{-1} \mu$

(c)

From the graph of $F = \dfrac{0.6(50)}{0.6 \sin \theta + \cos \theta}$ for $0 \le \theta \le 1$, we see that

$\dfrac{dF}{d\theta} = 0 \quad \Rightarrow \quad \theta \approx 0.54$. Checking this with part (b) and $\mu = 0.6$,

we calculate $\theta = \tan^{-1} 0.6 \approx 0.54$. So the value from the graph is consistent with the value in part (b).

33. $\dfrac{d}{dx} (\sin x) = \cos x \quad \Rightarrow \quad \dfrac{d^2}{dx^2} (\sin x) = -\sin x \quad \Rightarrow \quad \dfrac{d^3}{dx^3} (\sin x) = -\cos x \quad \Rightarrow \quad \dfrac{d^4}{dx^4} (\sin x) = \sin x.$

The derivatives of $\sin x$ occur in a cycle of four. Since $99 = 4(24) + 3$, we have

$\dfrac{d^{99}}{dx^{99}} (\sin x) = \dfrac{d^3}{dx^3} (\sin x) = -\cos x.$

34. Let $f(x) = x \sin x$ and $h(x) = \sin x$, so $f(x) = xh(x)$. Then
$f'(x) = h(x) + xh'(x)$, $f''(x) = h'(x) + h'(x) + xh''(x) = 2h'(x) + xh''(x)$,
$f'''(x) = 2h''(x) + h''(x) + xh'''(x) = 3h''(x) + xh'''(x), \cdots, f^{(n)}(x) = nh^{(n-1)}(x) + xh^{(n)}(x)$. Since

$34 = 4(8) + 2$, we have $h^{(34)}(x) = h^{(2)}(x) = \dfrac{d^2}{dx^2} (\sin x) = -\sin x$ and $h^{(35)}(x) = -\cos x$. Thus,

$\dfrac{d^{35}}{dx^{35}} (x \sin x) = 35h^{(34)}(x) + xh^{(35)}(x) = -35 \sin x - x \cos x.$

35. $y = A \sin x + B \cos x \quad \Rightarrow \quad y' = A \cos x - B \sin x \quad \Rightarrow \quad y'' = -A \sin x - B \cos x$. Substituting these expressions for y, y', and y'' into the given differential equation $y'' + y' - 2y = \sin x$ gives us
$(-A \sin x - B \cos x) + (A \cos x - B \sin x) - 2(A \sin x + B \cos x) = \sin x \quad \iff$
$-3A \sin x - B \sin x + A \cos x - 3B \cos x = \sin x \quad \iff \quad (-3A - B) \sin x + (A - 3B) \cos x = 1 \sin x$, so we
must have $-3A - B = 1$ and $A - 3B = 0$ (since 0 is the coefficient of $\cos x$ on the right side). Solving for A and
B, we add the first equation to three times the second to get $B = -\frac{1}{10}$ and $A = -\frac{3}{10}$.

36. (a) If $x \to 0$, then $5x \to 0$, and hence $\theta \, (= 5x) \to 0$. $\lim\limits_{x \to 0} \dfrac{\sin 5x}{x} = \lim\limits_{\theta \to 0} \dfrac{\sin \theta}{\frac{1}{5}\theta} = 5 \lim\limits_{\theta \to 0} \dfrac{\sin \theta}{\theta} = 5(1) = 5.$

(b) Let $f(x) = \sin 5x$. Then

$$\frac{d}{dx}(\sin 5x) = f'(x) = \lim_{h \to 0} \frac{f(x+h) - f(x)}{h} = \lim_{h \to 0} \frac{\sin[5(x+h)] - \sin 5x}{h}$$

$$= \lim_{h \to 0} \frac{\sin(5x + 5h) - \sin 5x}{h} = \lim_{h \to 0} \frac{\sin 5x \cos 5h + \cos 5x \sin 5h - \sin 5x}{h}$$

$$= \lim_{h \to 0} \left(\sin 5x \cdot \frac{\cos 5h - 1}{h} + \cos 5x \frac{\sin 5h}{h} \right)$$

$$= \sin 5x \lim_{h \to 0} \frac{\cos 5h - 1}{h} + \cos 5x \lim_{h \to 0} \frac{\sin 5h}{h}$$

The first limit can be shown to equal 0 in a manner similar to part (a) and Equation 3. The second limit is equal to 5, by part (a). Thus, we have $f'(x) = (\sin 5x)(0) + (\cos 5x)(5) = 5 \cos 5x$.

37. $\lim\limits_{x \to 0} \dfrac{\tan 4x}{x} = \lim\limits_{x \to 0} \left(\dfrac{\sin 4x}{x} \cdot \dfrac{1}{\cos 4x} \right) = \lim\limits_{x \to 0} \left(\dfrac{4 \sin 4x}{4x} \cdot \dfrac{1}{\cos 4x} \right) = 4 \lim\limits_{x \to 0} \dfrac{\sin 4x}{4x} \cdot \lim\limits_{x \to 0} \dfrac{1}{\cos 4x} = 4 \cdot 1 \cdot 1 = 4$

38. $\lim\limits_{x \to 0} x \cot x = \lim\limits_{x \to 0} x \cdot \dfrac{\cos x}{\sin x} = \lim\limits_{x \to 0} \dfrac{x \cos x}{\sin x} = \lim\limits_{x \to 0} \dfrac{\dfrac{x \cos x}{x}}{\dfrac{\sin x}{x}} = \lim\limits_{x \to 0} \dfrac{\dfrac{\cos x}{1}}{\dfrac{\sin x}{x}} = \dfrac{\lim\limits_{x \to 0} \cos x}{\lim\limits_{x \to 0} \dfrac{\sin x}{x}} = \dfrac{1}{1} = 1$

39. $\lim\limits_{\theta \to 0} \dfrac{\sin \theta}{\theta + \tan \theta} = \dfrac{\lim\limits_{\theta \to 0} \dfrac{\sin \theta}{\theta}}{\lim\limits_{\theta \to 0} \dfrac{\theta + \tan \theta}{\theta}} = \dfrac{1}{\lim\limits_{\theta \to 0} \left(1 + \dfrac{\sin \theta}{\theta} \cdot \dfrac{1}{\cos \theta} \right)} = \dfrac{1}{1 + 1 \cdot 1} = \dfrac{1}{2}$

40. (a) Let $\theta = \dfrac{1}{x}$. Then as $x \to \infty$, $\theta \to 0$, and $\lim\limits_{x \to \infty} x \sin \dfrac{1}{x} = \lim\limits_{\theta \to 0} \dfrac{1}{\theta} \sin \theta = \lim\limits_{\theta \to 0} \dfrac{\sin \theta}{\theta} = 1.$

(b) Since $-1 \le \sin(1/x) \le 1$, we have (as illustrated in the figure) $-|x| \le x \sin(1/x) \le |x|$. We know that $\lim\limits_{x \to 0} (|x|) = 0$ and $\lim\limits_{x \to 0} (-|x|) = 0$; so by the Squeeze Theorem,

$\lim\limits_{x \to 0} x \sin(1/x) = 0.$

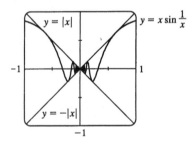

(c)

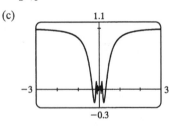

41. By the definition of radian measure, $s = r\theta$, where r is the radius of the circle.

By drawing the bisector of the angle θ, we can see that $\sin \dfrac{\theta}{2} = \dfrac{d/2}{r} \Rightarrow d = 2r \sin \dfrac{\theta}{2}.$

So $\lim\limits_{\theta \to 0^+} \dfrac{s}{d} = \lim\limits_{\theta \to 0^+} \dfrac{r\theta}{2r \sin(\theta/2)} = \lim\limits_{\theta \to 0^+} \dfrac{2 \cdot (\theta/2)}{2 \sin(\theta/2)} = \lim\limits_{\theta \to 0} \dfrac{\theta/2}{\sin(\theta/2)} = 1.$ [This is just the reciprocal of the limit

$\lim\limits_{x \to 0} \dfrac{\sin x}{x} = 1$ combined with the fact that as $\theta \to 0$, $\dfrac{\theta}{2} \to 0$ also.]

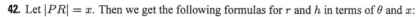

42. Let $|PR| = x$. Then we get the following formulas for r and h in terms of θ and x:

$$\sin\frac{\theta}{2} = \frac{r}{x} \quad\Rightarrow\quad r = x\sin\frac{\theta}{2} \text{ and } \cos\frac{\theta}{2} = \frac{h}{x} \quad\Rightarrow\quad h = x\cos\frac{\theta}{2}. \text{ Now}$$

$A(\theta) = \frac{1}{2}\pi r^2$ and $B(\theta) = \frac{1}{2}(2r)h = rh$. So

$$\lim_{\theta\to0+}\frac{A(\theta)}{B(\theta)} = \lim_{\theta\to0+}\frac{\frac{1}{2}\pi r^2}{rh} = \frac{1}{2}\pi\lim_{\theta\to0+}\frac{r}{h} = \frac{1}{2}\pi\lim_{\theta\to0+}\frac{x\sin(\theta/2)}{x\cos(\theta/2)}$$

$$= \frac{1}{2}\pi\lim_{\theta\to0+}\tan(\theta/2) = 0.$$

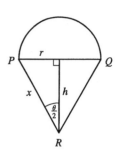

◆3.5 The Chain Rule • • • • • • • • • • • • • • • •

1. Let $u = g(x) = 4x$ and $y = f(u) = \sin u$. Then $\dfrac{dy}{dx} = \dfrac{dy}{du}\dfrac{du}{dx} = (\cos u)(4) = 4\cos 4x$.

2. Let $u = g(x) = 4 + 3x$ and $y = f(u) = \sqrt{u} = u^{1/2}$. Then $\dfrac{dy}{dx} = \dfrac{dy}{du}\dfrac{du}{dx} = \frac{1}{2}u^{-1/2}(3) = \dfrac{3}{2\sqrt{u}} = \dfrac{3}{2\sqrt{4+3x}}$.

3. Let $u = g(x) = 1 - x^2$ and $y = f(u) = u^{10}$. Then $\dfrac{dy}{dx} = \dfrac{dy}{du}\dfrac{du}{dx} = (10u^9)(-2x) = -20x(1-x^2)^9$.

4. Let $u = g(x) = \sin x$ and $y = f(u) = \tan u$. Then $\dfrac{dy}{dx} = \dfrac{dy}{du}\dfrac{du}{dx} = (\sec^2 u)(\cos x) = \sec^2(\sin x)\cdot\cos x$, or

equivalently, $[\sec(\sin x)]^2\cos x$.

5. Let $u = g(x) = \sqrt{x}$ and $y = f(u) = e^u$.

Then $\dfrac{dy}{dx} = \dfrac{dy}{du}\dfrac{du}{dx} = (e^u)\left(\frac{1}{2}x^{-1/2}\right) = e^{\sqrt{x}}\cdot\dfrac{1}{2\sqrt{x}} = \dfrac{e^{\sqrt{x}}}{2\sqrt{x}}$.

6. Let $u = g(x) = e^x$ and $y = f(u) = \sin u$. Then $\dfrac{dy}{dx} = \dfrac{dy}{du}\dfrac{du}{dx} = (\cos u)(e^x) = e^x\cos e^x$.

7. $F(x) = \sqrt[4]{1 + 2x + x^3} = (1 + 2x + x^3)^{1/4} \quad\Rightarrow$

$$F'(x) = \frac{1}{4}(1 + 2x + x^3)^{-3/4}\cdot\frac{d}{dx}(1 + 2x + x^3) = \frac{1}{4(1 + 2x + x^3)^{3/4}}\cdot(2 + 3x^2)$$

$$= \frac{2 + 3x^2}{4(1 + 2x + x^3)^{3/4}} = \frac{2 + 3x^2}{4\sqrt[4]{(1 + 2x + x^3)^3}}.$$

8. $F(x) = (x^2 - x + 1)^3 \quad\Rightarrow\quad F'(x) = 3(x^2 - x + 1)^2(2x - 1)$

9. $g(t) = \dfrac{1}{(t^4 + 1)^3} = (t^4 + 1)^{-3} \quad\Rightarrow\quad g'(t) = -3(t^4 + 1)^{-4}(4t^3) = -12t^3(t^4 + 1)^{-4} = \dfrac{-12t^3}{(t^4 + 1)^4}$

10. $f(t) = \sqrt[3]{1 + \tan t} = (1 + \tan t)^{1/3} \quad\Rightarrow\quad f'(t) = \frac{1}{3}(1 + \tan t)^{-2/3}\sec^2 t = \dfrac{\sec^2 t}{3\sqrt[3]{(1 + \tan t)^2}}$

11. $y = \cos(a^3 + x^3) \quad\Rightarrow\quad y' = -\sin(a^3 + x^3)\cdot 3x^2 \quad [a^3 \text{ is just a constant}] \quad = -3x^2\sin(a^3 + x^3)$

12. $y = a^3 + \cos^3 x \quad\Rightarrow\quad y' = 3(\cos x)^2(-\sin x) \quad [a^3 \text{ is just a constant}] \quad = -3\sin x\cos^2 x$

13. $y = e^{-mx} \quad\Rightarrow\quad y' = e^{-mx}\dfrac{d}{dx}(-mx) = e^{-mx}(-m) = -me^{-mx}$

14. $y = 4\sec 5x \quad\Rightarrow\quad y' = 4\sec 5x\tan 5x(5) = 20\sec 5x\tan 5x$

15. $f(x) = xe^{-x^2}$ $\Rightarrow$ $f'(x) = xe^{-x^2}(-2x) + e^{-x^2} \cdot 1 = e^{-x^2}(-2x^2 + 1) = e^{-x^2}(1 - 2x^2)$

16. $g(x) = e^{-5x}\cos 3x$ $\Rightarrow$ $g'(x) = e^{-5x}(-3\sin 3x) + (\cos 3x)(-5e^{-5x}) = -e^{-5x}(3\sin 3x + 5\cos 3x)$

17. $G(x) = (3x - 2)^{10}(5x^2 - x + 1)^{12}$ $\Rightarrow$

$\quad G'(x) = (3x-2)^{10}(12)(5x^2 - x + 1)^{11}(10x - 1) + (5x^2 - x + 1)^{12}(10)(3x-2)^9(3)$

$\qquad = 6(3x-2)^9(5x^2 - x + 1)^{11}[2(3x-2)(10x-1) + 5(5x^2 - x + 1)]$

$\qquad = 6(3x-2)^9(5x^2 - x + 1)^{11}[(60x^2 - 46x + 4) + (25x^2 - 5x + 5)]$

$\qquad = 6(3x-2)^9(5x^2 - x + 1)^{11}(85x^2 - 51x + 9)$

18. $g(t) = (6t^2 + 5)^3(t^3 - 7)^4$ $\Rightarrow$

$\quad g'(t) = (6t^2 + 5)^3(4)(t^3 - 7)^3(3t^2) + (t^3 - 7)^4(3)(6t^2 + 5)^2(12t)$

$\qquad = 12t(6t^2 + 5)^2(t^3 - 7)^3[t(6t^2 + 5) + 3(t^3 - 7)]$

$\qquad = 12t(6t^2 + 5)^2(t^3 - 7)^3(9t^3 + 5t - 21)$

19. $y = e^{x\cos x}$ $\Rightarrow$ $y' = e^{x\cos x} \cdot \dfrac{d}{dx}(x\cos x) = e^{x\cos x}[x(-\sin x) + (\cos x) \cdot 1] = e^{x\cos x}(\cos x - x\sin x)$

20. Using Formula 5 and the Chain Rule, $y = 10^{1-x^2}$ $\Rightarrow$

$\quad y' = 10^{1-x^2}(\ln 10) \cdot \dfrac{d}{dx}(1 - x^2) = -2x(\ln 10)10^{1-x^2}.$

21. This function is a quotient raised to a power. To find its derivative, we use the Chain Rule by differentiating the

power first and then multiplying by the derivative of the quotient. $F(y) = \left(\dfrac{y-6}{y+7}\right)^3$ $\Rightarrow$

$\quad F'(y) = 3\left(\dfrac{y-6}{y+7}\right)^2 \dfrac{(y+7)(1) - (y-6)(1)}{(y+7)^2} = 3\left(\dfrac{y-6}{y+7}\right)^2 \dfrac{13}{(y+7)^2} = \dfrac{39(y-6)^2}{(y+7)^4}$

22. $s(t) = \sqrt[4]{\dfrac{t^3+1}{t^3-1}} = \left(\dfrac{t^3+1}{t^3-1}\right)^{1/4}$ $\Rightarrow$

$\quad s'(t) = \dfrac{1}{4}\left(\dfrac{t^3+1}{t^3-1}\right)^{-3/4} \dfrac{(t^3-1)(3t^2) - (t^3+1)(3t^2)}{(t^3-1)^2} = \dfrac{1}{4}\left(\dfrac{t^3+1}{t^3-1}\right)^{-3/4} \dfrac{3t^2(t^3 - 1 - t^3 - 1)}{(t^3-1)^2}$

$\qquad = \dfrac{1}{4}\left(\dfrac{t^3+1}{t^3-1}\right)^{-3/4} \dfrac{3t^2(-2)}{(t^3-1)^2} = \dfrac{1}{2}\left(\dfrac{t^3+1}{t^3-1}\right)^{-3/4} \dfrac{-3t^2}{(t^3-1)^2}$

23. $y = \dfrac{r}{\sqrt{r^2+1}}$ $\Rightarrow$

$\quad y' = \dfrac{\sqrt{r^2+1}(1) - r \cdot \frac{1}{2}(r^2+1)^{-1/2}(2r)}{\left(\sqrt{r^2+1}\right)^2} = \dfrac{\sqrt{r^2+1} - \dfrac{r^2}{\sqrt{r^2+1}}}{\left(\sqrt{r^2+1}\right)^2} = \dfrac{\dfrac{\sqrt{r^2+1}\sqrt{r^2+1} - r^2}{\sqrt{r^2+1}}}{\left(\sqrt{r^2+1}\right)^2}$

$\qquad = \dfrac{(r^2+1) - r^2}{\left(\sqrt{r^2+1}\right)^3} = \dfrac{1}{(r^2+1)^{3/2}}$ or $(r^2+1)^{-3/2}$

(continued)

Another solution: Write y as a product and make use of the Product Rule.

$$y = r(r^2 + 1)^{-1/2} \quad \Rightarrow \quad y' = r \cdot -\tfrac{1}{2}(r^2 + 1)^{-3/2}(2r) + (r^2 + 1)^{-1/2} \cdot 1$$

$$= (r^2 + 1)^{-3/2}\left[-r^2 + (r^2 + 1)^1\right] = (r^2 + 1)^{-3/2}(1) = (r^2 + 1)^{-3/2}$$

The step that students usually have trouble with is factoring out $(r^2 + 1)^{-3/2}$. But this is no different than factoring out x^2 from $x^2 + x^5$; that is, we are just factoring out a factor with the *smallest* exponent that appears on it. In this case, $-\tfrac{3}{2}$ is smaller than $-\tfrac{1}{2}$.

24. $y = \dfrac{e^{2u}}{e^u + e^{-u}} \quad \Rightarrow$

$$y' = \frac{(e^u + e^{-u})(e^{2u} \cdot 2) - e^{2u}(e^u - e^{-u})}{(e^u + e^{-u})^2} = \frac{e^{2u}(2e^u + 2e^{-u} - e^u + e^{-u})}{(e^u + e^{-u})^2} = \frac{e^{2u}(e^u + 3e^{-u})}{(e^u + e^{-u})^2}$$

Another solution: Eliminate negative exponents by first changing the form of y.

$$y = \frac{e^{2u}}{e^u + e^{-u}} \cdot \frac{e^u}{e^u} = \frac{e^{3u}}{e^{2u} + 1} \quad \Rightarrow$$

$$y' = \frac{(e^{2u} + 1)(3e^{3u}) - e^{3u}(2e^{2u})}{(e^{2u} + 1)^2} = \frac{e^{3u}(3e^{2u} + 3 - 2e^{2u})}{(e^{2u} + 1)^2} = \frac{e^{3u}(e^{2u} + 3)}{(e^{2u} + 1)^2}$$

25. Using Formula 5 and the Chain Rule, $y = 2^{\sin \pi x} \quad \Rightarrow$

$$y' = 2^{\sin \pi x}(\ln 2) \cdot \frac{d}{dx}(\sin \pi x) = 2^{\sin \pi x}(\ln 2) \cdot \cos \pi x \cdot \pi = 2^{\sin \pi x}(\pi \ln 2) \cos \pi x$$

26. $y = \tan^2(3\theta) = (\tan 3\theta)^2 \quad \Rightarrow \quad y' = 2(\tan 3\theta) \cdot \dfrac{d}{d\theta}(\tan 3\theta) = 2 \tan 3\theta \cdot \sec^2 3\theta \cdot 3 = 6 \tan 3\theta \sec^2 3\theta$

27. $y = \cot^2(\sin \theta) = [\cot(\sin \theta)]^2 \quad \Rightarrow$

$$y' = 2\left[\cot(\sin \theta)\right] \cdot \frac{d}{d\theta}[\cot(\sin \theta)] = 2 \cot(\sin \theta) \cdot \left[-\csc^2(\sin \theta) \cdot \cos \theta\right] = -2 \cos \theta \, \cot(\sin \theta) \, \csc^2(\sin \theta)$$

28. $y = \sin(\sin(\sin x)) \quad \Rightarrow \quad y' = \cos(\sin(\sin x))\dfrac{d}{dx}(\sin(\sin x)) = \cos(\sin(\sin x)) \, \cos(\sin x) \, \cos x$

29. $y = \sin\left(\tan \sqrt{\sin x}\right) \quad \Rightarrow$

$$y' = \cos\left(\tan \sqrt{\sin x}\right) \cdot \frac{d}{dx}\left(\tan \sqrt{\sin x}\right) = \cos\left(\tan \sqrt{\sin x}\right) \sec^2 \sqrt{\sin x} \cdot \frac{d}{dx}(\sin x)^{1/2}$$

$$= \cos\left(\tan \sqrt{\sin x}\right) \sec^2 \sqrt{\sin x} \cdot \tfrac{1}{2}(\sin x)^{-1/2} \cdot \cos x$$

$$= \cos\left(\tan \sqrt{\sin x}\right)\left(\sec^2 \sqrt{\sin x}\right)\left(\frac{1}{2\sqrt{\sin x}}\right)(\cos x)$$

30. $y = \sqrt{x + \sqrt{x + \sqrt{x}}} \quad \Rightarrow \quad y' = \tfrac{1}{2}\left(x + \sqrt{x + \sqrt{x}}\right)^{-1/2}\left[1 + \tfrac{1}{2}(x + \sqrt{x})^{-1/2}\left(1 + \tfrac{1}{2}x^{-1/2}\right)\right]$

31. $y = \sin(\sin x) \quad \Rightarrow \quad y' = \cos(\sin x) \cdot \cos x$. At $(\pi, 0)$, $y' = \cos(\sin \pi) \cdot \cos \pi = \cos(0) \cdot (-1) = 1(-1) = -1$, and an equation of the tangent line is $y - 0 = -1(x - \pi)$, or $y = -x + \pi$.

32. $y = x^2 e^{-x} \quad \Rightarrow \quad y' = x^2(-e^{-x}) + e^{-x}(2x) = 2xe^{-x} - x^2 e^{-x}$. At $\left(1, \tfrac{1}{e}\right)$, $y' = 2e^{-1} - e^{-1} = \tfrac{1}{e}$. So an equation of the tangent line is $y - \tfrac{1}{e} = \tfrac{1}{e}(x - 1)$ or $y = \tfrac{1}{e}x$.

33. (a) $y = \dfrac{2}{1+e^{-x}}$ $\Rightarrow$ $y' = \dfrac{(1+e^{-x})(0) - 2(-e^{-x})}{(1+e^{-x})^2} = \dfrac{2e^{-x}}{(1+e^{-x})^2}.$

(b)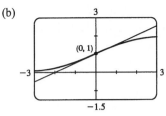

At $(0,1)$, $y' = \dfrac{2e^0}{(1+e^0)^2} = \dfrac{2(1)}{(1+1)^2} = \dfrac{2}{2^2} = \dfrac{1}{2}.$

So an equation of the tangent line is $y - 1 = \frac{1}{2}(x - 0)$ or $y = \frac{1}{2}x + 1.$

34. (a) For $x > 0$, $|x| = x$, and $y = f(x) = \dfrac{x}{\sqrt{2 - x^2}}$ $\Rightarrow$

(b)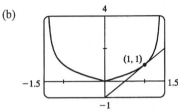

$f'(x) = \dfrac{\sqrt{2 - x^2}\,(1) - x\left(\frac{1}{2}\right)\left(2 - x^2\right)^{-1/2}(-2x)}{\left(\sqrt{2 - x^2}\right)^2} \cdot \dfrac{(2 - x^2)^{1/2}}{(2 - x^2)^{1/2}}$

$= \dfrac{(2 - x^2) + x^2}{(2 - x^2)^{3/2}} = \dfrac{2}{(2 - x^2)^{3/2}}$

So at $(1,1)$, the slope of the tangent line is $f'(1) = 2$ and its equation is $y - 1 = 2(x - 1)$ or $y = 2x - 1.$

35. (a) $f(x) = \dfrac{\sqrt{1 - x^2}}{x}$ $\Rightarrow$

(b)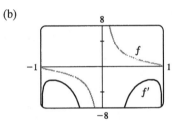

$f'(x) = \dfrac{x \cdot \frac{1}{2}\left(1 - x^2\right)^{-1/2}(-2x) - \sqrt{1 - x^2}\,(1)}{x^2} \cdot \dfrac{\sqrt{1 - x^2}}{\sqrt{1 - x^2}}$

$= \dfrac{-x^2 - \left(1 - x^2\right)}{x^2\sqrt{1 - x^2}} = \dfrac{-1}{x^2\sqrt{1 - x^2}}$

Notice that all tangents to the graph of f have negative slopes and $f'(x) < 0$ always.

36. (a) $f(x) = 2\cos x + \sin^2 x$ $\Rightarrow$

(b)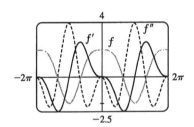

$f'(x) = 2(-\sin x) + 2\sin x(\cos x)$

$= \sin 2x - 2\sin x$ $\Rightarrow$

$f''(x) = 2\cos 2x - 2\cos x$

$= 2(\cos 2x - \cos x)$

We can see that our answers are plausible, since f has horizontal tangents where $f'(x) = 0$, and f' has horizontal tangents where $f''(x) = 0.$

37. $F(x) = f(g(x))$ $\Rightarrow$
$F'(x) = f'(g(x)) \cdot g'(x)$, so $F'(3) = f'(g(3)) \cdot g'(3) = f'(6) \cdot g'(3) = 7 \cdot 4 = 28$. Notice that we did not use $f'(3) = 2.$

38. $w = u \circ v$ $\Rightarrow$ $w(x) = u(v(x))$ $\Rightarrow$ $w'(x) = u'(v(x)) \cdot v'(x)$, so
$w'(0) = u'(v(0)) \cdot v'(0) = u'(2) \cdot v'(0) = 4 \cdot 5 = 20$. The other pieces of information, $u(0) = 1$, $u'(0) = 3$, and $v'(2) = 6$, were not needed.

39. (a) $h(x) = f(g(x)) \Rightarrow h'(x) = f'(g(x)) \cdot g'(x)$, so $h'(1) = f'(g(1)) \cdot g'(1) = f'(2) \cdot 6 = 5 \cdot 6 = 30$.

(b) $H(x) = g(f(x)) \Rightarrow H'(x) = g'(f(x)) \cdot f'(x)$, so $H'(1) = g'(f(1)) \cdot f'(1) = g'(3) \cdot 4 = 9 \cdot 4 = 36$.

40. (a) $F(x) = f(f(x)) \Rightarrow F'(x) = f'(f(x)) \cdot f'(x)$, so $F'(2) = f'(f(2)) \cdot f'(2) = f'(1) \cdot 5 = 4 \cdot 5 = 20$.

(b) $G(x) = g(g(x)) \Rightarrow G'(x) = g'(g(x)) \cdot g'(x)$, so $G'(3) = g'(g(3)) \cdot g'(3) = g'(2) \cdot 9 = 7 \cdot 9 = 63$.

41. (a) $u(x) = f(g(x)) \Rightarrow u'(x) = f'(g(x))g'(x)$. So $u'(1) = f'(g(1))g'(1) = f'(3)g'(1)$. To find $f'(3)$, note

that f is linear from $(2, 4)$ to $(6, 3)$, so its slope is $\dfrac{3 - 4}{6 - 2} = -\dfrac{1}{4}$. To find $g'(1)$, note that g is linear from $(0, 6)$

to $(2, 0)$, so its slope is $\dfrac{0 - 6}{2 - 0} = -3$. Thus, $f'(3)g'(1) = \left(-\frac{1}{4}\right)(-3) = \frac{3}{4}$.

(b) $v(x) = g(f(x)) \Rightarrow v'(x) = g'(f(x))f'(x)$. So $v'(1) = g'(f(1))f'(1) = g'(2)f'(1)$, which does not
exist since $g'(2)$ does not exist.

(c) $w(x) = g(g(x)) \Rightarrow w'(x) = g'(g(x))g'(x)$. So $w'(1) = g'(g(1))g'(1) = g'(3)g'(1)$. To find $g'(3)$, note

that g is linear from $(2, 0)$ to $(5, 2)$, so its slope is $\dfrac{2 - 0}{5 - 2} = \dfrac{2}{3}$. Thus, $g'(3)g'(1) = \left(\frac{2}{3}\right)(-3) = -2$.

42. (a) $h(x) = f(f(x)) \Rightarrow h'(x) = f'(f(x))f'(x)$.

So $h'(2) = f'(f(2))f'(2) = f'(1)f'(2) \approx (-1)(-1) = 1$.

(b) $g(x) = f(x^2) \Rightarrow g'(x) = f'(x^2) \cdot \dfrac{d}{dx}(x^2) = f'(x^2)(2x)$.

So $g'(2) = f'(2^2)(2 \cdot 2) = 4f'(4) \approx 4(1.5) = 6$.

43. $h(x) = f(g(x)) \Rightarrow h'(x) = f'(g(x))g'(x)$. So $h'(0.5) = f'(g(0.5))g'(0.5) = f'(0.1)g'(0.5)$. We can
estimate the derivatives by taking the average of two secant slopes.

For $f'(0.1)$: $m_1 = \dfrac{14.8 - 12.6}{0.1 - 0} = 22$, $m_2 = \dfrac{18.4 - 14.8}{0.2 - 0.1} = 36$. So $f'(0.1) \approx \dfrac{m_1 + m_2}{2} = \dfrac{22 + 36}{2} = 29$.

For $g'(0.5)$: $m_1 = \dfrac{0.10 - 0.17}{0.5 - 0.4} = -0.7$, $m_2 = \dfrac{0.05 - 0.10}{0.6 - 0.5} = -0.5$. So $g'(0.5) \approx \dfrac{m_1 + m_2}{2} = -0.6$.

Hence, $h'(0.5) = f'(0.1)g'(0.5) \approx (29)(-0.6) = -17.4$.

44. $g(x) = f(f(x)) \Rightarrow g'(x) = f'(f(x))f'(x)$. So $g'(1) = f'(f(1))f'(1) = f'(2)f'(1)$.

For $f'(2)$: $m_1 = \dfrac{3.1 - 2.4}{2.0 - 1.5} = 1.4$, $m_2 = \dfrac{4.4 - 3.1}{2.5 - 2.0} = 2.6$. So $f'(2) \approx \dfrac{m_1 + m_2}{2} = 2$.

For $f'(1)$: $m_1 = \dfrac{2.0 - 1.8}{1.0 - 0.5} = 0.4$, $m_2 = \dfrac{2.4 - 2.0}{1.5 - 1.0} = 0.8$. So $f'(1) \approx \dfrac{m_1 + m_2}{2} = 0.6$.

Hence, $g'(1) = f'(2)f'(1) \approx (2)(0.6) = 1.2$.

45. (a) $f(x) = \sqrt{x} \Rightarrow f'(x) = 1/(2\sqrt{x})$, so f is not differentiable at $x = 0$. Since h is differentiable on $[0, \infty)$
and $\sqrt{x}$ is differentiable on $(0, \infty)$, it follows that $G(x) = h(\sqrt{x})$ is differentiable on $(0, \infty)$.

(b) By the Chain Rule, $G'(x) = h'(\sqrt{x})\dfrac{d}{dx}\sqrt{x} = h'(\sqrt{x}) \cdot \dfrac{1}{2\sqrt{x}} = \dfrac{h'(\sqrt{x})}{2\sqrt{x}}$.

46. (a) $F(x) = f(x^\alpha) \Rightarrow F'(x) = f'(x^\alpha)\dfrac{d}{dx}(x^\alpha) = f'(x^\alpha)\alpha x^{\alpha - 1}$

(b) $G(x) = [f(x)]^\alpha \Rightarrow G'(x) = \alpha[f(x)]^{\alpha - 1}f'(x)$

47. (a) $F(x) = f(e^x) \Rightarrow F'(x) = f'(e^x)\dfrac{d}{dx}(e^x) = f'(e^x)e^x$

(b) $G(x) = e^{f(x)} \Rightarrow G'(x) = e^{f(x)}\dfrac{d}{dx}f(x) = e^{f(x)}f'(x)$

48. $f(x) = xg(x^2) \Rightarrow f'(x) = xg'(x^2) 2x + g(x^2) \cdot 1 = 2x^2g'(x^2) + g(x^2) \Rightarrow$
$f''(x) = 2x^2g''(x^2) 2x + g'(x^2) 4x + g'(x^2) 2x = 4x^3g''(x^2) + 4xg'(x^2) + 2xg'(x^2)$
$\qquad = 6xg'(x^2) + 4x^3g''(x^2)$

49. For the tangent line to be horizontal, $f'(x) = 0$. $f(x) = 2\sin x + \sin^2 x \Rightarrow$
$f'(x) = 2\cos x + 2\sin x \cos x = 0 \Leftrightarrow 2\cos x (1 + \sin x) = 0 \Leftrightarrow \cos x = 0$ or $\sin x = -1$, so
$x = \frac{\pi}{2} + 2n\pi$ or $\frac{3\pi}{2} + 2n\pi$, where n is any integer. Now $f\left(\frac{\pi}{2}\right) = 3$ and $f\left(\frac{3\pi}{2}\right) = -1$, so the points on the curve
with a horizontal tangent are $\left(\frac{\pi}{2} + 2n\pi, 3\right)$ and $\left(\frac{3\pi}{2} + 2n\pi, -1\right)$, where n is any integer.

50. $y = e^{-x^2} \Rightarrow y' = e^{-x^2}(-2x) \Rightarrow y'' = e^{-x^2}(-2) + (-2x)e^{-x^2}(-2x) = 2e^{-x^2}(2x^2 - 1)$.
$y'' = 0 \Leftrightarrow 2x^2 - 1 = 0 \Leftrightarrow x = \pm\frac{\sqrt{2}}{2}$. The curve is concave downward when $y'' < 0$. This is the case on
the interval $\left(-\frac{\sqrt{2}}{2}, \frac{\sqrt{2}}{2}\right)$.

51. $y = Ae^{-x} + Bxe^{-x} \Rightarrow$
$y' = A(-e^{-x}) + B[x(-e^{-x}) + e^{-x} \cdot 1] = -Ae^{-x} + Be^{-x} - Bxe^{-x} = (B - A)e^{-x} - Bxe^{-x} \Rightarrow$
$y'' = (B - A)(-e^{-x}) - B[x(-e^{-x}) + e^{-x} \cdot 1] = (A - B)e^{-x} - Be^{-x} + Bxe^{-x} = (A - 2B)e^{-x} + Bxe^{-x}$,
so $y'' + 2y' + y = (A - 2B)e^{-x} + Bxe^{-x} + 2[(B - A)e^{-x} - Bxe^{-x}] + Ae^{-x} + Bxe^{-x}$
$\qquad = [(A - 2B) + 2(B - A) + A]e^{-x} + [B - 2B + B]xe^{-x} = 0.$

52. $y = e^{rx} \Rightarrow y' = re^{rx} \Rightarrow y'' = r^2e^{rx}$, so
$y'' + 5y' - 6y = r^2e^{rx} + 5re^{rx} - 6e^{rx} = e^{rx}(r^2 + 5r - 6) = e^{rx}(r + 6)(r - 1) = 0 \Rightarrow$
$(r + 6)(r - 1) = 0 \Rightarrow r = 1$ or -6.

53. The use of $D, D^2, \ldots, D^n$ is just a derivative notation (see page 161). In general, $Df(2x) = 2f'(2x)$,
$D^2 f(2x) = 4f''(2x), \ldots, D^n f(2x) = 2^n f^{(n)}(2x)$. Since $f(x) = \cos x$ and $50 = 4(12) + 2$, we have
$f^{(50)}(x) = f^{(2)}(x) = -\cos x$, so $D^{50}\cos 2x = -2^{50}\cos 2x$.

54. $f(x) = xe^{-x}, f'(x) = e^{-x} - xe^{-x} = (1 - x)e^{-x}, f''(x) = -e^{-x} + (1 - x)(-e^{-x}) = (x - 2)e^{-x}$. Similarly,
$f'''(x) = (3 - x)e^{-x}, f^{(4)}(x) = (x - 4)e^{-x}, \ldots, f^{(1000)}(x) = (x - 1000)e^{-x}.$

55. $s(t) = 10 + \frac{1}{4}\sin(10\pi t) \Rightarrow$ the velocity after t seconds is
$v(t) = s'(t) = \frac{1}{4}\cos(10\pi t)(10\pi) = \frac{5\pi}{2}\cos(10\pi t)$ cm/s.

56. (a) $s = A\cos(\omega t + \delta) \Rightarrow$ velocity $= s' = -\omega A\sin(\omega t + \delta)$.

(b) If $A \neq 0$ and $\omega \neq 0$, then $s' = 0 \Leftrightarrow \sin(\omega t + \delta) = 0 \Leftrightarrow \omega t + \delta = n\pi \Leftrightarrow t = \frac{n\pi - \delta}{\omega}$,
n an integer.

57. (a) $B(t) = 4.0 + 0.35\sin\frac{2\pi t}{5.4} \Rightarrow \frac{dB}{dt} = \left(0.35\cos\frac{2\pi t}{5.4}\right)\left(\frac{2\pi}{5.4}\right) = \frac{0.7\pi}{5.4}\cos\frac{2\pi t}{5.4} = \frac{7\pi}{54}\cos\frac{2\pi t}{5.4}$

(b) At $t = 1$, $\frac{dB}{dt} = \frac{7\pi}{54}\cos\frac{2\pi}{5.4} \approx 0.16$.

58. $L(t) = 12 + 2.8\sin\left(\frac{2\pi}{365}(t - 80)\right) \Rightarrow L'(t) = 2.8\cos\left(\frac{2\pi}{365}(t - 80)\right)\left(\frac{2\pi}{365}\right)$.
On March 21, $t = 80$, and $L'(80) \approx 0.0482$ hours per day. On May 21, $t = 141$, and $L'(141) \approx 0.02398$, which is
approximately one-half of $L'(80)$.

59. $s(t) = 2e^{-1.5t} \sin 2\pi t \Rightarrow$

$v(t) = s'(t) = 2\left[e^{-1.5t}(\cos 2\pi t)(2\pi) + (\sin 2\pi t)e^{-1.5t}(-1.5)\right] = 2e^{-1.5t}(2\pi \cos 2\pi t - 1.5 \sin 2\pi t)$

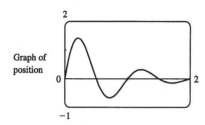

Graph of position

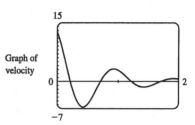

Graph of velocity

60. (a) $\displaystyle\lim_{t\to\infty} p(t) = \lim_{t\to\infty} \frac{1}{1+ae^{-kt}} = \frac{1}{1+a\cdot 0} = 1$, since $k > 0 \Rightarrow -kt \to -\infty \Rightarrow e^{-kt} \to 0.$

(b) $p(t) = \left(1+ae^{-kt}\right)^{-1} \Rightarrow \dfrac{dp}{dt} = -\left(1+ae^{-kt}\right)^{-2}\left(-kae^{-kt}\right) = \dfrac{kae^{-kt}}{\left(1+ae^{-kt}\right)^2}$

(c)

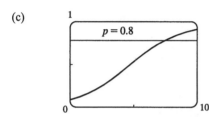

From the graph of $p(t) = \left(1 + 10e^{-0.5t}\right)^{-1}$, it seems that

$p(t) = 0.8$ (indicating that 80% of the population has heard the rumor) when $t \approx 7.4$ hours.

61. By the Chain Rule, $a(t) = \dfrac{dv}{dt} = \dfrac{dv}{ds}\dfrac{ds}{dt} = \dfrac{dv}{ds}v(t) = v(t)\dfrac{dv}{ds}$. The derivative dv/dt is the rate of change of the velocity with respect to time (in other words, the acceleration) whereas the derivative dv/ds is the rate of change of the velocity with respect to the displacement.

62. (a) The derivative dV/dr represents the rate of change of the volume with respect to the radius and the derivative dV/dt represents the rate of change of the volume with respect to time.

(b) Since $V = \dfrac{4}{3}\pi r^3$, $\dfrac{dV}{dt} = \dfrac{dV}{dr}\dfrac{dr}{dt} = 4\pi r^2\dfrac{dr}{dt}$.

63. (a) Using a calculator or CAS, we obtain the model $Q = ab^t$ with $a = 100.0124369$ and $b = 0.000045145933$.
We can change this model to one with base e and exponent $\ln b$: $Q = ae^{t\ln b} = 100.0124369e^{-10.00553063t}$.

(b) $Q'(t) = ab^t \ln b$. $Q'(0.04) \approx -670.63\ \mu A$. The result of Example 2 in Section 2.1 was $-670\ \mu A$.

64. (a) $P = ab^t$ or $P = ae^{t\ln b}$ with $a = 4.502714 \times 10^{-20}$ and
$b = 1.029953851$, where P is measured in thousands of people.
The fit appears to be very good.

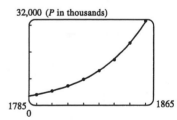

(b) **For 1800:** $m_1 = \dfrac{5308 - 3929}{1800 - 1790} = 137.9$, $m_2 = \dfrac{7240 - 5308}{1810 - 1800} = 193.2$.

So $P'(1800) \approx (m_1 + m_2)/2 = 165.55$ thousand people/year.

For 1850: $m_1 = \dfrac{23{,}192 - 17{,}063}{1850 - 1840} = 612.9$, $m_2 = \dfrac{31{,}443 - 23{,}192}{1860 - 1850} = 825.1$.

So $P'(1850) \approx (m_1 + m_2)/2 = 719$ thousand people/year.

(c) $P'(t) = ab^t \ln b$. $P'(1800) \approx 156.85$ and $P'(1850) \approx 686.07$. These estimates are somewhat less than the ones in part (b).

(d) $P(1870) \approx 41{,}946.56$. The difference of 3.4 million people is most likely due to the Civil War (1861–1865).

65. $x = t \sin t$, $y = t \cos t$. To find the value of t that corresponds to the point $(0, -\pi)$, we can solve $0 = t \sin t$, which says that either $t = 0$ or $\sin t = 0$. If $\sin t = 0$, then $t = 0, \pm\pi, \ldots$. Since $y = -\pi = t \cos t$, we see that $t = \pi$ is the desired value. $\dfrac{dy}{dt} = \cos t - t \sin t$, $\dfrac{dx}{dt} = \sin t + t \cos t$, and $\dfrac{dy}{dx} = \dfrac{dy/dt}{dx/dt} = \dfrac{\cos t - t \sin t}{\sin t + t \cos t}$. When $t = \pi$, $(x, y) = (0, -\pi)$ and $\dfrac{dy}{dx} = \dfrac{-1}{-\pi} = \dfrac{1}{\pi}$, so an equation of the tangent is $y + \pi = \dfrac{1}{\pi}(x - 0)$ or $y = \dfrac{1}{\pi}x - \pi$.

66. $x = \sin t$, $y = \sin(t + \sin t)$; $(0, 0)$.
$$\frac{dy}{dx} = \frac{dy/dt}{dx/dt} = \frac{\cos(t + \sin t)(1 + \cos t)}{\cos t} = \cos(t + \sin t)\frac{1 + \cos t}{\cos t} = \cos(t + \sin t)\left(\frac{1}{\cos t} + 1\right)$$
$$= (\sec t + 1)\cos(t + \sin t).$$

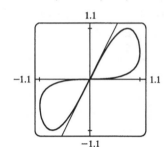

Now $x = \sin t$ is 0 when $t = 0$ and $t = \pi$, so there are two tangents at the point $(0, 0)$ since both $t = 0$ and $t = \pi$ correspond to the origin. The tangent corresponding to $t = 0$ has slope $(\sec 0 + 1)\cos(0 + \sin 0) = 2\cos 0 = 2$, and its equation is $y = 2x$. The tangent corresponding to $t = \pi$ has slope $(\sec \pi + 1)\cos(\pi + \sin \pi) = 0$, so it is the x-axis; that is, $y = 0$.

67. (a) $x = t^2$, $y = t^3 - 3t$ $\Rightarrow$ $\dfrac{dy}{dx} = \dfrac{dy/dt}{dx/dt} = \dfrac{3t^2 - 3}{2t}$. At the point $(3, 0)$,

$x = 3$ $\Rightarrow$ $t^2 = 3$ $\Rightarrow$ $t = \pm\sqrt{3}$ $\Rightarrow$ $\dfrac{dy}{dx} = \dfrac{3(\pm\sqrt{3})^2 - 3}{2(\pm\sqrt{3})} = \dfrac{6}{2(\pm\sqrt{3})} = \pm\dfrac{3}{\sqrt{3}} = \pm\sqrt{3}$. When $t = \sqrt{3}$, an equation of the tangent line is $y - 0 = \sqrt{3}(x - 3)$ or $y = \sqrt{3}\,x - 3\sqrt{3}$. When $t = -\sqrt{3}$, an equation of the tangent line is $y - 0 = -\sqrt{3}(x - 3)$ or $y = -\sqrt{3}\,x + 3\sqrt{3}$.

(b) Horizontal tangent:

$dy/dx = 0$ $\Leftrightarrow$ $3t^2 - 3 = 0$ $\Leftrightarrow$ $3(t^2 - 1) = 0$ $\Leftrightarrow$
$t^2 = 1$ $\Leftrightarrow$ $t = \pm 1$.
$t = 1$ corresponds to the point
$(x, y) = (t^2, t^3 - 3t) = (1^2, 1^3 - 3 \cdot 1) = (1, -2)$ and
$t = -1$ to $(1, 2)$. Vertical tangent: dy/dx is
undefined $\Leftrightarrow$ $2t = 0$ $\Leftrightarrow$ $t = 0$.
The value $t = 0$ corresponds to the origin; that is, $(0, 0)$.

(c)

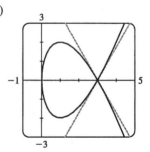

68. (a) $x = r(\theta - \sin \theta)$, $y = r(1 - \cos \theta)$ $\Rightarrow$ $\dfrac{dy}{dx} = \dfrac{dy/d\theta}{dx/d\theta} = \dfrac{r(\sin \theta)}{r(1 - \cos \theta)} = \dfrac{\sin \theta}{1 - \cos \theta}$. When $\theta = \frac{\pi}{3}$,

$\dfrac{dy}{dx} = \dfrac{\frac{\sqrt{3}}{2}}{1 - \frac{1}{2}} = \sqrt{3}$, $(x, y) = \left(r\left(\frac{\pi}{3} - \frac{\sqrt{3}}{2}\right), \frac{1}{2}r\right)$, and the tangent is $y - \frac{1}{2}r = \sqrt{3}\left[x - r\left(\frac{\pi}{3} - \frac{\sqrt{3}}{2}\right)\right]$.

(b) Horizontal tangent: $dy/dx = 0 \Leftrightarrow \sin\theta = 0$ (and $\cos\theta \neq 1$)

$\Leftrightarrow \theta = (2n+1)\pi$. The corresponding points

are $((2n+1)\pi r, 2r)$.

Vertical tangent: dy/dx is undefined $\Leftrightarrow 1 - \cos\theta = 0 \Leftrightarrow$

$\cos\theta = 1 \Leftrightarrow \theta = 2n\pi$. The corresponding points are $(2n\pi r, 0)$.

(c)

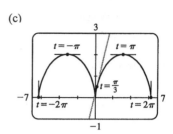

69. (a) Derive gives $g'(t) = \dfrac{45(t-2)^8}{(2t+1)^{10}}$ without simplifying. With either Maple or Mathematica, we first get

$g'(t) = 9\dfrac{(t-2)^8}{(2t+1)^9} - 18\dfrac{(t-2)^9}{(2t+1)^{10}}$, and the simplification command results in the above expression.

(b) Derive gives $y' = 2(x^3 - x + 1)^3(2x+1)^4(17x^3 + 6x^2 - 9x + 3)$ without simplifying.

With either Maple or Mathematica, we first get

$y' = 10(2x+1)^4(x^3 - x + 1)^4 + 4(2x+1)^5(x^3 - x + 1)^3(3x^2 - 1)$. If we use Mathematica's Factor or

Simplify, or Maple's factor, we get the above expression, but Maple's simplify gives the polynomial

expansion instead. For locating horizontal tangents, the factored form is the most helpful.

70. (a) $f(x) = \left(\dfrac{x^4 - x + 1}{x^4 + x + 1}\right)^{1/2}$. Derive gives $f'(x) = \dfrac{(3x^4 - 1)\sqrt{\dfrac{x^4 - x + 1}{x^4 + x + 1}}}{(x^4 + x + 1)(x^4 - x + 1)}$ whereas either Maple or

Mathematica give $f'(x) = \dfrac{3x^4 - 1}{\sqrt{\dfrac{x^4 - x + 1}{x^4 + x + 1}}\,(x^4 + x + 1)^2}$ after simplification.

(b) $f'(x) = 0 \Leftrightarrow 3x^4 - 1 = 0 \Leftrightarrow x = \pm\sqrt[4]{\tfrac{1}{3}} \approx \pm 0.7598$.

(c) $f'(x) = 0$ where f has horizontal tangents. f' has two maxima and

one minimum where f has inflection points.

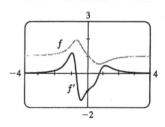

71. (a) $\dfrac{d}{dx}(\sin^n x \cos nx) = n\sin^{n-1} x \cos x \cos nx + \sin^n x(-n\sin nx)$ [Product Rule]

$= n\sin^{n-1} x(\cos nx \cos x - \sin nx \sin x)$ [factor out $n\sin^{n-1} x$]

$= n\sin^{n-1} x \cos(nx + x)$ [Addition Formula for cosine]

$= n\sin^{n-1} x \cos[(n+1)x]$ [factor out x]

(b) $\dfrac{d}{dx}(\cos^n x \cos nx) = n\cos^{n-1} x(-\sin x)\cos nx + \cos^n x(-n\sin nx)$ [Product Rule]

$= -n\cos^{n-1} x(\cos nx \sin x + \sin nx \cos x)$ [factor out $-n\cos^{n-1} x$]

$= -n\cos^{n-1} x \sin(nx + x)$ [Addition Formula for sine]

$= -n\cos^{n-1} x \sin[(n+1)x]$ [factor out x]

72. "The rate of change of y^5 with respect to x is eighty times the rate of change of y with respect to x" $\Leftrightarrow$

$\dfrac{d}{dx} y^5 = 80 \dfrac{dy}{dx}$ $\Leftrightarrow$ $5y^4 \dfrac{dy}{dx} = 80 \dfrac{dy}{dx}$ $\Leftrightarrow$ $5y^4 = 80$ (Note that $dy/dx \neq 0$ since the curve never has a

horizontal tangent) $\Leftrightarrow$ $y^4 = 16$ $\Leftrightarrow$ $y = 2$ (since $y > 0$ for all x)

73. Since $\theta° = \left(\dfrac{\pi}{180}\right) \theta$ rad, we have $\dfrac{d}{d\theta} (\sin \theta°) = \dfrac{d}{d\theta} \left(\sin \dfrac{\pi}{180}\theta\right) = \dfrac{\pi}{180} \cos \dfrac{\pi}{180}\theta = \dfrac{\pi}{180} \cos \theta°.$

74. (a) $f(x) = |x| = \sqrt{x^2} = \left(x^2\right)^{1/2}$ $\Rightarrow$ $f'(x) = \frac{1}{2}\left(x^2\right)^{-1/2} (2x) = x/\sqrt{x^2} = x/|x|$

(b) $f(x) = |\sin x| = \sqrt{\sin^2 x}$ $\Rightarrow$

$f'(x) = \frac{1}{2}\left(\sin^2 x\right)^{-1/2} 2 \sin x \cos x = \dfrac{\sin x}{|\sin x|} \cos x = \begin{cases} \cos x & \text{if } \sin x > 0 \\ -\cos x & \text{if } \sin x < 0 \end{cases}$

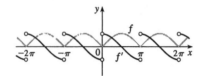

f is not differentiable when $x = n\pi$, n an integer.

(c) $g(x) = \sin|x| = \sin\sqrt{x^2}$ $\Rightarrow$ $g'(x) = \cos|x| \cdot \dfrac{x}{|x|} = \dfrac{x}{|x|} \cos x = \begin{cases} \cos x & \text{if } x > 0 \\ -\cos x & \text{if } x < 0 \end{cases}$

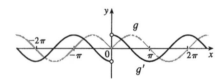

g is not differentiable at 0.

75. $\dfrac{d^2 y}{dx^2} = \dfrac{d}{dx}\left(\dfrac{dy}{dx}\right)$ [Leibniz notation for the second derivative]

$= \dfrac{d}{dx}\left(\dfrac{dy}{du}\dfrac{du}{dx}\right)$ [Chain Rule]

$= \dfrac{dy}{du} \cdot \dfrac{d}{dx}\left(\dfrac{du}{dx}\right) + \dfrac{du}{dx} \cdot \dfrac{d}{dx}\left(\dfrac{dy}{du}\right)$ [Product Rule]

$= \dfrac{dy}{du} \cdot \dfrac{d^2 u}{dx^2} + \dfrac{du}{dx} \cdot \dfrac{d}{du}\left(\dfrac{dy}{du}\right) \cdot \dfrac{du}{dx}$ [dy/du is a function of u]

$= \dfrac{dy}{du} \dfrac{d^2 u}{dx^2} + \dfrac{d^2 y}{du^2}\left(\dfrac{du}{dx}\right)^2$

Or: Using function notation for $y = f(u)$ and $u = g(x)$, we have $y = f(g(x))$, so $y' = f'(g(x)) \cdot g'(x)$ [by the Chain Rule] $\Rightarrow$

$(y')' = [f'(g(x)) \cdot g'(x)]' = f'(g(x)) \cdot g''(x) + g'(x) \cdot f''(g(x)) \cdot g'(x) = f'(g(x)) \cdot g''(x) + f''(g(x)) \cdot [g'(x)]^2.$

76. $V = \frac{4}{3}\pi r^3$ $\Leftrightarrow$ $\dfrac{dV}{dt} = 4\pi r^2 \dfrac{dr}{dt}$. But $\dfrac{dV}{dt}$ is proportional to the surface area, so $\dfrac{dV}{dt} = k \cdot 4\pi r^2$ for some

constant k. Therefore, $4\pi r^2 \dfrac{dr}{dt} = k \cdot 4\pi r^2$ $\Leftrightarrow$ $\dfrac{dr}{dt} = k =$ constant. An antiderivative of k with respect to t is

kt, so $r = kt + C$. When $t = 0$, the radius r must equal the original radius r_0, so $C = r_0$, and $r = kt + r_0$. To find

k we use the fact that when $t = 3$, $r = 3k + r_0$ and $V = \frac{1}{2}V_0$ $\Rightarrow$ $\frac{4}{3}\pi(3k + r_0)^3 = \frac{1}{2} \cdot \frac{4}{3}\pi r_0^3$ $\Rightarrow$

$(3k + r_0)^3 = \frac{1}{2}r_0^3$ $\Rightarrow$ $3k + r_0 = \frac{1}{\sqrt[3]{2}}r_0$ $\Rightarrow$ $k = \frac{1}{3}r_0\left(\frac{1}{\sqrt[3]{2}} - 1\right)$. Since $r = kt + r_0$,

$r = \frac{1}{3}r_0\left(\frac{1}{\sqrt[3]{2}} - 1\right)t + r_0$. When the snowball has melted completely we have $r = 0$ $\Rightarrow$

$\frac{1}{3}r_0\left(\frac{1}{\sqrt[3]{2}} - 1\right)t + r_0 = 0$ which gives $t = \dfrac{3\sqrt[3]{2}}{\sqrt[3]{2} - 1}$. Hence, it takes $\dfrac{3\sqrt[3]{2}}{\sqrt[3]{2} - 1} - 3 = \dfrac{3}{\sqrt[3]{2} - 1} \approx 11$ h 33 min

longer.

Laboratory Project Bézier Curves

1. The parametric equations for a cubic Bézier curve are

$$x = x_0(1 - t)^3 + 3x_1 t(1 - t)^2 + 3x_2 t^2(1 - t) + x_3 t^3$$
$$y = y_0(1 - t)^3 + 3y_1 t(1 - t)^2 + 3y_2 t^2(1 - t) + y_3 t^3$$

where $0 \le t \le 1$. We are given the points $P_0\,(x_0, y_0) = (4, 1)$, $P_1\,(x_1, y_1) = (28, 48)$, $P_2\,(x_2, y_2) = (50, 42)$, and $P_3\,(x_3, y_3) = (40, 5)$. The curve is then given by

$$x(t) = 4(1 - t)^3 + 3 \cdot 28t(1 - t)^2 + 3 \cdot 50t^2(1 - t) + 40t^3$$

$$y(t) = 1(1 - t)^3 + 3 \cdot 48t(1 - t)^2 + 3 \cdot 42t^2(1 - t) + 5t^3$$

where $0 \le t \le 1$. The line segments are of the form $x = x_0 + (x_1 - x_0)t$, $y = y_0 + (y_1 - y_0)t$:

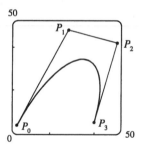

P_0P_1	$x = 4 + 24t,$	$y = 1 + 47t$
P_1P_2	$x = 28 + 22t,$	$y = 48 - 6t$
P_2P_3	$x = 50 - 10t,$	$y = 42 - 37t$

2. It suffices to show that the slope of the tangent at P_0 is the same as that of line segment P_0P_1, namely $\dfrac{y_1 - y_0}{x_1 - x_0}$. We

calculate the slope of the tangent to the Bézier curve:

$$\frac{dy/dt}{dx/dt} = \frac{-3y_0(1 - t)^2 + 3y_1\left[-2t(1 - t) + (1 - t)^2\right] + 3y_2\left[-t^2 + (2t)(1 - t)\right] + 3y_3 t^2}{-3x_0^2(1 - t) + 3x_1\left[-2t(1 - t) + (1 - t)^2\right] + 3x_2\left[-t^2 + (2t)(1 - t)\right] + 3x_3 t^2}$$

At point P_0, $t = 0$, so the slope of the tangent is $\dfrac{-3y_0 + 3y_1}{-3x_0 + 3x_1} = \dfrac{y_1 - y_0}{x_1 - x_0}$. So the tangent to the curve at P_0 passes

through P_1. Similarly, the slope of the tangent at point P_3 (where $t = 1$) is $\dfrac{-3y_2 + 3y_3}{-3x_2 + 3x_3} = \dfrac{y_3 - y_2}{x_3 - x_2}$, which is also

the slope of line P_2P_3.

3. It seems that if P_1 were to the right of P_2, a loop would appear. We try setting $P_1 = (110, 30)$, and the resulting curve does indeed have a loop.

4. Based on the behavior of the Bézier curve in Problems 1–3, we suspect that the four control points should be in an exaggerated C shape. We try P_0 $(10, 12)$, P_1 $(4, 15)$, P_2 $(4, 5)$, and P_3 $(10, 8)$, and these produce a decent C. If you are using a CAS, it may be necessary to instruct it to make the x- and y-scales the same so as not to distort the figure (this is called a "constrained projection" in Maple.)

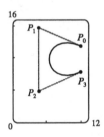

5. We use the same P_0 and P_1 as in Problem 4, and use part of our C as the top of an S. To prevent the center line from slanting up too much, we move P_2 up to $(4, 6)$ and P_3 down and to the left, to $(8, 7)$. In order to have a smooth joint between the top and bottom halves of the S (and a symmetric S), we determine points P_4, P_5, and P_6 by rotating points P_2, P_1, and P_0 about the center of the letter (point P_3). The points are therefore P_4 $(12, 8)$, P_5 $(12, -1)$, and P_6 $(6, 2)$.

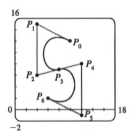

Applied Project	**Where Should a Pilot Start Descent?**

1. Condition (i) will hold if and only if all of the following four conditions hold:

(α) $P(0) = 0$

(β) $P'(0) = 0$ (for a smooth landing)

(γ) $P'(\ell) = 0$ (since the plane is cruising horizontally when it begins its descent)

(δ) $P(\ell) = h$.

First of all, condition α implies that $P(0) = d = 0$, so $P(x) = ax^3 + bx^2 + cx \Rightarrow P'(x) = 3ax^2 + 2bx + c$. But $P'(0) = c = 0$ by condition β. So $P'(\ell) = 3a\ell^2 + 2b\ell = \ell(3a\ell + 2b)$. Now by condition γ,

$$3a\ell + 2b = 0 \quad\Rightarrow\quad a = -\frac{2b}{3\ell}. \text{ Therefore, } P(x) = -\frac{2b}{3\ell}x^3 + bx^2. \text{ Setting } P(\ell) = h \text{ for condition } \delta, \text{ we get}$$

$$P(\ell) = -\frac{2b}{3\ell}\ell^3 + b\ell^2 = h \quad\Rightarrow\quad -\frac{2}{3}b\ell^2 + b\ell^2 = h \quad\Rightarrow\quad \frac{1}{3}b\ell^2 = h \quad\Rightarrow\quad b = \frac{3h}{\ell^2} \quad\Rightarrow\quad a = -\frac{2h}{\ell^3}. \text{ So}$$

$$y = P(x) = -\frac{2h}{\ell^3}x^3 + \frac{3h}{\ell^2}x^2.$$

2. By condition (ii), $\dfrac{dx}{dt} = -v$ for all t, so $x(t) = \ell - vt$. Condition (iii) states that $\left|\dfrac{d^2y}{dt^2}\right| \le k$. By the Chain Rule,

we have $\dfrac{dy}{dt} = \dfrac{dy}{dx}\dfrac{dx}{dt} = -\dfrac{2h}{\ell^3}(3x^2)\dfrac{dx}{dt} + \dfrac{3h}{\ell^2}(2x)\dfrac{dx}{dt} = \dfrac{6hx^2v}{\ell^3} - \dfrac{6hxv}{\ell^2}$ (for $x \le \ell$) $\Rightarrow$

$\dfrac{d^2y}{dt^2} = \dfrac{6hv}{\ell^3}(2x)\dfrac{dx}{dt} - \dfrac{6hv}{\ell^2}\dfrac{dx}{dt} = -\dfrac{12hv^2}{\ell^3}x + \dfrac{6hv^2}{\ell^2}$. In particular, when $t = 0$, $x = \ell$ and so

$\dfrac{d^2y}{dt^2}\bigg|_{t=0} = -\dfrac{12hv^2}{\ell^3}\ell + \dfrac{6hv^2}{\ell^2} = -\dfrac{6hv^2}{\ell^2}$. Thus, $\left|\dfrac{d^2y}{dt^2}\right|_{t=0} = \dfrac{6hv^2}{\ell^2} \le k$. (This condition also follows from

taking $x = 0$.)

3. We substitute $k = 860 \text{ mi/h}^2$, $h = 35{,}000 \text{ ft} \times \dfrac{1 \text{ mi}}{5280 \text{ ft}}$, and $v = 300 \text{ mi/h}$ into the result of part (b):

$$\frac{6\left(35{,}000 \cdot \frac{1}{5280}\right)(300)^2}{\ell^2} \le 860 \quad\Rightarrow\quad \ell \ge 300\sqrt{6 \cdot \frac{35{,}000}{5280 \cdot 860}} \approx 64.5 \text{ miles.}$$

4. Substituting the values of h and ℓ in Problem 3 into $P(x) = -\dfrac{2h}{\ell^3}x^3 + \dfrac{3h}{\ell^2}x^2$ gives us $P(x) = ax^3 + bx^2$, where

$a \approx 4.937 \times 10^{-5}$ and $b \approx 4.78 \times 10^{-3}$.

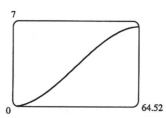

3.6 Implicit Differentiation · · · · · · · · · · · · · · · ·

1. (a) $\dfrac{d}{dx}\left(xy + 2x + 3x^2\right) = \dfrac{d}{dx}(4) \;\Rightarrow\; (x \cdot y' + y \cdot 1) + 2 + 6x = 0 \;\Rightarrow\; xy' = -y - 2 - 6x \;\Rightarrow$

$y' = \dfrac{-y - 2 - 6x}{x}$ or $y' = -6 - \dfrac{y + 2}{x}$.

(b) $xy + 2x + 3x^2 = 4 \;\Rightarrow\; xy = 4 - 2x - 3x^2 \;\Rightarrow\; y = \dfrac{4 - 2x - 3x^2}{x} = \dfrac{4}{x} - 2 - 3x$, so $y' = -\dfrac{4}{x^2} - 3$.

(c) From part (a), $y' = \dfrac{-y - 2 - 6x}{x} = \dfrac{-(4/x - 2 - 3x) - 2 - 6x}{x} = \dfrac{-4/x - 3x}{x} = -\dfrac{4}{x^2} - 3$.

2. (a) $\dfrac{d}{dx}\left(4x^2 + 9y^2\right) = \dfrac{d}{dx}(36) \;\Rightarrow\; 8x + 18y \cdot y' = 0 \;\Rightarrow\; y' = -\dfrac{8x}{18y} = -\dfrac{4x}{9y}$

(b) $4x^2 + 9y^2 = 36 \;\Rightarrow\; 9y^2 = 36 - 4x^2 \;\Rightarrow\; y^2 = \tfrac{4}{9}\left(9 - x^2\right) \;\Rightarrow\; y = \pm\tfrac{2}{3}\sqrt{9 - x^2}$, so

$y' = \pm\tfrac{2}{3} \cdot \tfrac{1}{2}\left(9 - x^2\right)^{-1/2}(-2x) = \mp\dfrac{2x}{3\sqrt{9 - x^2}}$

(c) From part (a), $y' = -\dfrac{4x}{9y} = -\dfrac{4x}{9\left(\pm\tfrac{2}{3}\sqrt{9 - x^2}\right)} = \mp\dfrac{2x}{3\sqrt{9 - x^2}}$.

3. $\dfrac{d}{dx}\left(x^3 + x^2 y + 4y^2\right) = \dfrac{d}{dx}(6) \;\Rightarrow\; 3x^2 + \left(x^2 y' + y \cdot 2x\right) + 8yy' = 0 \;\Rightarrow\; x^2 y' + 8yy' = -3x^2 - 2xy$

$\Rightarrow\; (x^2 + 8y)y' = -3x^2 - 2xy \;\Rightarrow\; y' = -\dfrac{3x^2 + 2xy}{x^2 + 8y} = -\dfrac{x(3x + 2y)}{x^2 + 8y}$

4. $\dfrac{d}{dx}\left(x^2 - 2xy + y^3\right) = \dfrac{d}{dx}(c) \;\Rightarrow\; 2x - 2(xy' + y \cdot 1) + 3y^2 y' = 0 \;\Rightarrow\; 2x - 2y = 2xy' - 3y^2 y' \;\Rightarrow$

$2x - 2y = y'\left(2x - 3y^2\right) \;\Rightarrow\; y' = \dfrac{2x - 2y}{2x - 3y^2}$

5. $\dfrac{d}{dx}\left(x^2 y + xy^2\right) = \dfrac{d}{dx}(3x) \;\Rightarrow\; \left(x^2 y' + y \cdot 2x\right) + \left(x \cdot 2yy' + y^2 \cdot 1\right) = 3 \;\Rightarrow$

$x^2 y' + 2xyy' = 3 - 2xy - y^2 \;\Rightarrow\; y'\left(x^2 + 2xy\right) = 3 - 2xy - y^2 \;\Rightarrow\; y' = \dfrac{3 - 2xy - y^2}{x^2 + 2xy}$

6. $\dfrac{d}{dx}\left(y^5 + x^2 y^3\right) = \dfrac{d}{dx}\left(1 + ye^{x^2}\right) \;\Rightarrow\; 5y^4 y' + \left(x^2 \cdot 3y^2 y' + y^3 \cdot 2x\right) = 0 + y \cdot e^{x^2} \cdot 2x + e^{x^2} \cdot y' \;\Rightarrow$

$y'\left(5y^4 + 3x^2 y^2 - e^{x^2}\right) = 2xye^{x^2} - 2xy^3 \;\Rightarrow\; y' = \dfrac{2xy\left(e^{x^2} - y^2\right)}{5y^4 + 3x^2 y^2 - e^{x^2}}$

7. $\sqrt{xy} = 1 + x^2 y \;\Rightarrow\; \tfrac{1}{2}(xy)^{-1/2}(xy' + y \cdot 1) = 0 + x^2 y' + y \cdot 2x \;\Rightarrow\; \dfrac{x}{2\sqrt{xy}}\,y' + \dfrac{y}{2\sqrt{xy}} = x^2 y' + 2xy$

$\Rightarrow\; y'\left(\dfrac{x}{2\sqrt{xy}} - x^2\right) = 2xy - \dfrac{y}{2\sqrt{xy}} \;\Rightarrow\; y'\left(\dfrac{x - 2x^2\sqrt{xy}}{2\sqrt{xy}}\right) = \dfrac{4xy\sqrt{xy} - y}{2\sqrt{xy}} \;\Rightarrow\; y' = \dfrac{4xy\sqrt{xy} - y}{x - 2x^2\sqrt{xy}}$

8. $\sqrt{1 + x^2y^2} = 2xy \quad \Rightarrow \quad \frac{1}{2}\left(1 + x^2y^2\right)^{-1/2}\left(x^2 \cdot 2yy' + y^2 \cdot 2x\right) = 2(xy' + y \cdot 1) \quad \Rightarrow$

$\dfrac{2x^2y}{2\sqrt{1+x^2y^2}}\, y' + \dfrac{2xy^2}{2\sqrt{1+x^2y^2}} = 2xy' + 2y \quad \Rightarrow \quad y'\left(\dfrac{x^2y}{\sqrt{1+x^2y^2}} - 2x\right) = 2y - \dfrac{xy^2}{\sqrt{1+x^2y^2}} \quad \Rightarrow$

$y'\left(\dfrac{x^2y - 2x\sqrt{1+x^2y^2}}{\sqrt{1+x^2y^2}}\right) = \dfrac{2y\sqrt{1+x^2y^2} - xy^2}{\sqrt{1+x^2y^2}} \quad \Rightarrow$

$y' = \dfrac{2y\sqrt{1+x^2y^2} - xy^2}{x^2y - 2x\sqrt{1+x^2y^2}} = \dfrac{y\left(2\sqrt{1+x^2y^2} - xy\right)}{x\left(xy - 2\sqrt{1+x^2y^2}\right)} = -\dfrac{y}{x}$

Another method: Since $1 + x^2y^2$ is positive, we can square both sides first and then differentiate implicitly.

9. $\dfrac{d}{dx}\,(4\cos x \sin y) = \dfrac{d}{dx}\,(1) \quad \Rightarrow \quad 4\left[\cos x \cdot \cos y \cdot y' + \sin y \cdot (-\sin x)\right] = 0 \quad \Rightarrow$

$y'(4\cos x \cos y) = 4\sin x \sin y \quad \Rightarrow \quad y' = \dfrac{4\sin x \sin y}{4\cos x \cos y} = \tan x \tan y$

10. $x\cos y + y\cos x = 1 \quad \Rightarrow \quad x(-\sin y)y' + \cos y + y(-\sin x) + \cos x \cdot y' = 0 \quad \Rightarrow \quad y' = \dfrac{y\sin x - \cos y}{\cos x - x\sin y}$

11. $\cos(x - y) = xe^x \quad \Rightarrow \quad -\sin(x - y)(1 - y') = xe^x + e^x \quad \Rightarrow \quad 1 - y' = -\dfrac{(x+1)e^x}{\sin(x-y)} \quad \Rightarrow$

$y' = 1 + \dfrac{(x+1)e^x}{\sin(x-y)}$

12. $\sin x + \cos y = \sin x \cos y \quad \Rightarrow \quad \cos x - \sin y \cdot y' = \sin x\,(-\sin y \cdot y') + \cos y \cos x \quad \Rightarrow$

$(\sin x \sin y - \sin y)y' = \cos x \cos y - \cos x \quad \Rightarrow \quad y' = \dfrac{\cos x(\cos y - 1)}{\sin y(\sin x - 1)}$

13. $\dfrac{d}{dx}\left(\dfrac{x^2}{16} - \dfrac{y^2}{9}\right) = \dfrac{d}{dx}\,(1) \quad \Rightarrow \quad \dfrac{x}{8} - \dfrac{2yy'}{9} = 0 \quad \Rightarrow \quad y' = \dfrac{9x}{16y}$. When $x = -5$ and $y = \frac{9}{4}$ we have

$y' = \dfrac{9(-5)}{16(9/4)} = -\dfrac{5}{4}$, so an equation of the tangent line is $y - \frac{9}{4} = -\frac{5}{4}(x+5)$ or $y = -\frac{5}{4}x - 4$.

14. $\dfrac{x^2}{9} + \dfrac{y^2}{36} = 1 \quad \Rightarrow \quad \dfrac{2x}{9} + \dfrac{yy'}{18} = 0 \quad \Rightarrow \quad y' = -\dfrac{4x}{y}$. When $x = -1$ and $y = 4\sqrt{2}$ we have

$y' = -\dfrac{4(-1)}{4\sqrt{2}} = \dfrac{1}{\sqrt{2}}$, so an equation of the tangent line is $y - 4\sqrt{2} = \frac{1}{\sqrt{2}}(x+1)$ or $y = \frac{1}{\sqrt{2}}(x+9)$.

15. $y^2 = x^3\,(2 - x) = 2x^3 - x^4 \quad \Rightarrow \quad 2yy' = 6x^2 - 4x^3 \quad \Rightarrow \quad y' = \dfrac{3x^2 - 2x^3}{y}$. When $x = y = 1$,

$y' = \dfrac{3(1)^2 - 2(1)^3}{1} = 1$, so an equation of the tangent line is $y - 1 = 1(x - 1)$ or $y = x$.

16. $x^{2/3} + y^{2/3} = 4 \quad \Rightarrow \quad \frac{2}{3}x^{-1/3} + \frac{2}{3}y^{-1/3}y' = 0 \quad \Rightarrow \quad \dfrac{1}{\sqrt[3]{x}} + \dfrac{y'}{\sqrt[3]{y}} = 0 \quad \Rightarrow \quad y' = -\dfrac{\sqrt[3]{y}}{\sqrt[3]{x}}$. When $x = -3\sqrt{3}$

and $y = 1$, we have $y' = -\dfrac{1}{(-3\sqrt{3})^{1/3}} = -\dfrac{(-3\sqrt{3})^{2/3}}{-3\sqrt{3}} = \dfrac{3}{3\sqrt{3}} = \dfrac{1}{\sqrt{3}}$, so an equation of the tangent line is

$y - 1 = \frac{1}{\sqrt{3}}\left(x + 3\sqrt{3}\right)$ or $y = \frac{1}{\sqrt{3}}x + 4$.

17. $2(x^2+y^2)^2 = 25(x^2-y^2) \Rightarrow 4(x^2+y^2)(2x+2yy') = 25(2x-2yy') \Rightarrow$

$4(x+yy')(x^2+y^2) = 25(x-yy') \Rightarrow 4yy'(x^2+y^2) + 25yy' = 25x - 4x(x^2+y^2) \Rightarrow$

$y' = \dfrac{25x - 4x(x^2+y^2)}{25y + 4y(x^2+y^2)}$. When $x=3$ and $y=1$, $y' = \frac{75-120}{25+40} = -\frac{45}{65} = -\frac{9}{13}$, so an equation of the tangent

line is $y - 1 = -\frac{9}{13}(x-3)$ or $y = -\frac{9}{13}x + \frac{40}{13}$.

18. $x^2y^2 = (y+1)^2(4-y^2) \Rightarrow 2x^2yy' + 2xy^2 = (y+1)^2(-2yy') + (4-y^2)\cdot 2(y+1)y' \Rightarrow$

$xy^2 = [(y+1)(4-y^2) - y(y+1)^2 - x^2y]y' \Rightarrow y' = \dfrac{xy^2}{(y+1)(4-y^2) - y(y+1)^2 - x^2y} = 0$ when

$x = 0$. So an equation of the tangent line at $(0,-2)$ is $y + 2 = 0(x-0)$ or $y = -2$.

19. (a) $y^2 = 5x^4 - x^2 \Rightarrow 2yy' = 5(4x^3) - 2x \Rightarrow y' = \dfrac{10x^3 - x}{y}$. **(b)**

So at the point $(1,2)$ we have $y' = \dfrac{10(1)^3 - 1}{2} = \dfrac{9}{2}$, and an

equation of the tangent line is $y - 2 = \frac{9}{2}(x-1)$ or $y = \frac{9}{2}x - \frac{5}{2}$.

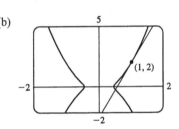

20. (a) $y^2 = x^3 + 3x^2 \Rightarrow 2yy' = 3x^2 + 3(2x) \Rightarrow y' = \dfrac{3x^2 + 6x}{2y}$. So at the point $(1,-2)$ we have

$y' = \dfrac{3(1)^2 + 6(1)}{2(-2)} = -\dfrac{9}{4}$, and an equation of the tangent line is $y + 2 = -\frac{9}{4}(x-1)$ or $y = -\frac{9}{4}x + \frac{1}{4}$.

(b) The curve has a horizontal tangent where $y' = 0 \Leftrightarrow$ **(c)**

$3x^2 + 6x = 0 \Leftrightarrow 3x(x+2) = 0 \Leftrightarrow x = 0$ or $x = -2$. But

note that at $x = 0$, $y = 0$ also, so the derivative does not exist. At

$x = -2$, $y^2 = (-2)^3 + 3(-2)^2 = -8 + 12 = 4$, so $y = \pm 2$. So the

two points at which the curve has a horizontal tangent are $(-2,-2)$

and $(-2,2)$.

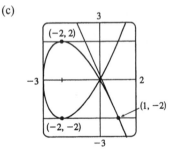

21. (a)

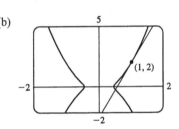

There are eight points with horizontal tangents:

four at $x \approx 1.57735$ and four at $x \approx 0.42265$.

(b) $y' = \dfrac{3x^2 - 6x + 2}{2(2y^3 - 3y^2 - y + 1)} \Rightarrow y' = -1$ at

$(0,1)$ and $y' = \frac{1}{3}$ at $(0,2)$.

Equations of the tangent lines are $y = -x + 1$

and $y = \frac{1}{3}x + 2$.

(c) $y' = 0 \Rightarrow 3x^2 - 6x + 2 = 0 \Rightarrow$

$x = 1 \pm \frac{1}{3}\sqrt{3}$

(d) By multiplying the right side of the equation by $x - 3$, we obtain the first graph.

By modifying the equation in other ways, we can generate the other graphs.

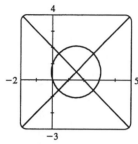

$$y\left(y^2 - 1\right)(y - 2)$$
$$= x(x - 1)(x - 2)(x - 3)$$

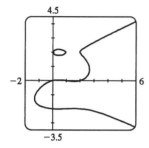

$$y\left(y^2 - 4\right)(y - 2)$$
$$= x(x - 1)(x - 2)$$

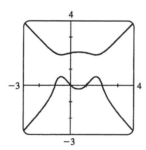

$$y(y + 1)\left(y^2 - 1\right)(y - 2)$$
$$= x(x - 1)(x - 2)$$

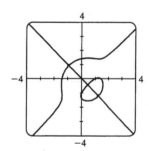

$$(y + 1)\left(y^2 - 1\right)(y - 2)$$
$$= (x - 1)(x - 2)$$

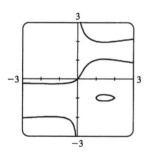

$$x(y + 1)\left(y^2 - 1\right)(y - 2)$$
$$= y(x - 1)(x - 2)$$

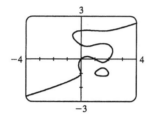

$$y\left(y^2 + 1\right)(y - 2)$$
$$= x\left(x^2 - 1\right)(x - 2)$$

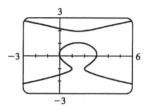

$$y(y + 1)\left(y^2 - 2\right)$$
$$= x(x - 1)\left(x^2 - 2\right)$$

22. (a)

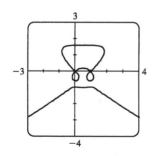

(b) There are 9 points with horizontal tangents: 3 at $x = 0$, 3 at $x = \frac{1}{2}$, and 3 at $x = 1$. The three horizontal tangents along the top of the wagon are hard to find, but by limiting the y-range of the graph (to $[1.6, 1.7]$, for example) they are distinguishable.

23. From Exercise 17, a tangent to the lemniscate will be horizontal if $y' = 0 \Rightarrow 25x - 4x(x^2 + y^2) = 0 \Rightarrow$
$x[25 - 4(x^2 + y^2)] = 0 \Rightarrow x^2 + y^2 = \frac{25}{4}$ (1). (Note that when x is 0, y is also 0, and there is no horizontal
tangent at the origin.) Substituting $\frac{25}{4}$ for $x^2 + y^2$ in the equation of the lemniscate, $2(x^2 + y^2)^2 = 25(x^2 - y^2)$,
we get $x^2 - y^2 = \frac{25}{8}$ (2). Solving (1) and (2), we have $x^2 = \frac{75}{16}$ and $y^2 = \frac{25}{16}$, so the four points are $\left(\pm \frac{5\sqrt{3}}{4}, \pm \frac{5}{4}\right)$.

24. $\dfrac{x^2}{a^2} + \dfrac{y^2}{b^2} = 1 \Rightarrow \dfrac{2x}{a^2} + \dfrac{2yy'}{b^2} = 0 \Rightarrow y' = -\dfrac{b^2 x}{a^2 y} \Rightarrow$ the equation of the tangent at (x_0, y_0) is

$y - y_0 = \dfrac{-b^2 x_0}{a^2 y_0}(x - x_0)$. Multiplying both sides by $\dfrac{y_0}{b^2}$ gives $\dfrac{y_0 y}{b^2} - \dfrac{y_0^2}{b^2} = -\dfrac{x_0 x}{a^2} + \dfrac{x_0^2}{a^2}$. Since (x_0, y_0) lies on

the ellipse, we have $\dfrac{x_0 x}{a^2} + \dfrac{y_0 y}{b^2} = \dfrac{x_0^2}{a^2} + \dfrac{y_0^2}{b^2} = 1$.

25. (a) $x^4 + y^4 = 16 \Rightarrow 4x^3 + 4y^3 y' = 0 \Rightarrow y^3 y' = -x^3 \Rightarrow y' = -x^3/y^3$

(b) $y'' = -\dfrac{y^3(3x^2) - (x^3)(3y^2 y')}{(y^3)^2} = -\dfrac{3x^2 y^3 - 3x^3 y^2(-x^3/y^3)}{y^6} \cdot \dfrac{y}{y} = -\dfrac{3x^2 y^4 + 3x^6}{y^7}$

(c) $y'' = -\dfrac{3x^2(y^4 + x^4)}{y^7} = -\dfrac{3x^2(16)}{y^7} = -48\dfrac{x^2}{y^7}$

26. $x^2 + 6xy + y^2 = 8 \Rightarrow 2x + 6xy' + 6y + 2yy' = 0 \Rightarrow (3x + y)y' = -x - 3y \Rightarrow$
$y' = -\dfrac{x + 3y}{3x + y} \Rightarrow$

$y'' = -\dfrac{(3x + y)(1 + 3y') - (x + 3y)(3 + y')}{(3x + y)^2} = -\dfrac{-8y + 8xy'}{(3x + y)^2} = \dfrac{8(y - xy')}{(3x + y)^2}$

$= \dfrac{8[y - x(-x - 3y)/(3x + y)]}{(3x + y)^2} \cdot \dfrac{3x + y}{3x + y} = \dfrac{8[y(3x + y) + x(x + 3y)]}{(3x + y)^3}$

$= \dfrac{8(x^2 + 6xy + y^2)}{(3x + y)^3} = \dfrac{64}{(3x + y)^3}$

At the last step, we used the fact that x and y must satisfy the original equation, $x^2 + 6xy + y^2 = 8$.

27. $y = \sin^{-1}(x^2) \Rightarrow y' = \dfrac{1}{\sqrt{1 - (x^2)^2}} \dfrac{d}{dx}(x^2) = \dfrac{2x}{\sqrt{1 - x^4}}$

28. $y = (\sin^{-1} x)^2 \Rightarrow y' = 2(\sin^{-1} x) \dfrac{d}{dx}(\sin^{-1} x) \Rightarrow y' = \dfrac{2\sin^{-1} x}{\sqrt{1 - x^2}}$

29. $y = 2\sqrt{x} \tan^{-1}\sqrt{x} \Rightarrow$

$y' = 2\sqrt{x} \cdot \dfrac{d}{dx}(\tan^{-1}\sqrt{x}) + \tan^{-1}\sqrt{x} \cdot \dfrac{d}{dx}(2\sqrt{x})$

$= 2\sqrt{x} \cdot \dfrac{1}{1 + (\sqrt{x})^2} \cdot \dfrac{1}{2\sqrt{x}} + \tan^{-1}\sqrt{x} \cdot \dfrac{2}{2\sqrt{x}} = \dfrac{1}{1 + x} + \dfrac{\tan^{-1}\sqrt{x}}{\sqrt{x}}$

30. $h(x) = \sqrt{1 - x^2} \arcsin x \Rightarrow$

$h'(x) = \sqrt{1 - x^2} \cdot \dfrac{1}{\sqrt{1 - x^2}} + \arcsin x\left[\frac{1}{2}(1 - x^2)^{-1/2}(-2x)\right] = 1 - \dfrac{x \arcsin x}{\sqrt{1 - x^2}}$

31. $H(x) = (1 + x^2) \arctan x \Rightarrow H'(x) = (1 + x^2)\dfrac{1}{1 + x^2} + (\arctan x)(2x) = 1 + 2x \arctan x$

32. $y = \tan^{-1}\left(x - \sqrt{x^2+1}\right)$ $\Rightarrow$

$$y' = \frac{1}{1+\left(x-\sqrt{x^2+1}\right)^2}\left(1 - \frac{x}{\sqrt{x^2+1}}\right) = \frac{1}{1+x^2-2x\sqrt{x^2+1}+x^2+1}\left(\frac{\sqrt{x^2+1}-x}{\sqrt{x^2+1}}\right)$$

$$= \frac{\sqrt{x^2+1}-x}{2\left(1+x^2-x\sqrt{x^2+1}\right)\sqrt{x^2+1}} = \frac{\sqrt{x^2+1}-x}{2\left(\sqrt{x^2+1}+x^2\sqrt{x^2+1}-x^3-x\right)}$$

$$= \frac{\sqrt{x^2+1}-x}{2\left[\sqrt{x^2+1}\,(1+x^2)-x(x^2+1)\right]} = \frac{\sqrt{x^2+1}-x}{2\left[(1+x^2)\left(\sqrt{x^2+1}-x\right)\right]} = \frac{1}{2(1+x^2)}$$

33. $y = \arcsin(\tan\theta)$ $\Rightarrow$ $y' = \dfrac{1}{\sqrt{1-(\tan\theta)^2}} \cdot \dfrac{d}{d\theta}(\tan\theta) = \dfrac{\sec^2\theta}{\sqrt{1-\tan^2\theta}}$

34. Let $y = \cos^{-1}x$. Then $\cos y = x$ and $0 \le y \le \pi$ $\Rightarrow$ $\dfrac{d}{dx}(\cos y) = \dfrac{d}{dx}(x)$ $\Rightarrow$ $-\sin y \dfrac{dy}{dx} = 1$ $\Rightarrow$

$\dfrac{dy}{dx} = -\dfrac{1}{\sin y} = -\dfrac{1}{\sqrt{1-\cos^2 y}} = -\dfrac{1}{\sqrt{1-x^2}}$ (Note that $\sin y \ge 0$ for $0 \le y \le \pi$.)

35. $f(x) = e^x - x^2 \arctan x$ $\Rightarrow$

$$f'(x) = e^x - \left[x^2\left(\frac{1}{1+x^2}\right) + (\arctan x)(2x)\right]$$

$$= e^x - \frac{x^2}{1+x^2} - 2x\arctan x$$

This is reasonable because the graphs show that f is increasing when f' is positive, and f' is zero when f has a minimum.

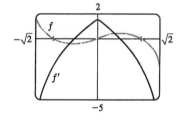

36. $f(x) = x \arcsin\left(1-x^2\right)$ $\Rightarrow$

$$f'(x) = x\left[\frac{-2x}{\sqrt{1-(1-x^2)^2}}\right] + \arcsin\left(1-x^2\right)\cdot 1$$

$$= \arcsin\left(1-x^2\right) - \frac{2x^2}{\sqrt{2x^2-x^4}}$$

This is reasonable because the graphs show that f is increasing when f' is positive, and that f has an inflection point when f' changes from increasing to decreasing.

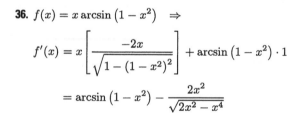

37. $2x^2 + y^2 = 3$ and $x = y^2$ intersect when $2x^2 + x - 3 = 0$ $\Leftrightarrow$ $(2x+3)(x-1) = 0$ $\Leftrightarrow$ $x = -\frac{3}{2}$ or 1, but $-\frac{3}{2}$ is extraneous since $x = y^2$ is nonnegative. When $x = 1$, $1 = y^2$ $\Rightarrow$ $y = \pm 1$, so there are two points of intersection: $(1, \pm 1)$. $2x^2 + y^2 = 3$ $\Rightarrow$ $4x + 2yy' = 0$ $\Rightarrow$ $y' = -2x/y$, and $x = y^2$ $\Rightarrow$ $1 = 2yy'$ $\Rightarrow$ $y' = 1/(2y)$. At $(1, 1)$, the slopes are $m_1 = -2(1)/1 = -2$ and $m_2 = 1/(2\cdot 1) = \frac{1}{2}$, so the curves are orthogonal (since m_1 and m_2 are negative reciprocals of each other). By symmetry, the curves are also orthogonal at $(1, -1)$.

38. $x^2 - y^2 = 5$ and $4x^2 + 9y^2 = 72$ intersect when $4x^2 + 9(x^2 - 5) = 72$ $\Leftrightarrow$ $13x^2 = 117$ $\Leftrightarrow$ $x = \pm 3$, so there are four points of intersection: $(\pm 3, \pm 2)$. $x^2 - y^2 = 5$ $\Rightarrow$ $2x - 2yy' = 0$ $\Rightarrow$ $y' = x/y$, and $4x^2 + 9y^2 = 72$ $\Rightarrow$ $8x + 18yy' = 0$ $\Leftrightarrow$ $y' = -4x/9y$. At $(3, 2)$, the slopes are $m_1 = \frac{3}{2}$ and $m_2 = -\frac{2}{3}$, so the curves are orthogonal. By symmetry, the curves are also orthogonal at $(3, -2)$, $(-3, 2)$ and $(-3, -2)$.

39.

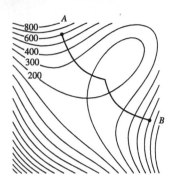

40. The orthogonal family represents the direction of the wind.

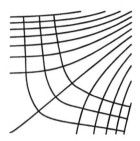

41. $x^2 + y^2 = r^2$ is a circle with center O and $ax + by = 0$ is a line through O.

$x^2 + y^2 = r^2 \implies 2x + 2yy' = 0 \implies y' = -x/y$, so the slope of the tangent line at P_0 (x_0, y_0) is $-x_0/y_0$. The slope of the line OP_0 is y_0/x_0, which is the negative reciprocal of $-x_0/y_0$. Hence, the curves are orthogonal, and the families of curves are orthogonal trajectories of each other.

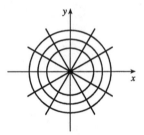

42. The circles $x^2 + y^2 = ax$ and $x^2 + y^2 = by$ intersect at the origin where the tangents are vertical and horizontal. If (x_0, y_0) is the other point of intersection, then $x_0^2 + y_0^2 = ax_0$ (1) and $x_0^2 + y_0^2 = by_0$ (2). Now $x^2 + y^2 = ax \implies$

$2x + 2yy' = a \implies y' = \dfrac{a - 2x}{2y}$ and $x^2 + y^2 = by \implies$

$2x + 2yy' = by' \implies y' = \dfrac{2x}{b - 2y}$. Thus, the curves are orthogonal at

$(x_0, y_0) \iff \dfrac{a - 2x_0}{2y_0} = -\dfrac{b - 2y_0}{2x_0} \iff 2ax_0 - 4x_0^2 = 4y_0^2 - 2by_0 \iff$

$ax_0 + by_0 = 2(x_0^2 + y_0^2)$, which is true by (1) and (2).

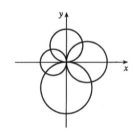

43. $y = cx^2 \implies y' = 2cx$ and $x^2 + 2y^2 = k \implies 2x + 4yy' = 0 \implies$

$2yy' = -x \implies y' = -\dfrac{x}{2(y)} = -\dfrac{x}{2(cx^2)} = -\dfrac{1}{2cx}$, so the curves are orthogonal.

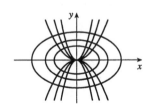

44. $y = ax^3 \implies y' = 3ax^2$ and $x^2 + 3y^2 = b \implies 2x + 6yy' = 0 \implies$

$3yy' = -x \implies y' = -\dfrac{x}{3(y)} = -\dfrac{x}{3(ax^3)} = -\dfrac{1}{3ax^2}$, so the curves are orthogonal.

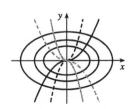

45. If the circle has radius r, its equation is $x^2 + y^2 = r^2$ $\Rightarrow$ $2x + 2yy' = 0$ $\Rightarrow$ $y' = -\dfrac{x}{y}$, so the slope of the

tangent line at $P(x_0, y_0)$ is $-\dfrac{x_0}{y_0}$. The negative reciprocal of that slope is $\dfrac{-1}{-x_0/y_0} = \dfrac{y_0}{x_0}$, which is the slope of

OP, so the tangent line at P is perpendicular to the radius OP.

46. $\sqrt{x} + \sqrt{y} = \sqrt{c}$ $\Rightarrow$ $\dfrac{1}{2\sqrt{x}} + \dfrac{y'}{2\sqrt{y}} = 0$ $\Rightarrow$ $y' = -\dfrac{\sqrt{y}}{\sqrt{x}}$ $\Rightarrow$ an equation of the tangent line at (x_0, y_0) is

$y - y_0 = -\dfrac{\sqrt{y_0}}{\sqrt{x_0}}(x - x_0)$. Now $x = 0$ $\Rightarrow$ $y = y_0 - \dfrac{\sqrt{y_0}}{\sqrt{x_0}}(-x_0) = y_0 + \sqrt{x_0}\sqrt{y_0}$, so the y-intercept is

$y_0 + \sqrt{x_0}\sqrt{y_0}$. And $y = 0$ $\Rightarrow$ $-y_0 = -\dfrac{\sqrt{y_0}}{\sqrt{x_0}}(x - x_0)$ $\Rightarrow$ $x - x_0 = \dfrac{y_0\sqrt{x_0}}{\sqrt{y_0}}$ $\Rightarrow$

$x = x_0 + \sqrt{x_0}\sqrt{y_0}$, so the x-intercept is $x_0 + \sqrt{x_0}\sqrt{y_0}$. The sum of the intercepts is

$\left(y_0 + \sqrt{x_0}\sqrt{y_0}\right) + \left(x_0 + \sqrt{x_0}\sqrt{y_0}\right) = x_0 + 2\sqrt{x_0}\sqrt{y_0} + y_0 = \left(\sqrt{x_0} + \sqrt{y_0}\right)^2 = \left(\sqrt{c}\right)^2 = c$.

47. To find the points at which the ellipse $x^2 - xy + y^2 = 3$ crosses the x-axis, let $y = 0$ and solve for x.

$y = 0$ $\Rightarrow$ $x^2 - x(0) + 0^2 = 3$ $\Leftrightarrow$ $x = \pm\sqrt{3}$. So the graph of the ellipse crosses the x-axis at the points

$(\pm\sqrt{3}, 0)$. Using implicit differentiation to find y', we get $2x - xy' - y + 2yy' = 0$ $\Rightarrow$ $y'(2y - x) = y - 2x$

$\Leftrightarrow$ $y' = \dfrac{y - 2x}{2y - x}$. So y' at $(\sqrt{3}, 0)$ is $\dfrac{0 - 2\sqrt{3}}{2(0) - \sqrt{3}} = 2$ and y' at $(-\sqrt{3}, 0)$ is $\dfrac{0 + 2\sqrt{3}}{2(0) + \sqrt{3}} = 2$. Thus, the tangent

lines at these points are parallel.

48. (a) We use implicit differentiation to find $y' = \dfrac{y - 2x}{2y - x}$ as in Exercise 47. (b)

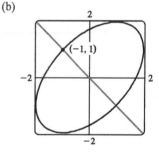

The slope of the tangent line at $(-1, 1)$ is $m = \dfrac{1 - 2(-1)}{2(1) - (-1)} = \dfrac{3}{3} = 1$,

so the slope of the normal line is $-\dfrac{1}{m} = -1$, and its equation is

$y - 1 = -1(x + 1)$ $\Leftrightarrow$ $y = -x$. Substituting $-x$ for y in the

equation of the ellipse, we get $x^2 - x(-x) + (-x)^2 = 3$ $\Rightarrow$

$3x^2 = 3$ $\Leftrightarrow$ $x = \pm 1$. So the normal line must intersect the ellipse

again at $x = 1$, and since the equation of the line is $y = -x$, the other

point of intersection must be $(1, -1)$.

49. $x^2y^2 + xy = 2$ $\Rightarrow$ $x^2 \cdot 2yy' + y^2 \cdot 2x + x \cdot y' + y \cdot 1 = 0$ $\Leftrightarrow$ $y'(2x^2y + x) = -2xy^2 - y$ $\Leftrightarrow$

$y' = -\dfrac{2xy^2 + y}{2x^2y + x}$. So $-\dfrac{2xy^2 + y}{2x^2y + x} = -1$ $\Leftrightarrow$ $2xy^2 + y = 2x^2y + x$ $\Leftrightarrow$ $y(2xy + 1) = x(2xy + 1)$ $\Leftrightarrow$

$y(2xy + 1) - x(2xy + 1) = 0$ $\Leftrightarrow$ $(2xy + 1)(y - x) = 0$ $\Leftrightarrow$ $xy = -\frac{1}{2}$ or $y = x$. But $xy = -\frac{1}{2}$ $\Rightarrow$

$x^2y^2 + xy = \frac{1}{4} - \frac{1}{2} \ne 2$, so we must have $x = y$. Then $x^2y^2 + xy = 2$ $\Rightarrow$ $x^4 + x^2 = 2$ $\Leftrightarrow$

$x^4 + x^2 - 2 = 0$ $\Leftrightarrow$ $(x^2 + 2)(x^2 - 1) = 0$. So $x^2 = -2$, which is impossible, or $x^2 = 1$ $\Leftrightarrow$ $x = \pm 1$.

Since $x = y$, the points on the curve where the tangent line has a slope of -1 are $(-1, -1)$ and $(1, 1)$.

50. $x^2 + 4y^2 = 36 \Rightarrow 2x + 8yy' = 0 \Rightarrow y' = -\dfrac{x}{4y}$. Let (a, b) be a point on $x^2 + 4y^2 = 36$ whose tangent line

passes through $(12, 3)$. The tangent line is then $y - 3 = -\dfrac{a}{4b}(x - 12)$, so $b - 3 = -\dfrac{a}{4b}(a - 12)$. Multiplying

both sides by $4b$ gives $4b^2 - 12b = -a^2 + 12a$, so $4b^2 + a^2 = 12(a + b)$. But $4b^2 + a^2 = 36$, so $36 = 12(a + b)$

$\Rightarrow a + b = 3 \Rightarrow b = 3 - a$. Substituting $3 - a$ for b into $x^2 + 4y^2 = 36$ gives

$a^2 + 4(3 - a)^2 = 36 \Leftrightarrow a^2 + 36 - 24a + 4a^2 = 36 \Leftrightarrow 5a^2 - 24a = 0 \Leftrightarrow a(5a - 24) = 0$, so

$a = 0$ or $a = \frac{24}{5}$. If $a = 0$, $b = 3 - 0 = 3$, and if $a = \frac{24}{5}$, $b = 3 - \frac{24}{5} = -\frac{9}{5}$. So the two points on the ellipse are

$(0, 3)$ and $\left(\frac{24}{5}, -\frac{9}{5}\right)$. Using $y - 3 = -\dfrac{a}{4b}(x - 12)$ with $(a, b) = (0, 3)$ gives us the tangent line $y - 3 = 0$ or

$y = 3$. With $(a, b) = \left(\frac{24}{5}, -\frac{9}{5}\right)$, we have $y - 3 = -\dfrac{24/5}{4(-9/5)}(x - 12) \Leftrightarrow y - 3 = \frac{2}{3}(x - 12) \Leftrightarrow$

$y = \frac{2}{3}x - 5$. A graph of the ellipse and the tangent lines confirms our results.

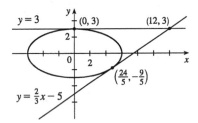

51. (a) If $y = f^{-1}(x)$, then $f(y) = x$. Differentiating implicitly with respect to x and remembering that y is a function

of x, we get $f'(y)\dfrac{dy}{dx} = 1$, so $\dfrac{dy}{dx} = \dfrac{1}{f'(y)} \Rightarrow (f^{-1})'(x) = \dfrac{1}{f'(f^{-1}(x))}$.

(b) $f(4) = 5 \Rightarrow f^{-1}(5) = 4$. By part (a), $(f^{-1})'(5) = 1/f'(f^{-1}(5)) = 1/f'(4) = 1/\left(\frac{2}{3}\right) = \frac{3}{2}$.

52. (a) $f(x) = 2x + \cos x \Rightarrow f'(x) = 2 - \sin x > 0$ for all x. Thus, f is increasing for all x and is therefore

one-to-one.

(b) Since f is one-to-one, $f^{-1}(1) = k \Leftrightarrow f(k) = 1$. By inspection, we see that $f(0) = 2(0) + \cos 0 = 1$, so

$k = f^{-1}(1) = 0$.

(c) $(f^{-1})'(1) = 1/f'(f^{-1}(1)) = 1/f'(0) = 1/(2 - \sin 0) = \frac{1}{2}$

53. (a) $y = J(x)$ and $xy'' + y' + xy = 0 \Rightarrow xJ''(x) + J'(x) + xJ(x) = 0$. If $x = 0$, we have $0 + J'(0) + 0 = 0$,

so $J'(0) = 0$.

(b) Differentiating $xy'' + y' + xy = 0$ implicitly, we get $xy''' + y'' \cdot 1 + y'' + xy' + y \cdot 1 = 0 \Rightarrow$

$xy''' + 2y'' + xy' + y = 0$, so $xJ'''(x) + 2J''(x) + xJ'(x) + J(x) = 0$. If $x = 0$, we have

$0 + 2J''(0) + 0 + 1$ $[J(0) = 1$ is given$] = 0 \Rightarrow 2J''(0) = -1 \Rightarrow J''(0) = -\frac{1}{2}$.

54. $x^2 + 4y^2 = 5 \Rightarrow 2x + 4(2yy') = 0 \Rightarrow y' = -\dfrac{x}{4y}$. Now let h be the height of the lamp, and let (a, b) be the

point of tangency of the line passing through the points $(3, h)$ and $(-5, 0)$. This line has slope

$(h - 0)/[3 - (-5)] = \frac{1}{8}h$. But the slope of the tangent line through the point (a, b) can be expressed as $y' = -\dfrac{a}{4b}$,

or as $\dfrac{b - 0}{a - (-5)} = \dfrac{b}{a + 5}$ [since the line passes through $(-5, 0)$ and (a, b)], so $-\dfrac{a}{4b} = \dfrac{b}{a + 5} \Leftrightarrow$

$4b^2 = -a^2 - 5a \Leftrightarrow a^2 + 4b^2 = -5a$. But $a^2 + 4b^2 = 5$ [since (a, b) is on the ellipse], so $5 = -5a \Leftrightarrow$

$a = -1$. Then $4b^2 = -a^2 - 5a = -1 - 5(-1) = 4 \Rightarrow b = 1$, since the point is on the top half of the ellipse.

So $\dfrac{h}{8} = \dfrac{b}{a + 5} = \dfrac{1}{-1 + 5} = \dfrac{1}{4} \Rightarrow h = 2$. So the lamp is located 2 units above the x-axis.

Derivatives of Logarithmic Functions • • • • • • • •

1. The differentiation formula for logarithmic functions, $\dfrac{d}{dx}(\log_a x) = \dfrac{1}{x \ln a}$, is simplest when $a = e$ because $\ln e = 1$.

2. $f(x) = \ln(x^2 + 10) \;\Rightarrow\; f'(x) = \dfrac{1}{x^2 + 10} \dfrac{d}{dx}(x^2 + 10) = \dfrac{2x}{x^2 + 10}$

3. $f(\theta) = \ln(\cos\theta) \;\Rightarrow\; f'(\theta) = \dfrac{1}{\cos\theta}\dfrac{d}{d\theta}(\cos\theta) = \dfrac{-\sin\theta}{\cos\theta} = -\tan\theta$

4. $f(x) = \cos(\ln x) \;\Rightarrow\; f'(x) = -\sin(\ln x)\cdot\dfrac{1}{x} = \dfrac{-\sin(\ln x)}{x}$

5. $f(x) = \log_2(1 - 3x) \;\Rightarrow\; f'(x) = \dfrac{1}{(1-3x)\ln 2}\dfrac{d}{dx}(1-3x) = \dfrac{-3}{(1-3x)\ln 2}$ or $\dfrac{3}{(3x-1)\ln 2}$

6. $f(x) = \log_{10}\left(\dfrac{x}{x-1}\right) = \log_{10} x - \log_{10}(x-1) \;\Rightarrow\; f'(x) = \dfrac{1}{x\ln 10} - \dfrac{1}{(x-1)\ln 10}$ or $-\dfrac{1}{x(x-1)\ln 10}$

7. $f(x) = \sqrt[5]{\ln x} = (\ln x)^{1/5} \;\Rightarrow\; f'(x) = \tfrac{1}{5}(\ln x)^{-4/5}\dfrac{d}{dx}(\ln x) = \dfrac{1}{5(\ln x)^{4/5}}\cdot\dfrac{1}{x} = \dfrac{1}{5x\sqrt[5]{(\ln x)^4}}$

8. $f(x) = \ln\sqrt[5]{x} = \ln x^{1/5} = \tfrac{1}{5}\ln x \;\Rightarrow\; f'(x) = \dfrac{1}{5}\cdot\dfrac{1}{x} = \dfrac{1}{5x}$

9. $f(x) = \sqrt{x}\,\ln x \;\Rightarrow\; f'(x) = \sqrt{x}\left(\dfrac{1}{x}\right) + (\ln x)\cdot\dfrac{1}{2\sqrt{x}} = \dfrac{1}{\sqrt{x}} + \dfrac{\ln x}{2\sqrt{x}} = \dfrac{2 + \ln x}{2\sqrt{x}}$

10. $f(t) = \dfrac{1 + \ln t}{1 - \ln t} \;\Rightarrow\;$

$$f'(t) = \dfrac{(1 - \ln t)(1/t) - (1 + \ln t)(-1/t)}{(1 - \ln t)^2} = \dfrac{(1/t)[(1 - \ln t) + (1 + \ln t)]}{(1 - \ln t)^2} = \dfrac{2}{t(1 - \ln t)^2}$$

11. $F(t) = \ln\dfrac{(2t+1)^3}{(3t-1)^4} = \ln(2t+1)^3 - \ln(3t-1)^4 = 3\ln(2t+1) - 4\ln(3t-1) \;\Rightarrow\;$

$$F'(t) = 3\cdot\dfrac{1}{2t+1}\cdot 2 - 4\cdot\dfrac{1}{3t-1}\cdot 3 = \dfrac{6}{2t+1} - \dfrac{12}{3t-1}, \text{ or combined, } \dfrac{-6(t+3)}{(2t+1)(3t-1)}.$$

12. $h(x) = \ln\left(x + \sqrt{x^2 - 1}\right) \;\Rightarrow\;$

$$h'(x) = \dfrac{1}{x + \sqrt{x^2-1}}\left(1 + \dfrac{x}{\sqrt{x^2-1}}\right) = \dfrac{1}{x + \sqrt{x^2-1}}\cdot\dfrac{\sqrt{x^2-1} + x}{\sqrt{x^2-1}} = \dfrac{1}{\sqrt{x^2-1}}$$

13. $y = \dfrac{\ln x}{1+x} \;\Rightarrow\; y' = \dfrac{(1+x)(1/x) - (\ln x)(1)}{(1+x)^2} = \dfrac{\dfrac{1+x}{x} - \dfrac{x\ln x}{x}}{(1+x)^2} = \dfrac{1 + x - x\ln x}{x(1+x)^2}$

14. $y = \ln(x^4\sin^2 x) = \ln x^4 + \ln(\sin x)^2 = 4\ln x + 2\ln\sin x \;\Rightarrow\; y' = 4\cdot\dfrac{1}{x} + 2\cdot\dfrac{1}{\sin x}\cdot\cos x = \dfrac{4}{x} + 2\cot x$

15. $y = \ln|x^3 - x^2| \;\Rightarrow\; y' = \dfrac{1}{x^3 - x^2}(3x^2 - 2x) = \dfrac{x(3x-2)}{x^2(x-1)} = \dfrac{3x-2}{x(x-1)}$

16. $G(u) = \ln\sqrt{\dfrac{3u+2}{3u-2}} = \tfrac{1}{2}[\ln(3u+2) - \ln(3u-2)] \;\Rightarrow\; G'(u) = \dfrac{1}{2}\left(\dfrac{3}{3u+2} - \dfrac{3}{3u-2}\right) = \dfrac{-6}{9u^2 - 4}$

17. $y = \ln(e^{-x} + xe^{-x}) = \ln(e^{-x}(1+x)) = \ln(e^{-x}) + \ln(1+x) = -x + \ln(1+x) \;\Rightarrow\;$

$y' = -1 + \dfrac{1}{1+x} = \dfrac{-1 - x + 1}{1+x} = -\dfrac{x}{1+x}$

18. $y = [\ln(1 + e^x)]^2 \;\Rightarrow\; y' = 2\,[\ln(1 + e^x)] \cdot \dfrac{1}{1 + e^x} \cdot e^x = \dfrac{2e^x \ln(1 + e^x)}{1 + e^x}$

19. $y = e^x \ln x \;\Rightarrow\; y' = e^x \cdot \dfrac{1}{x} + (\ln x) \cdot e^x = e^x\left(\dfrac{1}{x} + \ln x\right) \;\Rightarrow$

$y'' = e^x\left(-\dfrac{1}{x^2} + \dfrac{1}{x}\right) + \left(\dfrac{1}{x} + \ln x\right)e^x = e^x\left(-\dfrac{1}{x^2} + \dfrac{1}{x} + \dfrac{1}{x} + \ln x\right) = e^x\left(\ln x + \dfrac{2}{x} - \dfrac{1}{x^2}\right)$

20. $y = \ln(\sec x + \tan x) \;\Rightarrow\; y' = \dfrac{\sec x \tan x + \sec^2 x}{\sec x + \tan x} = \sec x \;\Rightarrow\; y'' = \sec x \tan x$

21. $f(x) = \dfrac{x}{1 - \ln(x - 1)} \;\Rightarrow$

$f'(x) = \dfrac{[1 - \ln(x - 1)] \cdot 1 - x \cdot \dfrac{-1}{x - 1}}{[1 - \ln(x - 1)]^2} = \dfrac{\dfrac{(x - 1)\,[1 - \ln(x - 1)] + x}{x - 1}}{[1 - \ln(x - 1)]^2} = \dfrac{x - 1 - (x - 1)\ln(x - 1) + x}{(x - 1)[1 - \ln(x - 1)]^2}$

$= \dfrac{2x - 1 - (x - 1)\ln(x - 1)}{(x - 1)\,[1 - \ln(x - 1)]^2}$

$\text{Dom}(f) = \{x \mid x - 1 > 0 \;\;\text{and}\;\; 1 - \ln(x - 1) \neq 0\} = \{x \mid x > 1 \;\;\text{and}\;\; \ln(x - 1) \neq 1\}$

$= \{x \mid x > 1 \;\;\text{and}\;\; x - 1 \neq e^1\} = \{x \mid x > 1 \;\;\text{and}\;\; x \neq 1 + e\} = (1, 1 + e) \cup (1 + e, \infty)$

22. $f(x) = \ln \ln \ln x \;\Rightarrow\; f'(x) = \dfrac{1}{\ln \ln x} \cdot \dfrac{1}{\ln x} \cdot \dfrac{1}{x}.$

$\text{Dom}(f) = \{x \mid \ln \ln x > 0\} = \{x \mid \ln x > 1\} = \{x \mid x > e\} = (e, \infty).$

23. $y = \ln(x^2 - 3) \;\Rightarrow\; y' = \dfrac{1}{x^2 - 3} \cdot 2x = \dfrac{2x}{x^2 - 3}.$

$y'(2) = \dfrac{2(2)}{2^2 - 3} = 4$, so an equation of the tangent line at $(2, 0)$ is $y - 0 = 4(x - 2)$ or $y = 4x - 8$.

24. $y = \dfrac{\ln x}{x} \;\Rightarrow\; y' = \dfrac{x(1/x) - \ln x}{x^2} = \dfrac{1 - \ln x}{x^2}.$

$y'(1) = \dfrac{1 - 0}{1^2} = 1$ and $y'(e) = \dfrac{1 - 1}{e^2} = 0 \;\Rightarrow\;$ equations of

tangent lines are $y - 0 = 1(x - 1)$ or $y = x - 1$ and

$y - 1/e = 0(x - e)$ or $y = 1/e$.

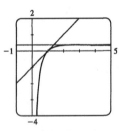

25. (a) The domain of $f(x) = x \ln x$ is $(0, \infty)$. $f'(x) = x(1/x) + (\ln x) \cdot 1 = 1 + \ln x$. So $f'(x) < 0$ when

$1 + \ln x < 0 \;\Leftrightarrow\; \ln x < -1 \;\Leftrightarrow\; x < e^{-1}.$ Therefore, f is decreasing on $(0, 1/e).$

(b) $f'(x) = 1 + \ln x \;\Rightarrow\; f''(x) = 1/x > 0$ for $x > 0$. So the curve is concave upward on $(0, \infty).$

26. $f(x) = \sin x + \ln x \;\Rightarrow\; f'(x) = \cos x + 1/x.$ This is reasonable,

because the graph shows that f increases when f' is positive, and

$f'(x) = 0$ when f has a horizontal tangent.

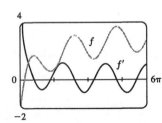

27. $y = (2x+1)^5 (x^4-3)^6 \;\Rightarrow\; \ln y = \ln\left((2x+1)^5(x^4-3)^6\right) \;\Rightarrow$

$\ln y = 5\ln(2x+1) + 6\ln(x^4-3) \;\Rightarrow\; \dfrac{1}{y}\,y' = 5\cdot\dfrac{1}{2x+1}\cdot 2 + 6\cdot\dfrac{1}{x^4-3}\cdot 4x^3 \;\Rightarrow$

$y' = y\left(\dfrac{10}{2x+1} + \dfrac{24x^3}{x^4-3}\right) = (2x+1)^5(x^4-3)^6\left(\dfrac{10}{2x+1} + \dfrac{24x^3}{x^4-3}\right).$ [The answer could be simplified to

$y' = 2(2x+1)^4(x^4-3)^5(29x^4 + 12x^3 - 15)$, but this is unnecessary.]

28. $y = \sqrt{x}\,e^{x^2}(x^2+1)^{10} \;\Rightarrow\; \ln y = \ln\sqrt{x} + \ln e^{x^2} + \ln(x^2+1)^{10} \;\Rightarrow\; \ln y = \tfrac{1}{2}\ln x + x^2 + 10\ln(x^2+1)$

$\Rightarrow\; \dfrac{1}{y}\,y' = \dfrac{1}{2}\cdot\dfrac{1}{x} + 2x + 10\cdot\dfrac{1}{x^2+1}\cdot 2x \;\Rightarrow\; y' = \sqrt{x}\,e^{x^2}(x^2+1)^{10}\left(\dfrac{1}{2x} + 2x + \dfrac{20x}{x^2+1}\right)$

29. $y = \dfrac{\sin^2 x\,\tan^4 x}{(x^2+1)^2} \;\Rightarrow\; \ln y = \ln\left(\sin^2 x\,\tan^4 x\right) - \ln\left(x^2+1\right)^2 \;\Rightarrow$

$\ln y = \ln(\sin x)^2 + \ln(\tan x)^4 - \ln(x^2+1)^2 \;\Rightarrow\; \ln y = 2\ln\sin x + 4\ln\tan x - 2\ln(x^2+1) \;\Rightarrow$

$\dfrac{1}{y}\,y' = 2\cdot\dfrac{1}{\sin x}\cdot\cos x + 4\cdot\dfrac{1}{\tan x}\cdot\sec^2 x - 2\cdot\dfrac{1}{x^2+1}\cdot 2x \;\Rightarrow$

$y' = \dfrac{\sin^2 x\,\tan^4 x}{(x^2+1)^2}\left(2\cot x + \dfrac{4\sec^2 x}{\tan x} - \dfrac{4x}{x^2+1}\right)$

30. $y = \sqrt[4]{\dfrac{x^2+1}{x^2-1}} \;\Rightarrow\; \ln y = \tfrac{1}{4}\ln(x^2+1) - \tfrac{1}{4}\ln(x^2-1) \;\Rightarrow\; \dfrac{1}{y}y' = \dfrac{1}{4}\cdot\dfrac{1}{x^2+1}\cdot 2x - \dfrac{1}{4}\cdot\dfrac{1}{x^2-1}\cdot 2x \;\Rightarrow$

$y' = \sqrt[4]{\dfrac{x^2+1}{x^2-1}}\cdot\dfrac{1}{2}\left(\dfrac{x}{x^2+1} - \dfrac{x}{x^2-1}\right) = \dfrac{1}{2}\sqrt[4]{\dfrac{x^2+1}{x^2-1}}\left(\dfrac{-2x}{x^4-1}\right) = \dfrac{x}{1-x^4}\sqrt[4]{\dfrac{x^2+1}{x^2-1}}$

31. $y = x^x \;\Rightarrow\; \ln y = \ln x^x \;\Rightarrow\; \ln y = x\ln x \;\Rightarrow\; y'/y = x(1/x) + (\ln x)\cdot 1 \;\Rightarrow$
$y' = y(1 + \ln x) \;\Rightarrow\; y' = x^x(1 + \ln x)$

32. $y = x^{1/x} \;\Rightarrow\; \ln y = \dfrac{1}{x}\ln x \;\Rightarrow\; \dfrac{y'}{y} = \dfrac{1}{x}\left(\dfrac{1}{x}\right) + (\ln x)\left(-\dfrac{1}{x^2}\right) \;\Rightarrow\; y' = x^{1/x}\dfrac{1-\ln x}{x^2}$

33. $y = x^{\sin x} \;\Rightarrow\; \ln y = \ln x^{\sin x} \;\Rightarrow\; \ln y = \sin x\ln x \;\Rightarrow\; \dfrac{y'}{y} = (\sin x)\cdot\dfrac{1}{x} + (\ln x)(\cos x) \;\Rightarrow$

$y' = y\left(\dfrac{\sin x}{x} + \ln x\cos x\right) \;\Rightarrow\; y' = x^{\sin x}\left(\dfrac{\sin x}{x} + \ln x\cos x\right)$

34. $y = (\sin x)^x \;\Rightarrow\; \ln y = x\ln(\sin x) \;\Rightarrow\; \dfrac{y'}{y} = x\cdot\dfrac{1}{\sin x}\cdot\cos x + [\ln(\sin x)]\cdot 1 \;\Rightarrow$
$y' = (\sin x)^x\left[x\cot x + \ln(\sin x)\right]$

35. $y = (\ln x)^x \;\Rightarrow\; \ln y = \ln(\ln x)^x \;\Rightarrow\; \ln y = x\ln\ln x \;\Rightarrow\; \dfrac{y'}{y} = x\cdot\dfrac{1}{\ln x}\cdot\dfrac{1}{x} + (\ln\ln x)\cdot 1 \;\Rightarrow$

$y' = y\left(\dfrac{x}{x\ln x} + \ln\ln x\right) \;\Rightarrow\; y' = (\ln x)^x\left(\dfrac{1}{\ln x} + \ln\ln x\right)$

36. $y = x^{\ln x} \;\Rightarrow\; \ln y = \ln x\ln x = (\ln x)^2 \;\Rightarrow\; \dfrac{y'}{y} = 2\ln x\left(\dfrac{1}{x}\right) \;\Rightarrow\; y' = x^{\ln x}\left(\dfrac{2\ln x}{x}\right)$

37. $y = \ln(x^2+y^2) \;\Rightarrow\; y' = \dfrac{1}{x^2+y^2}\dfrac{d}{dx}(x^2+y^2) \;\Rightarrow\; y' = \dfrac{2x+2yy'}{x^2+y^2} \;\Rightarrow\; x^2y' + y^2y' = 2x + 2yy'$

$\Rightarrow\; x^2y' + y^2y' - 2yy' = 2x \;\Rightarrow\; (x^2+y^2-2y)y' = 2x \;\Rightarrow\; y' = \dfrac{2x}{x^2+y^2-2y}$

38. $x^y = y^x$ $\Rightarrow$ $y \ln x = x \ln y$ $\Rightarrow$ $y \cdot \dfrac{1}{x} + (\ln x) \cdot y' = x \cdot \dfrac{1}{y} \cdot y' + \ln y$ $\Rightarrow$ $y' \ln x - \dfrac{x}{y} y' = \ln y - \dfrac{y}{x}$ $\Rightarrow$

$y' = \dfrac{\ln y - y/x}{\ln x - x/y}$

39. $f(x) = \ln(x-1)$ $\Rightarrow$ $f'(x) = 1/(x-1) = (x-1)^{-1}$ $\Rightarrow$ $f''(x) = -(x-1)^{-2}$ $\Rightarrow$
$f'''(x) = 2(x-1)^{-3}$ $\Rightarrow$ $f^{(4)}(x) = -2 \cdot 3(x-1)^{-4}$ $\Rightarrow$ $\cdots$ $\Rightarrow$
$f^{(n)}(x) = (-1)^{n-1} \cdot 2 \cdot 3 \cdot 4 \cdot \cdots \cdot (n-1)(x-1)^{-n} = (-1)^{n-1} \dfrac{(n-1)!}{(x-1)^n}$

40. $y = x^8 \ln x$, so $D^9 y = D^8 y' = D^8 \left(8x^7 \ln x + x^7\right)$. But the eighth derivative of x^7 is 0, so we now have

$$D^8 \left(8x^7 \ln x\right) = D^7 \left(8 \cdot 7x^6 \ln x + 8x^6\right) = D^7 \left(8 \cdot 7x^6 \ln x\right)$$
$$= D^6 \left(8 \cdot 7 \cdot 6x^5 \ln x\right) = \cdots = D \left(8! \, x^0 \ln x\right) = 8!/x.$$

41. If $f(x) = \ln(1+x)$, then $f'(x) = \dfrac{1}{1+x}$, so $f'(0) = 1$.

Thus, $\displaystyle\lim_{x \to 0} \dfrac{\ln(1+x)}{x} = \lim_{x \to 0} \dfrac{f(x)}{x} = \lim_{x \to 0} \dfrac{f(x) - f(0)}{x - 0} = f'(0) = 1$.

42. Let $m = n/x$. Then $n = xm$, and as $n \to \infty$, $m \to \infty$.

Therefore, $\displaystyle\lim_{n \to \infty} \left(1 + \dfrac{x}{n}\right)^n = \lim_{m \to \infty} \left(1 + \dfrac{1}{m}\right)^{mx} = \left[\lim_{m \to \infty} \left(1 + \dfrac{1}{m}\right)^m\right]^x = e^x$ by Equation 6.

Discovery Project | **Hyperbolic Functions**

1. (a)

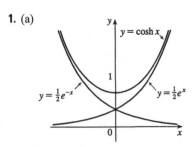

(b) The domain of $y = \cosh x$ is $\mathbb{R}$.
The range is $y \ge 1$.

2.

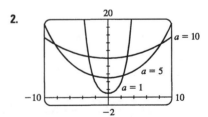

The value of a is the y-intercept. As a increases, the graph flattens out.

3.

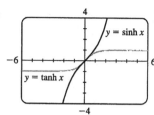

From the graphs, it appears that cosh is even and that sinh and tanh are odd.

$$f(x) = \cosh x = \frac{e^x + e^{-x}}{2} \quad \Rightarrow$$

$$f(-x) = \frac{e^{-x} + e^{-(-x)}}{2} = \frac{e^{-x} + e^x}{2} = f(x), \text{ so cosh is even.}$$

$$f(x) = \sinh x = \frac{e^x - e^{-x}}{2} \quad \Rightarrow \quad f(-x) = \frac{e^{-x} - e^{-(-x)}}{2} = \frac{e^{-x} - e^x}{2} = -\frac{e^x - e^{-x}}{2} = -f(x),$$

so sinh is odd.

$$f(x) = \tanh x = \frac{\sinh x}{\cosh x} \quad \Rightarrow \quad f(-x) = \frac{\sinh(-x)}{\cosh(-x)} = \frac{-\sinh x}{\cosh x} = -f(x), \text{ so tanh is odd.}$$

4. $\cosh^2 x - \sinh^2 x = \left(\dfrac{e^x + e^{-x}}{2}\right)^2 - \left(\dfrac{e^x - e^{-x}}{2}\right)^2 = \dfrac{e^{2x} + 2 + e^{-2x}}{4} - \dfrac{e^{2x} - 2 + e^{-2x}}{4} = \dfrac{4}{4} = 1.$

5. The curve looks like one branch of a hyperbola. We can confirm this by
using the identity proved in Problem 4; $x^2 - y^2 = \cosh^2 t - \sinh^2 t = 1$.
So the curve is the right branch of the hyperbola $x^2 - y^2 = 1$.

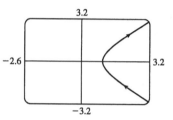

6. $\sinh x \cosh y + \cosh x \sinh y = \left[\frac{1}{2}\left(e^x - e^{-x}\right)\right]\left[\frac{1}{2}\left(e^y + e^{-y}\right)\right] + \left[\frac{1}{2}\left(e^x - e^{-x}\right)\right]\left[\frac{1}{2}\left(e^y + e^{-y}\right)\right]$

$$= \tfrac{1}{4}\left[\left(e^{x+y} + e^{x-y} - e^{-x+y} - e^{-x-y}\right) + \left(e^{x+y} - e^{x-y} + e^{-x+y} - e^{-x-y}\right)\right]$$

$$= \tfrac{1}{4}\left(2e^{x+y} - 2e^{-x-y}\right) = \tfrac{1}{2}\left[e^{x+y} - e^{-(x+y)}\right] = \sinh(x+y)$$

7. Substituting $-y$ for y in Problem 6 and using the results from Problem 3 gives us
$\sinh(x - y) = \sinh x \cosh y - \cosh x \sinh y$. By analogy with the trigonometric identity $\sin 2x = 2 \sin x \cos x$,
we might guess that $\sinh 2x = 2 \sinh x \cosh x$ and we can prove it by putting $y = x$ in the identity in Problem 6.
In view of the trigonometric identity $\cos(x + y) = \cos x \cos y - \sin x \sin y$, we expect that there is a similar
hyperbolic identity. By a calculation similar to that in Problem 6, we can prove that
$\cosh(x + y) = \cosh x \cosh y + \sinh x \sinh y$. Then, by putting $y = x$, we get $\cosh 2x = \cosh^2 x + \sinh^2 x$. By
substituting $-y$ for y gives us $\cosh(x - y) = \cosh x \cosh y - \sinh x \sinh y$. Also, using the identities for
$\sinh(x \pm y)$ and $\cosh(x \pm y)$, we get

$$\tanh(x \pm y) = \frac{\sinh(x \pm y)}{\cosh(x \pm y)} = \frac{(\sinh x \cosh y \pm \cosh x \sinh y)/(\cosh x \cosh y)}{(\cosh x \cosh y \pm \sinh x \sinh y)/(\cosh x \cosh y)} = \frac{\tanh x \pm \tanh y}{1 \pm \tanh x \tanh y}.$$

8. (a) $\dfrac{d}{dx}(\sinh x) = \dfrac{d}{dx}\left(\dfrac{e^x - e^{-x}}{2}\right) = \dfrac{e^x + e^{-x}}{2} = \cosh x$

(b) $\dfrac{d}{dx}(\cosh x) = \dfrac{d}{dx}\left(\dfrac{e^x + e^{-x}}{2}\right) = \dfrac{e^x - e^{-x}}{2} = \sinh x$

$$\dfrac{d}{dx}(\tanh x) = \dfrac{d}{dx}\left(\dfrac{\sinh x}{\cosh x}\right) = \dfrac{\cosh x \cosh x - \sinh x \sinh x}{(\cosh x)^2}$$

$$= \dfrac{\cosh^2 x - \sinh^2 x}{\cosh^2 x} = \dfrac{1}{\cosh^2 x} = \operatorname{sech}^2 x$$

9. (a) sinh is an increasing function on its domain, so it passes the Horizontal Line Test, and is one-to-one.

(b) Let $y = \sinh^{-1} x$. Then $\sinh y = x$. If we differentiate this equation implicitly with respect to x, we get

$\cosh y \dfrac{dy}{dx} = 1$. Since $\cosh^2 y - \sinh^2 y = 1$ and $\cosh y \ge 0$, we have $\cosh y = \sqrt{1 + \sinh^2 y}$, so

$\dfrac{dy}{dx} = \dfrac{1}{\cosh y} = \dfrac{1}{\sqrt{1 + \sinh^2 y}} = \dfrac{1}{\sqrt{1 + x^2}}$.

(c) Let $y = \sinh^{-1} x$. Then $x = \sinh y = \dfrac{e^y - e^{-y}}{2}$, so $e^y - 2x - e^{-y} = 0$ or, multiplying by e^y,

$e^{2y} - 2x e^y - 1 = 0$. This is really a quadratic equation in e^y: $(e^y)^2 - 2x(e^y) - 1 = 0$. Solving by the

quadratic formula, we get $e^y = \dfrac{2x \pm \sqrt{4x^2 + 4}}{2} = x \pm \sqrt{x^2 + 1}$. Note that $e^y > 0$, but $x - \sqrt{x^2 + 1} < 0$

(because $x < \sqrt{x^2 + 1}$). Thus, the minus sign is inadmissible and we have $e^y = x + \sqrt{x^2 + 1}$. Therefore,

$y = \ln(e^y) = \ln\left(x + \sqrt{x^2 + 1}\right)$.

(d) $\dfrac{d}{dx}\left[\ln\left(x + \sqrt{x^2 + 1}\right)\right] = \dfrac{1}{x + \sqrt{x^2 + 1}}\left[1 + \tfrac{1}{2}(x^2 + 1)^{-1/2}(2x)\right] = \dfrac{1}{x + \sqrt{x^2 + 1}}\left(1 + \dfrac{x}{\sqrt{x^2 + 1}}\right)$

$= \dfrac{1}{x + \sqrt{x^2 + 1}} \cdot \dfrac{\sqrt{x^2 + 1} + x}{\sqrt{x^2 + 1}} = \dfrac{1}{\sqrt{x^2 + 1}}$

10. (a) From the graph in Problem 3, tanh is an increasing function on its domain, so it passes the Horizontal Line Test, and is one-to-one.

(b) Let $y = \tanh^{-1} x$. Then $\tanh y = x$ $\Rightarrow$ $\operatorname{sech}^2 y \cdot y' = 1$ $\Rightarrow$ $y' = \dfrac{1}{\operatorname{sech}^2 y} = \dfrac{1}{1 - \tanh^2 y} = \dfrac{1}{1 - x^2}$.

To show that $\operatorname{sech}^2 y = 1 - \tanh^2 y$, divide the equation $\cosh^2 y - \sinh^2 y = 1$ by $\cosh^2 y$.

(c) Let $y = \tanh^{-1} x$. Then $x = \tanh y = \dfrac{\sinh y}{\cosh y} = \dfrac{e^y - e^{-y}}{e^y + e^{-y}} \cdot \dfrac{e^y}{e^y} = \dfrac{e^{2y} - 1}{e^{2y} + 1}$ $\Rightarrow$

$x e^{2y} + x = e^{2y} - 1$ $\Rightarrow$ $1 + x = e^{2y} - x e^{2y}$ $\Rightarrow$ $e^{2y} = \dfrac{1 + x}{1 - x}$ $\Rightarrow$ $2y = \ln\left(\dfrac{1 + x}{1 - x}\right)$ $\Rightarrow$

$y = \dfrac{1}{2}\ln\left(\dfrac{1 + x}{1 - x}\right)$.

(d) $\dfrac{d}{dx}\left[\dfrac{1}{2}\ln\left(\dfrac{1 + x}{1 - x}\right)\right] = \dfrac{d}{dx}\left[\tfrac{1}{2}\ln(1 + x) - \tfrac{1}{2}\ln(1 - x)\right] = \dfrac{1}{2}\dfrac{1}{1 + x} - \dfrac{1}{2}\dfrac{1}{1 - x}(-1)$

$= \dfrac{(1 - x) + (1 + x)}{2(1 + x)(1 - x)} = \dfrac{2}{2(1 - x^2)} = \dfrac{1}{1 - x^2}$

11. The tangent to $y = \cosh x$ has slope 1 when $y' = \sinh x = 1$ $\Rightarrow$ $x = \sinh^{-1} 1 = \ln\left(1 + \sqrt{2}\right)$, by

Problem 9(c). Since $\sinh x = 1$, $y = \cosh x = \sqrt{1 + \sinh^2 x} = \sqrt{1 + 1^2} = \sqrt{2}$. The point is

$\left(\ln\left(1 + \sqrt{2}\right), \sqrt{2}\right)$.

3.8 Linear Approximations and Differentials · · · · · · ·

1. $f(x) = x^3 \Rightarrow f'(x) = 3x^2$, so $f(1) = 1$ and $f'(1) = 3$. With $a = 1$, $L(x) = f(a) + f'(a)(x - a)$
becomes $L(x) = f(1) + f'(1)(x - 1) = 1 + 3(x - 1) = 3x - 2$.

2. $f(x) = \ln x \Rightarrow f'(x) = 1/x$, so $f(1) = 0$ and $f'(1) = 1$.
Thus, $L(x) = f(1) + f'(1)(x - 1) = 0 + 1(x - 1) = x - 1$.

3. $f(x) = \cos x \Rightarrow f'(x) = -\sin x$, so $f\left(\frac{\pi}{2}\right) = 0$ and $f'\left(\frac{\pi}{2}\right) = -1$. Thus,
$L(x) = f\left(\frac{\pi}{2}\right) + f'\left(\frac{\pi}{2}\right)\left(x - \frac{\pi}{2}\right) = 0 - 1\left(x - \frac{\pi}{2}\right) = -x + \frac{\pi}{2}$.

4. $f(x) = \sqrt[3]{x} = x^{1/3} \Rightarrow f'(x) = \frac{1}{3}x^{-2/3}$, so $f(-8) = -2$ and $f'(-8) = \frac{1}{12}$.
Thus, $L(x) = f(-8) + f'(-8)(x + 8) = -2 + \frac{1}{12}(x + 8) = \frac{1}{12}x - \frac{4}{3}$.

5. $f(x) = \sqrt{1 - x} \Rightarrow f'(x) = \dfrac{-1}{2\sqrt{1 - x}}$, so $f(0) = 1$ and

$f'(0) = -\frac{1}{2}$. Therefore,

$$\sqrt{1 - x} = f(x) \approx f(0) + f'(0)(x - 0)$$
$$= 1 + \left(-\frac{1}{2}\right)(x - 0) = 1 - \frac{1}{2}x$$

So $\sqrt{0.9} = \sqrt{1 - 0.1} \approx 1 - \frac{1}{2}(0.1) = 0.95$ and
$\sqrt{0.99} = \sqrt{1 - 0.01} \approx 1 - \frac{1}{2}(0.01) = 0.995$.

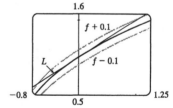

6. $g(x) = \sqrt[3]{1 + x} = (1 + x)^{1/3} \Rightarrow g'(x) = \frac{1}{3}(1 + x)^{-2/3}$,
so $g(0) = 1$ and $g'(0) = \frac{1}{3}$.
Therefore, $\sqrt[3]{1 + x} = g(x) \approx g(0) + g'(0)(x - 0) = 1 + \frac{1}{3}x$.
So $\sqrt[3]{0.95} = \sqrt[3]{1 + (-0.05)} \approx 1 + \frac{1}{3}(-0.05) = 0.98\overline{3}$, and
$\sqrt[3]{1.1} = \sqrt[3]{1 + 0.1} \approx 1 + \frac{1}{3}(0.1) = 1.0\overline{3}$.

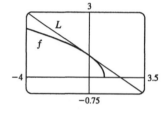

7. $f(x) = \sqrt{1 + x} \Rightarrow f'(x) = \dfrac{1}{2\sqrt{1 + x}}$, so $f(0) = 1$ and $f'(0) = \frac{1}{2}$.

Thus, $f(x) \approx f(0) + f'(0)(x - 0) = 1 + \frac{1}{2}(x - 0) = 1 + \frac{1}{2}x$.
We need $\sqrt{1 + x} - 0.1 < 1 + \frac{1}{2}x < \sqrt{1 + x} + 0.1$. By zooming in or
using an intersect feature, we see that this is true when $-0.69 < x < 1.09$.

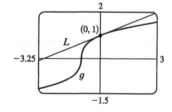

8. $f(x) = \tan x \Rightarrow f'(x) = \sec^2 x$, so $f(0) = 0$ and $f'(0) = 1$.
Thus, $f(x) \approx f(0) + f'(0)(x - 0) = 0 + 1(x - 0) = x$.
We need $\tan x - 0.1 < x < \tan x + 0.1$, which is true when
$-0.63 < x < 0.63$.

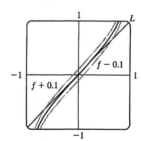

9. $f(x) = \dfrac{1}{(1+2x)^4} = (1+2x)^{-4}$ $\Rightarrow$

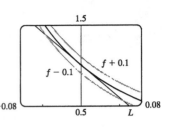

$f'(x) = -4(1+2x)^{-5}(2) = \dfrac{-8}{(1+2x)^5}$, so $f(0) = 1$ and $f'(0) = -8$.

Thus, $f(x) \approx f(0) + f'(0)(x-0) = 1 + (-8)(x-0) = 1 - 8x$.

We need $1/(1+2x)^4 - 0.1 < 1 - 8x < 1/(1+2x)^4 + 0.1$, which is true

when $-0.045 < x < 0.055$.

10. $f(x) = e^x$ $\Rightarrow$ $f'(x) = e^x$, so $f(0) = 1$ and $f'(0) = 1$.

Thus, $f(x) \approx f(0) + f'(0)(x-0) = 1 + 1(x-0) = 1 + x$.

We need $e^x - 0.1 < 1 + x < e^x + 0.1$, which is true when

$-0.483 < x < 0.416$.

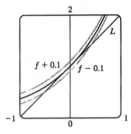

11. $y = f(x) = \sec x$ $\Rightarrow$ $f'(x) = \sec x \tan x$, so $f(0) = 1$ and $f'(0) = 1 \cdot 0 = 0$. The linear approximation of f
at 0 is $f(0) + f'(0)(x-0) = 1 + 0(x) = 1$. Since 0.08 is close to 0, approximating $\sec 0.08$ with 1 is reasonable.

12. If $y = x^6$, $y' = 6x^5$ and the tangent line approximation at $(1,1)$ has slope 6. If the change in x is 0.01, the change
in y on the tangent line is 0.06, and approximating $(1.01)^6$ with 1.06 is reasonable.

13. $y = f(x) = \ln x$ $\Rightarrow$ $f'(x) = 1/x$, so $f(1) = 0$ and $f'(1) = 1$. The linear approximation of f at 1 is
$f(1) + f'(1)(x-1) = 0 + 1(x-1) = x - 1$. Now $f(1.05) = \ln 1.05 \approx 1.05 - 1 = 0.05$, so the approximation
is reasonable.

14. (a) $f(x) = (x-1)^2$ $\Rightarrow$ $f'(x) = 2(x-1)$, so $f(0) = 1$ and $f'(0) = -2$. Thus,
$f(x) \approx L_f(x) = f(0) + f'(0)(x-0) = 1 - 2x$.
$g(x) = e^{-2x}$ $\Rightarrow$ $g'(x) = -2e^{-2x}$, so $g(0) = 1$ and $g'(0) = -2$. Thus,
$g(x) \approx L_g(x) = g(0) + g'(0)(x-0) = 1 - 2x$.
$h(x) = 1 + \ln(1-2x)$ $\Rightarrow$ $h'(x) = \dfrac{-2}{1-2x}$, so $h(0) = 1$ and $h'(0) = -2$. Thus,
$h(x) \approx L_h(x) = h(0) + h'(0)(x-0) = 1 - 2x$.
Notice that $L_f = L_g = L_h$. This happens because f, g, and h have the same function values and the same
derivative values at $a = 0$.

(b)

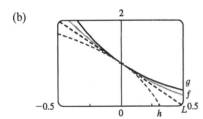

The linear approximation appears to be the best for the
function f since it is closer to f for a larger domain than it is
to g and h. The approximation looks worst for h since h
moves away from L faster than f and g do.

15. (a) $f(x) = \sin x \;\Rightarrow\; f'(x) = \cos x$, so $f(0) = 0$ and $f'(0) = 1$.

Thus, $f(x) \approx f(0) + f'(0)(x - 0) = 0 + 1(x - 0) = x$.

(b)

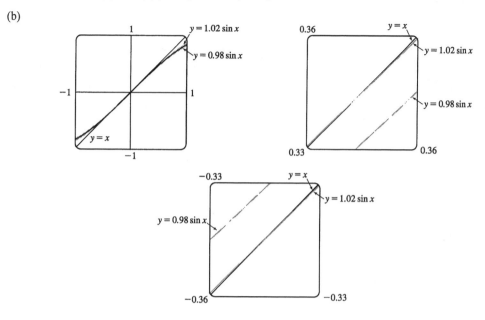

We want to know the values of x for which $y = x$ approximates $y = \sin x$ with less than a 2% difference; that is, the values of x for which

$$\left| \frac{x - \sin x}{\sin x} \right| < 0.02 \quad\Leftrightarrow\quad -0.02 < \frac{x - \sin x}{\sin x} < 0.02 \quad\Leftrightarrow$$

$$\begin{cases} -0.02 \sin x < x - \sin x < 0.02 \sin x & \text{if } \sin x > 0 \\ -0.02 \sin x > x - \sin x > 0.02 \sin x & \text{if } \sin x < 0 \end{cases} \Leftrightarrow \begin{cases} 0.98 \sin x < x < 1.02 \sin x & \text{if } \sin x > 0 \\ 1.02 \sin x < x < 0.98 \sin x & \text{if } \sin x < 0 \end{cases}$$

In the first figure, we see that the graphs are very close to each other near $x = 0$. Changing the viewing rectangle and using an intersect feature (see the second figure) we find that $y = x$ intersects $y = 1.02 \sin x$ at $x \approx 0.344$. By symmetry, they also intersect at $x \approx -0.344$ (see the third figure.). Converting 0.344 radians to degrees, we get $0.344 \left(\frac{180°}{\pi} \right) \approx 19.7° \approx 20°$, which verifies the statement.

16. (a) The linear approximation of f at $a = 1$ is

$f(x) \approx f(1) + f'(1)(x - 1) = 2 + \sqrt{1^3 + 1}\,(x - 1) = 2 + \sqrt{2}\,(x - 1)$. So at $x = 1.1$,

$f(x) \approx 2 + 0.1\sqrt{2} \approx 2.1414$.

(b) The true value of $f(1.1)$ is greater than the linear estimate, since the derivative of the function is getting larger while the derivative of the approximation is constant.

17. (a) $y = e^{x/10} \;\Rightarrow\; dy = e^{x/10} \cdot \frac{1}{10}\,dx = \frac{1}{10}e^{x/10}dx$

(b) $x = 0$ and $dx = 0.1 \;\Rightarrow\; dy = \frac{1}{10}e^{0/10}(0.1) = 0.01$.

$\Delta y = f(x + \Delta x) - f(x) = e^{(x + \Delta x)/10} - e^x = e^{(0 + 0.1)/10} - e^0 = e^{1/100} - 1 \approx 0.0101$

18. (a) $y = \sqrt{x} \ \Rightarrow \ dy = \frac{1}{2}x^{-1/2}dx = \frac{1}{2\sqrt{x}}\,dx$

(b) $x = 1$ and $dx = 1 \ \Rightarrow \ dy = \frac{1}{2(1)}(1) = \frac{1}{2}$.

$\Delta y = f(x + \Delta x) - f(x) = \sqrt{1+1} - \sqrt{1} = \sqrt{2} - 1 \approx 0.414$.

(c)

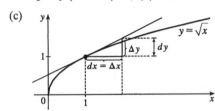

Remember, Δy represents the amount that the curve $y = f(x)$ rises or falls when x changes by an amount dx, whereas dy represents the amount that the tangent line rises or falls (the change in the linearization).

19. (a) If x is the edge length, then $V = x^3 \ \Rightarrow \ dV = 3x^2\,dx$. When $x = 30$ and $dx = 0.1$,

$dV = 3(30)^2(0.1) = 270$, so the maximum possible error in computing the volume of the cube is about 270 cm^3. The relative error is calculated by dividing the change in V, ΔV, by V. We approximate ΔV with dV.

$$\text{Relative error} = \frac{\Delta V}{V} \approx \frac{dV}{V} = \frac{3x^2\,dx}{x^3} = 3\frac{dx}{x} = 3\left(\frac{0.1}{30}\right) = 0.01.$$

Percentage error = relative error $\times\ 100\% = 0.01 \times 100\% = 1\%$.

(b) $S = 6x^2 \ \Rightarrow \ dS = 12x\,dx$. When $x = 30$ and $dx = 0.1$, $dS = 12(30)(0.1) = 36$, so the maximum possible error in computing the surface area of the cube is about 36 cm^2.

$$\text{Relative error} = \frac{\Delta S}{S} \approx \frac{dS}{S} = \frac{12x\,dx}{6x^2} = 2\frac{dx}{x} = 2\left(\frac{0.1}{30}\right) = 0.00\overline{6}.$$

Percentage error = relative error $\times\ 100\% = 0.00\overline{6} \times 100\% = 0.\overline{6}\%$.

20. (a) $A = \pi r^2 \ \Rightarrow \ dA = 2\pi r\,dr$. When $r = 24$ and $dr = 0.2$, $dA = 2\pi(24)(0.2) = 9.6\pi$, so the maximum possible error in the calculated area of the disk is about $9.6\pi \approx 30$ cm^2.

(b) Relative error $= \dfrac{\Delta A}{A} \approx \dfrac{dA}{A} = \dfrac{2\pi r\,dr}{\pi r^2} = \dfrac{2\,dr}{r} = \dfrac{2(0.2)}{24} = \dfrac{0.2}{12} = \dfrac{1}{60} = 0.01\overline{6}$.

Percentage error = relative error $\times\ 100\% = 0.01\overline{6} \times 100\% = 1.\overline{6}\%$.

21. For a hemispherical dome, $V = \frac{2}{3}\pi r^3 \ \Rightarrow \ dV = 2\pi r^2\,dr$. When $r = \frac{1}{2}(50) = 25$ m and

$dr = 0.05$ cm $= 0.0005$ m, $dV = 2\pi(25)^2(0.0005) = \frac{5\pi}{8}$, so the amount of paint needed is about $\frac{5\pi}{8} \approx 2$ m^3.

22. $F = kR^4 \ \Rightarrow \ dF = 4kR^3\,dR \ \Rightarrow \ \dfrac{dF}{F} = \dfrac{4kR^3\,dR}{kR^4} = 4\left(\dfrac{dR}{R}\right)$. Thus, the relative change in F is about

4 times the relative change in R. So a 5% increase in the radius corresponds to a 20% increase in blood flow.

Laboratory Project   Taylor Polynomials

1. We first write the functions described in conditions (i), (ii), and (iii):

$$P(x) = A + Bx + Cx^2 \qquad f(x) = \cos x$$
$$P'(x) = B + 2Cx \qquad f'(x) = -\sin x$$
$$P''(x) = 2C \qquad f''(x) = -\cos x$$

So, taking $a = 0$, our three conditions become

$$P(0) = f(0): \qquad A = \cos 0 = 1$$
$$P'(0) = f'(0): \qquad B = -\sin 0 = 0$$
$$P''(0) = f''(0): \qquad 2C = -\cos 0 = -1 \quad \Rightarrow \quad C = -\tfrac{1}{2}$$

The desired quadratic function is $P(x) = 1 - \tfrac{1}{2}x^2$, so the quadratic approximation is $\cos x \approx 1 - \tfrac{1}{2}x^2$.

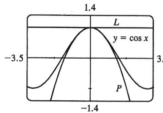

The figure shows a graph of the cosine function together with its linear approximation $L(x) = 1$ and quadratic approximation $P(x) = 1 - \tfrac{1}{2}x^2$ near 0. You can see that the quadratic approximation is much better than the linear one.

2. Accuracy to within 0.1 means that $\left|\cos x - \left(1 - \tfrac{1}{2}x^2\right)\right| < 0.1 \iff$
$-0.1 < \cos x - \left(1 - \tfrac{1}{2}x^2\right) < 0.1 \iff 0.1 > \left(1 - \tfrac{1}{2}x^2\right) - \cos x > -0.1 \iff$
$\cos x + 0.1 > 1 - \tfrac{1}{2}x > \cos x - 0.1 \iff \cos x - 0.1 < 1 - \tfrac{1}{2}x^2 < \cos x + 0.1.$

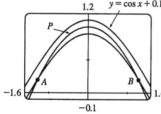

From the figure we see that this is true between A and B. Zooming in or using an intersect feature, we find that the x-coordinates of B and A are about ± 1.26. Thus, the approximation $\cos x \approx 1 - \tfrac{1}{2}x^2$ is accurate to within 0.1 when $-1.26 < x < 1.26$.

3. If $P(x) = A + B(x - a) + C(x - a)^2$, then $P'(x) = B + 2C(x - a)$ and $P''(x) = 2C$. Applying the conditions (i), (ii), and (iii), we get

$$P(a) = f(a): \qquad A = f(a)$$
$$P'(a) = f'(a): \qquad B = f'(a)$$
$$P''(a) = f''(a): \qquad 2C = f''(a) \quad \Rightarrow \quad C = \tfrac{1}{2}f''(a)$$

Thus, $P(x) = A + B(x - a) + C(x - a)^2$ can be written in the form
$P(x) = f(a) + f'(a)(x - a) + \tfrac{1}{2}f''(a)(x - a)^2.$

4. From Example 2 in Section 3.8, we have $f(1) = 2$, $f'(1) = \frac{1}{4}$, and

$f'(x) = \frac{1}{2}(x+3)^{-1/2}$. So $f''(x) = -\frac{1}{4}(x+3)^{-3/2}$ $\Rightarrow$

$f''(1) = -\frac{1}{32}$. From Problem 3, the quadratic approximation $P(x)$ is

$$\sqrt{x+3} \approx f(1) + f'(1)(x-1) + \frac{1}{2}f''(1)(x-1)^2$$

$$= 2 + \frac{1}{4}(x-1) - \frac{1}{64}(x-1)^2$$

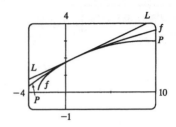

The figure shows the function $f(x) = \sqrt{x+3}$ together with its linear approximation $L(x) = \frac{1}{4}x + \frac{7}{4}$ and its quadratic approximation $P(x)$. You can see that $P(x)$ is a better approximation than $L(x)$ and this is borne out by the numerical values in the following chart.

	from $L(x)$	actual value	from $P(x)$
$\sqrt{3.98}$	1.9950	1.99499373...	1.99499375
$\sqrt{4.05}$	2.0125	2.01246118...	2.01246094
$\sqrt{4.2}$	2.0500	2.04939015...	2.04937500

5. $T_n(x) = c_0 + c_1(x-a) + c_2(x-a)^2 + c_3(x-a)^3 + \cdots + c_n(x-a)^n$. If we put $x = a$ in this equation, then all terms after the first are 0 and we get $T_n(a) = c_0$. Now we differentiate $T_n(x)$ and obtain

$T_n'(x) = c_1 + 2c_2(x-a) + 3c_3(x-a)^2 + 4c_4(x-a)^3 + \cdots + nc_n(x-a)^{n-1}$. Substituting $x = a$ gives

$T_n'(a) = c_1$. Differentiating again, we have

$T_n''(x) = 2c_2 + 2 \cdot 3c_3(x-a) + 3 \cdot 4c_4(x-a^2) + \cdots + (n-1)nc_n(x-a)^{n-2}$ and so $T_n''(a) = 2c_2$. Continuing in this manner, we get

$T_n'''(x) = 2 \cdot 3c_3 + 2 \cdot 3 \cdot 4c_4(x-a) + \cdots + (n-2)(n-1)nc_n(x-a)^{n-3}$ and $T_n'''(a) = 2 \cdot 3c_3$.

By now we see the pattern. If we continue to differentiate and substitute $x = a$, we obtain $T_n^{(4)}(a) = 2 \cdot 3 \cdot 4c_4$ and in general, for any integer k between 1 and n,

$$T_n^{(k)}(a) = 2 \cdot 3 \cdot 4 \cdot 5 \cdots \cdot kc_k = k! \, c_k \quad \Rightarrow \quad c_k = \frac{T_n^{(k)}(a)}{k!}$$

Because we want T_n and f to have the same derivatives at a, we require that $c_k = \dfrac{f^{(k)}(a)}{k!}$ for $k = 1, 2, \ldots, n$.

6. $T_n(x) = f(a) + f'(a)(x - a) + \dfrac{f''(a)}{2!}(x - a)^2 + \cdots + \dfrac{f^{(n)}(a)}{n!}(x - a)^n$. To compute the coefficients in this equation we need to calculate the derivatives of f at 0:

$$f(x) = \cos x \qquad\qquad f(0) = \cos 0 = 1$$
$$f'(x) = -\sin x \qquad\qquad f'(0) = -\sin 0 = 0$$
$$f''(x) = -\cos x \qquad\qquad f''(0) = -1$$
$$f'''(x) = \sin x \qquad\qquad f'''(0) = 0$$
$$f^{(4)}(x) = \cos x \qquad\qquad f^{(4)}(0) = 1$$

We see that the derivatives repeat in a cycle of length 4, so $f^{(5)}(0) = 0$, $f^{(6)}(0) = -1$, $f^{(7)}(0) = 0$, and $f^{(8)}(0) = 1$. From the original expression for $T_n(x)$, with $n = 8$ and $a = 0$, we have

$$T_8(x) = f(0) + f'(0)(x - 0) + \frac{f''(0)}{2!}(x - 0)^2 + \frac{f'''(0)}{3!}(x - 0)^3 + \cdots + \frac{f^{(8)}(0)}{8!}(x - 0)^8$$

$$= 1 + 0 \cdot x + \frac{-1}{2!}x^2 + 0 \cdot x^3 + \frac{1}{4!}x^4 + 0 \cdot x^5 + \frac{-1}{6!}x^6 + 0 \cdot x^7 + \frac{1}{8!}x^8$$

$$= 1 - \frac{x^2}{2!} + \frac{x^4}{4!} - \frac{x^6}{6!} + \frac{x^8}{8!}$$

and the desired approximation is $\cos x \approx 1 - \dfrac{x^2}{2!} + \dfrac{x^4}{4!} - \dfrac{x^6}{6!} + \dfrac{x^8}{8!}$. The Taylor polynomials T_2, T_4, and T_6 consist of the terms of T_8. Therefore, $T_2(x) = 1 - \dfrac{x^2}{2!}$, $T_4(x) = 1 - \dfrac{x^2}{2!} + \dfrac{x^4}{4!}$, and $T_6(x) = 1 - \dfrac{x^2}{2!} + \dfrac{x^4}{4!} - \dfrac{x^6}{6!}$. We graph T_2, T_4, T_6, T_8, and f:

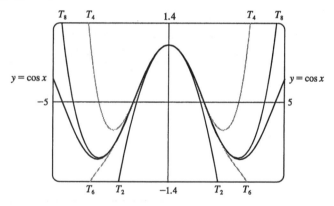

Notice that $T_2(x)$ is a good approximation to $\cos x$ near 0, $T_4(x)$ is a good approximation on a larger interval, $T_6(x)$ is a better approximation, and $T_8(x)$ is better still. Each successive Taylor polynomial is a good approximation on a larger interval than the previous one.

3 Review

—————————————— • CONCEPT CHECK • ——————————————

1. (a) The Power Rule: If n is any real number, then $\dfrac{d}{dx}(x^n) = nx^{n-1}$. The derivative of a variable base raised to a constant power is the power times the base raised to the power minus one.

(b) The Constant Multiple Rule: If c is a constant and f is a differentiable function, then $\dfrac{d}{dx}[cf(x)] = c\dfrac{d}{dx}f(x)$. The derivative of a constant times a function is the constant times the derivative of the function.

(c) The Sum Rule: If f and g are both differentiable, then $\dfrac{d}{dx}[f(x)+g(x)] = \dfrac{d}{dx}f(x) + \dfrac{d}{dx}g(x)$. The derivative of a sum of functions is the sum of the derivatives.

(d) The Difference Rule: If f and g are both differentiable, then $\dfrac{d}{dx}[f(x)-g(x)] = \dfrac{d}{dx}f(x) - \dfrac{d}{dx}g(x)$. The derivative of a difference of functions is the difference of the derivatives.

(e) The Product Rule: If f and g are both differentiable, then $\dfrac{d}{dx}[f(x)g(x)] = f(x)\dfrac{d}{dx}g(x) + g(x)\dfrac{d}{dx}f(x)$. The derivative of a product of two functions is the first function times the derivative of the second function plus the second function times the derivative of the first function.

(f) The Quotient Rule: If f and g are both differentiable, then $\dfrac{d}{dx}\left[\dfrac{f(x)}{g(x)}\right] = \dfrac{g(x)\dfrac{d}{dx}f(x) - f(x)\dfrac{d}{dx}g(x)}{[g(x)]^2}$. The derivative of a quotient of functions is the denominator times the derivative of the numerator minus the numerator times the derivative of the denominator, all divided by the square of the denominator.

(g) The Chain Rule: If f and g are both differentiable and $F = f \circ g$ is the composite function defined by $F(x) = f(g(x))$, then F is differentiable and F' is given by the product $F'(x) = f'(g(x))g'(x)$. The derivative of a composite function is the derivative of the outer function evaluated at the inner function times the derivative of the inner function.

2. (a) $y = x^n \ \Rightarrow \ y' = nx^{n-1}$

(b) $y = e^x \ \Rightarrow \ y' = e^x$

(c) $y = a^x \ \Rightarrow \ y' = a^x \ln a$

(d) $y = \ln x \ \Rightarrow \ y' = 1/x$

(e) $y = \log_a x \ \Rightarrow \ y' = 1/(x \ln a)$

(f) $y = \sin x \ \Rightarrow \ y' = \cos x$

(g) $y = \cos x \ \Rightarrow \ y' = -\sin x$

(h) $y = \tan x \ \Rightarrow \ y' = \sec^2 x$

(i) $y = \csc x \ \Rightarrow \ y' = -\csc x \cot x$

(j) $y = \sec x \ \Rightarrow \ y' = \sec x \tan x$

(k) $y = \cot x \ \Rightarrow \ y' = -\csc^2 x$

(l) $y = \sin^{-1} x \ \Rightarrow \ y' = 1/\sqrt{1-x^2}$

(m) $y = \tan^{-1} x \ \Rightarrow \ y' = 1/(1+x^2)$

3. (a) e is the number such that $\displaystyle\lim_{h\to 0} \dfrac{e^h - 1}{h} = 1$.

(b) $e = \displaystyle\lim_{x\to 0}(1+x)^{1/x}$

(c) The differentiation formula for $y = a^x$ $[y' = a^x \ln a]$ is simplest when $a = e$ because $\ln e = 1$.

(d) The differentiation formula for $y = \log_a x$ $[y' = 1/(x \ln a)]$ is simplest when $a = e$ because $\ln e = 1$.

4. (a) Implicit differentiation consists of differentiating both sides of an equation involving x and y with respect to x, and then solving the resulting equation for y'.

(b) Logarithmic differentiation consists of taking natural logarithms of both sides of an equation $y = f(x)$, simplifying, differentiating implicitly with respect to x, and then solving the resulting equation for y'.

5. The linearization L of f at $x = a$ is $L(x) = f(a) + f'(a)(x - a)$.

───────────────────────── ▲ **TRUE–FALSE QUIZ** ▲ ─────────────────────────

1. True.   This is the Sum Rule.

2. False.   See the warning before the Product Rule.

3. True.   This is the Chain Rule.

4. True by the Chain Rule.

5. False. $\dfrac{d}{dx} f(\sqrt{x}) = \dfrac{f'(\sqrt{x})}{2\sqrt{x}}$ by the Chain Rule.

6. False. e^2 is a constant, so $y' = 0$.

7. False. $\dfrac{d}{dx} 10^x = 10^x \ln 10$

8. False. $\ln 10$ is a constant, so its derivative is 0.

9. True. $\dfrac{d}{dx}\left(\tan^2 x\right) = 2 \tan x \sec^2 x$, and $\dfrac{d}{dx}\left(\sec^2 x\right) = 2 \sec x \left(\sec x \tan x\right) = 2 \tan x \sec^2 x$.

10. False. $f(x) = |x^2 + x| = x^2 + x$ for $x \geq 0$ or $x \leq -1$ and $|x^2 + x| = -(x^2 + x)$ for $-1 < x < 0$. So $f'(x) = 2x + 1$ for $x > 0$ or $x < -1$ and $f'(x) = (-2x + 1)$ for $-1 < x < 0$. But $|2x + 1| = 2x + 1$ for $x \geq -\frac{1}{2}$ and $|2x + 1| = -2x - 1$ for $x < -\frac{1}{2}$.

11. True. $g(x) = x^5 \;\Rightarrow\; g'(x) = 5x^4 \;\Rightarrow\; g'(2) = 5(2)^4 = 80$, and by the definition of the derivative,
$$\lim_{x \to 2} \frac{g(x) - g(2)}{x - 2} = g'(2) = 80.$$

12. False.   A tangent line to the parabola $y = x^2$ has slope $dy/dx = 2x$, so at $(-2, 4)$ the slope of the tangent is $2(-2) = -4$ and an equation of the tangent line is $y - 4 = -4(x + 2)$. [The given equation, $y - 4 = 2x(x + 2)$, is not even linear!]

───────────────────────── ◆ **EXERCISES** ◆ ─────────────────────────

1. $y = \left(x^4 - 3x^2 + 5\right)^3 \;\Rightarrow$

$y' = 3\left(x^4 - 3x^2 + 5\right)^2 \dfrac{d}{dx}\left(x^4 - 3x^2 + 5\right) = 3\left(x^4 - 3x^2 + 5\right)^2 \left(4x^3 - 6x\right) = 6x\left(x^4 - 3x^2 + 5\right)^2 \left(2x^2 - 3\right)$

2. $y = \cos(\tan x) \;\Rightarrow\; y' = -\sin(\tan x) \dfrac{d}{dx}(\tan x) = -\sin(\tan x)(\sec^2 x)$

3. $y = \sqrt{x} + \dfrac{1}{\sqrt[3]{x^4}} = x^{1/2} + x^{-4/3} \;\Rightarrow\; y' = \frac{1}{2}x^{-1/2} - \frac{4}{3}x^{-7/3} = \dfrac{1}{2\sqrt{x}} - \dfrac{4}{3\sqrt[3]{x^7}}$

4. $y = \dfrac{3x - 2}{\sqrt{2x + 1}}$ $\Rightarrow$

$$y' = \frac{\sqrt{2x + 1}\,(3) - (3x - 2)\frac{1}{2}(2x + 1)^{-1/2}(2)}{\left(\sqrt{2x + 1}\right)^2} \cdot \frac{(2x + 1)^{1/2}}{(2x + 1)^{1/2}} = \frac{3(2x + 1) - (3x - 2)}{(2x + 1)^{3/2}} = \frac{3x + 5}{(2x + 1)^{3/2}}$$

5. $y = 2x\sqrt{x^2 + 1}$ $\Rightarrow$

$$y' = 2x \cdot \tfrac{1}{2}(x^2 + 1)^{-1/2}(2x) + \sqrt{x^2 + 1}\,(2) = \frac{2x^2}{\sqrt{x^2 + 1}} + 2\sqrt{x^2 + 1} = \frac{2x^2 + 2(x^2 + 1)}{\sqrt{x^2 + 1}} = \frac{2(2x^2 + 1)}{\sqrt{x^2 + 1}}$$

6. $y = \dfrac{e^x}{1 + x^2}$ $\Rightarrow$ $y' = \dfrac{(1 + x^2)e^x - e^x(2x)}{(1 + x^2)^2} = \dfrac{e^x(x^2 - 2x + 1)}{(1 + x^2)^2} = \dfrac{e^x(x - 1)^2}{(1 + x^2)^2}$

7. $y = e^{\sin 2\theta}$ $\Rightarrow$ $y' = e^{\sin 2\theta}\,\dfrac{d}{d\theta}(\sin 2\theta) = e^{\sin 2\theta}(\cos 2\theta)(2) = 2\cos 2\theta\, e^{\sin 2\theta}$

8. $y = e^{-t}(t^2 - 2t + 2)$ $\Rightarrow$

$$y' = e^{-t}(2t - 2) + (t^2 - 2t + 2)(-e^{-t}) = e^{-t}(2t - 2 - t^2 + 2t - 2) = e^{-t}(-t^2 + 4t - 4)$$

9. $y = \dfrac{t}{1 - t^2}$ $\Rightarrow$ $y' = \dfrac{(1 - t^2)(1) - t(-2t)}{(1 - t^2)^2} = \dfrac{1 - t^2 + 2t^2}{(1 - t^2)^2} = \dfrac{t^2 + 1}{(1 - t^2)^2}$

10. $y = \sin^{-1}(e^x)$ $\Rightarrow$ $y' = \dfrac{1}{\sqrt{1 - (e^x)^2}} \cdot e^x = e^x / \sqrt{1 - e^{2x}}$

11. $y = xe^{-1/x}$ $\Rightarrow$ $y' = xe^{-1/x}(1/x^2) + e^{-1/x} \cdot 1 = e^{-1/x}(1/x + 1)$

12. $y = x^r e^{sx}$ $\Rightarrow$ $y' = x^r(se^{sx}) + e^{sx}(rx^{r-1}) = e^{sx}x^{r-1}(sx + r)$

13. $\dfrac{d}{dx}(xy^4 + x^2 y) = \dfrac{d}{dx}(x + 3y)$ $\Rightarrow$ $x \cdot 4y^3 y' + y^4 \cdot 1 + x^2 \cdot y' + y \cdot 2x = 1 + 3y'$ $\Rightarrow$

$$y'(4xy^3 + x^2 - 3) = 1 - y^4 - 2xy \quad \Rightarrow \quad y' = \frac{1 - y^4 - 2xy}{4xy^3 + x^2 - 3}$$

14. $y = \ln(\csc 5x)$ $\Rightarrow$ $y' = \dfrac{1}{\csc 5x}(-\csc 5x \cot 5x)(5) = -5\cot 5x$

15. $y = \dfrac{\sec 2\theta}{1 + \tan 2\theta}$ $\Rightarrow$

$$y' = \frac{(1 + \tan 2\theta)(\sec 2\theta \tan 2\theta \cdot 2) - (\sec 2\theta)(\sec^2 2\theta \cdot 2)}{(1 + \tan 2\theta)^2} = \frac{2\sec 2\theta \left[(1 + \tan 2\theta)\tan 2\theta - \sec^2 2\theta\right]}{(1 + \tan 2\theta)^2}$$

$$= \frac{2\sec 2\theta\,(\tan 2\theta + \tan^2 2\theta - \sec^2 2\theta)}{(1 + \tan 2\theta)^2} = \frac{2\sec 2\theta\,(\tan 2\theta - 1)}{(1 + \tan 2\theta)^2} \quad [1 + \tan^2 x = \sec^2 x]$$

16. $\dfrac{d}{dx}(x^2 \cos y + \sin 2y) = \dfrac{d}{dx}(xy)$ $\Rightarrow$ $x^2(-\sin y \cdot y') + (\cos y)(2x) + \cos 2y \cdot 2y' = x \cdot y' + y \cdot 1$ $\Rightarrow$

$$y'(-x^2 \sin y + 2\cos 2y - x) = y - 2x\cos y \quad \Rightarrow \quad y' = \frac{y - 2x\cos y}{2\cos 2y - x^2 \sin y - x}$$

17. $y = e^{cx}(c\sin x - \cos x)$ $\Rightarrow$

$$y' = e^{cx}(c\cos x + \sin x) + ce^{cx}(c\sin x - \cos x)$$

$$= e^{cx}(c^2 \sin x - c\cos x + c\cos x + \sin x) = e^{cx}(c^2 \sin x + \sin x) = e^{cx}\sin x\,(c^2 + 1)$$

18. $y = \ln(x^2 e^x) = \ln x^2 + \ln e^x = 2\ln x + x$ $\Rightarrow$ $y' = 2/x + 1$

19. $y = \log_5(1 + 2x)$ $\Rightarrow$ $y' = \dfrac{1}{(1 + 2x)\ln 5}\,\dfrac{d}{dx}(1 + 2x) = \dfrac{2}{(1 + 2x)\ln 5}$

20. $y = (\ln x)^{\cos x}$ $\Rightarrow$ $\ln y = \cos x \, \ln(\ln x)$ $\Rightarrow$ $\dfrac{y'}{y} = \cos x \cdot \dfrac{1}{\ln x} \cdot \dfrac{1}{x} + (\ln \ln x)(-\sin x)$ $\Rightarrow$

$y' = (\ln x)^{\cos x} \left(\dfrac{\cos x}{x \ln x} - \sin x \, \ln \ln x \right)$

21. $y = \ln \sin x - \frac{1}{2} \sin^2 x$ $\Rightarrow$ $y' = \dfrac{1}{\sin x} \cdot \cos x - \frac{1}{2} \cdot 2 \sin x \cdot \cos x = \cot x - \sin x \cos x$

22. $y = \dfrac{\left(x^2 + 1\right)^4}{(2x+1)^3 (3x-1)^5}$ $\Rightarrow$

$\ln y = \ln \dfrac{\left(x^2+1\right)^4}{(2x+1)^3(3x-1)^5} = \ln\left(x^2+1\right)^4 - \ln[(2x+1)^3(3x-1)^5]$

$\qquad = 4\ln\left(x^2+1\right) - [\ln(2x+1)^3 + \ln(3x-1)^5] = 4\ln\left(x^2+1\right) - 3\ln(2x+1) - 5\ln(3x-1)$ $\Rightarrow$

$\dfrac{y'}{y} = 4 \cdot \dfrac{1}{x^2+1} \cdot 2x - 3 \cdot \dfrac{1}{2x+1} \cdot 2 - 5 \cdot \dfrac{1}{3x-1} \cdot 3$ $\Rightarrow$

$y' = \dfrac{\left(x^2+1\right)^4}{(2x+1)^3(3x-1)^5}\left(\dfrac{8x}{x^2+1} - \dfrac{6}{2x+1} - \dfrac{15}{3x-1} \right)$. [The answer could be simplified to

$y' = -\dfrac{\left(x^2 + 56x + 9\right)\left(x^2+1\right)^3}{(2x+1)^4(3x-1)^6}$, but this is unnecessary.]

23. $y = x \tan^{-1}(4x)$ $\Rightarrow$ $y' = x \cdot \dfrac{1}{1 + (4x)^2} \cdot 4 + \tan^{-1}(4x) \cdot 1 = \dfrac{4x}{1 + 16x^2} + \tan^{-1}(4x)$

24. $y = e^{\cos x} + \cos(e^x)$ $\Rightarrow$ $y' = e^{\cos x}(-\sin x) + [-\sin(e^x) \cdot e^x] = -\sin x \, e^{\cos x} - e^x \sin(e^x)$

25. $y = \ln |\sec 5x + \tan 5x|$ $\Rightarrow$

$y' = \dfrac{1}{\sec 5x + \tan 5x}(\sec 5x \tan 5x \cdot 5 + \sec^2 5x \cdot 5) = \dfrac{5\sec 5x \,(\tan 5x + \sec 5x)}{\sec 5x + \tan 5x} = 5\sec 5x$

26. $y = 10^{\tan \pi \theta}$ $\Rightarrow$ $y' = 10^{\tan \pi \theta} \cdot \ln 10 \cdot \sec^2 \pi \theta \cdot \pi = \pi(\ln 10)10^{\tan \pi \theta} \sec^2 \pi \theta$

27. $y = \cot\left(3x^2 + 5\right)$ $\Rightarrow$ $y' = -\csc^2\left(3x^2+5\right)(6x) = -6x \csc^2\left(3x^2+5\right)$

28. $y = \ln \left| \dfrac{x^2 - 4}{2x+5} \right| = \ln |x^2 - 4| - \ln|2x+5|$ $\Rightarrow$ $y' = \dfrac{2x}{x^2-4} - \dfrac{2}{2x+5}$ or $\dfrac{2(x+1)(x+4)}{(x+2)(x-2)(2x+5)}$

29. $y = \sin\left(\tan \sqrt{1+x^3}\right)$ $\Rightarrow$ $y' = \cos\left(\tan \sqrt{1+x^3}\right)\left(\sec^2 \sqrt{1+x^3}\right)\left[3x^2 / \left(2\sqrt{1+x^3}\right)\right]$

30. $y = \arctan(\arcsin \sqrt{x})$ $\Rightarrow$ $y' = \dfrac{1}{1 + (\arcsin \sqrt{x})^2} \cdot \dfrac{1}{\sqrt{1-x}} \cdot \dfrac{1}{2\sqrt{x}}$

31. $f(x) = 1/(2x-1)^5 = (2x-1)^{-5}$ $\Rightarrow$

$f'(x) = -5(2x-1)^{-6}(2) = -10(2x-1)^{-6}$ $\Rightarrow$ $f''(x) = (-10)(-6)(2x-1)^{-7}(2) = 120(2x-1)^{-7}$.

$f''(0) = 120(-1)^{-7} = -120$

32. $x^6 + y^6 = 1$ $\Rightarrow$ $6x^5 + 6y^5 y' = 0$ $\Rightarrow$ $y' = -x^5/y^5$ $\Rightarrow$

$y'' = -\dfrac{y^5\left(5x^4\right) - x^5\left(5y^4 y'\right)}{\left(y^5\right)^2} = -\dfrac{5x^4 y^4 \left[y - x\left(-x^5/y^5\right)\right]}{y^{10}} = -\dfrac{5x^4\left[\left(y^6 + x^6\right)/y^5\right]}{y^6} = -\dfrac{5x^4}{y^{11}}$

33. $f(x) = 2^x$ $\Rightarrow$ $f'(x) = 2^x \ln 2$ $\Rightarrow$ $f''(x) = (2^x \ln 2)\ln 2 = 2^x (\ln 2)^2$ $\Rightarrow$

$f'''(x) = (2^x \ln 2)(\ln 2)^2 = 2^x (\ln 2)^3$ $\Rightarrow$ $\cdots$ $\Rightarrow$ $f^{(n)}(x) = (2^x \ln 2)(\ln 2)^{n-1} = 2^x (\ln 2)^n$

34. $\sqrt{x} + \sqrt{y} = 3$ $\Rightarrow$ $\dfrac{1}{2\sqrt{x}} + \dfrac{1}{2\sqrt{y}} y' = 0$ $\Rightarrow$ $\dfrac{1}{\sqrt{y}} y' = -\dfrac{1}{\sqrt{x}}$ $\Rightarrow$ $y' = -\dfrac{\sqrt{y}}{\sqrt{x}}$.

At $(4,1)$, $y' = -\frac{1}{2}$, so the tangent is $y - 1 = -\frac{1}{2}(x-4)$ or $y = -\frac{1}{2}x + 3$.

35. (a) $f(x) = x\sqrt{5-x}$ $\Rightarrow$

$$f'(x) = x\left[\tfrac{1}{2}(5-x)^{-1/2}(-1)\right] + \sqrt{5-x} = \frac{-x}{2\sqrt{5-x}} + \sqrt{5-x} \cdot \frac{2\sqrt{5-x}}{2\sqrt{5-x}}$$

$$= \frac{-x}{2\sqrt{5-x}} + \frac{2(5-x)}{2\sqrt{5-x}} = \frac{-x+10-2x}{2\sqrt{5-x}} = \frac{10-3x}{2\sqrt{5-x}}$$

(b) At $(1,2)$: $f'(1) = \tfrac{7}{4}$. So an equation of the tangent line is $y - 2 = \tfrac{7}{4}(x-1)$ or $y = \tfrac{7}{4}x + \tfrac{1}{4}$.

At $(4,4)$: $f'(4) = -\tfrac{2}{2} = -1$. So an equation of the tangent line is $y - 4 = -1(x-4)$ or $y = -x + 8$.

(c)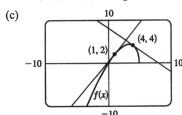

(d)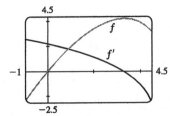

The graphs look reasonable, since f' is positive where f has tangents with positive slope, and f' is negative where f has tangents with negative slope.

36. (a) $f(x) = 4x - \tan x$ $\Rightarrow$ $f'(x) = 4 - \sec^2 x$ $\Rightarrow$ $f''(x) = -2\sec x\,(\sec x\,\tan x) = -2\sec^2 x\,\tan x.$

(b)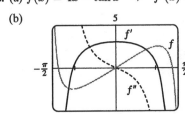

We can see that our answers are reasonable, since the graph of f' is 0 where f has a horizontal tangent, and the graph of f' is positive where f has tangents with positive slope and negative where f has tangents with negative slope. The same correspondence holds between the graphs of f' and f''.

37. $f(x) = xe^{\sin x}$ $\Rightarrow$ $f'(x) = x\left[e^{\sin x}(\cos x)\right] + e^{\sin x}(1) = e^{\sin x}(x\cos x + 1)$. As a check on our work, we notice from the graphs that $f'(x) > 0$ when f is increasing. Also, we see in the larger viewing rectangle a certain similarity in the graphs of f and f': the sizes of the oscillations of f and f' are linked.

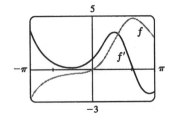

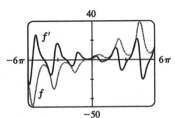

38. (a)

(b) The average rate of change is larger on $[2,3]$.

(c) The instantaneous rate of change (the slope of the tangent) is larger at $x = 2$.

(d) $f(x) = x - 2\sin x$ $\Rightarrow$ $f'(x) = 1 - 2\cos x$, so

$f'(2) = 1 - 2\cos 2 \approx 1.8323$ and

$f'(5) = 1 - 2\cos 5 \approx 0.4327$.

So $f'(2) > f'(5)$, as predicted in part (c).

39. (a) $h(x) = f(x)g(x) \Rightarrow h'(x) = f(x)g'(x) + g(x)f'(x) \Rightarrow$
$h'(2) = f(2)g'(2) + g(2)f'(2) = (3)(4) + (5)(-2) = 12 - 10 = 2$

(b) $F(x) = f(g(x)) \Rightarrow F'(x) = f'(g(x))g'(x) \Rightarrow F'(2) = f'(g(2))g'(2) = f'(5)(4) = 11 \cdot 4 = 44$

40. (a) $P(x) = f(x)g(x) \Rightarrow P'(x) = f(x)g'(x) + g(x)f'(x) \Rightarrow$
$P'(2) = f(2)g'(2) + g(2)f'(2) = (1)\left(\frac{6-0}{3-0}\right) + (4)\left(\frac{0-3}{3-0}\right) = (1)(2) + (4)(-1) = 2 - 4 = -2$

(b) $Q(x) = \dfrac{f(x)}{g(x)} \Rightarrow Q'(x) = \dfrac{g(x)f'(x) - f(x)g'(x)}{[g(x)]^2} \Rightarrow$
$Q'(2) = \dfrac{g(2)f'(2) - f(2)g'(2)}{[g(2)]^2} = \dfrac{(4)(-1) - (1)(2)}{4^2} = \dfrac{-6}{16} = -\dfrac{3}{8}$

(c) $C(x) = f(g(x)) \Rightarrow C'(x) = f'(g(x))g'(x) \Rightarrow$
$C'(2) = f'(g(2))g'(2) = f'(4)g'(2) = \left(\frac{6-0}{5-3}\right)(2) = (3)(2) = 6$

41. $f(x) = x^2 g(x) \Rightarrow f'(x) = x^2 g'(x) + g(x)(2x) = x\left[xg'(x) + 2g(x)\right]$

42. $f(x) = g(x^2) \Rightarrow f'(x) = g'(x^2)(2x) = 2xg'(x^2)$

43. $f(x) = [g(x)]^2 \Rightarrow f'(x) = 2[g(x)]^1 \cdot g'(x) = 2g(x)g'(x)$

44. $f(x) = g(g(x)) \Rightarrow f'(x) = g'(g(x))g'(x)$

45. $f(x) = g(e^x) \Rightarrow f'(x) = g'(e^x)e^x$

46. $f(x) = e^{g(x)} \Rightarrow f'(x) = e^{g(x)}g'(x)$

47. $f(x) = \ln|g(x)| \Rightarrow f'(x) = \dfrac{1}{g(x)}g'(x) = \dfrac{g'(x)}{g(x)}$

48. $f(x) = g(\ln x) \Rightarrow f'(x) = g'(\ln x) \cdot \dfrac{1}{x} = \dfrac{g'(\ln x)}{x}$

49. $h(x) = \dfrac{f(x)g(x)}{f(x) + g(x)} \Rightarrow$

$h'(x) = \dfrac{[f(x) + g(x)]\,[f(x)g'(x) + g(x)f'(x)] - f(x)g(x)\,[f'(x) + g'(x)]}{[f(x) + g(x)]^2}$

$= \dfrac{[f(x)]^2\,g'(x) + f(x)g(x)f'(x) + f(x)g(x)g'(x) + [g(x)]^2\,f'(x) - f(x)g(x)f'(x) - f(x)g(x)g'(x)}{[f(x) + g(x)]^2}$

$= \dfrac{f'(x)[g(x)]^2 + g'(x)[f(x)]^2}{[f(x) + g(x)]^2}$

50. Using the Chain Rule repeatedly, $h(x) = f(g(\sin 4x)) \Rightarrow$

$h'(x) = f'(g(\sin 4x)) \cdot \dfrac{d}{dx}\left(g(\sin 4x)\right) = f'(g(\sin 4x)) \cdot g'(\sin 4x) \cdot \dfrac{d}{dx}\left(\sin 4x\right)$

$= f'(g(\sin 4x))g'(\sin 4x)(\cos 4x)(4)$

51. $y = [\ln(x + 4)]^2 \Rightarrow y' = 2[\ln(x + 4)]^1 \cdot \dfrac{1}{x + 4} \cdot 1 = 2\dfrac{\ln(x + 4)}{x + 4}$ and $y' = 0 \Leftrightarrow \ln(x + 4) = 0 \Leftrightarrow$
$x + 4 = e^0 \Rightarrow x + 4 = 1 \Leftrightarrow x = -3$, so the tangent is horizontal at the point $(-3, 0)$.

52. (a) The line $x - 4y = 1$ has slope $\frac{1}{4}$. A tangent to $y = e^x$ has slope $\frac{1}{4}$ when $y' = e^x = \frac{1}{4} \Rightarrow$
$x = \ln\frac{1}{4} = -\ln 4$. Since $y = e^x$, the y-coordinate is $\frac{1}{4}$ and the point of tangency is $\left(-\ln 4, \frac{1}{4}\right)$. Thus, an
equation of the tangent line is $y - \frac{1}{4} = \frac{1}{4}(x + \ln 4)$ or $y = \frac{1}{4}x + \frac{1}{4}(\ln 4 + 1)$.

(b) The slope of the tangent at the point (a, e^a) is $\dfrac{d}{dx}\, e^x \Big|_{x=a} = e^a$. Thus, an equation of the tangent line is

$y - e^a = e^a(x - a)$. We substitute $x = 0$, $y = 0$ into this equation, since we want the line to pass through the origin: $0 - e^a = e^a(0 - a) \Leftrightarrow -e^a = e^a(-a) \Leftrightarrow a = 1$. So an equation of the tangent line at the point $(a, e^a) = (1, e)$ is $y - e = e(x - 1)$ or $y = ex$.

53. $x^2 + 2y^2 = 1 \Rightarrow 2x + 4yy' = 0 \Rightarrow y' = -x/(2y) = 1 \Leftrightarrow x = -2y$. Since the points lie on the ellipse,

we have $(-2y)^2 + 2y^2 = 1 \Rightarrow 6y^2 = 1 \Rightarrow y = \pm\frac{1}{\sqrt{6}}$. The points are $\left(-\frac{2}{\sqrt{6}}, \frac{1}{\sqrt{6}}\right)$ and $\left(\frac{2}{\sqrt{6}}, -\frac{1}{\sqrt{6}}\right)$.

54. (a) $f(x) = \dfrac{\ln x}{x} \Rightarrow f'(x) = \dfrac{x(1/x) - (\ln x)\cdot 1}{x^2} = \dfrac{1 - \ln x}{x^2}$.

$f'(x) > 0 \Rightarrow 1 - \ln x > 0 \Rightarrow \ln x < 1 \Rightarrow x < e$. Since the domain of f is $(0, \infty)$, f is increasing on $(0, e)$.

(b) $f''(x) = \dfrac{x^2(-1/x) - (1 - \ln x)(2x)}{(x^2)^2} = \dfrac{x[-1 - 2(1 - \ln x)]}{x^4} = \dfrac{2\ln x - 3}{x^3}$.

$f''(x) > 0 \Rightarrow 2\ln x - 3 > 0 \Rightarrow \ln x > \frac{3}{2} \Rightarrow x > e^{3/2} \approx 4.48$.

f is concave upward on $\left(e^{3/2}, \infty\right)$.

55. $s(t) = Ae^{-ct}\cos(\omega t + \delta) \Rightarrow$

$v(t) = s'(t) = A\{e^{-ct}[-\omega\sin(\omega t + \delta)] + \cos(\omega t + \delta)(-ce^{-ct})\}$

$= -Ae^{-ct}[\omega\sin(\omega t + \delta) + c\cos(\omega t + \delta)] \Rightarrow$

$a(t) = v'(t) = -A\{e^{-ct}[\omega^2\cos(\omega t + \delta) - c\omega\sin(\omega t + \delta)]$

$\qquad + [\omega\sin(\omega t + \delta) + c\cos(\omega t + \delta)](-ce^{-ct})\}$

$= -Ae^{-ct}[\omega^2\cos(\omega t + \delta) - c\omega\sin(\omega t + \delta) - c\omega\sin(\omega t + \delta) - c^2\cos(\omega t + \delta)]$

$= -Ae^{-ct}[(\omega^2 - c^2)\cos(\omega t + \delta) - 2c\omega\sin(\omega t + \delta)]$

$= Ae^{-ct}[(c^2 - \omega^2)\cos(\omega t + \delta) + 2c\omega\sin(\omega t + \delta)]$

56. (a) $y = t^3 - 12t + 3 \Rightarrow v(t) = y' = 3t^2 - 12 \Rightarrow a(t) = v'(t) = 6t$

(b) $v(t) = 3(t^2 - 4) > 0$ when $t > 2$, so it moves upward when $t > 2$ and downward when $0 \le t < 2$.

(c) Distance upward $= y(3) - y(2) = -6 - (-13) = 7$,

Distance downward $= y(0) - y(2) = 3 - (-13) = 16$. Total distance $= 7 + 16 = 23$.

(d)

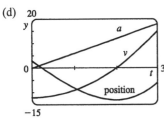

(e) The particle is speeding up when v and a have the same sign, that is, when $t > 2$. The particle is slowing down when v and a have opposite signs; that is, when $0 < t < 2$.

57. The linear density ρ is the rate of change of mass m with respect to length x. $m = x(1 + \sqrt{x}) = x + x^{3/2} \Rightarrow$

$\rho = dm/dx = 1 + \frac{3}{2}\sqrt{x}$, so the linear density when $x = 4$ is $1 + \frac{3}{2}\sqrt{4} = 4$ kg/m.

58. (a) $V = \frac{1}{3}\pi r^2 h \Rightarrow dV/dh = \frac{1}{3}\pi r^2$ (r constant)

(b) $V = \frac{1}{3}\pi r^2 h \Rightarrow dV/dr = \frac{2}{3}\pi rh$ (h constant)

59. (a) $C(x) = 920 + 2x - 0.02x^2 + 0.00007x^3$ $\Rightarrow$ $C'(x) = 2 - 0.04x + 0.00021x^2$

(b) $C'(100) = 2 - 4 + 2.1 = \$0.10/\text{unit}$. This value represents the rate at which costs are increasing as the hundredth unit is produced, and is the approximate cost of producing the 101st unit.

(c) The cost of producing the 101st item is $C(101) - C(100) = 990.10107 - 990 = \$0.10107$, slightly larger than $C'(100)$.

(d) $C''(x) = -0.04 + 0.00042x = 0$ $\Rightarrow$ $x = \frac{0.04}{0.00042} \approx 95.24$ and C'' changes from negative to positive at this value of x. This is the value of x at which the marginal cost is minimized.

60. (a) $\lim\limits_{t \to \infty} C(t) = \lim\limits_{t \to \infty} \left[K\left(e^{-at} - e^{-bt}\right) \right] = K \lim\limits_{t \to \infty} \left(e^{-at} - e^{-bt}\right) = K(0 - 0) = 0$ because $-at \to -\infty$ and $-bt \to -\infty$ as $t \to \infty$.

(b) $C(t) = K\left(e^{-at} - e^{-bt}\right)$ $\Rightarrow$ $C'(t) = K\left(e^{-at}(-a) - e^{-bt}(-b)\right) = K\left(-ae^{-at} + be^{-bt}\right)$

(c) $C'(t) = 0$ $\Rightarrow$ $be^{-bt} = ae^{-at}$ $\Rightarrow$ $\dfrac{b}{a} = e^{(-a+b)t}$ $\Rightarrow$ $\ln\dfrac{b}{a} = (b-a)t$ $\Rightarrow$ $t = \dfrac{\ln(b/a)}{b-a}$

61. (a) $f(x) = \sqrt[3]{1+3x} = (1+3x)^{1/3}$ $\Rightarrow$ $f'(x) = (1+3x)^{-2/3}$, so the linearization of f at $a = 0$ is
$L(x) = f(0) + f'(0)(x-0) = 1^{1/3} + 1^{-2/3}x = 1 + x$. Thus, $\sqrt[3]{1+3x} \approx 1 + x$ $\Rightarrow$
$\sqrt[3]{1.03} = \sqrt[3]{1 + 3(0.01)} \approx 1 + (0.01) = 1.01$.

(b) The linear approximation is $\sqrt[3]{1+3x} \approx 1 + x$, so for the required accuracy we want $\sqrt[3]{1+3x} - 0.1 < 1 + x < \sqrt[3]{1+3x} + 0.1$. From the graph, it appears that this is true when $-0.23 < x < 0.40$.

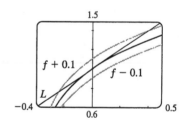

62. $A = x^2 + \frac{1}{2}\pi\left(\frac{1}{2}x\right)^2 = \left(1 + \frac{\pi}{8}\right)x^2$ $\Rightarrow$ $dA = \left(2 + \frac{\pi}{4}\right)x\,dx$.

When $x = 60$ and $dx = 0.1$, $dA = \left(2 + \frac{\pi}{4}\right)60(0.1) = 12 + \frac{3\pi}{2}$, so

the maximum error is approximately $12 + \frac{3\pi}{2} \approx 16.7 \text{ cm}^2$.

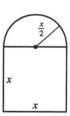

63. $\lim\limits_{\theta \to \pi/3} \dfrac{\cos\theta - 0.5}{\theta - \pi/3} = \left[\dfrac{d}{d\theta} \cos\theta\right]_{\theta = \pi/3} = -\sin\dfrac{\pi}{3} = -\dfrac{\sqrt{3}}{2}$

64. $\dfrac{d}{dx}[f(2x)] = x^2$ $\Rightarrow$ $f'(2x) \cdot 2 = x^2$ $\Rightarrow$ $f'(2x) = \frac{1}{2}x^2$. Let $t = 2x$. Then $f'(t) = \frac{1}{2}\left(\frac{1}{2}t\right)^2 = \frac{1}{8}t^2$,

so $f'(x) = \frac{1}{8}x^2$.

65. $\displaystyle\lim_{x\to 0}\frac{\sqrt{1+\tan x}-\sqrt{1+\sin x}}{x^3}=\lim_{x\to 0}\frac{\left(\sqrt{1+\tan x}-\sqrt{1+\sin x}\right)\left(\sqrt{1+\tan x}+\sqrt{1+\sin x}\right)}{x^3\left(\sqrt{1+\tan x}+\sqrt{1+\sin x}\right)}$

$\displaystyle =\lim_{x\to 0}\frac{(1+\tan x)-(1+\sin x)}{x^3\left(\sqrt{1+\tan x}+\sqrt{1+\sin x}\right)}=\lim_{x\to 0}\frac{\sin x\,(1/\cos x-1)}{x^3\left(\sqrt{1+\tan x}+\sqrt{1+\sin x}\right)}\cdot\frac{\cos x}{\cos x}$

$\displaystyle =\lim_{x\to 0}\frac{\sin x\,(1-\cos x)}{x^3\left(\sqrt{1+\tan x}+\sqrt{1+\sin x}\right)\cos x}\cdot\frac{1+\cos x}{1+\cos x}$

$\displaystyle =\lim_{x\to 0}\frac{\sin x\cdot\sin^2 x}{x^3\left(\sqrt{1+\tan x}+\sqrt{1+\sin x}\right)\cos x\,(1+\cos x)}$

$\displaystyle =\left(\lim_{x\to 0}\frac{\sin x}{x}\right)^3\lim_{x\to 0}\frac{1}{\left(\sqrt{1+\tan x}+\sqrt{1+\sin x}\right)\cos x\,(1+\cos x)}$

$\displaystyle =1^3\cdot\frac{1}{\left(\sqrt{1}+\sqrt{1}\right)\cdot 1\cdot(1+1)}=\frac{1}{4}$

66. Let (b,c) be on the curve, that is, $b^{2/3}+c^{2/3}=a^{2/3}$. Now $x^{2/3}+y^{2/3}=a^{2/3}\ \Rightarrow\ \frac{2}{3}x^{-1/3}+\frac{2}{3}y^{-1/3}\dfrac{dy}{dx}=0$,

so $\dfrac{dy}{dx}=-\dfrac{y^{1/3}}{x^{1/3}}=-\left(\dfrac{y}{x}\right)^{1/3}$, so at (b,c) the slope of the tangent line is $-(c/b)^{1/3}$ and an equation of the tangent

line is $y-c=-(c/b)^{1/3}(x-b)$ or $y=-(c/b)^{1/3}x+(c+b^{2/3}c^{1/3})$. Setting $y=0$, we find that the x-intercept

is $b^{1/3}c^{2/3}+b=b^{1/3}(c^{2/3}+b^{2/3})$ and setting $x=0$ we find that the y-intercept is

$c+b^{2/3}c^{1/3}=c^{1/3}(c^{2/3}+b^{2/3})$. So the length of the tangent line between these two points is

$$\sqrt{[b^{1/3}(c^{2/3}+b^{2/3})]^2+[c^{1/3}(c^{2/3}+b^{2/3})]^2}=\sqrt{b^{2/3}(a^{2/3})^2+c^{2/3}(a^{2/3})^2}$$

$$=\sqrt{(b^{2/3}+c^{2/3})a^{4/3}}=\sqrt{a^{2/3}a^{4/3}}$$

$$=\sqrt{a^2}=a=\text{constant}$$

Focus on Problem Solving

1. We must find a value x_0 such that the normal lines to the parabola $y = x^2$ at $x = \pm x_0$ intersect at a point one unit

from the points $(\pm x_0, x_0^2)$. The normals to $y = x^2$ at $x = \pm x_0$ have slopes $-\dfrac{1}{\pm 2x_0}$ and pass through $(\pm x_0, x_0^2)$

respectively, so the normals have the equations $y - x_0^2 = -\dfrac{1}{2x_0}(x - x_0)$ and $y - x_0^2 = \dfrac{1}{2x_0}(x + x_0)$. The

common y-intercept is $x_0^2 + \frac{1}{2}$. We want to find the value of x_0 for which the distance from $\left(0, x_0^2 + \frac{1}{2}\right)$ to $\left(x_0, x_0^2\right)$

equals 1. The square of the distance is $(x_0 - 0)^2 + \left[x_0^2 - \left(x_0^2 + \frac{1}{2}\right)\right]^2 = x_0^2 + \frac{1}{4} = 1$ $\Leftrightarrow$ $x_0 = \pm\frac{\sqrt{3}}{2}$. For these

values of x_0, the y-intercept is $x_0^2 + \frac{1}{2} = \frac{5}{4}$, so the center of the circle is at $\left(0, \frac{5}{4}\right)$.

Another solution: Let the center of the circle be $(0, a)$. Then the equation of the circle is $x^2 + (y - a)^2 = 1$.

Solving with the equation of the parabola, $y = x^2$, we get $x^2 + \left(x^2 - a\right)^2 = 1$ $\Leftrightarrow$ $x^2 + x^4 - 2ax^2 + a^2 = 1$

$\Leftrightarrow$ $x^4 + (1 - 2a)x^2 + a^2 - 1 = 0$. The parabola and the circle will be tangent to each other when this quadratic

equation in x^2 has equal roots; that is, when the discriminant is 0. Thus, $(1 - 2a)^2 - 4(a^2 - 1) = 0$ $\Leftrightarrow$

$1 - 4a + 4a^2 - 4a^2 + 4 = 0$ $\Leftrightarrow$ $4a = 5$, so $a = \frac{5}{4}$. The center of the circle is $\left(0, \frac{5}{4}\right)$.

2. $y = x^3 - 3x + 4$ $\Rightarrow$ $y' = 3x^2 - 3$, and $y = 3\left(x^2 - x\right)$ $\Rightarrow$
$y' = 6x - 3$. The slopes of the tangents of the two curves are equal
when $3x^2 - 3 = 6x - 3$; that is, when $x = 0$ or 2. At $x = 0$, both
tangents have slope -3, but the curves do not intersect. At $x = 2$,
both tangents have slope 9 and the curves intersect at $(2, 6)$. So
there is a common tangent line at $(2, 6)$, $y = 9x - 12$.

3. (a) $f(x) = \sqrt{1 - \sqrt{2 - \sqrt{3 - x}}}$

$$D = \left\{x \mid 3 - x \geq 0, 2 - \sqrt{3 - x} \geq 0, 1 - \sqrt{2 - \sqrt{3 - x}} \geq 0\right\}$$

$$= \left\{x \mid 3 \geq x, 2 \geq \sqrt{3 - x}, 1 \geq \sqrt{2 - \sqrt{3 - x}}\right\}$$

$$= \left\{x \mid 3 \geq x, 4 \geq 3 - x, 1 \geq 2 - \sqrt{3 - x}\right\}$$

$$= \left\{x \mid x \leq 3, x \geq -1, 1 \leq \sqrt{3 - x}\right\} = \left\{x \mid x \leq 3, x \geq -1, 1 \leq 3 - x\right\}$$

$$= \left\{x \mid x \leq 3, x \geq -1, x \leq 2\right\} = \left\{x \mid -1 \leq x \leq 2\right\} = [-1, 2]$$

(b) $f(x) = \sqrt{1 - \sqrt{2 - \sqrt{3 - x}}}$ $\Rightarrow$

(c)

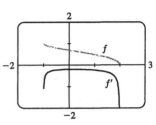

$$f'(x) = \frac{1}{2\sqrt{1 - \sqrt{2 - \sqrt{3 - x}}}} \cdot \frac{d}{dx}\left(1 - \sqrt{2 - \sqrt{3 - x}}\right)$$

$$= \frac{1}{2\sqrt{1 - \sqrt{2 - \sqrt{3 - x}}}} \cdot \frac{-1}{2\sqrt{2 - \sqrt{3 - x}}} \cdot \frac{d}{dx}\left(2 - \sqrt{3 - x}\right)$$

$$= -\frac{1}{8\sqrt{1 - \sqrt{2 - \sqrt{3 - x}}}\sqrt{2 - \sqrt{3 - x}}\sqrt{3 - x}}$$

Note that f is always decreasing
and f' is always negative.

4. $\displaystyle \lim_{x \to a} \frac{f(x) - f(a)}{\sqrt{x} - \sqrt{a}} = \lim_{x \to a} \left[\frac{f(x) - f(a)}{\sqrt{x} - \sqrt{a}} \cdot \frac{\sqrt{x} + \sqrt{a}}{\sqrt{x} + \sqrt{a}}\right] = \lim_{x \to a} \left[\frac{f(x) - f(a)}{x - a} \cdot (\sqrt{x} + \sqrt{a})\right]$

$$= \lim_{x \to a} \frac{f(x) - f(a)}{x - a} \cdot \lim_{x \to a} (\sqrt{x} + \sqrt{a}) = f'(a) \cdot (\sqrt{a} + \sqrt{a}) = 2\sqrt{a}\, f'(a)$$

5. We can assume without loss of generality that $\theta = 0$ at time $t = 0$, so that $\theta = 12\pi t$ rad. [The angular velocity of the wheel is 360 rpm $= 360 \cdot (2\pi\text{ rad})/(60\text{ s}) = 12\pi$ rad/s.] Then the position of A as a function of time is

$$A = (40\cos\theta, 40\sin\theta) = (40\cos 12\pi t, 40\sin 12\pi t), \text{ so } \sin\alpha = \frac{y}{1.2\text{ m}} = \frac{40\sin\theta}{120} = \frac{\sin\theta}{3} = \tfrac{1}{3}\sin 12\pi t.$$

(a) Differentiating the expression for $\sin\alpha$, we get $\cos\alpha \cdot \dfrac{d\alpha}{dt} = \tfrac{1}{3} \cdot 12\pi \cdot \cos 12\pi t = 4\pi\cos\theta$.

When $\theta = \frac{\pi}{3}$, we have $\sin\alpha = \tfrac{1}{3}\sin\theta = \frac{\sqrt{3}}{6}$, so $\cos\alpha = \sqrt{1 - \left(\frac{\sqrt{3}}{6}\right)^2} = \sqrt{\frac{11}{12}}$ and

$$\frac{d\alpha}{dt} = \frac{4\pi\cos\frac{\pi}{3}}{\cos\alpha} = \frac{2\pi}{\sqrt{11/12}} = \frac{4\pi\sqrt{3}}{\sqrt{11}} \approx 6.56 \text{ rad/s}.$$

(b) By the Law of Cosines, $|AP|^2 = |OA|^2 + |OP|^2 - 2|OA|\,|OP|\cos\theta$ $\Rightarrow$

$$120^2 = 40^2 + |OP|^2 - 2 \cdot 40\,|OP|\cos\theta \quad \Rightarrow \quad |OP|^2 - (80\cos\theta)\,|OP| - 12{,}800 = 0 \quad \Rightarrow$$

$$|OP| = \tfrac{1}{2}\left(80\cos\theta \pm \sqrt{6400\cos^2\theta + 51{,}200}\right) = 40\cos\theta \pm 40\sqrt{\cos^2\theta + 8}$$

$$= 40\left(\cos\theta + \sqrt{8 + \cos^2\theta}\right) \text{ cm} \quad (\text{since } |OP| > 0)$$

As a check, note that $|OP| = 160$ cm when $\theta = 0$ and $|OP| = 80\sqrt{2}$ cm when $\theta = \frac{\pi}{2}$.

(c) By part (b), the x-coordinate of P is given by $x = 40\left(\cos\theta + \sqrt{8 + \cos^2\theta}\right)$, so

$$\frac{dx}{dt} = \frac{dx}{d\theta}\frac{d\theta}{dt} = 40\left(-\sin\theta - \frac{2\cos\theta\sin\theta}{2\sqrt{8 + \cos^2\theta}}\right) \cdot 12\pi = -480\pi\sin\theta\left(1 + \frac{\cos\theta}{\sqrt{8 + \cos^2\theta}}\right) \text{ cm/s}.$$

In particular, $dx/dt = 0$ cm/s when $\theta = 0$ and $dx/dt = -480\pi$ cm/s when $\theta = \frac{\pi}{2}$.

6. The equation of T_1 is $y - x_1^2 = 2x_1(x - x_1) = 2x_1x - 2x_1^2$ or

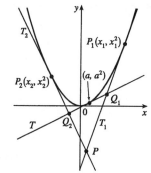

$y = 2x_1x - x_1^2$. The equation of T_2 is $y = 2x_2x - x_2^2$. Solving for the point

of intersection, we get $2x(x_1 - x_2) = x_1^2 - x_2^2 \Rightarrow x = \frac{1}{2}(x_1 + x_2)$.

Therefore, the coordinates of P are $\left(\frac{1}{2}(x_1 + x_2), x_1x_2\right)$. So if the point of

contact of T is (a, a^2), then Q_1 is $\left(\frac{1}{2}(a + x_1), ax_1\right)$ and Q_2 is

$\left(\frac{1}{2}(a + x_2), ax_2\right)$.

Therefore, $|PQ_1|^2 = \frac{1}{4}(a - x_2)^2 + x_1^2(a - x_2)^2 = (a - x_2)^2 \left(\frac{1}{4} + x_1^2\right)$ and

$|PP_1|^2 = \frac{1}{4}(x_1 - x_2)^2 + x_1^2(x_1 - x_2)^2 = (x_1 - x_2)^2 \left(\frac{1}{4} + x_1^2\right)$. So $\dfrac{|PQ_1|^2}{|PP_1|^2} = \dfrac{(a - x_2)^2}{(x_1 - x_2)^2}$, and similarly

$\dfrac{|PQ_2|^2}{|PP_2|^2} = \dfrac{(x_1 - a)^2}{(x_1 - x_2)^2}$. Finally, $\dfrac{|PQ_1|}{|PP_1|} + \dfrac{|PQ_2|}{|PP_2|} = \dfrac{a - x_2}{x_1 - x_2} + \dfrac{x_1 - a}{x_1 - x_2} = 1$.

7. Consider the statement that $\dfrac{d^n}{dx^n}(e^{ax}\sin bx) = r^n e^{ax}\sin(bx + n\theta)$. For $n = 1$,

$\dfrac{d}{dx}(e^{ax}\sin bx) = ae^{ax}\sin bx + be^{ax}\cos bx$, and

$$re^{ax}\sin(bx + \theta) = re^{ax}[\sin bx \cos\theta + \cos bx \sin\theta] = re^{ax}\left(\frac{a}{r}\sin bx + \frac{b}{r}\cos bx\right)$$

$$= ae^{ax}\sin bx + be^{ax}\cos bx$$

since $\tan\theta = \dfrac{b}{a} \Rightarrow \sin\theta = \dfrac{b}{r}$ and $\cos\theta = \dfrac{a}{r}$.

So the statement is true for $n = 1$. Assume it is true for $n = k$. Then

$$\dfrac{d^{k+1}}{dx^{k+1}}(e^{ax}\sin bx) = \dfrac{d}{dx}\left[r^k e^{ax}\sin(bx + k\theta)\right] = r^k ae^{ax}\sin(bx + k\theta) + r^k e^{ax}b\cos(bx + k\theta)$$

$$= r^k e^{ax}[a\sin(bx + k\theta) + b\cos(bx + k\theta)]$$

But

$$\sin[bx + (k+1)\theta] = \sin[(bx + k\theta) + \theta] = \sin(bx + k\theta)\cos\theta + \sin\theta\cos(bx + k\theta)$$

$$= \frac{a}{r}\sin(bx + k\theta) + \frac{b}{r}\cos(bx + k\theta)$$

Hence, $a\sin(bx + k\theta) + b\cos(bx + k\theta) = r\sin[bx + (k+1)\theta]$. So

$$\dfrac{d^{k+1}}{dx^{k+1}}(e^{ax}\sin bx) = r^k e^{ax}[a\sin(bx + k\theta) + b\cos(bx + k\theta)] = r^k e^{ax}[r\sin(bx + (k+1)\theta)]$$

$$= r^{k+1}e^{ax}[\sin(bx + (k+1)\theta)]$$

Therefore, the statement is true for all n by mathematical induction.

8. We recognize this limit as the definition of the derivative of the function $f(x) = e^{\sin x}$ at $x = \pi$, since it is of the

form $\displaystyle\lim_{x \to \pi} \frac{f(x) - f(\pi)}{x - \pi}$. Therefore, the limit is equal to $f'(\pi) = (\cos \pi)e^{\sin \pi} = -1 \cdot e^0 = -1$.

9. It seems from the figure that as P approaches the point $(0, 2)$ from the right, $x_T \to \infty$ and $y_T \to 2^+$. As P

approaches the point $(3, 0)$ from the left, it appears that $x_T \to 3^+$ and $y_T \to \infty$. So we guess that $x_T \in (3, \infty)$ and

$y_T \in (2, \infty)$. It is more difficult to estimate the range of values for x_N and y_N. We might perhaps guess that

$x_N \in (0, 3)$, and $y_N \in (-\infty, 0)$ or $(-2, 0)$.

In order to actually solve the problem, we implicitly differentiate the equation of the ellipse to find the equation

of the tangent line: $\dfrac{x^2}{9} + \dfrac{y^2}{4} = 1 \;\Rightarrow\; \dfrac{2x}{9} + \dfrac{2y}{4}y' = 0$, so $y' = -\dfrac{4}{9}\dfrac{x}{y}$. So at the point (x_0, y_0) on the ellipse, an

equation of the tangent line is $y - y_0 = -\dfrac{4}{9}\dfrac{x_0}{y_0}(x - x_0)$ or $4x_0x + 9y_0y = 4x_0^2 + 9y_0^2$. This can be written as

$\dfrac{x_0 x}{9} + \dfrac{y_0 y}{4} = \dfrac{x_0^2}{9} + \dfrac{y_0^2}{4} = 1$, because (x_0, y_0) lies on the ellipse. So an equation of the tangent line is

$\dfrac{x_0 x}{9} + \dfrac{y_0 y}{4} = 1$.

Therefore, the x-intercept x_T for the tangent line is given by $\dfrac{x_0 x_T}{9} = 1 \;\Leftrightarrow\; x_T = \dfrac{9}{x_0}$, and the y-intercept y_T

is given by $\dfrac{y_0 y_T}{4} = 1 \;\Leftrightarrow\; y_T = \dfrac{4}{y_0}$.

So as x_0 takes on all values in $(0, 3)$, x_T takes on all values in $(3, \infty)$, and as y_0 takes on all values in $(0, 2)$,

y_T takes on all values in $(2, \infty)$.

At the point (x_0, y_0) on the ellipse, the slope of the normal line is $-\dfrac{1}{y'(x_0, y_0)} = \dfrac{9}{4}\dfrac{y_0}{x_0}$, and its equation is

$y - y_0 = \dfrac{9}{4}\dfrac{y_0}{x_0}(x - x_0)$. So the x-intercept x_N for the normal line is given by $0 - y_0 = \dfrac{9}{4}\dfrac{y_0}{x_0}(x_N - x_0) \;\Rightarrow$

$x_N = -\dfrac{4x_0}{9} + x_0 = \dfrac{5x_0}{9}$, and the y-intercept y_N is given by $y_N - y_0 = \dfrac{9}{4}\dfrac{y_0}{x_0}(0 - x_0) \;\Rightarrow$

$y_N = -\dfrac{9y_0}{4} + y_0 = -\dfrac{5y_0}{4}$.

So as x_0 takes on all values in $(0, 3)$, x_N takes on all values in $\left(0, \frac{5}{3}\right)$, and as y_0 takes on all values in $(0, 2)$,

y_N takes on all values in $\left(-\frac{5}{2}, 0\right)$.

10. $\displaystyle\lim_{x \to 0} \frac{f(x)}{g(x)} = \lim_{x \to 0} \frac{f(x) - 0}{g(x) - 0} = \lim_{x \to 0} \frac{f(x) - f(0)}{g(x) - g(0)} = \lim_{x \to 0} \frac{\dfrac{f(x) - f(0)}{x - 0}}{\dfrac{g(x) - g(0)}{x - 0}}$

$\displaystyle = \frac{\lim\limits_{x \to 0} \dfrac{f(x) - f(0)}{x - 0}}{\lim\limits_{x \to 0} \dfrac{g(x) - g(0)}{x - 0}} = \frac{f'(0)}{g'(0)}$

11. If we divide $1 - x$ into x^n by long division, we find that $f(x) = \dfrac{x^n}{1-x} = -x^{n-1} - x^{n-2} - \cdots - x - 1 + \dfrac{1}{1-x}$.

This can also be seen by multiplying the last expression by $1 - x$ and canceling terms on the right-hand side. So we

let $g(x) = 1 + x + x^2 + \cdots + x^{n-1}$, so that $f(x) = \dfrac{1}{1-x} - g(x) \;\Rightarrow\; f^{(n)}(x) = \left(\dfrac{1}{1-x}\right)^{(n)} - g^{(n)}(x)$. But

g is a polynomial of degree $(n-1)$, so its nth derivative is 0, and therefore $f^{(n)}(x) = \left(\dfrac{1}{1-x}\right)^{(n)}$. Now

$$\frac{d}{dx}(1-x)^{-1} = (-1)(1-x)^{-2}(-1) = (1-x)^{-2}, \quad \frac{d^2}{dx^2}(1-x)^{-1} = (-2)(1-x)^{-3}(-1) = 2(1-x)^{-3},$$

$$\frac{d^3}{dx^3}(1-x)^{-1} = (-3)\cdot 2(1-x)^{-4}(-1) = 3\cdot 2(1-x)^{-4}, \quad \frac{d^4}{dx^4}(1-x)^{-1} = 4\cdot 3\cdot 2(1-x)^{-5}, \text{ and so on. So}$$

after n differentiations, we will have $f^{(n)}(x) = \left(\dfrac{1}{1-x}\right)^{(n)} = \dfrac{n!}{(1-x)^{n+1}}$.

12.

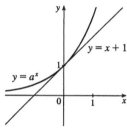

We see that at $x = 0$, $f(x) = a^x = 1 + x = 1$, so if $y = a^x$ is to lie above $y = 1 + x$, the two curves must just touch at $(0, 1)$, that is, we must have $f'(0) = 1$.

[To see this analytically, note that $a^x \geq 1 + x \;\Rightarrow\; a^x - 1 \geq x \;\Rightarrow\;$

$\dfrac{a^x - 1}{x} \geq 1$ for $x > 0$, so $f'(0) = \lim\limits_{x \to 0^+} \dfrac{a^x - 1}{x} \geq 1$. Similarly, for $x < 0$,

$a^x - 1 \geq x \;\Rightarrow\; \dfrac{a^x - 1}{x} \leq 1$, so $f'(0) = \lim\limits_{x \to 0^-} \dfrac{a^x - 1}{x} \leq 1$. Since

$1 \leq f'(0) \leq 1$, we must have $f'(0) = 1$.] But $f'(x) = a^x \ln a \;\Rightarrow\;$

$f'(0) = \ln a$, so we have $\ln a = 1 \;\Leftrightarrow\; a = e$.

Another method: The inequality certainly holds for $x \leq -1$, so consider $x > -1$, $x \neq 0$. Then $a^x \geq 1 + x \;\Rightarrow\;$

$a \geq (1+x)^{1/x}$ for $x > 0 \;\Rightarrow\; a \geq \lim\limits_{x \to 0^+}(1+x)^{1/x} = e$, by Equation 3.7.5. Also, $a^x \geq 1 + x \;\Rightarrow\;$

$a \leq (1+x)^{1/x}$ for $x < 0 \;\Rightarrow\; a \leq \lim\limits_{x \to 0^-}(1+x)^{1/x} = e$. So since $e \leq a \leq e$, we must have $a = e$.

13. $y = \dfrac{x}{\sqrt{a^2 - 1}} - \dfrac{2}{\sqrt{a^2 - 1}} \arctan \dfrac{\sin x}{a + \sqrt{a^2 - 1} + \cos x}$. Let $k = a + \sqrt{a^2 - 1}$. Then

$$y' = \frac{1}{\sqrt{a^2 - 1}} - \frac{2}{\sqrt{a^2 - 1}} \cdot \frac{1}{1 + \sin^2 x/(k + \cos x)^2} \cdot \frac{\cos x\,(k + \cos x) + \sin^2 x}{(k + \cos x)^2}$$

$$= \frac{1}{\sqrt{a^2 - 1}} - \frac{2}{\sqrt{a^2 - 1}} \cdot \frac{k \cos x + \cos^2 x + \sin^2 x}{(k + \cos x)^2 + \sin^2 x} = \frac{1}{\sqrt{a^2 - 1}} - \frac{2}{\sqrt{a^2 - 1}} \cdot \frac{k \cos x + 1}{k^2 + 2k \cos x + 1}$$

$$= \frac{k^2 + 2k \cos x + 1 - 2k \cos x - 2}{\sqrt{a^2 - 1}\,(k^2 + 2k \cos x + 1)} = \frac{k^2 - 1}{\sqrt{a^2 - 1}\,(k^2 + 2k \cos x + 1)}$$

But $k^2 = 2a^2 + 2a\sqrt{a^2 - 1} - 1 = 2a(a + \sqrt{a^2 - 1}) - 1 = 2ak - 1$, so $k^2 + 1 = 2ak$, and $k^2 - 1 = 2(ak - 1)$.

So $y' = \dfrac{2(ak-1)}{\sqrt{a^2-1}\,(2ak+2k\cos x)} = \dfrac{ak-1}{\sqrt{a^2-1}\,k(a+\cos x)}$. But $ak-1 = a^2 + a\sqrt{a^2-1} - 1 = k\sqrt{a^2-1}$,

so $y' = 1/(a+\cos x)$.

14. (a) $f(x) = x(x-2)(x-6) = x^3 - 8x^2 + 12x \;\Rightarrow\; f'(x) = 3x^2 - 16x + 12$. The average of the first pair of

zeros is $(0+2)/2 = 1$. At $x = 1$, the slope of the tangent line is $f'(1) = -1$, so an equation of the tangent line

has the form $y = -1x + b$. Since $f(1) = 5$, we have $5 = -1 + b \;\Rightarrow\; b = 6$ and the tangent has equation

$y = -x + 6$. Similarly, at $x = \dfrac{0+6}{2} = 3$, $y = -9x + 18$; at $x = \dfrac{2+6}{2} = 4$, $y = -4x$. From the graph, we

see that each tangent line drawn at the average of two zeros intersects the graph of f at the third zero.

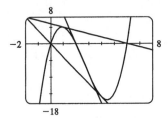

(b) A CAS gives $f'(x) = (x-b)(x-c) + (x-a)(x-c) + (x-a)(x-b)$ or

$f'(x) = 3x^2 - 2(a+b+c)x + ab + ac + bc$. Using the Simplify command, we get

$f'\left(\dfrac{a+b}{2}\right) = -\dfrac{(a-b)^2}{4}$ and $f\left(\dfrac{a+b}{2}\right) = -\dfrac{(a-b)^2}{8}(a+b-2c)$, so an equation of the tangent line at

$x = \dfrac{a+b}{2}$ is

$$y = -\dfrac{(a-b)^2}{4}\left(x - \dfrac{a+b}{2}\right) - \dfrac{(a-b)^2}{8}(a+b-2c)$$

To find the x-intercept, let $y = 0$ and use the Solve command. The result is $x = c$.

Using Derive, we can begin by authoring the expression $(x-a)(x-b)(x-c)$. Now load the utility file

Dif_apps. Next we author tangent (#1, x, (a + b)/2)—this is the command to find an equation of the tangent

line of the function in #1 whose independent variable is x at the x-value $(a+b)/2$. We then simplify that

expression and obtain the equation $y = \#3$. The form in expression #3 makes it easy to see that the x-intercept

is the third zero, namely c. In a similar fashion we see that b is the x-intercept for the tangent line at $(a+c)/2$

and a is the x-intercept for the tangent line at $(b+c)/2$.

```
#1:    (x - a) · (x - b) · (x - c)                                    Author the function y=

                                                          a + b
#2:    TANGENT ⎛(x - a) · (x - b) · (x - c), x, ─────⎞     Tangent (#1, x, (a+b)/2)
                                                            2

           2            2
       (a  - 2·a·b + b ) · (c - x)
#3:    ─────────────────────────────                       0.0s Simp (#2)
                   4
```

15. (a)

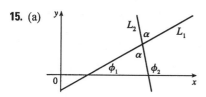

If the two lines L_1 and L_2 have slopes m_1 and m_2 and angles of inclination ϕ_1 and ϕ_2, then $m_1 = \tan\phi_1$ and $m_2 = \tan\phi_2$. The triangle in the figure shows that $\phi_1 + \alpha + (180° - \phi_2) = 180°$ and so $\alpha = \phi_2 - \phi_1$. Therefore, using the identity for $\tan(x - y)$, we have

$$\tan\alpha = \tan(\phi_2 - \phi_1) = \frac{\tan\phi_2 - \tan\phi_1}{1 + \tan\phi_2 \tan\phi_1} \text{ and so}$$

$$\tan\alpha = \frac{m_2 - m_1}{1 + m_1 m_2}.$$

(b) (i) The parabolas intersect when $x^2 = (x - 2)^2 \;\Rightarrow\; x = 1$. If $y = x^2$, then $y' = 2x$, so the slope of the tangent to $y = x^2$ at $(1, 1)$ is $m_1 = 2(1) = 2$. If $y = (x - 2)^2$, then $y' = 2(x - 2)$, so the slope of the tangent to $y = (x - 2)^2$ at $(1, 1)$ is $m_2 = 2(1 - 2) = -2$. Therefore,

$$\tan\alpha = \frac{m_2 - m_1}{1 + m_1 m_2} = \frac{-2 - 2}{1 + 2(-2)} = \tfrac{4}{3} \text{ and so } \alpha = \tan^{-1}\left(\tfrac{4}{3}\right) \approx 53°.$$

(ii) $x^2 - y^2 = 3$ and $x^2 - 4x + y^2 + 3 = 0$ intersect when $x^2 - 4x + (x^2 - 3) + 3 = 0 \;\Leftrightarrow\; 2x(x - 2) = 0$ $\Rightarrow\; x = 0$ or 2, but 0 is extraneous. If $x = 2$, then $y = \pm 1$. If $x^2 - y^2 = 3$ then $2x - 2yy' = 0 \;\Rightarrow\;$ $y' = x/y$ and $x^2 - 4x + y^2 + 3 = 0 \;\Rightarrow\; 2x - 4 + 2yy' = 0 \;\Rightarrow\; y' = \dfrac{2 - x}{y}$. At $(2, 1)$ the slopes are $m_1 = 2$ and $m_2 = 0$, so $\tan\alpha = \frac{0 - 2}{1 + 2 \cdot 0} = -2 \;\Rightarrow\; \alpha \approx 117°$. At $(2, -1)$ the slopes are $m_1 = -2$ and $m_2 = 0$, so $\tan\alpha = \frac{0 - (-2)}{1 + (-2)(0)} = 2 \;\Rightarrow\; \alpha \approx 63°$.

16. $y^2 = 4px \;\Rightarrow\; 2yy' = 4p \;\Rightarrow\; y' = 2p/y \;\Rightarrow\;$ slope of tangent at $P(x_1, y_1)$ is $m_1 = 2p/y_1$. The slope of FP is $m_2 = \dfrac{y_1}{x_1 - p}$, so by the formula from Problem 15(a),

$$\tan\alpha = \frac{y_1/(x_1 - p) - 2p/y_1}{1 + (2p/y_1)[y_1/(x_1 - p)]} \cdot \frac{y_1(x_1 - p)}{y_1(x_1 - p)} = \frac{y_1^2 - 2p(x_1 - p)}{y_1(x_1 - p) + 2py_1}$$

$$= \frac{4px_1 - 2px_1 + 2p^2}{x_1 y_1 - py_1 + 2py_1} = \frac{2p(p + x_1)}{y_1(p + x_1)} = \frac{2p}{y_1} = \text{slope of tangent at } P = \tan\beta$$

Since $0 \le \alpha, \beta \le \frac{\pi}{2}$, this proves that $\alpha = \beta$.

17. Since $\angle ROQ = \angle OQP = \theta$, the triangle QOR is isosceles, so $|QR| = |RO| = x$. By the Law of Cosines, $x^2 = x^2 + r^2 - 2rx\cos\theta$. Hence, $2rx\cos\theta = r^2$, so $x = \dfrac{r^2}{2r\cos\theta} = \dfrac{r}{2\cos\theta}$. Note that as $y \to 0^+$, $\theta \to 0^+$ (since $\sin\theta = y/r$), and hence $x \to \dfrac{r}{2\cos 0} = \dfrac{r}{2}$. Thus, as P is taken closer and closer to the x-axis, the point R approaches the midpoint of the radius AO.

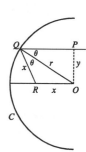

18. Suppose that $y = mx + c$ is a tangent line to the ellipse. Then it intersects the ellipse at only one point, so the

discriminant of the equation $\dfrac{x^2}{a^2} + \dfrac{(mx+c)^2}{b^2} = 1 \;\Leftrightarrow\; (b^2 + a^2m^2)x^2 + 2mca^2x + a^2c^2 - a^2b^2 = 0$ must be

0; that is,

$$0 = \left(2mca^2\right)^2 - 4(b^2 + a^2m^2)(a^2c^2 - a^2b^2)$$

$$= 4a^4c^2m^2 - 4a^2b^2c^2 + 4a^2b^4 - 4a^4c^2m^2 + 4a^4b^2m^2 = 4a^2b^2(a^2m^2 + b^2 - c^2)$$

Therefore, $a^2m^2 + b^2 - c^2 = 0$.

Now if a point (α, β) lies on the line $y = mx + c$, then $c = \beta - m\alpha$, so from above,

$$0 = a^2m^2 + b^2 - (\beta - m\alpha)^2 = (a^2 - \alpha^2)m^2 + 2\alpha\beta m + b^2 - \beta^2 \;\Leftrightarrow\; m^2 + \frac{2\alpha\beta}{a^2 - \alpha^2}m + \frac{b^2 - \beta^2}{a^2 - \alpha^2} = 0.$$

(a) Suppose that the two tangent lines from the point (α, β) to the ellipse have slopes m and $\dfrac{1}{m}$. Then m and $\dfrac{1}{m}$

are roots of the equation $z^2 + \dfrac{2\alpha\beta}{a^2 - \alpha^2}z + \dfrac{b^2 - \beta^2}{a^2 - \alpha^2} = 0$. This implies that $(z - m)\left(z - \dfrac{1}{m}\right) = 0 \;\Leftrightarrow\;$

$z^2 - \left(m + \dfrac{1}{m}\right)z + m\left(\dfrac{1}{m}\right) = 0$, so equating the constant terms in the two quadratic equations, we get

$\dfrac{b^2 - \beta^2}{a^2 - \alpha^2} = m\left(\dfrac{1}{m}\right) = 1$, and hence $b^2 - \beta^2 = a^2 - \alpha^2$. So (α, β) lies on the hyperbola $x^2 - y^2 = a^2 - b^2$.

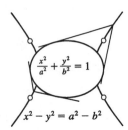

(b) If the two tangent lines from the point (α, β) to the ellipse have slopes m and $-\dfrac{1}{m}$, then m and $-\dfrac{1}{m}$ are roots

of the quadratic equation, and so $(z - m)\left(z + \dfrac{1}{m}\right) = 0$, and equating the constant terms as in part (a), we get

$\dfrac{b^2 - \beta^2}{a^2 - \alpha^2} = -1$, and hence $b^2 - \beta^2 = \alpha^2 - a^2$. So the point (α, β) lies on the circle $x^2 + y^2 = a^2 + b^2$.

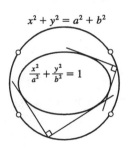

19. $y = x^4 - 2x^2 - x \implies y' = 4x^3 - 4x - 1$. The equation of the tangent line at $x = a$ is

$y - (a^4 - 2a^2 - a) = (4a^3 - 4a - 1)(x - a)$ or $y = (4a^3 - 4a - 1)x + (-3a^4 + 2a^2)$ and similarly for $x = b$.

So if at $x = a$ and $x = b$ we have the same tangent line, then $4a^3 - 4a - 1 = 4b^3 - 4b - 1$ and

$-3a^4 + 2a^2 = -3b^4 + 2b^2$. The first equation gives $a^3 - b^3 = a - b \implies (a - b)(a^2 + ab + b^2) = (a - b)$.

Assuming $a \neq b$, we have $1 = a^2 + ab + b^2$. The second equation gives $3(a^4 - b^4) = 2(a^2 - b^2) \implies$

$3(a^2 - b^2)(a^2 + b^2) = 2(a^2 - b^2)$ which is true if $a = -b$. Substituting into $1 = a^2 + ab + b^2$ gives

$1 = a^2 - a^2 + a^2 \implies a = \pm 1$ so that $a = 1$ and $b = -1$ or vice versa. Thus, the points $(1, -2)$ and $(-1, 0)$

have a common tangent line.

As long as there are only two such points, we are done. So we show that these are in fact the only two such

points. Suppose that $a^2 - b^2 \neq 0$. Then $3(a^2 - b^2)(a^2 + b^2) = 2(a^2 - b^2)$ gives $3(a^2 + b^2) = 2$ or $a^2 + b^2 = \frac{2}{3}$.

Thus, $ab = (a^2 + ab + b^2) - (a^2 + b^2) = 1 - \frac{2}{3} = \frac{1}{3}$, so $b = \dfrac{1}{3a}$. Hence, $a^2 + \dfrac{1}{9a^2} = \dfrac{2}{3}$, so $9a^4 + 1 = 6a^2$

$\implies \quad 0 = 9a^4 - 6a^2 + 1 = (3a^2 - 1)^2$. So $3a^2 - 1 = 0 \implies a^2 = \frac{1}{3} \implies b^2 = \dfrac{1}{9a^2} = \frac{1}{3} = a^2$, contradicting

our assumption that $a^2 \neq b^2$.

20. Suppose that the normal lines at the three points (a_1, a_1^2), (a_2, a_2^2), and (a_3, a_3^2) intersect at a common point. Now

if one of the a_i is 0 (suppose $a_1 = 0$) then by symmetry $a_2 = -a_3$, so $a_1 + a_2 + a_3 = 0$. So we can assume that

none of the a_i is 0.

The slope of the tangent line at (a_i, a_i^2) is $2a_i$, so the slope of the normal line is $-\dfrac{1}{2a_i}$ and its equation is

$y - a_i^2 = -\dfrac{1}{2a_i}(x - a_i)$. We solve for the x-coordinate of the intersection of the normal lines from (a_1, a_1^2)

and (a_2, a_2^2):

$y = a_1^2 - \dfrac{1}{2a_1}(x - a_1) = a_2^2 - \dfrac{1}{2a_2}(x - a_2) \implies$

$x\left(\dfrac{1}{2a_2} - \dfrac{1}{2a_1}\right) = a_2^2 - a_1^2 \implies x\left(\dfrac{a_1 - a_2}{2a_1 a_2}\right) = (-a_1 - a_2)(a_1 + a_2) \iff x = -2a_1 a_2(a_1 + a_2)$ $(\star)$.

Similarly, solving for the x-coordinate of the intersections of the normal lines from (a_1, a_1^2) and (a_3, a_3^2) gives

$x = -2a_1 a_3(a_1 + a_3)$ $(\dagger)$.

Equating $(\star)$ and $(\dagger)$ gives

$a_2(a_1 + a_2) = a_3(a_1 + a_3) \iff a_1(a_2 - a_3) = a_3^2 - a_2^2 = -(a_2 + a_3)(a_2 - a_3) \iff$

$a_1 = -(a_2 + a_3) \iff a_1 + a_2 + a_3 = 0.$

21.

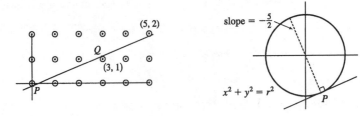

Because of the periodic nature of the lattice points, it suffices to consider the points in the 5×2 grid shown. We can see that the minimum value of r occurs when there is a line with slope $\frac{2}{5}$ which touches the circle centered at $(3, 1)$ and the circles centered at $(0, 0)$ and $(5, 2)$. To find P, the point at which the line is tangent to the circle at $(0, 0)$, we simultaneously solve $x^2 + y^2 = r^2$ and $y = -\frac{5}{2}x \Rightarrow x^2 + \frac{25}{4}x^2 = r^2 \Rightarrow x^2 = \frac{4}{29}r^2 \Rightarrow x = \frac{2}{\sqrt{29}}r, y = -\frac{5}{\sqrt{29}}r$. To find Q, we either use symmetry or solve $(x - 3)^2 + (y - 1)^2 = r^2$ and $y - 1 = -\frac{5}{2}(x - 3)$. As above, we get $x = 3 - \frac{2}{\sqrt{29}}r, y = 1 + \frac{5}{\sqrt{29}}r$. Now the slope of the line PQ is $\frac{2}{5}$, so

$$
m_{PQ} = \frac{1 + \frac{5}{\sqrt{29}}r - \left(-\frac{5}{\sqrt{29}}r\right)}{3 - \frac{2}{\sqrt{29}}r - \frac{2}{\sqrt{29}}r} = \frac{1 + \frac{10}{\sqrt{29}}r}{3 - \frac{4}{\sqrt{29}}r} = \frac{\sqrt{29} + 10r}{3\sqrt{29} - 4r} = \frac{2}{5}
$$

$$
\Rightarrow \qquad 5\sqrt{29} + 50r = 6\sqrt{29} - 8r
$$

$$
\Leftrightarrow \qquad 58r = \sqrt{29}
$$

$$
\Leftrightarrow \qquad r = \frac{\sqrt{29}}{58}
$$

So the minimum value of r for which any line with slope $\frac{2}{5}$ intersects circles with radius r centered at the lattice points on the plane is $r = \frac{\sqrt{29}}{58} \approx 0.093$.

Applications of Differentiation

 Related Rates $\bullet$ $\bullet$ $\bullet$ $\bullet$ $\bullet$ $\bullet$ $\bullet$ $\bullet$ $\bullet$ $\bullet$ $\bullet$ $\bullet$ $\bullet$

1. $V = x^3 \quad \Rightarrow \quad \dfrac{dV}{dt} = \dfrac{dV}{dx}\dfrac{dx}{dt} = 3x^2\dfrac{dx}{dt}$

2. (a) $A = \pi r^2 \quad \Rightarrow \quad \dfrac{dA}{dt} = \dfrac{dA}{dr}\dfrac{dr}{dt} = 2\pi r\dfrac{dr}{dt}$

   (b) $\dfrac{dA}{dt} = 2\pi r\dfrac{dr}{dt} = 2\pi(30\text{ m})(1\text{ m/s}) = 60\pi\text{ m}^2/\text{s}$

3. $y = x^3 + 2x \quad \Rightarrow \quad \dfrac{dy}{dt} = \dfrac{dy}{dx}\dfrac{dx}{dt} = (3x^2 + 2)(5) = 5(3x^2 + 2)$. When $x = 2$, $\dfrac{dy}{dt} = 5(14) = 70$.

4. $y = \sqrt{1+x^3} \quad \Rightarrow \quad \dfrac{dy}{dt} = \dfrac{dy}{dx}\dfrac{dx}{dt} = \tfrac{1}{2}(1+x^3)^{-1/2}\left(3x^2\right)\dfrac{dx}{dt} = \dfrac{3x^2}{2\sqrt{1+x^3}}\dfrac{dx}{dt}$. With $\dfrac{dy}{dt} = 4$ when $x = 2$ and

   $y = 3$, we have $4 = \dfrac{3(4)}{2(3)}\dfrac{dx}{dt} \quad \Rightarrow \quad \dfrac{dx}{dt} = 2$ cm/s.

5. (a) Given: the rate of decrease of the surface area is 1 cm^2/min. If we let   (c)

     t be time (in minutes) and S be the surface area (in cm^2), then we are

     given that $dS/dt = -1$ cm^2/s.

   (b) Unknown: the rate of decrease of the diameter when the diameter is

     10 cm. If we let x be the diameter, then we want to find dx/dt when

     $x = 10$ cm.

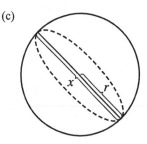

   (d) If the radius is r and the diameter $x = 2r$, then $r = \tfrac{1}{2}x$ and $S = 4\pi r^2 = 4\pi\left(\tfrac{1}{2}x\right)^2 = \pi x^2 \quad \Rightarrow$

     $\dfrac{dS}{dt} = \dfrac{dS}{dx}\dfrac{dx}{dt} = 2\pi x\dfrac{dx}{dt}$.

   (e) $-1 = \dfrac{dS}{dt} = 2\pi x\dfrac{dx}{dt} \quad \Rightarrow \quad \dfrac{dx}{dt} = -\dfrac{1}{2\pi x}$. When $x = 10$, $\dfrac{dx}{dt} = -\dfrac{1}{20\pi}$. So the rate of decrease is

     $\frac{1}{20\pi}$ cm/min.

6. (a) Given: at noon, ship A is 150 km west of ship B; ship A is sailing east at 35 km/h, and ship B is sailing north at

     25 km/h. If we let t be time (in hours), x be the distance traveled by ship A (in km), and y be the distance

     traveled by ship B (in km), then we are given that $dx/dt = 35$ km/h and $dy/dt = 25$ km/h.

   (b) Unknown: the rate at which the distance between the ships is changing at   (c)

     4:00 P.M. If we let z be the distance between the ships, then we want to

     find dz/dt when $t = 4$ h.

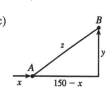

(d) $z^2 = (150 - x)^2 + y^2$ ⟹ $2z\dfrac{dz}{dt} = 2(150 - x)\left(-\dfrac{dx}{dt}\right) + 2y\dfrac{dy}{dt}$

(e) At 4:00 P.M., $x = 4(35) = 140$ and $y = 4(25) = 100$ ⟹ $z = \sqrt{(150 - 140)^2 + 100^2} = \sqrt{10,100}$. So

$$\frac{dz}{dt} = \frac{1}{z}\left[(x - 150)\frac{dx}{dt} + y\frac{dy}{dt}\right] = \frac{-10(35) + 100(25)}{\sqrt{10,100}} = \frac{215}{\sqrt{101}} \approx 21.4 \text{ km/h.}$$

7. (a) Given: a plane flying horizontally at an altitude of 1 mi and a speed of 500 mi/h passes directly over a radar station. If we let t be time (in hours) and x be the horizontal distance traveled by the plane (in mi), then we are given that $dx/dt = 500$ mi/h.

(b) Unknown: the rate at which the distance from the plane to the station is increasing when it is 2 mi from the station. If we let y be the distance from the plane to the station, then we want to find dy/dt when $y = 2$ mi.

(c)
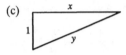

(d) By the Pythagorean Theorem, $y^2 = x^2 + 1$ ⟹ $2y(dy/dt) = 2x(dx/dt)$.

(e) $\dfrac{dy}{dt} = \dfrac{x}{y}\dfrac{dx}{dt} = \dfrac{x}{y}(500)$. Since $y^2 = x^2 + 1$, when $y = 2$, $x = \sqrt{3}$, so $\dfrac{dy}{dt} = \dfrac{\sqrt{3}}{2}(500) = 250\sqrt{3} \approx 433$ mi/h.

8. (a) Given: a man 6 ft tall walks away from a street light mounted on a 15-ft-tall pole at a rate of 5 ft/s. If we let t be time (in s) and x be the distance from the pole to the man (in ft), then we are given that $dx/dt = 5$ ft/s.

(b) Unknown: the rate at which the tip of his shadow is moving when he is 40 ft from the pole. If we let y be the distance from the man to the tip of his shadow (in ft), then we want to find $\dfrac{d}{dt}(x + y)$ when $x = 40$ ft.

(c)
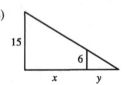

(d) By similar triangles, $\dfrac{15}{6} = \dfrac{x + y}{y}$ ⟹ $15y = 6x + 6y$ ⟹ $9y = 6x$ ⟹ $y = \frac{2}{3}x$.

(e) The tip of the shadow moves at a rate of $\dfrac{d}{dt}(x + y) = \dfrac{d}{dt}\left(x + \frac{2}{3}x\right) = \dfrac{5}{3}\dfrac{dx}{dt} = \frac{5}{3}(5) = \frac{25}{3}$ ft/s.

9.
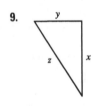

We are given that $\dfrac{dx}{dt} = 60$ mi/h and $\dfrac{dy}{dt} = 25$ mi/h. $z^2 = x^2 + y^2$ ⟹

$$2z\frac{dz}{dt} = 2x\frac{dx}{dt} + 2y\frac{dy}{dt} \Rightarrow z\frac{dz}{dt} = x\frac{dx}{dt} + y\frac{dy}{dt} \Rightarrow \frac{dz}{dt} = \frac{1}{z}\left(x\frac{dx}{dt} + y\frac{dy}{dt}\right).$$

After 2 hours, $x = 2(60) = 120$ and $y = 2(25) = 50$ ⟹ $z = \sqrt{120^2 + 50^2} = 130$,

so $\dfrac{dz}{dt} = \dfrac{1}{z}\left(x\dfrac{dx}{dt} + y\dfrac{dy}{dt}\right) = \dfrac{120(60) + 50(25)}{130} = 65$ mi/h.

10.

We are given that $\dfrac{dx}{dt} = 1.6$ m/s. By similar triangles, $\dfrac{y}{12} = \dfrac{2}{x}$ ⟹ $y = \dfrac{24}{x}$

⟹ $\dfrac{dy}{dt} = -\dfrac{24}{x^2}\dfrac{dx}{dt} = -\dfrac{24}{x^2}(1.6)$. When $x = 8$, $\dfrac{dy}{dt} = -\dfrac{24(1.6)}{64} = -0.6$ m/s,

so the shadow is decreasing at a rate of 0.6 m/s.

11.

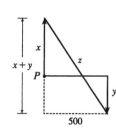

We are given that $\dfrac{dx}{dt} = 4$ ft/s and $\dfrac{dy}{dt} = 5$ ft/s. $z^2 = (x+y)^2 + 500^2 \Rightarrow$

$2z\dfrac{dz}{dt} = 2(x+y)\left(\dfrac{dx}{dt} + \dfrac{dy}{dt}\right)$. 15 minutes after the woman starts, we have

$x = (4\text{ ft/s})(20\text{ min})(60\text{ s/min}) = 4800$ ft and $y = 5 \cdot 15 \cdot 60 = 4500 \Rightarrow$

$z = \sqrt{(4800+4500)^2 + 500^2} = \sqrt{86{,}740{,}000}$, so

$\dfrac{dz}{dt} = \dfrac{x+y}{z}\left(\dfrac{dx}{dt} + \dfrac{dy}{dt}\right) = \dfrac{4800+4500}{\sqrt{86{,}740{,}000}}(5+4) = \dfrac{837}{\sqrt{8674}} \approx 8.99$ ft/s.

12. We are given that $\dfrac{dx}{dt} = 24$ ft/s.

(a)

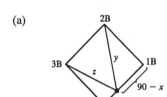

$y^2 = (90-x)^2 + 90^2 \Rightarrow 2y\dfrac{dy}{dt} = 2(90-x)\left(-\dfrac{dx}{dt}\right).$

When $x = 45$, $y = \sqrt{45^2 + 90^2} = 45\sqrt{5}$, so

$\dfrac{dy}{dt} = \dfrac{90-x}{y}\left(-\dfrac{dx}{dt}\right) = \dfrac{45}{45\sqrt{5}}(-24) = -\dfrac{24}{\sqrt{5}},$

so the distance from second base is decreasing at a rate of $\dfrac{24}{\sqrt{5}} \approx 10.7$ ft/s.

(b) Due to the symmetric nature of the problem in part (a), we expect to get the same answer—and we do.

$z^2 = x^2 + 90^2 \Rightarrow 2z\dfrac{dz}{dt} = 2x\dfrac{dx}{dt}$. When $x = 45$, $z = 45\sqrt{5}$, so $\dfrac{dz}{dt} = \dfrac{45}{45\sqrt{5}}(24) = \dfrac{24}{\sqrt{5}} \approx 10.7$ ft/s.

13. $A = \frac{1}{2}bh$, where b is the base and h is the altitude. We are given that $\dfrac{dh}{dt} = 1$ cm/min and $\dfrac{dA}{dt} = 2$ cm^2/min.

Using the Product Rule, we have $\dfrac{dA}{dt} = \dfrac{1}{2}\left(b\dfrac{dh}{dt} + h\dfrac{db}{dt}\right)$. When $h = 10$ and $A = 100$, we have

$100 = \frac{1}{2}b(10) \Rightarrow \frac{1}{2}b = 10 \Rightarrow b = 20$, so $2 = \dfrac{1}{2}\left(20\cdot 1 + 10\dfrac{db}{dt}\right) \Rightarrow 4 = 20 + 10\dfrac{db}{dt} \Rightarrow$

$\dfrac{db}{dt} = \dfrac{4-20}{10} = -1.6$ cm/min.

14.

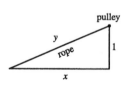

Given $\dfrac{dy}{dt} = -1$ m/s, find $\dfrac{dx}{dt}$ when $x = 8$ m. $y^2 = x^2 + 1 \Rightarrow$

$2y\dfrac{dy}{dt} = 2x\dfrac{dx}{dt} \Rightarrow \dfrac{dx}{dt} = \dfrac{y}{x}\dfrac{dy}{dt} = -\dfrac{y}{x}$. When $x = 8$, $y = \sqrt{65}$, so

$\dfrac{dx}{dt} = -\dfrac{\sqrt{65}}{8}$. Thus, the boat approaches the dock at $\dfrac{\sqrt{65}}{8} \approx 1.01$ m/s.

15.

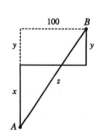

We are given that $\dfrac{dx}{dt} = 35$ km/h and $\dfrac{dy}{dt} = 25$ km/h. $z^2 = (x+y)^2 + 100^2$

$\Rightarrow 2z\dfrac{dz}{dt} = 2(x+y)\left(\dfrac{dx}{dt} + \dfrac{dy}{dt}\right)$. At 4:00 P.M., $x = 4(35) = 140$ and

$y = 4(25) = 100 \Rightarrow z = \sqrt{(140+100)^2 + 100^2} = \sqrt{67{,}600} = 260$, so

$\dfrac{dz}{dt} = \dfrac{x+y}{z}\left(\dfrac{dx}{dt} + \dfrac{dy}{dt}\right) = \dfrac{140+100}{260}(35+25) = \dfrac{720}{13} \approx 55.4$ km/h.

16. Let D denote the distance from the origin $(0,0)$ to the point on the curve $y = \sqrt{x}$.

$$D = \sqrt{(x-0)^2 + (y-0)^2} = \sqrt{x^2 + (\sqrt{x})^2} = \sqrt{x^2 + x} \quad\Rightarrow$$

$$\frac{dD}{dt} = \frac{1}{2}(x^2 + x)^{-1/2}(2x+1)\frac{dx}{dt} = \frac{2x+1}{2\sqrt{x^2+x}}\frac{dx}{dt}. \text{ With } \frac{dx}{dt} = 3 \text{ when } x = 4,$$

$$\frac{dD}{dt} = \frac{9}{2\sqrt{20}}(3) = \frac{27}{4\sqrt{5}} \approx 3.02 \text{ cm/s}.$$

17.

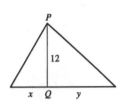

Using Q for the origin, we are given $\dfrac{dx}{dt} = -2$ ft/s and need to find $\dfrac{dy}{dt}$ when

$x = -5$. Using the Pythagorean Theorem twice, we have

$\sqrt{x^2 + 12^2} + \sqrt{y^2 + 12^2} = 39$, the total length of the rope. Differentiating

with respect to t, we get $\dfrac{x}{\sqrt{x^2+12^2}}\dfrac{dx}{dt} + \dfrac{y}{\sqrt{y^2+12^2}}\dfrac{dy}{dt} = 0$, so

$\dfrac{dy}{dt} = -\dfrac{x\sqrt{y^2+12^2}}{y\sqrt{x^2+12^2}}\dfrac{dx}{dt}$. Now when $x = -5$, $39 = \sqrt{(-5)^2 + 12^2} + \sqrt{y^2+12^2} = 13 + \sqrt{y^2+12^2} \quad\Leftrightarrow$

$\sqrt{y^2+12^2} = 26$, and $y = \sqrt{26^2 - 12^2} = \sqrt{532}$. So when $x = -5$,

$\dfrac{dy}{dt} = -\dfrac{(-5)(26)}{\sqrt{532}(13)}(-2) = -\dfrac{10}{\sqrt{133}} \approx -0.87$ ft/s. So cart B is moving towards Q at about 0.87 ft/s.

18.

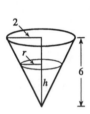

If $C = $ the rate at which water is pumped in, then $\dfrac{dV}{dt} = C - 10{,}000$, where

$V = \frac{1}{3}\pi r^2 h$ is the volume at time t. By similar triangles, $\dfrac{r}{2} = \dfrac{h}{6} \quad\Rightarrow$

$r = \frac{1}{3}h \quad\Rightarrow\quad V = \frac{1}{3}\pi\left(\frac{1}{3}h\right)^2 h = \frac{\pi}{27}h^3 \quad\Rightarrow\quad \dfrac{dV}{dt} = \frac{\pi}{9}h^2\dfrac{dh}{dt}$. When

$h = 200$, $\dfrac{dh}{dt} = 20$, so $C - 10{,}000 = \frac{\pi}{9}(200)^2(20) \quad\Rightarrow$

$C = 10{,}000 + \frac{800{,}000}{9}\pi \approx 289{,}253$ cm³/min.

19.

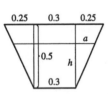

The figure is labeled in meters. The area A of a trapezoid is

$\frac{1}{2}(\text{base}_1 + \text{base}_2)(\text{height})$, and the volume V of the 10-meter-long trough is

$10A$. Thus, the volume of the trapezoid with height h is

$V = (10)\frac{1}{2}[0.3 + (0.3 + 2a)]\,h$. By similar triangles, $\dfrac{a}{h} = \dfrac{0.25}{0.5} = \dfrac{1}{2}$, so

$2a = h \quad\Rightarrow\quad V = 5(0.6 + h)h = 3h + 5h^2$. Now $\dfrac{dV}{dt} = \dfrac{dV}{dh}\dfrac{dh}{dt} \quad\Rightarrow\quad 0.2 = (3 + 10h)\dfrac{dh}{dt} \quad\Rightarrow$

$\dfrac{dh}{dt} = \dfrac{0.2}{3 + 10h}$. When $h = 0.3$, $\dfrac{dh}{dt} = \dfrac{0.2}{3 + 10(0.3)} = \dfrac{0.2}{6}$ m/min $= \dfrac{10}{3}$ cm/min.

20.

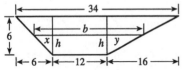

The figure is drawn without the top 3 feet.

$V = \frac{1}{2}(b + 12)h(20) = 10(b + 12)h$ and, from similar triangles,

$\dfrac{x}{h} = \dfrac{6}{6}$ and $\dfrac{y}{h} = \dfrac{16}{6} = \dfrac{8}{3}$, so $b = x + 12 + y = h + 12 + \dfrac{8h}{3} = 12 + \dfrac{11h}{3}$. Thus,

$V = 10\left(24 + \dfrac{11h}{3}\right)h = 240h + \dfrac{110h^2}{3}$ and so $0.8 = \dfrac{dV}{dt} = \left(240 + \dfrac{220}{3}h\right)\dfrac{dh}{dt}$. When $h = 5$,

$\dfrac{dh}{dt} = \dfrac{0.8}{240 + 5(220/3)} = \dfrac{3}{2275} \approx 0.00132$ ft/min.

21.

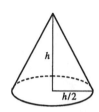

We are given that $\dfrac{dV}{dt} = 30$ ft^3/min. $V = \tfrac{1}{3}\pi r^2 h = \tfrac{1}{3}\pi\left(\dfrac{h}{2}\right)^2 h = \dfrac{\pi h^3}{12}$

$\Rightarrow \dfrac{dV}{dt} = \dfrac{dV}{dh}\dfrac{dh}{dt} \Rightarrow 30 = \dfrac{\pi h^2}{4}\dfrac{dh}{dt} \Rightarrow \dfrac{dh}{dt} = \dfrac{120}{\pi h^2}$. When

$h = 10$ ft, $\dfrac{dh}{dt} = \dfrac{120}{10^2\pi} = \dfrac{6}{5\pi} \approx 0.38$ ft/min.

22.

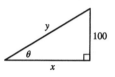

We are given $dx/dt = 8$ ft/s. $\cot\theta = \dfrac{x}{100} \Rightarrow x = 100\cot\theta \Rightarrow$

$\dfrac{dx}{dt} = -100\csc^2\theta\,\dfrac{d\theta}{dt} \Rightarrow \dfrac{d\theta}{dt} = -\dfrac{\sin^2\theta}{100}\cdot 8$. When $y = 200$,

$\sin\theta = \dfrac{100}{200} = \dfrac{1}{2} \Rightarrow \dfrac{d\theta}{dt} = -\dfrac{(1/2)^2}{100}\cdot 8 = -\dfrac{1}{50}$ rad/s. The angle is

decreasing at a rate of $\tfrac{1}{50}$ rad/s.

23.

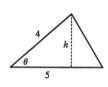

$A = \tfrac{1}{2}bh$, but $b = 5$ m and $\sin\theta = \dfrac{h}{4} \Rightarrow h = 4\sin\theta$, so

$A = \tfrac{1}{2}(5)(4\sin\theta) = 10\sin\theta$. We are given $\dfrac{d\theta}{dt} = 0.06$ rad/s, so

$\dfrac{dA}{dt} = \dfrac{dA}{d\theta}\dfrac{d\theta}{dt} = 10\cos\theta\,\dfrac{d\theta}{dt} = 0.6\cos\theta$. When $\theta = \tfrac{\pi}{3}$,

$\dfrac{dA}{dt} = 0.6\left(\cos\tfrac{\pi}{3}\right) = (0.6)\left(\tfrac{1}{2}\right) = 0.3$ m^2/s.

24.

We are given $d\theta/dt = 2°$/min $= \tfrac{\pi}{90}$ rad/min. By the Law of Cosines,

$x^2 = 12^2 + 15^2 - 2(12)(15)\cos\theta = 369 - 360\cos\theta \Rightarrow$

$2x\dfrac{dx}{dt} = 360\sin\theta\,\dfrac{d\theta}{dt} \Rightarrow \dfrac{dx}{dt} = \dfrac{180\sin\theta}{x}\dfrac{d\theta}{dt}$. When $\theta = 60°$,

$x = \sqrt{369 - 360\cos 60°} = \sqrt{189} = 3\sqrt{21}$, so

$\dfrac{dx}{dt} = \dfrac{180\sin 60°}{3\sqrt{21}}\cdot\dfrac{\pi}{90} = \dfrac{\pi\sqrt{3}}{3\sqrt{21}} = \dfrac{\sqrt{7}\,\pi}{21} \approx 0.396$ m/min.

25. Differentiating both sides of $PV = C$ with respect to t and using the Product Rule gives us $P\dfrac{dV}{dt} + V\dfrac{dP}{dt} = 0$

$\Rightarrow \dfrac{dV}{dt} = -\dfrac{V}{P}\dfrac{dP}{dt}$. When $V = 600$, $P = 150$ and $\dfrac{dP}{dt} = 20$, so we have $\dfrac{dV}{dt} = -\dfrac{600}{150}(20) = -80$. Thus, the

volume is decreasing at a rate of 80 cm^3/min.

26. $PV^{1.4} = C \Rightarrow P\cdot 1.4V^{0.4}\dfrac{dV}{dt} + V^{1.4}\dfrac{dP}{dt} = 0 \Rightarrow \dfrac{dV}{dt} = -\dfrac{V^{1.4}}{P\cdot 1.4V^{0.4}}\dfrac{dV}{dt} = -\dfrac{V}{1.4P}\dfrac{dP}{dt}$. When

$V = 400$, $P = 80$ and $\dfrac{dP}{dt} = -10$, so we have $\dfrac{dV}{dt} = -\dfrac{400}{1.4(80)}(-10) = \dfrac{250}{7}$. Thus, the volume is increasing at

a rate of $\tfrac{250}{7} \approx 36$ cm^3/min.

27. With $R_1 = 80$ and $R_2 = 100$, $\dfrac{1}{R} = \dfrac{1}{R_1} + \dfrac{1}{R_2} = \dfrac{1}{80} + \dfrac{1}{100} = \dfrac{180}{8000} = \dfrac{9}{400}$, so $R = \dfrac{400}{9}$. Differentiating

$\dfrac{1}{R} = \dfrac{1}{R_1} + \dfrac{1}{R_2}$ with respect to t, we have $-\dfrac{1}{R^2}\dfrac{dR}{dt} = -\dfrac{1}{R_1^2}\dfrac{dR_1}{dt} - \dfrac{1}{R_2^2}\dfrac{dR_2}{dt}$ $\Rightarrow$

$\dfrac{dR}{dt} = R^2\left(\dfrac{1}{R_1^2}\dfrac{dR_1}{dt} + \dfrac{1}{R_2^2}\dfrac{dR_2}{dt}\right)$. When $R_1 = 80$ and $R_2 = 100$,

$\dfrac{dR}{dt} = \dfrac{400^2}{9^2}\left[\dfrac{1}{80^2}(0.3) + \dfrac{1}{100^2}(0.2)\right] = \dfrac{107}{810} \approx 0.132\ \Omega/\text{s}.$

28. We want to find $\dfrac{dB}{dt}$ when $L = 18$ using $B = 0.007W^{2/3}$ and $W = 0.12L^{2.53}$.

$$\dfrac{dB}{dt} = \dfrac{dB}{dW}\dfrac{dW}{dL}\dfrac{dL}{dt} = \left(0.007 \cdot \tfrac{2}{3}W^{-1/3}\right)\left(0.12 \cdot 2.53 \cdot L^{1.53}\right)\left(\dfrac{20-15}{10{,}000{,}000}\right)$$

$$= \left[0.007 \cdot \tfrac{2}{3}\left(0.12 \cdot 18^{2.53}\right)^{-1/3}\right]\left(0.12 \cdot 2.53 \cdot 18^{1.53}\right)\left(\dfrac{5}{10^7}\right) \approx 1.045 \times 10^{-8}\ \text{g/yr}$$

29. (a)

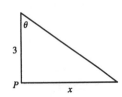

By the Pythagorean Theorem, $4000^2 + y^2 = \ell^2$. Differentiating with respect to t, we obtain $2y\dfrac{dy}{dt} = 2\ell\dfrac{d\ell}{dt}$. We know that $\dfrac{dy}{dt} = 600$, so when $y = 3000$,

$\ell = \sqrt{4000^2 + 3000^2} = \sqrt{25{,}000{,}000} = 5000$ and

$\dfrac{d\ell}{dt} = \dfrac{y}{\ell}\dfrac{dy}{dt} = \dfrac{3000}{5000}(600) = \dfrac{1800}{5} = 360\ \text{ft/s}.$

(b) Here $\tan\theta = \dfrac{y}{4000}$ $\Rightarrow$ $\dfrac{d}{dt}(\tan\theta) = \dfrac{d}{dt}\left(\dfrac{y}{4000}\right)$ $\Rightarrow$ $\sec^2\theta\dfrac{d\theta}{dt} = \dfrac{1}{4000}\dfrac{dy}{dt}$ $\Rightarrow$ $\dfrac{d\theta}{dt} = \dfrac{\cos^2\theta}{4000}\dfrac{dy}{dt}$.

When $y = 3000$, $\dfrac{dy}{dt} = 600$, $\ell = 5000$ and $\cos\theta = \dfrac{4000}{\ell} = \dfrac{4000}{5000} = \dfrac{4}{5}$, so

$\dfrac{d\theta}{dt} = \dfrac{(4/5)^2}{4000}(600) = 0.096\ \text{rad/s}.$

30.

We are given that $\dfrac{d\theta}{dt} = 4(2\pi) = 8\pi\ \text{rad/min}$. $x = 3\tan\theta$ $\Rightarrow$

$\dfrac{dx}{dt} = 3\sec^2\theta\dfrac{d\theta}{dt}$. When $x = 1$, $\tan\theta = \tfrac{1}{3}$, so $\sec^2\theta = 1 + \left(\tfrac{1}{3}\right)^2 = \tfrac{10}{9}$ and

$\dfrac{dx}{dt} = 3\left(\tfrac{10}{9}\right)(8\pi) = \tfrac{80\pi}{3} \approx 83.8\ \text{km/min}.$

31.

We are given that $\dfrac{dx}{dt} = 300\ \text{km/h}$. By the Law of Cosines,

$y^2 = x^2 + 1^2 - 2(1)(x)\cos 120° = x^2 + 1 - 2x\left(-\tfrac{1}{2}\right) = x^2 + x + 1$, so

$2y\dfrac{dy}{dt} = 2x\dfrac{dx}{dt} + \dfrac{dx}{dt}$ $\Rightarrow$ $\dfrac{dy}{dt} = \dfrac{2x+1}{2y}\dfrac{dx}{dt}$. After 1 minute,

$x = \tfrac{300}{60} = 5$ $\Rightarrow$ $y = \sqrt{5^2 + 5 + 1} = \sqrt{31}$ $\Rightarrow$

$\dfrac{dy}{dt} = \dfrac{2(5)+1}{2\sqrt{31}}(300) = \dfrac{1650}{\sqrt{31}} \approx 296\ \text{km/h}.$

32.

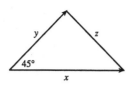

We are given that $\dfrac{dx}{dt} = 3$ mi/h and $\dfrac{dy}{dt} = 2$ mi/h. By the Law of Cosines,

$$z^2 = x^2 + y^2 - 2xy \cos 45° = x^2 + y^2 - \sqrt{2}\,xy \;\;\Rightarrow$$

$$2z\dfrac{dz}{dt} = 2x\dfrac{dx}{dt} + 2y\dfrac{dy}{dt} - \sqrt{2}\,x\dfrac{dy}{dt} - \sqrt{2}\,y\dfrac{dx}{dt}.$$ After 15 minutes $\left[= \tfrac{1}{4}\,\text{h}\right]$,

we have $x = \tfrac{3}{4}$ and $y = \tfrac{2}{4} = \tfrac{1}{2} \;\Rightarrow\; z^2 = \left(\tfrac{3}{4}\right)^2 + \left(\tfrac{2}{4}\right)^2 - \sqrt{2}\left(\tfrac{3}{4}\right)\left(\tfrac{2}{4}\right) \;\Rightarrow$

$$z = \dfrac{\sqrt{13 - 6\sqrt{2}}}{4}\ \text{and}$$

$$\dfrac{dz}{dt} = \dfrac{2}{\sqrt{13 - 6\sqrt{2}}}\left[2\left(\tfrac{3}{4}\right)3 + 2\left(\tfrac{1}{2}\right)2 - \sqrt{2}\left(\tfrac{3}{4}\right)2 - \sqrt{2}\left(\tfrac{1}{2}\right)3\right] = \dfrac{2}{\sqrt{13 - 6\sqrt{2}}}\ \dfrac{13 - 6\sqrt{2}}{2} = \sqrt{13 - 6\sqrt{2}}$$

$$\approx 2.125\ \text{mi/h}.$$

33.

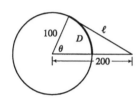

Let the distance between the runner and the friend be ℓ. Then by the Law of Cosines,

$$\ell^2 = 200^2 + 100^2 - 2 \cdot 200 \cdot 100 \cdot \cos\theta = 50{,}000 - 40{,}000\cos\theta\ (\star).$$

Differentiating implicitly with respect to t, we obtain

$$2\ell\dfrac{d\ell}{dt} = -40{,}000(-\sin\theta)\dfrac{d\theta}{dt}.$$ Now if D is the distance run when

the angle is θ radians, then by the formula for the length of an arc on a circle, $s = r\theta$, we have $D = 100\theta$, so

$$\theta = \dfrac{1}{100}D \;\Rightarrow\; \dfrac{d\theta}{dt} = \dfrac{1}{100}\dfrac{dD}{dt} = \dfrac{7}{100}.$$ To substitute into the expression for $\dfrac{d\ell}{dt}$, we must know $\sin\theta$ at the time

when $\ell = 200$, which we find from $(\star)$: $200^2 = 50{,}000 - 40{,}000\cos\theta \;\Leftrightarrow\; \cos\theta = \tfrac{1}{4} \;\Rightarrow$

$$\sin\theta = \sqrt{1 - \left(\tfrac{1}{4}\right)^2} = \dfrac{\sqrt{15}}{4}.$$ Substituting, we get $2(200)\dfrac{d\ell}{dt} = 40{,}000\dfrac{\sqrt{15}}{4}\left(\dfrac{7}{100}\right) \;\Rightarrow$

$$d\ell/dt = \dfrac{7\sqrt{15}}{4} \approx 6.78\ \text{m/s}.$$ Whether the distance between them is increasing or decreasing depends on the

direction in which the runner is running.

34.

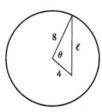

The hour hand of a clock goes around once every 12 hours or, in radians per

hour, $\dfrac{2\pi}{12} = \dfrac{\pi}{6}$ rad/h. The minute hand goes around once an hour, or at the rate

of 2π rad/h. So the angle θ between them (measuring clockwise from the

minute hand to the hour hand) is changing at the rate of

$$d\theta/dt = \tfrac{\pi}{6} - 2\pi = -\tfrac{11\pi}{6}\ \text{rad/h}.$$ Now, to relate θ to ℓ, we use the Law of

Cosines: $\ell^2 = 4^2 + 8^2 - 2 \cdot 4 \cdot 8 \cdot \cos\theta = 80 - 64\cos\theta\ (\star).$

Differentiating implicitly with respect to t, we get $2\ell\dfrac{d\ell}{dt} = -64(-\sin\theta)\dfrac{d\theta}{dt}.$ At 1:00, the angle between the two

hands is one-twelfth of the circle, that is, $\dfrac{2\pi}{12} = \dfrac{\pi}{6}$ radians. We use $(\star)$ to find ℓ at 1:00:

$$\ell = \sqrt{80 - 64\cos\tfrac{\pi}{6}} = \sqrt{80 - 32\sqrt{3}}.$$ Substituting, we get $2\ell\dfrac{d\ell}{dt} = 64\sin\tfrac{\pi}{6}\left(-\tfrac{11\pi}{6}\right) \;\Rightarrow$

$$\dfrac{d\ell}{dt} = \dfrac{64\left(\tfrac{1}{2}\right)\left(-\tfrac{11\pi}{6}\right)}{2\sqrt{80 - 32\sqrt{3}}} = -\dfrac{88\pi}{3\sqrt{80 - 32\sqrt{3}}} \approx -18.6.$$ So at 1:00, the distance between the tips of the hands is

decreasing at a rate of 18.6 mm/h ≈ 0.005 mm/s.

Maximum and Minimum Values • • • • • • • • •

1. A function f has an **absolute minimum** at $x = c$ if $f(c)$ is the smallest function value on the entire domain of f, whereas f has a **local minimum** at c if $f(c)$ is the smallest function value when x is near c.

2. (a) The Extreme Value Theorem

(b) See the Closed Interval Method.

3. Absolute maximum at b; absolute minimum at d; local maxima at b and e; local minima at d and s; neither a maximum nor a minimum at a, c, r, and t.

4. Absolute maximum at e; absolute minimum at t; local maxima at c, e, and s; local minima at b, c, d, and r; neither a maximum nor a minimum at a.

5. Absolute maximum value is $f(4) = 4$; absolute minimum value is $f(7) = 0$; local maximum values are $f(4) = 4$ and $f(6) = 3$; local minimum values are $f(2) = 1$ and $f(5) = 2$.

6. Absolute maximum value is $f(7) = 5$; absolute minimum value is $f(1) = 0$; local maximum values are $f(0) = 2$, $f(3) = 4$, and $f(5) = 3$; local minimum values are $f(1) = 0$, $f(4) = 2$, and $f(6) = 1$.

7. The highest point must occur at $x = 0$ and the lowest point must occur at $x = 3$.

8.

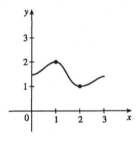

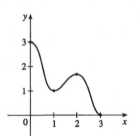

9. The figure has $f'(2) = 0$, so 2 is a critical number. There is an absolute maximum and an absolute minimum, but f has no *local* maximum or minimum.

10.

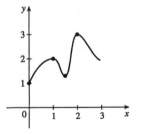

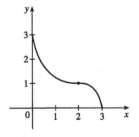

11. (a)

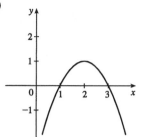

(b)

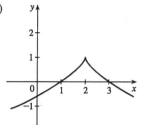

(c)

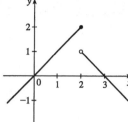

12. (a) Note that a local maximum cannot occur at an endpoint.

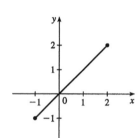

(b)

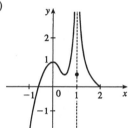

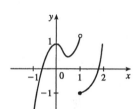

Note: By the Extreme Value Theorem, f must *not* be continuous.

13. (a) *Note:* By the Extreme Value Theorem, f must *not* be continuous; because if it were, it would attain an absolute minimum.

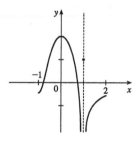

(b)

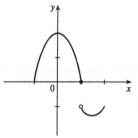

14. (a)

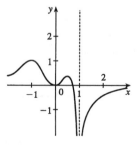

(b)

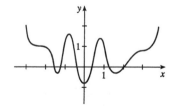

15. $f(x) = 8 - 3x$, $x \geq 1$. Absolute maximum $f(1) = 5$; no local maximum. No absolute or local minimum.

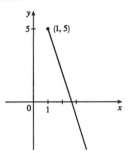

16. $f(x) = 3 - 2x$, $x \leq 5$. Absolute minimum $f(5) = -7$; no local minimum. No absolute or local maximum.

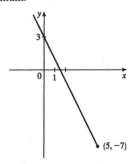

17. $f(x) = x^2$, $0 < x < 2$. No absolute or local maximum or minimum value.

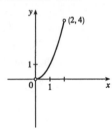

18. $f(x) = e^x$. No absolute or local maximum or minimum value.

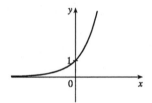

19. $f(\theta) = \sin\theta$, $-2\pi \leq \theta \leq 2\pi$. Absolute and local maxima $f\left(-\frac{3\pi}{2}\right) = f\left(\frac{\pi}{2}\right) = 1$. Absolute and local minima $f\left(-\frac{\pi}{2}\right) = f\left(\frac{3\pi}{2}\right) = -1$.

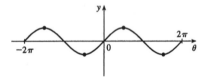

20. $f(\theta) = \tan\theta$, $-\frac{\pi}{4} \leq \theta < \frac{\pi}{2}$. Absolute minimum $f\left(-\frac{\pi}{4}\right) = -1$; no local minimum. No absolute or local maximum.

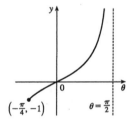

21. $f(x) = 1 - \sqrt{x}$. Absolute maximum $f(0) = 1$; no local maximum. No absolute or local minimum.

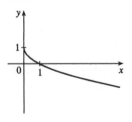

22. $f(x) = \begin{cases} x^2 & \text{if } -1 \leq x < 0 \\ 2 - x^2 & \text{if } 0 \leq x \leq 1 \end{cases}$

Absolute and local maximum $f(0) = 2$. No absolute or local minimum.

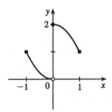

23. $f(x) = 5x^2 + 4x \Rightarrow f'(x) = 10x + 4$. $f'(x) = 0 \Rightarrow x = -\frac{2}{5}$, so $-\frac{2}{5}$ is the only critical number.

24. $f(x) = x^3 + x^2 - x \Rightarrow f'(x) = 3x^2 + 2x - 1$. $f'(x) = 0 \Rightarrow (x+1)(3x-1) = 0 \Rightarrow x = -1, \frac{1}{3}$.
These are the only critical numbers.

25. $s(t) = 3t^4 + 4t^3 - 6t^2 \Rightarrow s'(t) = 12t^3 + 12t^2 - 12t$. $s'(t) = 0 \Rightarrow 12t(t^2 + t - 1) \Rightarrow t = 0$ or
$t^2 + t - 1 = 0$. Using the quadratic formula to solve the latter equation gives us
$$t = \frac{-1 \pm \sqrt{1^2 - 4(1)(-1)}}{2(1)} = \frac{-1 \pm \sqrt{5}}{2} \approx 0.618, -1.618. \text{ The three critical numbers are } 0, \frac{-1 \pm \sqrt{5}}{2}.$$

26. $g(t) = |3t - 4| = \begin{cases} 3t - 4 & \text{if } 3t - 4 \geq 0 \\ -(3t - 4) & \text{if } 3t - 4 < 0 \end{cases} = \begin{cases} 3t - 4 & \text{if } t \geq \frac{4}{3} \\ 4 - 3t & \text{if } t < \frac{4}{3} \end{cases}$

$g'(t) = \begin{cases} 3 & \text{if } t > \frac{4}{3} \\ -3 & \text{if } t < \frac{4}{3} \end{cases}$ and $g'(t)$ does not exist at $t = \frac{4}{3}$, so $t = \frac{4}{3}$ is a critical number.

27. $f(r) = \dfrac{r}{r^2 + 1} \Rightarrow f'(r) = \dfrac{(r^2 + 1)1 - r(2r)}{(r^2 + 1)^2} = \dfrac{-r^2 + 1}{(r^2 + 1)^2} = 0 \Leftrightarrow r^2 = 1 \Leftrightarrow r = \pm 1$, so these are
the critical numbers. Note that $f'(r)$ always exists since $r^2 + 1 \neq 0$.

28. $f(z) = \dfrac{z + 1}{z^2 + z + 1} \Rightarrow f'(z) = \dfrac{(z^2 + z + 1)1 - (z + 1)(2z + 1)}{(z^2 + z + 1)^2} = \dfrac{-z^2 - 2z}{(z^2 + z + 1)^2} = 0 \Leftrightarrow$
$z(z + 2) = 0 \Rightarrow z = 0, -2$ are the critical numbers. (Note that $z^2 + z + 1 \neq 0$ since the discriminant < 0.)

29. $F(x) = x^{4/5}(x - 4)^2 \Rightarrow$
$F'(x) = x^{4/5} \cdot 2(x - 4) + (x - 4)^2 \cdot \frac{4}{5}x^{-1/5} = \frac{1}{5}x^{-1/5}(x - 4)[5 \cdot x \cdot 2 + (x - 4) \cdot 4]$
$= \dfrac{(x - 4)(14x - 16)}{5x^{1/5}} = \dfrac{2(x - 4)(7x - 8)}{5x^{1/5}} = 0 \text{ when } x = 4, \frac{8}{7}; \text{ and } F'(0) \text{ does not exist.}$
Critical numbers are $0, \frac{8}{7}, 4$.

30. $G(x) = \sqrt[3]{x^2 - x} \Rightarrow G'(x) = \frac{1}{3}(x^2 - x)^{-2/3}(2x - 1)$. $G'(x)$ does not exist when $x^2 - x = 0$ or $x = 0, 1$.
$G'(x) = 0 \Leftrightarrow 2x - 1 = 0 \Leftrightarrow x = \frac{1}{2}$. So the critical numbers are $x = 0, \frac{1}{2}, 1$.

31. $f(\theta) = \sin^2(2\theta) \Rightarrow f'(\theta) = 2\sin(2\theta)\cos(2\theta)(2) = 2(2\sin 2\theta \cos 2\theta) = 2[\sin(2 \cdot 2\theta)]$ [double-angle
formula for the sine] $= 2\sin 4\theta = 0 \Leftrightarrow \sin 4\theta = 0 \Leftrightarrow 4\theta = n\pi$, n an integer. So $\theta = n\pi/4$ are the critical
numbers.

32. $g(\theta) = \theta + \sin\theta \Rightarrow g'(\theta) = 1 + \cos\theta = 0 \Leftrightarrow \cos\theta = -1$. The critical numbers are
$\theta = \pi + 2n\pi = (2n + 1)\pi$, n an integer.

33. $f(x) = x \ln x \Rightarrow f'(x) = x(1/x) + (\ln x) \cdot 1 = \ln x + 1$. $f'(x) = 0 \Leftrightarrow \ln x = -1 \Leftrightarrow$
$x = e^{-1} = 1/e$. Therefore, the only critical number is $x = 1/e$.

34. $f(x) = xe^{2x} \Rightarrow f'(x) = x(2e^{2x}) + e^{2x} = e^{2x}(2x + 1)$. Since e^{2x} is never 0, we have $f'(x) = 0$ only when
$2x + 1 = 0 \Leftrightarrow x = -\frac{1}{2}$. So $-\frac{1}{2}$ is the only critical number.

35. $f(x) = 3x^2 - 12x + 5$, $[0, 3]$. $f'(x) = 6x - 12 = 0 \Leftrightarrow x = 2$. Applying the Closed Interval Method, we find
that $f(0) = 5$, $f(2) = -7$, and $f(3) = -4$. So $f(0) = 5$ is the absolute maximum and $f(2) = -7$ is the absolute
minimum.

36. $f(x) = x^3 - 3x + 1$, $[0, 3]$. $f'(x) = 3x^2 - 3 = 0 \Leftrightarrow x = \pm 1$, but -1 is not in $[0, 3]$. $f(0) = 1$, $f(1) = -1$,
and $f(3) = 19$. So $f(3) = 19$ is the absolute maximum and $f(1) = -1$ is the absolute minimum.

37. $f(x) = x^4 - 2x^2 + 3$, $[-2, 3]$. $f'(x) = 4x^3 - 4x = 4x(x^2 - 1) = 4x(x+1)(x-1) = 0$ ⟺ $x = -1, 0, 1$.
$f(-2) = 11$, $f(-1) = 2$, $f(0) = 3$, $f(1) = 2$, $f(3) = 66$. So $f(3) = 66$ is the absolute maximum and
$f(\pm 1) = 2$ is the absolute minimum.

38. $f(x) = \sqrt{9 - x^2}$, $[-1, 2]$. $f'(x) = -x/\sqrt{9 - x^2} = 0$ ⟺ $x = 0$. $f'(x)$ does not exist at $x = \pm 3$, but neither
value is in $[-1, 2]$. $f(-1) = 2\sqrt{2} \approx 2.8$, $f(0) = 3$, $f(2) = \sqrt{5} \approx 2.2$. So $f(0) = 3$ is the absolute maximum and
$f(2) = \sqrt{5}$ is the absolute minimum.

39. $f(x) = x^2 + \dfrac{2}{x}$, $[\frac{1}{2}, 2]$. $f'(x) = 2x - \dfrac{2}{x^2} = 2\dfrac{x^3 - 1}{x^2} = 0$ ⟺ $x^3 - 1 = 0$ ⟺ $(x-1)(x^2 + x + 1) = 0$,
but $x^2 + x + 1 \neq 0$, so $x = 1$. The denominator is 0 at $x = 0$, but not in the desired interval. $f(\frac{1}{2}) = \frac{17}{4} = 4.25$,
$f(1) = 3$, $f(2) = 5$. So $f(2) = 5$ is the absolute maximum and $f(1) = 3$ is the absolute minimum.

40. $f(x) = \dfrac{x}{x^2 + 4}$, $[0, 3]$. $f'(x) = \dfrac{(x^2 + 4)1 - x(2x)}{(x^2 + 4)^2} = \dfrac{4 - x^2}{(x^2 + 4)^2} = 0$ ⟺ $x = \pm 2$, but -2 is not in the
interval $[0, 3]$. $f(0) = 0$, $f(2) = \frac{1}{4} = 0.25$, $f(3) = \frac{3}{13} \approx 0.23$. So $f(2) = \frac{1}{4}$ is the absolute maximum and
$f(0) = 0$ is the absolute minimum.

41. $f(x) = \sin x + \cos x$, $[0, \frac{\pi}{3}]$. $f'(x) = \cos x - \sin x = 0$ ⟺ $\sin x = \cos x$ ⟹ $\dfrac{\sin x}{\cos x} = 1$ ⟹ $\tan x = 1$
⟹ $x = \frac{\pi}{4}$. $f(0) = 1$, $f(\frac{\pi}{4}) = \sqrt{2} \approx 1.41$, $f(\frac{\pi}{3}) = \frac{\sqrt{3}+1}{2} \approx 1.37$. So $f(\frac{\pi}{4}) = \sqrt{2}$ is the absolute maximum
and $f(0) = 1$ is the absolute minimum.

42. $f(x) = x - 2\cos x$, $[-\pi, \pi]$. $f'(x) = 1 + 2\sin x = 0$ ⟺ $\sin x = -\frac{1}{2}$ ⟺ $x = -\frac{5\pi}{6}, -\frac{\pi}{6}$.
$f(-\pi) = 2 - \pi \approx -1.14$, $f(-\frac{5\pi}{6}) = \sqrt{3} - \frac{5\pi}{6} \approx -0.886$, $f(-\frac{\pi}{6}) = -\frac{\pi}{6} - \sqrt{3} \approx -2.26$,
$f(\pi) = \pi + 2 \approx 5.14$. So $f(\pi) = \pi + 2$ is the absolute maximum and $f(-\frac{\pi}{6}) = -\frac{\pi}{6} - \sqrt{3}$ is the absolute
minimum.

43. $f(x) = xe^{-x}$, $[0, 2]$. $f'(x) = x(-e^{-x}) + e^{-x} = e^{-x}(1 - x) = 0$ ⟺ $x = 1$. $f(0) = 0$,
$f(1) = e^{-1} = 1/e \approx 0.37$, $f(2) = 2/e^2 \approx 0.27$. So $f(1) = 1/e$ is the absolute maximum and $f(0) = 0$ is the
absolute minimum.

44. $f(x) = \dfrac{\ln x}{x}$, $[1, 3]$. $f'(x) = \dfrac{x(1/x) - \ln x}{x^2} = \dfrac{1 - \ln x}{x^2} = 0$ ⟺ $1 - \ln x = 0$ ⟺ $\ln x = 1$ ⟺ $x = e$.
$f(1) = 0/1 = 0$, $f(e) = 1/e \approx 0.368$, $f(3) = (\ln 3)/3 \approx 0.366$. So $f(e) = 1/e$ is the absolute maximum and
$f(1) = 0$ is the absolute minimum.

45.

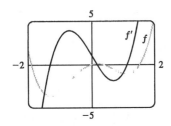

We see that $f'(x) = 0$ at about $x = -1.3$, 0.2,
and 1.1. Since f' exists everywhere, these are the
only critical numbers.

46.

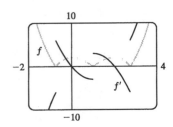

We see that $f'(x) = 0$ at about $x = 0.0$ and 2.0,
and that $f'(x)$ does not exist at about $x = -0.7$,
1.0, and 2.7, so the critical numbers of f are
about -0.7, 0.0, 1.0, 2.0, and 2.7.

47. (a)

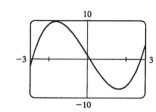

From the graph, it appears that the absolute maximum value is about $f(-1.63) = 9.71$, and the absolute minimum value is about $f(1.63) = -7.71$. These values make sense because the graph is symmetric about the point $(0, 1)$. ($y = x^3 - 8x$ is symmetric about the origin.)

(b) $f(x) = x^3 - 8x + 1 \Rightarrow f'(x) = 3x^2 - 8$. So $f'(x) = 0 \Rightarrow x = \pm\sqrt{\frac{8}{3}}$.

$$f\left(\pm\sqrt{\tfrac{8}{3}}\right) = \left(\pm\sqrt{\tfrac{8}{3}}\right)^3 - 8\left(\pm\sqrt{\tfrac{8}{3}}\right) + 1 = \pm\tfrac{8}{3}\sqrt{\tfrac{8}{3}} \mp 8\sqrt{\tfrac{8}{3}} + 1$$

$$= -\tfrac{16}{3}\sqrt{\tfrac{8}{3}} + 1 = 1 - \tfrac{32\sqrt{6}}{9} \text{ (minimum)} \quad \text{or} \quad \tfrac{16}{3}\sqrt{\tfrac{8}{3}} + 1 = 1 + \tfrac{32\sqrt{6}}{9} \text{ (maximum)}$$

(From the graph, we see that the extreme values do not occur at the endpoints.)

48. (a)

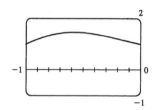

From the graph, it appears that the absolute maximum value is about $f(-0.58) = 1.47$, and the absolute minimum value is about $f(-1) = f(0) = 1.00$; that is, at both endpoints.

(b) $f(x) = e^{x^3 - x} \Rightarrow f'(x) = e^{x^3 - x}(3x^2 - 1)$. So $f'(x) = 0$ on $[-1, 0] \Rightarrow x = -\sqrt{1/3}$.

$f(-1) = f(0) = 1$ (minima) and $f\left(-\sqrt{1/3}\right) = e^{-\sqrt{3}/9 + \sqrt{3}/3} = e^{2\sqrt{3}/9}$ (maximum).

49. (a)

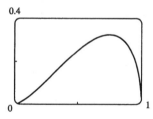

From the graph, it appears that the absolute maximum value is about $f(0.75) = 0.32$, and the absolute minimum value is $f(0) = f(1) = 0$; that is, at both endpoints.

(b) $f(x) = x\sqrt{x - x^2} \Rightarrow f'(x) = x \cdot \dfrac{1 - 2x}{2\sqrt{x - x^2}} + \sqrt{x - x^2} = \dfrac{(x - 2x^2) + (2x - 2x^2)}{2\sqrt{x - x^2}} = \dfrac{3x - 4x^2}{2\sqrt{x - x^2}}$.

So $f'(x) = 0 \Rightarrow 3x - 4x^2 = 0 \Rightarrow x(3 - 4x) = 0 \Rightarrow x = 0$ or $\tfrac{3}{4}$. $f(0) = f(1) = 0$ (minima), and

$f\left(\tfrac{3}{4}\right) = \tfrac{3}{4}\sqrt{\tfrac{3}{4} - \left(\tfrac{3}{4}\right)^2} = \tfrac{3\sqrt{3}}{16}$ (maximum).

50. (a)

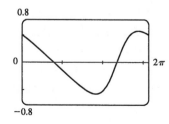

From the graph, it appears that the absolute maximum value is about $f(5.76) = 0.58$, and the absolute minimum value is about $f(3.67) = -0.58$.

(b) $f(x) = \dfrac{\cos x}{2 + \sin x}$ $\Rightarrow$ $f'(x) = \dfrac{(2 + \sin x)(-\sin x) - (\cos x)(\cos x)}{(2 + \sin x)^2} = \dfrac{-1 - 2\sin x}{(2 + \sin x)^2}$. So $f'(x) = 0$

$\Rightarrow$ $\sin x = -\frac{1}{2}$ $\Rightarrow$ $x = \frac{7\pi}{6}$ or $\frac{11\pi}{6}$. Now $f\left(\frac{7\pi}{6}\right) = \dfrac{-\sqrt{3}/2}{3/2} = -\dfrac{1}{\sqrt{3}}$ (minimum), and

$f\left(\frac{11\pi}{6}\right) = \dfrac{\sqrt{3}/2}{3/2} = \dfrac{1}{\sqrt{3}}$ (maximum).

51. The density is defined as $\rho = \dfrac{\text{mass}}{\text{volume}} = \dfrac{1000}{V(T)}$ (in g/cm^3). But a critical point of ρ will also be a critical point of

V [since $\dfrac{d\rho}{dT} = -1000V^{-2}\dfrac{dV}{dT}$ and V is never 0], and V is easier to differentiate than ρ.

$V(T) = 999.87 - 0.06426T + 0.0085043T^2 - 0.0000679T^3$ $\Rightarrow$

$V'(T) = -0.06426 + 0.0170086T - 0.0002037T^2$. Setting this equal to 0 and using the quadratic formula to find

T, we get $T = \dfrac{-0.0170086 \pm \sqrt{0.0170086^2 - 4 \cdot 0.0002037 \cdot 0.06426}}{2(-0.0002037)} \approx 3.9665\,°$ or $79.5318\,°$. Since we are

only interested in the region $0\,° \le T \le 30\,°$, we check the density ρ at the endpoints and at $3.9665\,°$:

$\rho(0) \approx \dfrac{1000}{999.87} \approx 1.00013$; $\rho(30) \approx \dfrac{1000}{1003.7641} \approx 0.99625$; $\rho(3.9665) \approx \dfrac{1000}{999.7447} \approx 1.000255$. So water has

its maximum density at about $3.9665\,°$C.

52. $F = \dfrac{\mu W}{\mu \sin\theta + \cos\theta}$ $\Rightarrow$ $\dfrac{dF}{d\theta} = \dfrac{(\mu\sin\theta + \cos\theta)(0) - \mu W(\mu\cos\theta - \sin\theta)}{(\mu\sin\theta + \cos\theta)^2} = \dfrac{-\mu W(\mu\cos\theta - \sin\theta)}{(\mu\sin\theta + \cos\theta)^2}$. So

$\dfrac{dF}{d\theta} = 0$ $\Rightarrow$ $\mu\cos\theta - \sin\theta = 0$ $\Rightarrow$ $\mu = \dfrac{\sin\theta}{\cos\theta} = \tan\theta$. Substituting $\tan\theta$ for μ in F gives us

$F = \dfrac{(\tan\theta)W}{(\tan\theta)\sin\theta + \cos\theta} = \dfrac{W\tan\theta}{\dfrac{\sin^2\theta}{\cos\theta} + \cos\theta} = \dfrac{W\tan\theta\cos\theta}{\sin^2\theta + \cos^2\theta} = \dfrac{W\sin\theta}{1} = W\sin\theta.$

If $\tan\theta = \mu$, then $\sin\theta = \dfrac{\mu}{\sqrt{\mu^2 + 1}}$ (see the figure), so $F = \dfrac{\mu}{\sqrt{\mu^2 + 1}}W$. We

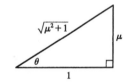

compare this with the value of F at the endpoints: $F(0) = \mu W$ and $F\left(\frac{\pi}{2}\right) = W$.

Now because $\dfrac{\mu}{\sqrt{\mu^2 + 1}} \le 1$ and $\dfrac{\mu}{\sqrt{\mu^2 + 1}} \le \mu$, we have that $\dfrac{\mu}{\sqrt{\mu^2 + 1}}W$

is less than or equal to each of $F(0)$ and $F\left(\frac{\pi}{2}\right)$. Hence, $\dfrac{\mu}{\sqrt{\mu^2 + 1}}W$ is the absolute minimum value of $F(\theta)$, and it

occurs when $\tan\theta = \mu$.

53. We apply the Closed Interval Method to the continuous function

$I(t) = 0.00009045t^5 + 0.001438t^4 - 0.06561t^3 + 0.4598t^2 - 0.6270t + 99.33$ on $[0, 10]$. Its derivative is

$I'(t) = 0.00045225t^4 + 0.005752t^3 - 0.19683t^2 + 0.9196t - 0.6270$. Since I' exists for all t, the only critical

numbers of I occur when $I'(t) = 0$. We use a root-finder on a computer algebra system (or a graphing device) to

find that $I'(t) = 0$ when $t \approx -29.7186$, 0.8231, 5.1309, or 11.0459, but only the second and third roots lie in the

interval $[0, 10]$. The values of I at these critical numbers are $I(0.8231) \approx 99.09$ and $I(5.1309) \approx 100.67$. The

values of I at the endpoints of the interval are $I(0) = 99.33$ and $I(10) \approx 96.86$. Comparing these four numbers,

we see that food was most expensive at $t \approx 5.1309$ (corresponding roughly to August, 1989) and cheapest at

$t = 10$ (midyear 1994).

54. (a)

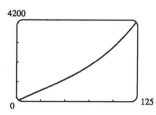

The equation of the graph in the figure is

$v(t) = 0.00146t^3 - 0.11553t^2 + 24.9816 9t - 21.26872.$

(b) $a(t) = v'(t) =$

$0.00438t^2 - 0.23106t + 24.98169 \Rightarrow$

$a'(t) = 0.00876t - 0.23106. \ a'(t) = 0 \Rightarrow$

$t_1 = \frac{0.23106}{0.00876} \approx 26.4. \ a(0) \approx 24.98,$

$a(t_1) \approx 21.93, \text{ and } a(125) \approx 64.54.$ The

maximum acceleration is about 64.5 ft/s² and

the minimum acceleration is about

21.93 ft/s².

55. (a) $v(r) = k(r_0 - r)r^2 = kr_0 r^2 - kr^3 \Rightarrow$

$v'(r) = 2kr_0 r - 3kr^2. \ v'(r) = 0 \Rightarrow$

$kr(2r_0 - 3r) = 0 \Rightarrow r = 0 \text{ or } \frac{2}{3}r_0 \text{ (but 0 is not in}$

the interval). Evaluating v at $\frac{1}{2}r_0$, $\frac{2}{3}r_0$, and r_0, we get

$v\left(\frac{1}{2}r_0\right) = \frac{1}{8}kr_0^3, \ v\left(\frac{2}{3}r_0\right) = \frac{4}{27}kr_0^3, \text{ and } v(r_0) = 0.$

Since $\frac{4}{27} > \frac{1}{8}$, v attains its maximum value at

$r = \frac{2}{3}r_0$. This supports the statement in the text.

(b) From part (a), the maximum value of v is

$\frac{4}{27}kr_0^3.$

(c)

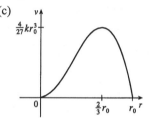

56. (a) $f(x) = ax^3 + bx^2 + cx + d, \ a \neq 0.$ So $f'(x) = 3ax^2 + 2bx + c$ is a quadratic and hence has either 2, 1, or 0 real roots, so $f(x)$ has either 2, 1 or 0 critical numbers.

Case (i) (2 critical numbers): $\quad f(x) = x^3 - 3x \Rightarrow f'(x) = 3x^2 - 3,$

so $x = -1, 1$ are critical numbers.

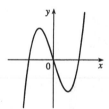

Case (ii) (1 critical number): $\quad f(x) = x^3 \Rightarrow f'(x) = 3x^2,$

so $x = 0$ is the only critical number.

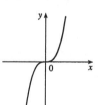

Case (iii) (no critical number): $\quad f(x) = x^3 + 3x \Rightarrow f'(x) = 3x^2 + 3,$

so there are no real roots.

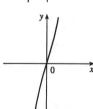

(b) Since there are at most two critical numbers, it can have at most two local extreme values and by (i) this can occur. By (iii) it can have no local extreme value. However, if there is only one critical number, then there is no local extreme value.

Applied Project	**The Calculus of Rainbows**

1. From Snell's Law, we have $\sin \alpha = k \sin \beta \approx \frac{4}{3} \sin \beta \iff \beta \approx \arcsin\left(\frac{3}{4} \sin \alpha\right)$. We substitute this into $D(\alpha) = \pi + 2\alpha - 4\beta = \pi + 2\alpha - 4\arcsin\left(\frac{3}{4} \sin \alpha\right)$, and then differentiate to find the minimum:

$$D'(\alpha) = 2 - 4\left[1 - \left(\frac{3}{4} \sin \alpha\right)^2\right]^{-1/2}\left(\frac{3}{4} \cos \alpha\right) = 2 - \frac{3 \cos \alpha}{\sqrt{1 - \frac{9}{16} \sin^2 \alpha}}. \text{ This is 0 when } \frac{3 \cos \alpha}{\sqrt{1 - \frac{9}{16} \sin^2 \alpha}} = 2$$

$\iff \frac{9}{4} \cos^2 \alpha = 1 - \frac{9}{16} \sin^2 \alpha \iff \frac{9}{4} \cos^2 \alpha = 1 - \frac{9}{16}(1 - \cos^2 \alpha) \iff \frac{27}{16} \cos^2 \alpha = \frac{7}{16} \iff$

$\cos \alpha = \sqrt{\frac{7}{27}} \iff \alpha = \arccos\sqrt{\frac{7}{27}} \approx 59.4°$, and so the local minimum is $D(59.4°) \approx 2.4$ radians $\approx 138°$. To see that this is an absolute minimum, we check the endpoints, which in this case are $\alpha = 0$ and $\alpha = \frac{\pi}{2}$:

$D(0) = \pi$ radians $= 180°$, and $D\left(\frac{\pi}{2}\right) \approx 166°$.

Another method: We first calculate $\frac{d\beta}{d\alpha}$: $\sin \alpha = \frac{4}{3} \sin \beta \iff \cos \alpha = \frac{4}{3} \cos \beta \frac{d\beta}{d\alpha} \iff \frac{d\beta}{d\alpha} = \frac{3 \cos \alpha}{4 \cos \beta}$, so

since $D'(\alpha) = 2 - 4\frac{d\beta}{d\alpha} = 0 \iff \frac{d\beta}{d\alpha} = \frac{1}{2}$, the minimum occurs when $3 \cos \alpha = 2 \cos \beta$. Now we square both sides and substitute $\sin \alpha = \frac{4}{3} \sin \beta$, leading to the same result.

2. If we repeat Problem 1 with k in place of $\frac{4}{3}$, we get $D(\alpha) = \pi + 2\alpha - 4\arcsin\left(\frac{1}{k} \sin \alpha\right) \Rightarrow$

$$D'(\alpha) = 2 - \frac{4 \cos \alpha}{k\sqrt{1 - [(\sin \alpha)/k]^2}}, \text{ which is 0 when } \frac{2 \cos \alpha}{k} = \sqrt{1 - \left(\frac{\sin \alpha}{k}\right)^2} \iff$$

$\left(\frac{2 \cos \alpha}{k}\right)^2 = 1 - \left(\frac{\sin \alpha}{k}\right)^2 \iff 4 \cos^2 \alpha = k^2 - \sin^2 \alpha \iff 3 \cos^2 \alpha = k^2 - 1 \iff$

$\alpha = \arccos\sqrt{\frac{k^2 - 1}{3}}$. So for $k \approx 1.3318$ (red light) the minimum occurs at $\alpha_1 \approx 1.038$ radians, and so the rainbow angle is about $\pi - D(\alpha_1) \approx 42.3°$. For $k \approx 1.3435$ (violet light) the minimum occurs at $\alpha_2 \approx 1.026$ radians, and so the rainbow angle is about $\pi - D(\alpha_2) \approx 40.6°$.

Another method: As in Problem 1, we can instead find $D'(\alpha)$ in terms of $\frac{d\beta}{d\alpha}$, and then substitute $\frac{d\beta}{d\alpha} = \frac{\cos \alpha}{k \cos \beta}$.

3. At each reflection or refraction, the light is bent in a counterclockwise direction: the bend at A is $\alpha - \beta$, the bend at B is $\pi - 2\beta$, the bend at C is again $\pi - 2\beta$, and the bend at D is $\alpha - \beta$. So the total bend is

$$D(\alpha) = 2(\alpha - \beta) + 2(\pi - 2\beta) = 2\alpha - 6\beta + 2\pi, \text{ as required. We substitute } \beta = \arcsin\left(\frac{\sin \alpha}{k}\right) \text{ and}$$

differentiate, to get $D'(\alpha) = 2 - \frac{6 \cos \alpha}{k\sqrt{1 - [(\sin \alpha)/k]^2}}$, which is 0 when $\frac{3 \cos \alpha}{k} = \sqrt{1 - \left(\frac{\sin \alpha}{k}\right)^2} \iff$

$9 \cos^2 \alpha = k^2 - \sin^2 \alpha \iff 8 \cos^2 \alpha = k^2 - 1 \iff \cos \alpha = \sqrt{\frac{1}{8}(k^2 - 1)}$. If $k = \frac{4}{3}$, then the minimum occurs at $\alpha_1 = \arccos \sqrt{\dfrac{(4/3)^2 - 1}{8}} \approx 1.254$ radians. Thus, the

minimum *counterclockwise* rotation is $D(\alpha_1) \approx 231°$, which is equivalent to a *clockwise* rotation of $360° - 231° = 129°$ (see the figure). So the rainbow angle for the secondary rainbow is about $180° - 129° = 51°$, as required. In general, the rainbow angle for the secondary rainbow is

$$\pi - [2\pi - D(\alpha)] = D(\alpha) - \pi.$$

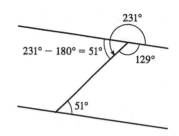

4. In the primary rainbow, the rainbow angle gets smaller as k gets larger, as we found in Problem 2, so the colors appear from top to bottom in order of increasing k. But in the secondary rainbow, the rainbow angle gets larger as k gets larger. To see this, we find the minimum deviations for red light and for violet light in the secondary rainbow.

For $k \approx 1.3318$ (red light) the minimum occurs at $\alpha_1 \approx \arccos \sqrt{\dfrac{1.3318^2 - 1}{8}} \approx 1.255$ radians, and so the rainbow angle is $D(\alpha_1) - \pi \approx 50.6°$. For $k \approx 1.3435$ (violet light) the minimum occurs at

$\alpha_2 \approx \arccos \sqrt{\dfrac{1.3435^2 - 1}{8}} \approx 1.248$ radians, and so the rainbow angle is $D(\alpha_2) - \pi \approx 53.6°$. Consequently, the rainbow angle is larger for colors with higher indices of refraction, and the colors appear from bottom to top in order of increasing k, the reverse of their order in the primary rainbow.

Note that our calculations above also explain why the secondary rainbow is more spread out than the primary rainbow: in the primary rainbow, the difference between rainbow angles for red and violet light is about $1.7°$, whereas in the secondary rainbow it is about $3°$.

◆ 4.3 Derivatives and the Shapes of Curves • • • • • • •

1. $\dfrac{f(8) - f(0)}{8 - 0} = \dfrac{6 - 4}{8} = \dfrac{1}{4}$. The values of c which satisfy $f'(c) = \frac{1}{4}$ seem to be about $c = 0.8, 3.2, 4.4,$ and 6.1.

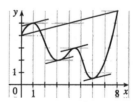

2. (a) g is concave upward on $(-1, 2)$ and $(7, 8)$.

(b) g is concave downward on $(2, 4)$ and $(4, 7)$.

(c) The only point of inflection is $(2, 2)$. Note that 7 is not in the domain of this function.

3. (a) Use the Increasing/Decreasing (I/D) Test.

(b) Use the Concavity Test.

(c) At any value of x where the concavity changes, we have an inflection point at $(x, f(x))$.

4. (a) See the First Derivative Test.

(b) See the Second Derivative Test and the note that precedes Example 5.

5. There is an inflection point at $x = 1$ because $f''(x)$ changes from negative to positive there, and so the graph of f changes from concave downward to concave upward. There is an inflection point at $x = 7$ because $f''(x)$ changes from positive to negative there, and so the graph of f changes from concave upward to concave downward.

6. (a) f is increasing on the intervals where $f'(x) > 0$, namely, $(2, 4)$ and $(6, 9)$.

(b) f has a local maximum where it changes from increasing to decreasing, that is, where f' changes from positive to negative (at $x = 4$). Similarly, where f' changes from negative to positive, f has a local minimum (at $x = 2$ and at $x = 6$).

(c) When f' is increasing, its derivative f'' is positive and hence, f is concave upward. This happens on $(1, 3)$, $(5, 7)$, and $(8, 9)$. Similarly, f is concave downward when f' is decreasing — that is, on $(0, 1)$, $(3, 5)$, and $(7, 8)$.

(d) f has inflection points at $x = 1, 3, 5, 7,$ and 8, since the direction of concavity changes at each of these values.

7. (a) $f(x) = x^3 - 12x + 1$ $\Rightarrow$ $f'(x) = 3x^2 - 12 = 3(x + 2)(x - 2)$. So $f'(x) > 0$ $\Leftrightarrow$ $x > 2$ or $x < -2$ and $f'(x) < 0$ $\Leftrightarrow$ $-2 < x < 2$. So f is increasing on $(-\infty, -2)$ and $(2, \infty)$ and decreasing on $(-2, 2)$.

(b) f changes from increasing to decreasing at $x = -2$ and from decreasing to increasing at $x = 2$. Thus, $f(-2) = 17$ is a local maximum and $f(2) = -15$ is a local minimum.

(c) $f''(x) = 6x$. $f''(x) > 0$ $\Leftrightarrow$ $x > 0$ and $f''(x) < 0$ $\Leftrightarrow$ $x < 0$. Thus, f is concave upward on $(0, \infty)$ and concave downward on $(-\infty, 0)$. There is an inflection point where the concavity changes, at $(0, f(0)) = (0, 1)$.

8. (a) $f(x) = 1 + 8x - x^8$ $\Rightarrow$ $f'(x) = 8 - 8x^7 = 8\left(1 - x^7\right)$. Thus, $f'(x) > 0$ $\Leftrightarrow$ $1 - x^7 > 0$ $\Leftrightarrow$ $x^7 < 1$ $\Leftrightarrow$ $x < 1$ and $f'(x) < 0$ $\Leftrightarrow$ $x > 1$. So f is increasing on $(-\infty, 1)$ and decreasing on $(1, \infty)$.

(b) f changes from increasing to decreasing at $x = 1$. Thus, $f(1) = 8$ is a local maximum.

(c) $f''(x) = -56x^6$. $f''(x) < 0$ for $x \neq 0$, so f is concave downward on $(-\infty, 0)$ and on $(0, \infty)$ by the Concavity Test. In fact, f is CD on $\mathbb{R}$ because f' is decreasing on $\mathbb{R}$. There are no inflection points.

9. (a) $f(x) = x - 2 \sin x$ on $(0, 3\pi)$ $\Rightarrow$ $f'(x) = 1 - 2 \cos x$. $f'(x) > 0$ $\Leftrightarrow$ $1 - 2 \cos x > 0$ $\Leftrightarrow$ $\cos x < \frac{1}{2}$ $\Leftrightarrow$ $\frac{\pi}{3} < x < \frac{5\pi}{3}$ or $\frac{7\pi}{3} < x < 3\pi$. $f'(x) < 0$ $\Leftrightarrow$ $\cos x > \frac{1}{2}$ $\Leftrightarrow$ $0 < x < \frac{\pi}{3}$ or $\frac{5\pi}{3} < x < \frac{7\pi}{3}$. So f is increasing on $\left(\frac{\pi}{3}, \frac{5\pi}{3}\right)$ and $\left(\frac{7\pi}{3}, 3\pi\right)$, and f is decreasing on $\left(0, \frac{\pi}{3}\right)$ and $\left(\frac{5\pi}{3}, \frac{7\pi}{3}\right)$.

(b) f changes from increasing to decreasing at $x = \frac{5\pi}{3}$, and from decreasing to increasing at $x = \frac{\pi}{3}$ and at $x = \frac{7\pi}{3}$. Thus, $f\left(\frac{5\pi}{3}\right) = \frac{5\pi}{3} + \sqrt{3} \approx 6.97$ is a local maximum and $f\left(\frac{\pi}{3}\right) = \frac{\pi}{3} - \sqrt{3} \approx -0.68$ and $f\left(\frac{7\pi}{3}\right) = \frac{7\pi}{3} - \sqrt{3} \approx 5.60$ are local minima.

(c) $f''(x) = 2 \sin x > 0$ $\Leftrightarrow$ $0 < x < \pi$ and $2\pi < x < 3\pi$, $f''(x) < 0$ $\Leftrightarrow$ $\pi < x < 2\pi$. Thus, f is concave upward on $(0, \pi)$ and $(2\pi, 3\pi)$, and f is concave downward on $(\pi, 2\pi)$. There are inflection points at (π, π) and $(2\pi, 2\pi)$.

10. (a) $f(x) = x/(1 + x)^2$ $\Rightarrow$
$$f'(x) = \frac{(1 + x)^2 (1) - (x)2(1 + x)}{[(1 + x)^2]^2} = \frac{(1 + x)[(1 + x) - 2x]}{(1 + x)^4} = \frac{(1 + x)(1 - x)}{(1 + x)^4} = \frac{1 - x}{(1 + x)^3}. \text{ So}$$
$f'(x) > 0$ $\Leftrightarrow$ $-1 < x < 1$ and $f'(x) < 0$ $\Leftrightarrow$ $x < -1$ or $x > 1$. So f is increasing on $(-1, 1)$ and f is decreasing on $(-\infty, -1)$ and $(1, \infty)$.

(b) f changes from increasing to decreasing at $x = 1$. $x = -1$ is not in the domain of f. Thus, $f(1) = \frac{1}{4}$ is a local maximum.

(c) $f''(x) = \dfrac{(1+x)^3(-1) - (1-x)3(1+x)^2}{[(1+x)^3]^2} = \dfrac{(1+x)^2\,[-1(1+x) - 3(1-x)]}{(1+x)^6} = \dfrac{2x-4}{(1+x)^4}.$

$f''(x) > 0 \;\Leftrightarrow\; x > 2$ and $f''(x) < 0 \;\Leftrightarrow\; x < 2$ $(x \neq -1)$. Thus, f is concave upward on $(2, \infty)$ and f is concave downward on $(-\infty, -1)$ and $(-1, 2)$. There is an inflection point at $\left(2, \frac{2}{9}\right)$.

11. (a) $y = f(x) = xe^x \;\Rightarrow\; f'(x) = xe^x + e^x = e^x(x+1)$. So $f'(x) > 0 \;\Leftrightarrow\; x+1 > 0 \;\Leftrightarrow\; x > -1$. Thus, f is increasing on $(-1, \infty)$ and decreasing on $(-\infty, -1)$.

(b) f changes from decreasing to increasing at its only critical number, $x = -1$. Thus, $f(-1) = -e^{-1}$ is a local minimum.

(c) $f'(x) = e^x(x+1) \;\Rightarrow\; f''(x) = e^x(1) + (x+1)e^x = e^x(x+2)$. So $f''(x) > 0 \;\Leftrightarrow\; x+2 > 0 \;\Leftrightarrow\; x > -2$. Thus, f is concave upward on $(-2, \infty)$ and concave downward on $(-\infty, -2)$. Since the concavity changes direction at $x = -2$, the point $\left(-2, -2e^{-2}\right)$ is an inflection point.

12. (a) $y = f(x) = x^2e^x \;\Rightarrow\; f'(x) = x^2e^x + 2xe^x = x(x+2)e^x$. So $f'(x) > 0 \;\Leftrightarrow\; x(x+2) > 0 \;\Leftrightarrow\;$ either $x < -2$ or $x > 0$. Therefore f is increasing on $(-\infty, -2)$ and $(0, \infty)$, and decreasing on $(-2, 0)$.

(b) f changes from increasing to decreasing at $x = -2$, so $f(-2) = 4e^{-2}$ is a local maximum. f changes from decreasing to increasing at $x = 0$, so $f(0) = 0$ is a local minimum.

(c) $f'(x) = \left(x^2 + 2x\right)e^x \;\Rightarrow\; f''(x) = \left(x^2 + 2x\right)e^x + e^x(2x + 2) = e^x\left(x^2 + 4x + 2\right)$. $f''(x) = 0 \;\Leftrightarrow\; x^2 + 4x + 2 = 0 \;\Leftrightarrow\; x = -2 \pm \sqrt{2}$. $f''(x) < 0 \;\Leftrightarrow\; -2 - \sqrt{2} < x < -2 + \sqrt{2}$, so f is concave downward on $\left(-2 - \sqrt{2}, -2 + \sqrt{2}\right)$ and concave upward on $\left(-\infty, -2 - \sqrt{2}\right)$ and $\left(-2 + \sqrt{2}, \infty\right)$. There are inflection points at $\left(-2 - \sqrt{2}, f\left(-2 - \sqrt{2}\right)\right) \approx (-3.41, 0.38)$ and $\left(-2 + \sqrt{2}, f\left(-2 + \sqrt{2}\right)\right) \approx (-0.59, 0.19)$.

13. (a) $y = f(x) = \dfrac{\ln x}{\sqrt{x}}$. (Note that f is only defined for $x > 0$.)

$f'(x) = \dfrac{\sqrt{x}\,(1/x) - \ln x\left(\frac{1}{2}x^{-1/2}\right)}{x} = \dfrac{\dfrac{1}{\sqrt{x}} - \dfrac{\ln x}{2\sqrt{x}}}{x} \cdot \dfrac{2\sqrt{x}}{2\sqrt{x}} = \dfrac{2 - \ln x}{2x^{3/2}} > 0 \;\Leftrightarrow\;$

$2 - \ln x > 0 \;\Leftrightarrow\; \ln x < 2 \;\Leftrightarrow\; x < e^2$. Therefore f is increasing on $\left(0, e^2\right)$ and decreasing on $\left(e^2, \infty\right)$.

(b) f changes from increasing to decreasing at $x = e^2$, so $f\left(e^2\right) = \dfrac{\ln e^2}{\sqrt{e^2}} = \dfrac{2}{e}$ is a local maximum.

(c) $f''(x) = \dfrac{2x^{3/2}(-1/x) - (2 - \ln x)\left(3x^{1/2}\right)}{\left(2x^{3/2}\right)^2} = \dfrac{-2x^{1/2} + 3x^{1/2}(\ln x - 2)}{4x^3}$

$= \dfrac{x^{1/2}(-2 + 3\ln x - 6)}{4x^3} = \dfrac{3\ln x - 8}{4x^{5/2}}.$

$f''(x) = 0 \;\Leftrightarrow\; \ln x = \frac{8}{3} \;\Leftrightarrow\; x = e^{8/3}$. $f''(x) > 0 \;\Leftrightarrow\; x > e^{8/3}$, so f is concave upward on $\left(e^{8/3}, \infty\right)$ and concave downward on $\left(0, e^{8/3}\right)$. There is an inflection point at $\left(e^{8/3}, \frac{8}{3}e^{-4/3}\right) \approx (14.39, 0.70).$

14. (a) $y = f(x) = x \ln x \implies f'(x) = x(1/x) + \ln x = 1 + \ln x.$ $f'(x) > 0 \iff \ln x + 1 > 0 \iff$
$\ln x > -1 \iff x > e^{-1}.$ Therefore f is increasing on $(1/e, \infty)$ and decreasing on $(0, 1/e)$.

(b) f changes from decreasing to increasing at $x = 1/e$, so $f(1/e) = -1/e$ is a local minimum.

(c) $f''(x) = 1/x > 0$ for $x > 0$. So f is concave upward on its entire domain, and has no inflection point.

15. $f(x) = x + \sqrt{1-x} \implies f'(x) = 1 + \frac{1}{2}(1-x)^{-1/2}(-1) = 1 - \dfrac{1}{2\sqrt{1-x}}.$ Note that f is defined for

$1 - x \geq 0$; that is, for $x \leq 1.$ $f'(x) = 0 \implies 2\sqrt{1-x} = 1 \implies \sqrt{1-x} = \frac{1}{2} \implies 1 - x = \frac{1}{4} \implies$
$x = \frac{3}{4}.$ f' does not exist at $x = 1$, but we can't have a local maximum or minimum at an endpoint.

First Derivative Test: $f'(x) > 0 \implies x < \frac{3}{4}$ and $f'(x) < 0 \implies \frac{3}{4} < x < 1.$ Since f' changes from
positive to negative at $x = \frac{3}{4}$, $f\left(\frac{3}{4}\right) = \frac{5}{4}$ is a local maximum.

Second Derivative Test: $f''(x) = -\frac{1}{2}\left(-\frac{1}{2}\right)(1-x)^{-3/2}(-1) = -\dfrac{1}{4\left(\sqrt{1-x}\right)^3}.$ $f''\left(\frac{3}{4}\right) = -2 < 0 \implies$

$f\left(\frac{3}{4}\right) = \frac{5}{4}$ is a local maximum.

Preference: The First Derivative Test may be slightly easier to apply in this case.

16. (a) $f(x) = x^4(x-1)^3 \implies$
$f'(x) = x^4 \cdot 3(x-1)^2 + (x-1)^3 \cdot 4x^3 = x^3(x-1)^2 [3x + 4(x-1)] = x^3(x-1)^2(7x-4)$
The critical numbers are 0, 1, and $\frac{4}{7}$.

(b) $f''(x) = 3x^2(x-1)^2(7x-4) + x^3 \cdot 2(x-1)(7x-4) + x^3(x-1)^2 \cdot 7$
$= x^2(x-1)\left[3(x-1)(7x-4) + 2x(7x-4) + 7x(x-1)\right]$
Now $f''(0) = f''(1) = 0$, so the Second Derivative Test gives no information for $x = 0$ or $x = 1.$
$f''\left(\frac{4}{7}\right) = \left(\frac{4}{7}\right)^2\left(\frac{4}{7} - 1\right)\left[0 + 0 + 7\left(\frac{4}{7}\right)\left(\frac{4}{7} - 1\right)\right] = \left(\frac{4}{7}\right)^2\left(-\frac{3}{7}\right)(4)\left(-\frac{3}{7}\right) > 0,$ so there is a local minimum
at $x = \frac{4}{7}$.

(c) f' is positive on $(-\infty, 0)$, negative on $\left(0, \frac{4}{7}\right)$, positive on $\left(\frac{4}{7}, 1\right)$, and positive on $(1, \infty)$. So f has a local
maximum at $x = 0$, a local minimum at $x = \frac{4}{7}$, and no local maximum or minimum at $x = 1$.

17. (a) $f(x) = 2x^3 - 3x^2 - 12x \implies f'(x) = 6x^2 - 6x - 12 = 6(x^2 - x - 2) = 6(x-2)(x+1).$ $f'(x) > 0$
$\iff x < -1$ or $x > 2$ and $f'(x) < 0 \iff -1 < x < 2.$ So f is increasing on $(-\infty, -1)$ and $(2, \infty)$, and f
is decreasing on $(-1, 2)$.

(b) Since f changes from increasing to decreasing at $x = -1$, $f(-1) = 7$ is a local maximum value. Since f
changes from decreasing to increasing at $x = 2$, $f(2) = -20$ is a local minimum value.

(c) $f''(x) = 6(2x-1) \implies f''(x) > 0$ on $\left(\frac{1}{2}, \infty\right)$ and $f''(x) < 0$ on   (d)
$\left(-\infty, \frac{1}{2}\right)$. So f is concave upward on $\left(\frac{1}{2}, \infty\right)$ and concave
downward on $\left(-\infty, \frac{1}{2}\right)$. There is a change in concavity at $x = \frac{1}{2}$,
and we have an inflection point at $\left(\frac{1}{2}, -\frac{13}{2}\right)$.

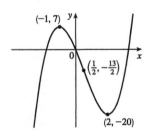

18. (a) $g(x) = 200 + 8x^3 + x^4$ $\Rightarrow$ $g'(x) = 24x^2 + 4x^3 = 4x^2(6 + x) = 0$ when $x = -6$ and when $x = 0$.
$g'(x) > 0$ $\Leftrightarrow$ $x > -6$ $(x \neq 0)$ and $g'(x) < 0$ $\Leftrightarrow$ $x < -6$, so g is decreasing on $(-\infty, -6)$ and g is
increasing on $(-6, \infty)$, with a horizontal tangent at $x = 0$.

(b) $g(-6) = -232$ is a local minimum value. There is no local
maximum value.

(d)

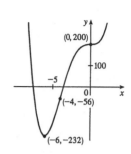

(c) $g''(x) = 48x + 12x^2 = 12x(4 + x) = 0$ when $x = -4$ and when
$x = 0$. $g''(x) > 0$ $\Leftrightarrow$ $x < -4$ or $x > 0$ and $g''(x) < 0$ $\Leftrightarrow$
$-4 < x < 0$, so g is CU on $(-\infty, -4)$ and $(0, \infty)$, and g is CD on
$(-4, 0)$. Inflection points at $(-4, -56)$ and $(0, 200)$

19. (a) $h(x) = 3x^5 - 5x^3 + 3$ $\Rightarrow$ $h'(x) = 15x^4 - 15x^2 = 15x^2(x^2 - 1) = 0$ when $x = 0, \pm 1$. Since $15x^2$ is
nonnegative, $h'(x) > 0$ $\Leftrightarrow$ $x^2 > 1$ $\Leftrightarrow$ $|x| > 1$ $\Leftrightarrow$ $x > 1$ or $x < -1$, so h is increasing on
$(-\infty, -1)$ and $(1, \infty)$ and decreasing on $(-1, 1)$, with a horizontal tangent at $x = 0$.

(b) Local maximum $h(-1) = 5$, local minimum $h(1) = 1$

(c) $h''(x) = 60x^3 - 30x = 30x(2x^2 - 1)$

$\quad = 60x\left(x + \frac{1}{\sqrt{2}}\right)\left(x - \frac{1}{\sqrt{2}}\right)$ $\Rightarrow$

$h''(x) > 0$ when $x > \frac{1}{\sqrt{2}}$ or $-\frac{1}{\sqrt{2}} < x < 0$, so h is CU on

$\left(-\frac{1}{\sqrt{2}}, 0\right)$ and $\left(\frac{1}{\sqrt{2}}, \infty\right)$ and CD on $\left(-\infty, -\frac{1}{\sqrt{2}}\right)$ and $\left(0, \frac{1}{\sqrt{2}}\right)$.

Inflection points at $(0, 3)$ and $\left(\pm\frac{1}{\sqrt{2}}, 3 \mp \frac{7}{8}\sqrt{2}\right)$ [about

$(-0.71, 4.24)$ and $(0.71, 1.76)$].

(d)

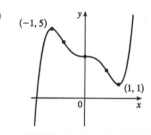

20. (a) $Q(x) = x - 3x^{1/3}$ $\Rightarrow$ $Q'(x) = 1 - \dfrac{1}{x^{2/3}} > 0$ $\Leftrightarrow$ $x^{2/3} > 1$ $\Leftrightarrow$ $x^2 > 1$ $\Leftrightarrow$ $x < -1$ or $x > 1$, so
Q is increasing on $(-\infty, -1)$, and $(1, \infty)$, and decreasing on $(-1, 1)$.

(b) $Q'(x) = 0$ $\Leftrightarrow$ $x = \pm 1$; $Q(1) = -2$ is a local minimum,
and $Q(-1) = 2$ is a local maximum.

(c) $Q''(x) = \frac{2}{3}x^{-5/3} > 0$ $\Leftrightarrow$ $x > 0$, so Q is CU on $(0, \infty)$
and CD on $(-\infty, 0)$. Inflection point at $(0, 0)$.

(d)

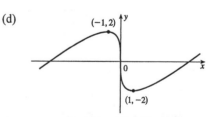

21. (a) $f(x) = x\sqrt{5 - x}$ $\Rightarrow$

$f'(x) = x \cdot \frac{1}{2}(5 - x)^{-1/2}(-1) + (5 - x)^{1/2} \cdot 1 = \frac{1}{2}(5 - x)^{-1/2}[-x + 2(5 - x)] = \dfrac{10 - 3x}{2\sqrt{5 - x}} > 0$ $\Leftrightarrow$

$x < \frac{10}{3}$, so f is increasing on $\left(-\infty, \frac{10}{3}\right)$ and decreasing on $\left(\frac{10}{3}, 5\right)$. [Note that the domain of f is $(-\infty, 5)$.]

(b) Local maximum $f\left(\frac{10}{3}\right) = \frac{10}{9}\sqrt{15} \approx 4.3$; no local minimum

(d)

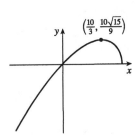

(c) $f''(x) = \dfrac{2(5-x)^{1/2}(-3) - (10-3x) \cdot 2\left(\frac{1}{2}\right)(5-x)^{-1/2}(-1)}{\left(2\sqrt{5-x}\right)^2}$

$= \dfrac{(5-x)^{-1/2}[-6(5-x) + (10-3x)]}{4(5-x)} = \dfrac{3x-20}{4(5-x)^{3/2}}$

$f''(x) < 0$ for $x < 5$, so f is CD on $(-\infty, 5)$. No IP

22. (a) $f(x) = 2x + \cot x,\ 0 < x < \pi.\ f'(x) = 2 - \csc^2 x > 0$ when $\csc^2 x < 2 \quad \Leftrightarrow \quad \sin x > \frac{1}{\sqrt{2}} \quad \Leftrightarrow$

$\frac{\pi}{4} < x < \frac{3\pi}{4}$, so f is increasing on $\left(\frac{\pi}{4}, \frac{3\pi}{4}\right)$ and decreasing on $\left(0, \frac{\pi}{4}\right)$ and $\left(\frac{3\pi}{4}, \pi\right)$.

(b) $f\left(\frac{\pi}{4}\right) = 1 + \frac{\pi}{2}$ is a local minimum, $f\left(\frac{3\pi}{4}\right) = \frac{3\pi}{2} - 1$ is a local maximum.

(c) $f''(x) = -2\csc x\,(-\csc x \cot x) = 2\csc^2 x \cot x > 0$

$\Leftrightarrow \quad \cot x > 0 \quad \Leftrightarrow \quad 0 < x < \frac{\pi}{2}$, so f is CU on $\left(0, \frac{\pi}{2}\right)$,

CD on $\left(\frac{\pi}{2}, \pi\right)$. There is an IP at $\left(\frac{\pi}{2}, \pi\right)$.

(d)

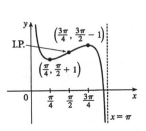

23. (a) $f(x) = 2\cos x + \sin^2 x,\ -\pi \le x \le \pi.\ f'(x) = -2\sin x + 2\sin x \cos x = 2\sin x\,(\cos x - 1)$. Since

$\cos x \le 1,\ \cos x - 1 \le 0$, so the sign of $f'(x)$ is the opposite of the sign of $\sin x$. Thus, $f'(x) > 0 \quad \Leftrightarrow$

$\sin x < 0 \quad \Leftrightarrow \quad -\pi < x < 0$, so f is increasing on $(-\pi, 0)$ and decreasing on $(0, \pi)$.

(b) f changes from increasing to decreasing at $x = 0$, so $f(0) = 2$ is a local maximum. The absolute minimum

value of -2 occurs at $x = \pm\pi$ (the endpoints), but there is no local minimum.

(c) $f'(x) = -2\sin x + 2\sin x \cos x = -2\sin x + \sin 2x \quad \Rightarrow$

$f''(x) = -2\cos x + 2\cos 2x = 2(2\cos^2 x - \cos x - 1)$

$= 2(2\cos x + 1)(\cos x - 1) > 0 \quad \Leftrightarrow$

$\cos x < -\frac{1}{2}\ [\cos x - 1 \le 0] \quad \Leftrightarrow \quad x \in \left(-\pi, -\frac{2\pi}{3}\right)$ and

$\left(\frac{2\pi}{3}, \pi\right)$, so f is CU on these intervals and CD on $\left(-\frac{2\pi}{3}, \frac{2\pi}{3}\right)$. Note

that $f'' < 0$ on $\left(-\frac{2\pi}{3}, 0\right)$ and $\left(0, \frac{2\pi}{3}\right)$, so f is CD on these intervals

by the Concavity Test. In fact, since f' is decreasing on $\left(-\frac{2\pi}{3}, \frac{2\pi}{3}\right)$,

f is CD on $\left(-\frac{2\pi}{3}, \frac{2\pi}{3}\right)$. There are IP at $\left(\pm\frac{2\pi}{3}, -\frac{1}{4}\right)$.

(d)

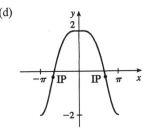

24. (a) $f(x) = \ln(1 + x^2) \quad \Rightarrow \quad f'(x) = \dfrac{2x}{1+x^2} > 0 \quad \Leftrightarrow \quad x > 0$, so f is increasing on $(0, \infty)$ and decreasing

on $(-\infty, 0)$.

(b) $f(0) = 0$ is a local minimum.

(c) $f''(x) = \dfrac{(1+x^2)(2) - 2x(2x)}{(1+x^2)^2} = \dfrac{2(1-x^2)}{(1+x^2)^2} > 0 \quad \Leftrightarrow$

$1 - x^2 > 0 \quad \Leftrightarrow \quad |x| < 1$, so f is CU on $(-1, 1)$, CD on

$(-\infty, -1)$ and $(1, \infty)$. There are IP at $(1, \ln 2)$ and $(-1, \ln 2)$.

(d)

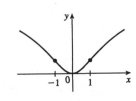

25. (a) $\lim\limits_{x\to\pm\infty}\dfrac{1+x^2}{1-x^2}=\lim\limits_{x\to\pm\infty}\dfrac{(1/x^2)+1}{(1/x^2)-1}=-1$, so $y=-1$ is a HA. $\lim\limits_{x\to1^-}\dfrac{1+x^2}{1-x^2}=\infty$, $\lim\limits_{x\to1^+}\dfrac{1+x^2}{1-x^2}=-\infty$,

$\lim\limits_{x\to-1^-}\dfrac{1+x^2}{1-x^2}=-\infty$, $\lim\limits_{x\to-1^+}\dfrac{1+x^2}{1-x^2}=\infty$. So $x=1$ and $x=-1$ are VA.

(b) $f(x)=\dfrac{1+x^2}{1-x^2}$ $\Rightarrow$ $f'(x)=\dfrac{(1-x^2)(2x)-(1+x^2)(-2x)}{(1-x^2)^2}=\dfrac{2x(1-x^2+1+x^2)}{(1-x^2)^2}=\dfrac{4x}{(1-x^2)^2}>0$

$\Leftrightarrow$ $x>0$ ($x\neq1$), so f increases on $(0,1)$, $(1,\infty)$ and decreases on $(-\infty,-1)$, $(-1,0)$.

(c) $f(0)=1$ is a local minimum.

(d) $f''(x)=\dfrac{(1-x^2)^2\cdot4-4x\cdot2(1-x^2)(-2x)}{[(1-x^2)^2]^2}$

$=\dfrac{4(1-x^2)(1-x^2+4x^2)}{(1-x^2)^4}=\dfrac{4(1+3x^2)}{(1-x^2)^3}$

Since the numerator is always positive, the sign of $f''(x)$ is the same as the sign of $1-x^2$. Thus, $f''(x)>0$ $\Leftrightarrow$ $1-x^2>0$ $\Leftrightarrow$ $x^2<1$ $\Leftrightarrow$ $|x|<1$ $\Leftrightarrow$ $-1<x<1$, so f is CU on $(-1,1)$ and CD on $(-\infty,-1)$ and $(1,\infty)$. There is no IP since $x=\pm1$ are not in the domain of f.

(e)
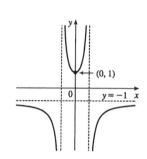

26. (a) $\lim\limits_{x\to\pm\infty}\dfrac{x}{(x-1)^2}=0$, so $y=0$ is a HA. $\lim\limits_{x\to1}\dfrac{x}{(x-1)^2}=\infty$, so $x=1$ is a VA.

(b) $f(x)=\dfrac{x}{(x-1)^2}$ $\Rightarrow$ $f'(x)=\dfrac{(x-1)^2(1)-x(2)(x-1)}{[(x-1)^2]^2}=\dfrac{(x-1)[(x-1)-2x]}{(x-1)^4}=\dfrac{-x-1}{(x-1)^3}=0$

$\Rightarrow$ $x=-1$. f' is negative on $(-\infty,-1)$ and $(1,\infty)$ and positive on $(-1,1)$, so $f(x)$ is decreasing on $(-\infty,-1)$ and $(1,\infty)$ and increasing on $(-1,1)$.

(c) Local minimum $f(-1)=-\frac{1}{4}$, no local maximum.

(d) $f''(x)=\dfrac{(x-1)^3(-1)+(x+1)(3)(x-1)^2}{(x-1)^6}=\dfrac{2(x+2)}{(x-1)^4}$. This

is negative on $(-\infty,-2)$, and positive on $(-2,1)$ and $(1,\infty)$. So f is CD on $(-\infty,-2)$ and CU on $(-2,1)$ and $(1,\infty)$. f has an inflection point at $\left(-2,-\frac{2}{9}\right)$.

(e)
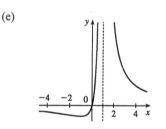

27. (a) $\lim\limits_{x\to\pm\infty}\left[x/(x^2+9)\right]=0$, so $y=0$ is a HA; no VA

(b) $f(x)=x/(x^2+9)$ $\Rightarrow$ $f'(x)=\dfrac{(x^2+9)(1)-x(2x)}{(x^2+9)^2}=\dfrac{9-x^2}{(x^2+9)^2}>0$ $\Leftrightarrow$ $9-x^2>0$ $\Leftrightarrow$

$x^2<9$ $\Leftrightarrow$ $|x|<3$ $\Leftrightarrow$ $-3<x<3$, so f is increasing on $(-3,3)$ and decreasing on $(-\infty,-3)$ and $(3,\infty)$.

(c) Local minimum $f(-3)=-\frac{1}{6}$, local maximum $f(3)=\frac{1}{6}$

(d) $f''(x) = \dfrac{(x^2+9)^2(-2x) - (9-x^2) \cdot 2(x^2+9)(2x)}{\left[(x^2+9)^2\right]^2} = \dfrac{(2x)(x^2+9)\left[-(x^2+9) - 2(9-x^2)\right]}{(x^2+9)^4}$

$= \dfrac{2x(x^2-27)}{(x^2+9)^3} = 0 \ \Leftrightarrow \ x = 0, \pm\sqrt{27} = \pm 3\sqrt{3}$

$f''(x) > 0 \ \Leftrightarrow \ -3\sqrt{3} < x < 0 \text{ or } x > 3\sqrt{3}$, so f is CU on

$(-3\sqrt{3}, 0)$ and $(3\sqrt{3}, \infty)$, and CD on $(-\infty, -3\sqrt{3})$ and

$(0, 3\sqrt{3})$. There are three inflection points: $(0,0)$ and

$(\pm 3\sqrt{3}, \pm\tfrac{1}{12}\sqrt{3})$.

(e)

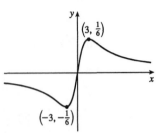

28. (a) $\displaystyle\lim_{x\to\pi/2^-} x\tan x = \infty$ and $\displaystyle\lim_{x\to-\pi/2^+} x\tan x = \infty$, so $x = \tfrac{\pi}{2}$ and $x = -\tfrac{\pi}{2}$ are VA.

(b) $f(x) = x\tan x, \ -\tfrac{\pi}{2} < x < \tfrac{\pi}{2}$. $f'(x) = x\sec^2 x + \tan x > 0$

$\Leftrightarrow \ 0 < x < \tfrac{\pi}{2}$, so f increases on $\left(0, \tfrac{\pi}{2}\right)$ and decreases

on $\left(-\tfrac{\pi}{2}, 0\right)$.

(c) Local minimum $f(0) = 0$.

(d) $f''(x) = 2\sec^2 x + 2x\tan x \sec^2 x > 0$ for $-\tfrac{\pi}{2} < x < \tfrac{\pi}{2}$, so f is

CU on $\left(-\tfrac{\pi}{2}, \tfrac{\pi}{2}\right)$. No IP

(e)

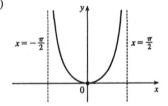

29. (a) $\displaystyle\lim_{x\to\pm\infty} e^{-1/(x+1)} = 1$ since $-1/(x+1) \to 0$, so $y = 1$ is a HA. $\displaystyle\lim_{x\to-1^+} e^{-1/(x+1)} = 0$ since

$-1/(x+1) \to -\infty$, $\displaystyle\lim_{x\to-1^-} e^{-1/(x+1)} = \infty$ since $-1/(x+1) \to \infty$, so $x = -1$ is a VA.

(b) $f(x) = e^{-1/(x+1)} \ \Rightarrow \ f'(x) = e^{-1/(x+1)}\left[-(-1)\dfrac{1}{(x+1)^2}\right]$ [Reciprocal Rule] $= e^{-1/(x+1)}/(x+1)^2$

$\Rightarrow \ f'(x) > 0$ for all x except -1, so f is increasing on $(-\infty, -1)$ and $(-1, \infty)$.

(c) No local maximum or minimum

(d) $f''(x) = \dfrac{(x+1)^2 e^{-1/(x+1)}\left[1/(x+1)^2\right] - e^{-1/(x+1)}\left[2(x+1)\right]}{\left[(x+1)^2\right]^2}$

$= \dfrac{e^{-1/(x+1)}\left[1 - (2x+2)\right]}{(x+1)^4} = -\dfrac{e^{-1/(x+1)}(2x+1)}{(x+1)^4} \ \Rightarrow$

$f''(x) > 0 \ \Leftrightarrow \ 2x+1 < 0 \ \Leftrightarrow \ x < -\tfrac{1}{2}$, so f is CU on $(-\infty, -1)$ and $\left(-1, -\tfrac{1}{2}\right)$, and CD on $\left(-\tfrac{1}{2}, \infty\right)$.

f has an IP at $\left(-\tfrac{1}{2}, e^{-2}\right)$.

(e)

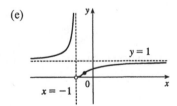

30. (a) f is periodic with period π, so we consider only $-\frac{\pi}{2} < x < \frac{\pi}{2}$. $\lim\limits_{x \to 0} \ln\left(\tan^2 x\right) = -\infty$,

$\lim\limits_{x \to (\pi/2)^-} \ln\left(\tan^2 x\right) = \infty$, and $\lim\limits_{x \to (\pi/2)^+} \ln\left(\tan^2 x\right) = \infty$, so $x = 0$, $x = \pm\frac{\pi}{2}$ are VA.

(b) $f(x) = \ln\left(\tan^2 x\right) \;\Rightarrow\; f'(x) = \dfrac{2 \tan x \sec^2 x}{\tan^2 x} = 2\,\dfrac{\sec^2 x}{\tan x} > 0 \;\Leftrightarrow\; \tan x > 0 \;\Leftrightarrow\; 0 < x < \frac{\pi}{2}$, so f

is increasing on $\left(0, \frac{\pi}{2}\right)$ and decreasing on $\left(-\frac{\pi}{2}, 0\right)$.

(c) No maximum or minimum

(d) $f'(x) = \dfrac{2}{\sin x \cos x} = \dfrac{4}{\sin 2x} \;\Rightarrow\; f''(x) = \dfrac{-8 \cos 2x}{\sin^2 2x} < 0$ (e)

$\Leftrightarrow\; \cos 2x > 0 \;\Leftrightarrow\; -\frac{\pi}{4} < x < \frac{\pi}{4}$, so f is CD on $\left(-\frac{\pi}{4}, 0\right)$

and $\left(0, \frac{\pi}{4}\right)$, and CU on $\left(-\frac{\pi}{2}, -\frac{\pi}{4}\right)$ and $\left(\frac{\pi}{4}, \frac{\pi}{2}\right)$. IP are $\left(\pm\frac{\pi}{4}, 0\right)$.

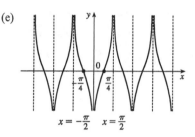

31. (a) From the graphs of

$f(x) = 3x^5 - 40x^3 + 30x^2$, it seems that f

is concave upward on $(-2, 0.25)$ and

$(2, \infty)$, and concave downward on

$(-\infty, -2)$ and $(0.25, 2)$, with inflection

points at about $(-2, 350)$, $(0.25, 1)$, and

$(2, -100)$.

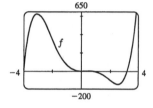

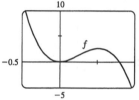

(b)

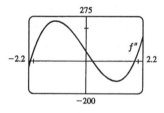

From the graph of $f''(x) = 60x^3 - 240x + 60$, it seems that f is CU

on $(-2.1, 0.25)$ and $(1.9, \infty)$, and CD on $(-\infty, -2.1)$ and

$(0.25, 1.9)$, with inflection points at about $(-2.1, 386)$, $(0.25, 1.3)$

and $(1.9, -87)$. (We have to check back on the graph of f to find the

y-coordinates of the inflection points.)

32. (a)

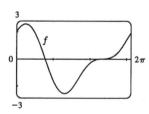

From the graph of $f(x) = 2 \cos x + \sin 2x$, it

seems that f is CU on $(1.5, 3.5)$ and $(4.5, 6.0)$,

and CD on $(0, 1.5)$, $(3.5, 4.5)$ and $(6.0, 2\pi)$, with

inflection points at about $(1.5, 0.3)$, $(3.5, -1.3)$,

$(4.5, 0.0)$ and $(6.0, 1.5)$.

(b)

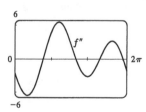

From the graph of $f''(x) = -2 \cos x - 4 \sin 2x$,

it seems that f is CU on $(1.57, 3.39)$ and

$(4.71, 6.03)$ and CD on $(0, 1.57)$, $(3.39, 4.71)$

and $(6.03, 2\pi)$, with inflection points at about

$(1.57, 0.00)$, $(3.39, -1.45)$, $(4.71, 0.00)$ and

$(6.03, 1.45)$.

33. (a)

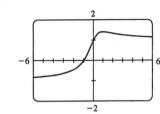

From the graph, we get us an estimate of $f(1) \approx 1.41$ as a local maximum, and no local minimum. $f(x) = \dfrac{x+1}{\sqrt{x^2+1}}$ $\Rightarrow$

$f'(x) = \dfrac{1-x}{(x^2+1)^{3/2}}$. $f'(x) = 0$ $\Leftrightarrow$ $x = 1$.

$f(1) = \frac{2}{\sqrt{2}} = \sqrt{2}$ is the exact value.

(b) From the graph in part (a), f increases most rapidly somewhere between $x = -\frac{1}{2}$ and $x = -\frac{1}{4}$. To find the exact value, we need to find the maximum value of f', which we can do by finding the critical numbers of f'.

$f''(x) = \dfrac{2x^2 - 3x - 1}{(x^2+1)^{5/2}} = 0$ $\Leftrightarrow$ $x = \dfrac{3 \pm \sqrt{17}}{4}$. $x = \dfrac{3 + \sqrt{17}}{4}$ corresponds to the *minimum* value of f'.

The maximum value of f' is at $\left(\dfrac{3 - \sqrt{17}}{4}, \sqrt{\dfrac{7}{6} - \dfrac{\sqrt{17}}{6}} \right) \approx (-0.28, 0.69)$.

34. (a)

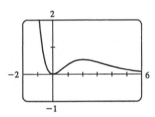

Tracing the graph gives us estimates of $f(0) = 0$ for a local minimum and $f(2) = 0.54$ for a local maximum. $f(x) = x^2 e^{-x}$ $\Rightarrow$

$f'(x) = xe^{-x}(2 - x)$. $f'(x) = 0$ $\Leftrightarrow$ $x = 0$ or 2. $f(0) = 0$ and $f(2) = 4e^{-2}$ are the exact values.

(b) From the graph in part (a), f increases most rapidly around $x = \frac{3}{4}$. To find the exact value, we need to find the maximum value of f', which we can do by finding the critical numbers of f'. $f''(x) = e^{-x}(x^2 - 4x + 2) = 0$

$\Rightarrow$ $x = 2 \pm \sqrt{2}$. $x = 2 + \sqrt{2}$ corresponds to the *minimum* value of f'. The maximum value of f' is at

$\left(2 - \sqrt{2}, (2 - \sqrt{2})^2 e^{-2+\sqrt{2}} \right) \approx (0.59, 0.19)$.

35. In Maple, we define f and then use the command

`plot(diff(diff(f,x),x),x=-3..3);`. In Mathematica, we define f and then use `Plot[Dt[Dt[f,x],x],{x,-3,3}]`. We see that $f'' > 0$ for $x > 0.1$ and $f'' < 0$ for $x < 0.1$. So f is concave up on $(0.1, \infty)$ and concave down on $(-\infty, 0.1)$.

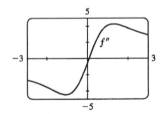

36. It appears that f'' is positive (and thus f is concave up) on $(-1.8, 0.3)$ and $(1.5, \infty)$ and negative (so f is concave down) on $(-\infty, -1.8)$ and $(0.3, 1.5)$.

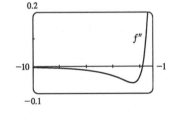

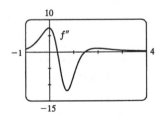

37. $y = -\dfrac{W}{24EI}x^4 + \dfrac{WL}{12EI}x^3 - \dfrac{WL^2}{24EI}x^2 = -\dfrac{W}{24EI}x^2\left(x^2 - 2Lx + L^2\right)$

$= \dfrac{-W}{24EI}x^2(x-L)^2 = cx^2(x-L)^2$

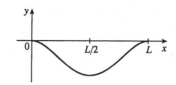

where $c = -\dfrac{W}{24EI}$ is a negative constant and $0 \le x \le L$. We sketch

$f(x) = cx^2(x-L)^2$ for $c = -1$. $f(0) = f(L) = 0$.

$f'(x) = cx^2[2(x-L)] + (x-L)^2(2cx) = 2cx(x-L)[x + (x-L)] = 2cx(x-L)(2x-L)$. So for

$0 < x < L$, $f'(x) > 0 \iff x(x-L)(2x-L) < 0$ (since $c < 0$) $\iff L/2 < x < L$ and $f'(x) < 0 \iff$

$0 < x < L/2$. So f is increasing on $(L/2, L)$ and decreasing on $(0, L/2)$, and there is a local and absolute

minimum at $(L/2, f(L/2)) = (L/2, cL^4/16)$.

$f'(x) = 2c\left[x(x-L)(2x-L)\right] \Rightarrow$

$f''(x) = 2c\left[1(x-L)(2x-L) + x(1)(2x-L) + x(x-L)(2)\right] = 2c\left(6x^2 - 6Lx + L^2\right) = 0 \iff$

$x = \dfrac{6L \pm \sqrt{12L^2}}{12} = \tfrac{1}{2}L \pm \tfrac{\sqrt{3}}{6}L$, and these are the x-coordinates of the two inflection points.

38. $F(x) = -\dfrac{k}{x^2} + \dfrac{k}{(x-2)^2}$, where $k > 0$ and $0 < x < 2$. For $0 < x < 2$,

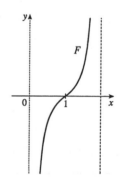

$x - 2 < 0$, so $F'(x) = \dfrac{2k}{x^3} - \dfrac{2k}{(x-2)^3} > 0$ and F is increasing.

$\lim\limits_{x \to 0^+} F(x) = -\infty$ and $\lim\limits_{x \to 2^-} F(x) = \infty$, so $x = 0$ and $x = 2$ are vertical

asymptotes. Notice that when the middle particle is at $x = 1$, the net force

acting on it is 0. When $x > 1$, the net force is positive, meaning that it acts to

the right. And if the particle approaches $x = 2$, the force on it rapidly

becomes very large. When $x < 1$, the net force is negative, so it acts to the

left. If the particle approaches 0, the force becomes very large to the left.

39. From the graph, we estimate that the most rapid increase in the

number of VCRs occurs at about $t = 7$. To maximize the first

derivative, we need to determine the values for which the second

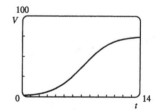

derivative is 0. $V(t) = \dfrac{75}{1 + 74e^{-0.6t}} \Rightarrow$

$V'(t) = -\dfrac{75\left[74e^{-0.6t}(-0.6)\right]}{\left(1 + 74e^{-0.6t}\right)^2} = \dfrac{3330e^{-0.6t}}{\left(1 + 74e^{-0.6t}\right)^2} \Rightarrow$

$V''(t) = \dfrac{\left(1 + 74e^{-0.6t}\right)^2\left[3330e^{-0.6t}(-0.6)\right] - \left(3330e^{-0.6t}\right)2\left(1 + 74e^{-0.6t}\right)\left[74e^{-0.6t}(-0.6)\right]}{\left[\left(1 + 74e^{-0.6t}\right)^2\right]^2}$

$= \dfrac{\left(1 + 74e^{-0.6t}\right)\left[3330e^{-0.6t}(-0.6)\right]\left[\left(1 + 74e^{-0.6t}\right) - 2\left(74e^{-0.6t}\right)\right]}{\left(1 + 74e^{-0.6t}\right)^4} = \dfrac{-1998e^{-0.6t}\left(1 - 74e^{-0.6t}\right)}{\left(1 + 74e^{-0.6t}\right)^3}$

$V''(t) = 0 \iff 1 = 74e^{-0.6t} \iff e^{0.6t} = 74 \iff 0.6t = \ln 74 \iff t = \tfrac{5}{3}\ln 74 \approx 7.173$ years, which

corresponds to early September 1987.

40. (a) As $|x| \to \infty$, $t = -x^2/(2\sigma^2) \to -\infty$, and $e^t \to 0$. The HA is $y = 0$. Since t takes on its maximum value at $x = 0$, so does e^t. Showing this result using derivatives, we have $f(x) = e^{-x^2/(2\sigma^2)}$ $\Rightarrow$

$f'(x) = e^{-x^2/(2\sigma^2)} \left(-x/\sigma^2 \right)$. $f'(x) = 0$ $\Leftrightarrow$ $x = 0$. Because f' changes from positive to negative at $x = 0$, $f(0) = 1$ is a local maximum. For inflection points, we find

$f''(x) = -\dfrac{1}{\sigma^2} \left[e^{-x^2/(2\sigma^2)} \cdot 1 + xe^{-x^2/(2\sigma^2)} \left(-x/\sigma^2 \right) \right] = \dfrac{-1}{\sigma^2} e^{-x^2/(2\sigma^2)} \left(1 - x^2/\sigma^2 \right)$.

$f''(x) = 0$ $\Leftrightarrow$ $x^2 = \sigma^2$ $\Leftrightarrow$ $x = \pm\sigma$. $f''(x) < 0$ $\Leftrightarrow$ $x^2 < \sigma^2$ $\Leftrightarrow$ $-\sigma < x < \sigma$. So f is CD on $(-\sigma, \sigma)$ and CU on $(-\infty, -\sigma)$ and (σ, ∞). IP at $\left(\pm\sigma, e^{-1/2} \right)$.

(b) Since we have IP at $x = \pm\sigma$, the inflection points move away from the y-axis as σ increases.

(c)

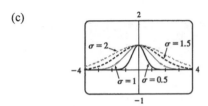

From the graph, we see that as σ increases, the graph tends to spread out and there is more area between the curve and the x-axis.

41. $f(x) = ax^3 + bx^2 + cx + d$ $\Rightarrow$ $f'(x) = 3ax^2 + 2bx + c$. We are given that $f(1) = 0$ and $f(-2) = 3$, so $f(1) = a + b + c + d = 0$ and $f(-2) = -8a + 4b - 2c + d = 3$. Also $f'(1) = 3a + 2b + c = 0$ and $f'(-2) = 12a - 4b + c = 0$ by Fermat's Theorem. Solving these four equations, we get $a = \frac{2}{9}, b = \frac{1}{3}, c = -\frac{4}{3}, d = \frac{7}{9}$, so the function is $f(x) = \frac{1}{9} \left(2x^3 + 3x^2 - 12x + 7 \right)$.

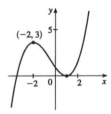

42. $f(x) = axe^{bx^2}$ $\Rightarrow$ $f'(x) = a \left[xe^{bx^2} \cdot 2bx + e^{bx^2} \cdot 1 \right] = ae^{bx^2} \left(2bx^2 + 1 \right)$. For $f(2) = 1$ to be a maximum value, we must have $f'(2) = 0$. $f(2) \stackrel{1}{=} 1$ $\Rightarrow$ $1 = 2ae^{4b}$ and $f'(2) = 0$ $\Rightarrow$ $0 = (8b + 1)ae^{4b}$. So $8b + 1 = 0$ $[a \neq 0]$ $\Rightarrow$ $b = -\frac{1}{8}$ and now $1 = 2ae^{-1/2}$ $\Rightarrow$ $a = \sqrt{e}/2$.

43. $f(x) = \tan x - x$ $\Rightarrow$ $f'(x) = \sec^2 x - 1 > 0$ for $0 < x < \frac{\pi}{2}$ since $\sec^2 x > 1$ for $0 < x < \frac{\pi}{2}$. So f is increasing on $\left(0, \frac{\pi}{2} \right)$. Thus, $f(x) > f(0) = 0$ for $0 < x < \frac{\pi}{2}$ $\Rightarrow$ $\tan x - x > 0$ $\Rightarrow$ $\tan x > x$ for $0 < x < \frac{\pi}{2}$.

44. (a) Let $f(x) = e^x - 1 - x$. Now $f(0) = e^0 - 1 = 0$, and for $x \geq 0$, we have $f'(x) = e^x - 1 \geq 0$. Now, since $f(0) = 0$ and f is increasing on $[0, \infty)$, $f(x) \geq 0$ for $x \geq 0$ $\Rightarrow$ $e^x - 1 - x \geq 0$ $\Rightarrow$ $e^x \geq 1 + x$.

(b) Let $f(x) = e^x - 1 - x - \frac{1}{2}x^2$. Thus, $f'(x) = e^x - 1 - x$, which is positive for $x \geq 0$ by part (a). Thus, $f(x)$ is increasing on $(0, \infty)$, so on that interval, $0 = f(0) \leq f(x) = e^x - 1 - x - \frac{1}{2}x^2$ $\Rightarrow$ $e^x \geq 1 + x + \frac{1}{2}x^2$.

(c) By part (a), the result holds for $n = 1$. Suppose that $e^x \geq 1 + x + \dfrac{x^2}{2!} + \cdots + \dfrac{x^k}{k!}$ for $x \geq 0$.

Let $f(x) = e^x - 1 - x - \dfrac{x^2}{2!} - \cdots - \dfrac{x^k}{k!} - \dfrac{x^{k+1}}{(k+1)!}$. Then $f'(x) = e^x - 1 - x - \cdots - \dfrac{x^k}{k!} \geq 0$

by assumption. Hence, $f(x)$ is increasing on $(0, \infty)$. So $0 \leq x$ implies that

$0 = f(0) \leq f(x) = e^x - 1 - x - \cdots - \dfrac{x^k}{k!} - \dfrac{x^{k+1}}{(k+1)!}$, and hence $e^x \geq 1 + x + \cdots + \dfrac{x^k}{k!} + \dfrac{x^{k+1}}{(k+1)!}$ for

$x \geq 0$. Therefore, for $x \geq 0$, $e^x \geq 1 + x + \dfrac{x^2}{2!} + \cdots + \dfrac{x^n}{n!}$ for every positive integer n, by mathematical

induction.

45. We are given that f is differentiable (and therefore continuous) everywhere. In particular, we can apply the Mean Value Theorem on the interval $[0, 4]$. There exists a number c in $(0, 4)$ such that $f(4) - f(0) = f'(c)(4 - 0)$, so $f(4) = f(0) + 4f'(c) = -3 + 4f'(c)$. We are given that $f'(x) \leq 5$ for all x, so in particular we know that $f'(c) \leq 5$. Multiplying both sides of this inequality by 4, we have $4f'(c) \leq 20$, so $f(4) = -3 + 4f'(c) \leq -3 + 20 = 17$. The largest possible value for $f(4)$ is 17.

46. By the Mean Value Theorem, $\dfrac{f(5) - f(2)}{5 - 2} = f'(c)$ for some $c \in (2, 5)$. Since $1 \leq f'(x) \leq 4$, we have

$1 \leq \dfrac{f(5) - f(2)}{5 - 2} \leq 4 \quad \Leftrightarrow \quad 1 \leq \dfrac{f(5) - f(2)}{3} \leq 4 \quad \Leftrightarrow \quad 3 \leq f(5) - f(2) \leq 12.$

47. Let $g(t)$ and $h(t)$ be the position functions of the two runners and let $f(t) = g(t) - h(t)$. By hypothesis, $f(0) = g(0) - h(0) = 0$ and $f(b) = g(b) - h(b) = 0$, where b is the finishing time. Then by the Mean Value

Theorem, there is a time c, with $0 < c < b$, such that $f'(c) = \dfrac{f(b) - f(0)}{b - 0}$. But $f(b) = f(0) = 0$, so $f'(c) = 0$.

Since $f'(c) = g'(c) - h'(c) = 0$, we have $g'(c) = h'(c)$. So at time c, both runners have the same velocity $g'(c) = h'(c)$.

48. Let $v(t)$ be the velocity of the car t hours after 2:00 P.M. Then $\dfrac{v(1/6) - v(0)}{1/6 - 0} = \dfrac{50 - 30}{1/6} = 120$. By the Mean

Value Theorem, there is a number c such that $0 < c < \frac{1}{6}$ with $v'(c) = 120$. Since $v'(t)$ is the acceleration at time t, the acceleration c hours after 2:00 P.M. is exactly 120 mi/h^2.

49. Let the cubic function be $f(x) = ax^3 + bx^2 + cx + d \Rightarrow f'(x) = 3ax^2 + 2bx + c \Rightarrow f''(x) = 6ax + 2b$. So f is CU when $6ax + 2b > 0 \Leftrightarrow x > -b/(3a)$, CD when $x < -b/(3a)$, and so the only point of inflection occurs when $x = -b/(3a)$. If the graph has three x-intercepts x_1, x_2 and x_3, then the expression for $f(x)$ must factor as $f(x) = a(x - x_1)(x - x_2)(x - x_3)$. Multiplying these factors together gives us $f(x) = a[x^3 - (x_1 + x_2 + x_3)x^2 + (x_1x_2 + x_1x_3 + x_2x_3)x - x_1x_2x_3]$. Equating the coefficients of the x^2-terms for the two forms of f gives us $b = -a(x_1 + x_2 + x_3)$. Hence, the x-coordinate of the point of inflection

is $-\dfrac{b}{3a} = -\dfrac{-a(x_1 + x_2 + x_3)}{3a} = \dfrac{x_1 + x_2 + x_3}{3}.$

50. $P(x) = x^4 + cx^3 + x^2 \;\Rightarrow\; P'(x) = 4x^3 + 3cx^2 + 2x \;\Rightarrow\; P''(x) = 12x^2 + 6cx + 2$. The graph of $P''(x)$ is a parabola. If $P''(x)$ has two roots, then it changes sign twice and so has two inflection points. This happens when the discriminant of $P''(x)$ is positive, that is, $(6c)^2 - 4 \cdot 12 \cdot 2 > 0 \;\Leftrightarrow\; 36c^2 - 96 > 0 \;\Leftrightarrow\;$ $|c| > \frac{2\sqrt{6}}{3} \approx 1.63$. If $36c^2 - 96 = 0 \;\Leftrightarrow\; c = \pm\frac{2\sqrt{6}}{3}$, $P''(x)$ is 0 at one point, but there is still no inflection point since $P''(x)$ never changes sign, and if $36c^2 - 96 < 0 \;\Leftrightarrow\; |c| < \frac{2\sqrt{6}}{3}$, then $P''(x)$ never changes sign, and so there is no inflection point.

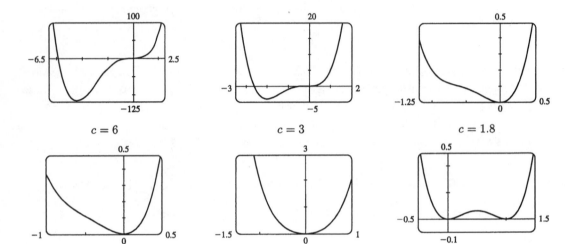

$c = 6$ $c = 3$ $c = 1.8$

$c = \frac{2\sqrt{6}}{3}$ $c = 0$ $c = -2$

For large positive c, the graph of f has two inflection points and a large dip to the left of the y-axis. As c decreases, the graph of f becomes flatter for $x < 0$, and eventually the dip rises above the x-axis, and then disappears entirely, along with the inflection points. As c continues to decrease, the dip and the inflection points reappear, to the right of the origin.

◆4.4◆ Graphing with Calculus *and* Calculators · · · · · · ·

1. $f(x) = 4x^4 - 7x^2 + 4x + 6 \;\Rightarrow\; f'(x) = 16x^3 - 14x + 4 \;\Rightarrow\; f''(x) = 48x^2 - 14$

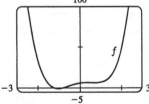
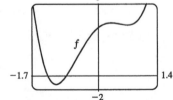
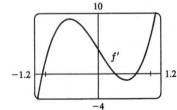

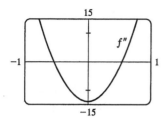

After finding suitable viewing rectangles (by ensuring that we have located all of the x-values where either $f' = 0$ or $f'' = 0$) we estimate from the graph of f' that f is increasing on $(-1.1, 0.3)$ and $(0.7, \infty)$ and decreasing on $(-\infty, -1.1)$ and $(0.3, 0.7)$, with a local maximum of $f(0.3) \approx 6.6$ and minima of $f(-1.1) \approx -1.1$ and $f(0.7) \approx 6.3$. We estimate from the graph of f'' that f is CU on $(-\infty, -0.5)$ and $(0.5, \infty)$ and CD on $(-0.5, 0.5)$, and that f has inflection points at about $(-0.5, 2.1)$ and $(0.5, 6.5)$.

2. $f(x) = 8x^5 + 45x^4 + 80x^3 + 90x^2 + 200x \quad \Rightarrow \quad f'(x) = 40x^4 + 180x^3 + 240x^2 + 180x + 200 \quad \Rightarrow$
$f''(x) = 160x^3 + 540x^2 + 480x + 180$

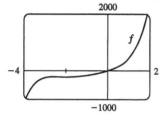

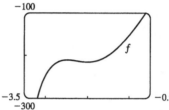

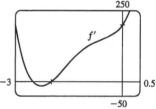

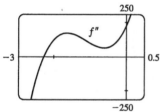

After finding suitable viewing rectangles, we estimate from the graph of f' that f is increasing on $(-\infty, -2.5)$ and $(-2.0, \infty)$ and decreasing on $(-2.5, -2.0)$. Maximum: $f(-2.5) \approx -211$. Minimum: $f(-2) \approx -216$. We estimate from the graph of f'' that f is CU on $(-2.3, \infty)$ and CD on $(-\infty, -2.3)$, and has an IP at $(-2.3, -213)$.

3. $f(x) = \sqrt[3]{x^2 - 3x - 5} \quad \Rightarrow \quad f'(x) = \frac{1}{3} \frac{2x - 3}{(x^2 - 3x - 5)^{2/3}} \quad \Rightarrow \quad f''(x) = -\frac{2}{9} \frac{x^2 - 3x + 24}{(x^2 - 3x - 5)^{5/3}}$

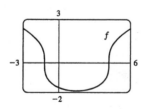

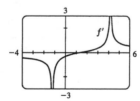

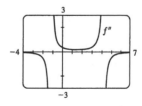

Note: With some CAS's, including Maple, it is necessary to define $f(x) = \frac{x^2 - 3x - 5}{|x^2 - 3x - 5|} \left| x^2 - 3x - 5 \right|^{1/3}$, since the CAS does not compute real cube roots of negative numbers. We estimate from the graph of f' that f is increasing on $(1.5, \infty)$, and decreasing on $(-\infty, -1.5)$. f has no maximum. Minimum: $f(1.5) \approx -1.9$. From the graph of f'', we estimate that f is CU on $(-1.2, 4.2)$ and CD on $(-\infty, -1.2)$ and $(4.2, \infty)$. IP at $(-1.2, 0)$ and $(4.2, 0)$.

4. $f(x) = \dfrac{x^4 + x^3 - 2x^2 + 2}{x^2 + x - 2}$ $\Rightarrow$ $f'(x) = 2\dfrac{x^5 + 2x^4 - 3x^3 - 4x^2 + 2x - 1}{(x^2 + x - 2)^2}$ $\Rightarrow$

$f''(x) = 2\dfrac{x^6 + 3x^5 - 3x^4 - 11x^3 + 12x^2 + 18x - 2}{(x^2 + x - 2)^3}$

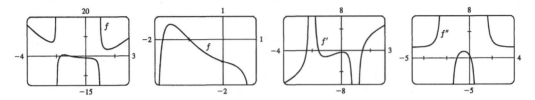

We estimate from the graph of f' that f is increasing on $(-2.4, -2)$, $(-2, -1.5)$ and $(1.5, \infty)$ and decreasing on $(-\infty, -2.4)$, $(-1.5, 1)$ and $(1, 1.5)$. Local maximum: $f(-1.5) \approx 0.7$.
Local minima: $f(-2.4) \approx 7.2$, $f(1.5) \approx 3.4$. From the graph of f'', we estimate that f is CU on $(-\infty, -2)$, $(-1.1, 0.1)$ and $(1, \infty)$ and CD on $(-2, -1.1)$ and $(0.1, 1)$.
f has IP at $(-1.1, 0.2)$ and $(0.1, -1.1)$.

5. $f(x) = \dfrac{x}{x^3 - x^2 - 4x + 1}$ $\Rightarrow$ $f'(x) = \dfrac{-2x^3 + x^2 + 1}{(x^3 - x^2 - 4x + 1)^2}$ $\Rightarrow$

$f''(x) = \dfrac{2(3x^5 - 3x^4 + 5x^3 - 6x^2 + 3x + 4)}{(x^3 - x^2 - 4x + 1)^3}$

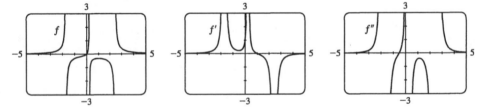

We estimate from the graph of f that $y = 0$ is a horizontal asymptote, and that there are vertical asymptotes at $x = -1.7$, $x = 0.24$, and $x = 2.46$. From the graph of f', we estimate that f is increasing on $(-\infty, -1.7)$, $(-1.7, 0.24)$, and $(0.24, 1)$, and that f is decreasing on $(1, 2.46)$ and $(2.46, \infty)$. There is a local maximum at $f(1) = -\frac{1}{3}$. From the graph of f'', we estimate that f is CU on $(-\infty, -1.7)$, $(-0.506, 0.24)$, and $(2.46, \infty)$, and that f is CD on $(-1.7, -0.506)$ and $(0.24, 2.46)$. There is an inflection point at $(-0.506, -0.192)$.

6. $f(x) = \tan x + 5\cos x$ $\Rightarrow$ $f'(x) = \sec^2 x - 5\sin x$ $\Rightarrow$ $f''(x) = 2\sec^2 x \tan x - 5\cos x$. Since f is periodic with period 2π, and defined for all x except odd multiples of $\frac{\pi}{2}$, we graph f and its derivatives on $\left[-\frac{\pi}{2}, \frac{3\pi}{2}\right]$.

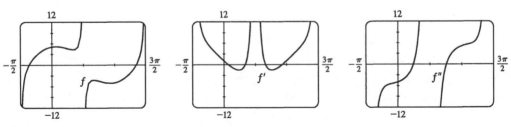

We estimate from the graph of f' that f is increasing on $\left(-\frac{\pi}{2}, 0.21\right)$, $\left(1.07, \frac{\pi}{2}\right)$, $\left(\frac{\pi}{2}, 2.07\right)$, and $\left(2.93, \frac{3\pi}{2}\right)$, and decreasing on $(0.21, 1.07)$ and $(2.07, 2.93)$.

Local minima: $f(1.07) \approx 4.23$, $f(2.93) \approx -5.10$. Local maxima: $f(0.21) \approx 5.10$, $f(2.07) \approx -4.23$.

From the graph of f'', we estimate that f is CU on $\left(0.76, \frac{\pi}{2}\right)$ and $\left(2.38, \frac{3\pi}{2}\right)$, and CD on $\left(-\frac{\pi}{2}, 0.76\right)$ and $\left(\frac{\pi}{2}, 2.38\right)$.

f has IP at $(0.76, 4.57)$ and $(2.38, -4.57)$.

7. $f(x) = x^2 \sin x$, $-7 \le x \le 7$ $\Rightarrow$ $f'(x) = 2x \sin x + x^2 \cos x$ $\Rightarrow$ $f''(x) = 2 \sin x + 4x \cos x - x^2 \sin x$

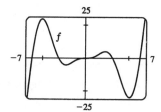 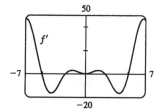 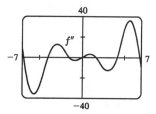

We estimate from the graph of f' that f is increasing on $(-7, -5.1)$, $(-2.3, 2.3)$, and $(5.1, 7)$ and decreasing on $(-5.1, -2.3)$, and $(2.3, 5.1)$.

Local maxima: $f(-5.1) \approx 24.1$, $f(2.3) \approx 3.9$. Local minima: $f(-2.3) \approx -3.9$, $f(5.1) \approx -24.1$.

From the graph of f'', we estimate that f is CU on $(-7, -6.8)$, $(-4.0, -1.5)$, $(0, 1.5)$, and $(4.0, 6.8)$ and CD on $(-6.8, -4.0)$, $(-1.5, 0)$, $(1.5, 4.0)$, and $(6.8, 7)$.

f has IP at $(-6.8, -24.4)$, $(-4.0, 12.0)$, $(-1.5, -2.3)$, $(0, 0)$, $(1.5, 2.3)$, $(4.0, -12.0)$ and $(6.8, 24.4)$.

8. $f(x) = \dfrac{e^x}{x^2 - 9}$ $\Rightarrow$ $f'(x) = \dfrac{e^x \left(x^2 - 2x - 9\right)}{\left(x^2 - 9\right)^2}$ $\Rightarrow$ $f''(x) = \dfrac{e^x \left(x^4 - 4x^3 - 12x^2 + 36x + 99\right)}{\left(x^2 - 9\right)^3}$

There are vertical asymptotes at $x = \pm 3$. It is difficult to show all the pertinent features in one viewing rectangle, so we'll show f, f', and f'' for $x < 3$ and also for $x > 3$.

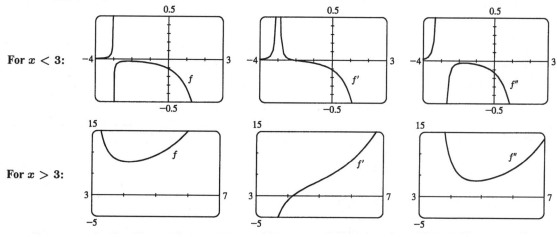

We estimate from the graphs of f' and f that f is increasing on $(-\infty, -3)$, $(-3, -2.16)$, and $(4.16, \infty)$ and decreasing on $(-2.16, 3)$ and $(3, 4.16)$. There is a local maximum at $f(-2.16) \approx -0.03$ and a local minimum at $f(4.16) \approx 7.71$. From the graphs of f'', we see that f is CU on $(-\infty, -3)$ and $(3, \infty)$ and CD on $(-3, 3)$. There is no inflection point.

9. $f(x) = 8x^3 - 3x^2 - 10 \Rightarrow f'(x) = 24x^2 - 6x \Rightarrow f''(x) = 48x - 6$

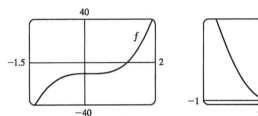 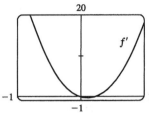 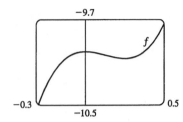

From the graphs, it appears that $f(x) = 8x^3 - 3x^2 - 10$ increases on $(-\infty, 0)$ and $(0.25, \infty)$ and decreases on $(0, 0.25)$; that f has a local maximum of $f(0) = -10.0$ and a local minimum of $f(0.25) \approx -10.1$; that f is CU on $(0.1, \infty)$ and CD on $(-\infty, 0.1)$; and that f has an IP at $(0.1, -10)$. To find the exact values, note that $f'(x) = 24x^2 - 6x = 6x(4x - 1)$, which is positive ($f$ is increasing) for $(-\infty, 0)$ and $\left(\frac{1}{4}, \infty\right)$, and negative ($f$ is decreasing) on $\left(0, \frac{1}{4}\right)$. By the FDT, f has a local maximum at $x = 0$: $f(0) = -10$; and f has a local minimum at $\frac{1}{4}$: $f\left(\frac{1}{4}\right) = \frac{1}{8} - \frac{3}{16} - 10 = -\frac{161}{16}$. $f''(x) = 48x - 6 = 6(8x - 1)$, which is positive ($f$ is CU) on $\left(\frac{1}{8}, \infty\right)$ and negative (f is CD) on $\left(-\infty, \frac{1}{8}\right)$. f has an IP at $\left(\frac{1}{8}, f\left(\frac{1}{8}\right)\right) = \left(\frac{1}{8}, -\frac{321}{32}\right)$.

10.

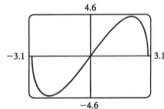

From the graph, it appears that f increases on $(-2.1, 2.1)$ and decreases on $(-3, -2.1)$ and $(2.1, 3)$; that f has a local maximum of $f(2.1) \approx 4.5$ and a local minimum of $f(-2.1) \approx -4.5$; that f is CU on $(-3.0, 0)$ and CD on $(0, 3.0)$, and that f has an IP at $(0, 0)$. $f(x) = x\sqrt{9 - x^2} \Rightarrow f'(x) = \dfrac{-x^2}{\sqrt{9 - x^2}} + \sqrt{9 - x^2} = \dfrac{9 - 2x^2}{\sqrt{9 - x^2}}$, which is positive ($f$ is increasing) on $\left(\dfrac{-3\sqrt{2}}{2}, \dfrac{3\sqrt{2}}{2}\right)$ and negative (f is decreasing) on $\left(-3, \dfrac{-3\sqrt{2}}{2}\right)$ and $\left(\dfrac{3\sqrt{2}}{2}, 3\right)$. By the FDT, f has a local maximum of $f\left(\dfrac{3\sqrt{2}}{2}\right) = \dfrac{3\sqrt{2}}{2}\sqrt{9 - \left(\dfrac{3\sqrt{2}}{2}\right)^2} = \dfrac{9}{2}$; and f has a local minimum of $f\left(\dfrac{-3\sqrt{2}}{2}\right) = -\dfrac{9}{2}$ (since f is an odd function). $f'(x) = \dfrac{-x^2}{\sqrt{9 - x^2}} + \sqrt{9 - x^2} \Rightarrow$

$f''(x) = \dfrac{\sqrt{9 - x^2}(-2x) + x^2\left(\frac{1}{2}\right)(9 - x^2)^{-1/2}(-2x)}{9 - x^2} - x(9 - x^2)^{-1/2} = \dfrac{-2x - x^3(9 - x^2)^{-1} - x}{\sqrt{9 - x^2}}$

$= \dfrac{-3x}{\sqrt{9 - x^2}} - \dfrac{x^3}{(9 - x^2)^{3/2}} = \dfrac{x(2x^2 - 27)}{(9 - x^2)^{3/2}}$

which is positive (f is CU) on $(-3, 0)$ and negative (f is CD) on $(0, 3)$. f has an IP at $(0, 0)$.

11.

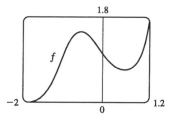

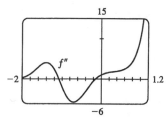

$f(x) = e^{x^3 - x} \to 0$ as $x \to -\infty$, and $f(x) \to \infty$ as $x \to \infty$. From the graph, it appears that f has a local minimum of about $f(0.58) = 0.68$, and a local maximum of about $f(-0.58) = 1.47$. To find the exact values, we calculate $f'(x) = (3x^2 - 1)e^{x^3 - x}$, which is 0 when $3x^2 - 1 = 0 \iff x = \pm\frac{1}{\sqrt{3}}$. The negative root corresponds to the local maximum $f\left(-\frac{1}{\sqrt{3}}\right) = e^{(-1/\sqrt{3})^3 - (-1/\sqrt{3})} = e^{2\sqrt{3}/9}$, and the positive root corresponds to the local minimum $f\left(\frac{1}{\sqrt{3}}\right) = e^{(1/\sqrt{3})^3 - (1/\sqrt{3})} = e^{-2\sqrt{3}/9}$. To estimate the inflection points, we calculate and graph

$$f''(x) = \frac{d}{dx}\left[(3x^2 - 1)e^{x^3 - x}\right] = (3x^2 - 1)e^{x^3 - x}(3x^2 - 1) + e^{x^3 - x}(6x) = e^{x^3 - x}(9x^4 - 6x^2 + 6x + 1).$$

From the graph, it appears that $f''(x)$ changes sign (and thus f has inflection points) at $x \approx -0.15$ and $x \approx -1.09$. From the graph of f, we see that these x-values correspond to inflection points at about $(-0.15, 1.15)$ and $(-1.09, 0.82)$.

12.

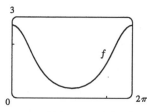

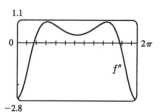

The function $f(x) = e^{\cos x}$ is periodic with period 2π, so we consider it only on the interval $[0, 2\pi]$. We see that it has local maxima of about $f(0) \approx 2.72$ and $f(2\pi) \approx 2.72$, and a local minimum of about $f(3.14) \approx 0.37$. To find the exact values, we calculate $f'(x) = -\sin x\, e^{\cos x}$. This is 0 when $-\sin x = 0 \iff x = 0, \pi$, or 2π (since we are considering only $x \in [0, 2\pi]$). Also $f'(x) > 0 \iff \sin x < 0 \iff \pi < x < 2\pi$. So $f(0) = f(2\pi) = e$ (both maxima) and $f(\pi) = e^{\cos \pi} = 1/e$ (minimum). To find the inflection points, we calculate and graph

$$f''(x) = \frac{d}{dx}(-\sin x\, e^{\cos x}) = -\cos x\, e^{\cos x} - \sin x\, (e^{\cos x})(-\sin x) = e^{\cos x}(\sin^2 x - \cos x).$$ From the graph

of $f''(x)$, we see that f has inflection points at $x \approx 0.90$ and at $x \approx 5.38$. These x-coordinates correspond to inflection points $(0.90, 1.86)$ and $(5.38, 1.86)$.

13.

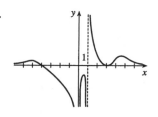

$f(x) = \dfrac{(x + 4)(x - 3)^2}{x^4(x - 1)}$ has VA at $x = 0$ and at $x = 1$ since

$\lim\limits_{x \to 0} f(x) = -\infty$, $\lim\limits_{x \to 1^-} f(x) = -\infty$ and $\lim\limits_{x \to 1^+} f(x) = \infty$.

$f(x) = \dfrac{\dfrac{x + 4}{x} \cdot \dfrac{(x - 3)^2}{x^2}}{\dfrac{x^4}{x^3} \cdot (x - 1)}$ [dividing numerator and denominator by x^3]

$= \dfrac{(1 + 4/x)(1 - 3/x)^2}{x(x - 1)} \to 0$ as $x \to \pm\infty$, so f is asymptotic to the x-axis. Since f is undefined at $x = 0$, it has no y-intercept. $f(x) = 0 \Rightarrow (x + 4)(x - 3)^2 = 0 \Rightarrow$ $x = -4$ or $x = 3$, so f has x-intercepts -4 and 3. Note, however, that the graph of f is only tangent to the x-axis and does not cross it at $x = 3$, since f is positive as $x \to 3^-$ and as $x \to 3^+$.

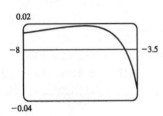

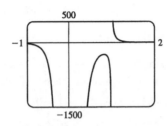

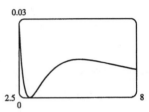

From these graphs, it appears that f has three maxima and one minimum. The maxima are approximately $f(-5.6) = 0.0182$, $f(0.82) = -281.5$ and $f(5.2) = 0.0145$ and we know (since the graph is tangent to the x-axis at $x = 3$) that the minimum is $f(3) = 0$.

14.

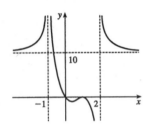

$f(x) = \dfrac{10x(x-1)^4}{(x-2)^3(x+1)^2}$ has VA at $x = -1$ and at $x = 2$ since

$$\lim_{x \to -1} f(x) = \infty, \quad \lim_{x \to 2^-} f(x) = -\infty \text{ and } \lim_{x \to 2^+} f(x) = \infty.$$

$f(x) = \dfrac{10(1 - 1/x)^4}{(1 - 2/x)^3(1 + 1/x)^2} \to 10$ as $x \to \pm\infty$, so f is asymptotic to

the line $y = 10$. $f(0) = 0$, so f has a y-intercept at 0. $f(x) = 0 \Rightarrow$ $10x(x-1)^4 = 0 \Rightarrow x = 0$ or $x = 1$. So f has x-intercepts 0 and 1. Note, however, that f does not change sign at $x = 1$, so the graph is tangent to the x-axis and does not cross it.

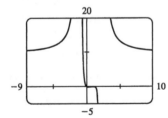

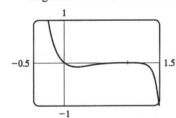

We know (since the graph is tangent to the x-axis at $x = 1$) that the maximum is $f(1) = 0$. From the graphs it appears that the minimum is about $f(0.2) = -0.1$.

15. $f(x) = \dfrac{x^2(x+1)^3}{(x-2)^2(x-4)^4} \Rightarrow f'(x) = -\dfrac{x(x+1)^2(x^3 + 18x^2 - 44x - 16)}{(x-2)^3(x-4)^5}$ (from CAS).

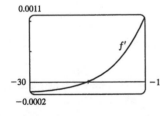

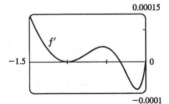

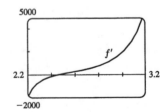

From the graphs of f', it seems that the critical points which indicate extrema occur at $x \approx -20$, -0.3, and 2.5, as estimated in Example 3. (There is another critical point at $x = -1$, but the sign of f' does not change there.) We differentiate again, obtaining $f''(x) = 2\dfrac{(x+1)(x^6 + 36x^5 + 6x^4 - 628x^3 + 684x^2 + 672x + 64)}{(x-2)^4(x-4)^6}$.

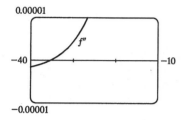 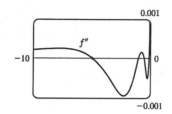 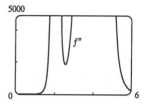

From the graphs of f'', it appears that f is CU on $(-35.3, -5.0)$, $(-1, -0.5)$, $(-0.1, 2)$, $(2, 4)$ and $(4, \infty)$ and CD on $(-\infty, -35.3)$, $(-5.0, -1)$ and $(-0.5, -0.1)$. We check back on the graphs of f to find the y-coordinates of the inflection points, and find that these points are approximately $(-35.3, -0.015)$, $(-5.0, -0.005)$, $(-1, 0)$, $(-0.5, 0.00001)$, and $(-0.1, 0.0000066)$.

16. $f(x) = \dfrac{10x(x-1)^4}{(x-2)^3(x+1)^2}$ $\Rightarrow$ $f'(x) = -20\dfrac{(x-1)^3(5x-1)}{(x-2)^4(x+1)^3}$ (from CAS).

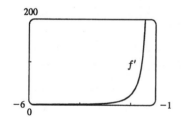 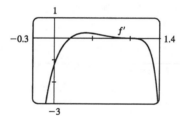 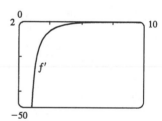

From the graphs of f', we estimate that f is increasing on $(-\infty, -1)$ and $(0.2, 1)$ and decreasing on $(-1, 0.2)$, $(1, 2)$ and $(2, \infty)$. Differentiating $f'(x)$, we get $f''(x) = 60\dfrac{(x-1)^2(5x^3 - 8x^2 + 17x - 6)}{(x-2)^5(x+1)^4}$.

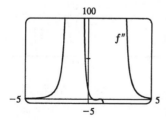 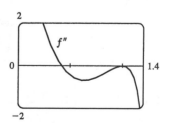

From the graphs of f'', it seems that f is CU on $(-\infty, -1.0)$, $(-1.0, 0.4)$ and $(2.0, \infty)$, and CD on $(0.4, 2)$. There is an inflection point at about $(0.4, -0.06)$.

17. $y = f(x) = \dfrac{\sin^2 x}{\sqrt{x^2+1}}$ with $0 \le x \le 3\pi$. From a CAS, $y' = \dfrac{\sin x \left[2\left(x^2+1\right)\cos x - x \sin x\right]}{\left(x^2+1\right)^{3/2}}$ and

$y'' = \dfrac{\left(4x^4 + 6x^2 + 5\right)\cos^2 x - 4x\left(x^2+1\right)\sin x \cos x - 2x^4 - 2x^2 - 3}{\left(x^2+1\right)^{5/2}}$.

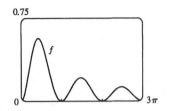

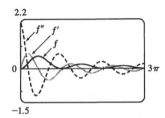

From the graph of f' and the formula for y', we determine that $y' = 0$ when $x = \pi$, 2π, 3π, or $x \approx 1.3$, 4.6, or 7.8. So f is increasing on $(0, 1.3)$, $(\pi, 4.6)$, and $(2\pi, 7.8)$. f is decreasing on $(1.3, \pi)$, $(4.6, 2\pi)$, and $(7.8, 3\pi)$. Local maxima: $f(1.3) \approx 0.6$, $f(4.6) \approx 0.21$, and $f(7.8) \approx 0.13$. Local minima: $f(\pi) = f(2\pi) = 0$. From the graph of f'', we see that $y'' = 0 \iff x \approx 0.6$, 2.1, 3.8, 5.4, 7.0, or 8.6. So f is CU on $(0, 0.6)$, $(2.1, 3.8)$, $(5.4, 7.0)$, and $(8.6, 3\pi)$. f is CD on $(0.6, 2.1)$, $(3.8, 5.4)$, and $(7.0, 8.6)$. There are IP at $(0.6, 0.25)$, $(2.1, 0.31)$, $(3.8, 0.10)$, $(5.4, 0.11)$, $(7.0, 0.061)$, and $(8.6, 0.065)$.

18. $f(x) = \dfrac{2x-1}{\sqrt[4]{x^4+x+1}} \Rightarrow f'(x) = \dfrac{4x^3+6x+9}{4(x^4+x+1)^{5/4}} \Rightarrow$

$f''(x) = -\dfrac{32x^6 + 96x^4 + 152x^3 - 48x^2 + 6x + 21}{16(x^4+x+1)^{9/4}}$

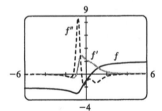

From the graph of f', f appears to be decreasing on $(-\infty, -0.94)$ and increasing on $(-0.94, \infty)$. There is a local minimum of $f(-0.94) \approx -3.01$. From the graph of f'', f appears to be CU on $(-1.25, -0.44)$ and CD on $(-\infty, -1.25)$ and $(-0.44, \infty)$. There are inflection points at $(-1.25, -2.87)$ and $(-0.44, -2.14)$.

19.

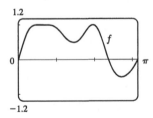

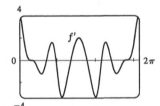

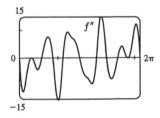

From the graph of $f(x) = \sin(x + \sin 3x)$ in the viewing rectangle $[0, \pi]$ by $[-1.2, 1.2]$, it looks like f has two maxima and two minima. If we calculate and graph $f'(x) = [\cos(x + \sin 3x)](1 + 3 \cos 3x)$ on $[0, 2\pi]$, we see that the graph of f' appears to be almost tangent to the x-axis at about $x = 0.7$. The graph of

$f'' = -[\sin(x + \sin 3x)](1 + 3\cos 3x)^2 + \cos(x + \sin 3x)(-9 \sin 3x)$ is even more interesting near this x-value: it seems to just touch the x-axis.

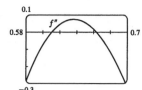

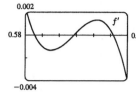

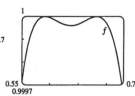

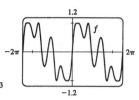

If we zoom in on this place on the graph of f'', we see that f'' actually does cross the axis twice near $x = 0.65$, indicating a change in concavity for a very short interval. If we look at the graph of f' on the same interval, we see that it changes sign three times near $x = 0.65$, indicating that what we had thought was a broad extremum at about $x = 0.7$ actually consists of three extrema (two maxima and a minimum). These maxima are roughly $f(0.59) = 1$ and $f(0.68) = 1$, and the minimum is roughly $f(0.64) = 0.99996$. There are also a maximum of about $f(1.96) = 1$ and minima of about $f(1.46) = 0.49$ and $f(2.73) = -0.51$. The points of inflection on $(0, \pi)$ are about $(0.61, 0.99998)$, $(0.66, 0.99998)$, $(1.17, 0.72)$, $(1.75, 0.77)$, and $(2.28, 0.34)$. On $(\pi, 2\pi)$, they are about $(4.01, -0.34)$, $(4.54, -0.77)$, $(5.11, -0.72)$, $(5.62, -0.99998)$, and $(5.67, -0.99998)$. There are also IP at $(0, 0)$ and $(\pi, 0)$. Note that the function is odd and periodic with period 2π, and it is also rotationally symmetric about all points of the form $((2n + 1)\pi, 0)$, n an integer.

20. From the graph, it appears that the leftmost point on the curve $x = t^4 - t^2$, $y = t + \ln t$ is about $(-0.25, 0.36)$. To find the exact coordinates, we find the value of t for which the graph has a vertical tangent; that is, $dx/dt = 0$ and $dy/dt \neq 0$. $dx/dt = 0 \Leftrightarrow 4t^3 - 2t = 0 \Leftrightarrow 2t(2t^2 - 1) = 0$ $\Leftrightarrow 2t(\sqrt{2}t + 1)(\sqrt{2}t - 1) = 0 \Leftrightarrow t = 0$ or $\pm\frac{1}{\sqrt{2}}$. The negative and 0 roots are inadmissible since $y(t)$ is only defined for $t > 0$, so the

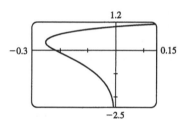

leftmost point must be $\left(x\left(\frac{1}{\sqrt{2}}\right), y\left(\frac{1}{\sqrt{2}}\right)\right) = \left(\left(\frac{1}{\sqrt{2}}\right)^4 - \left(\frac{1}{\sqrt{2}}\right)^2, \frac{1}{\sqrt{2}} + \ln \frac{1}{\sqrt{2}}\right) = \left(-\frac{1}{4}, \frac{1}{\sqrt{2}} - \frac{1}{2} \ln 2\right)$.

21.

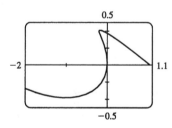

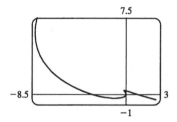

We graph the curve $x = t^4 - 2t^3 - 2t^2$, $y = t^3 - t$ in the viewing rectangle $[-2, 1.1]$ by $[-0.5, 0.5]$. This rectangle corresponds approximately to $t \in [-1, 0.8]$. We estimate that the curve has horizontal tangents at about $(-1, -0.4)$ and $(-0.17, 0.39)$ and vertical tangents at about $(0, 0)$ and $(-0.19, 0.37)$. We calculate

$\frac{dy}{dx} = \frac{dy/dt}{dx/dt} = \frac{3t^2 - 1}{4t^3 - 6t^2 - 4t}$. The horizontal tangents occur when $dy/dt = 3t^2 - 1 = 0 \Leftrightarrow t = \pm\frac{1}{\sqrt{3}}$, so both horizontal tangents are shown in our graph. $t = \frac{1}{\sqrt{3}}$ corresponds to the point

$\left(\frac{-2\sqrt{3}-5}{9}, \frac{-2\sqrt{3}}{9}\right) \approx (-0.94, -0.38)$ and $t = -\frac{1}{\sqrt{3}}$ corresponds to $\left(\frac{2\sqrt{3}-5}{9}, \frac{2\sqrt{3}}{9}\right) \approx (-0.17, 0.38)$. The

vertical tangents occur when $dx/dt = 2t(2t^2 - 3t - 2) = 0 \iff 2t(2t + 1)(t - 2) = 0 \iff t = 0, -\frac{1}{2}$
or 2. It seems that we have missed one vertical tangent, and indeed if we plot the curve on the t-interval $[-1.2, 2.2]$
we see that there is another vertical tangent at $(-8, 6)$. The t-values and points at which there are vertical tangents
are $t = 0$, $(0, 0)$; $t = -\frac{1}{2}$, $\left(-\frac{3}{16}, \frac{3}{8}\right)$; and $t = 2$, $(-8, 6)$.

22.

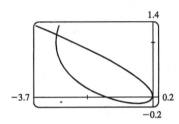

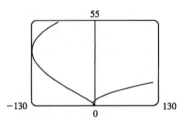

We graph the curve $x = t^4 + 4t^3 - 8t^2$, $y = 2t^2 - t$ in the viewing rectangle $[-3.7, 0.2]$ by $[-0.2, 1.4]$. It appears
that there is a horizontal tangent at about $(-0.4, -0.1)$, and vertical tangents at about $(-3, 1)$ and $(0, 0)$. We

calculate $\dfrac{dy}{dx} = \dfrac{dy/dt}{dx/dt} = \dfrac{4t - 1}{4t^3 + 12t^2 - 16t}$, so there is a horizontal tangent where $dy/dt = 4t - 1 = 0 \iff$

$t = \frac{1}{4}$. This point (the lowest point) is shown in the first graph. Its coordinates are $\left(-\frac{111}{256}, -\frac{1}{8}\right)$. There are vertical
tangents where $dx/dt = 4t^3 + 12t^2 - 16t = 0 \iff 4t(t^2 + 3t - 4) = 0 \iff 4t(t + 4)(t - 1) = 0$. We have
missed one vertical tangent corresponding to $t = -4$, and if we plot the graph for $t \in [-5, 3]$, we see that the curve
has another vertical tangent line at approximately $(-128, 36)$. The t-values and points at which there are vertical
tangents are $t = 0$, $(0, 0)$; $t = -4$, $(-128, 36)$; and $t = 1$, $(-3, 1)$.

23. $x = t^3 - ct$, $y = t^2$. For $c = 0$, there is a cusp at $(0, 0)$. For $c < 0$, there is a local minimum at $(0, 0)$. For $c > 0$,
there is a loop whose size increases as c increases ($c = \frac{1}{2}$ and $c = 1$ are shown in the figure). The curve intersects
itself on the y-axis; that is, when $x = 0 \iff t^3 - ct = 0 \iff t(t^2 - c) = 0 \iff t = 0, \pm\sqrt{c}$. Substituting
$\pm\sqrt{c}$ for t gives us $y = c$, so the point of intersection is $(0, c)$.

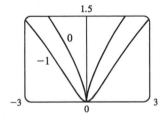

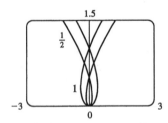

From the second figure, we see that the left- and rightmost points of the loop occur when there are vertical tangent
lines. $dx/dt = 0 \implies 3t^2 - c = 0 \implies t = \pm\sqrt{c/3}$. The rightmost point occurs when $t = -\sqrt{c/3}$ and has

coordinates $\left(\dfrac{2c\sqrt{3c}}{9}, \dfrac{c}{3}\right)$. The leftmost point occurs when $t = \sqrt{c/3}$ and has coordinates $\left(-\dfrac{2c\sqrt{3c}}{9}, \dfrac{c}{3}\right)$.

24. For $f(t) = C(e^{-at} - e^{-bt})$, C affects only vertical stretching, so we let $C = 1$. From the first figure, we notice that the graphs all pass through the origin, approach the t-axis as t increases, and approach $-\infty$ as $t \to -\infty$. Next we let $a = 2$ and produce the second figure.

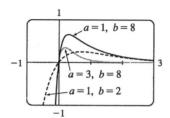

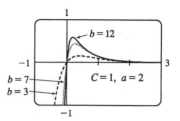

Here, as b increases, the slope of the tangent at the origin increases and the local maximum value increases.

$f(t) = e^{-2t} - e^{-bt}$ $\Rightarrow$ $f'(t) = be^{-bt} - 2e^{-2t}$. $f'(0) = b - 2$, which increases as b increases. $f'(t) = 0$ $\Rightarrow$

$be^{-bt} = 2e^{-2t}$ $\Rightarrow$ $\dfrac{b}{2} = e^{(b-2)t}$ $\Rightarrow$ $\ln \dfrac{b}{2} = (b-2)t$ $\Rightarrow$ $t = t_1 = \dfrac{\ln b - \ln 2}{b - 2}$, which decreases as b

increases (the maximum is getting closer to the y-axis). $f(t_1) = \dfrac{(b-2)2^{2/(b-2)}}{b^{1+2/(b-2)}}$. We can show that this value

increases as b increases by considering it to be a function of b and graphing its derivative with respect to b, which is always positive.

25. Note that $c = 0$ is a transitional value at which the graph consists of the x-axis. Also, we can see that if we

substitute $-c$ for c, the function $f(x) = \dfrac{cx}{1 + c^2 x^2}$ will be reflected in the x-axis, so we investigate only positive

values of c (except $c = -1$, as a demonstration of this reflective property). Also, f is an odd

function. $\lim\limits_{x \to \pm\infty} f(x) = 0$, so $y = 0$ is a horizontal asymptote for all c. We calculate

$f'(x) = \dfrac{(1 + c^2 x^2)c - cx(2c^2 x)}{(1 + c^2 x^2)^2} = -\dfrac{c(c^2 x^2 - 1)}{(1 + c^2 x^2)^2}$. $f'(x) = 0$ $\Leftrightarrow$ $c^2 x^2 - 1 = 0$ $\Leftrightarrow$ $x = \pm 1/c$. So there

is an absolute maximum of $f(1/c) = \frac{1}{2}$ and an absolute minimum of $f(-1/c) = -\frac{1}{2}$. These extrema have the

same value regardless of c, but the maximum points move closer to the y-axis as c increases.

$f''(x) = \dfrac{(-2c^3 x)(1 + c^2 x^2)^2 - (-c^3 x^2 + c)[2(1 + c^2 x^2)(2c^2 x)]}{(1 + c^2 x^2)^4}$

$= \dfrac{(-2c^3 x)(1 + c^2 x^2) + (c^3 x^2 - c)(4c^2 x)}{(1 + c^2 x^2)^3} = \dfrac{2c^3 x(c^2 x^2 - 3)}{(1 + c^2 x^2)^3}$

$f''(x) = 0$ $\Leftrightarrow$ $x = 0$ or $\pm\sqrt{3}/c$, so there are inflection points at $(0, 0)$
and at $\left(\pm\sqrt{3}/c, \pm\sqrt{3}/4\right)$.

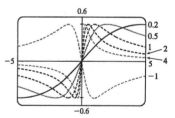

Again, the y-coordinate of the inflection points does not depend on c, but as c increases, both inflection points approach the y-axis.

26. We see that if $c \le 0$, $f(x) = \ln(x^2 + c)$ is only defined for $x^2 > -c$ $\Rightarrow$ $|x| > \sqrt{-c}$, and

$\lim\limits_{x \to \sqrt{-c}^+} f(x) = \lim\limits_{x \to -\sqrt{-c}^-} f(x) = -\infty$, since $\ln y \to -\infty$ as $y \to 0$. Thus, for $c < 0$, there are vertical

asymptotes at $x = \pm\sqrt{c}$, and as c decreases (that is, $|c|$ increases), the asymptotes get further apart. For $c = 0$,

$\lim\limits_{x \to 0} f(x) = -\infty$, so there is a vertical asymptote at $x = 0$. If $c > 0$, there are no asymptotes. To find the extrema and inflection points, we differentiate: $f(x) = \ln(x^2 + c)$ $\Rightarrow$ $f'(x) = \dfrac{1}{x^2 + c}(2x)$, so by the First Derivative

Test there is a local and absolute minimum at $x = 0$. Differentiating again, we get

$$f''(x) = \frac{1}{x^2 + c}(2) + 2x\left[-\left(x^2 + c\right)^{-2}(2x)\right] = \frac{2(c - x^2)}{(x^2 + c)^2}.$$

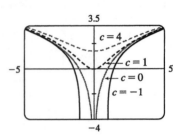

Now if $c \le 0$, f'' is always negative, so f is concave down on both

of the intervals on which it is defined. If $c > 0$, then f'' changes sign

when $c = x^2$ $\Leftrightarrow$ $x = \pm\sqrt{c}$. So for $c > 0$ there are inflection points

at $x = \pm\sqrt{c}$, and as c increases, the inflection points get further

apart.

27.

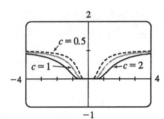
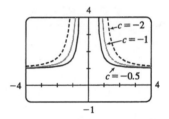

$c = 0$ is a transitional value — we get the graph of $y = 1$. For $c > 0$, we see that there is a HA at $y = 1$, and that

the graph spreads out as c increases. At first glance there appears to be a minimum at $(0, 0)$, but $f(0)$ is undefined,

so there is no minimum or maximum. For $c < 0$, we still have the HA at $y = 1$, but the range is $(1, \infty)$ rather than

$(0, 1)$. We also have a VA at $x = 0$. $f(x) = e^{-c/x^2}$ $\Rightarrow$ $f'(x) = e^{-c/x^2}\left(-2c/x^3\right)$ $\Rightarrow$

$f''(x) = \dfrac{2c(2c - 3x^2)}{x^6 e^{c/x^2}}$. $f'(x) \ne 0$ and $f'(x)$ exists for all $x \ne 0$ (and 0 is not in the domain of f), so there are no

maxima or minima. $f''(x) = 0$ $\Rightarrow$ $x = \pm\sqrt{2c/3}$, so if $c > 0$, the inflection points spread out as c increases,

and if $c < 0$, there are no IP. For $c > 0$, there are IP at $\left(\pm\sqrt{2c/3}, e^{-3/2}\right)$. Note that the y-coordinate of the IP is

constant.

28. Note that $f(x) = \dfrac{1}{(1 - x^2)^2 + cx^2}$ is an even function, and also that $\displaystyle\lim_{x \to \pm\infty} f(x) = 0$ for any value of c, so $y = 0$

is a horizontal asymptote. We calculate the derivatives:

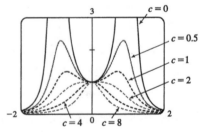

$$f'(x) = \frac{-4(1 - x^2)x + 2cx}{\left[(1 - x^2)^2 + cx^2\right]^2} = \frac{4x\left[x^2 + \left(\frac{1}{2}c - 1\right)\right]}{\left[(1 - x^2)^2 + cx^2\right]^2}, \text{ and}$$

$$f''(x) = 2\frac{10x^6 + (9c - 18)x^4 + (3c^2 - 12c + 6)x^2 + 2 - c}{\left[x^4 + (c - 2)x^2 + 1\right]^3}. \text{ We}$$

first consider the case $c > 0$. Then the denominator of f' is positive,

that is, $(1 - x^2)^2 + cx^2 > 0$ for all x, so f has domain

$\mathbb{R}$ and also $f > 0$. If $\frac{1}{2}c - 1 \ge 0$; that is, $c \ge 2$, then the only critical point is $f(0) = 1$, a maximum. Graphing a

few examples for $c \ge 2$ shows that there are two IP which approach the y-axis as $c \to \infty$.

$c = 2$ and $c = 0$ are transitional values of c at which the shape of the curve changes. For $0 < c < 2$, there are three critical points: $f(0) = 1$, a minimum, and $f\left(\pm\sqrt{1 - \frac{1}{2}c}\right) = \dfrac{1}{c(1 - c/4)}$, both maxima. As c decreases from 2 to 0, the maximum values get larger and larger, and the x-values at which they occur go from 0 to ± 1. Graphs show that there are four inflection points for $0 < c < 2$, and that they get farther away from the origin, both vertically and horizontally, as $c \to 0^+$. For $c = 0$, the function is simply asymptotic to the x-axis and to the lines $x = \pm 1$, approaching $+\infty$ from both sides of each. The y-intercept is 1, and $(0, 1)$ is a local minimum. There are no inflection points. Now if $c < 0$, we can write

$$f(x) = \frac{1}{\left(1 - x^2\right)^2 + cx^2} = \frac{1}{\left(1 - x^2\right)^2 - \left(\sqrt{-c}\,x\right)^2} = \frac{1}{\left(x^2 - \sqrt{-c}\,x - 1\right)\left(x^2 + \sqrt{-c}\,x - 1\right)}.$$ So f has vertical

asymptotes where $x^2 \pm \sqrt{-c}\,x - 1 = 0 \;\Leftrightarrow\; x = \left(-\sqrt{-c} \pm \sqrt{4 - c}\right)/2$ or $x = \left(\sqrt{-c} \pm \sqrt{4 - c}\right)/2$. As c decreases, the two exterior asymptotes move away from the origin, while the two interior ones move toward it. We graph a few examples to see the behavior of the graph near the asymptotes, and the nature of the critical points $x = 0$ and $x = \pm\sqrt{1 - \frac{1}{2}c}$:

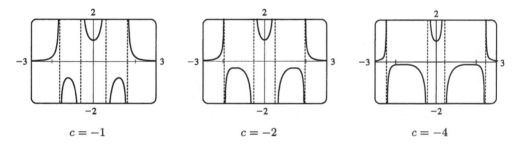

| $c = -1$ | $c = -2$ | $c = -4$ |

We see that there is one local minimum, $f(0) = 1$, and there are two local maxima, $f\left(\pm\sqrt{1 - \frac{1}{2}c}\right) = \dfrac{1}{c(1 - c/4)}$ as before. As c decreases, the x-values at which these maxima occur get larger, and the maximum values themselves approach 0, though they are always negative.

29. $f(x) = x^4 + cx^2 = x^2\left(x^2 + c\right)$. Note that f is an even function. For $c \geq 0$, the only x-intercept is the point $(0, 0)$. We calculate $f'(x) = 4x^3 + 2cx = 4x\left(x^2 + \frac{1}{2}c\right) \;\Rightarrow\; f''(x) = 12x^2 + 2c$. If $c \geq 0$, $x = 0$ is the only critical point and there is no inflection point. As we can see from the examples, there is no change in the basic shape of the graph for $c \geq 0$; it merely becomes steeper as c increases. For $c = 0$, the graph is the simple curve $y = x^4$. For $c < 0$, there are x-intercepts at 0 and at $\pm\sqrt{-c}$. Also, there is a maximum at $(0, 0)$, and there are minima at $\left(\pm\sqrt{-\frac{1}{2}c}, -\frac{1}{4}c^2\right)$. As $c \to -\infty$, the x-coordinates of these minima get larger in absolute value, and the minimum points move downward. There are inflection points at $\left(\pm\sqrt{-\frac{1}{6}c}, -\frac{5}{36}c^2\right)$, which also move away from the origin as $c \to -\infty$.

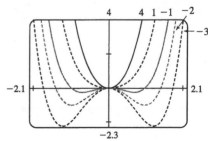

30. For $c = 0$, there is no inflection point; the curve is CU everywhere. If c increases, the curve simply becomes steeper, and there are still no inflection points. If c starts at 0 and decreases, a slight upward bulge appears near $x = 0$, so that there are two inflection points for any $c < 0$. This can be seen algebraically by calculating the second derivative: $f(x) = x^4 + cx^2 + x$ $\Rightarrow$ $f'(x) = 4x^3 + 2cx + 1$ $\Rightarrow$ $f''(x) = 12x^2 + 2c$. Thus, $f''(x) > 0$ when $c > 0$. For $c < 0$, there are inflection points when $x = \pm\sqrt{-\frac{1}{6}c}$. For $c = 0$, the graph has one critical number, at the absolute minimum somewhere around $x = -0.6$. As c increases, the number of critical points does not change. If c instead decreases from 0, we see that the graph eventually sprouts another local minimum, to the right of the origin, somewhere between $x = 1$ and $x = 2$. Consequently, there is also a maximum near $x = 0$. After a bit of experimentation, we find that at $c = -1.5$, there appear to be two critical numbers: the absolute minimum at about $x = -1$, and a horizontal tangent with no

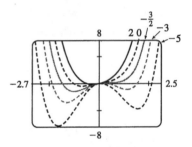

extremum at about $x = 0.5$. For any c smaller than this there will be 3 critical points, as shown in the graphs with $c = -3$ and with $c = -5$. To prove this algebraically, we calculate $f'(x) = 4x^3 + 2cx + 1$. Now if we substitute our value of $c = -1.5$, the formula for $f'(x)$ becomes $4x^3 - 3x + 1 = (x+1)(2x-1)^2$. This has a double root at $x = \frac{1}{2}$, indicating that the function has two critical points: $x = -1$ and $x = \frac{1}{2}$, just as we had guessed from the graph.

31. (a) $f(x) = cx^4 - 2x^2 + 1$. For $c = 0$, $f(x) = -2x^2 + 1$, a parabola whose vertex, $(0, 1)$, is the absolute maximum. For $c > 0$, $f(x) = cx^4 - 2x^2 + 1$ opens upward with two minimum points. As $c \to 0$, the minimum points spread apart and move downward; they are below the x-axis for $0 < c < 1$ and above for $c > 1$. For $c < 0$, the graph opens downward, and has an absolute maximum at $x = 0$ and no local minimum.

(b) $f'(x) = 4cx^3 - 4x = 4cx(x^2 - 1/c)$ $(c \neq 0)$. If $c \leq 0$, 0 is the only critical number. $f''(x) = 12cx^2 - 4$, so $f''(0) = -4$ and there is a local maximum at $(0, f(0)) = (0, 1)$, which lies on $y = 1 - x^2$. If $c > 0$, the critical numbers are 0 and $\pm 1/\sqrt{c}$. As before, there is a local maximum at $(0, f(0)) = (0, 1)$, which lies on $y = 1 - x^2$. $f''(\pm 1/\sqrt{c}) = 12 - 4 = 8 > 0$, so there is a local minimum at $x = \pm 1/\sqrt{c}$. Here $f(\pm 1/\sqrt{c}) = c(1/c^2) - 2/c + 1 = -1/c + 1$. But $(\pm 1/\sqrt{c}, -1/c + 1)$ lies on $y = 1 - x^2$ since $1 - (\pm 1/\sqrt{c})^2 = 1 - 1/c$.

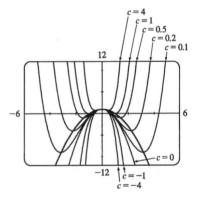

32. (a) $f(x) = 2x^3 + cx^2 + 2x$ $\Rightarrow$ $f'(x) = 6x^2 + 2cx + 2 = 2(3x^2 + cx + 1)$. $f'(x) = 0$ $\Leftrightarrow$ $x = \dfrac{-c \pm \sqrt{c^2 - 12}}{6}$. So f has critical points $\Leftrightarrow$ $c^2 - 12 \geq 0$ $\Leftrightarrow$ $|c| \geq 2\sqrt{3}$. For $c = \pm 2\sqrt{3}$, $f'(x) \geq 0$ on $(-\infty, \infty)$, so f' does not change signs at $-c/6$, and there is no extremum. If $c^2 - 12 > 0$, then f' changes from positive to negative at $x = \dfrac{-c - \sqrt{c^2 - 12}}{6}$ and from negative to positive at $x = \dfrac{-c + \sqrt{c^2 - 12}}{6}$. So f has a local maximum at $x = \dfrac{-c - \sqrt{c^2 - 12}}{6}$ and a local minimum at $x = \dfrac{-c + \sqrt{c^2 - 12}}{6}$.

(b) Let x_0 be a critical number for $f(x)$. Then $f'(x_0) = 0 \Rightarrow$

$$3x_0^2 + cx_0 + 1 = 0 \iff c = \frac{-1 - 3x_0^2}{x_0}. \text{ Now}$$

$$f(x_0) = 2x_0^3 + cx_0^2 + 2x_0 = 2x_0^3 + x_0^2\left(\frac{-1 - 3x_0^2}{x_0}\right) + 2x_0$$

$$= 2x_0^3 - x_0 - 3x_0^3 + 2x_0 = x_0 - x_0^3$$

So the point is $(x_0, y_0) = (x_0, x_0 - x_0^3)$; that is, the point lies on the

curve $y = x - x^3$.

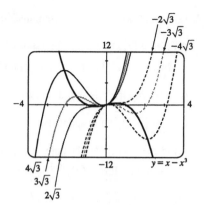

4.5 Indeterminate Forms and l'Hospital's Rule · · · · · ·

Note: The use of l'Hospital's Rule is indicated by an H above the equal sign: $\overset{H}{=}$

1. (a) $\lim\limits_{x \to a} \dfrac{f(x)}{g(x)}$ is an indeterminate form of type $\dfrac{0}{0}$.

(b) $\lim\limits_{x \to a} \dfrac{f(x)}{p(x)} = 0$ because the numerator approaches 0 while the denominator becomes large.

(c) $\lim\limits_{x \to a} \dfrac{h(x)}{p(x)} = 0$ because the numerator approaches a finite number while the denominator becomes large.

(d) If $\lim\limits_{x \to a} p(x) = \infty$ and $f(x) \to 0$ through positive values, then $\lim\limits_{x \to a} \dfrac{p(x)}{f(x)} = \infty$. [For example, take $a = 0$,

$p(x) = 1/x^2$, and $f(x) = x^2$.] If $f(x) \to 0$ through negative values, then $\lim\limits_{x \to a} \dfrac{p(x)}{f(x)} = -\infty$. [For example,

take $a = 0$, $p(x) = 1/x^2$, and $f(x) = -x^2$.] If $f(x) \to 0$ through both positive and negative values, then the

limit might not exist. [For example, take $a = 0$, $p(x) = 1/x^2$, and $f(x) = x$.] It is not possible to evaluate

this limit.

(e) $\lim\limits_{x \to a} \dfrac{p(x)}{q(x)}$ is an indeterminate form of type $\dfrac{\infty}{\infty}$.

2. (a) $\lim\limits_{x \to a} [f(x)p(x)]$ is an indeterminate form of type $0 \cdot \infty$.

(b) When x is near a, $p(x)$ is large and $h(x)$ is near 1, so $h(x)p(x)$ is large. Thus, $\lim\limits_{x \to a} [h(x)p(x)] = \infty$.

(c) When x is near a, $p(x)$ and $q(x)$ are both large, so $p(x)q(x)$ is large. Thus, $\lim\limits_{x \to a} [p(x)q(x)] = \infty$.

3. (a) When x is near a, $f(x)$ is near 0 and $p(x)$ is large, so $f(x) - p(x)$ is large negative. Thus,

$\lim\limits_{x \to a} [f(x) - p(x)] = -\infty$.

(b) $\lim\limits_{x \to a} [p(x) - q(x)]$ is an indeterminate form of type $\infty - \infty$.

(c) When x is near a, $p(x)$ and $q(x)$ are both large, so $p(x) + q(x)$ is large. Thus, $\lim\limits_{x \to a} [p(x) + q(x)] = \infty$.

4. (a) $\lim\limits_{x \to a} [f(x)]^{g(x)}$ is an indeterminate form of type 0^0.

(b) If $y = [f(x)]^{p(x)}$, then $\ln y = p(x) \ln f(x)$. When x is near a, $p(x) \to \infty$ and $\ln f(x) \to -\infty$, so $\ln y \to -\infty$. Therefore, $\lim\limits_{x \to a} [f(x)]^{p(x)} = \lim\limits_{x \to a} y = \lim\limits_{x \to a} e^{\ln y} = 0$, provided f^p is defined.

(c) $\lim\limits_{x \to a} [h(x)]^{p(x)}$ is an indeterminate form of type 1^∞.

(d) $\lim\limits_{x \to a} [p(x)]^{f(x)}$ is an indeterminate form of type ∞^0.

(e) If $y = [p(x)]^{q(x)}$, then $\ln y = q(x) \ln p(x)$. When x is near a, $q(x) \to \infty$ and $\ln p(x) \to \infty$, so $\ln y \to \infty$. Therefore, $\lim\limits_{x \to a} [p(x)]^{q(x)} = \lim\limits_{x \to a} y = \lim\limits_{x \to a} e^{\ln y} = \infty$.

(f) $\lim\limits_{x \to a} \sqrt[q(x)]{p(x)} = \lim\limits_{x \to a} [p(x)]^{1/q(x)}$ is an indeterminate form of type ∞^0.

5. We can simply factor the numerator to evaluate this limit.

$$\lim_{x \to -1} \frac{x^2 - 1}{x + 1} = \lim_{x \to -1} \frac{(x + 1)(x - 1)}{x + 1} = \lim_{x \to -1} (x - 1) = -2$$

6. $\lim\limits_{x \to 1} \dfrac{x^a - 1}{x^b - 1} \overset{H}{=} \lim\limits_{x \to 1} \dfrac{ax^{a-1}}{bx^{b-1}} = \dfrac{a}{b}$

7. $\lim\limits_{x \to 0} \dfrac{e^x - 1}{\sin x}$ is an indeterminate form of type $\frac{0}{0}$, so we'll apply l'Hospital's Rule.

$$\lim_{x \to 0} \frac{e^x - 1}{\sin x} \overset{H}{=} \lim_{x \to 0} \frac{e^x}{\cos x} = \frac{1}{1} = 1$$

8. $\lim\limits_{x \to 0} \dfrac{x + \tan x}{\sin x} \overset{H}{=} \lim\limits_{x \to 0} \dfrac{1 + \sec^2 x}{\cos x} = \dfrac{1 + 1^2}{1} = 2$

9. This limit has the form $\frac{0}{0}$. $\lim\limits_{x \to 0} \dfrac{\tan px}{\tan qx} \overset{H}{=} \lim\limits_{x \to 0} \dfrac{p \sec^2 px}{q \sec^2 qx} = \dfrac{p(1)^2}{q(1)^2} = \dfrac{p}{q}$

10. $\lim\limits_{x \to \pi} \dfrac{\tan x}{x} = \dfrac{\tan \pi}{\pi} = \dfrac{0}{\pi} = 0$

11. $\lim\limits_{x \to 0^+} [(\ln x)/x] = -\infty$ since $\ln x \to -\infty$ as $x \to 0^+$ and dividing by small values of x just increases the magnitude of the quotient $(\ln x)/x$. L'Hospital's Rule does not apply.

12. $\lim\limits_{x \to \infty} \dfrac{\ln \ln x}{x} \overset{H}{=} \lim\limits_{x \to \infty} \dfrac{\frac{1}{\ln x} \cdot \frac{1}{x}}{1} = \lim\limits_{x \to \infty} \dfrac{1}{x \ln x} = 0$

13. This limit has the form $\frac{0}{0}$. $\lim\limits_{t \to 0} \dfrac{5^t - 3^t}{t} \overset{H}{=} \lim\limits_{t \to 0} \dfrac{5^t \ln 5 - 3^t \ln 3}{1} = \ln 5 - \ln 3 = \ln \frac{5}{3}$

14. $\lim\limits_{x \to \infty} \dfrac{e^x}{x^3} \overset{H}{=} \lim\limits_{x \to \infty} \dfrac{e^x}{3x^2} \overset{H}{=} \lim\limits_{x \to \infty} \dfrac{e^x}{6x} \overset{H}{=} \lim\limits_{x \to \infty} \dfrac{e^x}{6} = \infty$

15. This limit has the form $\frac{0}{0}$. $\lim\limits_{x \to 0} \dfrac{e^x - 1 - x}{x^2} \overset{H}{=} \lim\limits_{x \to 0} \dfrac{e^x - 1}{2x} \overset{H}{=} \lim\limits_{x \to 0} \dfrac{e^x}{2} = \dfrac{1}{2}$

16. $\lim\limits_{x \to 0} \dfrac{\cos mx - \cos nx}{x^2} \overset{H}{=} \lim\limits_{x \to 0} \dfrac{-m \sin mx + n \sin nx}{2x} \overset{H}{=} \lim\limits_{x \to 0} \dfrac{-m^2 \cos mx + n^2 \cos nx}{2} = \frac{1}{2}(n^2 - m^2)$

17. This limit has the form $\frac{0}{0}$. $\lim\limits_{x \to 0} \dfrac{\sin^{-1} x}{x} \overset{H}{=} \lim\limits_{x \to 0} \dfrac{1/\sqrt{1 - x^2}}{1} = \lim\limits_{x \to 0} \dfrac{1}{\sqrt{1 - x^2}} = \dfrac{1}{1} = 1$

18. $\lim\limits_{x \to 0} \dfrac{x}{\tan^{-1}(4x)} \overset{H}{=} \lim\limits_{x \to 0} \dfrac{1}{\dfrac{1}{1 + (4x)^2} \cdot 4} = \lim\limits_{x \to 0} \dfrac{1 + 16x^2}{4} = \dfrac{1}{4}$

19. This limit has the form $\frac{\infty}{\infty}$. $\displaystyle\lim_{x\to\infty}\frac{x}{\ln(1+2e^x)}\overset{H}{=}\lim_{x\to\infty}\frac{1}{\frac{1}{1+2e^x}\cdot 2e^x}=\lim_{x\to\infty}\frac{1+2e^x}{2e^x}\overset{H}{=}\lim_{x\to\infty}\frac{2e^x}{2e^x}=1$

20. $\displaystyle\lim_{x\to 0}\frac{1-e^{-2x}}{\sec x}=\frac{1-1}{1}=0$. L'Hospital's Rule does not apply.

21. This limit has the form $0\cdot(-\infty)$. We need to write this product as a quotient, but keep in mind that we will have to differentiate both the numerator and the denominator. If we differentiate $\frac{1}{\ln x}$, we get a complicated expression that results in a more difficult limit. Instead we write the quotient as $\frac{\ln x}{x^{-1/2}}$.

$\displaystyle\lim_{x\to 0+}\sqrt{x}\,\ln x=\lim_{x\to 0+}\frac{\ln x}{x^{-1/2}}\overset{H}{=}\lim_{x\to 0+}\frac{1/x}{-\frac{1}{2}x^{-3/2}}\cdot\frac{-2x^{3/2}}{-2x^{3/2}}=\lim_{x\to 0+}(-2\sqrt{x})=0$

22. $\displaystyle\lim_{x\to-\infty}x^2e^x=\lim_{x\to-\infty}\frac{x^2}{e^{-x}}\overset{H}{=}\lim_{x\to-\infty}\frac{2x}{-e^{-x}}\overset{H}{=}\lim_{x\to-\infty}\frac{2}{e^{-x}}=\lim_{x\to-\infty}2e^x=0$

23. $\displaystyle\lim_{x\to\infty}e^{-x}\ln x=\lim_{x\to\infty}\frac{\ln x}{e^x}\overset{H}{=}\lim_{x\to\infty}\frac{1/x}{e^x}=\lim_{x\to\infty}\frac{1}{xe^x}=0$

24. $\displaystyle\lim_{x\to(\pi/2)^-}\sec 7x\cos 3x=\lim_{x\to(\pi/2)^-}\frac{\cos 3x}{\cos 7x}\overset{H}{=}\lim_{x\to(\pi/2)^-}\frac{-3\sin 3x}{-7\sin 7x}=\frac{3(-1)}{7(-1)}=\frac{3}{7}$

25. $\displaystyle\lim_{x\to\infty}x^3e^{-x^2}=\lim_{x\to\infty}\frac{x^3}{e^{x^2}}\overset{H}{=}\lim_{x\to\infty}\frac{3x^2}{2xe^{x^2}}=\lim_{x\to\infty}\frac{3x}{2e^{x^2}}\overset{H}{=}\lim_{x\to\infty}\frac{3}{4xe^{x^2}}=0$

26. $\displaystyle\lim_{x\to 1+}(x-1)\tan(\pi x/2)=\lim_{x\to 1+}\frac{x-1}{\cot(\pi x/2)}\overset{H}{=}\lim_{x\to 1+}\frac{1}{-\csc^2(\pi x/2)\frac{\pi}{2}}=-\frac{2}{\pi}$

27. $\displaystyle\lim_{x\to 0}\left(\frac{1}{x}-\csc x\right)=\lim_{x\to 0}\left(\frac{1}{x}-\frac{1}{\sin x}\right)=\lim_{x\to 0}\frac{\sin x-x}{x\sin x}$

$\overset{H}{=}\displaystyle\lim_{x\to 0}\frac{\cos x-1}{x\cos x+\sin x}\overset{H}{=}\lim_{x\to 0}\frac{-\sin x}{2\cos x-x\sin x}=\frac{0}{2}=0$

28. $\displaystyle\lim_{x\to 0}(\csc x-\cot x)=\lim_{x\to 0}\left(\frac{1}{\sin x}-\frac{\cos x}{\sin x}\right)=\lim_{x\to 0}\frac{1-\cos x}{\sin x}\overset{H}{=}\lim_{x\to 0}\frac{\sin x}{\cos x}=0$

29. As $x\to\infty$, $1/x\to 0$, and $e^{1/x}\to 1$. So the limit has the form $\infty-\infty$ and we will change the form to a product by factoring out x.

$\displaystyle\lim_{x\to\infty}\left(xe^{1/x}-x\right)=\lim_{x\to\infty}x\left(e^{1/x}-1\right)=\lim_{x\to\infty}\frac{e^{1/x}-1}{1/x}\overset{H}{=}\lim_{x\to\infty}\frac{e^{1/x}(-1/x^2)}{-1/x^2}=\lim_{x\to\infty}e^{1/x}=e^0=1$

30. $\displaystyle\lim_{x\to 1}\left(\frac{1}{\ln x}-\frac{1}{x-1}\right)=\lim_{x\to 1}\frac{x-1-\ln x}{(x-1)\ln x}\overset{H}{=}\lim_{x\to 1}\frac{1-1/x}{(x-1)(1/x)+\ln x}\cdot\frac{x}{x}$

$=\displaystyle\lim_{x\to 1}\frac{x-1}{x-1+x\ln x}\overset{H}{=}\lim_{x\to 1}\frac{1}{1+1+\ln x}=\frac{1}{2+0}=\frac{1}{2}$

31. The limit $\displaystyle\lim_{x\to 0+}x^{\sin x}$ has the indeterminate form 0^0. We'll begin finding the given limit by letting $y=x^{\sin x}$ and taking the natural logarithm of both sides. Then we'll find the limit of $\ln y$ and lastly—don't forget—we must convert to an exponential form to find the given limit. $y=x^{\sin x}\ \Rightarrow\ \ln y=\sin x\ln x$, so

$\displaystyle\lim_{x\to 0+}\ln y=\lim_{x\to 0+}\sin x\ln x=\lim_{x\to 0+}\frac{\ln x}{\csc x}\overset{H}{=}\lim_{x\to 0+}\frac{1/x}{-\csc x\cot x}=-\left(\lim_{x\to 0+}\frac{\sin x}{x}\right)\left(\lim_{x\to 0+}\tan x\right)$

$=-1\cdot 0=0\quad\Rightarrow\quad\displaystyle\lim_{x\to 0+}x^{\sin x}=\lim_{x\to 0+}e^{\ln y}=e^0=1$

32. $y = (\sin x)^{\tan x}$ $\Rightarrow$ $\ln y = \tan x \ln(\sin x)$, so

$$\lim_{x \to 0^+} \ln y = \lim_{x \to 0^+} \tan x \ln(\sin x) = \lim_{x \to 0^+} \frac{\ln(\sin x)}{\cot x} \overset{\text{H}}{=} \lim_{x \to 0^+} \frac{(\cos x)/\sin x}{-\csc^2 x} = \lim_{x \to 0^+} (-\sin x \cos x) = 0 \Rightarrow$$

$$\lim_{x \to 0^+} (\sin x)^{\tan x} = \lim_{x \to 0^+} e^{\ln y} = e^0 = 1.$$

33. $y = (1 - 2x)^{1/x}$ $\Rightarrow$ $\ln y = \frac{1}{x}\ln(1 - 2x)$, so $\lim_{x \to 0} \ln y = \lim_{x \to 0} \frac{\ln(1 - 2x)}{x} \overset{\text{H}}{=} \lim_{x \to 0} \frac{-2/(1 - 2x)}{1} = -2 \Rightarrow$

$$\lim_{x \to 0} (1 - 2x)^{1/x} = \lim_{x \to 0} e^{\ln y} = e^{-2}.$$

34. $y = \left(1 + \dfrac{a}{x}\right)^{bx}$ $\Rightarrow$ $\ln y = bx \ln\left(1 + \dfrac{a}{x}\right)$, so

$$\lim_{x \to \infty} \ln y = \lim_{x \to \infty} \frac{b\ln(1 + a/x)}{1/x} \overset{\text{H}}{=} \lim_{x \to \infty} \frac{b\left(\dfrac{1}{1 + a/x}\right)\left(-\dfrac{a}{x^2}\right)}{-1/x^2} = \lim_{x \to \infty} \frac{ab}{1 + a/x} = ab \Rightarrow$$

$$\lim_{x \to \infty} \left(1 + \frac{a}{x}\right)^{bx} = \lim_{x \to \infty} e^{\ln y} = e^{ab}.$$

35. As $x \to 0^+$, $\ln x \to -\infty$, and $-\ln x \to \infty$. So the given limit has the form ∞^0.

$y = (-\ln x)^x$ $\Rightarrow$ $\ln y = x\ln(-\ln x)$, so

$$\lim_{x \to 0^+} \ln y = \lim_{x \to 0^+} x\ln(-\ln x) = \lim_{x \to 0^+} \frac{\ln(-\ln x)}{1/x} \overset{\text{H}}{=} \lim_{x \to 0^+} \frac{[1/(-\ln x)](-1/x)}{-1/x^2} = \lim_{x \to 0^+} \frac{-x}{\ln x} = 0 \Rightarrow$$

$$\lim_{x \to 0^+} (-\ln x)^x = \lim_{x \to 0^+} e^{\ln y} = e^0 = 1.$$

36. $y = x^{(\ln 2)/(1 + \ln x)}$ $\Rightarrow$ $\ln y = \frac{\ln 2}{1 + \ln x}\ln x$ $\Rightarrow$

$$\lim_{x \to \infty} \ln y = \lim_{x \to \infty} \frac{(\ln 2)(\ln x)}{1 + \ln x} \overset{\text{H}}{=} \lim_{x \to \infty} \frac{(\ln 2)(1/x)}{1/x} = \lim_{x \to \infty} \ln 2 = \ln 2, \text{ so}$$

$$\lim_{x \to \infty} x^{(\ln 2)/(1 + \ln x)} = \lim_{x \to \infty} e^{\ln y} = e^{\ln 2} = 2.$$

37.

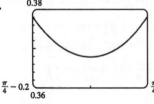

From the graph, it appears that $\lim_{x \to \infty} x[\ln(x + 5) - \ln x] = 5$.

To prove this, we first note that

$$\ln(x + 5) - \ln x = \ln\frac{x + 5}{x} = \ln\left(1 + \frac{5}{x}\right) \to \ln 1 = 0 \text{ as } x \to \infty. \text{ Thus,}$$

$$\lim_{x \to \infty} x[\ln(x + 5) - \ln x] = \lim_{x \to \infty} \frac{\ln(x + 5) - \ln x}{1/x}$$

$$\overset{\text{H}}{=} \lim_{x \to \infty} \frac{\dfrac{1}{x + 5} - \dfrac{1}{x}}{-1/x^2}$$

$$= \lim_{x \to \infty} \left[\frac{x - (x + 5)}{x(x + 5)} \cdot \frac{-x^2}{1}\right] = \lim_{x \to \infty} \frac{5x^2}{x^2 + 5x} = 5$$

38.

From the graph, it appears that $\lim_{x \to \pi/4} (\tan x)^{\tan 2x} \approx 0.368$.

The limit has the form 1^∞. Now $y = (\tan x)^{\tan 2x}$ $\Rightarrow$

$\ln y = \tan 2x \ln(\tan x)$, so

$$\lim_{x \to \pi/4} \ln y = \lim_{x \to \pi/4} \frac{\ln(\tan x)}{\cot 2x} \overset{\text{H}}{=} \lim_{x \to \pi/4} \frac{\sec^2 x/\tan x}{-2\csc^2 2x} = \frac{2/1}{-2(1)} = -1$$

$$\Rightarrow \lim_{x \to \pi/4} (\tan x)^{\tan 2x} = \lim_{x \to \pi/4} e^{\ln y} = e^{-1} = 1/e \approx 0.3679.$$

39.

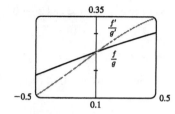

From the graph, it appears that

$$\lim_{x \to 0} \frac{f(x)}{g(x)} = \lim_{x \to 0} \frac{f'(x)}{g'(x)} = 0.25.\text{ We calculate}$$

$$\lim_{x \to 0} \frac{f(x)}{g(x)} = \lim_{x \to 0} \frac{e^x - 1}{x^3 + 4x} \overset{\text{H}}{=} \lim_{x \to 0} \frac{e^x}{3x^2 + 4} = \frac{1}{4}.$$

40.

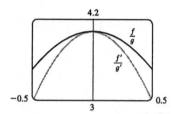

From the graph, it appears that $\lim_{x \to 0} \dfrac{f(x)}{g(x)} = \lim_{x \to 0} \dfrac{f'(x)}{g'(x)} = 4$.

We calculate

$$\lim_{x \to 0} \frac{f(x)}{g(x)} = \lim_{x \to 0} \frac{2x \sin x}{\sec x - 1} \overset{\text{H}}{=} \lim_{x \to 0} \frac{2(x \cos x + \sin x)}{\sec x \tan x}$$

$$\overset{\text{H}}{=} \lim_{x \to 0} \frac{2(-x \sin x + \cos x + \cos x)}{\sec x (\sec^2 x) + \tan x (\sec x \tan x)} = \frac{4}{1} = 4$$

41. $\lim_{x \to \infty} xe^{-x} = \lim_{x \to \infty} (x/e^x) \overset{\text{H}}{=} \lim_{x \to \infty} (1/e^x) = 0$, so $y = 0$ is a HA. $\lim_{x \to -\infty} xe^{-x} = -\infty.$ $f(x) = xe^{-x} \Rightarrow$

$f'(x) = x(-e^{-x}) + e^{-x} \cdot 1 = e^{-x}(1 - x) > 0 \iff 1 - x > 0 \iff x < 1$, so f is increasing on

$(-\infty, 1)$ and decreasing on $(1, \infty)$. By the FDT, $f(1) = 1/e$ is a local maximum.

$f''(x) = e^{-x}(-1) + (1 - x)(-e^{-x}) = e^{-x}(-1 - 1 + x) = e^{-x}(x - 2) > 0 \iff x - 2 > 0 \iff x > 2$,

so f is CU on $(2, \infty)$ and CD on $(-\infty, 2)$. IP is $\left(2, 2/e^2\right)$.

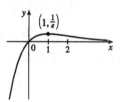

42. $\lim_{x \to \infty} \dfrac{e^x}{x} \overset{\text{H}}{=} \lim_{x \to \infty} \dfrac{e^x}{1} = \infty$, $\lim_{x \to -\infty} \dfrac{e^x}{x} = 0$, so $y = 0$ is a HA. $\lim_{x \to 0+} \dfrac{e^x}{x} = \infty$, $\lim_{x \to 0-} \dfrac{e^x}{x} = -\infty$, so $x = 0$ is a VA.

$f(x) = \dfrac{e^x}{x} \Rightarrow f'(x) = \dfrac{xe^x - e^x}{x^2} > 0 \iff (x - 1)e^x > 0 \iff x > 1$, so f is increasing on $(1, \infty)$,

and decreasing on $(-\infty, 0)$ and $(0, 1)$. By the FDT, $f(1) = e$ is a local minimum.

$f''(x) = \dfrac{x^2(xe^x) - (xe^x - e^x)(2x)}{(x^2)^2} = \dfrac{xe^x (x^2 - 2x + 2)}{x^4} = \dfrac{e^x (x^2 - 2x + 2)}{x^3} > 0 \iff x > 0$ since

$x^2 - 2x + 2 > 0$ for all x. So f is CU on $(0, \infty)$ and CD on $(-\infty, 0)$. No IP.

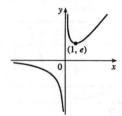

43. $\displaystyle\lim_{x\to\infty}\frac{\ln x}{x} \overset{H}{=} \lim_{x\to\infty}\frac{1/x}{1} = 0$, so $y = 0$ is a HA. Also $\displaystyle\lim_{x\to0^+}\frac{\ln x}{x} = -\infty$ since $\ln x \to -\infty$ and $x \to 0^+$, so $x = 0$

is a VA.

$f(x) = \dfrac{\ln x}{x} \quad\Rightarrow\quad f'(x) = \dfrac{x(1/x) - (\ln x)(1)}{x^2} = \dfrac{1 - \ln x}{x^2} = 0$ when $\ln x = 1 \;\Leftrightarrow\; x = e$. $f'(x) > 0 \;\Leftrightarrow\;$

$1 - \ln x > 0 \;\Leftrightarrow\; \ln x < 1 \;\Leftrightarrow\; 0 < x < e$. $f'(x) < 0 \;\Leftrightarrow\; x > e$. So f is increasing on $(0, e)$ and

decreasing on (e, ∞). By the FDT, $f(e) = 1/e$ is a local maximum.

$f''(x) = \dfrac{x^2(-1/x) - (1 - \ln x)(2x)}{(x^2)^2} = \dfrac{x(-1 - 2 + 2\ln x)}{x^4} = \dfrac{2\ln x - 3}{x^3}$, so $f''(x) > 0 \;\Leftrightarrow\; 2\ln x - 3 > 0$

$\Leftrightarrow\; \ln x > \dfrac{3}{2} \;\Leftrightarrow\; x > e^{3/2}$. $f''(x) < 0 \;\Leftrightarrow\; 0 < x < e^{3/2}$. So f is CU on $\left(e^{3/2}, \infty\right)$ and CD on

$\left(0, e^{3/2}\right)$. There is an inflection point at $\left(e^{3/2}, \frac{3}{2}e^{-3/2}\right)$.

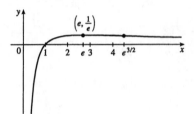

44. $\displaystyle\lim_{x\to\pm\infty} xe^{-x^2} = \lim_{x\to\pm\infty}\frac{x}{e^{x^2}} \overset{H}{=} \lim_{x\to\pm\infty}\frac{1}{2xe^{x^2}} = 0$, so $y = 0$ is a HA. $f(x) = xe^{-x^2} \quad\Rightarrow$

$f'(x) = xe^{-x^2}(-2x) + e^{-x^2}\cdot 1 = e^{-x^2}(1 - 2x^2) > 0 \;\Leftrightarrow\; x^2 < \frac{1}{2} \;\Leftrightarrow\; |x| < \frac{1}{\sqrt{2}}$, so f is increasing

on $\left(-\frac{1}{\sqrt{2}}, \frac{1}{\sqrt{2}}\right)$ and decreasing on $\left(-\infty, -\frac{1}{\sqrt{2}}\right)$ and $\left(\frac{1}{\sqrt{2}}, \infty\right)$. By the FDT,

$f\left(\frac{1}{\sqrt{2}}\right) = 1/\sqrt{2e}$ is a local maximum and $f\left(-\frac{1}{\sqrt{2}}\right) = -1/\sqrt{2e}$ is a local minimum.

$f''(x) = e^{-x^2}(-4x) + (1 - 2x^2)e^{-x^2}(-2x) = 2xe^{-x^2}(-2 - 1 + 2x^2) = 2xe^{-x^2}(2x^2 - 3) > 0 \;\Leftrightarrow$

$x > \sqrt{\frac{3}{2}}$ or $-\sqrt{\frac{3}{2}} < x < 0$, so f is CU on $\left(\sqrt{\frac{3}{2}}, \infty\right)$ and $\left(-\sqrt{\frac{3}{2}}, 0\right)$ and CD on $\left(-\infty, -\sqrt{\frac{3}{2}}\right)$ and $\left(0, \sqrt{\frac{3}{2}}\right)$.

IP are $(0, 0)$ and $\left(\pm\sqrt{\frac{3}{2}}, \pm\sqrt{\frac{3}{2}}e^{-3/2}\right)$.

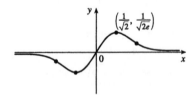

45. (a) $f(x) = x^2 \ln x$. The domain of f is $(0, \infty)$.

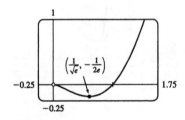

(b) $\lim\limits_{x\to0^+} x^2\ln x = \lim\limits_{x\to0^+} \dfrac{\ln x}{1/x^2} \overset{\text{H}}{=} \lim\limits_{x\to0^+} \dfrac{1/x}{-2/x^3} = \lim\limits_{x\to0^+} \left(-\dfrac{x^2}{2}\right) = 0$. There is a hole at $(0,0)$.

(c) It appears that there is an IP at about $(0.2, -0.06)$ and a local minimum at $(0.6, -0.18)$. $f(x) = x^2\ln x \;\Rightarrow$

$f'(x) = x^2(1/x) + (\ln x)(2x) = x(2\ln x + 1) > 0 \;\Leftrightarrow\; \ln x > -\tfrac{1}{2} \;\Leftrightarrow\; x > e^{-1/2}$, so f is increasing on

$(1/\sqrt{e}, \infty)$, decreasing on $(0, 1/\sqrt{e})$. By the FDT, $f(1/\sqrt{e}) = -1/(2e)$ is a local minimum. This point is

approximately $(0.6065, -0.1839)$, which agrees with our estimate.

$f''(x) = x(2/x) + (2\ln x + 1) = 2\ln x + 3 > 0 \;\Leftrightarrow\; \ln x > -\tfrac{3}{2} \;\Leftrightarrow\; x > e^{-3/2}$, so f is CU on

$\left(e^{-3/2}, \infty\right)$ and CD on $\left(0, e^{-3/2}\right)$.

IP is $\left(e^{-3/2}, -3/(2e^3)\right) \approx (0.2231, -0.0747)$.

46. (a) $f(x) = xe^{1/x}$. The domain of f is $(-\infty, 0) \cup (0, \infty)$.

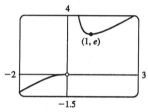
(1, e)

(b) $\lim\limits_{x\to0^+} xe^{1/x} = \lim\limits_{x\to0^+} \dfrac{e^{1/x}}{1/x} \overset{\text{H}}{=} \lim\limits_{x\to0^+} \dfrac{e^{1/x}(-1/x^2)}{-1/x^2} = \lim\limits_{x\to0^+} e^{1/x} = \infty$, so $x = 0$ is a VA.

Also $\lim\limits_{x\to0^-} xe^{1/x} = 0$ since $1/x \to -\infty \;\Rightarrow\; e^{1/x} \to 0$.

(c) It appears that there is a local minimum at $(1, 2.7)$. There are no IP and f is CD on $(-\infty, 0)$ and CU on $(0, \infty)$.

$f(x) = xe^{1/x} \;\Rightarrow\; f'(x) = xe^{1/x}\left(-\dfrac{1}{x^2}\right) + e^{1/x} = e^{1/x}\left(1 - \dfrac{1}{x}\right) > 0 \;\Leftrightarrow\; \dfrac{1}{x} < 1 \;\Leftrightarrow\; x < 0$ or

$x > 1$, so f is increasing on $(-\infty, 0)$ and $(1, \infty)$, and decreasing on $(0, 1)$. By the FDT, $f(1) = e$ is a local

minimum, which agrees with our estimate.

$f''(x) = e^{1/x}(1/x^2) + (1 - 1/x)e^{1/x}(-1/x^2) = \left(e^{1/x}/x^2\right)(1 - 1 + 1/x) = e^{1/x}/x^3 > 0 \;\Leftrightarrow\; x > 0$,

so f is CU on $(0, \infty)$ and CD on $(-\infty, 0)$. No IP.

47. (a) $f(x) = x^{1/x}$

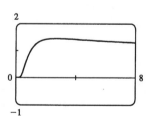

(b) Recall that $a^b = e^{b\ln a}$. $\lim\limits_{x\to0^+} x^{1/x} = \lim\limits_{x\to0^+} e^{(1/x)\ln x}$. As $x \to 0^+$, $\dfrac{\ln x}{x} \to -\infty$, so $x^{1/x} = e^{(1/x)\ln x} \to 0$.

This indicates that there is a hole at $(0,0)$. As $x \to \infty$, we have the indeterminate form ∞^0.

$\lim\limits_{x\to\infty} x^{1/x} = \lim\limits_{x\to\infty} e^{(1/x)\ln x}$, but $\lim\limits_{x\to\infty} \dfrac{\ln x}{x} \overset{\text{H}}{=} \lim\limits_{x\to\infty} \dfrac{1/x}{1} = 0$, so $\lim\limits_{x\to\infty} x^{1/x} = e^0 = 1$. This indicates that

$y = 1$ is a HA.

(c) Estimated maximum: $(2.72, 1.45)$. No estimated minimum. We use logarithmic differentiation to find any

critical numbers. $y = x^{1/x} \;\Rightarrow\; \ln y = \dfrac{1}{x}\ln x \;\Rightarrow\; \dfrac{y'}{y} = \dfrac{1}{x}\cdot\dfrac{1}{x} + (\ln x)\left(-\dfrac{1}{x^2}\right) \;\Rightarrow$

$y' = x^{1/x}\left(\dfrac{1-\ln x}{x^2}\right) = 0 \quad\Rightarrow\quad \ln x = 1 \quad\Rightarrow\quad x = e.$ For $0 < x < e,\ y' > 0$ and for $x > e,\ y' < 0$, so

$f(e) = e^{1/e}$ is a local maximum. This point is approximately $(2.7183, 1.4447)$, which agrees with our estimate.

(d)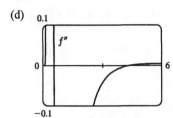

From the graph, we see that $f''(x) = 0$ at $x \approx 0.58$ and $x \approx 4.37$. Since f'' changes sign at these values, they are x-coordinates of inflection points.

48. (a) $f(x) = (\sin x)^{\sin x}$ is continuous where $\sin x > 0$, that is, on intervals of the form $(2n\pi, (2n+1)\pi)$, so we have graphed f on $(0, \pi)$.

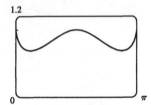

(b) $y = (\sin x)^{\sin x} \quad\Rightarrow\quad \ln y = \sin x \ln \sin x$, so

$$\lim_{x\to 0^+} \ln y = \lim_{x\to 0^+} \sin x \ln \sin x = \lim_{x\to 0^+} \frac{\ln \sin x}{\csc x} \overset{\text{H}}{=} \lim_{x\to 0^+} \frac{\cot x}{-\csc x \cot x} = \lim_{x\to 0^+}(-\sin x) = 0$$

$$\Rightarrow\quad \lim_{x\to 0^+} y = e^0 = 1.$$

(c) It appears that we have a local maximum at $(1.57, 1)$ and local minima at $(0.38, 0.69)$ and $(2.76, 0.69)$. $y = (\sin x)^{\sin x} \quad\Rightarrow\quad \ln y = \sin x \ln \sin x \quad\Rightarrow$

$$\frac{y'}{y} = (\sin x)\left(\frac{\cos x}{\sin x}\right) + (\ln \sin x)\cos x = \cos x(1 + \ln \sin x) \quad\Rightarrow\quad y' = (\sin x)^{\sin x}(\cos x)(1 + \ln \sin x).$$

$y' = 0 \quad\Rightarrow\quad \cos x = 0$ or $\ln \sin x = -1 \quad\Rightarrow\quad x_2 = \frac{\pi}{2}$ or $\sin x = e^{-1}$. On $(0, \pi)$, $\sin x = e^{-1} \quad\Rightarrow$ $x_1 = \sin^{-1}(e^{-1})$ and $x_3 = \pi - \sin^{-1}(e^{-1})$. Approximating these points gives us $(x_1, f(x_1)) \approx (0.3767, 0.6922)$, $(x_2, f(x_2)) \approx (1.5708, 1)$, and $(x_3, f(x_3)) \approx (2.7649, 0.6922)$. The approximations confirm our estimates.

(d) 12

From the graph, we see that $f''(x) = 0$ at $x \approx 0.94$ and $x \approx 2.20$. Since f'' changes sign at these values, they are x-coordinates of inflection points.

49. If $c < 0$, then $\displaystyle\lim_{x\to-\infty} f(x) = \lim_{x\to-\infty} \frac{x}{e^{cx}} \overset{\text{H}}{=} \lim_{x\to-\infty} \frac{1}{ce^{cx}} = 0$, and $\displaystyle\lim_{x\to\infty} f(x) = \infty$.

If $c > 0$, then $\displaystyle\lim_{x\to-\infty} f(x) = -\infty$, and $\displaystyle\lim_{x\to\infty} f(x) \overset{\text{H}}{=} \lim_{x\to\infty} \frac{1}{ce^{cx}} = 0$.

If $c = 0$, then $f(x) = x$, so $\displaystyle\lim_{x\to\pm\infty} f(x) = \pm\infty$ respectively.

So we see that $c = 0$ is a transitional value. We now exclude the case $c = 0$, since we know how the function

behaves in that case. To find the maxima and minima of f, we differentiate: $f(x) = xe^{-cx}$ $\Rightarrow$
$f'(x) = x(-ce^{-cx}) + e^{-cx} = (1 - cx)e^{-cx}$. This is 0 when $1 - cx = 0$ $\Leftrightarrow$ $x = 1/c$. If $c < 0$ then this
represents a minimum of $f(1/c) = 1/(ce)$, since $f'(x)$ changes from
negative to positive at $x = 1/c$; and if $c > 0$, it represents a maximum. As
$|c|$ increases, the maximum or minimum gets closer to the origin. To find
the inflection points, we differentiate again: $f'(x) = e^{-cx}(1 - cx)$ $\Rightarrow$
$f''(x) = e^{-cx}(-c) + (1 - cx)(-ce^{-cx}) = (cx - 2)ce^{-cx}$. This
changes sign when $cx - 2 = 0$ $\Leftrightarrow$ $x = 2/c$. So as $|c|$ increases, the
points of inflection get closer to the origin.

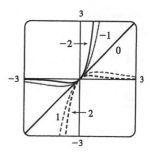

50.

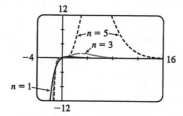

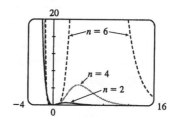

The first figure shows representative examples of $f(x) = x^n e^{-x}$ with n odd. n is even in the second figure. All
curves pass through the origin and approach $y = 0$ as $x \to \infty$. $f'(x) = \dfrac{x^n(n - x)}{xe^x} = 0$ $\Leftrightarrow$ $x = n$ or $x = 0$
(the latter for $n > 1$). At $x = 0$, we have a local minimum for n even. At $x = n$, we have a local maximum for all
n. As n increases, $(n, f(n))$ gets farther away from the origin. $f''(x) = \dfrac{x^n(x^2 - 2nx + n^2 - n)}{x^2 e^x} = 0$ $\Rightarrow$
$x = n \pm \sqrt{n}$ or $x = 0$ (the latter for $n > 2$). As n increases, the IP move farther away from the origin—they are
symmetric about the line $x = n$.

51. $\displaystyle\lim_{x\to\infty} \frac{e^x}{x^n} \overset{H}{=} \lim_{x\to\infty} \frac{e^x}{nx^{n-1}} \overset{H}{=} \lim_{x\to\infty} \frac{e^x}{n(n-1)x^{n-2}} \overset{H}{=} \cdots \overset{H}{=} \lim_{x\to\infty} \frac{e^x}{n!} = \infty$

52. $\displaystyle\lim_{x\to\infty} \frac{\ln x}{x^p} \overset{H}{=} \lim_{x\to\infty} \frac{1/x}{px^{p-1}} = \lim_{x\to\infty} \frac{1}{px^p} = 0$ since $p > 0$.

53. First we will find $\displaystyle\lim_{n\to\infty} \left(1 + \frac{i}{n}\right)^{nt}$, which is of the form 1^∞. $y = \left(1 + \dfrac{i}{n}\right)^{nt}$ $\Rightarrow$ $\ln y = nt \ln\left(1 + \dfrac{i}{n}\right)$, so

$\displaystyle\lim_{n\to\infty} \ln y = \lim_{n\to\infty} nt \ln\left(1 + \frac{i}{n}\right) = t \lim_{n\to\infty} \frac{\ln(1 + i/n)}{1/n} \overset{H}{=} t \lim_{n\to\infty} \frac{(-i/n^2)}{(1 + i/n)(-1/n^2)} = t \lim_{n\to\infty} \frac{i}{1 + i/n} = ti$

$\Rightarrow$ $\displaystyle\lim_{n\to\infty} y = e^{it}$. Thus, as $n \to \infty$, $A = A_0\left(1 + \dfrac{i}{n}\right)^{nt} \to A_0 e^{it}$.

54. (a) $\displaystyle\lim_{t\to\infty} v = \lim_{t\to\infty} \frac{mg}{c}\left(1 - e^{-ct/m}\right) = \frac{mg}{c} \lim_{t\to\infty} \left(1 - e^{-ct/m}\right)$

$\qquad = \dfrac{mg}{c}(1 - 0)$ [because $-ct/m \to -\infty$ as $t \to \infty$] $= \dfrac{mg}{c}$,

which is the speed the object approaches as time goes on, the so-called limiting velocity.

(b) $\lim\limits_{m\to\infty} v = \lim\limits_{m\to\infty} \dfrac{mg}{c}\left(1 - e^{-ct/m}\right) = \dfrac{g}{c}\lim\limits_{m\to\infty}\dfrac{1 - e^{-ct/m}}{1/m} \overset{\text{H}}{=} \dfrac{g}{c}\lim\limits_{m\to\infty}\dfrac{-e^{-ct/m}\left(ct/m^2\right)}{-1/m^2}$

$= \dfrac{g}{c}(ct)\lim\limits_{m\to\infty} e^{-ct/m} = gt(1)$ [because $-ct/m \to 0$ as $m \to \infty$] $= gt$.

The speed of a very heavy falling object is approximately proportional to the elapsed time—it doesn't depend on the mass.

55. We see that both numerator and denominator approach 0, so we can use l'Hospital's Rule:

$\lim\limits_{x\to a}\dfrac{\sqrt{2a^3x - x^4} - a\sqrt[3]{aax}}{a - \sqrt[4]{ax^3}} \overset{\text{H}}{=} \lim\limits_{x\to a}\dfrac{\frac{1}{2}\left(2a^3x - x^4\right)^{-1/2}\left(2a^3 - 4x^3\right) - a\left(\frac{1}{3}\right)(aax)^{-2/3}a^2}{-\frac{1}{4}\left(ax^3\right)^{-3/4}\left(3ax^2\right)}$

$= \dfrac{\frac{1}{2}\left(2a^3a - a^4\right)^{-1/2}\left(2a^3 - 4a^3\right) - \frac{1}{3}a^3\left(a^2a\right)^{-2/3}}{-\frac{1}{4}(aa^3)^{-3/4}\left(3aa^2\right)}$

$= \dfrac{\left(a^4\right)^{-1/2}\left(-a^3\right) - \frac{1}{3}a^3\left(a^3\right)^{-2/3}}{-\frac{3}{4}a^3\left(a^4\right)^{-3/4}} = \dfrac{-a - \frac{1}{3}a}{-\frac{3}{4}} = \frac{4}{3}\left(\frac{4}{3}a\right) = \frac{16}{9}a$

56. Let the radius of the circle be r. We see that $A(\theta)$ is the area of the whole figure (a sector of the circle with radius 1), minus the area of $\triangle OPR$. But the area of the sector of the circle is $\frac{1}{2}r^2\theta$ (see endpapers), and the area of the triangle is $\frac{1}{2}r\,|PQ| = \frac{1}{2}r(r\sin\theta) = \frac{1}{2}r^2\sin\theta$. So we have $A(\theta) = \frac{1}{2}r^2\theta - \frac{1}{2}r^2\sin\theta = \frac{1}{2}r^2(\theta - \sin\theta)$. Now by elementary trigonometry, $B(\theta) = \frac{1}{2}\,|QR|\,|PQ| = \frac{1}{2}(r - |OQ|)\,|PQ| = \frac{1}{2}(r - r\cos\theta)(r\sin\theta) = \frac{1}{2}r^2(1 - \cos\theta)\sin\theta$. So the limit we want is

$\lim\limits_{\theta\to 0^+}\dfrac{A(\theta)}{B(\theta)} = \lim\limits_{\theta\to 0^+}\dfrac{\frac{1}{2}r^2(\theta - \sin\theta)}{\frac{1}{2}r^2(1 - \cos\theta)\sin\theta} \overset{\text{H}}{=} \lim\limits_{\theta\to 0^+}\dfrac{1 - \cos\theta}{(1 - \cos\theta)\cos\theta + \sin\theta\,(\sin\theta)}$

$= \lim\limits_{\theta\to 0^+}\dfrac{1 - \cos\theta}{\cos\theta - \cos^2\theta + \sin^2\theta} \overset{\text{H}}{=} \lim\limits_{\theta\to 0^+}\dfrac{\sin\theta}{-\sin\theta - 2\cos\theta\,(-\sin\theta) + 2\sin\theta\,(\cos\theta)}$

$= \lim\limits_{\theta\to 0^+}\dfrac{\sin\theta}{-\sin\theta + 4\sin\theta\,\cos\theta} = \lim\limits_{\theta\to 0^+}\dfrac{1}{-1 + 4\cos\theta} = \dfrac{1}{-1 + 4\cos 0} = \dfrac{1}{3}$

57. Since $\lim\limits_{h\to 0}[f(x + h) - f(x - h)] = f(x) - f(x) = 0$ (f is differentiable and hence continuous) and $\lim\limits_{h\to 0}2h = 0$, we use l'Hospital's Rule:

$\lim\limits_{h\to 0}\dfrac{f(x + h) - f(x - h)}{2h} \overset{\text{H}}{=} \lim\limits_{h\to 0}\dfrac{f'(x + h)(1) - f'(x - h)(-1)}{2} = \dfrac{f'(x) + f'(x)}{2} = \dfrac{2f'(x)}{2} = f'(x)$

$\dfrac{f(x + h) - f(x - h)}{2h}$ is the slope of the secant line

between $(x - h, f(x - h))$ and $(x + h, f(x + h))$. As $h \to 0$, this line gets closer to the tangent line and its slope approaches $f'(x)$.

58. (a) For f to be continuous, we need $\lim\limits_{x\to 0} f(x) = f(0) = 1$. We note that for $x \neq 0$, $\ln f(x) = \ln|x|^x = x\ln|x|$.

So $\lim\limits_{x\to 0}\ln f(x) = \lim\limits_{x\to 0} x\ln|x| = \lim\limits_{x\to 0}\dfrac{\ln|x|}{1/x} \overset{\text{H}}{=} \lim\limits_{x\to 0}\dfrac{1/x}{-1/x^2} = 0$. Therefore,

$\lim\limits_{x\to 0} f(x) = \lim\limits_{x\to 0} e^{\ln f(x)} = e^0 = 1$. So f is continuous at 0.

(b) From the graphs, it appears that f is differentiable at 0.

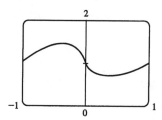
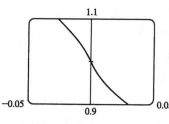
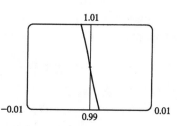

(c) To find f', we use logarithmic differentiation: $\ln f(x) = x \ln |x|$ $\Rightarrow$ $\dfrac{f'(x)}{f(x)} = x\left(\dfrac{1}{x}\right) + \ln |x|$ $\Rightarrow$

$f'(x) = f(x)(1 + \ln |x|) = |x|^x (1 + \ln |x|)$, $x \neq 0$. Now $f'(x) \to -\infty$ as $x \to 0$ [since $|x|^x \to 1$ and $(1 + \ln |x|) \to -\infty$], so the curve has a vertical tangent at $(0, 1)$ and is therefore not differentiable there. The fact cannot be seen in the graphs in part (b) because $\ln |x| \to -\infty$ very slowly as $x \to 0$.

◆ 4.6 Optimization Problems ・ ・ ・ ・ ・ ・ ・ ・ ・ ・ ・ ・

1. (a)

First Number	Second Number	Product
1	22	22
2	21	42
3	20	60
4	19	76
5	18	90
6	17	102
7	16	112
8	15	120
9	14	126
10	13	130
11	12	132

We needn't consider pairs where the first number is larger than the second, since we can just interchange the numbers in such cases. The answer appears to be 11 and 12, but we have considered only integers in the table.

(b) Call the two numbers x and y. Then $x + y = 23$, so $y = 23 - x$. Call the product P. Then
$P = xy = x(23 - x) = 23x - x^2$, so we wish to maximize the function $P(x) = 23x - x^2$. Since
$P'(x) = 23 - 2x$, we see that $P'(x) = 0$ $\Leftrightarrow$ $x = \frac{23}{2} = 11.5$. Thus, the maximum value of P is
$P(11.5) = (11.5)^2 = 132.25$ and it occurs when $x = y = 11.5$.
Or: Note that $P''(x) = -2 < 0$ for all x, so P is everywhere concave downward and the local maximum at
$x = 11.5$ must be an absolute maximum.

2. The two numbers are $x + 100$ and x. Minimize $f(x) = (x + 100)x = x^2 + 100x$. $f'(x) = 2x + 100 = 0$ $\Rightarrow$
$x = -50$. Since $f''(x) = 2 > 0$, there is an absolute minimum at $x = -50$. The two numbers are 50 and -50.

3. The two numbers are x and $\dfrac{100}{x}$, where $x > 0$. Minimize $f(x) = x + \dfrac{100}{x}$. $f'(x) = 1 - \dfrac{100}{x^2} = \dfrac{x^2 - 100}{x^2}$.

   The critical number is $x = 10$. Since $f'(x) < 0$ for $0 < x < 10$ and $f'(x) > 0$ for $x > 10$, there is an absolute minimum at $x = 10$. The numbers are 10 and 10.

4. Let $x > 0$ and let $f(x) = x + 1/x$. We wish to minimize $f(x)$. Now

   $f'(x) = 1 - \dfrac{1}{x^2} = \dfrac{1}{x^2}(x^2 - 1) = \dfrac{1}{x^2}(x+1)(x-1)$, so the only critical number in $(0, \infty)$ is 1.

   $f'(x) < 0$ for $0 < x < 1$ and $f'(x) > 0$ for $x > 1$, so f has an absolute minimum at $x = 1$, and $f(1) = 2$.

   Or: $f''(x) = 2/x^3 > 0$ for all $x > 0$, so f is concave upward everywhere and the critical point $(1, 2)$ must correspond to a local minimum for f.

5. If the rectangle has dimensions x and y, then its perimeter is $2x + 2y = 100$ m, so $y = 50 - x$. Thus, the area is

   $A = xy = x(50 - x)$. We wish to maximize the function $A(x) = x(50 - x) = 50x - x^2$, where $0 < x < 50$.

   Since $A'(x) = 50 - 2x = -2(x - 25)$, $A'(x) > 0$ for $0 < x < 25$ and $A'(x) < 0$ for $25 < x < 50$. Thus, A has an absolute maximum at $x = 25$, and $A(25) = 25^2 = 625$ m^2. The dimensions of the rectangle that maximize its area are $x = y = 25$ m. (The rectangle is a square.)

6. If the rectangle has dimensions x and y, then its area is $xy = 1000$ m^2, so $y = 1000/x$. The perimeter

   $P = 2x + 2y = 2x + 2000/x$. We wish to minimize the function $P(x) = 2x + 2000/x$ for $x > 0$.

   $P'(x) = 2 - 2000/x^2 = (2/x^2)(x^2 - 1000)$, so the only critical number in the domain of P is $x = \sqrt{1000}$.

   $P''(x) = 4000/x^3 > 0$, so P is concave upward throughout its domain and $P(\sqrt{1000}) = 4\sqrt{1000}$ is an absolute minimum value. The dimensions of the rectangle with minimal perimeter are $x = y = \sqrt{1000} = 10\sqrt{10}$ m. (The rectangle is a square.)

7. (a)

 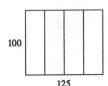 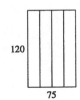

The areas of the three figures are 12,500, 12,500, and 9000 ft^2. There appears to be a maximum area of at least 12,500 ft^2.

(b) Let x denote the length of each of two sides and three dividers. Let y denote the length of the other two sides.

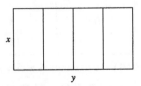

(c) Area $A = $ length $\times$ width $= y \cdot x$

(d) Length of fencing $= 750 \quad \Rightarrow \quad 5x + 2y = 750$

(e) $5x + 2y = 750 \quad \Rightarrow \quad y = 375 - \frac{5}{2}x \quad \Rightarrow \quad A(x) = \left(375 - \frac{5}{2}x\right)x = 375x - \frac{5}{2}x^2$

(f) $A'(x) = 375 - 5x = 0 \quad \Rightarrow \quad x = 75$. Since $A''(x) = -5 < 0$ there is an absolute maximum when $x = 75$.

Then $y = \frac{375}{2} = 187.5$. The largest area is $75\left(\frac{375}{2}\right) = 14{,}062.5$ ft^2. These values of x and y are between the values in the first and second figures in part (a). Our original estimate was low.

8. (a)

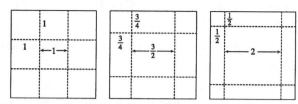

(b) Let x denote the length of the side of the square being cut out. Let y denote the length of the base.

The volumes of the resulting boxes are 1, 1.6875, and 2 ft^3. There appears to be a maximum volume of at least 2 ft^3.

(c) Volume $V = $ length $\times$ width $\times$ height $\Rightarrow$ $V = y \cdot y \cdot x = xy^2$

(d) Length of cardboard $= 3$ $\Rightarrow$ $x + y + x = 3$ $\Rightarrow$ $y + 2x = 3$

(e) $y + 2x = 3$ $\Rightarrow$ $y = 3 - 2x$ $\Rightarrow$ $V(x) = x(3 - 2x)^2$

(f) $V(x) = x(3 - 2x)^2$ $\Rightarrow$

$V'(x) = x \cdot 2(3 - 2x)(-2) + (3 - 2x)^2 \cdot 1 = (3 - 2x)[-4x + (3 - 2x)] = (3 - 2x)(-6x + 3),$

so the critical numbers are $x = \frac{3}{2}$ and $x = \frac{1}{2}$. Now $0 \le x \le \frac{3}{2}$ and $V(0) = V(\frac{3}{2}) = 0$, so the maximum is

$V(\frac{1}{2}) = (\frac{1}{2})(2)^2 = 2$ ft^3, which is the value found from our third figure in part (a).

9. Let b be the length of the base of the box and h the height. The surface area is $1200 = b^2 + 4hb$ $\Rightarrow$

$h = (1200 - b^2)/(4b)$. The volume is $V = b^2h = b^2(1200 - b^2)/4b = 300b - b^3/4$ $\Rightarrow$ $V'(b) = 300 - \frac{3}{4}b^2$.

$V'(b) = 0$ $\Rightarrow$ $300 = \frac{3}{4}b^2$ $\Rightarrow$ $b^2 = 400$ $\Rightarrow$ $b = \sqrt{400} = 20$. Since $V'(b) > 0$ for $0 < b < 20$ and

$V'(b) < 0$ for $b > 20$, there is an absolute maximum when $b = 20$ by the First Derivative Test for Absolute

Extreme Values (see page 310). If $b = 20$, then $h = (1200 - 20^2)/(4 \cdot 20) = 10$, so the largest possible volume is

$b^2h = (20)^2(10) = 4000$ cm^3.

10. Let b be the length of the base of the box and h the height. The volume is $32{,}000 = b^2h$ $\Rightarrow$ $h = 32{,}000/b^2$.

The surface area of the open box is $b^2 + 4hb = b^2 + 4(32{,}000/b^2)b = b^2 + 4(32{,}000)/b$. So

$V'(b) = 2b - 4(32{,}000)/b^2 = 2(b^3 - 64{,}000)/b^2 = 0$ $\Leftrightarrow$ $b = \sqrt[3]{64{,}000} = 40$. This gives an absolute

minimum since $V'(b) < 0$ if $0 < b < 40$ and $V'(b) > 0$ if $b > 40$. The box should be $40 \times 40 \times 20$.

11. (a) Let the rectangle have sides x and y and area A, so $A = xy$ or $y = A/x$. The problem is to minimize the

perimeter $= 2x + 2y = 2x + 2A/x = P(x)$. Now $P'(x) = 2 - 2A/x^2 = 2(x^2 - A)/x^2$. So the critical

number is $x = \sqrt{A}$. Since $P'(x) < 0$ for $0 < x < \sqrt{A}$ and $P'(x) > 0$ for $x > \sqrt{A}$, there is an absolute

minimum at $x = \sqrt{A}$. The sides of the rectangle are $\sqrt{A}$ and $A/\sqrt{A} = \sqrt{A}$, so the rectangle is a square.

(b) Let p be the perimeter and x and y the lengths of the sides, so $p = 2x + 2y$ $\Rightarrow$ $2y = p - 2x$ $\Rightarrow$

$y = \frac{1}{2}p - x$. The area is $A(x) = x(\frac{1}{2}p - x) = \frac{1}{2}px - x^2$. Now $A'(x) = 0$ $\Rightarrow$ $\frac{1}{2}p - 2x = 0$ $\Rightarrow$

$2x = \frac{1}{2}p$ $\Rightarrow$ $x = \frac{1}{4}p$. Since $A''(x) = -2 < 0$, there is an absolute maximum for A when $x = \frac{1}{4}p$ by the

Second Derivative Test. The sides of the rectangle are $\frac{1}{4}p$ and $\frac{1}{2}p - \frac{1}{4}p = \frac{1}{4}p$, so the rectangle is a square.

12.

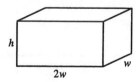

$V = lwh$ $\Rightarrow$ $10 = (2w)(w)h = 2w^2h$, so $h = 5/w^2$. The cost is

$10(2w^2) + 6[2(2wh) + 2(hw)] = 20w^2 + 36wh$, so

$C(w) = 20w^2 + 36w(5/w^2) = 20w^2 + 180/w$.

$C'(w) = 40w - 180/w^2 = 40(w^3 - \frac{9}{2})/w^2$ $\Rightarrow$ $w = \sqrt[3]{\frac{9}{2}}$ is the

critical number. There is an absolute minimum for C when $w = \sqrt[3]{\frac{9}{2}}$ since $C'(w) < 0$ for $0 < w < \sqrt[3]{\frac{9}{2}}$ and

$C'(w) > 0$ for $w > \sqrt[3]{\frac{9}{2}}$. $C(\sqrt[3]{\frac{9}{2}}) = 20(\sqrt[3]{\frac{9}{2}})^2 + \frac{180}{\sqrt[3]{9/2}} \approx \$163.54$.

13. The distance from a point (x, y) on the line $y = 4x + 7$ to the origin is $\sqrt{(x - 0)^2 + (y - 0)^2} = \sqrt{x^2 + y^2}$.
However, it is easier to work with the *square* of the distance; that is,

$D(x) = \left(\sqrt{x^2 + y^2} \right)^2 = x^2 + y^2 = x^2 + (4x + 7)^2$. Because the distance is positive, its minimum value will

occur at the same point as the minimum value of D.

$D'(x) = 2x + 2(4x + 7)(4) = 34x + 56$, so $D'(x) = 0 \iff x = -\frac{28}{17}$.

$D''(x) = 34 > 0$, so D is concave upward for all x. Thus, D has an absolute minimum at $x = -\frac{28}{17}$. The point

closest to the origin is $(x, y) = \left(-\frac{28}{17}, 4\left(-\frac{28}{17} \right) + 7 \right) = \left(-\frac{28}{17}, \frac{7}{17} \right)$.

14. The square of the distance from a point (x, y) on the parabola $x = -y^2$ is

$x^2 + (y + 3)^2 = y^4 + y^2 + 6y + 9 = D(y)$. Now $D'(y) = 4y^3 + 2y + 6 = 2(y + 1)(2y^2 - 2y + 3)$. Since

$2y^2 - 2y + 3 = 0$ has no real roots, $y = -1$ is the only critical number. Then $x = -(-1)^2 = -1$, so the point is

$(-1, -1)$.

15.

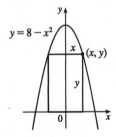

The height h of the equilateral triangle with sides of length L is $\frac{\sqrt{3}}{2} L$,

since $h^2 + (L/2)^2 = L^2 \;\Rightarrow\; h^2 = L^2 - \frac{1}{4}L^2 = \frac{3}{4}L^2 \;\Rightarrow\;$

$h = \frac{\sqrt{3}}{2}L$. Using similar triangles, $\dfrac{\frac{\sqrt{3}}{2}L - y}{x} = \dfrac{\frac{\sqrt{3}}{2}L}{L/2} = \sqrt{3} \;\Rightarrow\;$

$\sqrt{3}\,x = \dfrac{\sqrt{3}}{2}L - y \;\Rightarrow\; y = \dfrac{\sqrt{3}}{2}L - \sqrt{3}\,x \;\Rightarrow\; y = \dfrac{\sqrt{3}}{2}(L - 2x).$

The area of the inscribed rectangle is $A(x) = (2x)y = \sqrt{3}\,x(L - 2x) = \sqrt{3}\,Lx - 2\sqrt{3}\,x^2$, where $0 \le x \le L/2$.
Now $0 = A'(x) = \sqrt{3}\,L - 4\sqrt{3}\,x \;\Rightarrow\; x = \sqrt{3}\,L/(4\sqrt{3}) = L/4$. Since $A(0) = A(L/2) = 0$, the maximum

occurs when $x = L/4$, and $y = \frac{\sqrt{3}}{2}L - \frac{\sqrt{3}}{4}L = \frac{\sqrt{3}}{4}L$, so the dimensions are $L/2$ and $\frac{\sqrt{3}}{4}L$.

16.

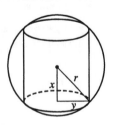

The rectangle has area $A(x) = 2xy = 2x(8 - x^2) = 16x - 2x^3$, where

$0 \le x \le 2\sqrt{2}$. Now $A'(x) = 16 - 6x^2 = 0 \;\Rightarrow\; x = 2\sqrt{\frac{2}{3}}$. Since

$A(0) = A(2\sqrt{2}) = 0$, there is a maximum when $x = 2\sqrt{\frac{2}{3}}$. Then

$y = \frac{16}{3}$, so the rectangle has dimensions $4\sqrt{\frac{2}{3}}$ and $\frac{16}{3}$.

17.

The cylinder has surface area

2(area of the base) + (lateral surface area)

$= 2\pi(\text{radius})^2 + 2\pi(\text{radius})(\text{height}) = 2\pi y^2 + 2\pi y(2x).$

Now $x^2 + y^2 = r^2 \;\Rightarrow\; y^2 = r^2 - x^2 \;\Rightarrow\; y = \sqrt{r^2 - x^2}$, so the

surface area is

$$S(x) = 2\pi(r^2 - x^2) + 4\pi x\sqrt{r^2 - x^2}, \quad 0 \le x \le r$$

$$= 2\pi r^2 - 2\pi x^2 + 4\pi\left(x\sqrt{r^2 - x^2} \right)$$

Thus, $S'(x) = 0 - 4\pi x + 4\pi \left[x \cdot \frac{1}{2}(r^2 - x^2)^{-1/2}(-2x) + (r^2 - x^2)^{1/2} \cdot 1 \right]$

$$= 4\pi \left[-x - \frac{x^2}{\sqrt{r^2 - x^2}} + \sqrt{r^2 - x^2} \right] = 4\pi \cdot \frac{-x\sqrt{r^2 - x^2} - x^2 + r^2 - x^2}{\sqrt{r^2 - x^2}}$$

$S'(x) = 0 \Rightarrow x\sqrt{r^2 - x^2} = r^2 - 2x^2$ $(\star)$ $\Rightarrow$ $\left(x\sqrt{r^2 - x^2} \right)^2 = (r^2 - 2x^2)^2 \Rightarrow$
$x^2(r^2 - x^2) = r^4 - 4r^2x^2 + 4x^4 \Rightarrow r^2x^2 - x^4 = r^4 - 4rx^2 + 4x^4 \Rightarrow 5x^4 - 5r^2x^2 + r^4 = 0$. This is a

quadratic equation in x^2. By the quadratic formula, $x^2 = \frac{5 \pm \sqrt{5}}{10} r^2$, but we reject the root with the $+$ sign since it

doesn't satisfy $(\star)$. [The right side is negative and the left side is positive.] So $x = \sqrt{\frac{5 - \sqrt{5}}{10}}\, r$. Since

$S(0) = S(r) = 0$, the maximum surface area occurs at the critical number and

$x^2 = \frac{5-\sqrt{5}}{10}r^2 \Rightarrow y^2 = r^2 - \frac{5-\sqrt{5}}{10}r^2 = \frac{5+\sqrt{5}}{10}r^2 \Rightarrow$ the surface area is

$2\pi\left(\frac{5+\sqrt{5}}{10}\right)r^2 + 4\pi\sqrt{\frac{5-\sqrt{5}}{10}}\sqrt{\frac{5+\sqrt{5}}{10}}r^2 = \pi r^2\left[2 \cdot \frac{5+\sqrt{5}}{10} + 4\frac{\sqrt{(5-\sqrt{5})(5+\sqrt{5})}}{10}\right] = \pi r^2\left[\frac{5+\sqrt{5}}{5} + \frac{2\sqrt{20}}{5}\right] = $

$\pi r^2\left[\frac{5+\sqrt{5}+2\cdot2\sqrt{5}}{5}\right] = \pi r^2\left[\frac{5+5\sqrt{5}}{5}\right] = \pi r^2(1+\sqrt{5}).$

18. 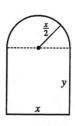 The area of the rectangle is $(2x)(2y) = 4xy$. Now $\frac{x^2}{a^2} + \frac{y^2}{b^2} = 1$ gives

$y = \frac{b}{a}\sqrt{a^2 - x^2}$, so we maximize $A(x) = 4\frac{b}{a}x\sqrt{a^2 - x^2}$.

$A'(x) = \frac{4b}{a}\left[x \cdot \frac{1}{2}(a^2 - x^2)^{-1/2}(-2x) + (a^2 - x^2)^{1/2} \cdot 1 \right]$

$\qquad = \frac{4b}{a}(a^2 - x^2)^{-1/2}\left[-x^2 + a^2 - x^2 \right] = \frac{4b}{a\sqrt{a^2 - x^2}}\left[a^2 - 2x^2 \right]$

So the critical number is $x = \frac{1}{\sqrt{2}}a$, and this clearly gives a maximum. Then $y = \frac{1}{\sqrt{2}}b$, so the maximum area is

$4\left(\frac{1}{\sqrt{2}}a\right)\left(\frac{1}{\sqrt{2}}b\right) = 2ab.$

19. The Perimeter $= 30 \Rightarrow 2y + x + \pi\left(\frac{x}{2}\right) = 30 \Rightarrow$

$y = \frac{1}{2}\left(30 - x - \frac{\pi x}{2}\right) = 15 - \frac{x}{2} - \frac{\pi x}{4}$. The area is the area of the

rectangle plus the area of the semicircle, or $xy + \frac{1}{2}\pi\left(\frac{x}{2}\right)^2$, so

$A(x) = x\left(15 - \frac{x}{2} - \frac{\pi x}{4}\right) + \frac{1}{8}\pi x^2 = 15x - \frac{1}{2}x^2 - \frac{\pi}{8}x^2.$

$A'(x) = 15 - \left(1 + \frac{\pi}{4}\right)x = 0 \Rightarrow x = \frac{15}{1 + \pi/4} = \frac{60}{4 + \pi}$. $A''(x) = -\left(1 + \frac{\pi}{4}\right) < 0$, so this gives a

maximum. The dimensions are $x = \frac{60}{4 + \pi}$ ft and $y = 15 - \frac{30}{4 + \pi} - \frac{15\pi}{4 + \pi} = \frac{60 + 15\pi - 30 - 15\pi}{4 + \pi} = \frac{30}{4 + \pi}$ ft,

so the height of the rectangle is half the base.

20.

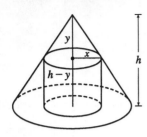

By similar triangles, $y/x = h/r$, so $y = hx/r$. The volume of the cylinder is $\pi x^2(h - y) = \pi hx^2 - (\pi h/r)x^3 = V(x)$. Now $V'(x) = 2\pi hx - (3\pi h/r)x^2 = \pi hx(2 - 3x/r)$. So $V'(x) = 0 \;\Rightarrow\; x = 0$ or $x = \frac{2}{3}r$. The maximum clearly occurs when $x = \frac{2}{3}r$ and then the volume is

$$\pi hx^2 - (\pi h/r)x^3 = \pi hx^2(1 - x/r) = \pi\left(\tfrac{2}{3}r\right)^2 h\left(1 - \tfrac{2}{3}\right) = \tfrac{4}{27}\pi r^2 h.$$

21.

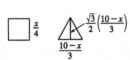

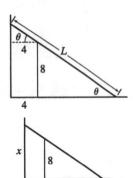

Let x be the length of the wire used for the square. The total area is

$$A(x) = \left(\frac{x}{4}\right)^2 + \frac{1}{2}\left(\frac{10 - x}{3}\right)\frac{\sqrt{3}}{2}\left(\frac{10 - x}{3}\right)$$

$$= \tfrac{1}{16}x^2 + \tfrac{\sqrt{3}}{36}(10 - x)^2, \quad 0 \le x \le 10$$

$$A'(x) = \tfrac{1}{8}x - \tfrac{\sqrt{3}}{18}(10 - x) = 0 \;\Leftrightarrow\; \tfrac{9}{72}x + \tfrac{4\sqrt{3}}{72}x - \tfrac{40\sqrt{3}}{72} = 0 \;\Leftrightarrow\; x = \tfrac{40\sqrt{3}}{9 + 4\sqrt{3}}. \text{ Now}$$

$$A(0) = \left(\tfrac{\sqrt{3}}{36}\right)100 \approx 4.81, \; A(10) = \tfrac{100}{16} = 6.25 \text{ and } A\left(\tfrac{40\sqrt{3}}{9 + 4\sqrt{3}}\right) \approx 2.72, \text{ so}$$

(a) The maximum area occurs when $x = 10$ m, and all the wire is used for the square.

(b) The minimum area occurs when $x = \tfrac{40\sqrt{3}}{9 + 4\sqrt{3}} \approx 4.35$ m.

22.

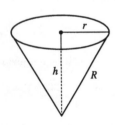

$L = 8\csc\theta + 4\sec\theta, \; 0 < \theta < \tfrac{\pi}{2},$

$\dfrac{dL}{d\theta} = -8\csc\theta\cot\theta + 4\sec\theta\tan\theta = 0$ when

$\sec\theta\tan\theta = 2\csc\theta\cot\theta \;\Leftrightarrow\; \tan^3\theta = 2 \;\Leftrightarrow\; \tan\theta = \sqrt[3]{2} \;\Leftrightarrow$

$\theta = \tan^{-1}\sqrt[3]{2}.$

$dL/d\theta < 0$ when $0 < \theta < \tan^{-1}\sqrt[3]{2}, \; dL/d\theta > 0$ when

$\tan^{-1}\sqrt[3]{2} < \theta < \tfrac{\pi}{2},$ so L has an absolute minimum when

$\theta = \tan^{-1}\sqrt[3]{2},$ and the shortest ladder has length

$L = 8\dfrac{\sqrt{1 + 2^{2/3}}}{2^{1/3}} + 4\sqrt{1 + 2^{2/3}} \approx 16.65$ ft.

Another method: Minimize $L^2 = x^2 + (4 + y)^2$, where $\dfrac{x}{4 + y} = \dfrac{8}{y}$.

23.

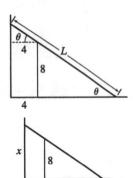

$h^2 + r^2 = R^2 \;\Rightarrow\; V = \tfrac{\pi}{3}r^2 h = \tfrac{\pi}{3}(R^2 - h^2)h = \tfrac{\pi}{3}(R^2 h - h^3).$

$V'(h) = \tfrac{\pi}{3}(R^2 - 3h^2) = 0$ when $h = \tfrac{1}{\sqrt{3}}R.$ This gives an absolute maximum, since $V'(h) > 0$ for $0 < h < \tfrac{1}{\sqrt{3}}R$ and $V'(h) < 0$ for $h > \tfrac{1}{\sqrt{3}}R.$ The maximum volume is

$$V\left(\tfrac{1}{\sqrt{3}}R\right) = \tfrac{\pi}{3}\left(\tfrac{1}{\sqrt{3}}R^3 - \tfrac{1}{3\sqrt{3}}R^3\right) = \tfrac{2}{9\sqrt{3}}\pi R^3.$$

24. (a) $E(v) = \dfrac{aLv^3}{v - u}$ $\Rightarrow$ $E'(v) = aL\dfrac{(v - u)3v^2 - v^3}{(v - u)^2} = 0$

when $2v^3 = 3uv^2$ $\Rightarrow$ $2v = 3u$ $\Rightarrow$ $v = \frac{3}{2}u$. The First

Derivative Test shows that this value of v gives the minimum

value of E.

(b)

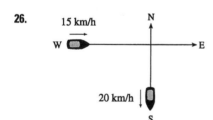

25. $S = 6sh - \frac{3}{2}s^2 \cot \theta + 3s^2 \frac{\sqrt{3}}{2} \csc \theta$

(a) $\dfrac{dS}{d\theta} = \frac{3}{2}s^2 \csc^2 \theta - 3s^2 \frac{\sqrt{3}}{2} \csc \theta \cot \theta$ or $\frac{3}{2}s^2 \csc \theta \left(\csc \theta - \sqrt{3} \cot \theta\right)$.

(b) $\dfrac{dS}{d\theta} = 0$ when $\csc \theta - \sqrt{3} \cot \theta = 0$ $\Rightarrow$ $\dfrac{1}{\sin \theta} - \sqrt{3}\dfrac{\cos \theta}{\sin \theta} = 0$ $\Rightarrow$ $\cos \theta = \frac{1}{\sqrt{3}}$. The First Derivative

Test shows that the minimum surface area occurs when $\theta = \cos^{-1}\left(\frac{1}{\sqrt{3}}\right) \approx 55°$.

(c)

$\sqrt{3}$ $\sqrt{2}$ θ 1

If $\cos \theta = \frac{1}{\sqrt{3}}$, then $\cot \theta = \frac{1}{\sqrt{2}}$ and $\csc \theta = \frac{\sqrt{3}}{\sqrt{2}}$, so the surface area is

$$S = 6sh - \frac{3}{2}s^2\frac{1}{\sqrt{2}} + 3s^2\frac{\sqrt{3}}{2}\frac{\sqrt{3}}{\sqrt{2}} = 6sh - \frac{3}{2\sqrt{2}}s^2 + \frac{9}{2\sqrt{2}}s^2$$

$$= 6sh + \frac{6}{2\sqrt{2}}s^2 = 6s\left(h + \frac{1}{2\sqrt{2}}s\right)$$

26.

15 km/h N W E 20 km/h S

Let t be the time, in hours, after 2:00 P.M. The position of the boat heading

south at time t is $(0, -20t)$. The position of the boat heading east at time t

is $(-15 + 15t, 0)$. If $D(t)$ is the distance between the boats at time t, we

minimize $f(t) = [D(t)]^2 = 20^2t^2 + 15^2(t - 1)^2$.

$f'(t) = 800t + 450(t - 1) = 1250t - 450 = 0$ when $t = \frac{450}{1250} = 0.36$ h.

0.36 h $\times \frac{60 \text{ min}}{\text{h}} = 21.6$ min $= 21$ min 36 s. Since $f''(t) > 0$, this gives a

minimum, so the boats are closest together at 2:21:36 P.M.

27.

3k x 10 − x k 10

The total illumination is $I(x) = \dfrac{3k}{x^2} + \dfrac{k}{(10 - x)^2}$, $0 < x < 10$. Then

$I'(x) = \dfrac{-6k}{x^3} + \dfrac{2k}{(10 - x)^3} = 0$ $\Rightarrow$ $6k(10 - x)^3 = 2kx^3$ $\Rightarrow$

$3(10 - x)^3 = x^3$ $\Rightarrow$ $\sqrt[3]{3}(10 - x) = x$ $\Rightarrow$ $10\sqrt[3]{3} - \sqrt[3]{3}x = x$

$\Rightarrow$ $10\sqrt[3]{3} = x + \sqrt[3]{3}x$ $\Rightarrow$ $10\sqrt[3]{3} = (1 + \sqrt[3]{3})x$ $\Rightarrow$

$x = \dfrac{10\sqrt[3]{3}}{1 + \sqrt[3]{3}} \approx 5.9$ ft. This gives a minimum since $I''(x) > 0$ for

$0 < x < 10$.

28.

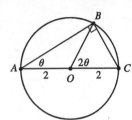

In isosceles triangle AOB, $\angle O = 180° - \theta - \theta$, so $\angle BOC = 2\theta$. The distance rowed is $4\cos\theta$ while the distance walked is the length of arc $BC = 2(2\theta) = 4\theta$. The time taken is given by

$$T(\theta) = \frac{4\cos\theta}{2} + \frac{4\theta}{4} = 2\cos\theta + \theta, \quad 0 \le \theta \le \tfrac{\pi}{2}.$$

$$T'(\theta) = -2\sin\theta + 1 = 0 \quad \Leftrightarrow \quad \sin\theta = \tfrac{1}{2} \quad \Rightarrow \quad \theta = \tfrac{\pi}{6}.$$

Check the value of T at $\theta = \tfrac{\pi}{6}$ and at the endpoints of the domain of T; that is, $\theta = 0$ and $\theta = \tfrac{\pi}{2}$. $T(0) = 2$, $T\left(\tfrac{\pi}{6}\right) = \sqrt{3} + \tfrac{\pi}{6} \approx 2.26$, and $T\left(\tfrac{\pi}{2}\right) = \tfrac{\pi}{2} \approx 1.57$. Therefore, the minimum value of T is $\tfrac{\pi}{2}$ when $\theta = \tfrac{\pi}{2}$; that is, the woman should walk all the way. Note that $T''(\theta) = -2\cos\theta < 0$ for $0 \le \theta < \tfrac{\pi}{2}$, so $\theta = \tfrac{\pi}{6}$ gives a maximum time.

29.

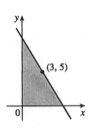

The line with slope m (where $m < 0$) through $(3, 5)$ has equation $y - 5 = m(x - 3)$ or $y = mx + (5 - 3m)$. The y-intercept is $5 - 3m$ and the x-intercept is $-5/m + 3$. So the triangle has area $A(m) = \tfrac{1}{2}(5 - 3m)(-5/m + 3) = 15 - 25/(2m) - \tfrac{9}{2}m$.

Now $A'(m) = \dfrac{25}{2m^2} - \dfrac{9}{2} = 0 \quad \Leftrightarrow \quad m^2 = \tfrac{25}{9} \quad \Rightarrow \quad m = -\tfrac{5}{3}$ (since $m < 0$).

$A''(m) = -\dfrac{25}{m^3} > 0$, so there is an absolute minimum when $m = -\tfrac{5}{3}$. Thus, an equation of the line is $y - 5 = -\tfrac{5}{3}(x - 3)$ or $y = -\tfrac{5}{3}x + 10$.

30. See the figure. The area is given by

$$A(x) = \tfrac{1}{2}\left(2\sqrt{a^2 - x^2}\right)x + \tfrac{1}{2}\left(2\sqrt{a^2 - x^2}\right)\left(\sqrt{x^2 + b^2 - a^2}\right) = \sqrt{a^2 - x^2}\left(x + \sqrt{x^2 + b^2 - a^2}\right) \text{ for }$$

$0 \le x \le a$. Now $A'(x) = \sqrt{a^2 - x^2}\left(1 + \dfrac{x}{\sqrt{x^2 + b^2 - a^2}}\right) + \left(x + \sqrt{x^2 + b^2 - a^2}\right)\dfrac{-x}{\sqrt{a^2 - x^2}} = 0 \quad \Leftrightarrow$

$$\frac{x}{\sqrt{a^2 - x^2}}\left(x + \sqrt{x^2 + b^2 - a^2}\right) = \sqrt{a^2 - x^2}\left(\frac{x + \sqrt{x^2 + b^2 - a^2}}{\sqrt{x^2 + b^2 - a^2}}\right).$$

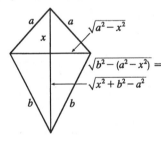

Except for the trivial case where $x = 0$, $a = b$ and $A(x) = 0$, we have $x + \sqrt{x^2 + b^2 - a^2} > 0$. Hence, cancelling this factor gives

$$\frac{x}{\sqrt{a^2 - x^2}} = \frac{\sqrt{a^2 - x^2}}{\sqrt{x^2 + b^2 - a^2}} \quad \Rightarrow \quad x\sqrt{x^2 + b^2 - a^2} = a^2 - x^2 \quad \Rightarrow$$

$$x^2\left(x^2 + b^2 - a^2\right) = a^4 - 2a^2x^2 + x^4 \quad \Rightarrow \quad x^2\left(b^2 - a^2\right) = a^4 - 2a^2x^2$$

$$\Rightarrow \quad x^2\left(b^2 + a^2\right) = a^4 \quad \Rightarrow \quad x = \frac{a^2}{\sqrt{a^2 + b^2}}.$$

Now we must check the value of A at this point as well as at the endpoints of the domain to see which gives the maximum value. $A(0) = a\sqrt{b^2 - a^2}$, $A(a) = 0$ and

$$A\left(\frac{a^2}{\sqrt{a^2 + b^2}}\right) = \sqrt{a^2 - \left(\frac{a^2}{\sqrt{a^2 + b^2}}\right)^2}\left[\frac{a^2}{\sqrt{a^2 + b^2}} + \sqrt{\left(\frac{a^2}{\sqrt{a^2 + b^2}}\right)^2 + b^2 - a^2}\right]$$

$$= \frac{ab}{\sqrt{a^2 + b^2}}\left[\frac{a^2}{\sqrt{a^2 + b^2}} + \frac{b^2}{\sqrt{a^2 + b^2}}\right] = \frac{ab\left(a^2 + b^2\right)}{a^2 + b^2} = ab$$

Since $b \geq \sqrt{b^2 - a^2}$, $A\left(a^2/\sqrt{a^2 + b^2}\right) \geq A(0)$. So there is an absolute maximum when $x = \dfrac{a^2}{\sqrt{a^2 + b^2}}$. In this

case the horizontal piece should be $\dfrac{2ab}{\sqrt{a^2 + b^2}}$ and the vertical piece should be $\dfrac{a^2 + b^2}{\sqrt{a^2 + b^2}} = \sqrt{a^2 + b^2}$.

31. Note that $|AD| = |AP| + |PD|$ $\Rightarrow$ $5 = x + |PD|$ $\Rightarrow$ $|PD| = 5 - x$. Using the Pythagorean Theorem for $\triangle PDB$ and $\triangle PDC$ gives us

$$L(x) = |AP| + |BP| + |CP| = x + \sqrt{(5-x)^2 + 2^2} + \sqrt{(5-x)^2 + 3^2}$$

$$= x + \sqrt{x^2 - 10x + 29} + \sqrt{x^2 - 10x + 34}$$

$$\Rightarrow \quad L'(x) = 1 + \frac{x-5}{\sqrt{x^2 - 10x + 29}} + \frac{x-5}{\sqrt{x^2 - 10x + 34}}.$$

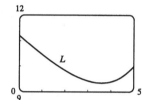

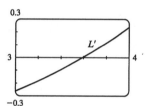

From the graphs of L and L', it seems that the minimum value of L is about $L(3.59) = 9.35$ m.

32. We note that since c is the consumption in gallons per hour, and v is the velocity in miles per hour, then

$\dfrac{c}{v} = \dfrac{\text{gallons/hour}}{\text{miles/hour}} = \dfrac{\text{gallons}}{\text{mile}}$ gives us the consumption in gallons per mile, that is, the quantity G. To find the

minimum, we calculate $\dfrac{dG}{dv} = \dfrac{d}{dv}\left(\dfrac{c}{v}\right) = \dfrac{v\dfrac{dc}{dv} - c\dfrac{dv}{dv}}{v^2} = \dfrac{v\dfrac{dc}{dv} - c}{v^2}$.

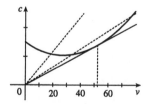

This is 0 when $v\dfrac{dc}{dv} - c = 0$ $\Leftrightarrow$ $\dfrac{dc}{dv} = \dfrac{c}{v}$. This implies that the

tangent line of $c(v)$ passes through the origin, and this occurs when

$v \approx 53$ mi/h. Note that the slope of the secant line through the origin and

a point $(v, c(v))$ on the graph is equal to $G(v)$, and it is intuitively clear

that G is minimized in the case where the secant is in fact a tangent.

33.

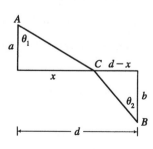

The total time is

$$T(x) = (\text{time from } A \text{ to } C) + (\text{time from } C \text{ to } B)$$

$$= \frac{\sqrt{a^2 + x^2}}{v_1} + \frac{\sqrt{b^2 + (d-x)^2}}{v_2}, \quad 0 < x < d$$

$$T'(x) = \frac{x}{v_1\sqrt{a^2 + x^2}} - \frac{d-x}{v_2\sqrt{b^2 + (d-x)^2}} = \frac{\sin\theta_1}{v_1} - \frac{\sin\theta_2}{v_2}$$

The minimum occurs when $T'(x) = 0$ $\Rightarrow$ $\dfrac{\sin\theta_1}{v_1} = \dfrac{\sin\theta_2}{v_2}$.

34.

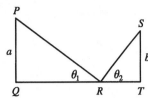

If $d = |QT|$, we minimize $f(\theta_1) = |PR| + |RS| = a\csc\theta_1 + b\csc\theta_2$.

Differentiating with respect to θ_1, and setting $\dfrac{df}{d\theta_1}$ equal to 0, we get

$$\frac{df}{d\theta_1} = 0 = -a\csc\theta_1\cot\theta_1 - b\csc\theta_2\cot\theta_2\frac{d\theta_2}{d\theta_1}.$$

So we need to find an expression for $\dfrac{d\theta_2}{d\theta_1}$. We can do this by observing that $|QT| = \text{constant} = a\cot\theta_1 + b\cot\theta_2$.

Differentiating this equation implicitly with respect to θ_1, we get $-a\csc^2\theta_1 - b\csc^2\theta_2\dfrac{d\theta_2}{d\theta_1} = 0$ ⇒

$\dfrac{d\theta_2}{d\theta_1} = -\dfrac{a\csc^2\theta_1}{b\csc^2\theta_2}$. We substitute this into the expression for $\dfrac{df}{d\theta_1}$ to get

$$-a\csc\theta_1\cot\theta_1 - b\csc\theta_2\cot\theta_2\left(-\frac{a\csc^2\theta_1}{b\csc^2\theta_2}\right) = 0 \;\Leftrightarrow\; -a\csc\theta_1\cot\theta_1 + a\frac{\csc^2\theta_1\cot\theta_2}{\csc\theta_2} = 0 \;\Leftrightarrow$$

$\cot\theta_1\csc\theta_2 = \csc\theta_1\cot\theta_2 \;\Leftrightarrow\; \dfrac{\cot\theta_1}{\csc\theta_1} = \dfrac{\cot\theta_2}{\csc\theta_2} \;\Leftrightarrow\; \cos\theta_1 = \cos\theta_2$. Since θ_1 and θ_2 are both acute, we

have $\theta_1 = \theta_2$.

35.

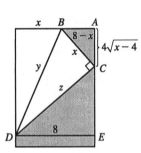

$y^2 = x^2 + z^2$, but triangles CDE and BCA are similar, so

$z/8 = x/(4\sqrt{x-4}) \;\Rightarrow\; z = 2x/\sqrt{x-4}$. Thus, we minimize

$f(x) = y^2 = x^2 + 4x^2/(x-4) = x^3/(x-4), \quad 4 < x \le 8$.

$$f'(x) = \frac{(x-4)(3x^2) - x^3}{(x-4)^2} = \frac{x^2[3(x-4) - x]}{(x-4)^2} = \frac{2x^2(x-6)}{(x-4)^2} = 0$$

when $x = 6$. $f'(x) < 0$ when $x < 6$, $f'(x) > 0$ when $x > 6$, so the

minimum occurs when $x = 6$ in.

36.

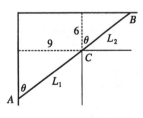

Paradoxically, we solve this maximum problem by solving a minimum

problem. Let L be the length of the line ACB going from wall to wall

touching the inner corner C. As $\theta \to 0$ or $\theta \to \frac{\pi}{2}$, we have $L \to \infty$ and

there will be an angle that makes L a minimum. A pipe of this length will

just fit around the corner.

From the diagram, $L = L_1 + L_2 = 9\csc\theta + 6\sec\theta \;\Rightarrow\; dL/d\theta = -9\csc\theta\cot\theta + 6\sec\theta\tan\theta = 0$ when

$6\sec\theta\tan\theta = 9\csc\theta\cot\theta \;\Leftrightarrow\; \tan^3\theta = \frac{9}{6} = 1.5 \;\Leftrightarrow\; \tan\theta = \sqrt[3]{1.5}$. Then $\sec^2\theta = 1 + \left(\frac{3}{2}\right)^{2/3}$ and

$\csc^2\theta = 1 + \left(\frac{3}{2}\right)^{-2/3}$, so the longest pipe has length $L = 9\left[1 + \left(\frac{3}{2}\right)^{-2/3}\right]^{1/2} + 6\left[1 + \left(\frac{3}{2}\right)^{2/3}\right]^{1/2} \approx 21.07$ ft.

Or, use $\theta = \tan^{-1}\left(\sqrt[3]{1.5}\right) \approx 0.852 \;\Rightarrow\; L = 9\csc\theta + 6\sec\theta \approx 21.07$ ft.

37.

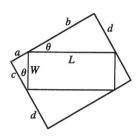

In the small triangle with sides a and c and hypotenuse W, $\sin \theta = \dfrac{a}{W}$ and $\cos \theta = \dfrac{c}{W}$. In the triangle with sides b and d and hypotenuse L, $\sin \theta = \dfrac{d}{L}$ and $\cos \theta = \dfrac{b}{L}$. Thus, $a = W \sin \theta$, $c = W \cos \theta$, $d = L \sin \theta$, and $b = L \cos \theta$, so the area of the circumscribed rectangle is

$$
\begin{aligned}
A(\theta) &= (a+b)(c+d) = (W \sin \theta + L \cos \theta)(W \cos \theta + L \sin \theta) \\
&= W^2 \sin \theta \cos \theta + WL \sin^2 \theta + LW \cos^2 \theta + L^2 \sin \theta \cos \theta \\
&= LW \sin^2 \theta + LW \cos^2 \theta + (L^2 + W^2) \sin \theta \cos \theta \\
&= LW\left(\sin^2 \theta + \cos^2 \theta\right) + (L^2 + W^2) \cdot \tfrac{1}{2} \cdot 2 \sin \theta \cos \theta \\
&= LW + \tfrac{1}{2}(L^2 + W^2) \sin 2\theta, \quad 0 \le \theta \le \tfrac{\pi}{2}
\end{aligned}
$$

This expression shows, without calculus, that the maximum value of $A(\theta)$ occurs when $\sin 2\theta = 1 \;\Leftrightarrow\; 2\theta = \tfrac{\pi}{2}$ $\Rightarrow \;\; \theta = \tfrac{\pi}{4}$. So the maximum area is $A\!\left(\tfrac{\pi}{4}\right) = LW + \tfrac{1}{2}(L^2 + W^2) = \tfrac{1}{2}(L^2 + 2LW + W^2) = \tfrac{1}{2}(L + W)^2$.

38.

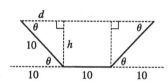

We maximize the cross-sectional area

$$
\begin{aligned}
A(\theta) &= 10h + 2\left(\tfrac{1}{2}dh\right) = 10h + dh = 10(10 \sin \theta) + (10 \cos \theta)(10 \sin \theta) \\
&= 100(\sin \theta + \sin \theta \cos \theta), \quad 0 \le \theta \le \tfrac{\pi}{2} \\
A'(\theta) &= 100\left(\cos \theta + \cos^2 \theta - \sin^2 \theta\right) = 100\left(\cos \theta + 2 \cos^2 \theta - 1\right) = 100(2 \cos \theta - 1)(\cos \theta + 1) \\
&= 0 \text{ when } \cos \theta = \tfrac{1}{2} \;\Leftrightarrow\; \theta = \tfrac{\pi}{3}. \quad (\cos \theta \ne -1 \text{ since } 0 \le \theta \le \tfrac{\pi}{2}.)
\end{aligned}
$$

Now $A(0) = 0$, $A\!\left(\tfrac{\pi}{2}\right) = 100$ and $A\!\left(\tfrac{\pi}{3}\right) = 75\sqrt{3} \approx 129.9$, so the maximum occurs when $\theta = \tfrac{\pi}{3}$.

39.

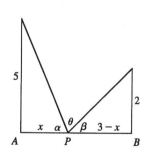

From the figure, $\tan \alpha = \dfrac{5}{x}$ and $\tan \beta = \dfrac{2}{3-x}$. Since

$$
\alpha + \beta + \theta = 180° = \pi, \; \theta = \pi - \tan^{-1}\!\left(\frac{5}{x}\right) - \tan^{-1}\!\left(\frac{2}{3-x}\right) \;\Rightarrow
$$

$$
\begin{aligned}
\frac{d\theta}{dx} &= -\frac{1}{1 + \left(\frac{5}{x}\right)^2}\left(-\frac{5}{x^2}\right) - \frac{1}{1 + \left(\frac{2}{3-x}\right)^2}\left[\frac{2}{(3-x)^2}\right] \\
&= \frac{x^2}{x^2 + 25} \cdot \frac{5}{x^2} - \frac{(3-x)^2}{(3-x)^2 + 4} \cdot \frac{2}{(3-x)^2}. \text{ Now}
\end{aligned}
$$

$$
\frac{d\theta}{dx} = 0 \;\Rightarrow\; \frac{5}{x^2 + 25} = \frac{2}{x^2 - 6x + 13} \;\Rightarrow\; 2x^2 + 50 = 5x^2 - 30x + 65 \;\Rightarrow
$$

$3x^2 - 30x + 15 = 0 \Rightarrow x^2 - 10x + 5 = 0 \Rightarrow x = 5 \pm 2\sqrt{5}$. We reject the root with the $+$ sign, since it is larger than 3. $d\theta/dx > 0$ for $x < 5 - 2\sqrt{5}$ and $d\theta/dx < 0$ for $x > 5 - 2\sqrt{5}$, so θ is maximized when $|AP| = x = 5 - 2\sqrt{5} \approx 0.53$.

40. Let x be the distance from the observer to the wall. Then, from the given figure,

$$\theta = \tan^{-1}\left(\frac{h+d}{x}\right) - \tan^{-1}\left(\frac{d}{x}\right), x > 0 \Rightarrow$$

$$\frac{d\theta}{dx} = \frac{1}{1 + [(h+d)/x]^2}\left[-\frac{h+d}{x^2}\right] - \frac{1}{1 + (d/x)^2}\left[-\frac{d}{x^2}\right] = -\frac{h+d}{x^2 + (h+d)^2} + \frac{d}{x^2 + d^2}$$

$$= \frac{d[x^2 + (h+d)^2] - (h+d)(x^2 + d^2)}{[x^2 + (h+d)^2](x^2 + d^2)} = \frac{h^2 d + hd^2 - hx^2}{[x^2 + (h+d)^2](x^2 + d^2)} = 0 \Leftrightarrow$$

$hx^2 = h^2 d + hd^2 \Leftrightarrow x^2 = hd + d^2 \Leftrightarrow x = \sqrt{d(h+d)}$. Since $d\theta/dx > 0$ for all $x < \sqrt{d(h+d)}$ and $d\theta/dx < 0$ for all $x > \sqrt{d(h+d)}$, the absolute maximum occurs when $x = \sqrt{d(h+d)}$.

41. (a)

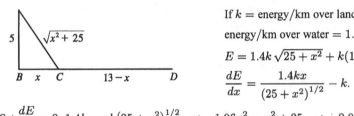

If $k = $ energy/km over land, then energy/km over water $= 1.4k$. So the total energy is

$$E = 1.4k\sqrt{25 + x^2} + k(13 - x), 0 \le x \le 13, \text{ and so}$$

$$\frac{dE}{dx} = \frac{1.4kx}{(25 + x^2)^{1/2}} - k.$$

Set $\dfrac{dE}{dx} = 0$: $1.4kx = k(25 + x^2)^{1/2} \Rightarrow 1.96x^2 = x^2 + 25 \Rightarrow 0.96x^2 = 25 \Rightarrow x = \frac{5}{\sqrt{0.96}} \approx 5.1$.

Testing against the value of E at the endpoints: $E(0) = 1.4k(5) + 13k = 20k$, $E(5.1) \approx 17.9k$, $E(13) \approx 19.5k$. Thus, to minimize energy, the bird should fly to a point about 5.1 km from B.

(b) If W/L is large, the bird would fly to a point C that is closer to B than to D to minimize the energy used flying over water. If W/L is small, the bird would fly to a point C that is closer to D than to B to minimize the distance of the flight. $E = W\sqrt{25 + x^2} + L(13 - x) \Rightarrow \dfrac{dE}{dx} = \dfrac{Wx}{\sqrt{25 + x^2}} - L = 0$ when

$\dfrac{W}{L} = \dfrac{\sqrt{25 + x^2}}{x}$. By the same sort of argument as in part (a), this ratio will give the minimal expenditure of energy if the bird heads for the point x km from B.

(c) For flight direct to D, $x = 13$, so from part (b), $W/L = \dfrac{\sqrt{25 + 13^2}}{13} \approx 1.07$. There is no value of W/L for which the bird should fly directly to B. But note that $\lim\limits_{x \to 0^+} (W/L) = \infty$, so if the point at which E is a minimum is close to B, then W/L is large.

(d) Assuming that the birds instinctively choose the path that minimizes the energy expenditure, we can use the equation for $dE/dx = 0$ from part (a) with $1.4k = c$, $x = 4$, and $k = 1$: $c(4) = 1 \cdot (25 + 4^2)^{1/2} \Rightarrow c = \sqrt{41}/4 \approx 1.6$.

42. (a) Let D be the point such that $a = |AD|$. From the figure, $\sin\theta = \dfrac{b}{|BC|} \Rightarrow |BC| = b\csc\theta$ and

$\cos\theta = \dfrac{|BD|}{|BC|} = \dfrac{a - |AB|}{|BC|} \Rightarrow |BC| = (a - |AB|)\sec\theta$. Eliminating $|BC|$ gives

$(a - |AB|)\sec\theta = b\csc\theta \quad\Rightarrow\quad b\cot\theta = a - |AB| \quad\Rightarrow\quad |AB| = a - b\cot\theta.$ The total resistance is

$$R(\theta) = C\frac{|AB|}{r_1^4} + C\frac{|BC|}{r_2^4} = C\left(\frac{a - b\cot\theta}{r_1^4} + \frac{b\csc\theta}{r_2^4}\right).$$

(b) $R'(\theta) = C\left(\dfrac{b\csc^2\theta}{r_1^4} - \dfrac{b\csc\theta\cot\theta}{r_2^4}\right) = bC\csc\theta\left(\dfrac{\csc\theta}{r_1^4} - \dfrac{\cot\theta}{r_2^4}\right).$

$R'(\theta) = 0 \quad\Leftrightarrow\quad \dfrac{\csc\theta}{r_1^4} = \dfrac{\cot\theta}{r_2^4} \quad\Leftrightarrow\quad \dfrac{r_2^4}{r_1^4} = \dfrac{\cot\theta}{\csc\theta} = \cos\theta.$

$R'(\theta) > 0 \quad\Leftrightarrow\quad \dfrac{\csc\theta}{r_1^4} > \dfrac{\cot\theta}{r_2^4} \quad\Rightarrow\quad \cos\theta < \dfrac{r_2^4}{r_1^4}$ and $R'(\theta) < 0$ when $\cos\theta > \dfrac{r_2^4}{r_1^4}$, so there is an absolute

minimum when $\cos\theta = r_2^4/r_1^4.$

(c) When $r_2 = \frac{2}{3}r_1$, we have $\cos\theta = \left(\frac{2}{3}\right)^4$, so $\theta = \cos^{-1}\left(\frac{2}{3}\right)^4 \approx 79°.$

43. (a) Distance = rate × time, so time = distance/rate. $T_1 = \dfrac{D}{c_1},$

$$T_2 = \frac{2|PR|}{c_1} + \frac{|RS|}{c_2} = \frac{2h\sec\theta}{c_1} + \frac{D - 2h\tan\theta}{c_2}, \quad T_3 = \frac{2\sqrt{h^2 + D^2/4}}{c_1} = \frac{\sqrt{4h^2 + D^2}}{c_1}.$$

(b) $\dfrac{dT_2}{d\theta} = \dfrac{2h}{c_1}\cdot\sec\theta\tan\theta - \dfrac{2h}{c_2}\sec^2\theta = 0$ when $2h\sec\theta\left(\dfrac{1}{c_1}\tan\theta - \dfrac{1}{c_2}\sec\theta\right) = 0 \quad\Rightarrow$

$\dfrac{1}{c_1}\dfrac{\sin\theta}{\cos\theta} - \dfrac{1}{c_2}\dfrac{1}{\cos\theta} = 0 \quad\Rightarrow\quad \dfrac{\sin\theta}{c_1\cos\theta} = \dfrac{1}{c_2\cos\theta} \quad\Rightarrow\quad \sin\theta = \dfrac{c_1}{c_2}.$ The First Derivative Test shows that

this gives a minimum.

(c) Using part (a) with $D = 1$ and $T_1 = 0.26$, we have $T_1 = \dfrac{D}{c_1} \quad\Rightarrow$

$c_1 = \frac{1}{0.26} \approx 3.85$ km/s. $T_3 = \dfrac{\sqrt{4h^2 + D^2}}{c_1} \quad\Rightarrow\quad 4h^2 + D^2 = T_3^2 c_1^2 \quad\Rightarrow$

$h = \frac{1}{2}\sqrt{T_3^2 c_1^2 - D^2} = \frac{1}{2}\sqrt{(0.34)^2(1/0.26)^2 - 1^2} \approx 0.42$ km. To find c_2, we use $\sin\theta = \dfrac{c_1}{c_2}$ from part (b)

and $T_2 = \dfrac{2h\sec\theta}{c_1} + \dfrac{D - 2h\tan\theta}{c_2}$ from part (a). From the figure,

$\sin\theta = \dfrac{c_1}{c_2} \quad\Rightarrow\quad \sec\theta = \dfrac{c_2}{\sqrt{c_2^2 - c_1^2}}$ and $\tan\theta = \dfrac{c_1}{\sqrt{c_2^2 - c_1^2}}$, so

$$T_2 = \frac{2hc_2}{c_1\sqrt{c_2^2 - c_1^2}} + \frac{D\sqrt{c_2^2 - c_1^2} - 2hc_1}{c_2\sqrt{c_2^2 - c_1^2}}.$$

Using the values for T_2 [given as 0.32], h, c_1, and D, we can graph

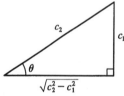

$Y_1 = T_2$ and $Y_2 = \dfrac{2hc_2}{c_1\sqrt{c_2^2 - c_1^2}} + \dfrac{D\sqrt{c_2^2 - c_1^2} - 2hc_1}{c_2\sqrt{c_2^2 - c_1^2}}$ and find their intersection points. Doing so gives us

$c_2 \approx 4.10$ and 7.66, but if $c_2 = 4.10$, then $\theta = \arcsin(c_1/c_2) \approx 69.6°$, which implies that point S is to the left

of point R in the diagram. So $c_2 = 7.66$ km/s.

44. (a) $I(x) \propto \dfrac{\text{strength of source}}{(\text{distance from source})^2}.$ Adding the intensities from the left and right lightbulbs,

$$I(x) = \frac{k}{x^2 + d^2} + \frac{k}{(10 - x)^2 + d^2} = \frac{k}{x^2 + d^2} + \frac{k}{x^2 - 20x + 100 + d^2}.$$

(b) The magnitude of the constant k won't affect the location of the point of maximum intensity, so for convenience we take $k = 1$. $I'(x) = -\dfrac{2x}{(x^2 + d^2)^2} - \dfrac{2(x - 10)}{(x^2 - 20x + 100 + d^2)^2}$.

Substituting $d = 5$ into the equations for $I(x)$ and $I'(x)$, we get

$$I_5(x) = \frac{1}{x^2 + 25} + \frac{1}{x^2 - 20x + 125} \quad \text{and} \quad I_5'(x) = -\frac{2x}{(x^2 + 25)^2} - \frac{2(x - 10)}{(x^2 - 20x + 125)^2}$$

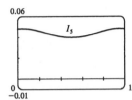

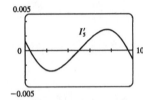

From the graphs, it appears that $I_5(x)$ has a minimum at $x = 5$ m.

(c) Substituting $d = 10$ into the equations for $I(x)$ and $I'(x)$ gives $I_{10}(x) = \dfrac{1}{x^2 + 100} + \dfrac{1}{x^2 - 20x + 200}$ and

$$I_{10}'(x) = -\frac{2x}{(x^2 + 100)^2} - \frac{2(x - 10)}{(x^2 - 20x + 200)^2}.$$

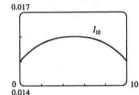

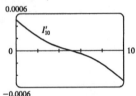

From the graphs, it seems that for $d = 10$, the intensity is minimized at the endpoints, that is, $x = 0$ and $x = 10$. The midpoint is now the most brightly lit point!

(d) From the first figures in parts (b) and (c), we see that the minimal illumination changes from the midpoint $(x = 5$ with $d = 5)$ to the endpoints $(x = 0$ and $x = 10$ with $d = 10)$.

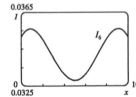

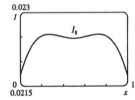

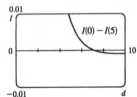

So we try $d = 6$ (see the first figure) and we see that the minimum value still occurs at $x = 5$. Next, we let $d = 8$ (see the second figure) and we see that the minimum value occurs at the endpoints. It appears that for some value of d between 6 and 8, we must have minima at both the midpoint and the endpoints, that is, $I(5)$ must equal $I(0)$. To find this value of d, we solve $I(0) = I(5)$ (with $k = 1$):

$$\frac{1}{d^2} + \frac{1}{100 + d^2} = \frac{1}{25 + d^2} + \frac{1}{25 + d^2} = \frac{2}{25 + d^2} \quad \Rightarrow$$

$$(25 + d^2)(100 + d^2) + d^2(25 + d^2) = 2d^2(100 + d^2) \quad \Rightarrow$$

$$2500 + 125d^2 + d^4 + 25d^2 + d^4 = 200d^2 + 2d^4 \quad \Rightarrow \quad 2500 = 50d^2 \quad \Rightarrow \quad d^2 = 50 \quad \Rightarrow$$

$d = 5\sqrt{2} \approx 7.071$ (for $0 \leq d \leq 10$). The third figure, a graph of $I(0) - I(5)$ with d independent, confirms that $I(0) - I(5) = 0$, that is, $I(0) = I(5)$, when $d = 5\sqrt{2}$. Thus, the point of minimal illumination changes abruptly from the midpoint to the endpoints when $d = 5\sqrt{2}$.

Applied Project	The Shape of a Can

1. In this case, the amount of metal used in the making of each top or bottom is $(2r)^2 = 4r^2$. So the quantity we want to minimize is $A = 2\pi rh + 2(4r^2)$. But $V = \pi r^2 h \Leftrightarrow h = V/\pi r^2$. Substituting this expression for h in A gives $A = 2V/r + 8r^2$. Differentiating A with respect to r, we get $dA/dr = -2V/r^2 + 16r = 0 \Rightarrow$

$16r^3 = 2V = 2\pi r^2 h \Leftrightarrow \dfrac{h}{r} = \dfrac{8}{\pi} \approx 2.55$. This gives a minimum because $\dfrac{d^2 A}{dr^2} = 16 + \dfrac{4V}{r^3} > 0$.

2.

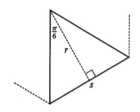

We need to find the area of metal used up by each end, that is, the area of each hexagon. We subdivide the hexagon into six congruent triangles, each sharing one side (s in the diagram) with the hexagon. We calculate the length of $s = 2r \tan \frac{\pi}{6} = \frac{2}{\sqrt{3}} r$, so the area of each triangle is $\frac{1}{2} sr = \frac{1}{\sqrt{3}} r^2$, and the total area of the hexagon is $6 \cdot \frac{1}{\sqrt{3}} r^2 = 2\sqrt{3} r^2$. So the quantity we want to minimize is $A = 2\pi rh + 2 \cdot 2\sqrt{3} r^2$.

Substituting for h as in Problem 1 and differentiating, we get $\dfrac{dA}{dr} = -\dfrac{2V}{r^2} + 8\sqrt{3} r$. Setting this equal to 0, we get

$8\sqrt{3} r^3 = 2V = 2\pi r^2 h \Rightarrow \dfrac{h}{r} = \dfrac{4\sqrt{3}}{\pi} \approx 2.21$. Again this minimizes A because $\dfrac{d^2 A}{dr^2} = 8\sqrt{3} + \dfrac{4V}{r^3} > 0$.

3. Let $C = 4\sqrt{3} r^2 + 2\pi rh + k(4\pi r + h) = 4\sqrt{3} r^2 + 2\pi r \left(\dfrac{V}{\pi r^2} \right) + k \left(4\pi r + \dfrac{V}{\pi r^2} \right)$. Then

$\dfrac{dC}{dr} = 8\sqrt{3} r - \dfrac{2V}{r^2} + 4k\pi - \dfrac{2kV}{\pi r^3}$. Setting this equal to 0, dividing by 2 and substituting $\dfrac{V}{r^2} = \pi h$ and $\dfrac{V}{\pi r^3} = \dfrac{h}{r}$

in the second and fourth terms respectively, we get $0 = 4\sqrt{3} r - \pi h + 2k\pi - \dfrac{kh}{r} \Leftrightarrow$

$k \left(2\pi - \dfrac{h}{r} \right) = \pi h - 4\sqrt{3} r \Rightarrow \dfrac{k}{r} \dfrac{2\pi - h/r}{\pi h/r - 4\sqrt{3}} = 1$. We now multiply by $\dfrac{\sqrt[3]{V}}{k}$, noting that

$\dfrac{\sqrt[3]{V}}{k} \dfrac{k}{r} = \sqrt[3]{\dfrac{V}{r^3}} = \sqrt[3]{\dfrac{\pi h}{r}}$, and get $\dfrac{\sqrt[3]{V}}{k} = \sqrt[3]{\dfrac{\pi h}{r}} \cdot \dfrac{2\pi - h/r}{\pi h/r - 4\sqrt{3}}$.

4.

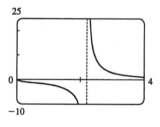

Let $\sqrt[3]{V}/k = T$ and $h/r = x$ so that $T(x) = \sqrt[3]{\pi x} \cdot \dfrac{2\pi - x}{\pi x - 4\sqrt{3}}$. We see from the graph of T that when the ratio $\sqrt[3]{V}/k$ is large; that is, either the volume of the can is large or the cost of joining (proportional to k) is small, the optimum value of h/r is about 2.21, but when $\sqrt[3]{V}/k$ is small, indicating small volume or expensive joining, the optimum value of h/r is larger. (The part of the graph for $\sqrt[3]{V}/k < 0$ has no physical meaning but confirms the location of the asymptote.)

5. Our conclusion is usually true in practice. But there are exceptions, such as cans of tuna, which may have to do with the shape of a reasonable slice of tuna. And for a comfortable grip on a soda or beer can, the geometry of the human hand is a restriction on the radius. Other possible considerations are packaging, transportation and stocking constraints, aesthetic appeal and other marketing concerns. Also, there may be better models than ours which prescribe a differently shaped can in special circumstances.

4.7 Applications to Economics • • • • • • • • • • • • •

1. (a) $C(0)$ represents the fixed costs of production, such as rent, utilities, machinery etc., which are incurred even when nothing is produced.

(b) The inflection point is the point at which $C''(x)$ changes from negative to positive; that is, the marginal cost $C'(x)$ changes from decreasing to increasing. Thus, the marginal cost is minimized at the inflection point.

(c) The marginal cost function is $C'(x)$. We graph it as in Example 1 in Section 2.8.

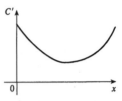

2. (a) We graph C' as in Example 1 in Section 2.8.

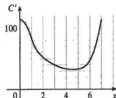

(b) By reading values of $C(x)$ from its graph, we can plot $c(x) = C(x)/x$.

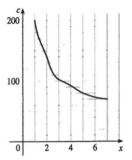

(c) Since the graph in part (b) is decreasing, we estimate that the minimum value of $c(x)$ occurs at $x = 7$. The average cost and the marginal cost are equal at that value. See the box preceding Example 1.

3. $c(x) = 21.4 - 0.002x$ and $c(x) = C(x)/x \;\Rightarrow\; C(x) = 21.4x - 0.002x^2$. $C'(x) = 21.4 - 0.004x$ and $C'(1000) = 17.4$. This means that the cost of producing the 1001st unit is about \$17.40.

4. (a) Profit is maximized when the marginal revenue is equal to the marginal cost; that is, when R and C have equal slopes. See the box preceding Example 2.

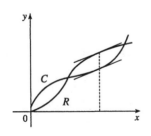

(b) $P(x) = R(x) - C(x)$ is sketched.

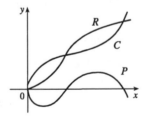

(c) The marginal profit function is defined as $P'(x)$.

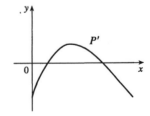

5. (a) The cost function is $C(x) = 40,000 + 300x + x^2$, so the cost at a production level of 1000 is

$C(1000) = \$1,340,000$. The average cost function is $c(x) = \dfrac{C(x)}{x} = \dfrac{40,000}{x} + 300 + x$ and

$c(1000) = \$1340/\text{unit}$. The marginal cost function is $C'(x) = 300 + 2x$ and $C'(1000) = \$2300/\text{unit}$.

(b) See the box preceding Example 1. We must have $C'(x) = c(x) \quad \Leftrightarrow \quad 300 + 2x = \dfrac{40,000}{x} + 300 + x \quad \Leftrightarrow$

$x = \dfrac{40,000}{x} \quad \Rightarrow \quad x^2 = 40,000 \quad \Rightarrow \quad x = \sqrt{40,000} = 200$. This gives a minimum value of the average cost

function $c(x)$ since $c''(x) = \dfrac{80,000}{x^3} > 0$.

(c) The minimum average cost is $c(200) = \$700/\text{unit}$.

6. (a) $C(x) = 2\sqrt{x} + \dfrac{x^2}{8000}$, $C(1000) = \$188.25$. $c(x) = \dfrac{C(x)}{x} = \dfrac{2}{\sqrt{x}} + \dfrac{x}{8000}$, $c(1000) = \$0.19/\text{unit}$.

$C'(x) = \dfrac{1}{\sqrt{x}} + \dfrac{x}{4000}$, $C'(1000) = \$0.28/\text{unit}$.

(b) We must have $C'(x) = c(x) \quad \Leftrightarrow \quad \dfrac{1}{\sqrt{x}} + \dfrac{x}{4000} = \dfrac{2}{\sqrt{x}} + \dfrac{x}{8000} \quad \Leftrightarrow \quad \dfrac{x}{8000} = \dfrac{1}{\sqrt{x}} \quad \Rightarrow$

$x^{3/2} = 8000 \quad \Rightarrow \quad x = 8000^{2/3} = 400$. This is a minimum since $c''(x) = \frac{3}{2}x^{-5/2} > 0$.

(c) The minimum average cost is $c(400) = \$0.15/\text{unit}$.

7. (a) $C(x) = 3700 + 5x - 0.04x^2 + 0.0003x^3 \quad \Rightarrow \quad C'(x) = 5 - 0.08x + 0.0009x^2$ (marginal cost).

$c(x) = \dfrac{C(x)}{x} = \dfrac{3700}{x} + 5 - 0.04x + 0.0003x^2$ (average cost).

(b)

100

C'(x)

$\dfrac{C(x)}{x}$

0   500

(c) $c'(x) = -\dfrac{3700}{x^2} - 0.04 + 0.0006x = 0 \quad \Rightarrow$

$3700 + 0.04x^2 - 0.0006x^3 = 0 \quad \Rightarrow$

$x_1 \approx 208.51$. $c(x_1) \approx \$27.45/\text{unit}$.

The graphs intersect at $(208.51, 27.45)$, so the
production level that minimizes average cost
is about 209 units.

(d) The marginal cost is given by $C'(x)$, so to find its minimum value we'll find the derivative of C'; that is, C''.
$C''(x) = -0.08 + 0.0018x = 0 \quad \Rightarrow \quad x_1 = \frac{800}{18} = 44.4\overline{4}$. $C'(x_1) = \$3.22/\text{unit}$.
$C'''(x) = 0.0018 > 0$ for all x, so this is the minimum marginal cost. C''' is the second derivative of C'.

8. (a) $C(x) = 339 + 25x - 0.09x^2 + 0.0004x^3 \quad \Rightarrow \quad C'(x) = 25 - 0.18x + 0.0012x^2$ (marginal cost).

$c(x) = \dfrac{C(x)}{x} = \dfrac{339}{x} + 25 - 0.09x + 0.0004x^2$ (average cost).

(b)

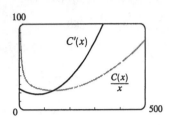

The graphs intersect at $(135.56, 22.65)$, so the production level that minimizes average cost is about 136 units.

(c) $c'(x) = -\dfrac{339}{x^2} - 0.09 + 0.0008x = 0 \Rightarrow$

$x_1 \approx 135.56$. $c(x_1) \approx \$22.65/\text{unit}$.

(d) $C''(x) = -0.18 + 0.0024x = 0 \Rightarrow$

$x = \frac{1800}{24} = 75$. $C'(75) = \$18.25/\text{unit}$.

$C'''(x) = 0.0024 > 0$ for all x, so this is the minimum marginal cost.

9. $C(x) = 680 + 4x + 0.01x^2$, $p(x) = 12 - x/500$. Then $R(x) = xp(x) = 12x - x^2/500$. If the profit is maximum, then $R'(x) = C'(x)$ [See the box preceding Example 2.] $\Leftrightarrow$ $12 - x/250 = 4 + 0.02x$ $\Leftrightarrow$ $8 = 0.024x$ $\Leftrightarrow$ $x = 8/0.024 = \frac{1000}{3}$. The profit is maximized if $P''(x) < 0$, but since $P''(x) = R''(x) - C''(x)$, we can just check the condition $R''(x) < C''(x)$. Now $R''(x) = -\frac{1}{250} < 0.02 = C''(x)$, so $x = \frac{1000}{3}$ gives a maximum.

10. $C(x) = 16{,}000 + 500x - 1.6x^2 + 0.004x^3$, $p(x) = 1700 - 7x$. Then $R(x) = xp(x) = 1700x - 7x^2$. If the profit is maximum, then $R'(x) = C'(x)$ $\Leftrightarrow$ $1700 - 14x = 500 - 3.2x + 0.012x^2$ $\Leftrightarrow$ $0.012x^2 + 10.8x - 1200 = 0$ $\Leftrightarrow$ $x^2 + 900x - 100{,}000 = 0$ $\Leftrightarrow$ $(x + 1000)(x - 100) = 0$ $\Leftrightarrow$ $x = 100$ (since $x > 0$). The profit is maximized if $P''(x) < 0$, but since $P''(x) = R''(x) - C''(x)$, we can just check the condition $R''(x) < C''(x)$. Now $R''(x) = -14 < -3.2 + 0.024x = C''(x)$ for $x > 0$, so there is a maximum at $x = 100$.

11. $C(x) = 0.001x^3 - 0.3x^2 + 6x + 900$. The marginal cost is $C'(x) = 0.003x^2 - 0.6x + 6$.

$C'(x)$ is increasing when $C''(x) > 0$ $\Leftrightarrow$ $0.006x - 0.6 > 0$ $\Leftrightarrow$ $x > 0.6/0.006 = 100$. So $C'(x)$ starts to increase when $x = 100$.

12. $C(x) = 0.0002x^3 - 0.25x^2 + 4x + 1500$. The marginal cost is $C'(x) = 0.0006x^2 - 0.50x + 4$.

$C'(x)$ is increasing when $C''(x) > 0$ $\Leftrightarrow$ $0.0012x - 0.5 > 0$ $\Leftrightarrow$ $x > 0.5/0.0012 \approx 417$. So $C'(x)$ starts to increase when $x = 417$.

13. (a) $C(x) = 1200 + 12x - 0.1x^2 + 0.0005x^3$. $R(x) = xp(x) = 29x - 0.00021x^2$.

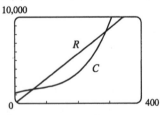

Since the profit is maximized when $R'(x) = C'(x)$, we examine the curves R and C in the figure, looking for x-values at which the slopes of the tangent lines are equal. It appears that $x = 200$ is a good estimate.

(b) $R'(x) = C'(x)$ $\Rightarrow$ $29 - 0.00042x = 12 - 0.2x + 0.0015x^2$ $\Rightarrow$ $0.0015x^2 - 0.19958x - 17 = 0$ $\Rightarrow$ $x \approx 192.06$ (for $x > 0$). As in Exercise 9, $R''(x) < C''(x)$ $\Rightarrow$ $-0.00042 < -0.2 + 0.003x$ $\Leftrightarrow$ $0.003x > 0.19958$ $\Leftrightarrow$ $x > 66.5$. Our value of 192 is in this range, so we have a maximum profit when we produce 192 yards of fabric.

14. (a) Cost = setup cost + manufacturing cost $\Rightarrow$ $C(x) = 500 + m(x) = 500 + 20x - 5x^{3/4} + 0.01x^2$. We

can solve $x(p) = 320 - 7.7p$ for p in terms of x to find the demand (or price) function.

$$x = 320 - 7.7p \quad \Rightarrow \quad 7.7p = 320 - x \quad \Rightarrow \quad p(x) = \frac{320 - x}{7.7}. \quad R(x) = xp(x) = \frac{320x - x^2}{7.7}.$$

(b) $C'(x) = R'(x) \quad \Rightarrow \quad 20 - \frac{15}{4}x^{-1/4} + 0.02x = \frac{320 - 2x}{7.7} \quad \Rightarrow \quad x \approx 81.53$ planes, and

$p(x) = \$30.97$ million. The maximum profit associated with these values is about $\$463.59$ million.

15. (a) We are given that the demand function p is linear and $p(27,000) = 10$, $p(33,000) = 8$, so the slope is

$\frac{10 - 8}{27,000 - 33,000} = -\frac{1}{3000}$ and an equation of the line is $y - 10 = \left(-\frac{1}{3000}\right)(x - 27,000) \quad \Rightarrow$

$y = p(x) = -\frac{1}{3000}x + 19 = 19 - (x/3000)$.

(b) The revenue is $R(x) = xp(x) = 19x - (x^2/3000) \quad \Rightarrow \quad R'(x) = 19 - (x/1500) = 0$ when $x = 28,500$.

Since $R''(x) = -1/1500 < 0$, the maximum revenue occurs when $x = 28,500 \quad \Rightarrow$ the price is

$p(28,500) = \$9.50$.

16. (a) Let $p(x)$ be the demand function. Then $p(x)$ is linear and $y = p(x)$ passes through $(20, 10)$ and $(18, 11)$, so the

slope is $-\frac{1}{2}$ and an equation of the line is $y - 10 = -\frac{1}{2}(x - 20) \quad \Leftrightarrow \quad y = -\frac{1}{2}x + 20$. Thus, the demand is

$p(x) = -\frac{1}{2}x + 20$ and the revenue is $R(x) = xp(x) = -\frac{1}{2}x^2 + 20x$.

(b) The cost is $C(x) = 6x$, so the profit is $P(x) = R(x) - C(x) = -\frac{1}{2}x^2 + 14x$. Then $0 = P'(x) = -x + 14$

$\Rightarrow \quad x = 14$. Since $P''(x) = -1 < 0$, the selling price for maximum profit is $p(14) = -\frac{1}{2}(14) + 20 = \$13$.

17. (a) As in Example 3, we see that the demand function p is linear. We are given that $p(1000) = 450$ and deduce that

$p(1100) = 440$, since a \$10 reduction in price increases sales by 100 per week. The slope for p is

$\frac{440 - 450}{1100 - 1000} = -\frac{1}{10}$, so an equation is $p - 450 = -\frac{1}{10}(x - 1000)$ or $p(x) = -\frac{1}{10}x + 550$.

(b) $R(x) = xp(x) = -\frac{1}{10}x^2 + 550x$. $R'(x) = -\frac{1}{5}x + 550 = 0$ when $x = 5(550) = 2750$.

$p(2750) = 275$, so the rebate should be $450 - 275 = \$175$.

(c) $C(x) = 68,000 + 150x \quad \Rightarrow$

$P(x) = R(x) - C(x) = -\frac{1}{10}x^2 + 550x - 68,000 - 150x = -\frac{1}{10}x^2 + 400x - 68,000$,

$P'(x) = -\frac{1}{5}x + 400 = 0$ when $x = 2000$. $p(2000) = 350$. Therefore, the rebate to maximize profits should

be $450 - 350 = \$100$.

18. Let x denote the number of \$10 increases in rent. Then the price is $p(x) = 800 + 10x$, and the number of units

occupied is $100 - x$. Now the revenue is

$$R(x) = (\text{rental price per unit}) \times (\text{number of units rented})$$

$$= (800 + 10x)(100 - x) = -10x^2 + 200x + 80,000 \text{ for } 0 \le x \le 100 \quad \Rightarrow$$

$R'(x) = -20x + 200 = 0 \quad \Leftrightarrow \quad x = 10$. This is a maximum since $R''(x) = -20 < 0$ for all x. Now we must

check the value of $R(x) = (800 + 10x)(100 - x)$ at $x = 10$ and at the endpoints of the domain to see which value

of x gives the maximum value of R. $R(0) = 80,000$, $R(10) = (900)(90) = 81,000$, and

$R(100) = (1800)(0) = 0$. Thus, the maximum revenue of \$81,000/week occurs when 90 units are occupied at a

rent of \$900/week.

4.8 Newton's Method · · · · · · · · · · · · ·

1.

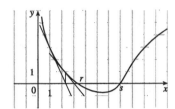

The tangent line at $x = 1$ intersects the x-axis at $x \approx 2.3$, so $x_2 \approx 2.3$. The tangent line at $x = 2.3$ intersects the x-axis at $x \approx 3$, so $x_3 \approx 3.0$.

2.

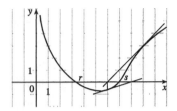

The tangent line at $x = 9$ intersects the x-axis at $x \approx 6.0$, so $x_2 \approx 6.0$. The tangent line at $x = 6.0$ intersects the x-axis at $x \approx 8.0$, so $x_3 \approx 8.0$.

3. Since $x_1 = 3$ and $y = 5x - 4$ is tangent to $y = f(x)$ at $x = 3$, we simply need to find where the tangent line intersects the x-axis. $y = 0 \Rightarrow 5x_2 - 4 = 0 \Rightarrow x_2 = \frac{4}{5}$.

4. (a)

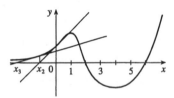

If $x_1 = 0$, then x_2 is negative, and x_3 is even more negative. The sequence of approximations does not converge, that is, Newton's method fails.

(b)

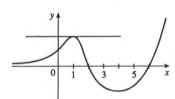

If $x_1 = 1$, the tangent line is horizontal and Newton's method fails.

(c)

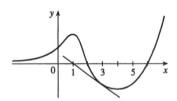

If $x_1 = 3$, then $x_2 = 1$ and we have the same situation as in part (b). Newton's method fails again.

(d)

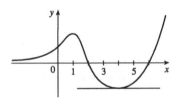

If $x_1 = 4$, the tangent line is horizontal and Newton's method fails.

(e)

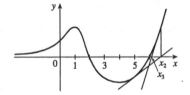

If $x_1 = 5$, then x_2 is greater than 6, x_3 gets closer to 6, and the sequence of approximations converges to 6. Newton's method succeeds!

5. $f(x) = x^4 - 20 \Rightarrow f'(x) = 4x^3$, so $x_{n+1} = x_n - \dfrac{f(x_n)}{f'(x_n)} = x_n - \dfrac{x_n^4 - 20}{4x_n^3}$.

Now $x_1 = 2 \Rightarrow x_2 = 2 - \dfrac{2^4 - 20}{4(2)^3} = 2.125 \Rightarrow x_3 = 2.125 - \dfrac{(2.125)^4 - 20}{4(2.125)^3} \approx 2.1148$.

6. $f(x) = x^3 - x^2 - 1 \Rightarrow f'(x) = 3x^2 - 2x$, so $x_{n+1} = x_n - \dfrac{f(x_n)}{f'(x_n)} = x_n - \dfrac{x_n^3 - x_n^2 - 1}{3x_n^2 - 2x_n}$.

Now $x_1 = 1 \Rightarrow x_2 = 1 - \dfrac{1 - 1 - 1}{3 - 2} = 2 \Rightarrow x_3 = 2 - \dfrac{2^3 - 2^2 - 1}{3 \cdot 2^2 - 2 \cdot 2} = 1.625$.

7. To approximate $x = \sqrt[3]{30}$ (so that $x^3 = 30$), we can take $f(x) = x^3 - 30$. So $f'(x) = 3x^2$, and thus,

$x_{n+1} = x_n - \dfrac{x_n^3 - 30}{3x_n^2}$. Since $\sqrt[3]{27} = 3$ and 27 is close to 30, we'll use $x_1 = 3$. We need to find approximations

until they agree to eight decimal places. $x_1 = 3 \Rightarrow x_2 \approx 3.11111111$, $x_3 \approx 3.10723734$,

$x_4 \approx 3.10723251 \approx x_5$. So $\sqrt[3]{30} \approx 3.10723251$, to eight decimal places.

Here is a quick and easy method for finding the iterations for Newton's method on a programmable calculator. (The screens shown are from the TI-83 Plus, but the method is similar on other calculators.) Assign $f(x) = x^3 - 30$ to Y_1, and $f'(x) = 3x^2$ to Y_2. Now store $x_1 = 3$ in X and then enter $X - Y_1/Y_2 \rightarrow X$ to get $x_2 = 3.\overline{1}$. By successively pressing the ENTER key, you get the approximations $x_3, x_4, \ldots$.

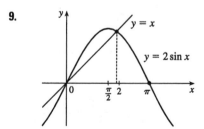
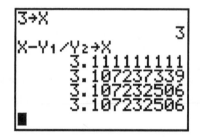

8. $f(x) = x^7 - 1000 \Rightarrow f'(x) = 7x^6$, so $x_{n+1} = x_n - \dfrac{x_n^7 - 1000}{7x_n^6}$. We need to find approximations until they agree to eight decimal places. $x_1 = 3 \Rightarrow x_2 \approx 2.76739173$, $x_3 \approx 2.69008741$, $x_4 \approx 2.68275645$, $x_5 \approx 2.68269580 \approx x_6$. So $\sqrt[7]{1000} \approx 2.68269580$, to eight decimal places.

9.

From the graph it appears that there is a root near 2, so we take $x_1 = 2$.

Write the equation as $f(x) = 2\sin x - x = 0$. Then $f'(x) = 2\cos x - 1$,

so $x_{n+1} = x_n - \dfrac{2\sin x_n - x_n}{2\cos x_n - 1}$. Now $x_1 = 2$, $x_2 \approx 1.900996$,

$x_3 \approx 1.895512$, $x_4 \approx 1.895494 \approx x_5$. So the root is 1.895494, to six decimal places.

10. $f(x) = x^4 + x - 4 \Rightarrow f'(x) = 4x^3 + 1 \Rightarrow x_{n+1} = x_n - \dfrac{x_n^4 + x_n - 4}{4x_n^3 + 1}$. $x_1 = 1.5 \Rightarrow x_2 \approx 1.323276$,

$x_3 \approx 1.285346$, $x_4 \approx 1.283784$, $x_5 \approx 1.283782 \approx x_6$. So the root is 1.283782, to six decimal places.

11.

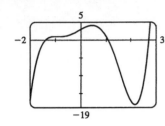

$f(x) = x^5 - x^4 - 5x^3 - x^2 + 4x + 3 \quad \Rightarrow$

$f'(x) = 5x^4 - 4x^3 - 15x^2 - 2x + 4 \quad \Rightarrow$

$x_{n+1} = x_n - \dfrac{x_n^5 - x_n^4 - 5x_n^3 - x_n^2 + 4x_n + 3}{5x_n^4 - 4x_n^3 - 15x_n^2 - 2x_n + 4}$. From the graph of f,

there appear to be roots near -1.4, 1.1, and 2.7.

$x_1 = -1.4$

$x_2 \approx -1.39210970$

$x_3 \approx -1.39194698$

$x_4 \approx -1.39194691 \approx x_5$

$x_1 = 1.1$

$x_2 \approx 1.07780402$

$x_3 \approx 1.07739442$

$x_4 \approx 1.07739428 \approx x_5$

$x_1 = 2.7$

$x_2 \approx 2.72046250$

$x_3 \approx 2.71987870$

$x_4 \approx 2.71987822 \approx x_5$

To eight decimal places, the roots of the equation are -1.39194691, 1.07739428, and 2.71987822.

12.

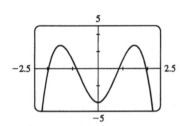

Solving $x^2(4 - x^2) = \dfrac{4}{x^2 + 1}$ is the same as solving

$f(x) = 4x^2 - x^4 - \dfrac{4}{x^2 + 1} = 0$. $f'(x) = 8x - 4x^3 + \dfrac{8x}{(x^2 + 1)^2} \quad \Rightarrow$

$x_{n+1} = x_n - \dfrac{4x_n^2 - x_n^4 - 4/(x_n^2 + 1)}{8x_n - 4x_n^3 + 8x_n/(x_n^2 + 1)^2}$. From the graph of $f(x)$,

there appear to be roots near $x = \pm 1.9$ and $x = \pm 0.8$. Since f is even, we

only need to find the positive roots.

$x_1 = 0.8$

$x_2 \approx 0.84287645$

$x_3 \approx 0.84310820$

$x_4 \approx 0.84310821 \approx x_5$

$x_1 = 1.9$

$x_2 \approx 1.94689103$

$x_3 \approx 1.94383891$

$x_4 \approx 1.94382538 \approx x_5$

To eight decimal places, the roots of the equation are ± 0.84310821 and ± 1.94382538.

13.

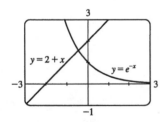

Solving $e^{-x} = 2 + x$ is the same as solving $f(x) = e^{-x} - x - 2 = 0$.

$f'(x) = -e^{-x} - 1 \quad \Rightarrow \quad x_{n+1} = x_n - \dfrac{e^{-x_n} - x_n - 2}{-e^{-x_n} - 1}$. From the

graph of $y = e^{-x}$ and $y = 2 + x$, there appears to be a root near

$x = -0.5$. Now $x_1 = -0.5 \quad \Rightarrow \quad x_2 \approx -0.44385167$,

$x_3 \approx -0.44285470$, $x_4 \approx -0.44285440 \approx x_5$. To eight decimal places,

the root of the equation is -0.44285440.

14.

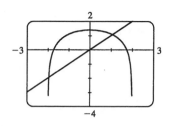

From the graph, $y = \ln(4 - x^2)$ and $y = x$ intersect twice, at $x \approx -2$ and at $x \approx 1$. $f(x) = \ln(4 - x^2) - x$ $\Rightarrow$

$f'(x) = \dfrac{-2x}{4 - x^2} - 1$, so $x_{n+1} = x_n - \dfrac{\ln(4 - x_n^2) - x_n}{[-2x_n/(4 - x_n^2)] - 1}$.

Trying $x_1 = -2$ won't work because it's not in the domain of $y = \ln(4 - x^2)$. Trying $x_1 = -1.9$ also fails after one iteration because the approximation x_2 is less than -2. We try $x_1 = -1.99$.

$x_1 = -1.99$
$x_2 \approx -1.97753026$
$x_3 \approx -1.96741777$
$x_4 \approx -1.96475281$
$x_5 \approx -1.96463580$
$x_6 \approx -1.96463560 \approx x_7$

$x_1 = 1.1$
$x_2 \approx 1.05864851$
$x_3 \approx 1.05800655$
$x_4 \approx 1.05800640 \approx x_5$

To eight decimal places, the roots of the equation are -1.96463560 and 1.05800640.

15.

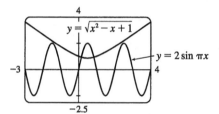

From the graph, we see that there are roots of this equation near 0.2 and 0.8. $f(x) = \sqrt{x^2 - x + 1} - 2\sin\pi x$ $\Rightarrow$

$f'(x) = \dfrac{2x - 1}{2\sqrt{x^2 - x + 1}} - 2\pi\cos\pi x$, so

$x_{n+1} = x_n - \dfrac{\sqrt{x_n^2 - x_n + 1} - 2\sin\pi x_n}{\dfrac{2x_n - 1}{2\sqrt{x_n^2 - x_n + 1}} - 2\pi\cos\pi x_n}$.

Taking $x_1 = 0.2$, we get $x_2 \approx 0.15212015$, $x_3 \approx 0.15438067$, $x_4 \approx 0.15438500 \approx x_5$. Taking $x_1 = 0.8$, we get $x_2 \approx 0.84787985$, $x_3 \approx 0.84561933$, $x_4 \approx 0.84561500 \approx x_5$. To eight decimal places, the roots of the equation are 0.15438500 and 0.84561500.

16.

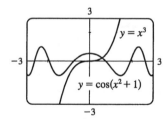

From the graph, we see that the only root of this equation is near 0.6. $f(x) = \cos(x^2 + 1) - x^3$ $\Rightarrow$ $f'(x) = -2x\sin(x^2 + 1) - 3x^2$,

so $x_{n+1} = x_n - \dfrac{\cos(x_n^2 + 1) - x_n^3}{-2x_n\sin(x_n^2 + 1) - 3x_n^2}$. Taking $x_1 = 0.6$, we

get $x_2 \approx 0.59699955$, $x_3 \approx 0.59698777 \approx x_3$. To eight decimal places, the root of the equation is 0.59698777.

17.

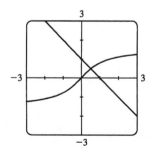

From the graph of $y = \tan^{-1} x$ and $y = 1 - x$, there appears to be a point of intersection near $x = 0.5$. Solving $\tan^{-1} x = 1 - x$ is the same as solving $f(x) = \tan^{-1} x + x - 1 = 0$. $f(x) = \tan^{-1} x + x - 1$ $\Rightarrow$

$f'(x) = \dfrac{1}{1 + x^2} + 1$, so $x_{n+1} = x_n - \dfrac{\tan^{-1} x_n + x_n - 1}{1/(1 + x_n^2) + 1}$.

Now $x_1 = 0.5$ $\Rightarrow$ $x_2 \approx 0.52019577$, $x_3 \approx 0.52026899 \approx x_4$.
To eight decimal places, the root of the equation is 0.52026899.

18.

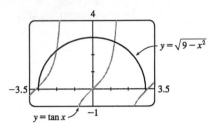

From the graph, $y = \tan x$ and $y = \sqrt{9 - x^2}$ intersect three times, at $x \approx -3$, $x \approx -2$, and $x \approx 1.2$. $f(x) = \tan x - \sqrt{9 - x^2}$ $\Rightarrow$ $f'(x) = \sec^2 x + \dfrac{x}{\sqrt{9 - x^2}}$, so

$$x_{n+1} = x_n - \frac{\tan x_n - \sqrt{9 - x_n^2}}{\sec^2 x_n + x_n/\sqrt{9 - x_n^2}}.$$ Trying $x_1 = -3$ won't

work because it's not in the domain of $f'(x)$. Trying $x_1 = -2.9$ also fails after one iteration because the approximation x_2 is less than -3. We try -2.99.

$x_1 = -2.99$	$x_1 = -2$	$x_1 = 1.2$
$x_2 \approx -2.99821730$	$x_2 \approx -1.98954336$	$x_2 \approx 1.22202993$
$x_3 \approx -2.99675310$	$x_3 \approx -1.98982579$	$x_3 \approx 1.22089613$
$x_4 \approx -2.99644398$	$x_4 \approx -1.98982601 \approx x_5$	$x_4 \approx 1.22089273 \approx x_5$
$x_5 \approx -2.99643623 \approx x_6$		

19. (a) $f(x) = x^2 - a$ $\Rightarrow$ $f'(x) = 2x$, so Newton's method gives

$$x_{n+1} = x_n - \frac{x_n^2 - a}{2x_n} = x_n - \frac{1}{2}x_n + \frac{a}{2x_n} = \frac{1}{2}x_n + \frac{a}{2x_n} = \frac{1}{2}\left(x_n + \frac{a}{x_n}\right).$$

(b) Using (a) with $a = 1000$ and $x_1 = \sqrt{900} = 30$, we get $x_2 \approx 31.666667$, $x_3 \approx 31.622807$, and $x_4 \approx 31.622777 \approx x_5$. So $\sqrt{1000} \approx 31.622777$.

20. (a) $f(x) = \dfrac{1}{x} - a$ $\Rightarrow$ $f'(x) = -\dfrac{1}{x^2}$, so $x_{n+1} = x_n - \dfrac{1/x_n - a}{-1/x_n^2} = x_n + x_n - ax_n^2 = 2x_n - ax_n^2$.

(b) Using (a) with $a = 1.6894$ and $x_1 = \frac{1}{2} = 0.5$, we get $x_2 = 0.5754$, $x_3 \approx 0.588485$, and $x_4 \approx 0.588789 \approx x_5$. So $1/1.6984 \approx 0.588789$.

21. $f(x) = x^3 - 3x + 6$ $\Rightarrow$ $f'(x) = 3x^2 - 3$. If $x_1 = 1$, then $f'(x_1) = 0$ and the tangent line used for approximating x_2 is horizontal. Attempting to find x_2 results in trying to divide by zero.

22. $x^3 - x = 1$ $\Leftrightarrow$ $x^3 - x - 1 = 0$. $f(x) = x^3 - x - 1$ $\Rightarrow$ $f'(x) = 3x^2 - 1$, so $x_{n+1} = x_n - \dfrac{x_n^3 - x_n - 1}{3x_n^2 - 1}$.

(a) $x_1 = 1$, $x_2 = 1.5$, $x_3 \approx 1.347826$, $x_4 \approx 1.325200$, $x_5 \approx 1.324718 \approx x_6$

(b) $x_1 = 0.6$, $x_2 = 17.9$, $x_3 \approx 11.946802$, $x_4 \approx 7.985520$, $x_5 \approx 5.356909$, $x_6 \approx 3.624996$, $x_7 \approx 2.505589$, $x_8 \approx 1.820129$, $x_9 \approx 1.461044$, $x_{10} \approx 1.339323$, $x_{11} \approx 1.324913$, $x_{12} \approx 1.324718 \approx x_{13}$

(c) $x_1 = 0.57$, $x_2 \approx -54.165455$, $x_3 \approx -36.114293$, $x_4 \approx -24.082094$, $x_5 \approx -16.063387$, $x_6 \approx -10.721483$, $x_7 \approx -7.165534$, $x_8 \approx -4.801704$, $x_9 \approx -3.233425$, $x_{10} \approx -2.193674$, $x_{11} \approx -1.496867$, $x_{12} \approx -0.997546$, $x_{13} \approx -0.496305$, $x_{14} \approx -2.894162$, $x_{15} \approx -1.967962$, $x_{16} \approx -1.341355$, $x_{17} \approx -0.870187$, $x_{18} \approx -0.249949$, $x_{19} \approx -1.192219$, $x_{20} \approx -0.731952$, $x_{21} \approx 0.355213$, $x_{22} \approx -1.753322$, $x_{23} \approx -1.189420$, $x_{24} \approx -0.729123$, $x_{25} \approx 0.377844$, $x_{26} \approx -1.937872$, $x_{27} \approx -1.320350$, $x_{28} \approx -0.851919$, $x_{29} \approx -0.200959$, $x_{30} \approx -1.119386$, $x_{31} \approx -0.654291$, $x_{32} \approx 1.547010$, $x_{33} \approx 1.360051$, $x_{34} \approx 1.325828$, $x_{35} \approx 1.324719$, $x_{36} \approx 1.324718 \approx x_{37}$.

(d)

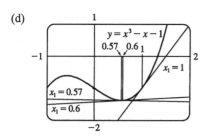

From the figure, we see that the tangent line corresponding to $x_1 = 1$ results in a sequence of approximations that converges quite quickly ($x_5 \approx x_6$). The tangent line corresponding to $x_1 = 0.6$ is close to being horizontal, so x_2 is quite far from the root. But the sequence still converges — just a little more slowly ($x_{12} \approx x_{13}$). Lastly, the tangent line corresponding to $x_1 = 0.57$ is very nearly horizontal, x_2 is farther away from the root, and the sequence takes more iterations to converge ($x_{36} \approx x_{37}$).

23. For $f(x) = x^{1/3}$, $f'(x) = \frac{1}{3}x^{-2/3}$ and

$$x_{n+1} = x_n - \frac{f(x_n)}{f'(x_n)} = x_n - \frac{x_n^{1/3}}{\frac{1}{3}x_n^{-2/3}} = x_n - 3x_n = -2x_n.$$

Therefore, each successive approximation becomes twice as large as the previous one in absolute value, so the sequence of approximations fails to converge to the root, which is 0. In the figure, we have $x_1 = 0.5$, $x_2 = -2(0.5) = -1$, and $x_3 = -2(-1) = 2$.

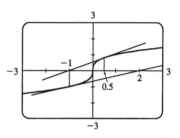

24. $f(x) = x^2 + \sin x \;\Rightarrow\; f'(x) = 2x + \cos x$. $f'(x)$ exists for all x, so to find the minimum of f, we can examine the zeros of f'. From the graph of f', we see that a good choice for x_1 is $x_1 = -0.5$. Use $g(x) = 2x + \cos x$ and $g'(x) = 2 - \sin x$ to obtain $x_2 \approx -0.450627$, $x_3 \approx -0.450184 \approx x_4$. Since $f''(x) = 2 - \sin x > 0$ for all x, $f(-0.450184) \approx -0.232466$ is the absolute minimum.

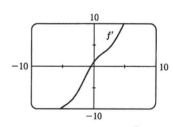

25.

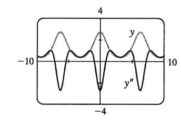

From the figure, we see that $y = f(x) = e^{\cos x}$ is periodic with period 2π. To find the x-coordinates of the IP, we only need to approximate the zeros of y'' on $[0, \pi]$. $f'(x) = -e^{\cos x} \sin x \;\Rightarrow\; f''(x) = e^{\cos x}(\sin^2 x - \cos x)$. Since $e^{\cos x} \neq 0$, we will use Newton's method with $g(x) = \sin^2 x - \cos x$, $g'(x) = 2\sin x \cos x + \sin x$, and $x_1 = 1$. $x_2 \approx 0.904173$, $x_3 \approx 0.904557 \approx x_4$. Thus, $(0.904557, 1.855277)$ is the IP.

26.

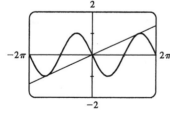

$f(x) = -\sin x \;\Rightarrow\; f'(x) = -\cos x$. At $x = a$, the slope of the tangent line is $f'(a) = -\cos a$. The line through the origin and $(a, f(a))$ is $y = \dfrac{-\sin a - 0}{a - 0}x$. If this line is to be tangent to f at $x = a$, then its slope must equal $f'(a)$. Thus, $\dfrac{-\sin a}{a} = -\cos a \;\Rightarrow\; \tan a = a$.

To solve this equation using Newton's method, let $g(x) = \tan x - x$,

$g'(x) = \sec^2 x - 1$, and $x_{n+1} = x_n - \dfrac{\tan x_n - x_n}{\sec^2 x_n - 1}$ with $x_1 = 4.5$ (estimated from the figure). $x_2 \approx 4.493614$, $x_3 \approx 4.493410$, $x_4 \approx 4.493409 \approx x_5$. Thus, the slope of the line that has the largest slope is $f'(x_5) \approx 0.217234$.

27.

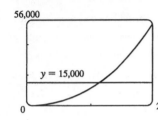

The volume of the silo, in terms of its radius, is

$$V(r) = \pi r^2(30) + \tfrac{1}{2}\left(\tfrac{4}{3}\pi r^3\right) = 30\pi r^2 + \tfrac{2}{3}\pi r^3.$$

From a graph of V, we see that $V(r) = 15{,}000$ at $r \approx 11$ ft. Now we use

Newton's method to solve the equation $V(r) - 15{,}000 = 0$.

$\dfrac{dV}{dr} = 60\pi r + 2\pi r^2$, so $r_{n+1} = r_n - \dfrac{30\pi r_n^2 + \tfrac{2}{3}\pi r_n^3 - 15{,}000}{60\pi r_n + 2\pi r_n^2}$. Taking

$r_1 = 11$, we get $r_2 \approx 11.2853$, $r_3 \approx 11.2807 \approx r_4$. So in order for the

silo to hold 15,000 ft³ of grain, its radius must be about 11.2807 ft.

28. Let the radius of the circle be r. Using $s = r\theta$, we have $5 = r\theta$ and so $r = 5/\theta$. From the Law of Cosines we get

$4^2 = r^2 + r^2 - 2 \cdot r \cdot r \cdot \cos\theta \quad \Leftrightarrow \quad 16 = 2r^2(1 - \cos\theta) = 2(5/\theta)^2\,(1 - \cos\theta).$

Multiplying by θ^2 gives $16\theta^2 = 50(1 - \cos\theta)$, so we take

$f(\theta) = 16\theta^2 + 50\cos\theta - 50$ and $f'(\theta) = 32\theta - 50\sin\theta$. The formula

for Newton's method is $\theta_{n+1} = \theta_n - \dfrac{16\theta_n^2 + 50\cos\theta_n - 50}{32\theta_n - 50\sin\theta_n}$. From the

graph of f, we can use $\theta_1 = 2.2$, giving us $\theta_2 \approx 2.2662$,

$\theta_3 \approx 2.2622 \approx \theta_4$. So correct to four decimal places, the angle is

2.2622 radians $\approx 130°$.

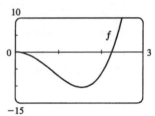

29. In this case, $A = 18{,}000$, $R = 375$, and $n = 5(12) = 60$. So the formula $A = \dfrac{R}{i}\left[1 - (1 + i)^{-n}\right]$ becomes

$18{,}000 = \dfrac{375}{x}\left[1 - (1 + x)^{-60}\right] \quad \Leftrightarrow \quad 48x = 1 - (1 + x)^{-60}$ [multiply each term by $(1 + x)^{60}$] $\Leftrightarrow$

$48x(1 + x)^{60} - (1 + x)^{60} + 1 = 0$. Let the LHS be called $f(x)$, so that

$$f'(x) = 48x(60)(1 + x)^{59} + 48(1 + x)^{60} - 60(1 + x)^{59}$$

$$= 12(1 + x)^{59}\left[4x(60) + 4(1 + x) - 5\right] = 12(1 + x)^{59}(244x - 1)$$

$x_{n+1} = x_n - \dfrac{48x_n(1 + x_n)^{60} - (1 + x_n)^{60} + 1}{12(1 + x_n)^{59}(244x_n - 1)}$. An interest rate of 1%/month seems like a reasonable estimate

for $x = i$. So let $x_1 = 1\% = 0.01$, and we get $x_2 \approx 0.0082202$, $x_3 \approx 0.0076802$, $x_4 \approx 0.0076291$,

$x_5 \approx 0.0076286 \approx x_6$. Thus, the dealer is charging a monthly interest rate of 0.76286% (or 9.55%/year,

compounded monthly).

30. (a) $p(x) = x^5 - (2 + r)x^4 + (1 + 2r)x^3 - (1 - r)x^2 + 2(1 - r)x + r - 1 \quad \Rightarrow$

$p'(x) = 5x^4 - 4(2 + r)x^3 + 3(1 + 2r)x^2 - 2(1 - r)x + 2(1 - r)$. So we use

$x_{n+1} = x_n - \dfrac{x_n^5 - (2 + r)x_n^4 + (1 + 2r)x_n^3 - (1 - r)x_n^2 + 2(1 - r)x_n + r - 1}{5x_n^4 - 4(2 + r)x_n^3 + 3(1 + 2r)x_n^2 - 2(1 - r)x_n + 2(1 - r)}$. We substitute in the value

$r \approx 3.04042 \times 10^{-6}$ in order to evaluate the approximations numerically. The libration point L_1 is slightly less

than 1 AU from the sun, so we take $x_1 = 0.95$ as our first approximation, and get $x_2 \approx 0.96682$, $x_3 \approx 0.97770$,

$x_4 \approx 0.98451$, $x_5 \approx 0.98830$, $x_6 \approx 0.98976$, $x_7 \approx 0.98998$, $x_8 \approx 0.98999 \approx x_9$. So, to five decimal places,

L_1 is located 0.98999 AU from the sun (or 0.01001 AU from Earth).

(b) In this case we use Newton's method with the function

$p(x) - 2rx^2 = x^5 - (2 + r)x^4 + (1 + 2r)x^3 - (1 + r)x^2 + 2(1 - r)x + r - 1 \quad \Rightarrow$

$\left[p(x) - 2rx^2\right]' = 5x^4 - 4(2 + r)x^3 + 3(1 + 2r)x^2 - 2(1 + r)x + 2(1 - r)$. So

$$x_{n+1} = x_n - \frac{x_n^5 - (2+r)x_n^4 + (1+2r)x_n^3 - (1+r)x_n^2 + 2(1-r)x_n + r - 1}{5x_n^4 - 4(2+r)x_n^3 + 3(1+2r)x_n^2 - 2(1+r)x_n + 2(1-r)}.$$ Again, we substitute

$r \approx 3.04042 \times 10^{-6}$. L_2 is slightly more than 1 AU from the sun and, judging from the result of part (a), probably less than 0.02 AU from Earth. So we take $x_1 = 1.02$ and get $x_2 \approx 1.01422$, $x_3 \approx 1.01118$, $x_4 \approx 1.01018$, $x_5 \approx 1.01008 \approx x_6$. So, to five decimal places, L_2 is located 1.01008 AU from the sun (or 0.01008 AU from Earth).

Antiderivatives • • • • • • • • • • • • • • • •

1. $f(x) = 6x^2 - 8x + 3 \;\Rightarrow\; F(x) = 6\dfrac{x^{2+1}}{2+1} - 8\dfrac{x^{1+1}}{1+1} + 3x + C = 2x^3 - 4x^2 + 3x + C$

Check: $F'(x) = 2 \cdot 3x^2 - 4 \cdot 2x + 3 + 0 = 6x^2 - 8x + 3 = f(x)$

2. $f(x) = 1 - x^3 + 12x^5 \;\Rightarrow\; F(x) = x - \dfrac{x^{3+1}}{3+1} + 12\dfrac{x^{5+1}}{5+1} + C = x - \frac{1}{4}x^4 + 2x^6 + C$

3. $f(x) = 5x^{1/4} - 7x^{3/4} \;\Rightarrow\; F(x) = 5\dfrac{x^{1/4+1}}{\frac{1}{4}+1} - 7\dfrac{x^{3/4+1}}{\frac{3}{4}+1} + C = 5\dfrac{x^{5/4}}{5/4} - 7\dfrac{x^{7/4}}{7/4} + C = 4x^{5/4} - 4x^{7/4} + C$

Check: $F'(x) = 4 \cdot \frac{5}{4}x^{1/4} - 4 \cdot \frac{7}{4}x^{3/4} = 5x^{1/4} - 7x^{3/4} = f(x)$

4. $f(x) = 2x + 3x^{1.7} \;\Rightarrow\; F(x) = x^2 + \frac{3}{2.7}x^{2.7} + C = x^2 + \frac{10}{9}x^{2.7} + C$

5. $f(x) = \dfrac{10}{x^9} = 10x^{-9}$ has domain $(-\infty, 0) \cup (0, \infty)$, so $F(x) = \begin{cases} \dfrac{10x^{-8}}{-8} + C_1 = -\dfrac{5}{4x^8} + C_1 & \text{if } x < 0 \\[2mm] -\dfrac{5}{4x^8} + C_2 & \text{if } x > 0 \end{cases}$

See Example 1(b) for a similar exercise.

6. $f(x) = \sqrt[3]{x^2} - \sqrt{x^3} = x^{2/3} - x^{3/2} \;\Rightarrow\; F(x) = \frac{1}{5/3}x^{5/3} - \frac{1}{5/2}x^{5/2} + C = \frac{3}{5}x^{5/3} - \frac{2}{5}x^{5/2} + C$

7. $g(t) = \dfrac{t^3 + 2t^2}{\sqrt{t}} = t^{5/2} + 2t^{3/2} \;\Rightarrow\; G(t) = \dfrac{t^{7/2}}{7/2} + \dfrac{2t^{5/2}}{5/2} + C = \frac{2}{7}t^{7/2} + \frac{4}{5}t^{5/2} + C$

Note that g has domain $(0, \infty)$.

8. $f(x) = \dfrac{3}{x^2} - \dfrac{5}{x^4} = 3x^{-2} - 5x^{-4}$ has domain $(-\infty, 0) \cup (0, \infty)$, so

$F(x) = \begin{cases} \dfrac{3x^{-1}}{-1} - \dfrac{5x^{-3}}{-3} + C_1 = -\dfrac{3}{x} + \dfrac{5}{3x^3} + C_1 & \text{if } x < 0 \\[3mm] -\dfrac{3}{x} + \dfrac{5}{3x^3} + C_2 & \text{if } x > 0 \end{cases}$

9. $f(t) = 3\cos t - 4\sin t \;\Rightarrow\; F(t) = 3(\sin t) - 4(-\cos t) + C = 3\sin t + 4\cos t + C$

10. $f(x) = 3e^x + 7\sec^2 x \;\Rightarrow\; F(x) = 3e^x + 7\tan x + C_n$ on the interval $\left(n\pi - \frac{\pi}{2}, n\pi + \frac{\pi}{2}\right)$.

11. $f(x) = 2x + 5(1 - x^2)^{-1/2} = 2x + \dfrac{5}{\sqrt{1 - x^2}} \;\Rightarrow\; F(x) = x^2 + 5\sin^{-1}x + C$

12. $f(x) = \dfrac{x^2 + x + 1}{x} = x + 1 + \dfrac{1}{x} \;\Rightarrow\; F(x) = \begin{cases} \frac{1}{2}x^2 + x + \ln|x| + C_1 & \text{if } x < 0 \\[2mm] \frac{1}{2}x^2 + x + \ln|x| + C_2 & \text{if } x > 0 \end{cases}$

13. $f(x) = 5x^4 - 2x^5 \Rightarrow F(x) = 5 \cdot \dfrac{x^5}{5} - 2 \cdot \dfrac{x^6}{6} + C = x^5 - \frac{1}{3}x^6 + C.$

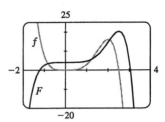

$F(0) = 4 \Rightarrow 0^5 - \frac{1}{3} \cdot 0^6 + C = 4 \Rightarrow C = 4,$ so

$F(x) = x^5 - \frac{1}{3}x^6 + 4.$ The graph confirms our answer since $f(x) = 0$

when F has a local maximum, f is positive when F is increasing, and f is

negative when F is decreasing.

14. $f(x) = 4 - 3(1 + x^2)^{-1} = 4 - \dfrac{3}{1 + x^2} \Rightarrow$

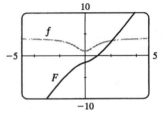

$F(x) = 4x - 3\tan^{-1} x + C.$ $F(1) = 0 \Rightarrow 4 - 3(\frac{\pi}{4}) + C = 0 \Rightarrow$

$C = \frac{3\pi}{4} - 4,$ so $F(x) = 4x - 3\tan^{-1} x + \frac{3\pi}{4} - 4.$ Note that f is positive

and F is increasing on $\mathbb{R}.$ Also, f has smaller values where the slopes of

the tangent lines of F are smaller.

15. $f''(x) = 6x + 12x^2 \Rightarrow f'(x) = 6 \cdot \dfrac{x^2}{2} + 12 \cdot \dfrac{x^3}{3} + C = 3x^2 + 4x^3 + C \Rightarrow$

$f(x) = 3 \cdot \dfrac{x^3}{3} + 4 \cdot \dfrac{x^4}{4} + Cx + D = x^3 + x^4 + Cx + D$ [C and D are just arbitrary constants]

16. $f''(x) = 2 + x^3 + x^6 \Rightarrow f'(x) = 2x + \frac{1}{4}x^4 + \frac{1}{7}x^7 + C \Rightarrow f(x) = x^2 + \frac{1}{20}x^5 + \frac{1}{56}x^8 + Cx + D$

17. $f''(x) = 1 + x^{4/5} \Rightarrow f'(x) = x + \frac{5}{9}x^{9/5} + C \Rightarrow$

$f(x) = \frac{1}{2}x^2 + \frac{5}{9} \cdot \frac{5}{14}x^{14/5} + Cx + D = \frac{1}{2}x^2 + \frac{25}{126}x^{14/5} + Cx + D$

18. $f''(x) = \cos x \Rightarrow f'(x) = \sin x + C \Rightarrow f(x) = -\cos x + Cx + D$

19. $f'(x) = 3\cos x + 5\sin x \Rightarrow f(x) = 3\sin x - 5\cos x + C.$

$f(0) = 4 \Rightarrow -5 + C = 4 \Rightarrow C = 9,$ so $f(x) = 3\sin x - 5\cos x + 9.$

20. $f'(x) = 4/\sqrt{1 - x^2} \Rightarrow f(x) = 4\sin^{-1} x + C.$ $f(\frac{1}{2}) = 4\sin^{-1}(\frac{1}{2}) + C = 4 \cdot \frac{\pi}{6} + C$ and $f(\frac{1}{2}) = 1 \Rightarrow$

$\frac{2\pi}{3} + C = 1 \Rightarrow C = 1 - \frac{2\pi}{3},$ so $f(x) = 4\sin^{-1} x + 1 - \frac{2\pi}{3}.$

21. $f''(x) = x \Rightarrow f'(x) = \frac{1}{2}x^2 + C.$ $f'(0) = 2 \Rightarrow C = 2,$ so $f'(x) = \frac{1}{2}x^2 + 2 \Rightarrow$

$f(x) = \frac{1}{6}x^3 + 2x + D.$ $f(0) = -3 \Rightarrow D = -3,$ so $f(x) = \frac{1}{6}x^3 + 2x - 3.$

22. $f''(x) = x + x^{1/2} \Rightarrow f'(x) = \frac{1}{2}x^2 + \frac{2}{3}x^{3/2} + C.$ $f'(1) = 2 \Rightarrow \frac{1}{2} + \frac{2}{3} + C = 2 \Rightarrow C = \frac{5}{6},$ so

$f'(x) = \frac{1}{2}x^2 + \frac{2}{3}x^{3/2} + \frac{5}{6} \Rightarrow f(x) = \frac{1}{6}x^3 + \frac{4}{15}x^{5/2} + \frac{5}{6}x + D.$ $f(1) = 1 \Rightarrow \frac{1}{6} + \frac{4}{15} + \frac{5}{6} + D = 1$

$\Rightarrow D = -\frac{4}{15},$ so $f(x) = \frac{1}{6}x^3 + \frac{4}{15}x^{5/2} + \frac{5}{6}x - \frac{4}{15}.$

23. $f''(x) = x^{-2}, x > 0 \Rightarrow f'(x) = -1/x + C \Rightarrow f(x) = -\ln|x| + Cx + D = -\ln x + Cx + D$ (since

$x > 0$). $f(1) = 0 \Rightarrow C + D = 0$ and $f(2) = 0 \Rightarrow -\ln 2 + 2C + D = 0 \Rightarrow$

$-\ln 2 + 2C - C$ (since $D = -C$) $= 0 \Rightarrow -\ln 2 + C = 0 \Rightarrow C = \ln 2$ and $D = -\ln 2.$ So

$f(x) = -\ln x + (\ln 2)x - \ln 2.$

24. $f''(x) = 3e^x + 5\sin x \Rightarrow f'(x) = 3e^x - 5\cos x + C.$ $f'(0) = 2 \Rightarrow 3 - 5 + C = 2 \Rightarrow C = 4,$ so

$f'(x) = 3e^x - 5\cos x + 4 \Rightarrow f(x) = 3e^x - 5\sin x + 4x + D.$ $f(0) = 1 \Rightarrow 3 + D = 1 \Rightarrow$

$D = -2,$ so $f(x) = 3e^x - 5\sin x + 4x - 2.$

25. Given $f'(x) = 2x + 1,$ we have $f(x) = x^2 + x + C.$ Since f passes through $(1, 6),$

$f(1) = 6 \Rightarrow 1^2 + 1 + C = 6 \Rightarrow C = 4.$ Therefore, $f(x) = x^2 + x + 4$ and $f(2) = 2^2 + 2 + 4 = 10.$

26. $f'(x) = x^3 \Rightarrow f(x) = \frac{1}{4}x^4 + C.$ $x + y = 0 \Rightarrow y = -x \Rightarrow m = -1.$ Now $m = f'(x) \Rightarrow$
$-1 = x^3 \Rightarrow x = -1 \Rightarrow y = 1$ (from the equation of the tangent line), so $(-1, 1)$ is a point on the graph
of f. From $f, 1 = \frac{1}{4}(-1)^4 + C \Rightarrow C = \frac{3}{4}.$ Therefore, the function is $f(x) = \frac{1}{4}x^4 + \frac{3}{4}.$

27.

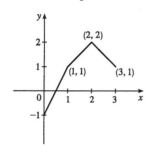

$$f'(x) = \begin{cases} 2 & \text{if } 0 \le x < 1 \\ 1 & \text{if } 1 < x < 2 \\ -1 & \text{if } 2 < x \le 3 \end{cases} \Rightarrow f(x) = \begin{cases} 2x + C & \text{if } 0 \le x < 1 \\ x + D & \text{if } 1 < x < 2 \\ -x + E & \text{if } 2 < x \le 3 \end{cases}$$

$f(0) = -1 \Rightarrow 2(0) + C = -1 \Rightarrow C = -1.$ Starting at the point
$(0, -1)$ and moving to the right on a line with slope 2 gets us to the point
$(1, 1)$. The slope for $1 < x < 2$ is 1, so we get to the point $(2, 2)$. Here we
have used the fact that f is continuous. We can include the point $x = 1$ on
either the first or the second part of f. The line connecting $(1, 1)$ to $(2, 2)$ is $y = x$, so $D = 0$. The slope for
$2 < x \le 3$ is -1, so we get to $(3, 1)$. $f(3) = 1 \Rightarrow -3 + E = 1 \Rightarrow E = 4.$ Thus,

$$f(x) = \begin{cases} 2x - 1 & \text{if } 0 \le x \le 1 \\ x & \text{if } 1 < x < 2 \\ -x + 4 & \text{if } 2 \le x \le 3 \end{cases}$$

Note that $f'(x)$ does not exist at $x = 1$ or at $x = 2$.

28. (a)

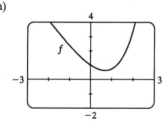

(b)

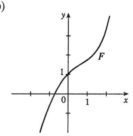

Since f is always positive, F is always increasing.

(c) $f(x) = e^x - 2x \Rightarrow F(x) = e^x - x^2 + C.$ $F(0) = 1 \Rightarrow 1 - 0 + C = 1 \Rightarrow C = 0,$
so $F(x) = e^x - x^2.$

(d) If we use a graphing device to graph $F(x) = e^x - x^2$, we see that the graph looks similar to the one in part (b).

29.

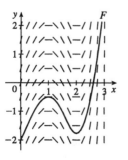

30.

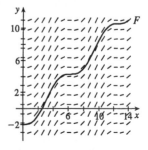

31.

x	$f(x)$
0	1
0.5	0.959
1.0	0.841
1.5	0.665
2.0	0.455
2.5	0.239
3.0	0.047

x	$f(x)$
3.5	−0.100
4.0	−0.189
4.5	−0.217
5.0	−0.192
5.5	−0.128
6.0	−0.047

We compute slopes [values of $f(x) = (\sin x)/x$ for $0 < x < 2\pi$] as in the table [$\lim_{x \to 0^+} f(x) = 1$] and draw a direction field as in Example 5. Then we use the direction field to graph F starting at $(0,0)$.

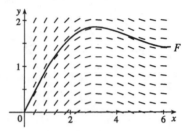

32.

x	$f(x)$
0	0
±0.2	0.041
±0.4	0.169
±0.6	0.410
±0.8	0.824
±1.0	1.557
±1.2	3.087
±1.4	8.117
±1.5	21.152

We compute slopes [values of $f(x) = x \tan x$ for $-\pi/2 < x < \pi/2$] as in the table and draw a direction field as in Example 5. Then we use the direction field to graph F starting at $(0,0)$ and extending in both directions. Note that if f is an even function, then the antiderivative F that passes through the origin is an odd function.

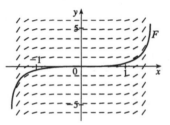

33.

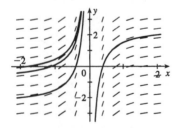

Remember that the given table values of f are the slopes of F at any x. For example, at $x = 1.4$, the slope of F is $f(1.4) = 0$.

34. (a)

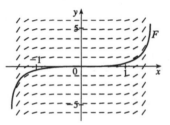

(b) The general antiderivative of $f(x) = x^{-2}$ is

$$F(x) = \begin{cases} -1/x + C_1 & \text{if } x < 0 \\ -1/x + C_2 & \text{if } x > 0 \end{cases}$$ since $f(x)$ is not defined

at $x = 0$. The graph of the general antiderivatives of $f(x)$ looks like the graph in part (a), as expected.

35. $v(t) = s'(t) = \sin t - \cos t \implies s(t) = -\cos t - \sin t + C$. $s(0) = -1 + C$ and $s(0) = 0 \implies$
$-1 + C = 0 \implies C = 1$, so $s(t) = -\cos t - \sin t + 1$.

36. $a(t) = v'(t) = 5 + 4t - 2t^2 \;\Rightarrow\; v(t) = 5t + 2t^2 - \frac{2}{3}t^3 + C.$ $v(0) = 3 \;\Rightarrow\; C = 3,$ so
$v(t) = 5t + 2t^2 - \frac{2}{3}t^3 + 3.$ $v(t) = s'(t) \;\Rightarrow\; s(t) = \frac{5}{2}t^2 + \frac{2}{3}t^3 - \frac{1}{6}t^4 + 3t + D.$ $s(0) = 10 \;\Rightarrow\; D = 10,$
so the particle's position after t seconds is given by $s(t) = \frac{5}{2}t^2 + \frac{2}{3}t^3 - \frac{1}{6}t^4 + 3t + 10.$

37. (a) We first observe that since the stone is dropped 450 m above the ground, $v(0) = 0$ and $s(0) = 450.$
$v'(t) = a(t) = -9.8 \;\Rightarrow\; v(t) = -9.8t + C.$ Now $v(0) = 0 \;\Rightarrow\; C = 0,$ so $v(t) = -9.8t \;\Rightarrow\;$
$s(t) = -4.9t^2 + D.$ Last, $s(0) = 450 \;\Rightarrow\; D = 450 \;\Rightarrow\; s(t) = 450 - 4.9t^2.$

(b) The stone reaches the ground when $s(t) = 0.$ $450 - 4.9t^2 = 0 \;\Rightarrow\; t^2 = 450/4.9 \;\Rightarrow\;$
$t_1 = \sqrt{450/4.9} \approx 9.58$ s.

(c) The velocity with which the stone strikes the ground is $v(t_1) = -9.8\sqrt{450/4.9} \approx -93.9$ m/s.

(d) This is just reworking parts (a) and (b) with $v(0) = -5.$ Using $v(t) = -9.8t + C, v(0) = -5 \;\Rightarrow\;$
$0 + C = -5 \;\Rightarrow\; v(t) = -9.8t - 5.$ So $s(t) = -4.9t^2 - 5t + D$ and $s(0) = 450 \;\Rightarrow\; D = 450 \;\Rightarrow\;$
$s(t) = -4.9t^2 - 5t + 450.$ Solving $s(t) = 0$ by using the quadratic formula gives us
$t = \left(5 \pm \sqrt{8845}\right)/(-9.8) \;\Rightarrow\; t_1 \approx 9.09$ s.

38. $v'(t) = a(t) = a \;\Rightarrow\; v(t) = at + C$ and $v_0 = v(0) = C \;\Rightarrow\; v(t) = at + v_0 \;\Rightarrow\; s(t) = \frac{1}{2}at^2 + v_0t + D$
$\Rightarrow\; s_0 = s(0) = D \;\Rightarrow\; s(t) = \frac{1}{2}at^2 + v_0t + s_0$

39. By Exercise 38 with $a = -9.8,$ $s(t) = -4.9t^2 + v_0t + s_0$ and $v(t) = s'(t) = -9.8t + v_0.$ So
$[v(t)]^2 = (-9.8t + v_0)^2 = (9.8)^2 t^2 - 19.6v_0t + v_0^2 = v_0^2 + 96.04t^2 - 19.6v_0t = v_0^2 - 19.6(-4.9t^2 + v_0t).$ But
$-4.9t^2 + v_0t$ is just $s(t)$ without the s_0 term; that is, $s(t) - s_0.$ Thus, $[v(t)]^2 = v_0^2 - 19.6\,[s(t) - s_0].$

40. For the first ball, $s_1(t) = -16t^2 + 48t + 432$ from Example 7. For the second ball, $a(t) = -32 \;\Rightarrow\;$
$v(t) = -32t + C,$ but $v(1) = -32(1) + C = 24 \;\Rightarrow\; C = 56,$ so $v(t) = -32t + 56 \;\Rightarrow\;$
$s(t) = -16t^2 + 56t + D,$ but $s(1) = -16(1)^2 + 56(1) + D = 432 \;\Rightarrow\; D = 392,$ and
$s_2(t) = -16t^2 + 56t + 392.$ The balls pass each other when $s_1(t) = s_2(t) \;\Rightarrow\;$
$-16t^2 + 48t + 432 = -16t^2 + 56t + 392 \;\Leftrightarrow\; 8t = 40 \;\Leftrightarrow\; t = 5$ s.
Another solution: From Exercise 38, we have $s_1(t) = -16t^2 + 48t + 432$ and $s_2(t) = -16t^2 + 24t + 432.$
We now want to solve $s_1(t) = s_2(t - 1) \;\Rightarrow\; -16t^2 + 48t + 432 = -16(t - 1)^2 + 24(t - 1) + 432 \;\Rightarrow\;$
$48t = 32t - 16 + 24t - 24 \;\Rightarrow\; 40 = 8t \;\Rightarrow\; t = 5$ s.

41. Marginal cost $= 1.92 - 0.002x = C'(x) \;\Rightarrow\; C(x) = 1.92x - 0.001x^2 + K.$ But
$C(1) = 1.92 - 0.001 + K = 562 \;\Rightarrow\; K = 560.081.$ Therefore, $C(x) = 1.92x - 0.001x^2 + 560.081 \;\Rightarrow\;$
$C(100) = 742.081,$ so the cost of producing 100 items is $742.08.

42. Let the mass, measured from one end, be $m(x).$ Then $m(0) = 0$ and $\rho = \dfrac{dm}{dx} = x^{-1/2} \;\Rightarrow\; m(x) = 2x^{1/2} + C$
and $m(0) = C = 0,$ so $m(x) = 2\sqrt{x}.$ Thus, the mass of the 100-centimeter rod is $m(100) = 2\sqrt{100} = 20$ g.

43. Using Exercise 38 with $a = -32,$ $v_0 = 0,$ and $s_0 = h$ (the height of the cliff), we know that the height at time t is
$s(t) = -16t^2 + h.$ $v(t) = s'(t) = -32t$ and $v(t) = -120 \;\Rightarrow\; -32t = -120 \;\Rightarrow\; t = 3.75,$ so
$0 = s(3.75) = -16(3.75)^2 + h \;\Rightarrow\; h = 16(3.75)^2 = 225$ ft.

44. $v'(t) = a(t) = -40.$ The initial velocity is 50 mi/h $= \frac{50 \cdot 5280}{3600} = \frac{220}{3}$ ft/s, so $v(t) = -40t + \frac{220}{3}.$ The car stops
when $v(t) = 0 \;\Leftrightarrow\; t = \frac{220}{3 \cdot 40} = \frac{11}{6}.$ Since $s(t) = -20t^2 + \frac{220}{3}t,$ the distance covered is
$s\left(\frac{11}{6}\right) = -20\left(\frac{11}{6}\right)^2 + \frac{220}{3} \cdot \frac{11}{6} = \frac{605}{9} \approx 67.2$ ft.

45. $a(t) = k$, the initial velocity is 30 mi/h $= 30 \cdot \frac{5280}{3600} = 44$ ft/s, and the final velocity (after 5 seconds) is

50 mi/h $= 50 \cdot \frac{5280}{3600} = \frac{220}{3}$ ft/s. So $v(t) = kt + C$ and $v(0) = 44 \;\Rightarrow\; C = 44$. Thus, $v(t) = kt + 44 \;\Rightarrow\;$

$v(5) = 5k + 44$. But $v(5) = \frac{220}{3}$, so $5k + 44 = \frac{220}{3} \;\Rightarrow\; 5k = \frac{88}{3} \;\Rightarrow\; k = \frac{88}{15} \approx 5.87$ ft/s^2.

46. $a(t) = -40 \;\Rightarrow\; v(t) = -40t + v_0$ where v_0 is the car's speed (in ft/s) when the brakes were applied. The car

stops when $-40t + v_0 = 0 \;\Leftrightarrow\; t = \frac{1}{40}v_0$. Now $s(t) = \frac{1}{2}(-40)t^2 + v_0 t = -20t^2 + v_0 t$. The car travels 160 ft

in the time that it takes to stop, so $s\left(\frac{1}{40}v_0\right) = 160 \;\Rightarrow\; 160 = -20\left(\frac{1}{40}v_0\right)^2 + v_0\left(\frac{1}{40}v_0\right) = \frac{1}{80}v_0^2 \;\Rightarrow\;$

$v_0^2 = 12,800 \;\Rightarrow\; v_0 = 80\sqrt{2} \approx 113$ ft/s (about 77 mi/h).

47. (a) The Mean Value Theorem says that there exists a number c in the interval (x_1, x_2) such that

$$H'(c) = \frac{H(x_2) - H(x_1)}{x_2 - x_1}. \text{ Since } H = G - F \text{ and } G \text{ and } F \text{ are antiderivatives of } f,$$

$H'(c) = G'(c) - F'(c) = f(c) - f(c) = 0$. So now $\dfrac{H(x_2) - H(x_1)}{x_2 - x_1} = 0 \;\Rightarrow\; H(x_2) - H(x_1) = 0$

$(x_2 \neq x_1) \;\Rightarrow\; H(x_2) = H(x_1)$. Since this is true for any $x_1 < x_2$ in I, H must be a constant function.

(b) We have $H = G - F$ and $H(x) = C$, so $C = G - F \;\Rightarrow\; G(x) = F(x) + C$. Thus, any antiderivative G can be expressed as $F(x) + C$.

48. Taking the upward direction to be positive we have that for $0 \leq t \leq 10$ (using the subscript 1 to refer to

$0 \leq t \leq 10$), $a_1(t) = -(9 - 0.9t) = v_1'(t) \;\Rightarrow\; v_1(t) = -9t + 0.45t^2 + v_0$, but $v_1(0) = v_0 = -10 \;\Rightarrow\;$

$v_1(t) = -9t + 0.45t^2 - 10 = s_1'(t) \;\Rightarrow\; s_1(t) = -\frac{9}{2}t^2 + 0.15t^3 - 10t + s_0$. But $s_1(0) = 500 = s_0 \;\Rightarrow\;$

$s_1(t) = -\frac{9}{2}t^2 + 0.15t^3 - 10t + 500$. $s_1(10) = -450 + 150 - 100 + 500 = 100$, so it takes more

than 10 seconds for the raindrop to fall. Now for $t > 10$, $a(t) = 0 = v'(t) \;\Rightarrow\;$

$v(t) = \text{constant} = v_1(10) = -9(10) + 0.45(10)^2 - 10 = -55 \;\Rightarrow\; v(t) = -55$. At 55 ft/s, it will take

$100/55 \approx 1.8$ s to fall the last 100 ft. Hence, the total time is $10 + \frac{100}{55} = \frac{130}{11} \approx 11.8$ s.

49. (a) First note that 90 mi/h $= 90 \times \frac{5280}{3600}$ ft/s $= 132$ ft/s. Then $a(t) = 4$ ft/s$^2 \;\Rightarrow\; v(t) = 4t + C$, but $v(0) = 0$

$\Rightarrow\; C = 0$. Now $4t = 132$ when $t = \frac{132}{4} = 33$ s, so it takes 33 s to reach 132 ft/s. Therefore, taking

$s(0) = 0$, we have $s(t) = 2t^2$, $0 \leq t \leq 33$. So $s(33) = 2178$ ft. 15 minutes $= 15(60) = 900$ s, so for

$33 < t \leq 933$ we have $v(t) = 132$ ft/s $\;\Rightarrow\; s(933) = 132(900) + 2178 = 120,978$ ft $= 22.9125$ mi.

(b) As in part (a), the train accelerates for 33 s and travels 2178 ft while doing so. Similarly, it decelerates for 33 s and travels 2178 ft at the end of its trip. During the remaining $900 - 66 = 834$ s it travels at 132 ft/s, so the distance traveled is $132 \cdot 834 = 110,088$ ft. Thus, the total distance is $2178 + 110,088 + 2178 = 114,444$ ft $= 21.675$ mi.

(c) 45 mi $= 45(5280) = 237,600$ ft. Subtract $2(2178)$ to take care of the speeding up and slowing down, and we have 233,244 ft at 132 ft/s for a trip of $233,244/132 = 1767$ s at 90 mi/h. The total time is $1767 + 2(33) = 1833$ s $= 30$ min 33 s $= 30.55$ min.

(d) $37.5(60) = 2250$ s. $2250 - 2(33) = 2184$ s at maximum speed. $2184(132) + 2(2178) = 292,644$ total feet or $292,644/5280 = 55.425$ mi.

50. (a) For $0 \leq t \leq 3$ we have $a(t) = 60t \;\Rightarrow\; v(t) = 30t^2 + C \;\Rightarrow\; v(0) = 0 = C \;\Rightarrow\; v(t) = 30t^2$, so

$s(t) = 10t^3 + C \;\Rightarrow\; s(0) = 0 = C \;\Rightarrow\; s(t) = 10t^3$. Note that $v(3) = 270$ and $s(3) = 270$.

For $3 < t \leq 17$: $a(t) = -g = -32$ ft/s $\;\Rightarrow\; v(t) = -32(t - 3) + C \;\Rightarrow\; v(3) = 270 = C \;\Rightarrow\;$

$v(t) = -32(t - 3) + 270 \;\Rightarrow\; s(t) = -16(t - 3)^2 + 270(t - 3) + C \;\Rightarrow\; s(3) = 270 = C \;\Rightarrow\;$

$s(t) = -16(t - 3)^2 + 270(t - 3) + 270$. Note that $v(17) = -178$ and $s(17) = 914$.

For $17 < t \leq 22$: The velocity increases linearly from -178 ft/s to -18 ft/s during this period, so

$$\frac{\Delta v}{\Delta t} = \frac{-18 - (-178)}{22 - 17} = \frac{160}{5} = 32. \text{ Thus, } v(t) = 32(t - 17) - 178 \quad \Rightarrow$$

$s(t) = 16(t - 17)^2 - 178(t - 17) + 914$ and $s(22) = 424$ ft.

For $t > 22$: $v(t) = -18 \quad \Rightarrow \quad s(t) = -18(t - 22) + C$. But $s(22) = 424 = C \quad \Rightarrow$
$s(t) = -18(t - 22) + 424$.

Therefore, until the rocket lands, we have

$$v(t) = \begin{cases} 30t^2 & \text{if } 0 \le t \le 3 \\ -32\,(t - 3) + 270 & \text{if } 3 < t \le 17 \\ 32(t - 17) - 178 & \text{if } 17 < t \le 22 \\ -18 & \text{if } t > 22 \end{cases}$$

and

$$s(t) = \begin{cases} 10t^3 & \text{if } 0 \le t \le 3 \\ -16(t - 3)^2 + 270(t - 3) + 270 & \text{if } 3 < t \le 17 \\ 16(t - 17)^2 - 178\,(t - 17) + 914 & \text{if } 17 < t \le 22 \\ -18(t - 22) + 424 & \text{if } t > 22 \end{cases}$$

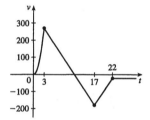 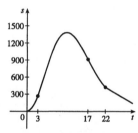

(b) To find the maximum height, set $v(t)$ on $3 < t \le 17$ equal to 0. $-32(t - 3) + 270 = 0 \quad \Rightarrow \quad t_1 = 11.4375$ s and the maximum height is $s(t_1) = -16(t_1 - 3)^2 + 270(t_1 - 3) + 270 = 1409.0625$ ft.

(c) To find the time to land, set $s(t) = -18(t - 22) + 424 = 0$. Then $t - 22 = \frac{424}{18} = 23.\overline{5}$, so $t \approx 45.6$ s.

 Review

─────────────── • CONCEPT CHECK • ───────────────

1. A function f has an **absolute maximum** at $x = c$ if $f(c)$ is the largest function value on the entire domain of f, whereas f has a **local maximum** at c if $f(c)$ is the largest function value when x is near c. See Figure 4 in Section 4.2.

2. (a) See Theorem 4.2.3.

   (b) See the Closed Interval Method before Example 6 in Section 4.2.

3. (a) See Theorem 4.2.4.

   (b) See Definition 4.2.5.

4. See the Mean Value Theorem in Section 4.3. Geometrical interpretation—there is some point P on the graph of a function f [on the interval (a, b)] where the tangent line is parallel to the secant line that connects $(a, f(a))$ and $(b, f(b))$.

5. (a) See the I/D Test before Example 2 in Section 4.3.

(b) See the Concavity Test before Example 4 in Section 4.3.

6. (a) See the First Derivative Test after Example 2 in Section 4.3.

(b) See the Second Derivative Test before Example 4 in Section 4.3.

(c) See the note before Example 5 in Section 4.3.

7. (a) See l'Hospital's Rule and the three notes that follow it in Section 4.5.

(b) Write fg as $\dfrac{f}{1/g}$ or $\dfrac{g}{1/f}$.

(c) Convert the difference into a quotient using a common denominator, rationalizing, factoring, or some other method.

(d) Convert the power to a product by taking the natural logarithm of both sides of $y = f^g$ or by writing f^g as $e^{g \ln f}$.

8. Without calculus you could get misleading graphs that fail to show the most interesting features of a function. See the first paragraph in Section 4.4.

9. (a) See Figure 3 in Section 4.8.

(b) $x_2 = x_1 - \dfrac{f(x_1)}{f'(x_1)}$

(c) $x_{n+1} = x_n - \dfrac{f(x_n)}{f'(x_n)}$

(d) Newton's method is likely to fail or to work very slowly when $f'(x_1)$ is close to 0.

10. (a) See the definition at the beginning of Section 4.9.

(b) If F_1 and F_2 are both antiderivatives of f on an interval I, then they differ by a constant.

──────────────── ▲ **TRUE–FALSE QUIZ** ▲ ────────────────

1. False.   For example, take $f(x) = x^3$, then $f'(x) = 3x^2$ and $f'(0) = 0$, but $f(0) = 0$ is not a maximum or minimum; $(0, 0)$ is an inflection point.

2. False.   For example, $f(x) = |x|$ has an absolute minimum at 0, but $f'(0)$ does not exist.

3. False.   For example, $f(x) = x$ is continuous on $(0, 1)$ but attains neither a maximum nor a minimum value on $(0, 1)$. Don't confuse this with f being continuous on the *closed* interval $[a, b]$, which would make the statement true.

4. True.   By the Mean Value Theorem, $f'(c) = \dfrac{f(1) - f(-1)}{1 - (-1)} = \dfrac{0}{2} = 0$. Note that $|c| < 1 \iff c \in (-1, 1)$.

5. True.   This is an example of part (b) of the I/D Test.

6. False.   For example, the curve $y = f(x) = 1$ has no inflection points but $f''(c) = 0$ for all c.

7. False. $f'(x) = g'(x) \Rightarrow f(x) = g(x) + C$. For example, if $f(x) = x + 2$ and $g(x) = x + 1$, then $f'(x) = g'(x) = 1$, but $f(x) \ne g(x)$.

8. False. Assume there is a function f such that $f(1) = -2$ and $f(3) = 0$. Then by the Mean Value Theorem there

exists a number $c \in (1, 3)$ such that $f'(c) = \dfrac{f(3) - f(1)}{3 - 1} = \dfrac{0 - (-2)}{2} = 1$. But $f'(x) > 1$ for all x, a

contradiction.

9. True. The graph of one such function is sketched.

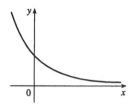

10. False. At any point $(a, f(a))$, we know that $f'(a) < 0$. So since the tangent line at $(a, f(a))$ is not horizontal, it

must cross the x-axis — at $x = b$, say. But since $f''(x) > 0$ for all x, the graph of f must lie above all of

its tangents; in particular, $f(b) > 0$. But this is a contradiction, since we are given that $f(x) < 0$ for all x.

11. True. By the Mean Value Theorem, there exists a number c in $(0, 1)$ such that

$f(1) - f(0) = f'(c)(1 - 0) = f'(c)$. Since $f'(c)$ is nonzero, $f(1) - f(0) \neq 0$, so $f(1) \neq f(0)$.

12. False. The most general antiderivative is $F(x) = -1/x + C_1$ for $x < 0$ and $F(x) = -1/x + C_2$ for $x > 0$

(see Example 1 in Section 4.10).

13. False. $\displaystyle\lim_{x \to 0} \frac{x}{e^x} = \frac{\displaystyle\lim_{x \to 0} x}{\displaystyle\lim_{x \to 0} e^x} = \frac{0}{1} = 0$, not 1.

◆ **EXERCISES** ◆

1. $f(x) = 10 + 27x - x^3$, $0 \le x \le 4$. $f'(x) = 27 - 3x^2 = -3(x^2 - 9) = -3(x + 3)(x - 3) = 0$ only when

$x = 3$ (since -3 is not in the domain). $f'(x) > 0$ for $x < 3$ and $f'(x) < 0$ for $x > 3$, so $f(3) = 64$ is a local

maximum value. Checking the endpoints, we find $f(0) = 10$ and $f(4) = 54$. Thus, $f(0) = 10$ is the absolute

minimum value and $f(3) = 64$ is the absolute maximum value.

2. $f(x) = x - \sqrt{x}$, $0 \le x \le 4$. $f'(x) = 1 - 1/(2\sqrt{x}) = 0 \iff 2\sqrt{x} = 1 \implies x = \frac{1}{4}$. $f'(x)$ does not exist

$\iff x = 0$. $f'(x) > 0$ for $0 < x < \frac{1}{4}$ and $f'(x) < 0$ for $\frac{1}{4} < x < 4$, so $f(\frac{1}{4}) = -\frac{1}{4}$ is a local and absolute

minimum value. $f(0) = 0$ and $f(4) = 2$, so $f(4) = 2$ is the absolute maximum value.

3. $f(x) = \dfrac{x}{x^2 + x + 1}$, $-2 \le x \le 0$. $f'(x) = \dfrac{(x^2 + x + 1)(1) - x(2x + 1)}{(x^2 + x + 1)^2} = \dfrac{1 - x^2}{(x^2 + x + 1)^2} = 0 \iff$

$x = -1$ (since 1 is not in the domain). $f'(x) < 0$ for $-2 < x < -1$ and $f'(x) > 0$ for $-1 < x < 0$, so

$f(-1) = -1$ is a local and absolute minimum value. $f(-2) = -\frac{2}{3}$ and $f(0) = 0$, so $f(0) = 0$ is an absolute

maximum value.

4. $f(x) = x^2 e^{-x}$, $0 \le x \le 3$. $f'(x) = xe^{-x}(2 - x) = 0 \implies x = 0$ or 2. $f''(x) = e^{-x}(x^2 - 4x + 2) \implies$

$f''(2) = -2e^{-2} < 0$, so $f(2) = 4e^{-2} \approx 0.54$ is a local maximum. Also $f(0) = 0$ and $f(3) = 9e^{-3} \approx 0.45$, so

the absolute minimum is $f(0) = 0$, and the absolute maximum is $f(2) = 4e^{-2}$.

5. (a) $f(x) = 2 - 2x - x^3$ is a polynomial, so there is no asymptote.　(e)

(b) $f'(x) = -2 - 3x^2 = -1(3x^2 + 2) < 0$, so f is decreasing on $\mathbb{R}$.

(c) No local extrema

(d) $f''(x) = -6x < 0$ on $(0, \infty)$ and $f''(x) > 0$ on $(-\infty, 0)$, so f is CD on $(0, \infty)$ and CU on $(-\infty, 0)$. There is an IP at $(0, 2)$.

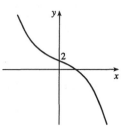

6. (a) $f(x) = x^4 + 4x^3$ is a polynomial, so there is no asymptote.　(e)

(b) $f'(x) = 4x^3 + 12x^2 = 4x^2(x + 3) > 0 \Leftrightarrow x > -3$, so f is increasing on $(-3, \infty)$ and decreasing on $(-\infty, -3)$.

(c) Local minimum $f(-3) = -27$, no local maximum

(d) $f''(x) = 12x^2 + 24x = 12x(x + 2) < 0 \Leftrightarrow -2 < x < 0$, so f is CD on $(-2, 0)$ and CU on $(-\infty, -2)$ and $(0, \infty)$. IP at $(0, 0)$ and $(-2, -16)$.

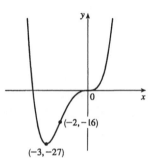

7. (a) $f(x) = x + \sqrt{1 - x}$ has no asymptote.　(e)

(b) $f'(x) = 1 - 1/(2\sqrt{1 - x}) = 0 \Leftrightarrow 2\sqrt{1 - x} = 1 \Leftrightarrow 1 - x = \frac{1}{4} \Leftrightarrow x = \frac{3}{4}$ and $f'(x) > 0 \Leftrightarrow x < \frac{3}{4}$, so f is increasing on $(-\infty, \frac{3}{4})$ and decreasing on $(\frac{3}{4}, 1)$.

(c) $f(\frac{3}{4}) = \frac{3}{4} + \sqrt{1 - \frac{3}{4}} = \frac{3}{4} + \sqrt{\frac{1}{4}} = \frac{3}{4} + \frac{1}{2} = \frac{5}{4}$ is a local maximum.

(d) $f''(x) = -\dfrac{1}{4(1 - x)^{3/2}} < 0$ on the domain of f, so f is CD on $(-\infty, 1)$. No IP.

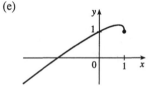

8. (a) $f(x) = \dfrac{1}{1 - x^2} = \dfrac{1}{(1 + x)(1 - x)}$ has vertical asymptotes　(e)

$x = \pm 1$. $\displaystyle\lim_{x \to \pm\infty} f(x) = 0$, so f has a horizontal asymptote of $y = 0$.

(b) $f'(x) = \dfrac{2x}{(1 - x^2)^2} = 0 \Leftrightarrow x = 0$, so f is decreasing on $(-\infty, -1)$ and $(-1, 0)$, and increasing on $(0, 1)$ and $(1, \infty)$.

(c) Local minimum $f(0) = 1$; no local maximum

(d) $f''(x) = \dfrac{(1 - x^2)^2 \cdot 2 - 2x \cdot 2(1 - x^2)(-2x)}{(1 - x^2)^4} = \dfrac{2(1 - x^2)^2 + 8x^2}{(1 - x^2)^3} = \dfrac{6x^2 + 2}{(1 - x^2)^3} < 0 \Rightarrow x^2 > 1$, so f is CD on $(-\infty, -1)$ and $(1, \infty)$, and CU on $(-1, 1)$. No IP.

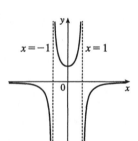

9. (a) $y = f(x) = \sin^2 x - 2\cos x$ has no asymptote.

(b) $y' = 2\sin x \cos x + 2\sin x = 2\sin x(\cos x + 1)$. $y' = 0 \Leftrightarrow \sin x = 0$ or $\cos x = -1 \Leftrightarrow x = n\pi$ or $x = (2n + 1)\pi$. $y' > 0$ when $\sin x > 0$, since $\cos x + 1 \geq 0$ for all x. Therefore, $y' > 0$ (and so f is increasing) on $(2n\pi, (2n + 1)\pi)$; $y' < 0$ (and so f is decreasing) on $((2n - 1)\pi, 2n\pi)$ or equivalently, $((2n + 1)\pi, (2n + 2)\pi)$.

(c) Local maxima are $f((2n + 1)\pi) = 2$; local minima are $f(2n\pi) = -2$.

(d) $y' = \sin 2x + 2\sin x$ $\Rightarrow$

$$y'' = 2\cos 2x + 2\cos x = 2(2\cos^2 x - 1) + 2\cos x = 4\cos^2 x + 2\cos x - 2$$
$$= 2(2\cos^2 x + \cos x - 1) = 2(2\cos x - 1)(\cos x + 1)$$

$y'' = 0$ $\Leftrightarrow$ $\cos x = \frac{1}{2}$ or -1 $\Leftrightarrow$ $x = 2n\pi \pm \frac{\pi}{3}$ or $x = (2n+1)\pi$. $y'' > 0$ (and so f is CU) on $\left(2n\pi - \frac{\pi}{3}, 2n\pi + \frac{\pi}{3}\right)$; $y'' \le 0$ (and so f is CD) on $\left(2n\pi + \frac{\pi}{3}, 2n\pi + \frac{5\pi}{3}\right)$. There are inflection points at $\left(2n\pi \pm \frac{\pi}{3}, -\frac{1}{4}\right)$.

(e)

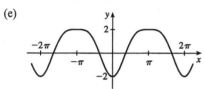

10. (a) $\lim\limits_{x\to\pm\infty} e^{2x - x^2} = 0$, so $y = 0$ is a HA.

(b) $y = f(x) = e^{2x - x^2}$ $\Rightarrow$ $f'(x) = 2(1 - x)e^{2x - x^2} > 0$
$\Leftrightarrow$ $x < 1$, so f is increasing on $(-\infty, 1)$ and decreasing on $(1, \infty)$.

(c) $f(1) = e$ is a local and absolute maximum.

(d) $f''(x) = 2(2x^2 - 4x + 1)e^{2x - x^2} = 0$ $\Leftrightarrow$ $x = 1 \pm \frac{\sqrt{2}}{2}$. $f''(x) > 0$ $\Leftrightarrow$ $x < 1 - \frac{\sqrt{2}}{2}$ or $x > 1 + \frac{\sqrt{2}}{2}$, so f is CU on $\left(-\infty, 1 - \frac{\sqrt{2}}{2}\right)$ and $\left(1 + \frac{\sqrt{2}}{2}, \infty\right)$, and CD on $\left(1 - \frac{\sqrt{2}}{2}, 1 + \frac{\sqrt{2}}{2}\right)$. IP at $\left(1 \pm \frac{\sqrt{2}}{2}, \sqrt{e}\right)$.

(e)

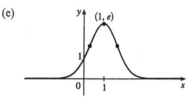

11. (a) $\lim\limits_{x\to\pm\infty}\left(e^x + e^{-3x}\right) = \infty$, no asymptote.

(b) $y = f(x) = e^x + e^{-3x}$ $\Rightarrow$
$f'(x) = e^x - 3e^{-3x} = e^{-3x}\left(e^{4x} - 3\right) > 0$ $\Leftrightarrow$ $e^{4x} > 3$ $\Leftrightarrow$
$4x > \ln 3$ $\Leftrightarrow$ $x > \frac{1}{4}\ln 3$, so f is increasing on $\left(\frac{1}{4}\ln 3, \infty\right)$
and decreasing on $\left(-\infty, \frac{1}{4}\ln 3\right)$.

(c) $f\left(\frac{1}{4}\ln 3\right) = 3^{1/4} + 3^{-3/4} \approx 1.75$ is a local and absolute minimum.

(d) $f''(x) = e^x + 9e^{-3x} > 0$, so f is CU on $(-\infty, \infty)$. No IP.

(e)

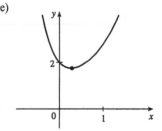

12. (a) $\lim\limits_{x\to\pm\infty} \ln(x^2 - 1) = \infty$, $\lim\limits_{x\to 1^+} \ln(x^2 - 1) = -\infty$,
$\lim\limits_{x\to -1^-} \ln(x^2 - 1) = -\infty$, so $x = 1$ and $x = -1$ are VA.

(b) $y = f(x) = \ln(x^2 - 1)$ $\Rightarrow$ $f'(x) = \dfrac{2x}{x^2 - 1} > 0$ for $x > 1$
and $f'(x) < 0$ for $x < -1$, so f is increasing on $(1, \infty)$ and decreasing on $(-\infty, -1)$. Note that the domain of f is $|x| > 1$.

(c) No maximum or minimum.

(d) $f''(x) = -2\dfrac{x^2 + 1}{(x^2 - 1)^2} < 0$, so f is CD on $(-\infty, -1)$ and $(1, \infty)$. No IP.

(e)

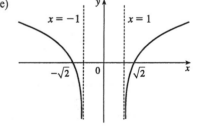

13. $f(x) = \dfrac{x^2 - 1}{x^3}$ $\Rightarrow$ $f'(x) = \dfrac{x^3(2x) - (x^2 - 1)3x^2}{x^6} = \dfrac{3 - x^2}{x^4}$ $\Rightarrow$

$f''(x) = \dfrac{x^4(-2x) - (3 - x^2)4x^3}{x^8} = \dfrac{2x^2 - 12}{x^5}$

Estimates: From the graphs of f' and f'', it appears that f is increasing on

$(-1.73, 0)$ and $(0, 1.73)$ and decreasing on $(-\infty, -1.73)$ and $(1.73, \infty)$;

f has a local maximum of about $f(1.73) = 0.38$ and a local minimum of

about $f(-1.7) = -0.38$; f is CU on $(-2.45, 0)$ and $(2.45, \infty)$, and CD

on $(-\infty, -2.45)$ and $(0, 2.45)$; and f has inflection points at about

$(-2.45, -0.34)$ and $(2.45, 0.34)$.

Exact: Now $f'(x) = \dfrac{3 - x^2}{x^4}$ is positive for $0 < x^2 < 3$, that is, f is

increasing on $(-\sqrt{3}, 0)$ and $(0, \sqrt{3}\,)$; and $f'(x)$ is negative (and so f is

decreasing) on $(-\infty, -\sqrt{3}\,)$ and $(\sqrt{3}, \infty)$. $f'(x) = 0$ when $x = \pm\sqrt{3}$.

f' goes from positive to negative at $x = \sqrt{3}$, so f has a local maximum of

$f(\sqrt{3}\,) = \dfrac{(\sqrt{3}\,)^2 - 1}{(\sqrt{3}\,)^3} = \dfrac{2\sqrt{3}}{9}$; and since f is odd, we know that maxima on

the interval $(0, \infty)$ correspond to minima on $(-\infty, 0)$, so f has a local

minimum of $f(-\sqrt{3}\,) = -\dfrac{2\sqrt{3}}{9}$. Also, $f''(x) = \dfrac{2x^2 - 12}{x^5}$ is positive (so

f is CU) on $(-\sqrt{6}, 0)$ and $(\sqrt{6}, \infty)$, and negative (so f is CD) on

$(-\infty, -\sqrt{6}\,)$ and $(0, \sqrt{6}\,)$. There are IP at $\left(\sqrt{6}, \dfrac{5\sqrt{6}}{36}\right)$ and

$\left(-\sqrt{6}, -\dfrac{5\sqrt{6}}{36}\right)$.

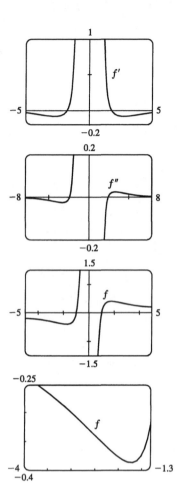

14. $f(x) = \dfrac{\sqrt[3]{x}}{1 - x} = x^{1/3}(1 - x)^{-1}$ $\Rightarrow$

$f'(x) = x^{1/3}(-1)(1 - x)^{-2}(-1) + (1 - x)^{-1}\left(\tfrac{1}{3}\right)x^{-2/3} = \dfrac{x^{-2/3}}{3}\dfrac{1 + 2x}{(x - 1)^2}$ $\Rightarrow$

$f''(x) = \dfrac{x^{-2/3}}{3}\dfrac{(x - 1)^2(2) - (1 + 2x)(2)(x - 1)}{(x - 1)^4} + \dfrac{1 + 2x}{(x - 1)^2}\left(\dfrac{-2x^{-5/3}}{9}\right) = -\dfrac{2x^{-5/3}}{9}\dfrac{5x^2 + 5x - 1}{(x - 1)^3}$

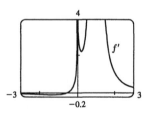

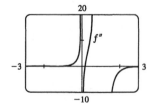

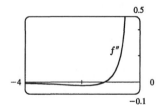

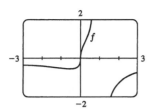
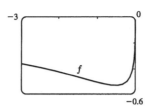
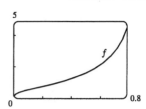

From the graphs, it appears that f is increasing on $(-0.50, 1)$ and $(1, \infty)$, with a vertical asymptote at $x = 1$, and decreasing on $(-\infty, -0.50)$; f has no local maximum, but a local minimum of about $f(-0.50) = -0.53$; f is CU on $(-1.17, 0)$ and $(0.17, 1)$ and CD on $(-\infty, -1.17)$, $(0, 0.17)$ and $(1, \infty)$; and f has inflection points at about $(-1.17, -0.49)$, $(0, 0)$ and $(0.17, 0.67)$. Note also that $\lim_{x \to \pm\infty} f(x) = 0$, so $y = 0$ is a horizontal asymptote.

15. $f(x) = 3x^6 - 5x^5 + x^4 - 5x^3 - 2x^2 + 2 \quad\Rightarrow\quad f'(x) = 18x^5 - 25x^4 + 4x^3 - 15x^2 - 4x \quad\Rightarrow$
$f''(x) = 90x^4 - 100x^3 + 12x^2 - 30x - 4$

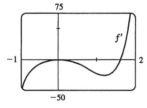
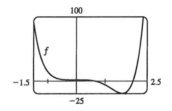
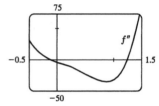

From the graphs of f' and f'', it appears that f is increasing on $(-0.23, 0)$ and $(1.62, \infty)$ and decreasing on $(-\infty, -0.23)$ and $(0, 1.62)$; f has a local maximum of about $f(0) = 2$ and local minima

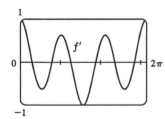
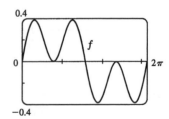

of about $f(-0.23) = 1.96$ and $f(1.62) = -19.2$; f is CU on $(-\infty, -0.12)$ and $(1.24, \infty)$ and CD on $(-0.12, 1.24)$; and f has inflection points at about $(-0.12, 1.98)$ and $(1.2, -12.1)$.

16. $f(x) = \sin x \cos^2 x \quad\Rightarrow\quad f'(x) = \cos^3 x - 2\sin^2 x \cos x \quad\Rightarrow\quad f''(x) = -7\sin x \cos^2 x + 2\sin^3 x$

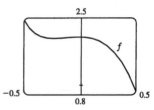

From the graphs of f' and f'', it appears that f is increasing on $(0, 0.62)$, $(1.57, 2.53)$, $(3.76, 4.71)$ and $(5.67, 2\pi)$ and decreasing on $(0.62, 1.57)$, $(2.53, 3.76)$ and $(4.71, 5.67)$; f has local maxima of about $f(0.62) = f(2.53) = 0.38$ and $f(4.71) = 0$ and local minima of about $f(1.57) = 0$ and

$f(3.76) = f(5.67) = -0.38$; f is CU on $(1.08, 2.06)$, $(3.14, 4.22)$ and $(5.20, 2\pi)$ and CD on $(0, 1.08)$, $(2.06, 3.14)$ and $(4.22, 5.20)$; and f has inflection points at about $(0, 0)$, $(1.08, 0.20)$, $(2.06, 0.20)$, $(3.14, 0)$, $(4.22, -0.20)$, $(5.20, -0.20)$ and $(2\pi, 0)$.

17.

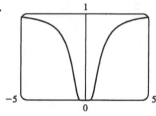

From the graph, we estimate the points of inflection to be about

$(\pm 0.82, 0.22)$. $f(x) = e^{-1/x^2}$ $\Rightarrow$ $f'(x) = 2x^{-3}e^{-1/x^2}$ $\Rightarrow$

$f''(x) = 2\left[x^{-3}\left(2x^{-3}\right)e^{-1/x^2} + e^{-1/x^2}\left(-3x^{-4}\right)\right]$

$\qquad = 2x^{-6}e^{-1/x^2}\left(2 - 3x^2\right)$.

This is 0 when $2 - 3x^2 = 0$ $\Leftrightarrow$ $x = \pm\sqrt{\frac{2}{3}}$, so the inflection points

are $\left(\pm\sqrt{\frac{2}{3}}, e^{-3/2}\right)$.

18. (a)

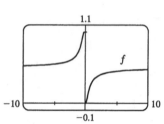

(c) From the graph of f, estimates for the IP are $(-0.4, 0.9)$ and $(0.4, 0.08)$.

(d) $f''(x) = -\dfrac{e^{1/x}\left[e^{1/x}(2x - 1) + 2x + 1\right]}{x^4(e^{1/x} + 1)^3}$

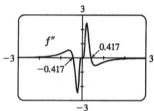

(b) $f(x) = \dfrac{1}{1 + e^{1/x}}$. $\displaystyle\lim_{x \to \infty} f(x) = \dfrac{1}{1 + 1} = \dfrac{1}{2}$,

$\displaystyle\lim_{x \to -\infty} f(x) = \dfrac{1}{1 + 1} = \dfrac{1}{2}$,

$\displaystyle\lim_{x \to 0+} f(x) = \dfrac{1}{1 + \infty} = 0$,

$\displaystyle\lim_{x \to 0-} f(x) = \dfrac{1}{1 + 0} = 1$

(e) From the graph, we see that f'' changes sign at $x = \pm 0.417$ ($x = 0$ is not in the domain of f). IP are approximately $(0.417, 0.083)$ and $(-0.417, 0.917)$.

19. $f(x) = \arctan(\cos(3\arcsin x))$. We use a CAS to compute f' and f'', and to graph f, f', and f'':

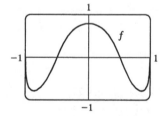

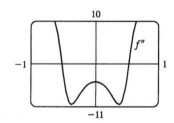

From the graph of f', it appears that the only maximum occurs at $x = 0$ and there are minima at $x = \pm 0.87$. From the graph of f'', it appears that there are inflection points at $x = \pm 0.52$.

20. $f(x) = \ln(2x + x\sin x)$. We use the CAS to calculate

$$f'(x) = \frac{2 + \sin x + x\cos x}{2x + x\sin x} \text{ and}$$

$$f''(x) = \frac{2x^2\sin x + 4\sin x - \cos^2 x + x^2 + 5}{x^2(\cos^2 x - 4\sin x - 5)}.$$

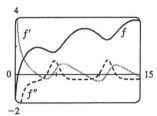

From the graphs, it seems that $f' > 0$ (and so f is increasing) on approximately the intervals $(0, 2.7)$, $(4.5, 8.2)$ and $(10.9, 14.3)$. It seems that f'' changes sign (indicating inflection points) at $x \approx 3.8$, 5.7, 10.0 and 12.0. Looking back at the graph of f, this implies that the inflection points have approximate coordinates $(3.8, 1.7)$, $(5.7, 2.1)$, $(10.0, 2.7)$, and $(12.0, 2.9)$.

21. The family of functions $f(x) = \ln(\sin x + C)$ all have the same period and all have maximum values at $x = \frac{\pi}{2} + 2\pi n$. Since the domain of ln is $(0, \infty)$, f has a graph only if $\sin x + C > 0$ somewhere. Since $-1 \leq \sin x \leq 1$, this happens if $C > -1$, that is, f has no graph if $C \leq -1$. Similarly, if $C > 1$, then $\sin x + C > 0$ and f is continuous on $(-\infty, \infty)$. As C increases, the graph of f is shifted vertically upward and flattens out.

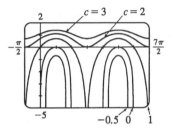

If $-1 < C \leq 1$, f is defined where $\sin x + C > 0 \Leftrightarrow \sin x > -C \Leftrightarrow \sin^{-1}(-C) < x < \pi - \sin^{-1}(-C)$. Since the period is 2π, the domain of f is $(2n\pi + \sin^{-1}(-C), (2n+1)\pi - \sin^{-1}(-C))$, n an integer.

22. We exclude the case $c = 0$, since in that case $f(x) = 0$ for all x. To find the maxima and minima, we differentiate:

$$f(x) = cxe^{-cx^2} \Rightarrow f'(x) = c\left[xe^{-cx^2}(-2cx) + e^{-cx^2}(1)\right] = ce^{-cx^2}(-2cx^2 + 1).$$ This is 0 where $-2cx^2 + 1 = 0 \Leftrightarrow x = \pm 1/\sqrt{2c}$. So if $c > 0$, there are two maxima or minima, whose x-coordinates approach 0 as c increases. The negative root gives a minimum and the positive root gives a maximum, by the First Derivative Test. By substituting back into the equation, we see that $f(\pm 1/\sqrt{2c}) = c(\pm 1/\sqrt{2c})e^{-c(\pm 1/\sqrt{2c})^2} = \pm\sqrt{c/2e}$. So as c increases, the extreme points become more pronounced. Note that if $c > 0$, then $\lim\limits_{x \to \pm\infty} f(x) = 0$. If $c < 0$, then there are no extreme values, and $\lim\limits_{x \to \pm\infty} f(x) = \mp\infty$.

To find the points of inflection, we differentiate again: $f'(x) = ce^{-cx^2}(-2cx^2 + 1) \Rightarrow$

$$f''(x) = c\left[e^{-cx^2}(-4cx) + (-2cx^2 + 1)\left(-2cxe^{-cx^2}\right)\right] = -2c^2xe^{-cx^2}(3 - 2cx^2).$$ This is 0 at $x = 0$ and where $3 - 2cx^2 = 0 \Leftrightarrow x = \pm\sqrt{3/(2c)} \Rightarrow$ IP at $\left(\pm\sqrt{3/(2c)}, \pm\sqrt{3c/2}\,e^{-3/2}\right)$. If $c > 0$ there are three inflection points, and as c increases, the x-coordinates of the nonzero inflection points approach 0. If $c < 0$, there is only one inflection point, the origin.

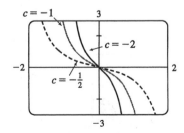

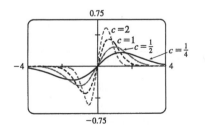

23. For $(1,6)$ to be on the curve $y = x^3 + ax^2 + bx + 1$, we have that $6 = 1 + a + b + 1 \Rightarrow b = 4 - a$. Now $y' = 3x^2 + 2ax + b$ and $y'' = 6x + 2a$. Also, for $(1,6)$ to be an inflection point it must be true that $y''(1) = 6(1) + 2a = 0 \Rightarrow a = -3 \Rightarrow b = 4 - (-3) = 7$.

24. (a) $g(x) = f(x^2) \Rightarrow g'(x) = 2xf'(x^2)$ by the Chain Rule. Since $f'(x) > 0$ for all $x \neq 0$, we must have $f'(x^2) > 0$ for $x \neq 0$, so $g'(x) = 0 \Leftrightarrow x = 0$. Now $g'(x)$ changes sign (from negative to positive) at $x = 0$, since one of its factors, $f'(x^2)$, is positive for all x, and its other factor, $2x$, changes from negative to positive at this point, so by the First Derivative Test, f has a local and absolute minimum at $x = 0$.

(b) $g'(x) = 2xf'(x^2) \Rightarrow g''(x) = 2\left[xf''(x^2)(2x) + f'(x^2)\right] = 4x^2 f''(x^2) + 2f'(x^2)$ by the Product Rule and the Chain Rule. But $x^2 > 0$ for all $x \neq 0$, $f''(x^2) > 0$ (since f is CU for $x > 0$), and $f'(x^2) > 0$ for all $x \neq 0$, so since all of its factors are positive, $g''(x) > 0$ for $x \neq 0$. Whether $g''(0)$ is positive or 0 doesn't matter (since the sign of g'' does not change there); g is concave upward on $\mathbb{R}$.

25. $\lim\limits_{x \to \pi} \dfrac{\sin x}{x^2 - \pi^2} \overset{\text{H}}{=} \lim\limits_{x \to \pi} \dfrac{\cos x}{2x} = -\dfrac{1}{2\pi}$

26. $\lim\limits_{x \to 0} \dfrac{e^{ax} - e^{bx}}{x} \overset{\text{H}}{=} \lim\limits_{x \to 0} \dfrac{ae^{ax} - be^{bx}}{1} = a - b$

27. $\lim\limits_{x \to \infty} \dfrac{\ln(\ln x)}{\ln x} \overset{\text{H}}{=} \lim\limits_{x \to \infty} \dfrac{(1/\ln x)(1/x)}{1/x} = \lim\limits_{x \to \infty} \dfrac{1}{\ln x} = 0$

28. $\lim\limits_{x \to 0} \dfrac{1 + \sin x - \cos x}{1 - \sin x - \cos x} \overset{\text{H}}{=} \lim\limits_{x \to 0} \dfrac{\cos x + \sin x}{-\cos x + \sin x} = \dfrac{1 + 0}{-1 + 0} = -1$

29. $\lim\limits_{x \to 0} \dfrac{\ln(1 - x) + x + \frac{1}{2}x^2}{x^3} \overset{\text{H}}{=} \lim\limits_{x \to 0} \dfrac{-\dfrac{1}{1 - x} + 1 + x}{3x^2} \overset{\text{H}}{=} \lim\limits_{x \to 0} \dfrac{-\dfrac{1}{(1-x)^2} + 1}{6x} \overset{\text{H}}{=} \lim\limits_{x \to 0} \dfrac{-\dfrac{2}{(1-x)^3}}{6} = -\dfrac{2}{6} = -\dfrac{1}{3}$

30. $\lim\limits_{x \to \pi/2} \left(\frac{\pi}{2} - x\right) \tan x = \lim\limits_{x \to \pi/2} \dfrac{\frac{\pi}{2} - x}{\cot x} \overset{\text{H}}{=} \lim\limits_{x \to \pi/2} \dfrac{-1}{-\csc^2 x} = \lim\limits_{x \to \pi/2} \sin^2 x = 1^2 = 1$

31. $\lim\limits_{x \to 0} \left(\csc^2 x - x^{-2}\right) = \lim\limits_{x \to 0} \left[\dfrac{1}{\sin^2 x} - \dfrac{1}{x^2}\right] = \lim\limits_{x \to 0} \dfrac{x^2 - \sin^2 x}{x^2 \sin^2 x} \overset{\text{H}}{=} \lim\limits_{x \to 0} \dfrac{2x - \sin 2x}{2x \sin^2 x + x^2 \sin 2x}$

$\overset{\text{H}}{=} \lim\limits_{x \to 0} \dfrac{2 - 2\cos 2x}{2\sin^2 x + 4x \sin 2x + 2x^2 \cos 2x} \overset{\text{H}}{=} \lim\limits_{x \to 0} \dfrac{4\sin 2x}{6\sin 2x + 12x \cos 2x - 4x^2 \sin 2x}$

$\overset{\text{H}}{=} \lim\limits_{x \to 0} \dfrac{8\cos 2x}{24\cos 2x - 32x \sin 2x - 8x^2 \cos 2x} = \dfrac{8}{24} = \dfrac{1}{3}$

32. $y = x^{1/(1-x)} \Rightarrow \ln y = \dfrac{\ln x}{1 - x}$, so $\lim\limits_{x \to 1} \ln y = \lim\limits_{x \to 1} \dfrac{\ln x}{1 - x} \overset{\text{H}}{=} \lim\limits_{x \to 1} \dfrac{1/x}{-1} = -1 \Rightarrow \lim\limits_{x \to 1} x^{1/(1-x)} = e^{-1}$.

33. We are given $d\theta/dt = -0.25$ rad/h.

$x = 400 \cot \theta \Rightarrow \dfrac{dx}{dt} = -400 \csc^2 \theta \dfrac{d\theta}{dt}$. When $\theta = \frac{\pi}{6}$,

$\dfrac{dx}{dt} = -400(2)^2(-0.25) = 400$ ft/h.

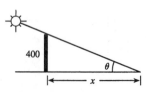

34. Given $dV/dt = 2$, find dh/dt when $h = 5$. $V = \frac{1}{3}\pi r^2 h$ and, from similar

triangles, $\dfrac{r}{h} = \dfrac{3}{10}$ $\Rightarrow$ $V = \dfrac{\pi}{3}\left(\dfrac{3h}{10}\right)^2 h = \dfrac{3\pi}{100}h^3$, so

$2 = \dfrac{dV}{dt} = \dfrac{9\pi}{100}h^2\dfrac{dh}{dt}$ $\Rightarrow$ $\dfrac{dh}{dt} = \dfrac{200}{9\pi h^2} = \dfrac{200}{9\pi(5)^2} = \dfrac{8}{9\pi}$ cm/s

when $h = 5$.

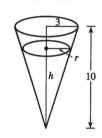
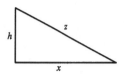

35. Given $dh/dt = 5$ and $dx/dt = 15$, find dz/dt. $z^2 = x^2 + h^2$ $\Rightarrow$

$2z\dfrac{dz}{dt} = 2x\dfrac{dx}{dt} + 2h\dfrac{dh}{dt}$ $\Rightarrow$ $\dfrac{dz}{dt} = \dfrac{1}{z}(15x + 5h)$. When $t = 3$,

$h = 45 + 3(5) = 60$ and $x = 15(3) = 45 \Rightarrow z = 75$, so

$\dfrac{dz}{dt} = \frac{1}{75}\left[15(45) + 5(60)\right] = 13$ ft/s.

36. We are given $dz/dt = 30$ ft/s. By similar triangles, $\dfrac{y}{z} = \dfrac{4}{\sqrt{241}}$

$\Rightarrow$ $y = \dfrac{4}{\sqrt{241}}z$, so $\dfrac{dy}{dt} = \dfrac{4}{\sqrt{241}}\dfrac{dz}{dt} = \dfrac{120}{\sqrt{241}} \approx 7.7$ ft/s.

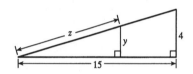

37. Call the two integers x and y. Then $x + 4y = 1000$, so $x = 1000 - 4y$. Their product is $P = xy = (1000 - 4y)y$, so our problem is to maximize the function $P(y) = 1000y - 4y^2$, where $0 < y < 250$ and y is an integer. $P'(y) = 1000 - 8y$, so $P'(y) = 0 \Leftrightarrow y = 125$. $P''(y) = -8 < 0$, so $P(125) = 62{,}500$ is an absolute maximum. Since the optimal y turned out to be an integer, we have found the desired pair of numbers, namely $x = 1000 - 4(125) = 500$ and $y = 125$.

38. On the hyperbola $xy = 8$, if $d(x)$ is the distance from the point $(x, y) = (x, 8/x)$ to the point $(3, 0)$, then $[d(x)]^2 = (x - 3)^2 + 64/x^2 = f(x)$. $f'(x) = 2(x - 3) - 128/x^3 = 0$ $\Rightarrow$ $x^4 - 3x^3 - 64 = 0$ $\Rightarrow$ $(x - 4)(x^3 + x^2 + 4x + 16) = 0$ $\Rightarrow$ $x = 4$ since the solution must have $x > 0$. Then $y = \frac{8}{4} = 2$, so the point is $(4, 2)$.

39.

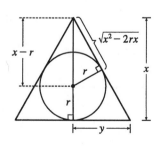

By similar triangles, $\dfrac{y}{x} = \dfrac{r}{\sqrt{x^2 - 2rx}}$, so the area of the triangle is

$A(x) = \frac{1}{2}(2y)x = xy = \dfrac{rx^2}{\sqrt{x^2 - 2rx}}$ $\Rightarrow$

$A'(x) = \dfrac{2rx\sqrt{x^2 - 2rx} - rx^2(x - r)/\sqrt{x^2 - 2rx}}{x^2 - 2rx}$

$= \dfrac{rx^2(x - 3r)}{(x^2 - 2rx)^{3/2}} = 0$ when $x = 3r$.

$A'(x) < 0$ when $2r < x < 3r$, $A'(x) > 0$ when $x > 3r$. So $x = 3r$ gives a minimum and $A(3r) = r(9r^2)/(\sqrt{3}\,r) = 3\sqrt{3}\,r^2$.

40.

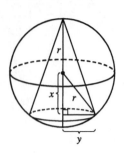

The volume of the cone is

$$V = \tfrac{1}{3}\pi y^2 (r + x) = \tfrac{1}{3}\pi (r^2 - x^2)(r + x), \quad -r \le x \le r.$$

$$V'(x) = \tfrac{\pi}{3}\left[(r^2 - x^2)(1) + (r + x)(-2x)\right]$$

$$= \tfrac{\pi}{3}\left[(r + x)(r - x - 2x)\right] = \tfrac{\pi}{3}(r + x)(r - 3x)$$

$$= 0 \text{ when } x = -r \text{ or } x = r/3.$$

Now $V(r) = 0 = V(-r)$, so the maximum occurs at $x = r/3$

and the volume is $V\!\left(\dfrac{r}{3}\right) = \dfrac{\pi}{3}\left(r^2 - \dfrac{r^2}{9}\right)\!\left(\dfrac{4r}{3}\right) = \dfrac{32\pi r^3}{81}.$

41.

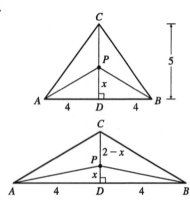

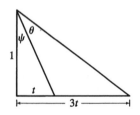

We minimize

$$L(x) = |PA| + |PB| + |PC| = 2\sqrt{x^2 + 16} + (5 - x),$$

$0 \le x \le 5$. $L'(x) = 2x/\sqrt{x^2 + 16} - 1 = 0 \iff$

$2x = \sqrt{x^2 + 16} \iff 4x^2 = x^2 + 16 \iff x = \tfrac{4}{\sqrt{3}}.$

$L(0) = 13$, $L\!\left(\tfrac{4}{\sqrt{3}}\right) \approx 11.9$, $L(5) \approx 12.8$, so the minimum

occurs when $x = \tfrac{4}{\sqrt{3}} \approx 2.3$.

If $|CD| = 2$, $L(x)$ changes from $(5 - x)$ to $(2 - x)$ with

$0 \le x \le 2$. But we still get $L'(x) = 0 \iff x = \tfrac{4}{\sqrt{3}}$,

which isn't in the interval $[0, 2]$. Now $L(0) = 10$ and

$L(2) = 2\sqrt{20} = 4\sqrt{5} \approx 8.9$. The minimum occurs when

$P = C$.

42.

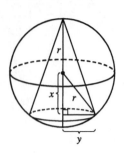

It suffices to maximize $\tan \theta$. Now

$$\frac{3t}{1} = \tan(\psi + \theta) = \frac{\tan\psi + \tan\theta}{1 - \tan\psi\,\tan\theta} = \frac{t + \tan\theta}{1 - t\tan\theta}.$$

So $3t(1 - t\tan\theta) = t + \tan\theta \implies 2t = (1 + 3t^2)\tan\theta \implies$

$$\tan\theta = \frac{2t}{1 + 3t^2}. \text{ Let } f(t) = \tan\theta = \frac{2t}{1 + 3t^2} \implies$$

$$f'(t) = \frac{2(1 + 3t^2) - 2t(6t)}{(1 + 3t^2)^2} = \frac{2(1 - 3t^2)}{(1 + 3t^2)^2} = 0 \iff$$

$$1 - 3t^2 = 0 \iff t = \tfrac{1}{\sqrt{3}} \text{ since } t \ge 0.$$

Now $f'(t) > 0$ for $0 \le t < \tfrac{1}{\sqrt{3}}$ and $f'(t) < 0$ for $t > \tfrac{1}{\sqrt{3}}$, so f has an absolute maximum when $t = \tfrac{1}{\sqrt{3}}$ and

$$\tan\theta = \frac{2(1/\sqrt{3})}{1 + 3(1/\sqrt{3})^2} = \tfrac{1}{\sqrt{3}} \implies \theta = \tfrac{\pi}{6}. \text{ Substituting for } t \text{ and } \theta \text{ in } 3t = \tan(\psi + \theta) \text{ gives us}$$

$$\sqrt{3} = \tan\!\left(\psi + \tfrac{\pi}{6}\right) \implies \psi = \tfrac{\pi}{6}.$$

43. $v = K\sqrt{\dfrac{L}{C} + \dfrac{C}{L}} \implies \dfrac{dv}{dL} = \dfrac{K}{2\sqrt{(L/C) + (C/L)}}\left(\dfrac{1}{C} - \dfrac{C}{L^2}\right) = 0 \iff \dfrac{1}{C} = \dfrac{C}{L^2} \iff L^2 = C^2 \iff$

$L = C$. This gives the minimum velocity since $v' < 0$ for $0 < L < C$ and $v' > 0$ for $L > C$.

44.

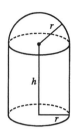

We minimize the surface area $S = \pi r^2 + 2\pi rh + \frac{1}{2}(4\pi r^2) = 3\pi r^2 + 2\pi rh$.

Solving $V = \pi r^2 h + \frac{2}{3}\pi r^3$ for h, we get $h = \dfrac{V - \frac{2}{3}\pi r^3}{\pi r^2} = \dfrac{V}{\pi r^2} - \frac{2}{3}r$, so

$$S(r) = 3\pi r^2 + 2\pi r\left[\frac{V}{\pi r^2} - \frac{2}{3}r\right] = \frac{5}{3}\pi r^2 + \frac{2V}{r}.$$

$$S'(r) = -\frac{2V}{r^2} + \frac{10}{3}\pi r = \frac{\frac{10}{3}\pi r^3 - 2V}{r^2} = 0 \iff \frac{10}{3}\pi r^3 = 2V$$

$\iff r^3 = \dfrac{3V}{5\pi} \iff r = \sqrt[3]{\dfrac{3V}{5\pi}}$. This gives an absolute minimum since $S'(r) < 0$ for $0 < r < \sqrt[3]{\dfrac{3V}{5\pi}}$ and

$S'(r) > 0$ for $r > \sqrt[3]{\dfrac{3V}{5\pi}}$. Thus, $h = \dfrac{V - \frac{2}{3}\pi \cdot \dfrac{3V}{5\pi}}{\pi \sqrt[3]{\dfrac{(3V)^2}{(5\pi)^2}}} = \dfrac{(V - \frac{2}{5}V)\sqrt[3]{(5\pi)^2}}{\pi\sqrt[3]{(3V)^2}} = \dfrac{3V\sqrt[3]{(5\pi)^2}}{5\pi\sqrt[3]{(3V)^2}} = \sqrt[3]{\dfrac{3V}{5\pi}} = r$.

45. Let x denote the number of $1 decreases in ticket price. Then the ticket price is $12 - 1(x)$, and the average attendance is $11{,}000 + 1000(x)$. Now the revenue per game is

$$R(x) = (\text{price per person}) \times (\text{number of people per game})$$

$$= (12 - x)(11{,}000 + 1000x) = -1000x^2 + 1000x + 132{,}000$$

for $0 \le x \le 4$ (since the seating capacity is 15,000) $\Rightarrow$ $R'(x) = -2000x + 1000 = 0 \iff x = 0.5$. This is a maximum since $R''(x) = -2000 < 0$ for all x. Now we must check the value of $R(x) = (12 - x)(11{,}000 + 1000x)$ at $x = 0.5$ and at the endpoints of the domain to see which value of x gives the maximum value of R. $R(0) = (12)(11{,}000) = 132{,}000$, $R(0.5) = (11.5)(11{,}500) = 132{,}250$, and $R(4) = (8)(15{,}000) = 120{,}000$. Thus, the maximum revenue of $132,250 per game occurs when the average attendance is 11,500 and the ticket price is $11.50.

46. (a) $C(x) = 1800 + 25x - 0.2x^2 + 0.001x^3$ and

$R(x) = xp(x) = 48.2x - 0.03x^2$. The profit is maximized when $C'(x) = R'(x)$.

From the figure, we estimate that the tangents are parallel when $x \approx 160$.

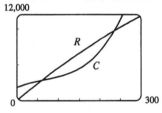

(b) $C'(x) = 25 - 0.4x + 0.003x^2$ and $R'(x) = 48.2 - 0.06x$. $C'(x) = R'(x) \Rightarrow$ $0.003x^2 - 0.34x - 23.2 = 0 \Rightarrow x_1 \approx 161.3 \ (x > 0)$. $R''(x) = -0.06$ and $C''(x) = -0.4 + 0.006x$, so $R''(x_1) = -0.06 < C''(x_1) \approx 0.57 \Rightarrow$ profit is maximized by producing 161 units.

(c) $c(x) = \dfrac{C(x)}{x} = \dfrac{1800}{x} + 25 - 0.2x + 0.001x^2$ is the average cost.

Since the average cost is minimized when the marginal cost equals the average cost, we graph $c(x)$ and $C'(x)$ and estimate the point of intersection. From the figure, $C'(x) = c(x) \iff x \approx 144$.

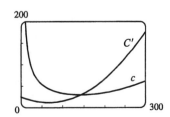

47. $f(x) = x^6 + 2x^2 - 8x + 3 \Rightarrow f'(x) = 6x^5 + 4x - 8$. We want to find the minimum of f, so we examine the graph of f' looking for values at which f' changes from negative to positive.

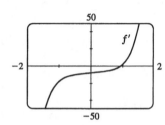

From the graph, we see that this occurs at $x \approx 1$. So we will use Newton's method with $g(x) = f'(x) = 6x^5 + 4x - 8$, $g'(x) = 30x^4 + 4$, and

$x_1 = 1$. $x_{n+1} = x_n - \dfrac{6x_n^5 + 4x_n - 8}{30x_n^4 + 4}$ gives us $x_2 \approx 0.941176$,

$x_3 \approx 0.934068$, $x_4 \approx 0.933975 \approx x_5$. Thus, $f(x_5) \approx -2.063421$ is the absolute minimum value of f.

48. $f(x) = x - 6\cos x \Rightarrow f'(x) = 1 + 6\sin x \Rightarrow x_{n+1} = x_n - \dfrac{x_n - 6\cos x_n}{1 + 6\sin x_n}$.

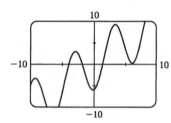

From the graph of f, it appears that there are roots near 1, -2 and -4.
If $x_1 = 1$, then $x_2 \approx 1.370620$, $x_3 \approx 1.344812$, $x_4 \approx 1.344751 \approx x_5$.
If $x_1 = -2$, then $x_2 \approx -1.888486$, $x_3 \approx -1.891518$,
$x_4 \approx -1.891520 \approx x_5$. If $x_1 = -4$, then $x_2 \approx -3.985898$,
$x_3 \approx -3.985826 \approx x_4$. To six decimal places, the roots of the equation are 1.344751, -1.891520 and -3.985826.

49. $f(x) = e^x - (2/\sqrt{x}) = e^x - 2x^{-1/2} \Rightarrow$

$F(x) = e^x - 2\dfrac{x^{-1/2+1}}{-1/2+1} + C = e^x - 2\dfrac{x^{1/2}}{1/2} + C = e^x - 4\sqrt{x} + C$

50. $g(t) = \dfrac{1+t}{\sqrt{t}} = \dfrac{1}{\sqrt{t}} + \dfrac{t}{\sqrt{t}} = t^{-1/2} + t^{1/2} \Rightarrow G(t) = 2t^{1/2} + \frac{2}{3}t^{3/2} + C$

51. $f'(x) = 2/(1+x^2) \Rightarrow f(x) = 2\arctan x + C$. $f(0) = 2\arctan 0 + C = 0 + C = C$ and $f(0) = -1 \Rightarrow C = -1$. Therefore, $f(x) = 2\arctan x - 1$.

52. $f'(x) = 1 + 2\sin x - \cos x \Rightarrow f(x) = x - 2\cos x - \sin x + C \Rightarrow 3 = f(0) = -2 + C \Rightarrow C = 5$, so $f(x) = x - 2\cos x - \sin x + 5$.

53. $f''(x) = x^3 + x \Rightarrow f'(x) = \frac{1}{4}x^4 + \frac{1}{2}x^2 + C$. Now $f'(0) = C$ and $f'(0) = 1 \Rightarrow f'(x) = \frac{1}{4}x^4 + \frac{1}{2}x^2 + 1$
$\Rightarrow f(x) = \frac{1}{20}x^5 + \frac{1}{6}x^3 + x + D$. Now $f(0) = D$ and $f(0) = -1 \Rightarrow f(x) = \frac{1}{20}x^5 + \frac{1}{6}x^3 + x - 1$.

54. $f''(x) = x^4 - 4x^2 + 3x - 2 \Rightarrow f'(x) = \frac{1}{5}x^5 - \frac{4}{3}x^3 + \frac{3}{2}x^2 - 2x + C \Rightarrow$
$f(x) = \frac{1}{30}x^6 - \frac{1}{3}x^4 + \frac{1}{2}x^3 - x^2 + Cx + D$. $0 = f(0) = D \Rightarrow f(x) = \frac{1}{30}x^6 - \frac{1}{3}x^4 + \frac{1}{2}x^3 - x^2 + Cx$.
$1 = f(1) = \frac{1}{30} - \frac{1}{3} + \frac{1}{2} - 1 + C \Rightarrow C = \frac{9}{5}$, so $f(x) = \frac{1}{30}x^6 - \frac{1}{3}x^4 + \frac{1}{2}x^3 - x^2 + \frac{9}{5}x$.

55. (a) Since f is 0 just to the left of the y-axis, we must have a minimum of F at the same place since we are increasing through $(0,0)$ on F. There must be a local maximum to the left of $x = -3$, since f changes from positive to negative there.

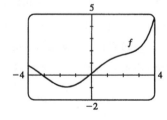

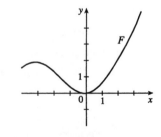

(b) $f(x) = 0.1e^x + \sin x \;\Rightarrow\; F(x) = 0.1e^x - \cos x + C.$
$F(0) = 0 \;\Rightarrow\; 0.1 - 1 + C = 0 \;\Rightarrow\; C = 0.9$, so
$F(x) = 0.1e^x - \cos x + 0.9.$

(c)

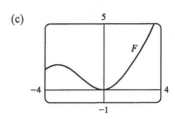

56. On $(0,1)$, $f(x) = x^2$ since $f'(x) = 2x$ and $f(0) = 0$. On $(1,3)$,
f is linear with slope -1 since $f'(x) = -1$. If $x > 3$, f is linear
with slope 1 since $f'(x) = 1$. Because f is an even function, we
can just reflect this graph through the y-axis to get the complete
graph.

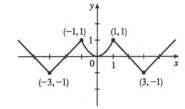

57. Choosing the positive direction to be upward, we have $a(t) = -9.8 \;\Rightarrow\; v(t) = -9.8t + v_0$, but $v(0) = 0 = v_0$
$\Rightarrow\; v(t) = -9.8t = s'(t) \;\Rightarrow\; s(t) = -4.9t^2 + s_0$, but $s(0) = s_0 = 500 \;\Rightarrow\; s(t) = -4.9t^2 + 500$. When
$s = 0$, $-4.9t^2 + 500 = 0 \;\Rightarrow\; t_1 = \sqrt{\frac{500}{4.9}} \approx 10.1 \;\Rightarrow\; v(t_1) = -9.8\sqrt{\frac{500}{4.9}} \approx -98.995$ m/s. Since the
canister has been designed to withstand an impact velocity of 100 m/s, the canister will *not burst*.

58. $f(x) = x^4 + x^3 + cx^2 \;\Rightarrow\; f'(x) = 4x^3 + 3x^2 + 2cx$. This is 0 when $x(4x^2 + 3x + 2c) = 0 \;\Leftrightarrow\; x = 0$
or $4x^2 + 3x + 2c = 0$. Using the quadratic formula, we find that the roots of this last equation are
$x = \dfrac{-3 \pm \sqrt{9 - 32c}}{8}$. Now if $9 - 32c < 0 \;\Leftrightarrow\; c > \frac{9}{32}$, then $x = 0$ is the only critical point, a minimum. If
$c = \frac{9}{32}$, then there are two critical points (a minimum at $x = 0$, and a horizontal tangent with no maximum or
minimum at $x = -\frac{3}{8}$) and if $c < \frac{9}{32}$, then there are three critical points except when $c = 0$, in which case the root
with the $+$ sign coincides with the critical point at $x = 0$. For $0 < c < \frac{9}{32}$, there is a minimum at
$x = -\dfrac{3}{8} - \dfrac{\sqrt{9 - 32c}}{8}$, a maximum at $x = -\dfrac{3}{8} + \dfrac{\sqrt{9 - 32c}}{8}$, and a minimum at $x = 0$. For $c = 0$, there is a
minimum at $x = -\frac{3}{4}$ and a horizontal tangent with no extremum at $x = 0$, and for $c < 0$, there is a maximum at
$x = 0$, and there are minima at $x = -\dfrac{3}{8} \pm \dfrac{\sqrt{9 - 32c}}{8}$. Now we calculate $f''(x) = 12x^2 + 6x + 2c$. The roots of
this equation are $x = \dfrac{-6 \pm \sqrt{36 - 4 \cdot 12 \cdot 2c}}{24}$. So if $36 - 96c \leq 0 \;\Leftrightarrow\; c \geq \frac{3}{8}$, then there is no inflection point.
If $c < \frac{3}{8}$, then there are two inflection points at $x = -\dfrac{1}{4} \pm \dfrac{\sqrt{9 - 24c}}{12}$.

Value of c	No. of CP	No. of IP
$c < 0$	3	2
$c = 0$	2	2
$0 < c < \frac{9}{32}$	3	2
$c = \frac{9}{32}$	2	2
$\frac{9}{32} < c < \frac{3}{8}$	1	2
$c \geq \frac{3}{8}$	1	0

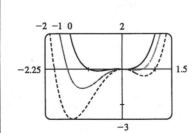

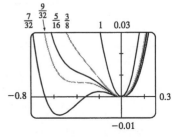

59. (a)

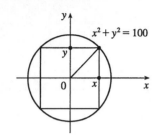

$x^2 + y^2 = 100$

The cross-sectional area of the rectangular beam is

$A = 2x \cdot 2y = 4xy = 4x\sqrt{100 - x^2}, \ 0 \le x \le 10$, so

$$\frac{dA}{dx} = 4x\left(\tfrac{1}{2}\right)(100 - x^2)^{-1/2}(-2x) + (100 - x^2)^{1/2} \cdot 4$$

$$= \frac{-4x^2}{(100 - x^2)^{1/2}} + 4(100 - x^2)^{1/2}$$

$$= \frac{4\left[-x^2 + (100 - x^2)\right]}{(100 - x^2)^{1/2}}.$$

$\dfrac{dA}{dx} = 0$ when $-x^2 + (100 - x^2) = 0 \ \Rightarrow \ x^2 = 50 \ \Rightarrow \ x = \sqrt{50} \approx 7.07 \ \Rightarrow$

$y = \sqrt{100 - \left(\sqrt{50}\right)^2} = \sqrt{50}$. Since $A(0) = A(10) = 0$, the rectangle of maximum area is a square.

(b)

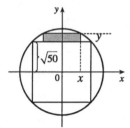

$\sqrt{50}$

The cross-sectional area of each rectangular plank (shaded in the figure) is

$A = 2x\left(y - \sqrt{50}\right) = 2x\left[\sqrt{100 - x^2} - \sqrt{50}\right], \ 0 \le x \le \sqrt{50}$, so

$$\frac{dA}{dx} = 2\left(\sqrt{100 - x^2} - \sqrt{50}\right) + 2x\left(\tfrac{1}{2}\right)(100 - x^2)^{-1/2}(-2x)$$

$$= 2(100 - x^2)^{1/2} - 2\sqrt{50} - \frac{2x^2}{(100 - x^2)^{1/2}}$$

Set $\dfrac{dA}{dx} = 0$: $(100 - x^2) - \sqrt{50}(100 - x^2)^{1/2} - x^2 = 0 \ \Rightarrow \ 100 - 2x^2 = \sqrt{50}(100 - x^2)^{1/2} \ \Rightarrow$

$10{,}000 - 400x^2 + 4x^4 = 50(100 - x^2) \ \Rightarrow \ 4x^4 - 350x^2 + 5000 = 0 \ \Rightarrow \ 2x^4 - 175x^2 + 2500 = 0$

$\Rightarrow \ x^2 = \dfrac{175 \pm \sqrt{10{,}625}}{4} \approx 69.52$ or $17.98 \ \Rightarrow \ x \approx 8.34$ or 4.24.

But $8.34 > \sqrt{50}$, so $x_1 \approx 4.24 \ \Rightarrow \ y - \sqrt{50} = \sqrt{100 - x_1^2} - \sqrt{50} \approx 1.99$. Each plank should have

dimensions about $8\tfrac{1}{2}$ inches by 2 inches.

(c) From the figure in part (a), the width is $2x$ and the depth is $2y$, so the strength is

$S = k(2x)(2y)^2 = 8kxy^2 = 8kx(100 - x^2) = 800kx - 8kx^3, \ 0 \le x \le 10$. $dS/dx = 800k - 24kx^2 = 0$

when $24kx^2 = 800k \ \Rightarrow \ x^2 = \dfrac{100}{3} \ \Rightarrow \ x = \dfrac{10}{\sqrt{3}} \ \Rightarrow \ y = \sqrt{\dfrac{200}{3}} = \dfrac{10\sqrt{2}}{\sqrt{3}} = \sqrt{2}\,x$. Since

$S(0) = S(10) = 0$, the maximum strength occurs when $x = \dfrac{10}{\sqrt{3}}$. The dimensions should be

$\dfrac{20}{\sqrt{3}} \approx 11.55$ inches by $\dfrac{20\sqrt{2}}{\sqrt{3}} \approx 16.33$ inches.

60. (a)

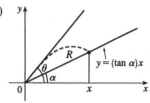

R

$y = (\tan \alpha)x$

$y = (\tan \theta)x - \dfrac{g}{2v^2 \cos^2 \theta}x^2$. The parabola intersects the

line when $(\tan \alpha)x = (\tan \theta)x - \dfrac{g}{2v^2 \cos^2 \theta}x^2 \ \Rightarrow$

$x = \dfrac{(\tan \theta - \tan \alpha)2v^2 \cos^2 \theta}{g} \ \Rightarrow$

$R(\theta) = \dfrac{x}{\cos \alpha} = \left(\dfrac{\sin \theta}{\cos \theta} - \dfrac{\sin \alpha}{\cos \alpha}\right)\dfrac{2v^2 \cos^2 \theta}{g \cos \alpha} = \left(\dfrac{\sin \theta}{\cos \theta} - \dfrac{\sin \alpha}{\cos \alpha}\right)(\cos \theta \ \cos \alpha)\dfrac{2v^2 \cos \theta}{g \cos^2 \alpha}$

$= (\sin \theta \ \cos \alpha - \sin \alpha \ \cos \theta)\dfrac{2v^2 \cos \theta}{g \cos^2 \alpha} = \sin(\theta - \alpha)\dfrac{2v^2 \cos \theta}{g \cos^2 \alpha}$

(b) $R'(\theta) = \dfrac{2v^2}{g\cos^2\alpha}\left[\cos\theta\cdot\cos(\theta-\alpha)+\sin(\theta-\alpha)(-\sin\theta)\right] = \dfrac{2v^2}{g\cos^2\alpha}\cos[\theta+(\theta-\alpha)]$

$= \dfrac{2v^2}{g\cos^2\alpha}\cos(2\theta-\alpha) = 0$ when $\cos(2\theta-\alpha)=0 \;\Rightarrow\; 2\theta-\alpha=\frac{\pi}{2} \;\Rightarrow$

$\theta = \dfrac{\pi/2+\alpha}{2} = \dfrac{\pi}{4}+\dfrac{\alpha}{2}$. The First Derivative Test shows that this gives a maximum value for $R(\theta)$.

[This could be done without calculus by applying the formula for $\sin x\cos y$ to $R(\theta)$.]

(c)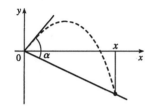

Replacing α by $-\alpha$ in part (a), we get $R(\theta) = \dfrac{2v^2\cos\theta\,\sin(\theta+\alpha)}{g\cos^2\alpha}$.

Proceeding as in part (b), or simply by replacing α by $-\alpha$ in the result of part (b), we see that $R(\theta)$ is maximized when $\theta = \dfrac{\pi}{4}-\dfrac{\alpha}{2}$.

61. (a) $I = \dfrac{k\cos\theta}{d^2} = \dfrac{k(h/d)}{d^2} = k\dfrac{h}{d^3} = k\dfrac{h}{\left(\sqrt{40^2+h^2}\right)^3} = k\dfrac{h}{(1600+h^2)^{3/2}} \;\Rightarrow$

$\dfrac{dI}{dh} = k\dfrac{(1600+h^2)^{3/2}-h\frac{3}{2}(1600+h^2)^{1/2}\cdot 2h}{\left[(1600+h^2)^{3/2}\right]^2} = \dfrac{k\,(1600+h^2)^{1/2}\,(1600+h^2-3h^2)}{(1600+h^2)^3}$

$= \dfrac{k(1600-2h^2)}{(1600+h^2)^{5/2}}$

Set $dI/dh = 0$: $1600-2h^2 = 0 \;\Rightarrow\; h^2 = 800 \;\Rightarrow\; h = \sqrt{800} = 20\sqrt{2}$. By the First Derivative Test, I has a local maximum at $h = 20\sqrt{2} \approx 28$ ft.

(b)

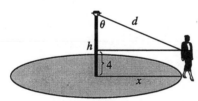

$\dfrac{dx}{dt} = 4\text{ ft/s}$

$I = \dfrac{k\cos\theta}{d^2} = \dfrac{k[(h-4)/d]}{d^2} = \dfrac{k(h-4)}{d^3} = \dfrac{k(h-4)}{[(h-4)^2+x^2]^{3/2}} = k(h-4)\left[(h-4)^2+x^2\right]^{-3/2}$

$\dfrac{dI}{dt} = \dfrac{dI}{dx}\cdot\dfrac{dx}{dt} = k(h-4)\left(-\frac{3}{2}\right)\left[(h-4)^2+x^2\right]^{-5/2}\cdot 2x\cdot\dfrac{dx}{dt}$

$= k(h-4)(-3x)\left[(h-4)^2+x^2\right]^{-5/2}\cdot 4 = \dfrac{-12xk(h-4)}{[(h-4)^2+x^2]^{5/2}}$

$\left.\dfrac{dI}{dt}\right|_{x=40} = -\dfrac{480k(h-4)}{[(h-4)^2+1600]^{5/2}}$

Focus on Problem Solving

1. Let $y = f(x) = e^{-x^2}$. The area of the rectangle under the curve from $-x$ to x is $A(x) = 2xe^{-x^2}$ where $x \geq 0$. We maximize $A(x)$: $A'(x) = 2e^{-x^2} - 4x^2e^{-x^2} = 2e^{-x^2}\left(1 - 2x^2\right) = 0 \Rightarrow x = \frac{1}{\sqrt{2}}$. This gives a maximum since $A'(x) > 0$ for $0 \leq x < \frac{1}{\sqrt{2}}$ and $A'(x) < 0$ for $x > \frac{1}{\sqrt{2}}$. We next determine the points of inflection of $f(x)$. Notice that $f'(x) = -2xe^{-x^2} = -A(x)$. So $f''(x) = -A'(x)$ and hence, $f''(x) < 0$ for $-\frac{1}{\sqrt{2}} < x < \frac{1}{\sqrt{2}}$ and $f''(x) > 0$ for $x < -\frac{1}{\sqrt{2}}$ and $x > \frac{1}{\sqrt{2}}$. So $f(x)$ changes concavity at $x = \pm\frac{1}{\sqrt{2}}$, and the two vertices of the rectangle of largest area are at the inflection points.

2. Let $f(x) = \sin x - \cos x$ on $[0, 2\pi]$ since f has period 2π. $f'(x) = \cos x + \sin x = 0 \Leftrightarrow \cos x = -\sin x \Leftrightarrow \tan x = -1 \Leftrightarrow x = \frac{3\pi}{4}$ or $\frac{7\pi}{4}$. Evaluating f at its critical numbers and endpoints, we get $f(0) = -1$, $f\left(\frac{3\pi}{4}\right) = \sqrt{2}$, $f\left(\frac{7\pi}{4}\right) = -\sqrt{2}$, and $f(2\pi) = -1$. So f has absolute maximum value $\sqrt{2}$ and absolute minimum value $-\sqrt{2}$. Thus, $-\sqrt{2} \leq \sin x - \cos x \leq \sqrt{2} \Rightarrow |\sin x - \cos x| \leq \sqrt{2}$.

3. First, we recognize some symmetry in the inequality: $\dfrac{e^{x+y}}{xy} \geq e^2 \Leftrightarrow \dfrac{e^x}{x} \cdot \dfrac{e^y}{y} \geq e \cdot e$. This suggests that we need to show that $\dfrac{e^x}{x} \geq e$ for $x > 0$. If we can do this, then the inequality $\dfrac{e^y}{y} \geq e$ is true, and the given inequality follows. $f(x) = \dfrac{e^x}{x} \Rightarrow f'(x) = \dfrac{xe^x - e^x}{x^2} = \dfrac{e^x(x-1)}{x^2} = 0 \Rightarrow x = 1$. By the First Derivative Test, we have a minimum of $f(1) = e$, so $e^x/x \geq e$ for all x.

4. $x^2y^2\left(4 - x^2\right)\left(4 - y^2\right) = x^2\left(4 - x^2\right)y^2\left(4 - y^2\right) = f(x)f(y)$, where $f(t) = t^2\left(4 - t^2\right)$. We will show that $0 \leq f(t) \leq 4$ for $|t| \leq 2$, which gives $0 \leq f(x)f(y) \leq 16$ for $|x| \leq 2$ and $|y| \leq 2$.
$f(t) = 4t^2 - t^4 \Rightarrow f'(t) = 8t - 4t^3 = 4t\left(2 - t^2\right) = 0 \Rightarrow t = 0$ or $\pm\sqrt{2}$.
$f(0) = 0$, $f\left(\pm\sqrt{2}\right) = 2(4 - 2) = 4$, and $f(2) = 0$. So 0 is the absolute minimum value of $f(t)$ on $[-2, 2]$ and 4 is the absolute maximum value of $f(t)$ on $[-2, 2]$. We conclude that $0 \leq f(t) \leq 4$ for $|t| \leq 2$ and hence, $0 \leq f(x)f(y) \leq 4^2$ or $0 \leq x^2\left(4 - x^2\right)y^2\left(4 - y^2\right) \leq 16$.

5. First we show that $x(1 - x) \leq \frac{1}{4}$ for all x. Let $f(x) = x(1 - x) = x - x^2$. Then $f'(x) = 1 - 2x$. This is 0 when $x = \frac{1}{2}$ and $f'(x) > 0$ for $x < \frac{1}{2}$, $f'(x) < 0$ for $x > \frac{1}{2}$, so the absolute maximum of f is $f\left(\frac{1}{2}\right) = \frac{1}{4}$. Thus, $x(1 - x) \leq \frac{1}{4}$ for all x.
Now suppose that the given assertion is false, that is, $a(1 - b) > \frac{1}{4}$ and $b(1 - a) > \frac{1}{4}$. Multiply these inequalities: $a(1 - b)b(1 - a) > \frac{1}{16} \Rightarrow [a(1 - a)][b(1 - b)] > \frac{1}{16}$. But we know that $a(1 - a) \leq \frac{1}{4}$ and $b(1 - b) \leq \frac{1}{4} \Rightarrow [a(1 - a)][b(1 - b)] \leq \frac{1}{16}$. Thus, we have a contradiction, so the given assertion is proved.

6. Let $P(a, 1 - a^2)$ be the point of contact. The equation of the tangent line at P is $y - (1 - a^2) = (-2a)(x - a)$
$\Rightarrow$ $y - 1 + a^2 = -2ax + 2a^2$ $\Rightarrow$ $y = -2ax + a^2 + 1$. To find the x-intercept, put $y = 0$: $2ax = a^2 + 1$ $\Rightarrow$
$x = \dfrac{a^2 + 1}{2a}$. To find the y-intercept, put $x = 0$: $y = a^2 + 1$. Therefore, the area of the triangle is

$\dfrac{1}{2}\left(\dfrac{a^2 + 1}{2a}\right)(a^2 + 1) = \dfrac{(a^2 + 1)^2}{4a}$. Therefore, we minimize the function $A(a) = \dfrac{(a^2 + 1)^2}{4a}$, $0 < a \le 1$.

$A'(a) = \dfrac{(4a)2(a^2 + 1)(2a) - (a^2 + 1)^2(4)}{16a^2} = \dfrac{(a^2 + 1)[4a^2 - (a^2 + 1)]}{4a^2} = \dfrac{(a^2 + 1)(3a^2 - 1)}{4a^2}$.

$A'(a) = 0$ when $3a^2 - 1 = 0$ $\Rightarrow$ $a = \frac{1}{\sqrt{3}}$. $A'(a) < 0$ for $a < \frac{1}{\sqrt{3}}$, $A'(a) > 0$ for $a > \frac{1}{\sqrt{3}}$. So by the First

Derivative Test, there is an absolute minimum when $a = \frac{1}{\sqrt{3}}$. The required point is $\left(\frac{1}{\sqrt{3}}, \frac{2}{3}\right)$.

7. Differentiating $x^2 + xy + y^2 = 12$ implicitly with respect to x gives $2x + y + x\dfrac{dy}{dx} + 2y\dfrac{dy}{dx} = 0$, so

$\dfrac{dy}{dx} = -\dfrac{2x + y}{x + 2y}$. At a highest or lowest point, $\dfrac{dy}{dx} = 0$ $\Leftrightarrow$ $y = -2x$. Substituting $-2x$ for y in the original

equation gives $x^2 + x(-2x) + (-2x)^2 = 12$, so $3x^2 = 12$ and $x = \pm 2$. If $x = 2$, then $y = -2x = -4$, and if
$x = -2$ then $y = 4$. Thus, the highest and lowest points are $(-2, 4)$ and $(2, -4)$.

8. Let the circle have radius r, so $|OP| = |OQ| = r$, where O is the center of the circle. Now $\angle POR$ has measure

$\frac{1}{2}\theta$, and $\angle OPR$ is a right angle, so $\tan \frac{1}{2}\theta = \dfrac{|PR|}{r}$ and the area of $\triangle OPR$ is $\frac{1}{2}|OP||PR| = \frac{1}{2}r^2 \tan \frac{1}{2}\theta$. The

area of the sector cut by OP and OR is $\frac{1}{2}r^2\left(\frac{1}{2}\theta\right) = \frac{1}{4}r^2\theta$. Let S be the intersection of PQ and OR. Then

$\sin \frac{1}{2}\theta = \dfrac{|PS|}{r}$ and $\cos \frac{1}{2}\theta = \dfrac{|OS|}{r}$, and the area of $\triangle OSP$ is

$\frac{1}{2}|OS||PS| = \frac{1}{2}\left(r \cos \frac{1}{2}\theta\right)\left(r \sin \frac{1}{2}\theta\right) = \frac{1}{2}r^2 \sin \frac{1}{2}\theta \cos \frac{1}{2}\theta = \frac{1}{4}r^2 \sin \theta$.

So $B(\theta) = 2\left(\frac{1}{2}r^2 \tan \frac{1}{2}\theta - \frac{1}{4}r^2\theta\right) = r^2\left(\tan \frac{1}{2}\theta - \frac{1}{2}\theta\right)$ and $A(\theta) = 2\left(\frac{1}{4}r^2\theta - \frac{1}{4}r^2 \sin \theta\right) = \frac{1}{2}r^2(\theta - \sin \theta)$.

Thus, $\displaystyle\lim_{\theta \to 0^+} \dfrac{A(\theta)}{B(\theta)} = \dfrac{\frac{1}{2}r^2(\theta - \sin \theta)}{r^2\left(\tan \frac{1}{2}\theta - \frac{1}{2}\theta\right)} = \dfrac{\theta - \sin \theta}{2\left(\tan \frac{1}{2}\theta - \frac{1}{2}\theta\right)} \overset{H}{=} \displaystyle\lim_{\theta \to 0^+} \dfrac{1 - \cos \theta}{2\left(\frac{1}{2}\sec^2 \frac{1}{2}\theta - \frac{1}{2}\right)}$

$= \displaystyle\lim_{\theta \to 0^+} \dfrac{1 - \cos \theta}{\sec^2 \frac{1}{2}\theta - 1} = \displaystyle\lim_{\theta \to 0^+} \dfrac{1 - \cos \theta}{\tan^2 \frac{1}{2}\theta} \overset{H}{=} \displaystyle\lim_{\theta \to 0^+} \dfrac{\sin \theta}{2\left(\tan \frac{1}{2}\theta\right)\left(\sec^2 \frac{1}{2}\theta\right)\frac{1}{2}}$

$= \displaystyle\lim_{\theta \to 0^+} \dfrac{\sin \theta \cos^3 \frac{1}{2}\theta}{\sin \frac{1}{2}\theta} = \displaystyle\lim_{\theta \to 0^+} \dfrac{\left(2 \sin \frac{1}{2}\theta \cos \frac{1}{2}\theta\right)\cos^3 \frac{1}{2}\theta}{\sin \frac{1}{2}\theta} = 2 \displaystyle\lim_{\theta \to 0^+} \cos^4\left(\frac{1}{2}\theta\right) = 2(1)^4 = 2$

9. $f(x) = \dfrac{1}{1 + |x|} + \dfrac{1}{1 + |x - 2|}$

$= \begin{cases} \dfrac{1}{1 - x} + \dfrac{1}{1 - (x - 2)} & \text{if } x < 0 \\[2mm] \dfrac{1}{1 + x} + \dfrac{1}{1 - (x - 2)} & \text{if } 0 \le x < 2 \\[2mm] \dfrac{1}{1 + x} + \dfrac{1}{1 + (x - 2)} & \text{if } x \ge 2 \end{cases}$ $\Rightarrow$ $f'(x) = \begin{cases} \dfrac{1}{(1 - x)^2} + \dfrac{1}{(3 - x)^2} & \text{if } x < 0 \\[2mm] \dfrac{-1}{(1 + x)^2} + \dfrac{1}{(3 - x)^2} & \text{if } 0 < x < 2 \\[2mm] \dfrac{-1}{(1 + x)^2} - \dfrac{1}{(x - 1)^2} & \text{if } x > 2 \end{cases}$

We see that $f'(x) > 0$ for $x < 0$ and $f'(x) < 0$ for $x > 2$. For $0 < x < 2$, we have

$f'(x) = \dfrac{1}{(3 - x)^2} - \dfrac{1}{(x + 1)^2} = \dfrac{(x^2 + 2x + 1) - (x^2 - 6x + 9)}{(3 - x)^2(x + 1)^2} = \dfrac{8(x - 1)}{(3 - x)^2(x + 1)^2}$, so $f'(x) < 0$ for

$0 < x < 1$, $f'(1) = 0$ and $f'(x) > 0$ for $1 < x < 2$. We have shown that $f'(x) > 0$ for $x < 0$; $f'(x) < 0$ for $0 < x < 1$; $f'(x) > 0$ for $1 < x < 2$; and $f'(x) < 0$ for $x > 2$. Therefore, by the First Derivative Test, the local maxima of f are at $x = 0$ and $x = 2$, where f takes the value $\frac{4}{3}$. Therefore, $\frac{4}{3}$ is the absolute maximum value of f.

10. If $f''(x) > 0$ for all x, then f' is increasing on $(-\infty, \infty)$, so $f'(0)$ must be greater than $f'(-1)$. But $f'(0) = 0 < \frac{1}{2} = f'(-1)$, so such a function cannot exist.

11. We first show that $\dfrac{x}{1+x^2} < \tan^{-1} x$ for $x > 0$. Let $f(x) = \tan^{-1} x - \dfrac{x}{1+x^2}$. Then

$$f'(x) = \frac{1}{1+x^2} - \frac{1(1+x^2) - x(2x)}{(1+x^2)^2} = \frac{(1+x^2) - (1-x^2)}{(1+x^2)^2} = \frac{2x^2}{(1+x^2)^2} > 0 \text{ for } x > 0. \text{ So } f(x) \text{ is}$$

increasing on $(0, \infty)$. Hence, $0 < x \;\Rightarrow\; 0 = f(0) < f(x) = \tan^{-1} x - \dfrac{x}{1+x^2}$. So $\dfrac{x}{1+x^2} < \tan^{-1} x$

for $0 < x$. We next show that $\tan^{-1} x < x$ for $x > 0$. Let $h(x) = x - \tan^{-1} x$. Then

$$h'(x) = 1 - \frac{1}{1+x^2} = \frac{x^2}{1+x^2} > 0. \text{ Hence, } h(x) \text{ is increasing on } (0, \infty). \text{ So for } 0 < x,$$

$0 = h(0) < h(x) = x - \tan^{-1} x$. Hence, $\tan^{-1} x < x$ for $x > 0$, and we conclude that $\dfrac{x}{1+x^2} < \tan^{-1} x < x$

for $x > 0$.

12. To sketch the region $\{(x, y) \mid 2xy \le |x - y| \le x^2 + y^2\}$, we consider two cases.

Case 1: $x \ge y$ This is the case in which (x, y) lies on or below the line $y = x$. The double inequality becomes $2xy \le x - y \le x^2 + y^2$. The right-hand inequality holds if and only if $x^2 - x + y^2 + y \ge 0 \;\Leftrightarrow$ $\left(x - \frac{1}{2}\right)^2 + \left(y + \frac{1}{2}\right)^2 \ge \frac{1}{2} \;\Leftrightarrow\; (x, y)$ lies on or outside the circle with radius $\frac{1}{\sqrt{2}}$ centered at $\left(\frac{1}{2}, -\frac{1}{2}\right)$. The left-hand inequality holds if and only if $2xy - x + y \le 0 \;\Leftrightarrow\; xy - \frac{1}{2}x + \frac{1}{2}y \le 0 \;\Leftrightarrow\; \left(x + \frac{1}{2}\right)\left(y - \frac{1}{2}\right) \le -\frac{1}{4}$ $\Leftrightarrow\; (x, y)$ lies on or below the hyperbola $\left(x + \frac{1}{2}\right)\left(y - \frac{1}{2}\right) = -\frac{1}{4}$, which passes through the origin and approaches the lines $y = \frac{1}{2}$ and $x = -\frac{1}{2}$ asymptotically.

Case 2: $y \ge x$ This is the case in which (x, y) lies on or above the line $y = x$. The double inequality becomes $2xy \le y - x \le x^2 + y^2$. The right-hand inequality holds if and only if $x^2 + x + y^2 - y \ge 0 \;\Leftrightarrow$ $\left(x + \frac{1}{2}\right)^2 + \left(y - \frac{1}{2}\right)^2 \ge \frac{1}{2} \;\Leftrightarrow\; (x, y)$ lies on or outside the circle of radius $\frac{1}{\sqrt{2}}$ centered at $\left(-\frac{1}{2}, \frac{1}{2}\right)$. The left-hand inequality holds if and only if $2xy + x - y \le 0 \;\Leftrightarrow\; xy + \frac{1}{2}x - \frac{1}{2}y \le 0 \;\Leftrightarrow\; \left(x - \frac{1}{2}\right)\left(y + \frac{1}{2}\right) \le -\frac{1}{4}$ $\Leftrightarrow\; (x, y)$ lies on or above the left-hand branch of the hyperbola $\left(x - \frac{1}{2}\right)\left(y + \frac{1}{2}\right) = -\frac{1}{4}$, which passes through the origin and approaches the lines $y = -\frac{1}{2}$ and $x = \frac{1}{2}$ asymptotically. Therefore, the region of interest consists of the points on or above the left branch of the hyperbola $\left(x - \frac{1}{2}\right)\left(y + \frac{1}{2}\right) = -\frac{1}{4}$ that are on or outside the circle $\left(x + \frac{1}{2}\right)^2 + \left(y - \frac{1}{2}\right)^2 = \frac{1}{2}$, together with the points on or below the right

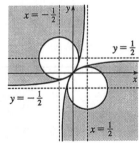

branch of the hyperbola $\left(x + \frac{1}{2}\right)\left(y - \frac{1}{2}\right) = -\frac{1}{4}$ that are on or outside the circle $\left(x - \frac{1}{2}\right)^2 + \left(y + \frac{1}{2}\right)^2 = \frac{1}{2}$. Note that the inequalities are unchanged when x and y are interchanged, so the region is symmetric about the line $y = x$. So we need only have analyzed case 1 and then reflected that region about the line $y = x$, instead of considering case 2.

13. $A = (x_1, x_1^2)$ and $B = (x_2, x_2^2)$, where x_1 and x_2 are the solutions of the quadratic equation $x^2 = mx + b$. Let $P = (x, x^2)$ and set $A_1 = (x_1, 0)$, $B_1 = (x_2, 0)$, and $P_1 = (x, 0)$. Let $f(x)$ denote the area of triangle PAB. Then $f(x)$ can be expressed in terms of the areas of three trapezoids as follows:

$$f(x) = \text{area}\,(A_1ABB_1) - \text{area}\,(A_1APP_1) - \text{area}\,(B_1BPP_1)$$
$$= \tfrac{1}{2}(x_1^2 + x_2^2)(x_2 - x_1) - \tfrac{1}{2}(x_1^2 + x^2)(x - x_1) - \tfrac{1}{2}(x^2 + x_2^2)(x_2 - x)$$

After expanding and canceling terms, we get
$$f(x) = \tfrac{1}{2}(x_2x_1^2 - x_1x_2^2 - xx_1^2 + x_1x^2 - x_2x^2 + xx_2^2) = \tfrac{1}{2}[x_1^2(x_2 - x) + x_2^2(x - x_1) + x^2(x_1 - x_2)]$$
$$f'(x) = \tfrac{1}{2}[-x_1^2 + x_2^2 + 2x(x_1 - x_2)]. \quad f''(x) = \tfrac{1}{2}[2(x_1 - x_2)] = x_1 - x_2 < 0 \text{ since } x_2 > x_1.$$
$$f'(x) = 0 \;\Rightarrow\; 2x(x_1 - x_2) = x_1^2 - x_2^2 \;\Rightarrow\; x_P = \tfrac{1}{2}(x_1 + x_2).$$

$$f(x_P) = \tfrac{1}{2}\left(x_1^2\left[\tfrac{1}{2}(x_2 - x_1)\right] + x_2^2\left[\tfrac{1}{2}(x_2 - x_1)\right] + \tfrac{1}{4}(x_1 + x_2)^2(x_1 - x_2)\right)$$
$$= \tfrac{1}{2}\left[\tfrac{1}{2}(x_2 - x_1)(x_1^2 + x_2^2) - \tfrac{1}{4}(x_2 - x_1)(x_1 + x_2)^2\right]$$
$$= \tfrac{1}{8}(x_2 - x_1)\left[2(x_1^2 + x_2^2) - (x_1^2 + 2x_1x_2 + x_2^2)\right]$$
$$= \tfrac{1}{8}(x_2 - x_1)(x_1^2 - 2x_1x_2 + x_2^2) = \tfrac{1}{8}(x_2 - x_1)(x_1 - x_2)^2 = \tfrac{1}{8}(x_2 - x_1)(x_2 - x_1)^2$$
$$= \tfrac{1}{8}(x_2 - x_1)^3$$

To put this in terms of m and b, we solve the system $y = x_1^2$ and $y = mx_1 + b$, giving us $x_1^2 - mx_1 - b = 0 \;\Rightarrow\; x_1 = \tfrac{1}{2}(m - \sqrt{m^2 + 4b})$. Similarly, $x_2 = \tfrac{1}{2}(m + \sqrt{m^2 + 4b})$. The area is then $\tfrac{1}{8}(x_2 - x_1)^3 = \tfrac{1}{8}(\sqrt{m^2 + 4b})^3$, and is attained at the point $P(x_P, x_P^2) = P(\tfrac{1}{2}m, \tfrac{1}{4}m^2)$.

Note: Another way to get an expression for $f(x)$ is to use the formula for an area of a triangle in terms of the coordinates of the vertices: $f(x) = \tfrac{1}{2}\left[(x_2x_1^2 - x_1x_2^2) + (x_1x^2 - xx_1^2) + (xx_2^2 - x_2x^2)\right]$.

14. If $L = \lim\limits_{x \to \infty} \left(\dfrac{x + a}{x - a}\right)^x$, then L has the indeterminate form 1^∞, so

$$\ln L = \lim_{x \to \infty} \ln\left(\frac{x + a}{x - a}\right)^x = \lim_{x \to \infty} x \ln\left(\frac{x + a}{x - a}\right) = \lim_{x \to \infty} \frac{\ln(x + a) - \ln(x - a)}{1/x}$$

$$\overset{\text{H}}{=} \lim_{x \to \infty} \frac{\dfrac{1}{x + a} - \dfrac{1}{x - a}}{-1/x^2} = \lim_{x \to \infty}\left[\frac{(x - a) - (x + a)}{(x + a)(x - a)} \cdot \frac{-x^2}{1}\right]$$

$$= \lim_{x \to \infty} \frac{2ax^2}{x^2 - a^2} = \lim_{x \to \infty} \frac{2a}{1 - a^2/x^2} = 2a.$$

Hence, $\ln L = 2a$, so $L = e^{2a}$. From the original equation, we want $L = e^1 \;\Rightarrow\; 2a = 1 \;\Rightarrow\; a = \tfrac{1}{2}$.

15. (a) $A = \tfrac{1}{2}bh$ with $\sin\theta = h/c$, so $A = \tfrac{1}{2}bc\sin\theta$. But A is a constant, so differentiating this equation with respect to t, we

get $\dfrac{dA}{dt} = 0 = \dfrac{1}{2}\left[bc\cos\theta\,\dfrac{d\theta}{dt} + b\dfrac{dc}{dt}\sin\theta + \dfrac{db}{dt}c\sin\theta\right]$

$\Rightarrow \quad bc\cos\theta\,\dfrac{d\theta}{dt} = -\sin\theta\left[b\dfrac{dc}{dt} + c\dfrac{db}{dt}\right] \quad \Rightarrow \quad \dfrac{d\theta}{dt} = -\tan\theta\left[\dfrac{1}{c}\dfrac{dc}{dt} + \dfrac{1}{b}\dfrac{db}{dt}\right].$

(b) We use the Law of Cosines to get the length of side a in terms of those of b and c, and then
we differentiate implicitly with respect to t: $a^2 = b^2 + c^2 - 2bc\cos\theta$ $\Rightarrow$

$$2a\frac{da}{dt} = 2b\frac{db}{dt} + 2c\frac{dc}{dt} - 2\left[bc(-\sin\theta)\frac{d\theta}{dt} + b\frac{dc}{dt}\cos\theta + \frac{db}{dt}c\cos\theta\right] \Rightarrow$$

$$\frac{da}{dt} = \frac{1}{a}\left(b\frac{db}{dt} + c\frac{dc}{dt} + bc\sin\theta\frac{d\theta}{dt} - b\frac{dc}{dt}\cos\theta - c\frac{db}{dt}\cos\theta\right).$$ Now we substitute our value of a from the

Law of Cosines and the value of $d\theta/dt$ from part (a), and simplify (primes signify differentiation by t):

$$\frac{da}{dt} = \frac{bb' + cc' + bc\sin\theta\,[-\tan\theta(c'/c + b'/b)] - (bc' + cb')(\cos\theta)}{\sqrt{b^2 + c^2 - 2bc\cos\theta}}$$

$$= \frac{bb' + cc' - [\sin^2\theta(bc' + cb') + \cos^2\theta(bc' + cb')]/\cos\theta}{\sqrt{b^2 + c^2 - 2bc\cos\theta}} = \frac{bb' + cc' - (bc' + cb')\sec\theta}{\sqrt{b^2 + c^2 - 2bc\cos\theta}}$$

16. *Case (i) (first graph):* For $x + y \geq 0$, that is, $y \geq -x$, $|x + y| = x + y \leq e^x$ $\Rightarrow$ $y \leq e^x - x$.
Note that $y = e^x - x$ is always above the line $y = -x$ and that $y = -x$ is a slant asymptote.

Case (ii) (second graph): For $x + y < 0$, that is, $y < -x$, $|x + y| = -x - y \leq e^x$ $\Rightarrow$ $y \geq -x - e^x$.
Note that $-x - e^x$ is always below the line $y = -x$ and $y = -x$ is a slant asymptote.

Putting the two pieces together gives the third graph.

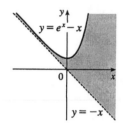 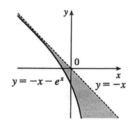 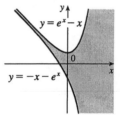

17. (a) Let $y = |AD|$, $x = |AB|$, and $1/x = |AC|$, so that $|AB| \cdot |AC| = 1$.
We compute the area $\mathcal{A}$ of $\triangle ABC$ in two ways. First,

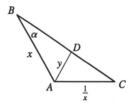

$\mathcal{A} = \frac{1}{2}|AB||AC|\sin\frac{2\pi}{3} = \frac{1}{2} \cdot 1 \cdot \frac{\sqrt{3}}{2} = \frac{\sqrt{3}}{4}$. Second,

$\mathcal{A} = (\text{area of } \triangle ABD) + (\text{area of } \triangle ACD)$

$\quad = \frac{1}{2}|AB||AD|\sin\frac{\pi}{3} + \frac{1}{2}|AD||AC|\sin\frac{\pi}{3}$

$\quad = \frac{1}{2}xy\frac{\sqrt{3}}{2} + \frac{1}{2}y(1/x)\frac{\sqrt{3}}{2} = \frac{\sqrt{3}}{4}y(x + 1/x)$

Equating the two expressions for the area, we get $\frac{\sqrt{3}}{4}y\left(x + \frac{1}{x}\right) = \frac{\sqrt{3}}{4}$ $\Leftrightarrow$ $y = \frac{1}{x + 1/x} = \frac{x}{x^2 + 1}$, $x > 0$.

Another method: Use the Law of Sines on the triangles ABD and ABC. In $\triangle ABD$, we have
$\angle A + \angle B + \angle D = 180°$ $\Leftrightarrow$ $60° + \alpha + \angle D = 180°$ $\Leftrightarrow$ $\angle D = 120° - \alpha$. Thus,

$$\frac{x}{y} = \frac{\sin(120° - \alpha)}{\sin\alpha} = \frac{\sin 120°\cos\alpha - \cos 120°\sin\alpha}{\sin\alpha} = \frac{\frac{\sqrt{3}}{2}\cos\alpha + \frac{1}{2}\sin\alpha}{\sin\alpha} \Rightarrow \frac{x}{y} = \frac{\sqrt{3}}{2}\cot\alpha + \frac{1}{2},$$

and by a similar argument with $\triangle ABC$, $\frac{\sqrt{3}}{2}\cot\alpha = x^2 + \frac{1}{2}$. Eliminating $\cot\alpha$ gives $\frac{x}{y} = \left(x^2 + \frac{1}{2}\right) + \frac{1}{2}$ $\Rightarrow$

$$y = \frac{x}{x^2 + 1}, x > 0.$$

(b) We differentiate our expression for y with respect to x to find the maximum:

$\dfrac{dy}{dx} = \dfrac{(x^2+1) - x(2x)}{(x^2+1)^2} = \dfrac{1-x^2}{(x^2+1)^2} = 0$ when $x = 1$. This indicates a maximum by the First Derivative

Test, since $y'(x) > 0$ for $0 < x < 1$ and $y'(x) < 0$ for $x > 1$, so the maximum value of y is $y(1) = \frac{1}{2}$.

18. (a)

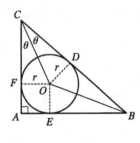

From geometry, two tangents to a circle from a given point have the same length, so $|CF| = |CD|$, $|AE| = |AF|$, and $|BD| = |BE|$. Thus,

$\frac{1}{2}(|BC| + |AC| - |AB|)$

$\quad = \frac{1}{2}[(|BD| + |DC|) + (|AF| + |FC|) - (|AE| + |EB|)]$

$\quad = \frac{1}{2}\left[\left(\underline{|BD|} + |CD|\right) + \left(\underline{|AF|} + |CD|\right) - \left(\underline{|AF|} + \underline{|BD|}\right)\right]$

$\quad = \frac{1}{2}[2|CD|] = |CD|$

(b) Using the result from part (a) and the fact that $a = |BC|$, we have $\tan\theta = \dfrac{r}{|CD|}$ $\Rightarrow$

$\dfrac{r}{\tan\theta} = |CD| = \frac{1}{2}(|AC| + |BC| - |AB|) = \frac{1}{2}(a\cos 2\theta + a - a\sin 2\theta)$ $\Leftrightarrow$

$\qquad r = \frac{1}{2}a\tan\theta\left(2\cos^2\theta - 1 + 1 - 2\sin\theta\,\cos\theta\right)$

$\qquad = \frac{1}{2}a\left(2\sin\theta\,\cos\theta - 2\sin^2\theta\right)$ [in terms of θ]

$\qquad = \frac{1}{2}a(\sin 2\theta + \cos 2\theta - 1)$ [in terms of 2θ]

(c) We differentiate r with respect to θ and set $dr/d\theta$ equal to 0 to find the maximum values:

$dr/d\theta = \frac{1}{2}a(2\cos 2\theta - 2\sin 2\theta) = a(\cos 2\theta - \sin 2\theta)$. Since $0 < \theta < \frac{\pi}{4}$, $dr/d\theta = 0$ $\Leftrightarrow$ $\cos 2\theta = \sin 2\theta$

$\Leftrightarrow$ $1 = \tan 2\theta$ $\Leftrightarrow$ $2\theta = \frac{\pi}{4}$ $\Leftrightarrow$ $\theta = \frac{\pi}{8}$. This gives a maximum by the First Derivative Test, since

$dr/d\theta > 0$ for $0 < \theta < \frac{\pi}{8}$, and $dr/d\theta < 0$ for $\frac{\pi}{8} < \theta < \frac{\pi}{4}$. The maximum value is

$r\left(\frac{\pi}{8}\right) = \frac{1}{2}a\left(\sin\frac{\pi}{4} + \cos\frac{\pi}{4} - 1\right) = \frac{1}{2}(\sqrt{2} - 1)a \approx 0.207a$.

19. Let $s_A(t)$ and $s_B(t)$ be the position functions for cars A and B and let $f(t) = s_A(t) - s_B(t)$. Since A passed B twice (B passed A once), there must be three values of t such that $f(t) = 0$. Let these times be denoted t_1, t_2, and t_3. By the Mean Value Theorem, we know that for some number c_1 in (t_1, t_2), $f'(c_1) = \dfrac{f(t_2) - f(t_1)}{t_2 - t_1}$, but

$f(t_2) - f(t_1) = 0$, so $f'(c_1) = 0$ $\Leftrightarrow$ $s'_A(c_1) - s'_B(c_1) = 0$ $\Leftrightarrow$ $v_A(c_1) - v_B(c_1) = 0$ $\Rightarrow$

$v_A(c_1) = v_B(c_1)$. By a similar argument, there exists some number c_2 in (t_2, t_3) such that $v_A(c_2) = v_B(c_2)$. Now let $g(t) = v_A(t) - v_B(t)$ and apply the Mean Value Theorem on $[c_1, c_2]$ with $c_1 < c < c_2$.

$g'(c) = \dfrac{g(c_2) - g(c_1)}{c_2 - c_1}$, but $g(c_2) = g(c_1) = 0$, so $g'(c) = 0$ $\Rightarrow$ $v'_A(c) - v'_B(c) = 0$ $\Rightarrow$

$a_A(c) - a_B(c) = 0$ $\Rightarrow$ $a_A(c) = a_B(c)$; that is, A and B had equal accelerations at $t = c$.

20. Let $x = |AE|$, $y = |AF|$ as shown. The area $\mathcal{A}$ of the $\triangle AEF$ is $\mathcal{A} = \frac{1}{2}xy$. We need to find a relationship between x and y, so that we can take the derivative $d\mathcal{A}/dx$ and then find the maximum and minimum areas. Now let A' be the point on which A ends up after the fold has been performed, and let P be the intersection of AA' and EF. Note that AA' is perpendicular to EF since we are reflecting A through the line EF to get to A', and that $|AP| = |PA'|$ for the same reason. But $|AA'| = 1$, since AA' is a radius of the circle. Since $|AP| + |PA'| = |AA'|$,

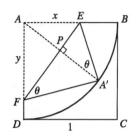

we have $|AP| = \frac{1}{2}$. Another way to express the area of the triangle is

$\mathcal{A} = \frac{1}{2}|EF||AP| = \frac{1}{2}\sqrt{x^2 + y^2}\left(\frac{1}{2}\right) = \frac{1}{4}\sqrt{x^2 + y^2}$. Equating the two expressions for $\mathcal{A}$, we get

$\frac{1}{2}xy = \frac{1}{4}\sqrt{x^2 + y^2} \Rightarrow 4x^2y^2 = x^2 + y^2 \Rightarrow y^2(4x^2 - 1) = x^2 \Rightarrow y = x/\sqrt{4x^2 - 1}$.

(Note that we could also have derived this result from the similarity of $\triangle A'PE$ and $\triangle A'FE$; that is,

$\dfrac{|A'P|}{|PE|} = \dfrac{|A'F|}{|A'E|} \quad\Rightarrow\quad \dfrac{\frac{1}{2}}{\sqrt{x^2 - \left(\frac{1}{2}\right)^2}} = \dfrac{y}{x} \Rightarrow y = \dfrac{\frac{1}{2}x}{\sqrt{4x^2 - 1}/2} = \dfrac{x}{\sqrt{4x^2 - 1}}$.)

Now we can substitute for y and calculate $\dfrac{d\mathcal{A}}{dx}$: $\mathcal{A} = \dfrac{1}{2}\dfrac{x^2}{\sqrt{4x^2 - 1}} \quad\Rightarrow$

$\dfrac{d\mathcal{A}}{dx} = \dfrac{1}{2}\left[\dfrac{\sqrt{4x^2 - 1}\,(2x) - x^2\left(\frac{1}{2}\right)\left(4x^2 - 1\right)^{-1/2}(8x)}{4x^2 - 1}\right]$. This is 0 when $2x\sqrt{4x^2 - 1} - 4x^3\left(4x^2 - 1\right)^{-1/2} = 0$

$\Leftrightarrow 2x\left(4x^2 - 1\right)^{-1/2}\left[\left(4x^2 - 1\right) - 2x^2\right] = 0 \quad\Rightarrow\quad \left(4x^2 - 1\right) - 2x^2 = 0 \ (x > 0) \Leftrightarrow 2x^2 = 1 \quad\Rightarrow$

$x = \frac{1}{\sqrt{2}}$. So this is one possible value for an extremum. We must also test the endpoints of the interval over which x ranges. The largest value that x can attain is 1, and the smallest value of x occurs when $y = 1 \Leftrightarrow$

$1 = x/\sqrt{4x^2 - 1} \Leftrightarrow x^2 = 4x^2 - 1 \Leftrightarrow 3x^2 = 1 \Leftrightarrow x = \frac{1}{\sqrt{3}}$. This will give the same value of $\mathcal{A}$ as will $x = 1$, since the geometric situation is the same (reflected through the line $y = x$). We calculate

$\mathcal{A}\left(\frac{1}{\sqrt{2}}\right) = \dfrac{1}{2}\dfrac{\left(1/\sqrt{2}\right)^2}{\sqrt{4\left(1/\sqrt{2}\right)^2 - 1}} = \dfrac{1}{4} = 0.25$, and $\mathcal{A}(1) = \dfrac{1}{2}\dfrac{1^2}{\sqrt{4(1)^2 - 1}} = \dfrac{1}{2\sqrt{3}} \approx 0.29$. So the maximum area

is $\mathcal{A}(1) = \mathcal{A}\left(\frac{1}{\sqrt{3}}\right) = \frac{1}{2\sqrt{3}}$ and the minimum area is $\mathcal{A}\left(\frac{1}{\sqrt{2}}\right) = \frac{1}{4}$.

Another method: Use the angle θ (see diagram above) as a variable:

$\mathcal{A} = \frac{1}{2}xy = \frac{1}{2}\left(\frac{1}{2}\sec\theta\right)\left(\frac{1}{2}\csc\theta\right) = \dfrac{1}{8\sin\theta\,\cos\theta} = \dfrac{1}{4\sin 2\theta}$. $\mathcal{A}$ is minimized when $\sin 2\theta$ is maximal, that is,

when $\sin 2\theta = 1 \Rightarrow 2\theta = \frac{\pi}{2} \Rightarrow \theta = \frac{\pi}{4}$. Also note that $A'E = x = \frac{1}{2}\sec\theta \le 1 \Rightarrow \sec\theta \le 2 \Rightarrow$

$\cos\theta \ge \frac{1}{2} \Rightarrow \theta \le \frac{\pi}{3}$, and similarly, $A'F = y = \frac{1}{2}\csc\theta \le 1 \Rightarrow \csc\theta \le 2 \Rightarrow \sin\theta \le \frac{1}{2} \Rightarrow \theta \ge \frac{\pi}{6}$.

As above, we find that $\mathcal{A}$ is maximized at these endpoints: $\mathcal{A}\left(\frac{\pi}{6}\right) = \dfrac{1}{4\sin\frac{\pi}{3}} = \dfrac{1}{2\sqrt{3}} = \dfrac{1}{4\sin\frac{2\pi}{3}} = \mathcal{A}\left(\frac{\pi}{3}\right)$; and

minimized at $\theta = \frac{\pi}{4}$: $\mathcal{A}\left(\frac{\pi}{4}\right) = \dfrac{1}{4\sin\frac{\pi}{2}} = \dfrac{1}{4}$.

21.

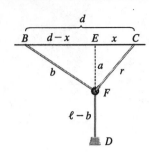

Let $a = |EF|$ and $b = |BF|$ as shown in the figure.
Since $\ell = |BF| + |FD|$, $|FD| = \ell - b$. Now

$$|ED| = |EF| + |FD| = a + \ell - b$$

$$= \sqrt{r^2 - x^2} + \ell - \sqrt{(d-x)^2 + a^2}$$

$$= \sqrt{r^2 - x^2} + \ell - \sqrt{(d-x)^2 + \left(\sqrt{r^2 - x^2}\right)^2}$$

$$= \sqrt{r^2 - x^2} + \ell - \sqrt{d^2 - 2dx + x^2 + r^2 - x^2}$$

Let $f(x) = \sqrt{r^2 - x^2} + \ell - \sqrt{d^2 + r^2 - 2dx}$.

$f'(x) = \frac{1}{2}\left(r^2 - x^2\right)^{-1/2}(-2x) - \frac{1}{2}\left(d^2 + r^2 - 2dx\right)^{-1/2}(-2d) = \dfrac{-x}{\sqrt{r^2 - x^2}} + \dfrac{d}{\sqrt{d^2 + r^2 - 2dx}}$.

$f'(x) = 0 \;\Rightarrow\; \dfrac{x}{\sqrt{r^2 - x^2}} = \dfrac{d}{\sqrt{d^2 + r^2 - 2dx}} \;\Rightarrow\; \dfrac{x^2}{r^2 - x^2} = \dfrac{d^2}{d^2 + r^2 - 2dx} \;\Rightarrow\;$

$d^2 x^2 + r^2 x^2 - 2dx^3 = d^2 r^2 - d^2 x^2 \;\Rightarrow\; 0 = 2dx^3 - 2d^2 x^2 - r^2 x^2 + d^2 r^2 \;\Rightarrow\;$

$0 = 2dx^2(x - d) - r^2(x^2 - d^2) \;\Rightarrow\; 0 = 2dx^2(x - d) - r^2(x + d)(x - d) \;\Rightarrow\;$

$0 = (x - d)\left[2dx^2 - r^2(x + d)\right]$

But $d > r > x$, so $x \neq d$. Thus, we solve $2dx^2 - r^2 x - dr^2 = 0$ for x:

$$x = \frac{-(-r^2) \pm \sqrt{(-r^2)^2 - 4(2d)(-dr^2)}}{2(2d)} = \frac{r^2 \pm \sqrt{r^4 + 8d^2 r^2}}{4d}.$$ Because $\sqrt{r^4 + 8d^2 r^2} > r^2$, the "negative"

can be discarded. Thus,

$$x = \frac{r^2 + \sqrt{r^2}\sqrt{r^2 + 8d^2}}{4d} = \frac{r^2 + r\sqrt{r^2 + 8d^2}}{4d} \quad (r > 0)$$

$$= \frac{r}{4d}\left(r + \sqrt{r^2 + 8d^2}\right)$$

The maximum value of $|ED|$ occurs at this value of x.

22.

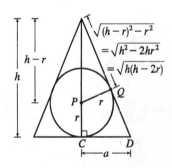

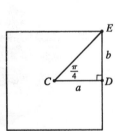

Let $a = \overline{CD}$ denote the distance from the center C of the base to the midpoint D of a side of the base. Since

$\triangle PQR$ is similar to $\triangle DCR$, $\dfrac{a}{h} = \dfrac{r}{\sqrt{h(h - 2r)}} \;\Rightarrow\; a = \dfrac{rh}{\sqrt{h(h - 2r)}} = r\dfrac{\sqrt{h}}{\sqrt{h - 2r}}$.

Let b denote one-half the length of a side of the base. The area A of the base is

$$A = 8(\text{area of } \triangle CDE) = 8\left(\tfrac{1}{2}ab\right) = 4a\left(a\tan\tfrac{\pi}{4}\right) = 4a^2.$$

The volume of the pyramid is $V = \tfrac{1}{3}Ah = \tfrac{1}{3}\left(4a^2\right)h = \dfrac{4}{3}\left(r\dfrac{\sqrt{h}}{\sqrt{h-2r}}\right)^2 h = \tfrac{4}{3}r^2\dfrac{h^2}{h-2r}$, with domain $h > 2r$.

Now $\dfrac{dV}{dh} = \dfrac{4}{3}r^2 \cdot \dfrac{(h-2r)(2h) - h^2(1)}{(h-2r)^2} = \dfrac{4}{3}r^2\dfrac{h^2 - 4hr}{(h-2r)^2} = \dfrac{4}{3}r^2\dfrac{h(h-4r)}{(h-2r)^2}$

and

$$\dfrac{d^2V}{dh^2} = \dfrac{4}{3}r^2 \cdot \dfrac{(h-2r)^2(2h-4r) - \left(h^2 - 4hr\right)(2)(h-2r)(1)}{\left[(h-2r)^2\right]^2}$$

$$= \dfrac{4}{3}r^2 \cdot \dfrac{2(h-2r)\left[\left(h^2 - 4hr + 4r^2\right) - \left(h^2 - 4hr\right)\right]}{(h-2r)^2}$$

$$= \dfrac{8}{3}r^2 \cdot \dfrac{4r^2}{(h-2r)^3} = \dfrac{32}{3}r^4 \cdot \dfrac{1}{(h-2r)^3}.$$

The first derivative is equal to zero for $h = 4r$ and the second derivative is positive for $h > 2r$, so the volume of the pyramid is minimized when $h = 4r$.

To extend our solution to a regular n-gon, we make the following changes:

(1) the number of sides of the base is n

(2) the number of triangles in the base is $2n$

(3) $\angle DCE = \dfrac{\pi}{n}$

(4) $b = a\tan\dfrac{\pi}{n}$

We then obtain the following results:

$A = na^2\tan\dfrac{\pi}{n}$, $V = \dfrac{nr^2}{3}\cdot\tan\left(\dfrac{\pi}{n}\right)\cdot\dfrac{h^2}{h-2r}$, $\dfrac{dV}{dh} = \dfrac{nr^2}{3}\cdot\tan\left(\dfrac{\pi}{n}\right)\cdot\dfrac{h(h-4r)}{(h-2r)^2}$, and

$\dfrac{d^2V}{dh^2} = \dfrac{8nr^4}{3}\cdot\tan\left(\dfrac{\pi}{n}\right)\cdot\dfrac{1}{(h-2r)^3}$. Notice that the answer, $h = 4r$, is independent of the number of sides of the base of the polygon!

23.

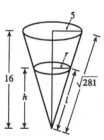

By similar triangles, $\dfrac{r}{5} = \dfrac{h}{16} \Rightarrow r = \dfrac{5h}{16}$. The volume of the cone is

$V = \tfrac{1}{3}\pi r^2 h = \tfrac{1}{3}\pi\left(\dfrac{5h}{16}\right)^2 h = \dfrac{25\pi}{768}h^3$, so $\dfrac{dV}{dt} = \dfrac{25\pi}{256}h^2\dfrac{dh}{dt}$. Now the rate of

change of the volume is also equal to the difference of what is being added
$(2 \text{ cm}^3/\text{min})$ and what is oozing out $(k\pi rl$, where πrl is the area of the cone and k

is a proportionality constant). Thus, $\dfrac{dV}{dt} = 2 - k\pi rl$.

Equating the two expressions for $\dfrac{dV}{dt}$ and substituting $h = 10$, $\dfrac{dh}{dt} = -0.3$, $r = \dfrac{5(10)}{16} = \dfrac{25}{8}$, and $\dfrac{l}{\sqrt{281}} = \dfrac{10}{16}$

$\Leftrightarrow l = \tfrac{5}{8}\sqrt{281}$, we get $\dfrac{25\pi}{256}(10)^2(-0.3) = 2 - k\pi\dfrac{25}{8}\cdot\dfrac{5}{8}\sqrt{281} \Leftrightarrow \dfrac{125k\pi\sqrt{281}}{64} = 2 + \dfrac{750\pi}{256}$. Solving for k

gives us $k = \dfrac{256 + 375\pi}{250\pi\sqrt{281}}$. To maintain a certain height, the rate of oozing, $k\pi rl$, must equal the rate of the liquid

being poured in; that is, $\dfrac{dV}{dt} = 0$. $k\pi rl = \dfrac{256 + 375\pi}{250\pi\sqrt{281}}\cdot\pi\cdot\dfrac{25}{8}\cdot\dfrac{5\sqrt{281}}{8} = \dfrac{256 + 375\pi}{128} \approx 11.204 \text{ cm}^3/\text{min}.$

24.

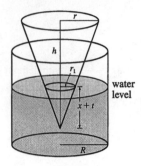

Assume the axes of the cone and the cylinder are parallel. Let H denote the initial height of the water. When the cone has been dropping for t seconds, the water level has risen x meters, so the tip of the cone is $x + 1t$ meters below the water line. We want to find dx/dt when $x + t = h$ (when the cone is completely submerged). Using similar triangles, $\dfrac{r_1}{x+t} = \dfrac{r}{h} \;\Rightarrow\; r_1 = \dfrac{r}{h}(x+t).$

volume of water and cone at time t	=	original volume of water	+	volume of submerged part of cone
$\pi R^2 (H + x)$	=	$\pi R^2 H$	+	$\frac{1}{3}\pi r_1^2 (x + t)$
$\pi R^2 H + \pi R^2 x$	=	$\pi R^2 H$	+	$\frac{1}{3}\pi \dfrac{r^2}{h^2}(x + t)^3$
$3h^2 R^2 x$	=	$r^2 (x + t)^3$		

Differentiating implicitly with respect to t gives us

$$3h^2 R^2 \frac{dx}{dt} = r^2 \left[3(x+t)^2 \frac{dx}{dt} + 3(x+t)^2 \frac{dt}{dt} \right] \quad \Rightarrow$$

$$\frac{dx}{dt} = \frac{r^2 (x+t)^2}{h^2 R^2 - r^2 (x+t)^2} \quad \Rightarrow$$

$$\left. \frac{dx}{dt} \right|_{x+t=h} = \frac{r^2 h^2}{h^2 R^2 - r^2 h^2} = \frac{r^2}{R^2 - r^2}$$

Thus, the water level is rising at a rate of $\dfrac{r^2}{R^2 - r^2}$ cm/s at the instant the cone is completely submerged.

Integrals

1. (a) Since f is *increasing*, we can obtain a *lower* estimate by using *left* endpoints. We are instructed to use five rectangles, so $n = 5$.

$$L_5 = \sum_{i=1}^{5} f(x_{i-1})\,\Delta x \quad [\Delta x = \tfrac{b-a}{n} = \tfrac{10-0}{5} = 2]$$

$$= f(x_0) \cdot 2 + f(x_1) \cdot 2 + f(x_2) \cdot 2 + f(x_3) \cdot 2 + f(x_4) \cdot 2$$

$$= 2\,[f(0) + f(2) + f(4) + f(6) + f(8)]$$

$$\approx 2(1 + 3 + 4.3 + 5.4 + 6.3) = 2(20) = 40$$

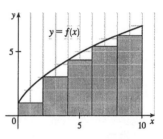

Since f is *increasing*, we can obtain an *upper* estimate by using *right* endpoints.

$$R_5 = \sum_{i=1}^{5} f(x_i)\,\Delta x$$

$$= 2\,[f(x_1) + f(x_2) + f(x_3) + f(x_4) + f(x_5)]$$

$$= 2\,[f(2) + f(4) + f(6) + f(8) + f(10)]$$

$$\approx 2(3 + 4.3 + 5.4 + 6.3 + 7) = 2(26) = 52$$

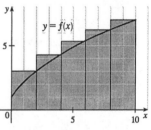

Comparing R_5 to L_5, we see that we have added the area of the rightmost rectangle, $f(10) \cdot 2$, to the sum and subtracted the area of the leftmost rectangle, $f(0) \cdot 2$, from the sum.

(b) $L_{10} = \sum_{i=1}^{10} f(x_{i-1})\,\Delta x \quad [\Delta x = \tfrac{10-0}{10} = 1]$

$$= 1\,[f(x_0) + f(x_1) + \cdots + f(x_9)]$$

$$= f(0) + f(1) + \cdots + f(9)$$

$$\approx 1 + 2.1 + 3 + 3.7 + 4.3 + 4.9 + 5.4 + 5.8 + 6.3 + 6.7$$

$$= 43.2$$

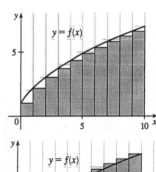

$$R_{10} = \sum_{i=1}^{10} f(x_i)\,\Delta x = f(1) + f(2) + \cdots + f(10)$$

$$= L_{10} + 1 \cdot f(10) - 1 \cdot f(0) \quad \begin{bmatrix} \text{add rightmost rectangle,} \\ \text{subtract leftmost} \end{bmatrix}$$

$$= 43.2 + 7 - 1 = 49.2$$

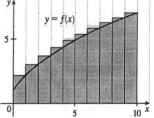

2. (a) (i) $L_6 = \sum\limits_{i=1}^{6} f(x_{i-1})\Delta x \quad [\Delta x = \frac{12-0}{6} = 2]$

$= 2[f(x_0) + f(x_1) + f(x_2) + f(x_3) + f(x_4) + f(x_5)]$

$= 2[f(0) + f(2) + f(4) + f(6) + f(8) + f(10)]$

$\approx 2(9 + 8.8 + 8.2 + 7.3 + 5.9 + 4.1)$

$= 2(43.3) = 86.6$

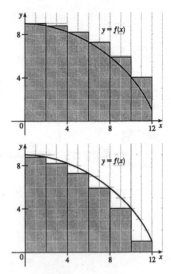

(ii) $R_6 = L_6 + 2 \cdot f(12) - 2 \cdot f(0)$

$\approx 86.6 + 2(1) - 2(9) = 70.6$

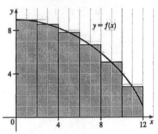

(iii) $M_6 = \sum\limits_{i=1}^{6} f(x_i^*)\,\Delta x$

$= 2[f(1) + f(3) + f(5) + f(7) + f(9) + f(11)]$

$\approx 2(8.9 + 8.5 + 7.8 + 6.6 + 5.1 + 2.8)$

$= 2(39.7) = 79.4$

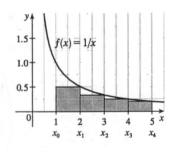

(b) Since f is *decreasing*, we obtain an *overestimate* by using *left* endpoints; that is, L_6.

(c) Since f is *decreasing*, we obtain an *underestimate* by using *right* endpoints; that is, R_6.

(d) M_6 gives the best estimate, since the area of each rectangle appears to be closer to the true area than the overestimates and underestimates in L_6 and R_6.

3. (a) $R_4 = \sum\limits_{i=1}^{4} f(x_i)\,\Delta x \quad [\Delta x = \frac{5-1}{4} = 1]$

$= f(x_1) \cdot 1 + f(x_2) \cdot 1 + f(x_3) \cdot 1 + f(x_4) \cdot 1$

$= f(2) + f(3) + f(4) + f(5)$

$= \frac{1}{2} + \frac{1}{3} + \frac{1}{4} + \frac{1}{5} = \frac{77}{60} = 1.28\overline{3}$

Since f is *decreasing* on $[1, 5]$, an *underestimate* is obtained by using the *right* endpoint approximation, R_4.

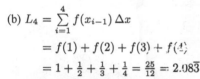

(b) $L_4 = \sum\limits_{i=1}^{4} f(x_{i-1})\,\Delta x$

$= f(1) + f(2) + f(3) + f(4)$

$= 1 + \frac{1}{2} + \frac{1}{3} + \frac{1}{4} = \frac{25}{12} = 2.08\overline{3}$

L_4 is an overestimate. Alternatively, we could just add the area of the leftmost rectangle and subtract the area of the rightmost; that is,

$L_4 = R_4 + f(1) \cdot 1 - f(5) \cdot 1$.

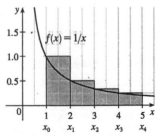

4. (a) $R_5 = \sum\limits_{i=1}^{5} f(x_i)\,\Delta x \quad [\Delta x = \frac{5-0}{5} = 1]$

$= f(x_1) \cdot 1 + f(x_2) \cdot 1 + f(x_3) \cdot 1 + f(x_4) \cdot 1 + f(x_5) \cdot 1$

$= f(1) + f(2) + f(3) + f(4) + f(5)$

$= 24 + 21 + 16 + 9 + 0 = 70$

Since f is decreasing on $[0,5]$, R_5 is an underestimate.

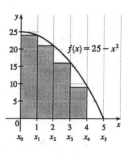

(b) $L_5 = \sum\limits_{i=1}^{5} f(x_{i-1})\,\Delta x$

$= f(0) + f(1) + f(2) + f(3) + f(4)$

$= 25 + 24 + 21 + 16 + 9 = 95$

L_5 is an overestimate.

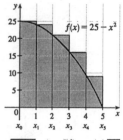

5. (a) $f(x) = 1 + x^2$ and $\Delta x = \dfrac{2 - (-1)}{3} = 1 \Rightarrow$

$R_3 = 1 \cdot f(0) + 1 \cdot f(1) + 1 \cdot f(2) = 1 \cdot 1 + 1 \cdot 2 + 1 \cdot 5 = 8.$

$\Delta x = \dfrac{2 - (-1)}{6} = 0.5 \Rightarrow$

$R_6 = 0.5[f(-0.5) + f(0) + f(0.5) + f(1) + f(1.5) + f(2)]$

$= 0.5(1.25 + 1 + 1.25 + 2 + 3.25 + 5)$

$= 0.5(13.75) = 6.875$

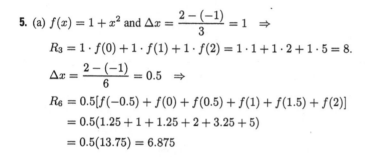

(b) $L_3 = 1 \cdot f(-1) + 1 \cdot f(0) + 1 \cdot f(1) = 1 \cdot 2 + 1 \cdot 1 + 1 \cdot 2 = 5$

$L_6 = 0.5[f(-1) + f(-0.5) + f(0) + f(0.5) + f(1) + f(1.5)]$

$= 0.5(2 + 1.25 + 1 + 1.25 + 2 + 3.25)$

$= 0.5(10.75) = 5.375$

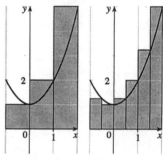

(c) $M_3 = 1 \cdot f(-0.5) + 1 \cdot f(0.5) + 1 \cdot f(1.5)$

$= 1 \cdot 1.25 + 1 \cdot 1.25 + 1 \cdot 3.25 = 5.75$

$M_6 = 0.5[f(-0.75) + f(-0.25) + f(0.25)$

$\qquad + f(0.75) + f(1.25) + f(1.75)]$

$= 0.5(1.5625 + 1.0625 + 1.0625 + 1.5625 + 2.5625 + 4.0625)$

$= 0.5(11.875) = 5.9375$

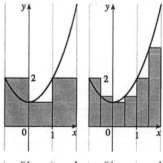

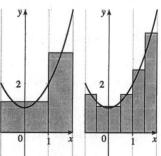

(d) M_6 appears to be the best estimate.

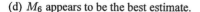

6. (a)

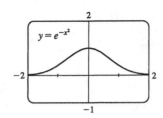

(b) $f(x) = e^{-x^2}$ and $\Delta x = \dfrac{2 - (-2)}{4} = 1 \quad \Rightarrow$

(i) $R_4 = 1 \cdot f(-1) + 1 \cdot f(0)$

$\qquad\quad + 1 \cdot f(1) + 1 \cdot f(2)$

$\qquad = e^{-1} + 1 + e^{-1} + e^{-4}$

$\qquad \approx 1.754$

(ii) $M_4 = 1 \cdot f(-1.5) + 1 \cdot f(-0.5)$

$\qquad\quad + 1 \cdot f(0.5) + 1 \cdot f(1.5)$

$\qquad = e^{-2.25} + e^{-0.25} + e^{-0.25} + e^{-2.25}$

$\qquad \approx 1.768$

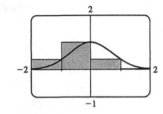

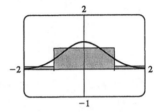

(c) (i) $R_8 = 0.5[f(-1.5) + f(-1) + f(-0.5) + f(0)$

$\qquad\qquad + f(0.5) + f(1) + f(1.5) + f(2)]$

$\qquad = e^{-2.25} + e^{-1} + e^{-0.25} + 1$

$\qquad\quad + e^{-0.25} + e^{-1} + e^{-2.25} + e^{-4}$

$\qquad \approx 1.761$

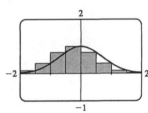

(ii) Due to the symmetry of the figure, we see that

$\qquad M_8 = (0.5)(2)[f(0.25) + f(0.75) + f(1.25) + f(1.75)]$

$\qquad\quad = e^{-0.0625} + e^{-0.5625} + e^{-1.5625} + e^{3.0625}$

$\qquad\quad \approx 1.766$

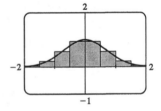

7. Here is one possible algorithm (ordered sequence of operations) for calculating the sums:

1 Let SUM = 0, X_MIN = 0, X_MAX = π, N = 10 (or 30 or 50, depending on which sum we are calculating), DELTA_X = (X_MAX − X_MIN)/N, and RIGHT_ENDPOINT = X_MIN + DELTA_X.

2 Repeat steps 2a, 2b in sequence until RIGHT_ENDPOINT > X_MAX.

2a Add sin (RIGHT_ENDPOINT) to SUM.

2b Add DELTA_X to RIGHT_ENDPOINT.

At the end of this procedure, (DELTA_X) · (SUM) is equal to the answer we are looking for. We find that

$$R_{10} = \frac{\pi}{10} \sum_{i=1}^{10} \sin\left(\frac{i\pi}{10}\right) \approx 1.9835, \ R_{30} = \frac{\pi}{30} \sum_{i=1}^{30} \sin\left(\frac{i\pi}{30}\right) \approx 1.9982, \text{ and } R_{50} = \frac{\pi}{50} \sum_{i=1}^{50} \sin\left(\frac{i\pi}{50}\right) \approx 1.9993.$$

It appears that the exact area is 2.

Shown below is program SUMRIGHT and its output from a TI-83 Plus calculator. To generalize the program, we have input (rather than assign) values for Xmin, Xmax, and N. Also, the function, sin x, is assigned to Y_1, enabling us to evaluate any right sum merely by changing Y_1 and running the program.

8. We can use the algorithm from Exercise 7 with X_MIN = 1, X_MAX = 2, and $1 / (\text{RIGHT\_ENDPOINT})^2$ instead

of sin (RIGHT_ENDPOINT) in step 2a. We find that $R_{10} = \dfrac{1}{10} \sum\limits_{i=1}^{10} \dfrac{1}{(1 + i/10)^2} \approx 0.4640$,

$R_{30} = \dfrac{1}{30} \sum\limits_{i=1}^{30} \dfrac{1}{(1 + i/30)^2} \approx 0.4877$, and $R_{50} = \dfrac{1}{50} \sum\limits_{i=1}^{50} \dfrac{1}{(1 + i/50)^2} \approx 0.4926$. It appears that the exact area

is $\frac{1}{2}$.

9. In Maple, we have to perform a number of steps before getting a numerical answer. After loading the student package [command: `with(student);`] we use the command `left_sum:=leftsum(x^(1/2),x=1..4,10 [or 30, or 50]);` which gives us the expression in summation notation. To get a numerical approximation to the sum, we use `evalf(left_sum);`. Mathematica does not have a special command for these sums, so we must type them in manually. For example, the first left sum is given by `(3/10)*Sum[Sqrt[1+3(i-1)/10],{i,1,10}]`, and we use the N command on the resulting output to get a numerical approximation.

In Derive, we use the LEFT_RIEMANN command to get the left sums, but must define the right sums ourselves. (We can define a new function using LEFT_RIEMANN with k ranging from 1 to n instead of from 0 to $n - 1$.)

(a) With $f(x) = \sqrt{x}$, $1 \le x \le 4$, the left sums are of the form $L_n = \dfrac{3}{n} \sum\limits_{i=1}^{n} \sqrt{1 + \dfrac{3(i-1)}{10}}$. Specifically,

$L_{10} \approx 4.5148$, $L_{30} \approx 4.6165$, and $L_{50} \approx 4.6366$. The right sums are of the form $R_n = \dfrac{3}{n} \sum\limits_{i=1}^{n} \sqrt{1 + \dfrac{3i}{n}}$. Specifically, $R_{10} \approx 4.8148$, $R_{30} \approx 4.7165$, and $R_{50} \approx 4.6966$.

(b) In Maple, we use the `leftbox` and `rightbox` commands (with the same arguments as `leftsum` and `rightsum` above) to generate the graphs.

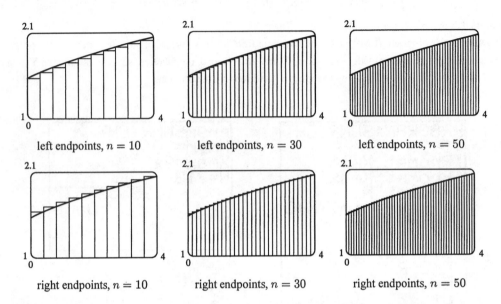

left endpoints, $n = 10$ left endpoints, $n = 30$ left endpoints, $n = 50$

right endpoints, $n = 10$ right endpoints, $n = 30$ right endpoints, $n = 50$

(c) We know that since $\sqrt{x}$ is an increasing function on $(1, 4)$, all of the left sums are smaller than the actual area, and all of the right sums are larger than the actual area. Since the left sum with $n = 50$ is about $4.637 > 4.6$ and the right sum with $n = 50$ is about $4.697 < 4.7$, we conclude that $4.6 < L_{50} <$ exact area $< R_{50} < 4.7$, so the exact area is between 4.6 and 4.7.

10. See the solution to Exercise 9 for the CAS commands for evaluating the sums.

(a) With $f(x) = \sin(\sin x)$, $0 \le x \le \frac{\pi}{2}$, the left sums are of the form $L_n = \dfrac{\pi}{2n} \displaystyle\sum_{i=1}^{n} \sin\left(\sin \dfrac{\pi\,(i-1)}{2n}\right)$. In particular, $L_{10} \approx 0.8251$, $L_{30} \approx 0.8710$, and $L_{50} \approx 0.8799$. The right sums are of the form $R_n = \dfrac{\pi}{2n} \displaystyle\sum_{i=1}^{n} \sin\left(\sin \dfrac{\pi i}{2n}\right)$. In particular, $R_{10} \approx 0.9573$, $R_{30} \approx 0.9150$, and $R_{50} \approx 0.9064$.

(b) In Maple, we use the `leftbox` and `rightbox` commands (with the same arguments as `leftsum` and `rightsum` above) to generate the graphs.

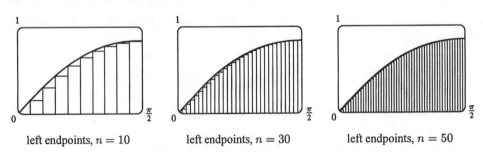

left endpoints, $n = 10$ left endpoints, $n = 30$ left endpoints, $n = 50$

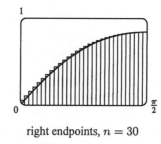
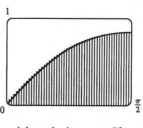

right endpoints, $n = 10$ right endpoints, $n = 30$ right endpoints, $n = 50$

(c) We know that since $\sin(\sin x)$ is an increasing function on $\left(0, \frac{\pi}{2}\right)$ [this is true because its derivative, $-\cos(\sin x)(-\cos x)$, is positive on that interval], all of the left sums are smaller than the actual area, and all of the right sums are larger than the actual area. Since the left sum with $n = 50$ is about $0.8799 > 0.87$ and the right sum with $n = 50$ is about $0.9064 < 0.91$, we conclude that $0.87 < L_{50} <$ exact area $< R_{50} < 0.91$, so the exact area is between 0.87 and 0.91.

11. Since v is an increasing function, L_6 will give us a lower estimate and R_6 will give us an upper estimate.

$L_6 = (0 \text{ ft/s})(0.5 \text{ s}) + (6.2)(0.5) + (10.8)(0.5) + (14.9)(0.5) + (18.1)(0.5) + (19.4)(0.5)$

$= 0.5(69.4) = 34.7 \text{ ft}$

$R_6 = 0.5(6.2 + 10.8 + 14.9 + 18.1 + 19.4 + 20.2) = 0.5(89.6) = 44.8 \text{ ft}$

12. We can find an upper estimate by using the final velocity for each time interval. Thus, the distance d traveled after 62 seconds can be approximated by

$$d = \sum_{i=1}^{6} v(t_i) \Delta t_i = (185 \text{ ft/s})(10 \text{ s}) + 319 \cdot 5 + 447 \cdot 5 + 742 \cdot 12 + 1325 \cdot 27 + 1445 \cdot 3 = 54{,}694 \text{ ft}$$

13. For a decreasing function, using left endpoints gives us an overestimate and using right endpoints results in an underestimate. We will use M_6 to get an estimate. $\Delta t = 1$, so

$$M_6 = 1[v(0.5) + v(1.5) + v(2.5) + v(3.5) + v(4.5) + v(5.5)]$$
$$\approx 55 + 40 + 28 + 18 + 10 + 4 = 155 \text{ ft}$$

For a very rough check on the above calculation, we can draw a line from $(0, 70)$ to $(6, 0)$ and calculate the area of the triangle: $\frac{1}{2}(70)(6) = 210$. This is clearly an overestimate, so our midpoint estimate of 155 is reasonable.

14. For an increasing function, using left endpoints gives us an underestimate and using right endpoints results in an overestimate. We will use M_6 to get an estimate. $\Delta t = \frac{30 - 0}{6} = 5 \text{ s} = \frac{5}{3600} \text{ h} = \frac{1}{720} \text{ h}$.

$$M_6 = \frac{1}{720}[v(2.5) + v(7.5) + v(12.5) + v(17.5) + v(22.5) + v(27.5)]$$
$$= \frac{1}{720}(31.25 + 66 + 88 + 103.5 + 113.75 + 119.25) = \frac{1}{720}(521.75) \approx 0.725 \text{ km}$$

For a very rough check on the above calculation, we can draw a line from $(0, 0)$ to $(30, 120)$ and calculate the area of the triangle: $\frac{1}{2}(30)(120) = 1800$. Divide by 3600 to get 0.5, which is clearly an underestimate, making our midpoint estimate of 0.725 seem reasonable. Of course, answers will vary due to different readings of the graph.

15. $f(x) = \sqrt[4]{x}$, $1 \le x \le 16$. $\Delta x = (16 - 1)/n = 15/n$ and $x_i = 1 + i\, \Delta x = 1 + 15i/n$.

$$A = \lim_{n \to \infty} R_n = \lim_{n \to \infty} \sum_{i=1}^{n} f(x_i)\, \Delta x = \lim_{n \to \infty} \sum_{i=1}^{n} \sqrt[4]{1 + \frac{15i}{n}} \cdot \frac{15}{n}.$$

16. $f(x) = \dfrac{\ln x}{x}$, $3 \le x \le 10$. $\Delta x = (10-3)/n = 7/n$ and $x_i = 3 + i\,\Delta x = 3 + 7i/n$.

$$A = \lim_{n\to\infty} R_n = \lim_{n\to\infty} \sum_{i=1}^{n} f(x_i)\,\Delta x = \lim_{n\to\infty} \sum_{i=1}^{n} \frac{\ln(3+7i/n)}{3+7i/n} \cdot \frac{7}{n}.$$

17. $\displaystyle\lim_{n\to\infty} \sum_{i=1}^{n} \frac{\pi}{4n} \tan\frac{i\pi}{4n}$ can be interpreted as the area of the region lying under the graph of $y = \tan x$ on the interval

$[0, \frac{\pi}{4}]$, since for $y = \tan x$ on $[0, \frac{\pi}{4}]$ with $\Delta x = \dfrac{\pi/4 - 0}{n} = \dfrac{\pi}{4n}$, $x_i = 0 + i\,\Delta x = \dfrac{i\pi}{4n}$, and $x_i^* = x_i$, the

expression for the area is $A = \displaystyle\lim_{n\to\infty} \sum_{i=1}^{n} f(x_i^*)\,\Delta x = \lim_{n\to\infty} \sum_{i=1}^{n} \tan\left(\frac{i\pi}{4n}\right)\frac{\pi}{4n}$. Note that this answer is not unique,

since the expression for the area is the same for the function $y = \tan(x + k\pi)$ on the interval $\left[k\pi, k\pi + \frac{\pi}{4}\right]$, where k is any integer.

18. (a) $\Delta x = \dfrac{1-0}{n} = \dfrac{1}{n}$ and $x_i = 0 + i\,\Delta x = \dfrac{i}{n}$. $A = \displaystyle\lim_{n\to\infty} R_n = \lim_{n\to\infty} \sum_{i=1}^{n} f(x_i)\,\Delta x = \lim_{n\to\infty} \sum_{i=1}^{n} \left(\frac{i}{n}\right)^3 \cdot \frac{1}{n}$.

(b) $\displaystyle\lim_{n\to\infty} \sum_{i=1}^{n} \frac{i^3}{n^3} \cdot \frac{1}{n} = \lim_{n\to\infty} \frac{1}{n^4} \sum_{i=1}^{n} i^3 = \lim_{n\to\infty} \frac{1}{n^4} \left[\frac{n(n+1)}{2}\right]^2 = \lim_{n\to\infty} \frac{(n+1)^2}{4n^2} = \frac{1}{4}\lim_{n\to\infty}\left(1 + \frac{1}{n}\right)^2 = \frac{1}{4}$.

19. (a) $y = f(x) = x^5$. $\Delta x = \dfrac{2-0}{n} = \dfrac{2}{n}$ and $x_i = 0 + i\,\Delta x = \dfrac{2i}{n}$.

$$A = \lim_{n\to\infty} R_n = \lim_{n\to\infty} \sum_{i=1}^{n} f(x_i)\,\Delta x = \lim_{n\to\infty} \sum_{i=1}^{n} \left(\frac{2i}{n}\right)^5 \cdot \frac{2}{n} = \lim_{n\to\infty} \sum_{i=1}^{n} \frac{32 i^5}{n^5} \cdot \frac{2}{n} = \lim_{n\to\infty} \frac{64}{n^6} \sum_{i=1}^{n} i^5.$$

(b) $\displaystyle\sum_{i=1}^{n} i^5 = \frac{n^2(n+1)^2(2n^2 + 2n - 1)}{12}$

(c) $\displaystyle\lim_{n\to\infty} \frac{64}{n^6} \cdot \frac{n^2(n+1)^2(2n^2 + 2n - 1)}{12} = \frac{64}{12}\lim_{n\to\infty} \frac{(n^2 + 2n + 1)(2n^2 + 2n - 1)}{n^2 \cdot n^2}$

$$= \frac{16}{3}\lim_{n\to\infty}\left(1 + \frac{2}{n} + \frac{1}{n^2}\right)\left(2 + \frac{2}{n} - \frac{1}{n^2}\right) = \frac{16}{3} \cdot 1 \cdot 2 = \frac{32}{3}$$

20. From Example 3(a), we have $A = \displaystyle\lim_{n\to\infty} \frac{2}{n} \sum_{i=1}^{n} e^{-2i/n}$. Using a CAS, $\displaystyle\sum_{i=1}^{n} e^{-2i/n} = \frac{e^{-2}(e^2 - 1)}{e^{2/n} - 1}$ and

$$\lim_{n\to\infty} \frac{2}{n} \cdot \frac{e^{-2}(e^2 - 1)}{e^{2/n} - 1} = e^{-2}(e^2 - 1) \approx 0.8647,$$ whereas the estimate from Example 3(b) using M_{10} was 0.8632.

21. $y = f(x) = \cos x$. $\Delta x = \dfrac{b-0}{n} = \dfrac{b}{n}$ and $x_i = 0 + i\,\Delta x = \dfrac{bi}{n}$.

$$A = \lim_{n\to\infty} R_n = \lim_{n\to\infty} \sum_{i=1}^{n} f(x_i)\,\Delta x = \lim_{n\to\infty} \sum_{i=1}^{n} \cos\left(\frac{bi}{n}\right) \cdot \frac{b}{n} = \lim_{n\to\infty} \left[\frac{b\sin\left(b\left(\frac{1}{2n} + 1\right)\right)}{2n\sin\left(\frac{b}{2n}\right)} - \frac{b}{2n}\right] = \sin b$$

If $b = \frac{\pi}{2}$, then $A = \sin\frac{\pi}{2} = 1$.

22. (a)

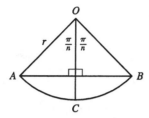

The diagram shows one of the n congruent triangles, $\triangle AOB$, with central angle $2\pi/n$. O is the center of the circle and AB is one of the sides of the polygon. Radius OC is drawn so as to bisect $\angle AOB$. It follows that OC intersects AB at right angles and bisects AB. Thus, $\triangle AOB$ is divided into two right triangles with legs of length $\frac{1}{2}(AB) = r\sin(\pi/n)$ and $r\cos(\pi/n)$.

$\triangle AOB$ has area $2 \cdot \frac{1}{2}[r\sin(\pi/n)][r\cos(\pi/n)] = r^2\sin(\pi/n)\cos(\pi/n) = \frac{1}{2}r^2\sin(2\pi/n)$, so $A_n = n \cdot \text{area}(\triangle AOB) = \frac{1}{2}nr^2\sin(2\pi/n)$.

(b) To use Equation 3.4.2, $\displaystyle\lim_{\theta \to 0}\frac{\sin\theta}{\theta} = 1$, we need to have the same expression in the denominator as we have in the argument of the sine function—in this case, $2\pi/n$.

$$\lim_{n\to\infty} A_n = \lim_{n\to\infty}\frac{1}{2}nr^2\sin(2\pi/n) = \lim_{n\to\infty}\frac{1}{2}nr^2\frac{\sin(2\pi/n)}{2\pi/n}\cdot\frac{2\pi}{n} = \lim_{n\to\infty}\frac{\sin(2\pi/n)}{2\pi/n}\pi r^2. \text{ Let } \theta = \frac{2\pi}{n}.$$

Then as $n \to \infty$, $\theta \to 0$, so $\displaystyle\lim_{n\to\infty}\frac{\sin(2\pi/n)}{2\pi/n}\pi r^2 = \lim_{\theta\to 0}\frac{\sin\theta}{\theta}\pi r^2 = (1)\,\pi r^2 = \pi r^2$.

 5.2 **The Definite Integral** • • • • • • • • • • • • • • • •

1. $R_4 = \displaystyle\sum_{i=1}^{4} f(x_i)\,\Delta x$ $[x_i^* = x_i$ is a right endpoint and $\Delta x = 0.5]$

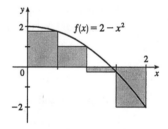

$= 0.5\,[f(0.5) + f(1) + f(1.5) + f(2)]$ $[f(x) = 2 - x^2]$

$= 0.5\,[1.75 + 1 + (-0.25) + (-2)]$

$= 0.5(0.5) = 0.25$

The Riemann sum represents the sum of the areas of the two rectangles above the x-axis minus the sum of the areas of the two rectangles below the x-axis; that is, the *net area* of the rectangles with respect to the x-axis.

2. $L_6 = \displaystyle\sum_{i=1}^{6} f(x_{i-1})\Delta x$ $[x_i^* = x_{i-1}$ is a left endpoint and $\Delta x = 0.5]$

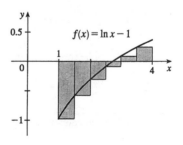

$= 0.5\,[f(1) + f(1.5) + f(2)$

$\qquad + f(2.5) + f(3) + f(3.5)]$ $[f(x) = \ln x - 1]$

$\approx 0.5(-1 - 0.5945349 - 0.3068528$

$\qquad - 0.0837093 + 0.0986123 + 0.2527630)$

$= 0.5(-1.6337217) \approx -0.816861$

The Riemann sum represents the sum of the areas of the two rectangles above the x-axis minus the sum of the areas of the four rectangles below the x-axis; that is, the *net area* of the rectangles with respect to the x-axis.

3. $M_5 = \sum_{i=1}^{5} f(\overline{x}_i)\,\Delta x$ $[x_i^* = \overline{x}_i = \frac{1}{2}(x_{i-1} + x_i)$ is a midpoint and $\Delta x = 1]$

$\qquad = 1\,[f(1.5) + f(2.5) + f(3.5)$

$\qquad\qquad + f(4.5) + f(5.5)]$ $[f(x) = \sqrt{x} - 2]$

$\qquad \approx -0.856759$

The Riemann sum represents the sum of the areas of the two rectangles above the x-axis minus the sum of the areas of the three rectangles below the x-axis.

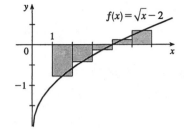

4. (a) $R_6 = \sum_{i=1}^{6} f(x_i)\,\Delta x$ $[x_i^* = x_i$ is a right endpoint and $\Delta x = 0.5]$

$\qquad = 0.5\,[f(0.5) + f(1) + f(1.5) + f(2)$

$\qquad\qquad + f(2.5) + f(3)]$ $[f(x) = x - 2\sin 2x]$

$\qquad \approx 5.353254$

The Riemann sum represents the sum of the areas of the four rectangles above the x-axis minus the sum of the areas of the two rectangles below the x-axis.

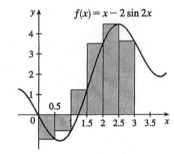

(b) $M_6 = \sum_{i=1}^{6} f(\overline{x}_i)\,\Delta x$ $[x_i^* = \overline{x}_i$ is a midpoint and $\Delta x = 0.5]$

$\qquad = 0.5[f(0.25) + f(0.75) + f(1.25) + f(1.75)$

$\qquad\qquad + f(2.25) + f(2.75)]$ $[f(x) = x - 2\sin 2x]$

$\qquad \approx 4.458461$

The Riemann sum represents the sum of the areas of the four rectangles above the x-axis minus the sum of the areas of the two rectangles below the x-axis.

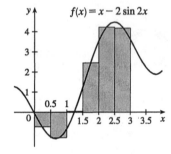

5. $\Delta x = (b - a)/n = (8 - 0)/4 = 8/4 = 2.$

(a) Using the right endpoints to approximate $\int_0^8 f(x)\,dx$, we have

$$\sum_{i=1}^{4} f(x_i)\,\Delta x = 2[f(2) + f(4) + f(6) + f(8)] \approx 2[1 + 2 + (-2) + 1] = 4.$$

(b) Using the left endpoints to approximate $\int_0^8 f(x)\,dx$, we have

$$\sum_{i=1}^{4} f(x_{i-1})\,\Delta x = 2[f(0) + f(2) + f(4) + f(6)] \approx 2[2 + 1 + 2 + (-2)] = 6.$$

(c) Using the midpoint of each subinterval to approximate $\int_0^8 f(x)\,dx$, we have

$$\sum_{i=1}^{4} f(\overline{x}_i)\,\Delta x = 2[f(1) + f(3) + f(5) + f(7)] \approx 2[3 + 2 + 1 + (-1)] = 10.$$

6. (a) Using the right endpoints to approximate $\int_{-3}^{3} g(x)\,dx$, we have

$$\sum_{i=1}^{6} g(x_i)\,\Delta x = 1[g(-2) + g(-1) + g(0) + g(1) + g(2) + g(3)]$$

$$\approx 1 - 0.5 - 1.5 - 1.5 - 0.5 + 2.5 = -0.5$$

(b) Using the left endpoints to approximate $\int_{-3}^{3} g(x)\, dx$, we have

$$\sum_{i=1}^{6} g(x_{i-1})\, \Delta x = 1[g(-3) + g(-2) + g(-1) + g(0) + g(1) + g(2)]$$

$$\approx 2 + 1 - 0.5 - 1.5 - 1.5 - 0.5 = -1$$

(c) Using the midpoint of each subinterval to approximate $\int_{-3}^{3} g(x)\, dx$, we have

$$\sum_{i=1}^{6} g(\overline{x}_i)\, \Delta x = 1[g(-2.5) + g(-1.5) + g(-0.5) + g(0.5) + g(1.5) + g(2.5)]$$

$$\approx 1.5 + 0 - 1 - 1.75 - 1 + 0.5 = -1.75$$

7. Since f is increasing, $L_5 \leq \int_{0}^{25} f(x)\, dx \leq R_5$.

$$\text{Lower estimate} = L_5 = \sum_{i=1}^{5} f(x_{i-1})\, \Delta x = 5[f(0) + f(5) + f(10) + f(15) + f(20)]$$

$$= 5(-42 - 37 - 25 - 6 + 15) = 5(-95) = -475$$

$$\text{Upper estimate} = R_5 = \sum_{i=1}^{5} f(x_i)\, \Delta x = 5[f(5) + f(10) + f(15) + f(20) + f(25)]$$

$$= 5(-37 - 25 - 6 + 15 + 36) = 5(-17) = -85$$

8. (a) Using the right endpoints to approximate $\int_{0}^{6} f(x)\, dx$, we have

$$\sum_{i=1}^{3} f(x_i)\, \Delta x = 2[f(2) + f(4) + f(6)] = 2(8.3 + 2.3 - 10.5) = 0.2$$

(b) Using the left endpoints to approximate $\int_{0}^{6} f(x)\, dx$, we have

$$\sum_{i=1}^{3} f(x_{i-1})\, \Delta x = 2[f(0) + f(2) + f(4)] = 2(9.3 + 8.3 + 2.3) = 39.8$$

(c) Using the midpoint of each interval to approximate $\int_{0}^{6} f(x)\, dx$, we have

$$\sum_{i=1}^{3} f(\overline{x}_i)\, \Delta x = 2[[f(1) + f(3) + f(5)]] = 2(9.0 + 6.5 - 7.6) = 15.8.$$

The estimate using the right endpoints must be less than $\int_{0}^{6} f(x)\, dx$, since if we take x_i^* to be the right endpoint x_i of each interval, then $f(x_i) \leq f(x)$ for all x on $[x_{i-1}, x_i]$, which implies that $f(x_i)\, \Delta x \leq \int_{x_{i-1}}^{x_i} f(x)\, dx$, and so the sum $\sum_{i=1}^{3} [f(x_i)\, \Delta x] \leq \sum_{i=1}^{3} \left[\int_{x_{i-1}}^{x_i} f(x)\, dx \right] = \int_{0}^{6} f(x)\, dx$. Similarly, if we take x_i^* to be the left endpoint x_{i-1} of each interval, then $f(x_{i-1}) \geq f(x)$ for all x on $[x_{i-1}, x_i]$, and so $\sum_{i=1}^{3} [f(x_{i-1})\, \Delta x] \geq \int_{0}^{6} f(x)\, dx$. We cannot say anything about the midpoint estimate.

9. $\Delta x = (10 - 0)/5 = 2$, so the endpoints are 0, 2, 4, 6, 8, and 10, and the midpoints are 1, 3, 5, 7, and 9. The Midpoint Rule gives

$$\int_{0}^{10} \sin \sqrt{x}\, dx \approx \sum_{i=1}^{5} f(\overline{x}_i)\, \Delta x = 2\left(\sin \sqrt{1} + \sin \sqrt{3} + \sin \sqrt{5} + \sin \sqrt{7} + \sin \sqrt{9}\right) \approx 6.4643.$$

10. $\Delta x = (\pi - 0)/6 = \frac{\pi}{6}$, so the endpoints are 0, $\frac{\pi}{6}$, $\frac{2\pi}{6}$, $\frac{3\pi}{6}$, $\frac{4\pi}{6}$, $\frac{5\pi}{6}$, and $\frac{6\pi}{6}$, and the midpoints are $\frac{\pi}{12}$, $\frac{3\pi}{12}$, $\frac{5\pi}{12}$, $\frac{7\pi}{12}$, $\frac{9\pi}{12}$, and $\frac{11\pi}{12}$. The Midpoint Rule gives

$$\int_{0}^{\pi} \sec(x/3)\, dx \approx \sum_{i=1}^{6} f(\overline{x}_i)\, \Delta x = \frac{\pi}{6}\left(\sec \frac{\pi}{36} + \sec \frac{3\pi}{36} + \sec \frac{5\pi}{36} + \sec \frac{7\pi}{36} + \sec \frac{9\pi}{36} + \sec \frac{11\pi}{36}\right) \approx 3.9379.$$

11. $\Delta x = (2 - 1)/10 = 0.1$, so the endpoints are $1.0, 1.1, \ldots, 2.0$ and the midpoints are $1.05, 1.15, \ldots, 1.95$.
The Midpoint Rule gives

$$\int_1^2 \sqrt{1 + x^2} \, dx \approx \sum_{i=1}^{10} f(\overline{x}_i) \, \Delta x = 0.1 \left[\sqrt{1 + (1.05)^2} + \sqrt{1 + (1.15)^2} + \cdots + \sqrt{1 + (1.95)^2} \right] \approx 1.8100.$$

12. $\Delta x = (4 - 2)/4 = 0.5$, so the endpoints are $2, 2.5, 3, 3.5$, and 4, and the midpoints are $2.25, 2.75, 3.25$, and 3.75.
The Midpoint Rule gives

$$\int_2^4 x \ln x \, dx \approx \sum_{i=1}^{4} f(\overline{x}_i) \, \Delta x \quad [f(x) = x \ln x]$$

$$= 0.5[f(2.25) + f(2.75) + f(3.25) + f(3.75)] \approx 6.6969.$$

13. In Maple, we use the command `with(student);` to load the sum and box commands, then
`m:=middlesum(sqrt(1+x^2),x=1..2,10);` which gives us the sum in summation notation, then
`M:=evalf(m);` which gives $M_{10} \approx 1.81001414$, confirming the result of Exercise 11. The command
`middlebox(sqrt(1+x^2),x=1..2,10);` generates the graph. Repeating for $n = 20$ and $n = 30$ gives
$M_{20} \approx 1.81007263$ and $M_{30} \approx 1.81008347$.

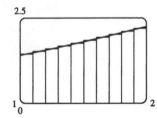 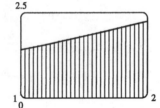 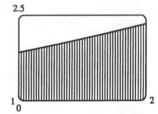

14. See the solution to Exercise 5.1.7 for a possible algorithm to calculate the sums. With $\Delta x = 0.01$ and subinterval
endpoints $1, 1.01, 1.02, \ldots, 1.99, 2$, we calculate that the left Riemann sum is

$$L_{100} = \sum_{i=1}^{100} \sqrt{1 + (x_{i-1})^2} \, \Delta x \approx 1.80598, \text{ and the right Riemann sum is } R_{100} = \sum_{i=1}^{100} \sqrt{1 + (x_i)^2} \, \Delta x \approx 1.81420.$$

Since $\sqrt{1 + x^2}$ is an increasing function, we must have $L_{100} \le \int_1^2 \sqrt{1 + x^2} \, dx \le R_{100}$, so
$1.805 < L_{100} \le \int_1^2 \sqrt{1 + x^2} \, dx \le R_{100} < 1.815$.
Therefore, the approximate value 1.8100 in Exercise 11 must be accurate to two decimal places.

15. We'll create the table of values to approximate $\int_0^\pi \sin x \, dx$ by using the
program in the solution to Exercise 5.1.7 with $Y_1 = \sin x$, $Xmin = 0$,
$Xmax = \pi$, and $n = 5, 10, 50$, and 100.

The values of R_n appear to be approaching 2.

n	R_n
5	1.933766
10	1.983524
50	1.999342
100	1.999836

16. $\int_0^2 e^{-x^2}\,dx$ with $n = 5, 10, 50$, and 100.

n	L_n	R_n
5	1.077467	0.684794
10	0.980007	0.783670
50	0.901705	0.862438
100	0.891896	0.872262

The value of the integral lies between 0.872 and 0.892. Note that $f(x) = e^{-x^2}$ is decreasing on $(0, 2)$. We cannot make a similar statement for $\int_{-1}^2 e^{-x^2}\,dx$ since f is increasing on $(-1, 0)$.

17. On $[0, \pi]$, $\displaystyle\lim_{n\to\infty} \sum_{i=1}^n x_i \sin x_i \,\Delta x = \int_0^\pi x \sin x\,dx$.

18. On $[1, 5]$, $\displaystyle\lim_{n\to\infty} \sum_{i=1}^n \frac{e^{x_i}}{1 + x_i}\,\Delta x = \int_1^5 \frac{e^x}{1 + x}\,dx$.

19. On $[0, 1]$, $\displaystyle\lim_{n\to\infty} \sum_{i=1}^n \left[2(x_i^*)^2 - 5x_i^*\right] \Delta x = \int_0^1 \left(2x^2 - 5x\right) dx$.

20. On $[1, 4]$, $\displaystyle\lim_{n\to\infty} \sum_{i=1}^n \sqrt{x_i^*}\,\Delta x = \int_1^4 \sqrt{x}\,dx$.

21. Note that $\Delta x = \dfrac{5 - (-1)}{n} = \dfrac{6}{n}$ and $x_i = -1 + i\,\Delta x = -1 + \dfrac{6i}{n}$.

$$\int_{-1}^5 (1 + 3x)\,dx = \lim_{n\to\infty} \sum_{i=1}^n f(x_i)\,\Delta x = \lim_{n\to\infty} \sum_{i=1}^n \left[1 + 3\left(-1 + \frac{6i}{n}\right)\right]\frac{6}{n}$$

$$= \lim_{n\to\infty} \frac{6}{n} \sum_{i=1}^n \left[-2 + \frac{18i}{n}\right] = \lim_{n\to\infty} \frac{6}{n}\left[\sum_{i=1}^n(-2) + \sum_{i=1}^n \frac{18i}{n}\right]$$

$$= \lim_{n\to\infty} \frac{6}{n}\left[-2n + \frac{18}{n}\sum_{i=1}^n i\right] = \lim_{n\to\infty} \frac{6}{n}\left[-2n + \frac{18}{n}\cdot\frac{n(n + 1)}{2}\right]$$

$$= \lim_{n\to\infty} \left[-12 + \frac{108}{n^2}\cdot\frac{n(n + 1)}{2}\right] = \lim_{n\to\infty} \left[-12 + 54\frac{n + 1}{n}\right]$$

$$= \lim_{n\to\infty} \left[-12 + 54\left(1 + \frac{1}{n}\right)\right] = -12 + 54\cdot 1 = 42$$

22. Note that $\Delta x = \dfrac{5 - 1}{n} = \dfrac{4}{n}$ and $x_i = 1 + i\,\Delta x = 1 + \dfrac{4i}{n}$.

$$\int_1^5 (2 + 3x - x^2)\,dx = \lim_{n\to\infty} \sum_{i=1}^n f(x_i)\,\Delta x = \lim_{n\to\infty} \frac{4}{n}\sum_{i=1}^n \left[2 + 3\left(1 + \frac{4i}{n}\right) - \left(1 + \frac{4i}{n}\right)^2\right]$$

$$= \lim_{n\to\infty} \frac{4}{n}\sum_{i=1}^n \left[-\frac{16i^2}{n^2} + \frac{4i}{n} + 4\right] = \lim_{n\to\infty} \left[-\frac{64}{n^3}\sum_{i=1}^n i^2 + \frac{16}{n^2}\sum_{i=1}^n i + \frac{16}{n}\sum_{i=1}^n 1\right]$$

$$= \lim_{n\to\infty} \left[-\frac{64}{n^3}\frac{n(n + 1)(2n + 1)}{6} + \frac{16}{n^2}\frac{n(n + 1)}{2} + \frac{16}{n}n\right]$$

$$= \lim_{n\to\infty} \left[-\frac{32}{3}\cdot 1\left(1 + \frac{1}{n}\right)\left(2 + \frac{1}{n}\right) + 8\cdot 1\left(1 + \frac{1}{n}\right) + 16\right] = -\frac{64}{3} + 8 + 16 = \frac{8}{3}$$

23. Note that $\Delta x = \dfrac{2-0}{n} = \dfrac{2}{n}$ and $x_i = 0 + i\,\Delta x = \dfrac{2i}{n}$.

$$\int_0^2 (2 - x^2)\,dx = \lim_{n\to\infty} \sum_{i=1}^n f(x_i)\,\Delta x = \lim_{n\to\infty} \sum_{i=1}^n \left(2 - \frac{4i^2}{n^2}\right)\left(\frac{2}{n}\right)$$

$$= \lim_{n\to\infty} \frac{2}{n}\left[\sum_{i=1}^n 2 - \frac{4}{n^2}\sum_{i=1}^n i^2\right] = \lim_{n\to\infty} \frac{2}{n}\left(2n - \frac{4}{n^2}\sum_{i=1}^n i^2\right)$$

$$= \lim_{n\to\infty} \left[4 - \frac{8}{n^3} \cdot \frac{n(n+1)(2n+1)}{6}\right] = \lim_{n\to\infty}\left(4 - \frac{4}{3}\cdot\frac{n+1}{n}\cdot\frac{2n+1}{n}\right)$$

$$= \lim_{n\to\infty}\left[4 - \frac{4}{3}\left(1 + \frac{1}{n}\right)\left(2 + \frac{1}{n}\right)\right] = 4 - \tfrac{4}{3}\cdot 1 \cdot 2 = \tfrac{4}{3}$$

24. $\displaystyle\int_0^5 (1 + 2x^3)\,dx = \lim_{n\to\infty}\sum_{i=1}^n f(x_i)\,\Delta x \quad [\Delta x = 5/n \text{ and } x_i = 5i/n]$

$$= \lim_{n\to\infty}\sum_{i=1}^n\left(1 + 2\cdot\frac{125 i^3}{n^3}\right)\left(\frac{5}{n}\right) = \lim_{n\to\infty}\frac{5}{n}\left[\sum_{i=1}^n 1 + \frac{250}{n^3}\sum_{i=1}^n i^3\right]$$

$$= \lim_{n\to\infty}\frac{5}{n}\left(1\cdot n + \frac{250}{n^3}\sum_{i=1}^n i^3\right) = \lim_{n\to\infty}\left[5 + \frac{1250}{n^4}\cdot\frac{n^2(n+1)^2}{4}\right]$$

$$= \lim_{n\to\infty}\left[5 + 312.5\cdot\frac{(n+1)^2}{n^2}\right] = \lim_{n\to\infty}\left[5 + 312.5\left(1 + \frac{1}{n}\right)^2\right]$$

$$= 5 + 312.5 = 317.5$$

25. Note that $\Delta x = \dfrac{2-1}{n} = \dfrac{1}{n}$ and $x_i = 1 + i\,\Delta x = 1 + i(1/n) = 1 + i/n$.

$$\int_1^2 x^3\,dx = \lim_{n\to\infty}\sum_{i=1}^n f(x_i)\,\Delta x = \lim_{n\to\infty}\sum_{i=1}^n\left(1 + \frac{i}{n}\right)^3\left(\frac{1}{n}\right) = \lim_{n\to\infty}\frac{1}{n}\sum_{i=1}^n\left(\frac{n+i}{n}\right)^3$$

$$= \lim_{n\to\infty}\frac{1}{n^4}\sum_{i=1}^n(n^3 + 3n^2 i + 3n i^2 + i^3) = \lim_{n\to\infty}\frac{1}{n^4}\left[\sum_{i=1}^n n^3 + \sum_{i=1}^n 3n^2 i + \sum_{i=1}^n 3n i^2 + \sum_{i=1}^n i^3\right]$$

$$= \lim_{n\to\infty}\frac{1}{n^4}\left[n\cdot n^3 + 3n^2\sum_{i=1}^n i + 3n\sum_{i=1}^n i^2 + \sum_{i=1}^n i^3\right]$$

$$= \lim_{n\to\infty}\left[1 + \frac{3}{n^2}\cdot\frac{n(n+1)}{2} + \frac{3}{n^3}\cdot\frac{n(n+1)(2n+1)}{6} + \frac{1}{n^4}\cdot\frac{n^2(n+1)^2}{4}\right]$$

$$= \lim_{n\to\infty}\left[1 + \frac{3}{2}\cdot\frac{n+1}{n} + \frac{1}{2}\cdot\frac{n+1}{n}\cdot\frac{2n+1}{n} + \frac{1}{4}\cdot\frac{(n+1)^2}{n^2}\right]$$

$$= \lim_{n\to\infty}\left[1 + \frac{3}{2}\left(1 + \frac{1}{n}\right) + \frac{1}{2}\left(1 + \frac{1}{n}\right)\left(2 + \frac{1}{n}\right) + \frac{1}{4}\left(1 + \frac{1}{n}\right)^2\right] = 1 + \frac{3}{2} + \frac{1}{2}\cdot 2 + \frac{1}{4} = 3.75$$

26. (a) $\Delta x = (4-0)/8 = 0.5$ and $x_i^* = x_i = 0.5i$.

$$\int_0^4 (x^2 - 3x)\,dx \approx \sum_{i=1}^{8} f(x_i^*)\,\Delta x$$

$$= 0.5\{[0.5^2 - 3(0.5)] + [1.0^2 - 3(1.0)] + \cdots$$
$$+ [3.5^2 - 3(3.5)] + [4.0^2 - 3(4.0)]\}$$
$$= \tfrac{1}{2}\left(-\tfrac{5}{4} - 2 - \tfrac{9}{4} - 2 - \tfrac{5}{4} + 0 + \tfrac{7}{4} + 4\right) = -1.5$$

(b)

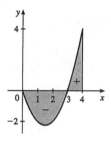

(c) $\displaystyle\int_0^4 (x^2 - 3x)\,dx = \lim_{n\to\infty} \sum_{i=1}^{n}\left[\left(\frac{4i}{n}\right)^2 - 3\left(\frac{4i}{n}\right)\right]\left(\frac{4}{n}\right)$

$$= \lim_{n\to\infty} \frac{4}{n}\left[\frac{16}{n^2}\sum_{i=1}^{n} i^2 - \frac{12}{n}\sum_{i=1}^{n} i\right]$$

$$= \lim_{n\to\infty}\left[\frac{64}{n^3}\cdot\frac{n(n+1)(2n+1)}{6} - \frac{48}{n^2}\cdot\frac{n(n+1)}{2}\right]$$

$$= \lim_{n\to\infty}\left[\frac{32}{3}\left(1+\frac{1}{n}\right)\left(2+\frac{1}{n}\right) - 24\left(1+\frac{1}{n}\right)\right]$$

$$= \tfrac{32}{3}\cdot 2 - 24 = -\tfrac{8}{3}$$

(d) $\int_0^4 (x^2 - 3x)\,dx = A_1 - A_2$,

where A_1 is the area marked $+$ and A_2 is the area marked $-$.

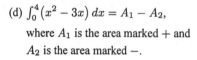

27. $\Delta x = (\pi - 0)/n = \pi/n$ and $x_i^* = x_i = \pi i/n$.

$$\int_0^\pi \sin 5x\,dx = \lim_{n\to\infty}\sum_{i=1}^{n}(\sin 5x_i)\left(\frac{\pi}{n}\right) = \lim_{n\to\infty}\sum_{i=1}^{n}\left(\sin\frac{5\pi i}{n}\right)\frac{\pi}{n} \overset{CAS}{=} \pi\lim_{n\to\infty}\frac{1}{n}\cot\left(\frac{5\pi}{2n}\right) \overset{CAS}{=} \pi\left(\frac{2}{5\pi}\right) = \frac{2}{5}$$

28. $\Delta x = (10-2)/n = 8/n$ and $x_i^* = x_i = 2 + 8i/n$.

$$\int_2^{10} x^6\,dx = \lim_{n\to\infty}\sum_{i=1}^{n}\left(2+\frac{8i}{n}\right)^6\left(\frac{8}{n}\right) = 8\lim_{n\to\infty}\frac{1}{n}\sum_{i=1}^{n}\left(2+\frac{8i}{n}\right)^6$$

$$\overset{CAS}{=} 8\lim_{n\to\infty}\frac{1}{n}\cdot\frac{64\left(58,593n^6 + 164,052n^5 + 131,208n^4 - 27,776n^2 + 2048\right)}{21n^5}$$

$$\overset{CAS}{=} 8\left(\frac{1,249,984}{7}\right) = \frac{9,999,872}{7} \approx 1,428,553.1$$

29. (a) Think of $\int_0^2 f(x)\,dx$ as the area of a trapezoid with bases 1 and 3 and height 2. The area of a trapezoid is $A = \tfrac{1}{2}(b+B)h$, so $\int_0^2 f(x)\,dx = \tfrac{1}{2}(1+3)2 = 4$.

(b) $\int_0^5 f(x)\,dx = \int_0^2 f(x)\,dx + \int_2^3 f(x)\,dx + \int_3^5 f(x)\,dx$

$$\underset{\text{trapezoid}}{}\quad\underset{\text{rectangle}}{}\quad\underset{\text{triangle}}{}$$

$$= \tfrac{1}{2}(1+3)2 + \quad 3\cdot 1 \quad + \quad \tfrac{1}{2}\cdot 2\cdot 3 \quad = 4 + 3 + 3 = 10$$

(c) $\int_5^7 f(x)\,dx$ is the negative of the area of the triangle with base 2 and height 3. $\int_5^7 f(x)\,dx = -\tfrac{1}{2}\cdot 2\cdot 3 = -3$.

(d) As in parts (a) and (c), $\int_7^9 f(x)\,dx = -\tfrac{1}{2}(3+2)2 = -5$. Thus,

$$\int_0^9 f(x)\,dx = \int_0^5 f(x)\,dx + \int_5^7 f(x)\,dx + \int_7^9 f(x)\,dx = 10 - 3 - 5 = 2.$$

30. (a) $\int_0^2 g(x)\, dx = \frac{1}{2} \cdot 4 \cdot 2 = 4$ (area of a triangle)

(b) $\int_2^6 g(x)\, dx = -\frac{1}{2}\pi(2)^2 = -2\pi$ (negative of the area of a semicircle)

(c) $\int_6^7 g(x)\, dx = \frac{1}{2} \cdot 1 \cdot 1 = \frac{1}{2}$ (area of a triangle)

$\int_0^7 g(x)\, dx = \int_0^2 g(x)\, dx + \int_2^6 g(x)\, dx + \int_6^7 g(x)\, dx = 4 - 2\pi + \frac{1}{2} = 4.5 - 2\pi$

31. $\int_1^3 (1 + 2x)\, dx$ can be interpreted as the area under the graph of $f(x) = 1 + 2x$

between $x = 1$ and $x = 3$. This is equal to the area of the rectangle plus the

area of the triangle, so $\int_1^3 (1 + 2x)\, dx = A = 2 \cdot 3 + \frac{1}{2} \cdot 2 \cdot 4 = 10$.

Or: Use the formula for the area of a trapezoid: $A = \frac{1}{2}(3 + 7)(2) = 10$.

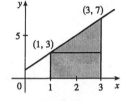

32. $\int_{-2}^2 \sqrt{4 - x^2}\, dx$ can be interpreted as the area under the graph of

$f(x) = \sqrt{4 - x^2}$ between $x = -2$ and $x = 2$. This is equal to half the area of

the circle with radius 2, so $\int_{-2}^2 \sqrt{4 - x^2}\, dx = \frac{1}{2}\pi \cdot 2^2 = 2\pi$.

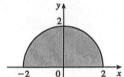

33. $\int_{-3}^0 \left(1 + \sqrt{9 - x^2}\right)\, dx$ can be interpreted as the area under the graph of

$f(x) = 1 + \sqrt{9 - x^2}$ between $x = -3$ and $x = 0$. This is equal to one-quarter

the area of the circle with radius 3, plus the area of the rectangle, so

$\int_{-3}^0 \left(1 + \sqrt{9 - x^2}\right)\, dx = \frac{1}{4}\pi \cdot 3^2 + 1 \cdot 3 = 3 + \frac{9}{4}\pi$.

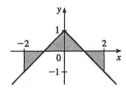

34. $\int_{-1}^3 (2 - x)\, dx$ can be interpreted as $A_1 - A_2$, where A_1 and A_2 are the areas

of the triangles shown. Thus, $\int_{-1}^3 (2 - x)\, dx = \frac{1}{2} \cdot 3 \cdot 3 - \frac{1}{2} \cdot 1 \cdot 1 = 4$.

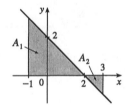

35. $\int_{-2}^2 (1 - |x|)\, dx$ can be interpreted as the area of the middle triangle minus the

areas of the outside triangles, so $\int_{-2}^2 (1 - |x|)\, dx = \frac{1}{2} \cdot 2 \cdot 1 - 2 \cdot \frac{1}{2} \cdot 1 \cdot 1 = 0$.

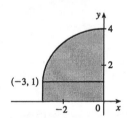

36. $\int_0^3 |3x - 5|\, dx$ can be interpreted as the area under the graph of the function

$f(x) = |3x - 5|$ between $x = 0$ and $x = 3$. This is equal to the sum of the

areas of the two triangles, so $\int_0^3 |3x - 5|\, dx = \frac{1}{2} \cdot \frac{5}{3} \cdot 5 + \frac{1}{2}(3 - \frac{5}{3})4 = \frac{41}{6}$.

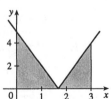

37. $\int_9^4 \sqrt{t}\, dt = -\int_4^9 \sqrt{t}\, dt$ (because we reversed the limits of integration)

$= -\int_4^9 \sqrt{x}\, dx$ (we can use any letter without changing the value of the integral)

$= -\frac{38}{3}$

38. $\int_1^1 x^2 \cos x \, dx = 0$ since the limits of integration are equal.

39. $\int_1^3 f(x) \, dx + \int_3^6 f(x) \, dx + \int_6^{12} f(x) \, dx = \int_1^6 f(x) \, dx + \int_6^{12} f(x) \, dx = \int_1^{12} f(x) \, dx$

40. $\int_2^{10} f(x) \, dx - \int_2^7 f(x) \, dx = \int_2^7 f(x) \, dx + \int_7^{10} f(x) \, dx - \int_2^7 f(x) \, dx = \int_7^{10} f(x) \, dx$

41. $\int_2^5 f(x) \, dx + \int_5^8 f(x) \, dx = \int_2^8 f(x) \, dx \quad \Rightarrow \quad \int_2^5 f(x) \, dx + 2.5 = 1.7 \quad \Rightarrow \quad \int_2^5 f(x) \, dx = 1.7 - 2.5 = -0.8$

42. $\int_0^1 f(t) \, dt + \int_1^3 f(t) \, dt + \int_3^4 f(t) \, dt = \int_0^4 f(t) \, dt \quad \Rightarrow \quad 2 + \int_1^3 f(t) \, dt + 1 = -6 \quad \Rightarrow$
$\int_1^3 f(t) \, dt = -6 - 2 - 1 = -9$

43. $\int_0^1 (5 - 6x^2) \, dx = \int_0^1 5 \, dx - 6 \int_0^1 x^2 \, dx = 5(1 - 0) - 6(\frac{1}{3}) = 5 - 2 = 3$

44. $\int_1^3 (2e^x - 1) \, dx = 2 \int_1^3 e^x \, dx - \int_1^3 1 \, dx = 2(e^3 - e) - 1(3 - 1) = 2e^3 - 2e - 2$

45. $\int_1^3 e^{x+2} \, dx = \int_1^3 e^x \cdot e^2 \, dx = e^2 \int_1^3 e^x \, dx = e^2(e^3 - e) = e^5 - e^3$

46. Using Integral Comparison Property 8,
$$m \le f(x) \le M \quad \Rightarrow \quad m(2 - 0) \le \int_0^2 f(x) \, dx \le M(2 - 0) \quad \Rightarrow \quad 2m \le \int_0^2 f(x) \, dx \le 2M.$$

47. On $[1, 3]$, $\ln 1 \le \ln x \le \ln 3 \quad \Rightarrow \quad 0(3 - 1) \le \int_1^3 \ln x \, dx \le (\ln 3)(3 - 1) \quad \Rightarrow \quad 0 \le \int_1^3 \ln x \, dx \le 2 \ln 3.$

48. If $0 \le x \le 2$, then $0 \le x^3 \le 8$, so $1 \le x^3 + 1 \le 9$ and $1 \le \sqrt{x^3 + 1} \le 3$. Thus,
$1(2 - 0) \le \int_0^2 \sqrt{x^3 + 1} \, dx \le 3(2 - 0)$; that is, $2 \le \int_0^2 \sqrt{x^3 + 1} \, dx \le 6.$

49. $\lim\limits_{n \to \infty} \sum\limits_{i=1}^n \dfrac{i^4}{n^5} = \lim\limits_{n \to \infty} \sum\limits_{i=1}^n \dfrac{i^4}{n^4} \cdot \dfrac{1}{n} = \lim\limits_{n \to \infty} \sum\limits_{i=1}^n \left(\dfrac{i}{n}\right)^4 \dfrac{1}{n}$. At this point, we need to recognize the limit as being of

the form $\lim\limits_{n \to \infty} \sum\limits_{i=1}^n f(x_i) \, \Delta x$, where $\Delta x = (1 - 0)/n = 1/n$, $x_i = 0 + i \, \Delta x = i/n$, and $f(x) = x^4$. Thus, the

definite integral is $\int_0^1 x^4 \, dx$.

5.3 Evaluating Definite Integrals • • • • • • • • • •

1. If $w'(t)$ is the rate of change of weight in pounds per year, then $w(t)$ represents the weight in pounds of the child at
age t. We know from the Total Change Theorem that $\int_5^{10} w'(t) \, dt = w(10) - w(5)$, so the integral represents the
increase in the child's weight (in pounds) between the ages of 5 and 10.

2. $\int_a^b I(t) \, dt = \int_a^b Q'(t) \, dt = Q(b) - Q(a)$ by the Total Change Theorem, so it represents the change in the charge Q
from time $t = a$ to $t = b$.

3. Since $r(t)$ is the rate at which oil leaks, we can write $r(t) = -V'(t)$, where $V(t)$ is the volume of oil at time t.
[Note that the minus sign is needed because V is decreasing, so $V'(t)$ is negative, but $r(t)$ is positive.] Thus, by the
Total Change Theorem, $\int_0^{120} r(t) \, dt = -\int_0^{120} V'(t) \, dt = -[V(120) - V(0)] = V(0) - V(120)$, which is the
number of gallons of oil that leaked from the tank in the first two hours (120 minutes).

4. By the Total Change Theorem, $\int_0^{15} n'(t) \, dt = n(15) - n(0) = n(15) - 100$ represents the increase in the bee
population in 15 weeks. So $100 + \int_0^{15} n'(t) \, dt = n(15)$ represents the total bee population after 15 weeks.

5. By the Total Change Theorem, $\int_{1000}^{5000} R'(x) \, dx = R(5000) - R(1000)$, so it represents the increase in revenue
when production is increased from 1000 units to 5000 units.

6. The slope of the trail is the rate of change of the elevation E, so $f(x) = E'(x)$. By the Total Change Theorem, $\int_3^5 f(x)\,dx = \int_3^5 E'(x)\,dx = E(5) - E(3)$ is the change in the elevation E between $x = 3$ miles and $x = 5$ miles from the start of the trail.

7. In general, the unit of measurement for $\int_a^b f(x)\,dx$ is the product of the unit for $f(x)$ and the unit for x. Since $f(x)$ is measured in newtons and x is measured in meters, the units for $\int_0^{100} f(x)\,dx$ are newton-meters. (A newton-meter is abbreviated N-m and is called a joule.)

8. The units for $a(x)$ are pounds per foot and the units for x are feet, so the units for da/dx are pounds per foot per foot, denoted $(\text{lb/ft})/\text{ft}$. The unit of measurement for $\int_2^8 a(x)\,dx$ is the product of pounds per foot and feet; that is, pounds.

9. $\displaystyle \int_{-1}^3 x^5\,dx = \left[\frac{x^6}{6}\right]_{-1}^3 = \frac{3^6}{6} - \frac{(-1)^6}{6} = \frac{729 - 1}{6} = \frac{364}{3}$

10. $\int_1^2 x^{-2}\,dx = \left[-x^{-1}\right]_1^2 = \left[-1/x\right]_1^2 = -\frac{1}{2} - (-1) = -\frac{1}{2} + 1 = \frac{1}{2}$

11. $\int_2^8 (4x + 3)\,dx = \left[\frac{4}{2}x^2 + 3x\right]_2^8 = (2 \cdot 8^2 + 3 \cdot 8) - (2 \cdot 2^2 + 3 \cdot 2) = 152 - 14 = 138$

12. $\int_0^4 (1 + 3y - y^2)\,dy = \left[y + \frac{3}{2}y^2 - \frac{1}{3}y^3\right]_0^4 = (4 + \frac{3}{2} \cdot 16 - \frac{1}{3} \cdot 64) - (0) = \frac{20}{3}$

13. $\displaystyle \int_0^4 \sqrt{x}\,dx = \int_0^4 x^{1/2}\,dx = \left[\frac{x^{3/2}}{3/2}\right]_0^4 = \left[\frac{2x^{3/2}}{3}\right]_0^4 = \frac{2(4)^{3/2}}{3} - 0 = \frac{2 \cdot 8}{3} = \frac{16}{3}$

14. $\int_\pi^{2\pi} \cos\theta\,d\theta = [\sin\theta]_\pi^{2\pi} = \sin 2\pi - \sin\pi = 0 - 0 = 0$

15. $\int_{-1}^0 (2x - e^x)\,dx = \left[x^2 - e^x\right]_{-1}^0 = (0 - 1) - (1 - e^{-1}) = -2 + 1/e$

16. $\displaystyle \int_0^1 x^{3/7}\,dx = \left[\frac{x^{10/7}}{10/7}\right]_0^1 = \left[\frac{7}{10}x^{10/7}\right]_0^1 = \frac{7}{10} - 0 = \frac{7}{10}$

17. $\displaystyle \int_1^2 \frac{3}{t^4}\,dt = 3\int_1^2 t^{-4}\,dt = 3\left[\frac{t^{-3}}{-3}\right]_1^2 = \frac{3}{-3}\left[\frac{1}{t^3}\right]_1^2 = -1\left(\frac{1}{8} - 1\right) = \frac{7}{8}$

18. $\displaystyle \int_1^4 \frac{1}{\sqrt{x}}\,dx = \int_1^4 x^{-1/2}\,dx = \left[\frac{x^{1/2}}{1/2}\right]_1^4 = \left[2x^{1/2}\right]_1^4 = 2\sqrt{4} - 2\sqrt{1} = 4 - 2 = 2$

19. $\displaystyle \int_1^2 \frac{x^2 + 1}{\sqrt{x}}\,dx = \int_1^2 \left(x^{3/2} + x^{-1/2}\right)dx = \left[\frac{x^{5/2}}{5/2} + \frac{x^{1/2}}{1/2}\right]_1^2 = \left[\frac{2}{5}x^{5/2} + 2x^{1/2}\right]_1^2$

$\qquad = \left(\frac{2}{5} \cdot 4\sqrt{2} + 2\sqrt{2}\right) - \left(\frac{2}{5} + 2\right) = \frac{18}{5}\sqrt{2} - \frac{12}{5}$

20. $\int_0^2 (x^3 - 1)^2\,dx = \int_0^2 (x^6 - 2x^3 + 1)\,dx = \left[\frac{1}{7}x^7 - 2(\frac{1}{4}x^4) + x\right]_0^2 = (\frac{128}{7} - 2 \cdot 4 + 2) - 0 = \frac{86}{7}$

21. $\int_{\pi/4}^{\pi/3} \sin t\,dt = [-\cos t]_{\pi/4}^{\pi/3} = (-\cos\frac{\pi}{3}) - (-\cos\frac{\pi}{4}) = -\frac{1}{2} + \frac{\sqrt{2}}{2} = \frac{\sqrt{2} - 1}{2}$

22. $\displaystyle \int_1^2 \frac{4 + u^2}{u^3}\,du = \int_1^2 \left(4u^{-3} + u^{-1}\right)du = \left[\frac{4}{-2}u^{-2} + \ln|u|\right]_1^2 = \left[\frac{-2}{u^2} + \ln u\right]_1^2$

$\qquad = \left(-\frac{1}{2} + \ln 2\right) - (-2 + \ln 1) = \frac{3}{2} + \ln 2$

23. $\displaystyle \int_0^1 u(\sqrt{u} + \sqrt[3]{u})\,du = \int_0^1 u\left(u^{1/2} + u^{1/3}\right)du = \int_0^1 \left(u^{3/2} + u^{4/3}\right)du = \left[\frac{u^{5/2}}{5/2} + \frac{u^{7/3}}{7/3}\right]_0^1$

$\qquad = \left[\frac{2}{5}u^{5/2} + \frac{3}{7}u^{7/3}\right]_0^1 = \frac{2}{5} + \frac{3}{7} = \frac{29}{35}$

24. $\int_0^5 (2e^x + 4\cos x)\,dx = [2e^x + 4\sin x]_0^5 = (2e^5 + 4\sin 5) - (2e^0 + 4\sin 0) = 2e^5 + 4\sin 5 - 2 \approx 290.99$

25. $\int_{\pi/6}^{\pi/3} \csc^2 \theta \, d\theta = [-\cot \theta]_{\pi/6}^{\pi/3} = (-\cot \frac{\pi}{3}) - (-\cot \frac{\pi}{6}) = -\frac{1}{3}\sqrt{3} + \sqrt{3} = \frac{2}{3}\sqrt{3}$

26. $\int_1^8 \dfrac{x-1}{\sqrt[3]{x^2}} \, dx = \int_1^8 \left(x^{1/3} - x^{-2/3}\right) dx = \left[\dfrac{x^{4/3}}{4/3} - \dfrac{x^{1/3}}{1/3}\right]_1^8 = \left[\dfrac{3}{4}x^{4/3} - 3x^{1/3}\right]_1^8$

$\qquad = \left(\frac{3}{4} \cdot 16 - 3 \cdot 2\right) - \left(\frac{3}{4} - 3\right) = \frac{33}{4}$

27. $\int_1^9 \dfrac{1}{2x} \, dx = \dfrac{1}{2} \int_1^9 \dfrac{1}{x} \, dx = \frac{1}{2} \left[\ln |x|\right]_1^9 = \frac{1}{2}(\ln 9 - \ln 1) = \frac{1}{2} \ln 9 - 0 = \ln 9^{1/2} = \ln 3$

28. $\int_{\ln 3}^{\ln 6} 8e^x \, dx = [8e^x]_{\ln 3}^{\ln 6} = 8\left(e^{\ln 6} - e^{\ln 3}\right) = 8(6-3) = 24$

29. $\int_8^9 2^t \, dt = \left[\dfrac{1}{\ln 2} 2^t\right]_8^9 = \dfrac{1}{\ln 2}(2^9 - 2^8) = \dfrac{1}{\ln 2} \cdot 2^8(2^1 - 1) = \dfrac{2^8}{\ln 2},$ or $\dfrac{256}{\ln 2}$

30. $\int_{\pi/3}^{\pi/2} \csc x \cot x \, dx = [-\csc x]_{\pi/3}^{\pi/2} = (-\csc \frac{\pi}{2}) - (-\csc \frac{\pi}{3}) = -1 + \frac{2}{3}\sqrt{3}$

31. $\int_1^{\sqrt{3}} \dfrac{6}{1+x^2} \, dx = 6[\tan^{-1} x]_1^{\sqrt{3}} = 6\left(\tan^{-1}\sqrt{3} - \tan^{-1} 1\right) = 6\left(\dfrac{\pi}{3} - \dfrac{\pi}{4}\right) = 6\left(\dfrac{\pi}{12}\right) = \dfrac{\pi}{2}$

32. $\int_0^{0.5} \dfrac{dx}{\sqrt{1-x^2}} = \left[\sin^{-1} x\right]_0^{0.5} = \sin^{-1}\left(\frac{1}{2}\right) - \sin^{-1} 0 = \dfrac{\pi}{6}$

33. $\int_0^{\pi/4} \dfrac{1 + \cos^2 \theta}{\cos^2 \theta} \, d\theta = \int_0^{\pi/4} \left(\dfrac{1}{\cos^2 \theta} + \dfrac{\cos^2 \theta}{\cos^2 \theta}\right) d\theta = \int_0^{\pi/4} \left(\sec^2 \theta + 1\right) d\theta$

$\qquad = [\tan \theta + \theta]_0^{\pi/4} = \left(\tan \frac{\pi}{4} + \frac{\pi}{4}\right) - (0+0) = 1 + \frac{\pi}{4}$

34. $\int_{-1}^2 |x - x^2| \, dx = \int_{-1}^0 (x^2 - x) \, dx + \int_0^1 (x - x^2) \, dx + \int_1^2 (x^2 - x) \, dx$

$\qquad = \left[\dfrac{x^3}{3} - \dfrac{x^2}{2}\right]_{-1}^0 + \left[\dfrac{x^2}{2} - \dfrac{x^3}{3}\right]_0^1 + \left[\dfrac{x^3}{3} - \dfrac{x^2}{2}\right]_1^2$

$\qquad = 0 - \left(-\frac{1}{3} - \frac{1}{2}\right) + \left(\frac{1}{2} - \frac{1}{3}\right) - 0 + \left(\frac{8}{3} - 2\right) - \left(\frac{1}{3} - \frac{1}{2}\right) = \frac{7}{3} + \frac{3}{2} - 2 = \frac{11}{6}$

35. It appears that the area under the graph is about $\frac{2}{3}$ of the area of the viewing rectangle, or about $\frac{2}{3}\pi \approx 2.1$. The actual area is

$\int_0^{\pi} \sin x \, dx = [-\cos x]_0^{\pi} = (-\cos \pi) - (-\cos 0) = -(-1) + 1 = 2.$

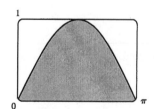

36. Splitting up the region as shown, we estimate that the area under the graph is $\frac{\pi}{3} + \frac{1}{4}\left(3 \cdot \frac{\pi}{3}\right) \approx 1.8$. The actual area is

$\int_0^{\pi/3} \sec^2 x \, dx = [\tan x]_0^{\pi/3} = \sqrt{3} - 0 = \sqrt{3} \approx 1.73.$

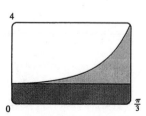

37. The graph shows that $y = x + x^2 - x^4$ has x-intercepts at $x = 0$ and at $x \approx 1.32$. So the area of the region that lies under the curve and above the x-axis is about

$$\int_0^{1.32} \left(x + x^2 - x^4\right) dx = \left[\tfrac{1}{2}x^2 + \tfrac{1}{3}x^3 - \tfrac{1}{5}x^5\right]_0^{1.32}$$
$$= \left[\tfrac{1}{2}(1.32)^2 + \tfrac{1}{3}(1.32)^3 - \tfrac{1}{5}(1.32)^5\right] - 0$$
$$\approx 0.84$$

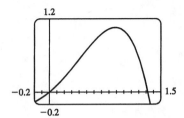

38. The graph shows that $y = 2x + 3x^4 - 2x^6$ has x-intercepts at $x = 0$ and at $x \approx 1.37$. So the area of the region that lies under the curve and above the x-axis is about

$$\int_0^{1.37} \left(2x + 3x^4 - 2x^6\right) dx = \left[x^2 + \tfrac{3}{5}x^5 - \tfrac{2}{7}x^7\right]_0^{1.37}$$
$$= \left[(1.37)^2 + \tfrac{3}{5}(1.37)^5 - \tfrac{2}{7}(1.37)^7\right] - 0$$
$$\approx 2.18$$

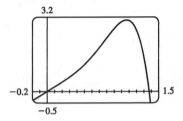

39. $\int_{-1}^{2} x^3\, dx = \left[\tfrac{1}{4}x^4\right]_{-1}^{2} = 4 - \tfrac{1}{4} = \tfrac{15}{4} = 3.75$

40. $\int_{\pi/4}^{5\pi/2} \sin x\, dx = \left[-\cos x\right]_{\pi/4}^{5\pi/2} = 0 + \tfrac{\sqrt{2}}{2} = \tfrac{\sqrt{2}}{2}$

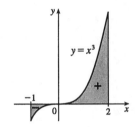

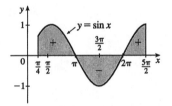

41. $\dfrac{d}{dx}\left[\sqrt{x^2+1} + C\right] = \dfrac{d}{dx}\left[(x^2+1)^{1/2} + C\right] = \tfrac{1}{2}(x^2+1)^{-1/2} \cdot 2x = \dfrac{x}{\sqrt{x^2+1}}$

42. $\dfrac{d}{dx}\left[x \sin x + \cos x + C\right] = x \cos x + (\sin x) \cdot 1 - \sin x = x \cos x$

43. $\int x\sqrt{x}\, dx = \int x^{3/2}\, dx = \tfrac{2}{5}x^{5/2} + C.$

The members of the family in the figure correspond to $C = 5, 3, 0, -2,$ and $-4.$

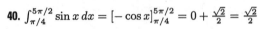

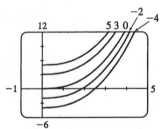

44. $\int (\cos x - 2\sin x)\, dx = \sin x + 2\cos x + C$

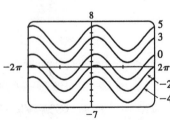

45. $\int (1-t)(2+t^2)\, dt = \int (2 - 2t + t^2 - t^3)\, dt = 2t - 2\dfrac{t^2}{2} + \dfrac{t^3}{3} - \dfrac{t^4}{4} + C = 2t - t^2 + \tfrac{1}{3}t^3 - \tfrac{1}{4}t^4 + C$

46. $\int x\left(1+2x^4\right) dx = \int \left(x + 2x^5\right) dx = \dfrac{x^2}{2} + 2\dfrac{x^6}{6} + C = \frac{1}{2}x^2 + \frac{1}{3}x^6 + C$

47. $\displaystyle\int \dfrac{\sin x}{1 - \sin^2 x} \, dx = \int \dfrac{\sin x}{\cos^2 x} \, dx = \int \dfrac{1}{\cos x} \cdot \dfrac{\sin x}{\cos x} \, dx = \int \sec x \, \tan x \, dx = \sec x + C$

48. $\displaystyle\int \dfrac{\sin 2x}{\sin x} \, dx = \int \dfrac{2 \sin x \cos x}{\sin x} \, dx = \int 2 \cos x \, dx = 2 \sin x + C$

49. $A = \int_0^2 \left(2y - y^2\right) dy = \left[y^2 - \frac{1}{3}y^3\right]_0^2 = \left(4 - \frac{8}{3}\right) - 0 = \frac{4}{3}$

50. $y = \sqrt[4]{x} \;\Rightarrow\; x = y^4$, so $A = \int_0^1 y^4 \, dy = \left[\frac{1}{5}y^5\right]_0^1 = \frac{1}{5}$.

51. (a) displacement $= \int_0^3 (3t - 5) \, dt = \left[\frac{3}{2}t^2 - 5t\right]_0^3 = \frac{27}{2} - 15 = -\frac{3}{2}$ m

(b) distance traveled $= \int_0^3 |3t - 5| \, dt = \int_0^{5/3} (5 - 3t) \, dt + \int_{5/3}^3 (3t - 5) \, dt$

$$= \left[5t - \frac{3}{2}t^2\right]_0^{5/3} + \left[\frac{3}{2}t^2 - 5t\right]_{5/3}^3 = \frac{25}{3} - \frac{3}{2} \cdot \frac{25}{9} + \frac{27}{2} - 15 - \left(\frac{3}{2} \cdot \frac{25}{9} - \frac{25}{3}\right) = \frac{41}{6} \text{ m}$$

52. (a) displacement $= \int_1^6 \left(t^2 - 2t - 8\right) dt = \left[\frac{1}{3}t^3 - t^2 - 8t\right]_1^6 = (72 - 36 - 48) - \left(\frac{1}{3} - 1 - 8\right) = -\frac{10}{3}$ m

(b) distance traveled $= \int_1^6 |t^2 - 2t - 8| \, dt = \int_1^6 |(t-4)(t+2)| \, dt$

$$= \int_1^4 \left(-t^2 + 2t + 8\right) dt + \int_4^6 \left(t^2 - 2t - 8\right) dt = \left[-\frac{1}{3}t^3 + t^2 + 8t\right]_1^4 + \left[\frac{1}{3}t^3 - t^2 - 8t\right]_4^6$$

$$= \left(-\frac{64}{3} + 16 + 32\right) - \left(-\frac{1}{3} + 1 + 8\right) + (72 - 36 - 48) - \left(\frac{64}{3} - 16 - 32\right) = \frac{98}{3} \text{ m}$$

53. (a) $v'(t) = a(t) = t + 4 \;\Rightarrow\; v(t) = \frac{1}{2}t^2 + 4t + C \;\Rightarrow\; v(0) = C = 5 \;\Rightarrow\; v(t) = \frac{1}{2}t^2 + 4t + 5$ m/s

(b) distance traveled $= \int_0^{10} |v(t)| \, dt = \int_0^{10} \left|\frac{1}{2}t^2 + 4t + 5\right| dt = \int_0^{10} \left(\frac{1}{2}t^2 + 4t + 5\right) dt$

$$= \left[\frac{1}{6}t^3 + 2t^2 + 5t\right]_0^{10} = \frac{500}{3} + 200 + 50 = 416\frac{2}{3} \text{ m}$$

54. (a) $v'(t) = 2t + 3 \;\Rightarrow\; v(t) = t^2 + 3t + C \;\Rightarrow\; v(0) = C = -4 \;\Rightarrow\; v(t) = t^2 + 3t - 4$

(b) distance traveled $= \int_0^3 |t^2 + 3t - 4| \, dt = \int_0^3 |(t+4)(t-1)| \, dt$

$$= \int_0^1 \left(-t^2 - 3t + 4\right) dt + \int_1^3 \left(t^2 + 3t - 4\right) dt$$

$$= \left[-\frac{1}{3}t^3 - \frac{3}{2}t^2 + 4t\right]_0^1 + \left[\frac{1}{3}t^3 + \frac{3}{2}t^2 - 4t\right]_1^3$$

$$= \left(-\frac{1}{3} - \frac{3}{2} + 4\right) + \left(9 + \frac{27}{2} - 12\right) - \left(\frac{1}{3} + \frac{3}{2} - 4\right) = \frac{89}{6} \text{ m}$$

55. Since $m'(x) = \rho(x)$, $m = \int_0^4 \rho(x) \, dx = \int_0^4 (9 + 2\sqrt{x}) \, dx = \left[9x + \frac{4}{3}x^{3/2}\right]_0^4 = 36 + \frac{32}{3} - 0 = \frac{140}{3} = 46\frac{2}{3}$ kg.

56. $n(10) - n(4) = \int_4^{10} (200 + 50t) \, dt = \left[200t + 25t^2\right]_4^{10} = 2000 + 2500 - (800 + 400) = 3300$

57. Let s be the position of the car. We know from Equation 2 that $s(100) - s(0) = \int_0^{100} v(t) \, dt$. We use the Midpoint Rule for $0 \le t \le 100$ with $n = 5$. Note that the length of each of the five time intervals is 20 seconds $= \frac{20}{3600}$ hour $= \frac{1}{180}$ hour. So the distance traveled is

$$\int_0^{100} v(t) \, dt \approx \frac{1}{180}[v(10) + v(30) + v(50) + v(70) + v(90)]$$

$$= \frac{1}{180}(38 + 58 + 51 + 53 + 47)$$

$$= \frac{247}{180} \approx 1.4 \text{ miles}$$

58. (a) The total amount spewed into the atmosphere is $Q(6) - Q(0) = \int_0^6 r(t)\,dt = Q(6)$ since $Q(0) = 0$. The rate $r(t)$ is positive, so Q is an increasing function. Thus, an upper estimate for $Q(6)$ is R_6 and a lower estimate for $Q(6)$ is L_6. $\Delta t = \dfrac{b-a}{n} = \dfrac{6-0}{6} = 1$.

$$R_6 = \sum_{i=1}^{6} r(t_i)\,\Delta t = 10 + 24 + 36 + 46 + 54 + 60 = 230 \text{ tonnes.}$$

$$L_6 = \sum_{i=1}^{6} r(t_{i-1})\,\Delta t = R_6 + r(0) - r(6) = 230 + 2 - 60 = 172 \text{ tonnes.}$$

(b) $\Delta t = \dfrac{b-a}{n} = \dfrac{6-0}{3} = 2$.

$Q(6) \approx M_3 = 2[r(1) + r(3) + r(5)] = 2(10 + 36 + 54) = 2(100) = 200$ tonnes.

59. From Equation 2, the increase in cost if the production level is raised from 2000 yards to 4000 yards is $C(4000) - C(2000) = \int_{2000}^{4000} C'(x)\,dx$.

$$\int_{2000}^{4000} C'(x)\,dx = \int_{2000}^{4000} (3 - 0.01x + 0.000006x^2)\,dx$$

$$= \left[3x - 0.005x^2 + 0.000002x^3\right]_{2000}^{4000} = 60{,}000 - 2{,}000 = \$58{,}000$$

60. Let w be the amount of water in the tank. We are given that the rate of water leaving the tank is $r(t) = -dw/dt$. So by the Total Change Theorem, the total loss of water from the tank after four hours is

$w(0) - w(4) = -[w(4) - w(0)] = -\int_0^4 w'(t)\,dt = \int_0^4 r(t)\,dt$. We use the Midpoint Rule with $n = 4$ and

$\Delta t = 1$: $\int_0^4 r(t)\,dt \approx \sum_{i=1}^{4} r(\overline{t}_i)(1) = r(0.5) + r(1.5) + r(2.5) + r(3.5) \approx 5.9 + 5.4 + 4.7 + 3.6 = 19.6$ L.

61. (a) We can find the area between the Lorenz curve and the line $y = x$ by subtracting the area under $y = L(x)$ from the area under $y = x$. Thus,

$$\text{coefficient of inequality} = \frac{\text{area between Lorenz curve and line } y = x}{\text{area under line } y = x} = \frac{\int_0^1 [x - L(x)]\,dx}{\int_0^1 x\,dx}$$

$$= \frac{\int_0^1 [x - L(x)]\,dx}{[x^2/2]_0^1} = \frac{\int_0^1 [x - L(x)]\,dx}{1/2} = 2\int_0^1 [x - L(x)]\,dx$$

(b) $L(x) = \frac{5}{12}x^2 + \frac{7}{12}x \Rightarrow L(50\%) = L\left(\frac{1}{2}\right) = \frac{5}{48} + \frac{7}{24} = \frac{19}{48} = 0.39583$, so the bottom 50% of the households receive at most about 40% of the income. Using the result in part (a),

$$\text{coefficient of inequality} = 2\int_0^1 [x - L(x)]\,dx = 2\int_0^1 \left(x - \frac{5}{12}x^2 - \frac{7}{12}x\right)dx$$

$$= 2\int_0^1 \left(\frac{5}{12}x - \frac{5}{12}x^2\right)dx = 2\int_0^1 \frac{5}{12}\left(x - x^2\right)dx$$

$$= \frac{5}{6}\left[\frac{1}{2}x^2 - \frac{1}{3}x^3\right]_0^1 = \frac{5}{6}\left(\frac{1}{2} - \frac{1}{3}\right) = \frac{5}{6}\left(\frac{1}{6}\right) = \frac{5}{36}$$

62. (a) From Exercise 4.2.54(a), $v(t) = 0.00146t^3 - 0.11553t^2 + 24.98169t - 21.26872$.

(b) $h(125) - h(0) = \int_0^{125} v(t)\,dt = \left[0.000365t^4 - 0.03851t^3 + 12.490845t^2 - 21.26872t\right]_0^{125} \approx 206{,}407$ ft

63. The second derivative is the derivative of the first derivative, so we'll apply the Total Change Theorem with $F = h'$.

$\int_1^2 h''(u)\,du = \int_1^2 (h')'(u)\,du = h'(2) - h'(1) = 5 - 2 = 3$. The other information is unnecessary.

64. $B = 3A \Rightarrow \int_0^b e^x\,dx = 3\int_0^a e^x\,dx \Rightarrow [e^x]_0^b = 3[e^x]_0^a \Rightarrow e^b - 1 = 3(e^a - 1) \Rightarrow$

$e^b = 3e^a - 2 \Rightarrow b = \ln(3e^a - 2)$

Discovery Project | **Area Functions**

1. (a)

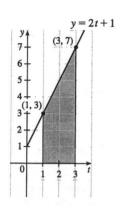

$$\text{Area of trapezoid} = \tfrac{1}{2}(b_1 + b_2)h$$
$$= \tfrac{1}{2}(3 + 7)2$$
$$= 10 \text{ square units}$$

Or:

Area of rectangle + area of triangle

$$= b_r h_r + \tfrac{1}{2}b_t h_t$$
$$= (2)(3) + \tfrac{1}{2}(2)(4) = 10 \text{ square units}$$

(b)

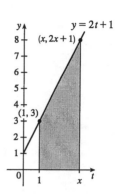

As in part (a),

$$A(x) = \tfrac{1}{2}[3 + (2x + 1)](x - 1)$$
$$= \tfrac{1}{2}(2x + 4)(x - 1)$$
$$= (x + 2)(x - 1)$$
$$= x^2 + x - 2 \text{ square units}$$

(c) $A'(x) = 2x + 1$. This is the y-coordinate of the point $(x, 2x + 1)$ on the given line.

2. (a)

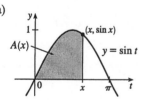

(b) $A(x) = \int_0^x \sin t\, dt = [-\cos t]_0^x$

$$= -\cos x - (-1) = 1 - \cos x$$

(c) $A'(x) = \sin x$. This is the y-coordinate of the point

$(x, \sin x)$ on the given curve.

(d)

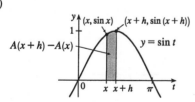

$A(x + h) - A(x)$ is the area under the curve $y = \sin t$ from $t = x$ to $t = x + h$.

(e)

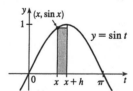

An approximating rectangle is shown in the figure. It has height $\sin x$, width h, and area $h \sin x$, so

$$A(x + h) - A(x) \approx h \sin x$$

$$\Rightarrow \quad \frac{A(x + h) - A(x)}{h} \approx \sin x.$$

(f) Part (e) says that the average rate of change of A is approximately $\sin x$. As h approaches 0, the quotient approaches the instantaneous rate of change—namely, $A'(x)$. So the result of part (c), $A'(x) = \sin x$, is geometrically plausible.

3. (a) $f(x) = \cos(x^2)$

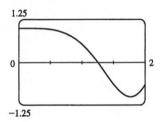

(b) $g(x)$ starts to decrease at that value of x where $\cos(t^2)$ changes from positive to negative; that is, at about $x = 1.25$.

(c) $g(x) = \int_0^x \cos(t^2)\,dt$. Using an integration command, we find that $g(0) = 0$, $g(0.2) \approx 0.200$, $g(0.4) \approx 0.399$, $g(0.6) \approx 0.592$, $g(0.8) \approx 0.768$, $g(1.0) \approx 0.905$, $g(1.2) \approx 0.974$, $g(1.4) \approx 0.950$, $g(1.6) \approx 0.826$, $g(1.8) \approx 0.635$, and $g(2.0) \approx 0.461$.

(d) We sketch the graph of g' using the method of Example 1 in Section 2.8. The graphs of $g'(x)$ and $f(x)$ look alike, so we guess that $g'(x) = f(x)$.

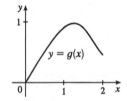

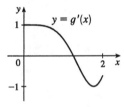

4. In Problems 1 and 2, we showed that if $g(x) = \int_a^x f(t)\,dt$, then $g'(x) = f(x)$, for the functions $f(t) = 2t + 1$ and $f(t) = \sin t$. In Problem 3 we guessed that the same is true for $f(t) = \cos(t^2)$, based on visual evidence. So we conjecture that $g'(x) = f(x)$ for any continuous function f. This turns out to be true and is proved in Section 5.4 (the Fundamental Theorem of Calculus).

5.4 The Fundamental Theorem of Calculus · · · · · · ·

1. The precise version of this statement is given by the Fundamental Theorem of Calculus. See the statement of this theorem and the paragraph that follows it on page 384.

2. (a) $g(x) = \int_0^x f(t)\,dt$, so $g(0) = \int_0^0 f(t)\,dt = 0$.

(d)

$g(1) = \int_0^1 f(t)\,dt = \frac{1}{2} \cdot 1 \cdot 1$ [area of triangle] $= \frac{1}{2}$.

$g(2) = \int_0^2 f(t)\,dt = \int_0^1 f(t)\,dt + \int_1^2 f(t)\,dt$ [below the x-axis]

$\quad = \frac{1}{2} - \frac{1}{2} \cdot 1 \cdot 1 = 0$.

$g(3) = g(2) + \int_2^3 f(t)\,dt = 0 - \frac{1}{2} \cdot 1 \cdot 1 = -\frac{1}{2}$.

$g(4) = g(3) + \int_3^4 f(t)\,dt = -\frac{1}{2} + \frac{1}{2} \cdot 1 \cdot 1 = 0$.

$g(5) = g(4) + \int_4^5 f(t)\,dt = 0 + 1.5 = 1.5$.

$g(6) = g(5) + \int_5^6 f(t)\,dt = 1.5 + 2.5 = 4$.

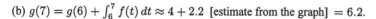

(b) $g(7) = g(6) + \int_6^7 f(t)\,dt \approx 4 + 2.2$ [estimate from the graph] $= 6.2$.

(c) The answers from part (a) and part (b) indicate that g has a minimum at $x = 3$ and a maximum at $x = 7$. This makes sense from the graph of f since we are subtracting area on $1 < x < 3$ and adding area on $3 < x < 7$.

3. (a) $g(x) = \int_0^x f(t)\,dt$.

(d)

$g(0) = \int_0^0 f(t)\,dt = 0$, $g(1) = \int_0^1 f(t)\,dt = 1 \cdot 2 = 2$ [rectangle],

$g(2) = \int_0^2 f(t)\,dt = \int_0^1 f(t)\,dt + \int_1^2 f(t)\,dt = g(1) + \int_1^2 f(t)\,dt$

$\quad = 2 + 1 \cdot 2 + \frac{1}{2} \cdot 1 \cdot 2 = 5$ [rectangle plus triangle],

$g(3) = \int_0^3 f(t)\,dt = g(2) + \int_2^3 f(t)\,dt = 5 + \frac{1}{2} \cdot 1 \cdot 4 = 7$,

$g(6) = g(3) + \int_3^6 f(t)\,dt$ [the integral is negative since f lies under the x-axis]

$\quad = 7 + \left[-\left(\frac{1}{2} \cdot 2 \cdot 2 + 1 \cdot 2 \right) \right] = 7 - 4 = 3$

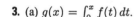

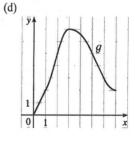

(b) g is increasing on $(0, 3)$ because as x increases from 0 to 3, we keep adding more area.

(c) g has a maximum value when we start subtracting area; that is, at $x = 3$.

4. (a) $g(-3) = \int_{-3}^{-3} f(t)\,dt = 0$, $g(3) = \int_{-3}^{3} f(t)\,dt = \int_{-3}^{0} f(t)\,dt + \int_{0}^{3} f(t)\,dt = 0$ by symmetry, since the area above the x-axis is the same as the area below the axis.

(b) From the graph, it appears that to the nearest $\frac{1}{2}$,

(e)

$g(-2) = \int_{-3}^{-2} f(t)\,dt \approx 1$, $g(-1) = \int_{-3}^{-1} f(t)\,dt \approx 3\frac{1}{2}$, and

$g(0) = \int_{-3}^{0} f(t)\,dt \approx 5\frac{1}{2}$.

(c) g is increasing on $(-3, 0)$ because as x increases from -3 to 0, we keep adding more area.

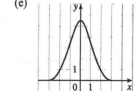

(d) g has a maximum value when we start subtracting area; that is, at $x = 0$.

(f) The graph of $g'(x)$ is the same as that of $f(x)$, as indicated by FTC1.

5.

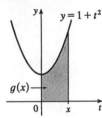

(a) By FTC1, $g(x) = \int_0^x (1+t^2)\,dt \Rightarrow g'(x) = f(x) = 1 + x^2$.

(b) By FTC2, $g(x) = \int_0^x (1+t^2)\,dt = \left[t + \tfrac{1}{3}t^3\right]_0^x = \left(x + \tfrac{1}{3}x^3\right) - 0$

$\Rightarrow g'(x) = 1 + x^2$.

6.

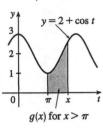

$g(x)$ for $x > \pi$

(a) By FTC1, $g(x) = \int_\pi^x (2 + \cos t)\,dt \Rightarrow$

$g'(x) = f(x) = 2 + \cos x$.

(b) By FTC2, $g(x) = \int_\pi^x (2 + \cos t)\,dt = \left[2t + \sin t\right]_\pi^x$

$= (2x + \sin x) - (2\pi + 0) = 2x + \sin x - 2\pi \Rightarrow$

$g'(x) = 2 + \cos x$.

7. $f(t) = \sqrt{1 + 2t}$ and $g(x) = \int_0^x \sqrt{1 + 2t}\,dt$, so by FTC1, $g'(x) = f(x) = \sqrt{1 + 2x}$.

8. $f(t) = \ln t$ and $g(x) = \int_1^x \ln t\,dt$, so by FTC1, $g'(x) = f(x) = \ln x$.

9. $f(t) = t^2 \sin t$ and $g(y) = \int_2^y t^2 \sin t\,dt$, so by FTC1, $g'(y) = f(y) = y^2 \sin y$.

10. $f(\theta) = \tan\theta$ and $F(x) = \int_x^{10} \tan\theta\,d\theta = -\int_{10}^x \tan\theta\,d\theta$, so by FTC1, $F'(x) = -f(x) = -\tan x$.

11. Let $u = \dfrac{1}{x}$. Then $\dfrac{du}{dx} = -\dfrac{1}{x^2}$. Also, $\dfrac{dh}{dx} = \dfrac{dh}{du}\dfrac{du}{dx}$, so

$h'(x) = \dfrac{d}{dx} \int_2^{1/x} \arctan t\,dt = \dfrac{d}{du} \int_2^u \arctan t\,dt \cdot \dfrac{du}{dx} = \arctan u \dfrac{du}{dx} = -\dfrac{\arctan(1/x)}{x^2}$.

12. Let $u = x^2$. Then $\dfrac{du}{dx} = 2x$. Also, $\dfrac{dh}{dx} = \dfrac{dh}{du}\dfrac{du}{dx}$, so

$h'(x) = \dfrac{d}{dx} \int_0^{x^2} \sqrt{1 + r^3}\,dr = \dfrac{d}{du} \int_0^u \sqrt{1 + r^3}\,dr \cdot \dfrac{du}{dx} = \sqrt{1 + u^3}(2x) = 2x\sqrt{1 + (x^2)^3} = 2x\sqrt{1 + x^6}$.

13. Let $u = \sqrt{x}$. Then $\dfrac{du}{dx} = \dfrac{1}{2\sqrt{x}}$. Also, $\dfrac{dy}{dx} = \dfrac{dy}{du}\dfrac{du}{dx}$, so

$y' = \dfrac{d}{dx} \int_3^{\sqrt{x}} \dfrac{\cos t}{t}\,dt = \dfrac{d}{du} \int_3^u \dfrac{\cos t}{t}\,dt \cdot \dfrac{du}{dx} = \dfrac{\cos u}{u} \cdot \dfrac{1}{2\sqrt{x}} = \dfrac{\cos\sqrt{x}}{\sqrt{x}} \cdot \dfrac{1}{2\sqrt{x}} = \dfrac{\cos\sqrt{x}}{2x}$.

14. Let $u = e^x$. Then $\dfrac{du}{dx} = e^x$. Also, $\dfrac{dy}{dx} = \dfrac{dy}{du}\dfrac{du}{dx}$, so

$y' = \dfrac{d}{dx} \int_{e^x}^0 \sin^3 t\,dt = \dfrac{d}{du} \int_u^0 \sin^3 t\,dt \cdot \dfrac{du}{dx} = -\dfrac{d}{du} \int_0^u \sin^3 t\,dt \cdot \dfrac{du}{dx} = -\sin^3 u \cdot e^x = -e^x \sin^3(e^x)$

15. $g(x) = \int_{2x}^{3x} \dfrac{u^2 - 1}{u^2 + 1}\,du = \int_{2x}^0 \dfrac{u^2 - 1}{u^2 + 1}\,du + \int_0^{3x} \dfrac{u^2 - 1}{u^2 + 1}\,du = -\int_0^{2x} \dfrac{u^2 - 1}{u^2 + 1}\,du + \int_0^{3x} \dfrac{u^2 - 1}{u^2 + 1}\,du \Rightarrow$

$g'(x) = -\dfrac{(2x)^2 - 1}{(2x)^2 + 1} \cdot \dfrac{d}{dx}(2x) + \dfrac{(3x)^2 - 1}{(3x)^2 + 1} \cdot \dfrac{d}{dx}(3x) = -2 \cdot \dfrac{4x^2 - 1}{4x^2 + 1} + 3 \cdot \dfrac{9x^2 - 1}{9x^2 + 1}$

16. $y = \int_{\cos x}^{5x} \cos(u^2)\,du = \int_0^{5x} \cos(u^2)\,du - \int_0^{\cos x} \cos(u^2)\,du \Rightarrow$

$y' = \cos(25x^2) \cdot \dfrac{d}{dx}(5x) - \cos(\cos^2 x) \cdot \dfrac{d}{dx}(\cos x) = \cos(25x^2) \cdot 5 - \cos(\cos^2 x) \cdot (-\sin x)$

$= 5\cos(25x^2) + \sin x \cos(\cos^2 x)$

17. $F(x) = \int_1^x f(t)\, dt \;\Rightarrow\; F'(x) = f(x) = \int_1^{x^2} \dfrac{\sqrt{1+u^4}}{u}\, du \;\left[\text{since } f(t) = \int_1^{t^2} \dfrac{\sqrt{1+u^4}}{u}\, du \right] \;\Rightarrow$

$F''(x) = f'(x) = \dfrac{\sqrt{1+(x^2)^4}}{x^2} \cdot \dfrac{d}{dx}(x^2) = \dfrac{\sqrt{1+x^8}}{x^2} \cdot 2x = \dfrac{2\sqrt{1+x^8}}{x}$. So $F''(2) = \sqrt{1+2^8} = \sqrt{257}$.

18. For the curve to be concave upward, we must have $y'' > 0$. $y = \int_0^x \dfrac{1}{1+t+t^2}\, dt \;\Rightarrow\; y' = \dfrac{1}{1+x+x^2} \;\Rightarrow$

$y'' = \dfrac{-(1+2x)}{(1+x+x^2)^2}$. For this expression to be positive, we must have $(1+2x) < 0$, since $(1+x+x^2)^2 > 0$ for

all x. $(1+2x) < 0 \;\Leftrightarrow\; x < -\frac{1}{2}$. Thus, the curve is concave upward on $\left(-\infty, -\frac{1}{2}\right)$.

19. (a) By FTC1, $g'(x) = f(x)$. So $g'(x) = f(x) = 0$ at $x = 1, 3, 5, 7$, and 9. g has local maxima at $x = 1$ and 5
(since $f = g'$ changes from positive to negative there) and local minima at $x = 3$ and 7. There is no local
maximum or minimum at $x = 9$, since f is not defined for $x > 9$.

(b) We can see from the graph that $\left|\int_0^1 f\, dt\right| < \left|\int_1^3 f\, dt\right| < \left|\int_3^5 f\, dt\right| < \left|\int_5^7 f\, dt\right| < \left|\int_7^9 f\, dt\right|$.

So $g(1) = \left|\int_0^1 f\, dt\right|$, $g(5) = \int_0^5 f\, dt = g(1) - \left|\int_1^3 f\, dt\right| + \left|\int_3^5 f\, dt\right|$, and

$g(9) = \int_0^9 f\, dt = g(5) - \left|\int_5^7 f\, dt\right| + \left|\int_7^9 f\, dt\right|$. Thus, $g(1) < g(5) < g(9)$, and so the absolute maximum of

$g(x)$ occurs at $x = 9$.

(c) g is concave downward on those intervals where $g'' < 0$. But
$g'(x) = f(x)$, so $g''(x) = f'(x)$, which is negative on
(approximately) $\left(\frac{1}{2}, 2\right)$, $(4, 6)$ and $(8, 9)$. So g is concave downward
on these intervals.

(d)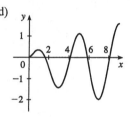

20. (a) By FTC1, $g'(x) = f(x)$. So $g'(x) = f(x) = 0$ at $x = 2, 4, 6, 8$, and 10. g has local maxima at $x = 2$ and 6
(since $f = g'$ changes from positive to negative there) and local minima at $x = 4$ and 8. There is no local
maximum or minimum at $x = 10$, since f is not defined for $x > 10$.

(b) We can see from the graph that $\left|\int_0^2 f\, dt\right| > \left|\int_2^4 f\, dt\right| > \left|\int_4^6 f\, dt\right| > \left|\int_6^8 f\, dt\right| > \left|\int_8^{10} f\, dt\right|$.

So $g(2) = \left|\int_0^2 f\, dt\right|$, $g(6) = \int_0^6 f\, dt = g(2) - \left|\int_2^4 f\, dt\right| + \left|\int_4^6 f\, dt\right|$, and

$g(10) = \int_0^{10} f\, dt = g(6) - \left|\int_6^8 f\, dt\right| + \left|\int_8^{10} f\, dt\right|$. Thus, $g(2) > g(6) > g(10)$, and so the absolute maximum

of $g(x)$ occurs at $x = 2$.

(c) g is concave downward on those intervals where $g'' < 0$. But
$g'(x) = f(x)$, so $g''(x) = f'(x)$, which is negative on $(1, 3)$, $(5, 7)$
and $(9, 10)$. So g is concave downward on these intervals.

(d)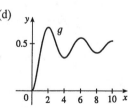

21. (a) The Fresnel Function $S(x) = \int_0^x \sin\left(\frac{\pi}{2}t^2\right) dt$ has local maximum values where $0 = S'(x) = \sin\left(\frac{\pi}{2}x^2\right)$ and S'
changes from positive to negative. For $x > 0$, this happens when $\frac{\pi}{2}x^2 = (2n-1)\pi$ [odd multiples of π] $\Leftrightarrow$
$x^2 = 2(2n-1) \;\Leftrightarrow\; x = \sqrt{4n-2}$, n any positive integer. For $x < 0$, S' changes from positive to negative

where $\frac{\pi}{2}x^2 = 2n\pi$ [even multiples of π] $\Leftrightarrow$ $x^2 = 4n$ $\Leftrightarrow$ $x = -2\sqrt{n}$. S' does not change sign at $x = 0$.

(b) S is concave upward on those intervals where $S''(x) > 0$. Differentiating our expression for $S'(x)$, we get

$S''(x) = \cos(\frac{\pi}{2}x^2)(2\frac{\pi}{2}x) = \pi x \cos(\frac{\pi}{2}x^2)$. For $x > 0$, $S''(x) > 0$ where $\cos(\frac{\pi}{2}x^2) > 0$ $\Leftrightarrow$ $0 < \frac{\pi}{2}x^2 < \frac{\pi}{2}$

or $(2n - \frac{1}{2})\pi < \frac{\pi}{2}x^2 < (2n + \frac{1}{2})\pi$, n any integer $\Leftrightarrow$ $0 < x < 1$ or $\sqrt{4n - 1} < x < \sqrt{4n + 1}$, n any

positive integer. For $x < 0$, $S''(x) > 0$ where $\cos(\frac{\pi}{2}x^2) < 0$ $\Leftrightarrow$ $(2n - \frac{3}{2})\pi < \frac{\pi}{2}x^2 < (2n - \frac{1}{2})\pi$, n any

integer $\Leftrightarrow$ $4n - 3 < x^2 < 4n - 1$ $\Leftrightarrow$ $\sqrt{4n - 3} < |x| < \sqrt{4n - 1}$ $\Rightarrow$ $\sqrt{4n - 3} < -x < \sqrt{4n - 1}$

$\Rightarrow$ $-\sqrt{4n - 3} > x > -\sqrt{4n - 1}$, so the intervals of upward concavity for $x < 0$ are

$(-\sqrt{4n - 1}, -\sqrt{4n - 3})$, n any positive integer. To summarize: S is concave upward on the intervals $(0, 1)$,

$(-\sqrt{3}, -1)$, $(\sqrt{3}, \sqrt{5})$, $(-\sqrt{7}, -\sqrt{5})$, $(\sqrt{7}, 3)$, ...

(c) In Maple, we use `plot({int(sin(Pi*t^2/2),t=0..x),0.2},x=0..2);`. Note that Maple

recognizes the Fresnel function, calling it `FresnelS(x)`. In Mathematica, we use

`Plot[{Integrate[Sin[Pi*t^2/2],{t,0,x}],0.2},{x,0,2}]`. In Derive, we load the utility file

`FRESNEL` and plot `FRESNEL_SIN(x)`. From the graphs, we see that $\int_0^x \sin(\frac{\pi}{2}t^2)\,dt = 0.2$ at $x \approx 0.74$.

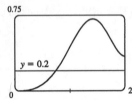

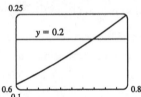

22. (a) In Maple, we should start by setting

`si:=int(sin(t)/t,t=0..x);`. In Mathematica, the command is

`si=Integrate[Sin[t]/t,{t,0,x}]`. Note that both systems

recognize this function; Maple calls it `Si(x)` and Mathematica calls it

`SinIntegral[x]`. In Maple, the command to generate the graph is

`plot(si,x=-4*Pi..4*Pi);`. In Mathematica, it is

`Plot[si,{x,-4*Pi,4*Pi}]`. In Derive, we load the utility file `EXP_INT` and plot `SI(x)`.

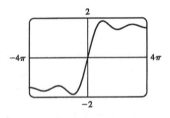

(b) $\text{Si}(x)$ has local maximum values where $\text{Si}'(x)$ changes from positive to negative, passing through 0. From the

Fundamental Theorem we know that $\text{Si}'(x) = \dfrac{d}{dx}\displaystyle\int_0^x \frac{\sin t}{t}\,dt = \dfrac{\sin x}{x}$, so we must have $\sin x = 0$ for a

maximum, and for $x > 0$ we must have $x = (2n - 1)\pi$, n any positive integer, for Si' to be changing from

positive to negative at x. For $x < 0$, we must have $x = 2n\pi$, n any positive integer, for a maximum, since the

denominator of $\text{Si}'(x)$ is negative for $x < 0$. Thus, the local maxima occur at

$x = \pi, -2\pi, 3\pi, -4\pi, 5\pi, -6\pi, \ldots$.

(c) To find the first inflection point, we solve $\text{Si}''(x) = \dfrac{\cos x}{x} - \dfrac{\sin x}{x^2} = 0$. We can see from the graph that the first

inflection point lies somewhere between $x = 3$ and $x = 5$. Using a root finder gives the value $x \approx 4.4934$. To

find the y-coordinate of the inflection point, we evaluate $\text{Si}(4.4934) \approx 1.6556$. So the coordinates of the first

inflection point to the right of the origin are about $(4.4934, 1.6556)$. Alternatively, we could graph $S''(x)$ and

estimate the first positive x-value at which it changes sign.

(d) It seems from the graph that the function has horizontal asymptotes at $y \approx 1.5$, with $\lim\limits_{x \to \pm\infty} \mathrm{Si}(x) \approx \pm 1.5$ respectively. Using the limit command, we get $\lim\limits_{x \to \infty} \mathrm{Si}(x) = \frac{\pi}{2}$. Since $\mathrm{Si}(x)$ is an odd function, $\lim\limits_{x \to -\infty} \mathrm{Si}(x) = -\frac{\pi}{2}$. So $\mathrm{Si}(x)$ has the horizontal asymptotes $y = \pm\frac{\pi}{2}$.

(e) We use the `fsolve` command in Maple (or `FindRoot` in Mathematica) to find that the solution is $x \approx 1.1$. Or, as in Exercise 21(c), we graph $y = \mathrm{Si}(x)$ and $y = 1$ on the same screen to see where they intersect.

23. By FTC2, $\int_1^x f'(t)\, dt = f(x) - f(1)$ $\Rightarrow$ $f(x) = f(1) + \int_1^x f'(t)\, dt = f(1) + \int_1^x (2^t/t)\, dt$. This integral cannot be expressed in a simpler form. Since we want $f(1) = 0$, we have $f(x) = \int_1^x (2^t/t)\, dt$.

24. (a) If $x < 0$, then $g(x) = \int_0^x f(t)\, dt = \int_0^x 0\, dt = 0$.

If $0 \le x \le 1$, then $g(x) = \int_0^x f(t)\, dt = \int_0^x t\, dt = \left[\frac{1}{2}t^2\right]_0^x = \frac{1}{2}x^2$.

If $1 < x \le 2$, then

$g(x) = \int_0^x f(t)\, dt = \int_0^1 f(t)\, dt + \int_1^x f(t)\, dt$

$\quad = g(1) + \int_1^x (2 - t)\, dt = \frac{1}{2}(1)^2 + \left[2t - \frac{1}{2}t^2\right]_1^x$

$\quad = \frac{1}{2} + \left(2x - \frac{1}{2}x^2\right) - \left(2 - \frac{1}{2}\right) = 2x - \frac{1}{2}x^2 - 1$.

If $x > 2$, then $g(x) = \int_0^x f(t)\, dt = g(2) + \int_2^x 0\, dt = 1 + 0 = 1$. So

$$g(x) = \begin{cases} 0 & \text{if } x < 0 \\ \frac{1}{2}x^2 & \text{if } 0 \le x \le 1 \\ 2x - \frac{1}{2}x^2 - 1 & \text{if } 1 < x \le 2 \\ 1 & \text{if } x > 2 \end{cases}$$

(b)

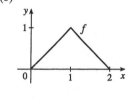

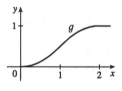

(c) f is not differentiable at its corners at $x = 0$, 1, and 2. f is differentiable on $(-\infty, 0)$, $(0, 1)$, $(1, 2)$ and $(2, \infty)$. g is differentiable on $(-\infty, \infty)$.

25. Using FTC1, we differentiate both sides of $6 + \int_a^x \dfrac{f(t)}{t^2}\, dt = 2\sqrt{x}$ to get $\dfrac{f(x)}{x^2} = 2 \cdot \dfrac{1}{2\sqrt{x}}$ $\Rightarrow$ $f(x) = x^{3/2}$.

To find a, we substitute $x = a$ in the original equation to obtain $6 + \int_a^a \dfrac{f(t)}{t^2}\, dt = 2\sqrt{a}$ $\Rightarrow$ $6 + 0 = 2\sqrt{a}$ $\Rightarrow$ $3 = \sqrt{a}$ $\Rightarrow$ $a = 9$.

26. (a) $C(t) = \dfrac{1}{t} \int_0^t [f(s) + g(s)]\, ds$. Using FTC1 and the Product Rule, we have

$C'(t) = \dfrac{1}{t}[f(t) + g(t)] - \dfrac{1}{t^2}\int_0^t [f(s) + g(s)]\, ds$. Set $C'(t) = 0$:

$\dfrac{1}{t}[f(t) + g(t)] - \dfrac{1}{t^2}\int_0^t [f(s) + g(s)]\, ds = 0$ $\Rightarrow$ $[f(t) + g(t)] - \dfrac{1}{t}\int_0^t [f(s) + g(s)]\, ds = 0$ $\Rightarrow$

$[f(t) + g(t)] - C(t) = 0$ $\Rightarrow$ $C(t) = f(t) + g(t)$.

(b) For $0 \le t \le 30$, we have $D(t) = \int_0^t \left(\dfrac{V}{15} - \dfrac{V}{450}s\right) ds = \left[\dfrac{V}{15}s - \dfrac{V}{900}s^2\right]_0^t = \dfrac{V}{15}t - \dfrac{V}{900}t^2$.

So $D(t) = V$ $\Rightarrow$ $\dfrac{V}{15}t - \dfrac{V}{900}t^2 = V$ $\Rightarrow$ $60t - t^2 = 900$ $\Rightarrow$ $t^2 - 60t + 900 = 0$ $\Rightarrow$

$(t - 30)^2 = 0$ $\Rightarrow$ $t = 30$. So the length of time T is 30 months.

(c) $C(t) = \dfrac{1}{t}\displaystyle\int_0^t \left(\dfrac{V}{15} - \dfrac{V}{450}s + \dfrac{V}{12{,}900}s^2\right)ds = \dfrac{1}{t}\left[\dfrac{V}{15}s - \dfrac{V}{900}s^2 + \dfrac{V}{38{,}700}s^3\right]_0^t$

$= \dfrac{1}{t}\left(\dfrac{V}{15}t - \dfrac{V}{900}t^2 + \dfrac{V}{38{,}700}t^3\right) = \dfrac{V}{15} - \dfrac{V}{900}t + \dfrac{V}{38{,}700}t^2 \quad \Rightarrow$

$C'(t) = -\dfrac{V}{900} + \dfrac{V}{19{,}350}t = 0$ when $\dfrac{1}{19{,}350}t = \dfrac{1}{900} \quad \Rightarrow \quad t = 21.5.$

$C(21.5) = \dfrac{V}{15} - \dfrac{V}{900}(21.5) + \dfrac{V}{38{,}700}(21.5)^2 \approx 0.05472V,\ C(0) = \dfrac{V}{15} \approx 0.06667V,$ and

$C(30) = \dfrac{V}{15} - \dfrac{V}{900}(30) + \dfrac{V}{38{,}700}(30)^2 \approx 0.05659V,$ so the absolute minimum is $C(21.5) \approx 0.05472V.$

(d) As in part (c), we have $C(t) = \dfrac{V}{15} - \dfrac{V}{900}t + \dfrac{V}{38{,}700}t^2$, so $C(t) = f(t) + g(t)$

$\Leftrightarrow \dfrac{V}{15} - \dfrac{V}{900}t + \dfrac{V}{38{,}700}t^2 = \dfrac{V}{15} - \dfrac{V}{450}t + \dfrac{V}{12{,}900}t^2 \quad \Leftrightarrow$

$t^2\left(\dfrac{1}{12{,}900} - \dfrac{1}{38{,}700}\right) = t\left(\dfrac{1}{450} - \dfrac{1}{900}\right) \quad \Leftrightarrow$

$t = \dfrac{1/900}{2/38{,}700} = \dfrac{43}{2} = 21.5.$ This is the value of t that we obtained as the critical

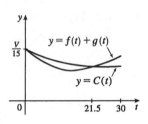

number of C in part (c), so we have verified the result of (a) in this case.

27. (a) Let $F(t) = \int_0^t f(s)\,ds$. Then, by FTC1, $F'(t) = f(t)$ = rate of depreciation, so $F(t)$ represents the loss in value over the interval $[0, t]$.

(b) $C(t) = \dfrac{1}{t}\left[A + \displaystyle\int_0^t f(s)\,ds\right] = \dfrac{A + F(t)}{t}$ represents the average expenditure per unit of t during the interval $[0, t]$, assuming that there has been only one overhaul during that time period. The company wants to minimize average expenditure.

(c) $C(t) = \dfrac{1}{t}\left[A + \displaystyle\int_0^t f(s)\,ds\right]$. Using FTC1, we have $C'(t) = -\dfrac{1}{t^2}\left[A + \displaystyle\int_0^t f(s)\,ds\right] + \dfrac{1}{t}f(t).$

$C'(t) = 0 \quad \Rightarrow \quad tf(t) = A + \displaystyle\int_0^t f(s)\,ds \quad \Rightarrow \quad f(t) = \dfrac{1}{t}\left[A + \displaystyle\int_0^t f(s)\,ds\right] = C(t).$

5.5 The Substitution Rule • • • • • • • • • • • •

1. Let $u = 3x$. Then $du = 3\,dx$, so $dx = \tfrac{1}{3}du$. Thus,

$\int \cos 3x\,dx = \int \cos u\left(\tfrac{1}{3}\,du\right) = \tfrac{1}{3}\int \cos u\,du = \tfrac{1}{3}\sin u + C = \tfrac{1}{3}\sin 3x + C.$ Don't forget that it is often very easy to check an indefinite integration by differentiating your answer. In this case,

$\dfrac{d}{dx}\left(\tfrac{1}{3}\sin 3x + C\right) = \tfrac{1}{3}(\cos 3x) \cdot 3 = \cos 3x,$ the desired result.

2. Let $u = 4 + x^2$. Then $du = 2x\,dx$, so $\int x(4 + x^2)^{10}\,dx = \int u^{10}\left(\tfrac{1}{2}\,du\right) = \tfrac{1}{2} \cdot \tfrac{1}{11}u^{11} + C = \tfrac{1}{22}(4 + x^2)^{11} + C.$

3. Let $u = x^3 + 1$. Then $du = 3x^2\,dx$, so $x^2\,dx = \tfrac{1}{3}du$. Thus,

$\int x^2\sqrt{x^3 + 1}\,dx = \int \sqrt{u}\left(\tfrac{1}{3}\,du\right) = \dfrac{1}{3}\dfrac{u^{3/2}}{3/2} + C = \tfrac{1}{3} \cdot \tfrac{2}{3}u^{3/2} + C = \tfrac{2}{9}(x^3 + 1)^{3/2} + C$

4. Let $u = \sqrt{x}$. Then $du = \dfrac{1}{2\sqrt{x}}\,dx$, so $\displaystyle\int \dfrac{\sin\sqrt{x}}{\sqrt{x}}\,dx = \int \sin u\,(2\,du) = 2(-\cos u) + C = -2\cos\sqrt{x} + C$.

5. Let $u = 1 + 2x$. Then $du = 2\,dx$, so

$$\int \frac{4}{(1+2x)^3}\,dx = 4\int u^{-3}\left(\tfrac{1}{2}\,du\right) = 2\frac{u^{-2}}{-2} + C = -\frac{1}{u^2} + C = -\frac{1}{(1+2x)^2} + C$$

6. Let $u = \sin\theta$. Then $du = \cos\theta\,d\theta$, so $\int e^{\sin\theta}\cos\theta\,d\theta = \int e^u\,du = e^u + C = e^{\sin\theta} + C$.

7. Let $u = x^2 + 3$. Then $du = 2x\,dx$, so $\int 2x\left(x^2+3\right)^4 dx = \int u^4\,du = \tfrac{1}{5}u^5 + C = \tfrac{1}{5}\left(x^2+3\right)^5 + C$.

8. Let $u = x^2$. Then $du = 2x\,dx$, so $\int xe^{x^2}\,dx = \int e^u\left(\tfrac{1}{2}\,du\right) = \tfrac{1}{2}e^u + C = \tfrac{1}{2}e^{x^2} + C$.

9. Let $u = \ln x$. Then $du = \dfrac{dx}{x}$, so $\displaystyle\int \dfrac{(\ln x)^2}{x}\,dx = \int u^2\,du = \tfrac{1}{3}u^3 + C = \tfrac{1}{3}(\ln x)^3 + C$.

10. Let $u = 1 - x^4$. Then $du = -4x^3\,dx$, so

$$\int x^3\left(1-x^4\right)^5 dx = \int u^5\left(-\tfrac{1}{4}\,du\right) = -\tfrac{1}{4}\left(\tfrac{1}{6}u^6\right) + C = -\tfrac{1}{24}\left(1-x^4\right)^6 + C$$

11. Let $u = x - 1$. Then $du = dx$, so $\int \sqrt{x-1}\,dx = \int u^{1/2}\,du = \tfrac{2}{3}u^{3/2} + C = \tfrac{2}{3}(x-1)^{3/2} + C$.

12. Let $u = 2 - x$. Then $du = -dx$, so $\int(2-x)^6\,dx = \int u^6(-du) = -\tfrac{1}{7}u^7 + C = -\tfrac{1}{7}(2-x)^7 + C$.

13. Let $u = 5 - 3x$. Then $du = -3\,dx$, so $\displaystyle\int \dfrac{dx}{5-3x} = -\dfrac{1}{3}\int \dfrac{1}{u}\,du = -\tfrac{1}{3}\ln|u| + C = -\tfrac{1}{3}\ln|5-3x| + C$.

14. Let $u = x^2 + 1$. Then $du = 2x\,dx$, so

$$\int \frac{x}{x^2+1}\,dx = \int \frac{\tfrac{1}{2}\,du}{u} = \frac{1}{2}\ln|u| + C = \frac{1}{2}\ln|x^2+1| + C = \tfrac{1}{2}\ln\left(x^2+1\right) + C \ \ \text{[since } x^2 + 1 > 0]$$

or $\ln\sqrt{x^2+1} + C$.

15. Let $u = 1 + x + 2x^2$. Then $du = (1 + 4x)\,dx$, so

$$\int \frac{1+4x}{\sqrt{1+x+2x^2}}\,dx = \int \frac{du}{\sqrt{u}} = \int u^{-1/2}\,du = \frac{u^{1/2}}{1/2} + C = 2\sqrt{1+x+2x^2} + C$$

16. Let $u = 1 - t^3$. Then $du = -3t^2\,dt$, so

$$\int t^2\cos\left(1-t^3\right)dt = \int \cos u\left(-\tfrac{1}{3}\,du\right) = -\tfrac{1}{3}\sin u + C = -\tfrac{1}{3}\sin\left(1-t^3\right) + C$$

17. Let $u = t + 1$. Then $du = dt$, so $\displaystyle\int \dfrac{2}{(t+1)^6}\,dt = 2\int u^{-6}\,du = -\tfrac{2}{5}u^{-5} + C = -\dfrac{2}{5(t+1)^5} + C$.

18. Let $u = 3 - 5y$. Then $du = -5\,dy$, so

$$\int \sqrt[5]{3-5y}\,dy = \int u^{1/5}\left(-\tfrac{1}{5}\,du\right) = -\tfrac{1}{5}\cdot\tfrac{5}{6}u^{6/5} + C = -\tfrac{1}{6}(3-5y)^{6/5} + C$$

19. Let $u = 3\theta$. Then $du = 3\,d\theta$, so $\int \sin 3\theta\,d\theta = \int \sin u\left(\tfrac{1}{3}du\right) = \tfrac{1}{3}(-\cos u) + C = -\tfrac{1}{3}\cos 3\theta + C$.

20. Let $u = \tan^{-1}x$. Then $du = \dfrac{dx}{1+x^2}$, so $\displaystyle\int \dfrac{\tan^{-1}x}{1+x^2}\,dx = \int u\,du = \dfrac{u^2}{2} + C = \dfrac{\left(\tan^{-1}x\right)^2}{2} + C$.

21. Let $u = 1 + e^x$. Then $du = e^x\,dx$, so $\int e^x\sqrt{1+e^x}\,dx = \int \sqrt{u}\,du = \tfrac{2}{3}u^{3/2} + C = \tfrac{2}{3}(1+e^x)^{3/2} + C$.

Or: Let $u = \sqrt{1+e^x}$. Then $u^2 = 1 + e^x$ and $2u\,du = e^x\,dx$, so

$$\int e^x\sqrt{1+e^x}\,dx = \int u\cdot 2u\,du = \tfrac{2}{3}u^3 + C = \tfrac{2}{3}(1+e^x)^{3/2} + C$$

22. Let $u = \sin x$. Then $du = \cos x\,dx$, so $\displaystyle\int \cot x\,dx = \int \dfrac{\cos x}{\sin x}\,dx = \int \dfrac{du}{u} = \ln|u| + C = \ln|\sin x| + C$.

23. Let $u = \cos x$. Then $du = -\sin x\,dx$, so $\int \cos^4 x \sin x\,dx = \int u^4(-du) = -\frac{1}{5}u^5 + C = -\frac{1}{5}\cos^5 x + C$.

24. Let $u = \frac{\pi}{x}$. Then $du = -\frac{\pi}{x^2}\,dx$, so $\int \frac{\cos(\pi/x)}{x^2}\,dx = \int \cos u\left(-\frac{1}{\pi}\,du\right) = -\frac{1}{\pi}\sin u + C = -\frac{1}{\pi}\sin\frac{\pi}{x} + C$.

25. Let $u = \cot x$. Then $du = -\csc^2 x\,dx$, so

$$\int \sqrt{\cot x}\,\csc^2 x\,dx = \int \sqrt{u}\,(-du) = -\frac{u^{3/2}}{3/2} + C = -\frac{2}{3}(\cot x)^{3/2} + C$$

26. Let $u = \sin x$. Then $du = \cos x\,dx$, so $\int \cos x \cos(\sin x)dx = \int \cos u\,du = \sin u + C = \sin(\sin x) + C$.

27. $\int \frac{e^x + 1}{e^x}\,dx = \int (1 + e^{-x})dx = x - e^{-x} + C$ [Substitute $u = -x$.]

28. Let $u = e^x + 1$. Then $du = e^x\,dx$, so $\int \frac{e^x}{e^x + 1}\,dx = \int \frac{du}{u} = \ln|u| + C = \ln(e^x + 1) + C$.

29. Let $u = \sec x$. Then $du = \sec x \tan x\,dx$, so

$$\int \sec^3 x \tan x\,dx = \int \sec^2 x\,(\sec x \tan x)\,dx = \int u^2\,du = \frac{1}{3}u^3 + C = \frac{1}{3}\sec^3 x + C$$

30. Let $u = \cos x$. Then $du = -\sin x\,dx$, so

$$\int \frac{\sin x}{1 + \cos^2 x}\,dx = \int \frac{-du}{1 + u^2} = -\tan^{-1} u + C = -\tan^{-1}(\cos x) + C$$

31. Let $u = 1 + x^2$. Then $du = 2x\,dx$, so

$$\int \frac{1 + x}{1 + x^2}\,dx = \int \frac{1}{1 + x^2}\,dx + \int \frac{x}{1 + x^2}\,dx = \tan^{-1} x + \int \frac{\frac{1}{2}du}{u} = \tan^{-1} x + \frac{1}{2}\ln|u| + C$$

$$= \tan^{-1} x + \frac{1}{2}\ln|1 + x^2| + C = \tan^{-1} x + \frac{1}{2}\ln(1 + x^2) + C \quad [\text{since } 1 + x^2 > 0].$$

32. Let $u = x^2$. Then $du = 2x\,dx$, so $\int \frac{x}{1 + x^4}\,dx = \int \frac{\frac{1}{2}du}{1 + u^2} = \frac{1}{2}\tan^{-1} u + C = \frac{1}{2}\tan^{-1}(x^2) + C$.

In Exercises 33–36, let $f(x)$ denote the integrand and $F(x)$ its antiderivative (with $C = 0$).

33. $f(x) = \frac{3x - 1}{(3x^2 - 2x + 1)^4}$.

$u = 3x^2 - 2x + 1 \quad\Rightarrow\quad du = (6x - 2)\,dx = 2(3x - 1)\,dx$, so

$$\int \frac{3x - 1}{(3x^2 - 2x + 1)^4}\,dx = \int \frac{1}{u^4}\left(\frac{1}{2}\,du\right) = \frac{1}{2}\int u^{-4}\,du$$

$$= -\frac{1}{6}u^{-3} + C = -\frac{1}{6(3x^2 - 2x + 1)^3} + C$$

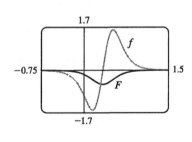

Notice that at $x = \frac{1}{3}$, f changes from negative to positive, and F has a local minimum.

34. $f(x) = \frac{x}{\sqrt{x^2 + 1}}$. $u = x^2 + 1 \quad\Rightarrow\quad du = 2x\,dx$, so

$$\int \frac{x}{\sqrt{x^2 + 1}}\,dx = \int \frac{1}{\sqrt{u}}\left(\frac{1}{2}\,du\right) = \frac{1}{2}\int u^{-1/2}\,du$$

$$= u^{1/2} + C = \sqrt{x^2 + 1} + C.$$

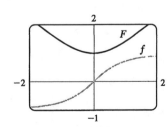

Note that at $x = 0$, f changes from negative to positive and F has a local minimum.

35. $f(x) = \sin^3 x \cos x$. $u = \sin x \implies du = \cos x \, dx$, so

$$\int \sin^3 x \cos x \, dx = \int u^3 \, du = \tfrac{1}{4}u^4 + C = \tfrac{1}{4}\sin^4 x + C$$

Note that at $x = \frac{\pi}{2}$, f changes from positive to negative and F has a local maximum. Also, both f and F are periodic with period π, so at $x = 0$ and at $x = \pi$, f changes from negative to positive and F has local minima.

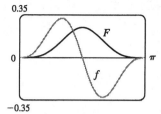

36. $f(\theta) = \tan^2 \theta \sec^2 \theta$. $u = \tan \theta \implies du = \sec^2 \theta \, d\theta$, so

$$\int \tan^2 \theta \sec^2 \theta \, d\theta = \int u^2 \, du = \tfrac{1}{3}u^3 + C = \tfrac{1}{3}\tan^3 \theta + C$$

Note that f is positive and F is increasing. At $x = 0$, $f = 0$ and F has a horizontal tangent.

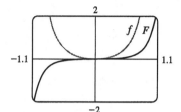

37. Let $u = x - 1$, so $du = dx$. When $x = 0$, $u = -1$; when $x = 2$, $u = 1$. Thus, $\int_0^2 (x-1)^{25} \, dx = \int_{-1}^1 u^{25} \, du = 0$ by Theorem 6(b), since $f(u) = u^{25}$ is an odd function.

38. Let $u = 4 + 3x$, so $du = 3 \, dx$. When $x = 0$, $u = 4$; when $x = 7$, $u = 25$. Thus,

$$\int_0^7 \sqrt{4 + 3x} \, dx = \int_4^{25} \sqrt{u}\left(\tfrac{1}{3}\,du\right) = \frac{1}{3}\left[\frac{u^{3/2}}{3/2}\right]_4^{25} = \frac{2}{9}\left(25^{3/2} - 4^{3/2}\right) = \frac{2}{9}(125 - 8) = \frac{234}{9} = 26$$

39. Let $u = 1 + 2x^3$, so $du = 6x^2 \, dx$. When $x = 0$, $u = 1$; when $x = 1$, $u = 3$. Thus,

$$\int_0^1 x^2 \left(1 + 2x^3\right)^5 \, dx = \int_1^3 u^5 \left(\tfrac{1}{6}\,du\right) = \tfrac{1}{6}\left[\tfrac{1}{6}u^6\right]_1^3 = \tfrac{1}{36}\left(3^6 - 1^6\right) = \tfrac{1}{36}(729 - 1) = \tfrac{728}{36} = \tfrac{182}{9}$$

40. Let $u = \sin x$, so $du = \cos x \, dx$. When $x = 0$, $u = 0$; when $x = \frac{\pi}{2}$, $u = 1$. Thus,

$$\int_0^{\pi/2} e^{\sin x} \cos x \, dx = \int_0^1 e^u \, du = [e^u]_0^1 = e - 1$$

41. Let $u = \pi t$, so $du = \pi \, dt$. When $t = 0$, $u = 0$; when $t = 1$, $u = \pi$. Thus, $\int_0^1 \cos \pi t \, dt = \int_0^\pi \cos u \left(\tfrac{1}{\pi}\,du\right) = \tfrac{1}{\pi}[\sin u]_0^\pi = \tfrac{1}{\pi}(0 - 0) = 0$

42. Let $u = 4t$, so $du = 4 \, dt$. When $t = 0$, $u = 0$; when $t = \frac{\pi}{4}$, $u = \pi$. Thus,

$$\int_0^{\pi/4} \sin 4t \, dt = \int_0^\pi \sin u \left(\tfrac{1}{4}\,du\right) = -\tfrac{1}{4}[\cos u]_0^\pi = -\tfrac{1}{4}(-1 - 1) = \tfrac{1}{2}$$

43. Let $u = \sqrt{x}$, so $du = \dfrac{1}{2\sqrt{x}}\,dx$. When $x = 1$, $u = 1$; when $x = 4$, $u = 2$. Thus,

$$\int_1^4 \frac{e^{\sqrt{x}}}{\sqrt{x}} \, dx = \int_1^2 e^u (2 \, du) = 2\,[e^u]_1^2 = 2\left(e^2 - e\right)$$

44. Let $u = 3x + 1$, so $du = 3dx$. When $x = 1$, $u = 4$; when $x = 2$, $u = 7$. Thus,

$$\int_1^2 \frac{dx}{3x + 1} = \int_4^7 \frac{1}{u}\left(\frac{1}{3}\,du\right) = \frac{1}{3}\left[\ln|u|\,\right]_4^7 = \frac{1}{3}(\ln 7 - \ln 4) = \frac{1}{3}\ln \frac{7}{4}$$

45. Let $u = x - 1$, so $u + 1 = x$ and $du = dx$. When $x = 1$, $u = 0$; when $x = 2$, $u = 1$. Thus,

$$\int_1^2 x\sqrt{x - 1} \, dx = \int_0^1 (u + 1)\sqrt{u} \, du = \int_0^1 \left(u^{3/2} + u^{1/2}\right) du = \left[\tfrac{2}{5}u^{5/2} + \tfrac{2}{3}u^{3/2}\right]_0^1 = \tfrac{2}{5} + \tfrac{2}{3} = \tfrac{16}{15}$$

46. $\displaystyle\int_{-\pi/2}^{\pi/2} \frac{x^2 \sin x}{1 + x^6} \, dx = 0$ by Theorem 6(b), since $f(x) = \dfrac{x^2 \sin x}{1 + x^6}$ is an odd function.

47. Let $u = 1 + 2x$, so $du = 2\,dx$. When $x = 0$, $u = 1$; when $x = 13$, $u = 27$. Thus,

$$\int_0^{13} \frac{dx}{\sqrt[3]{(1+2x)^2}} = \int_1^{27} u^{-2/3}\left(\tfrac{1}{2}\,du\right) = \left[\tfrac{1}{2} \cdot 3u^{1/3}\right]_1^{27} = \tfrac{3}{2}(3-1) = 3$$

48. Let $u = 1 + 2x$, so $x = \tfrac{1}{2}(u-1)$ and $du = 2\,dx$. When $x = 0$, $u = 1$; when $x = 4$, $u = 9$. Thus,

$$\int_0^4 \frac{x\,dx}{\sqrt{1+2x}} = \int_1^9 \frac{\tfrac{1}{2}(u-1)\,du}{\sqrt{u}}\frac{du}{2} = \tfrac{1}{4}\int_1^9 \left(u^{1/2} - u^{-1/2}\right)du = \tfrac{1}{4}\left[\tfrac{2}{3}u^{3/2} - 2u^{1/2}\right]_1^9$$

$$= \tfrac{1}{4} \cdot \tfrac{2}{3}\left[u^{3/2} - 3u^{1/2}\right]_1^9 = \tfrac{1}{6}\left[(27-9) - (1-3)\right] = \tfrac{20}{6} = \tfrac{10}{3}$$

49. $\displaystyle\int_{-\pi/6}^{\pi/6} \tan^3 \theta\,d\theta = 0$ by Theorem 6(b), since $f(\theta) = \tan^3 \theta$ is an odd function.

50. Let $u = a^2 - x^2$, so $du = -2x\,dx$. When $x = 0$, $u = a^2$; when $x = a$, $u = 0$. Thus,

$$\int_0^a x\sqrt{a^2 - x^2}\,dx = \int_{a^2}^0 u^{1/2}\left(-\tfrac{1}{2}\,du\right) = \tfrac{1}{2}\int_0^{a^2} u^{1/2}\,du = \tfrac{1}{2} \cdot \left[\tfrac{2}{3}u^{3/2}\right]_0^{a^2} = \tfrac{1}{3}a^3$$

51. Let $u = \ln x$, so $du = \dfrac{dx}{x}$. When $x = e$, $u = 1$; when $x = e^4$; $u = 4$. Thus,

$$\int_e^{e^4} \frac{dx}{x\sqrt{\ln x}} = \int_1^4 u^{-1/2}\,du = 2\left[u^{1/2}\right]_1^4 = 2(2-1) = 2$$

52. Let $u = \sin^{-1} x$, so $du = \dfrac{dx}{\sqrt{1-x^2}}$. When $x = 0$, $u = 0$; when $x = \tfrac{1}{2}$, $u = \tfrac{\pi}{6}$. Thus,

$$\int_0^{1/2} \frac{\sin^{-1} x}{\sqrt{1-x^2}}\,dx = \int_0^{\pi/6} u\,du = \left[\frac{u^2}{2}\right]_0^{\pi/6} = \frac{\pi^2}{72}$$

53. From the graph, it appears that the area under the curve is about

$1 + \left(\text{a little more than } \tfrac{1}{2} \cdot 1 \cdot 0.7\right)$, or about 1.4. The exact area is given by

$A = \int_0^1 \sqrt{2x+1}\,dx$. Let $u = 2x+1$, so $du = 2\,dx$. The limits change to

$2 \cdot 0 + 1 = 1$ and $2 \cdot 1 + 1 = 3$, and

$A = \int_1^3 \sqrt{u}\left(\tfrac{1}{2}\,du\right) = \tfrac{1}{2}\left[\tfrac{2}{3}u^{3/2}\right]_1^3 = \tfrac{1}{3}(3\sqrt{3} - 1) = \sqrt{3} - \tfrac{1}{3} \approx 1.399$.

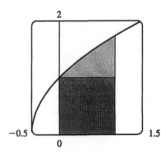

54. From the graph, it appears that the area under the curve is almost

$\tfrac{1}{2} \cdot \pi \cdot 2.6$, or about 4. The exact area is given by

$A = \int_0^\pi (2\sin x - \sin 2x)\,dx$

$= -2\left[\cos x\right]_0^\pi - \int_0^\pi \sin 2x\,dx$

$= -2(-1 - 1) - 0$ [by symmetry of the graph of $y = \sin 2x$]

$= 4$

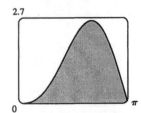

55. First write the integral as a sum of two integrals:
$\int_{-2}^{2}(x+3)\sqrt{4-x^2}\,dx = \int_{-2}^{2} x\sqrt{4-x^2}\,dx + \int_{-2}^{2} 3\sqrt{4-x^2}\,dx$. The first integral is 0 by Theorem 6(b), since
$f(x) = x\sqrt{4-x^2}$ is an odd function and we are integrating from $x = -2$ to $x = 2$. The second integral we
interpret as three times the area of a semicircle with radius 2, so the original integral is equal to
$0 + 3 \cdot \frac{1}{2}\left(\pi \cdot 2^2\right) = 6\pi$.

56. Let $u = x^2$. Then $du = 2x\,dx$ and the limits are unchanged ($0^2 = 0$ and $1^2 = 1$), so
$I = \int_0^1 x\sqrt{1-x^4}\,dx = \frac{1}{2}\int_0^1 \sqrt{1-u^2}\,du$. But this integral can be interpreted as the area of a quarter-circle with
radius 1. So $I = \frac{1}{2} \cdot \frac{1}{4}\left(\pi \cdot 1^2\right) = \frac{1}{8}\pi$.

57. First Figure   Let $u = \sqrt{x}$, so $du = \dfrac{1}{2\sqrt{x}}\,dx$ and $dx = 2\sqrt{x}\,du = 2u\,du$. When $x = 0$, $u = 0$; when

$x = 1$, $u = 1$. Thus, $A_1 = \displaystyle\int_0^1 e^{\sqrt{x}}\,dx = \int_0^1 e^u (2u\,du) = 2\int_0^1 ue^u\,du$.

Second Figure $A_2 = \int_0^1 2xe^x\,dx = 2\int_0^1 ue^u\,du$.

Third Figure   Let $u = \sin x$, so $du = \cos x\,dx$. When $x = 0$, $u = 0$; when $x = \frac{\pi}{2}$, $u = 1$. Thus,

$A_3 = \int_0^{\pi/2} e^{\sin x}\sin 2x\,dx = \int_0^{\pi/2} e^{\sin x}(2\sin x\,\cos x)\,dx = \int_0^1 e^u (2u\,du) = 2\int_0^1 ue^u\,du$.

Since $A_1 = A_2 = A_3$, all three areas are equal.

58. Let $r(t) = ae^{bt}$ with $a = 450.268$ and $b = 1.12567$, and $n(t) = $ population after t hours. Since $r(t) = n'(t)$,
$\int_0^3 r(t)\,dt = n(3) - n(0)$ is the total change in the population after three hours. Since we start with 400 bacteria,
the population will be

$$n(3) = 400 + \int_0^3 r(t)\,dt = 400 + \int_0^3 ae^{bt}\,dt = 400 + \frac{a}{b}\left[e^{bt}\right]_0^3 = 400 + \frac{a}{b}\left(e^{3b}-1\right)$$
$$\approx 400 + 11{,}313 = 11{,}713 \text{ bacteria}$$

59. The volume of inhaled air in the lungs at time t is

$$V(t) = \int_0^t f(u)\,du = \int_0^t \tfrac{1}{2}\sin\!\left(\tfrac{2\pi}{5}u\right)du = \int_0^{2\pi t/5} \tfrac{1}{2}\sin v\left(\tfrac{5}{2\pi}\,dv\right) \quad [\text{substitute } v = \tfrac{2\pi}{5}u,\ dv = \tfrac{2\pi}{5}\,du]$$
$$= \tfrac{5}{4\pi}\left[-\cos v\right]_0^{2\pi t/5} = \tfrac{5}{4\pi}\left[-\cos\!\left(\tfrac{2\pi}{5}t\right)+1\right] = \tfrac{5}{4\pi}\left[1-\cos\!\left(\tfrac{2\pi}{5}t\right)\right] \text{ liters}$$

60. Number of calculators $= x(4) - x(2) = \int_2^4 5000\left[1 - 100(t+10)^{-2}\right]dt$
$$= 5000\left[t + 100(t+10)^{-1}\right]_2^4 = 5000\left[(4 + \tfrac{100}{14}) - (2 + \tfrac{100}{12})\right] \approx 4048$$

61. Let $u = 2x$. Then $du = 2\,dx$, so $\int_0^2 f(2x)\,dx = \int_0^4 f(u)\left(\tfrac{1}{2}\,du\right) = \tfrac{1}{2}\int_0^4 f(u)\,du = \tfrac{1}{2}(10) = 5$.

62. Let $u = x^2$. Then $du = 2x\,dx$, so $\int_0^3 xf\left(x^2\right)dx = \int_0^9 f(u)\left(\tfrac{1}{2}\,du\right) = \tfrac{1}{2}\int_0^9 f(u)\,du = \tfrac{1}{2}(4) = 2$.

63. Let $u = -x$. Then $du = -dx$, so
$\int_a^b f(-x)\,dx = \int_{-a}^{-b} f(u)(-du) = \int_{-b}^{-a} f(u)\,du = \int_{-b}^{-a} f(x)\,dx$. From
the diagram, we see that the equality follows from the fact that we are
reflecting the graph of f, and the limits of integration, about the y-axis.

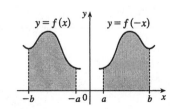

64. Let $u = x + c$. Then $du = dx$, so

$\int_a^b f(x+c)\, dx = \int_{a+c}^{b+c} f(u)\, du = \int_{a+c}^{b+c} f(x)\, dx$. From the diagram,

we see that the equality follows from the fact that we are translating the

graph of f, and the limits of integration, by a distance c.

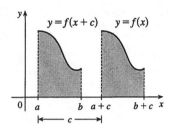

65. Let $u = 1 - x$. Then $x = 1 - u$ and $dx = -du$, so

$$\int_0^1 x^a (1-x)^b\, dx = \int_1^0 (1-u)^a\, u^b(-du) = \int_0^1 u^b(1-u)^a\, du = \int_0^1 x^b(1-x)^a\, dx$$

5.6 Integration by Parts • • • • • • • • • • • •

1. Let $u = \ln x$, $dv = x\, dx$ $\Rightarrow$ $du = dx/x$, $v = \frac{1}{2}x^2$. Then by Equation 2, $\int u\, dv = uv - \int v\, du$,

$\int x \ln x\, dx = \frac{1}{2}x^2 \ln x - \int \frac{1}{2}x^2(dx/x) = \frac{1}{2}x^2 \ln x - \frac{1}{2}\int x\, dx = \frac{1}{2}x^2 \ln x - \frac{1}{2} \cdot \frac{1}{2}x^2 + C$

$\qquad = \frac{1}{2}x^2 \ln x - \frac{1}{4}x^2 + C$

2. Let $u = \theta$, $dv = \cos\theta\, d\theta$ $\Rightarrow$ $du = d\theta$, $v = \sin\theta$. Then by Equation 2,

$\int \theta \cos\theta\, d\theta = \theta \sin\theta - \int \sin\theta\, d\theta = \theta \sin\theta + \cos\theta + C$.

Note: A mnemonic device which is helpful for selecting u when using integration by parts is the LIATE principle of precedence for u:

$\underline{\text{L}}$ogarithmic

$\underline{\text{I}}$nverse trigonometric

$\underline{\text{A}}$lgebraic

$\underline{\text{T}}$rigonometric

$\underline{\text{E}}$xponential

If the integrand has several factors, then we try to choose among them a u which appears as high as possible on the list. For example, in Exercise 3 the integrand is xe^{2x}, which is the product of an algebraic function (x) and an exponential function (e^{2x}). Since $\underline{\text{A}}$lgebraic appears before $\underline{\text{E}}$xponential, we choose $u = x$. Sometimes the integration turns out to be similar regardless of the selection of u and dv, but it is advisable to refer to LIATE when in doubt.

3. Let $u = x$, $dv = e^{2x}\, dx$ $\Rightarrow$ $du = dx$, $v = \frac{1}{2}e^{2x}$. Then by Equation 2,

$\int xe^{2x}\, dx = \frac{1}{2}xe^{2x} - \int \frac{1}{2}e^{2x}\, dx = \frac{1}{2}xe^{2x} - \frac{1}{4}e^{2x} + C$.

4. Let $u = \ln x$, $dv = x^4\, dx$ $\Rightarrow$ $du = (1/x)\, dx$, $v = \frac{1}{5}x^5$. Then

$\int x^4 \ln x\, dx = \frac{1}{5}x^5 \ln x - \int \frac{1}{5}x^5(1/x)\, dx = \frac{1}{5}x^5 \ln x - \frac{1}{5}\int x^4 dx = \frac{1}{5}x^5 \ln x - \frac{1}{5}\left(\frac{1}{5}x^5\right) + C$

$\qquad = \frac{1}{5}x^5 \ln x - \frac{1}{25}x^5 + C$, or $\frac{1}{25}x^5(5 \ln x - 1) + C$.

5. Let $u = x$, $dv = \sin 4x\, dx$ $\Rightarrow$ $du = dx$, $v = -\frac{1}{4}\cos 4x$. Then by Equation 2,

$\int x \sin 4x\, dx = -\frac{1}{4}x \cos 4x - \int \left(-\frac{1}{4}\cos 4x\right) dx = -\frac{1}{4}x \cos 4x + \frac{1}{4}\left(\frac{1}{4}\sin 4x\right) + C$

$\qquad = -\frac{1}{4}x \cos 4x + \frac{1}{16}\sin 4x + C$.

6. Let $u = \sin^{-1} x$, $dv = dx$ $\Rightarrow$ $du = \dfrac{dx}{\sqrt{1 - x^2}}$, $v = x$. Then

$\int \sin^{-1} x\, dx = x \sin^{-1} x - \int \dfrac{x}{\sqrt{1 - x^2}}\, dx$. Setting $t = 1 - x^2$, we get $dt = -2x\, dx$, so

$-\int \dfrac{x\, dx}{\sqrt{1 - x^2}} = -\int t^{-1/2}\left(-\frac{1}{2}\, dt\right) = \frac{1}{2}\left(2t^{1/2}\right) + C = t^{1/2} + C = \sqrt{1 - x^2} + C$. Hence,

$\int \sin^{-1} x\, dx = x \sin^{-1} x + \sqrt{1 - x^2} + C$.

7. First let $u = x^2$, $dv = \cos 3x\, dx$ $\Rightarrow$ $du = 2x\, dx$, $v = \frac{1}{3} \sin 3x$. Then by Equation 2, the original integral

$I = \int x^2 \cos 3x\, dx = \frac{1}{3}x^2 \sin 3x - \frac{2}{3} \int x \sin 3x\, dx$. To evaluate the last integral, we next let $U = x$,

$dV = \sin 3x\, dx$ $\Rightarrow$ $dU = dx$, $V = -\frac{1}{3} \cos 3x$. So

$\int x \sin 3x\, dx = -\frac{1}{3}x \cos 3x + \frac{1}{3} \int \cos 3x\, dx = -\frac{1}{3}x \cos 3x + \frac{1}{9} \sin 3x + C_1$. Substituting for $\int x \sin 3x\, dx$,

we get $I = \frac{1}{3}x^2 \sin 3x - \frac{2}{3}\left(-\frac{1}{3}x \cos 3x + \frac{1}{9} \sin 3x + C_1\right) = \frac{1}{3}x^2 \sin 3x + \frac{2}{9}x \cos 3x - \frac{2}{27} \sin 3x + C$,

where $C = -\frac{2}{3}C_1$.

8. First let $u = x^2$, $dv = \sin ax\, dx$ $\Rightarrow$ $du = 2x\, dx$, $v = -\dfrac{1}{a} \cos ax$. Then by Equation 2,

$I = \int x^2 \sin ax\, dx = -\dfrac{x^2}{a} \cos ax - \int \left(-\dfrac{1}{a}\right) \cos ax\, (2x\, dx) = -\dfrac{x^2}{a} \cos ax + \dfrac{2}{a} \int x \cos ax\, dx$. Next let

$U = x$, $dV = \cos ax\, dx$ $\Rightarrow$ $dU = dx$, $V = \dfrac{1}{a} \sin ax$. So

$\int x \cos ax\, dx = \dfrac{x}{a} \sin ax - \int \dfrac{1}{a} \sin ax\, dx = \dfrac{x}{a} \sin ax + \dfrac{1}{a^2} \cos ax + C_1$. Substituting for $\int x \cos ax\, dx$, we get

$I = -\dfrac{x^2}{a} \cos ax + \dfrac{2}{a}\left(\dfrac{x}{a} \sin ax + \dfrac{1}{a^2} \cos ax + C_1\right) = -\dfrac{x^2}{a} \cos ax + \dfrac{2x}{a^2} \sin ax + \dfrac{2}{a^3} \cos ax + C$.

9. First let $u = (\ln x)^2$, $dv = dx$ $\Rightarrow$ $du = 2\ln x \cdot \frac{1}{x}\, dx$, $v = x$. Then by Equation 2,

$I = \int (\ln x)^2\, dx = x(\ln x)^2 - 2\int x \ln x \cdot \frac{1}{x}\, dx = x(\ln x)^2 - 2\int \ln x\, dx$. Next let $U = \ln x$, $dV = dx$ $\Rightarrow$

$dU = 1/x\, dx$, $V = x$ to get $\int \ln x\, dx = x \ln x - \int x \cdot (1/x)\, dx = x \ln x - \int dx = x \ln x - x + C_1$. Thus,

$I = x(\ln x)^2 - 2(x \ln x - x + C_1) = x(\ln x)^2 - 2x \ln x + 2x + C$, where $C = -2C_1$.

10. Let $u = t^3$, $dv = e^t\, dt$ $\Rightarrow$ $du = 3t^2\, dt$, $v = e^t$. Then $I = \int t^3 e^t\, dt = t^3 e^t - \int 3t^2 e^t\, dt$. Integrate by parts
twice more with $dv = e^t\, dt$.

$$I = t^3 e^t - \left(3t^2 e^t - \int 6t e^t\, dt\right) = t^3 e^t - 3t^2 e^t + 6t e^t - \int 6 e^t\, dt$$

$$= t^3 e^t - 3t^2 e^t + 6t e^t - 6e^t + C = \left(t^3 - 3t^2 + 6t - 6\right)e^t + C$$

More generally, if $p(t)$ is a polynomial of degree n in t, then repeated integration by parts shows that

$\int p(t)\, e^t\, dt = \left[p(t) - p'(t) + p''(t) - p'''(t) + \cdots + (-1)^n\, p^{(n)}(t)\right] e^t + C$.

11. Let $u = \ln r$, $dv = r^3 dr$ $\Rightarrow$ $du = (1/r)\, dr$, $v = \frac{1}{4}r^4$. Then

$$\int r^3 \ln r\, dr = \frac{1}{4}r^4 \ln r - \int \frac{1}{4}r^4 (1/r)\, dr = \frac{1}{4}r^4 \ln r - \frac{1}{4}\int r^3 dr = \frac{1}{4}r^4 \ln r - \frac{1}{4}\left(\frac{1}{4}r^4\right) + C$$

$$= \frac{1}{4}r^4 \ln r - \frac{1}{16}r^4 + C, \text{ or } \frac{1}{16}r^4 (4\ln r - 1) + C.$$

12. First let $u = \sin(\ln t)$, $dv = dt$ $\Rightarrow$ $du = \cos(\ln t) \cdot \frac{1}{t}\,dt$, $v = t$. Then
$I = \int \sin(\ln t)\,dt = t\sin(\ln t) - \int \cos(\ln t)\,dt$. Next let $U = \cos(\ln t)$, $dV = dt$ $\Rightarrow$ $dU = -\sin(\ln t) \cdot \frac{1}{t}dt$,
$V = t$. Then $\int \cos(\ln t)\,dt = t\cos(\ln t) + \int \sin(\ln t)\,dt = t\cos(\ln t) + I$. Substituting for $\int \cos(\ln t)\,dt$, we get
$I = t\sin(\ln t) - [t\cos(\ln t) + I] = t\sin(\ln t) - t\cos(\ln t) - I$ $\Rightarrow$ $2I = t\sin(\ln t) - t\cos(\ln t) + C_1$.
Hence, $I = \frac{1}{2}t\sin(\ln t) - \frac{1}{2}t\cos(\ln t) + C$.

13. First let $u = \sin 3\theta$, $dv = e^{2\theta}\,d\theta$ $\Rightarrow$ $du = 3\cos 3\theta\,d\theta$, $v = \frac{1}{2}e^{2\theta}$.
Then $I = \int e^{2\theta} \sin 3\theta\,d\theta = \frac{1}{2}e^{2\theta}\sin 3\theta - \frac{3}{2}\int e^{2\theta}\cos 3\theta\,d\theta$.
Next let $U = \cos 3\theta$, $dV = e^{2\theta}\,d\theta$ $\Rightarrow$ $dU = -3\sin 3\theta\,d\theta$, $V = \frac{1}{2}e^{2\theta}$ to get
$\int e^{2\theta}\cos 3\theta\,d\theta = \frac{1}{2}e^{2\theta}\cos 3\theta + \frac{3}{2}\int e^{2\theta}\sin 3\theta\,d\theta$. Substituting in the previous formula gives
$I = \frac{1}{2}e^{2\theta}\sin 3\theta - \frac{3}{4}e^{2\theta}\cos 3\theta - \frac{9}{4}\int e^{2\theta}\sin 3\theta\,d\theta = \frac{1}{2}e^{2\theta}\sin 3\theta - \frac{3}{4}e^{2\theta}\cos 3\theta - \frac{9}{4}I$ $\Rightarrow$
$\frac{13}{4}I = \frac{1}{2}e^{2\theta}\sin 3\theta - \frac{3}{4}e^{2\theta}\cos 3\theta + C_1$. Hence, $I = \frac{1}{13}e^{2\theta}(2\sin 3\theta - 3\cos 3\theta) + C$, where $C = \frac{4}{13}C_1$.

14. First let $u = e^{-\theta}$, $dv = \cos 2\theta\,d\theta$ $\Rightarrow$ $du = -e^{-\theta}\,d\theta$, $v = \frac{1}{2}\sin 2\theta$. Then
$I = \int e^{-\theta}\cos 2\theta\,d\theta = \frac{1}{2}e^{-\theta}\sin 2\theta - \int \frac{1}{2}\sin 2\theta\,(-e^{-\theta}\,d\theta) = \frac{1}{2}e^{-\theta}\sin 2\theta + \frac{1}{2}\int e^{-\theta}\sin 2\theta\,d\theta$.
Next let $U = e^{-\theta}$, $dV = \sin 2\theta\,d\theta$ $\Rightarrow$ $dU = -e^{-\theta}\,d\theta$, $V = -\frac{1}{2}\cos 2\theta$, so
$\int e^{-\theta}\sin 2\theta\,d\theta = -\frac{1}{2}e^{-\theta}\cos 2\theta - \int (-\frac{1}{2})\cos 2\theta\,(-e^{-\theta}\,d\theta) = -\frac{1}{2}e^{-\theta}\cos 2\theta - \frac{1}{2}\int e^{-\theta}\cos 2\theta\,d\theta$. So
$I = \frac{1}{2}e^{-\theta}\sin 2\theta + \frac{1}{2}\left[(-\frac{1}{2}e^{-\theta}\cos 2\theta) - \frac{1}{2}I\right] = \frac{1}{2}e^{-\theta}\sin 2\theta - \frac{1}{4}e^{-\theta}\cos 2\theta - \frac{1}{4}I$
$\Rightarrow$ $\frac{5}{4}I = \frac{1}{2}e^{-\theta}\sin 2\theta - \frac{1}{4}e^{-\theta}\cos 2\theta + C_1$ $\Rightarrow$
$I = \frac{4}{5}\left(\frac{1}{2}e^{-\theta}\sin 2\theta - \frac{1}{4}e^{-\theta}\cos 2\theta + C_1\right) = \frac{2}{5}e^{-\theta}\sin 2\theta - \frac{1}{5}e^{-\theta}\cos 2\theta + C$.

15. Let $u = t$, $dv = e^{-t}\,dt$ $\Rightarrow$ $du = dt$, $v = -e^{-t}$. By Formula 6,
$\int_0^1 te^{-t}\,dt = \left[-te^{-t}\right]_0^1 + \int_0^1 e^{-t}\,dt = -1/e + \left[-e^{-t}\right]_0^1 = -1/e - 1/e + 1 = 1 - 2/e$.

16. Let $u = \ln t$, $dv = \sqrt{t}\,dt$ $\Rightarrow$ $du = dt/t$, $v = \frac{2}{3}t^{3/2}$. By Formula 6,
$\int_1^4 \sqrt{t}\ln t\,dt = \left[\frac{2}{3}t^{3/2}\ln t\right]_1^4 - \frac{2}{3}\int_1^4 \sqrt{t}\,dt = \frac{2}{3}\cdot 8 \cdot \ln 4 - 0 - \left[\frac{2}{3}\cdot\frac{2}{3}t^{3/2}\right]_1^4 = \frac{16}{3}\ln 4 - \frac{4}{9}(8-1) = \frac{16}{3}\ln 4 - \frac{28}{9}$.

17. Let $u = x$, $dv = \cos 2x\,dx$ $\Rightarrow$ $du = dx$, $v = \frac{1}{2}\sin 2x\,dx$. By Formula 6,
$\int_0^{\pi/2} x\cos 2x\,dx = \left[\frac{1}{2}x\sin 2x\right]_0^{\pi/2} - \frac{1}{2}\int_0^{\pi/2}\sin 2x\,dx = 0 + \left[\frac{1}{4}\cos 2x\right]_0^{\pi/2} = \frac{1}{4}(-1-1) = -\frac{1}{2}$.

18. First let $u = x^2 + 1$, $dv = e^{-x}\,dx$ $\Rightarrow$ $du = 2x\,dx$, $v = -e^{-x}$. By (6),
$\int_0^1 (x^2+1)e^{-x}\,dx = \left[-(x^2+1)e^{-x}\right]_0^1 + \int_0^1 2xe^{-x}\,dx = -2e^{-1} + 1 + 2\int_0^1 xe^{-x}\,dx$. Next let
$U = x$, $dV = e^{-x}\,dx$ $\Rightarrow$ $dU = dx$, $V = -e^{-x}$. By (6) again,
$\int_0^1 xe^{-x}\,dx = \left[-xe^{-x}\right]_0^1 + \int_0^1 e^{-x}\,dx = -e^{-1} + \left[-e^{-x}\right]_0^1 = -e^{-1} - e^{-1} + 1 = -2e^{-1} + 1$. So
$\int_0^1 (x^2+1)e^{-x}\,dx = -2e^{-1} + 1 + 2(-2e^{-1} + 1) = -2e^{-1} + 1 - 4e^{-1} + 2 = -6e^{-1} + 3$.

19. Let $u = \sin^{-1}x$, $dv = dx$ $\Rightarrow$ $du = \dfrac{dx}{\sqrt{1-x^2}}$, $v = x$. By Formula 6,

$I = \int_0^{1/2}\sin^{-1}x\,dx = \left[x\sin^{-1}x\right]_0^{1/2} - \int_0^{1/2}\dfrac{x\,dx}{\sqrt{1-x^2}} = \dfrac{1}{2}\cdot\dfrac{\pi}{6} - \int_0^{1/2}\dfrac{x\,dx}{\sqrt{1-x^2}}$. To evaluate the last

integral, let $t = 1 - x^2$, so $dt = -2x\,dx$ and $x\,dx = -\frac{1}{2}\,dt$. When $x = 0$, $t = 1$; when $x = \frac{1}{2}$, $t = \frac{3}{4}$. So
$\int_0^{1/2}\dfrac{x\,dx}{\sqrt{1-x^2}} = \int_1^{3/4}\dfrac{1}{\sqrt{t}}\left(-\dfrac{1}{2}dt\right) = \dfrac{1}{2}\int_{3/4}^1 t^{-1/2}dt = \dfrac{1}{2}\left[2t^{1/2}\right]_{3/4}^1 = \sqrt{1} - \sqrt{\dfrac{3}{4}} = 1 - \dfrac{\sqrt{3}}{2}$.
Thus, $I = \dfrac{\pi}{12} - \left(1 - \dfrac{\sqrt{3}}{2}\right) = \dfrac{\pi}{12} - 1 + \dfrac{\sqrt{3}}{2} = \dfrac{1}{12}\left(\pi - 12 + 6\sqrt{3}\right)$.

20. Let $u = x$, $dv = \csc^2 x \, dx$ $\Rightarrow$ $du = dx$, $v = -\cot x$. Then

$$\int_{\pi/4}^{\pi/2} x \csc^2 x \, dx = [-x \cot x]_{\pi/4}^{\pi/2} + \int_{\pi/4}^{\pi/2} \cot x \, dx = -\frac{\pi}{2} \cdot 0 + \frac{\pi}{4} \cdot 1 + [\ln|\sin x|]_{\pi/4}^{\pi/2} \quad \text{[see Exercise 5.5.22]}$$

$$= \frac{\pi}{4} + \ln 1 - \ln \frac{1}{\sqrt{2}} = \frac{\pi}{4} + 0 - \ln 2^{-1/2} = \frac{\pi}{4} + \frac{1}{2} \ln 2$$

21. $I = \int_1^4 \ln \sqrt{x} \, dx = \int_1^4 \ln x^{1/2} dx = \int_1^4 \frac{1}{2} \ln x \, dx = \frac{1}{2} \int_1^4 \ln x \, dx = \frac{1}{2} [x \ln x - x]_1^4$ as in Example 2. So
$I = \frac{1}{2}[(4\ln 4 - 4) - (0 - 1)] = 2\ln 4 - \frac{3}{2}$.

22. Let $u = \tan^{-1} x$, $dv = x \, dx$ $\Rightarrow$ $du = dx/(1 + x^2)$, $v = \frac{1}{2}x^2$.

Then $\int x \tan^{-1} x \, dx = \frac{1}{2}x^2 \tan^{-1} x - \frac{1}{2} \int \dfrac{x^2}{1 + x^2} \, dx$. To evaluate the last integral, use long division or observe

that $\displaystyle \int \frac{x^2}{1 + x^2} \, dx = \int \frac{(1 + x^2) - 1}{1 + x^2} \, dx = \int 1 \, dx - \int \frac{1}{1 + x^2} \, dx = x - \tan^{-1} x + C_1$. So
$\int x \tan^{-1} x \, dx = \frac{1}{2}x^2 \tan^{-1} x - \frac{1}{2}(x - \tan^{-1} x + C_1) = \frac{1}{2}(x^2 \tan^{-1} x + \tan^{-1} x - x) + C$.

23. Let $u = \ln(\sin \theta)$, $dv = \cos \theta \, d\theta$ $\Rightarrow$ $du = (1/\sin \theta) \cos \theta \, d\theta$, $v = \sin \theta$. Then

$$\int_{\pi/6}^{\pi/2} \cos \theta \ln(\sin \theta) \, d\theta = [\sin \theta \ln(\sin \theta)]_{\pi/6}^{\pi/2} - \int_{\pi/6}^{\pi/2} \cos \theta \, d\theta = (1 \cdot \ln 1) - \left(\frac{1}{2} \cdot \ln \frac{1}{2}\right) - [\sin \theta]_{\pi/6}^{\pi/2}$$

$$= 0 - \frac{1}{2} \ln 2^{-1} - \left(1 - \frac{1}{2}\right) = \frac{1}{2} \ln 2 - \frac{1}{2}, \text{ or } \frac{1}{2}(\ln 2 - 1).$$

24. Let $u = \sin(t - s)$, $dv = e^s \, ds$ $\Rightarrow$ $du = -\cos(t - s) \, ds$, $v = e^s$. Then
$I = \int_0^t e^s \sin(t - s) \, ds = [e^s \sin(t - s)]_0^t + \int_0^t e^s \cos(t - s) \, ds = e^t \sin 0 - e^0 \sin t + I_1$. For
I_1, let $U = \cos(t - s)$, $dV = e^s \, ds$ $\Rightarrow$ $dU = \sin(t - s) \, ds$, $V = e^s$. So
$I_1 = [e^s \cos(t - s)]_0^t - \int_0^t e^s \sin(t - s) ds = e^t \cos 0 - e^0 \cos t - I$. Thus, $I = -\sin t + e^t - \cos t - I$ $\Rightarrow$
$2I = e^t - \cos t - \sin t$ $\Rightarrow$ $I = \frac{1}{2}(e^t - \cos t - \sin t)$.

25. Let $w = \sqrt{x}$, so that $x = w^2$ and $dx = 2w \, dw$. Thus, $\int \sin \sqrt{x} \, dx = \int 2w \sin w \, dw$. Now use parts with $u = 2w$,
$dv = \sin w \, dw$, $du = 2 \, dw$, $v = -\cos w$ to get

$$\int 2w \sin w \, dw = -2w \cos w + \int 2 \cos w \, dw = -2w \cos w + 2 \sin w + C$$

$$= -2\sqrt{x} \cos \sqrt{x} + 2 \sin \sqrt{x} + C = 2(\sin \sqrt{x} - \sqrt{x} \cos \sqrt{x}) + C$$

26. Let $t = x^3$, so that $dt = 3x^2 \, dx$. Thus, $\int x^5 \cos(x^3) \, dx = \frac{1}{3} \int x^3 \cos(x^3) \cdot 3x^2 \, dx = \frac{1}{3} \int t \cos t \, dt$.
Now use parts with $u = t$, $dv = \cos t \, dt$, $du = dt$, $v = \sin t$ to get
$\frac{1}{3} \int t \cos t \, dt = \frac{1}{3}(t \sin t - \int \sin t \, dt) = \frac{1}{3}t \sin t + \frac{1}{3} \cos t + C = \frac{1}{3}x^3 \sin(x^3) + \frac{1}{3} \cos(x^3) + C$.

27. Let $x = \theta^2$, so that $dx = 2\theta \, d\theta$. Thus, $\int_{\sqrt{\pi/2}}^{\sqrt{\pi}} \theta^3 \cos(\theta^2) \, d\theta = \int_{\sqrt{\pi/2}}^{\sqrt{\pi}} \theta^2 \cos(\theta^2) \cdot \frac{1}{2}(2\theta \, d\theta) = \frac{1}{2} \int_{\pi/2}^{\pi} x \cos x \, dx$.
Now use parts with $u = x$, $dv = \cos x \, dx$, $du = dx$, $v = \sin x$ to get

$$\frac{1}{2} \int_{\pi/2}^{\pi} x \cos x \, dx = \frac{1}{2}([x \sin x]_{\pi/2}^{\pi} - \int_{\pi/2}^{\pi} \sin x \, dx) = \frac{1}{2}[x \sin x + \cos x]_{\pi/2}^{\pi}$$

$$= \frac{1}{2}(\pi \sin \pi + \cos \pi) - \frac{1}{2}\left(\frac{\pi}{2} \sin \frac{\pi}{2} + \cos \frac{\pi}{2}\right) = \frac{1}{2}(\pi \cdot 0 - 1) - \frac{1}{2}\left(\frac{\pi}{2} \cdot 1 + 0\right) = -\frac{1}{2} - \frac{\pi}{4}$$

28. Let $w = \sqrt{x}$, so that $x = w^2$ and $dx = 2w \, dw$. Thus, $\int_1^4 e^{\sqrt{x}} \, dx = \int_1^2 e^w 2w \, dw$. Now use parts with $u = 2w$,
$dv = e^w \, dw$, $du = 2 \, dw$, $v = e^w$ to get $\int_1^2 e^w 2w \, dw = [2we^w]_1^2 - 2 \int_1^2 e^w \, dw = 4e^2 - 2e - 2(e^2 - e) = 2e^2$.

In Exercises 29–32, let $f(x)$ denote the integrand and $F(x)$ its antiderivative (with $C = 0$).

29. Let $u = x$, $dv = \cos \pi x\, dx$ $\Rightarrow$ $du = dx$, $v = (\sin \pi x)/\pi$. Then

$$\int x \cos \pi x\, dx = x \cdot \frac{\sin \pi x}{\pi} - \int \frac{\sin \pi x}{\pi}\, dx = \frac{x \sin \pi x}{\pi} + \frac{\cos \pi x}{\pi^2} + C.$$

We see from the graph that this is reasonable, since F has extreme values where f is 0.

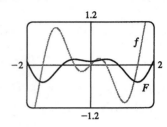

30. Let $u = \ln x$, $dv = x^{3/2}\, dx$ $\Rightarrow$ $du = \frac{1}{x}\, dx$, $v = \frac{2}{5}x^{5/2}$. Then

$$\int x^{3/2} \ln x\, dx = \frac{2}{5}x^{5/2} \ln x - \frac{2}{5}\int x^{3/2}\, dx = \frac{2}{5}x^{5/2} \ln x - \left(\frac{2}{5}\right)^2 x^{5/2} + C$$

$$= \frac{2}{5}x^{5/2} \ln x - \frac{4}{25}x^{5/2} + C.$$

We see from the graph that this is reasonable, since F has a minimum where f changes from negative to positive.

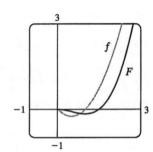

31. Let $u = 2x + 3$, $dv = e^x\, dx$ $\Rightarrow$ $du = 2\, dx$, $v = e^x$. Then
$\int (2x + 3)e^x\, dx = (2x + 3)e^x - 2\int e^x\, dx = (2x + 3)e^x - 2e^x + C = (2x + 1)\, e^x + C$. We see from the graph that this is reasonable, since F has a minimum where f changes from negative to positive.

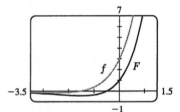

32. $\int x^3 e^{x^2}\, dx = \int x^2 \cdot xe^{x^2}\, dx = I$.

Let $u = x^2$, $dv = xe^{x^2}\, dx$ $\Rightarrow$ $du = 2x\, dx$, $v = \frac{1}{2}e^{x^2}$. Then

$I = \frac{1}{2}x^2 e^{x^2} - \int xe^{x^2}\, dx = \frac{1}{2}x^2 e^{x^2} - \frac{1}{2}e^{x^2} + C = \frac{1}{2}e^{x^2}\left(x^2 - 1\right) + C.$

We see from the graph that this is reasonable, since F has a minimum where f changes from negative to positive.

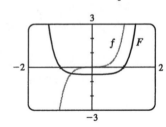

33. (a) Take $n = 2$ in Example 6 to get $\int \sin^2 x\, dx = -\frac{1}{2}\cos x \sin x + \frac{1}{2}\int 1\, dx = \dfrac{x}{2} - \dfrac{\sin 2x}{4} + C.$

(b) $\int \sin^4 x\, dx = -\frac{1}{4}\cos x \sin^3 x + \frac{3}{4}\int \sin^2 x\, dx = -\frac{1}{4}\cos x \sin^3 x + \frac{3}{8}x - \frac{3}{16}\sin 2x + C.$

34. (a) Let $u = \cos^{n-1} x$, $dv = \cos x\, dx$ $\Rightarrow$ $du = -(n - 1)\cos^{n-2} x \sin x\, dx$, $v = \sin x$ in (2):

$$\int \cos^n x\, dx = \cos^{n-1} x \sin x + (n - 1)\int \cos^{n-2} x \sin^2 x\, dx$$

$$= \cos^{n-1} x \sin x + (n - 1)\int \cos^{n-2} x\left(1 - \cos^2 x\right)\, dx$$

$$= \cos^{n-1} x \sin x + (n - 1)\int \cos^{n-2} x\, dx - (n - 1)\int \cos^n x\, dx$$

Rearranging terms gives $n \int \cos^n x\, dx = \cos^{n-1} x \sin x + (n - 1)\int \cos^{n-2} x\, dx$ or

$$\int \cos^n x\, dx = \frac{1}{n}\cos^{n-1} x \sin x + \frac{n - 1}{n}\int \cos^{n-2} x\, dx$$

(b) Take $n = 2$ in part (a) to get $\int \cos^2 x \, dx = \frac{1}{2} \cos x \sin x + \frac{1}{2} \int 1 \, dx = \dfrac{x}{2} + \dfrac{\sin 2x}{4} + C$.

(c) $\int \cos^4 x \, dx = \frac{1}{4} \cos^3 x \sin x + \frac{3}{4} \int \cos^2 x \, dx = \frac{1}{4} \cos^3 x \sin x + \frac{3}{8} x + \frac{3}{16} \sin 2x + C$

35. (a) From Example 6, $\displaystyle\int \sin^n x \, dx = -\frac{1}{n} \cos x \sin^{n-1} x + \frac{n-1}{n} \int \sin^{n-2} x \, dx$. Using (6),

$$\int_0^{\pi/2} \sin^n x \, dx = \left[-\frac{\cos x \sin^{n-1} x}{n} \right]_0^{\pi/2} + \frac{n-1}{n} \int_0^{\pi/2} \sin^{n-2} x \, dx$$

$$= (0 - 0) + \frac{n-1}{n} \int_0^{\pi/2} \sin^{n-2} x \, dx = \frac{n-1}{n} \int_0^{\pi/2} \sin^{n-2} x \, dx$$

(b) Using $n = 3$ in part (a), we have $\int_0^{\pi/2} \sin^3 x \, dx = \frac{2}{3} \int_0^{\pi/2} \sin x \, dx = \left[-\frac{2}{3} \cos x \right]_0^{\pi/2} = \frac{2}{3}$.

Using $n = 5$ in part (a), we have $\int_0^{\pi/2} \sin^5 x \, dx = \frac{4}{5} \int_0^{\pi/2} \sin^3 x \, dx = \frac{4}{5} \cdot \frac{2}{3} = \frac{8}{15}$.

(c) The formula holds for $n = 1$ (that is, $2n + 1 = 3$) by (b). Assume it holds for some $k \geq 1$. Then

$$\int_0^{\pi/2} \sin^{2k+1} x \, dx = \frac{2 \cdot 4 \cdot 6 \cdots \cdots (2k)}{3 \cdot 5 \cdot 7 \cdots \cdots (2k+1)}.$$ By Example 6,

$$\int_0^{\pi/2} \sin^{2k+3} x \, dx = \frac{2k+2}{2k+3} \int_0^{\pi/2} \sin^{2k+1} x \, dx = \frac{2k+2}{2k+3} \cdot \frac{2 \cdot 4 \cdot 6 \cdots \cdots (2k)}{3 \cdot 5 \cdot 7 \cdots \cdots (2k+1)}$$

$$= \frac{2 \cdot 4 \cdot 6 \cdots \cdots (2k)[2(k+1)]}{3 \cdot 5 \cdot 7 \cdots \cdots (2k+1)[2(k+1)+1]},$$

so the formula holds for $n = k + 1$. By induction, the formula holds for all $n \geq 1$.

36. Using Exercise 35(a), we see that the formula holds for $n = 1$, because

$$\int_0^{\pi/2} \sin^2 x \, dx = \frac{1}{2} \int_0^{\pi/2} 1 \, dx = \frac{1}{2} [x]_0^{\pi/2} = \frac{1}{2} \cdot \frac{\pi}{2}.$$

Now assume it holds for some $k \geq 1$. Then $\displaystyle\int_0^{\pi/2} \sin^{2k} x \, dx = \frac{1 \cdot 3 \cdot 5 \cdots \cdots (2k-1)}{2 \cdot 4 \cdot 6 \cdots \cdots (2k)} \frac{\pi}{2}$. By Exercise 35(a),

$$\int_0^{\pi/2} \sin^{2(k+1)} x \, dx = \frac{2k+1}{2k+2} \int_0^{\pi/2} \sin^{2k} x \, dx = \frac{2k+1}{2k+2} \cdot \frac{1 \cdot 3 \cdot 5 \cdots \cdots (2k-1)}{2 \cdot 4 \cdot 6 \cdots \cdots (2k)} \frac{\pi}{2}$$

$$= \frac{1 \cdot 3 \cdot 5 \cdots \cdots (2k-1)(2k+1)}{2 \cdot 4 \cdot 6 \cdots \cdots (2k)(2k+2)} \cdot \frac{\pi}{2},$$

so the formula holds for $n = k + 1$. By induction, the formula holds for all $n \geq 1$.

37. Let $u = (\ln x)^n$, $dv = dx$ $\Rightarrow$ $du = n(\ln x)^{n-1}(dx/x)$, $v = x$. By Equation 2,

$\int (\ln x)^n \, dx = x(\ln x)^n - \int nx(\ln x)^{n-1}(dx/x) = x(\ln x)^n - n \int (\ln x)^{n-1} \, dx$.

38. Let $u = x^n$, $dv = e^x \, dx$ $\Rightarrow$ $du = nx^{n-1} \, dx$, $v = e^x$. By Equation 2, $\int x^n e^x \, dx = x^n e^x - n \int x^{n-1} e^x \, dx$.

39. Take $n = 3$ in Exercise 37 to get

$\int (\ln x)^3 \, dx = x (\ln x)^3 - 3 \int (\ln x)^2 \, dx = x(\ln x)^3 - 3x(\ln x)^2 + 6x \ln x - 6x + C$ (by Exercise 9).

Or: Instead of using Exercise 9, apply Exercise 37 again with $n = 2$.

40. Take $n = 4$ in Exercise 38 to get

$$\int x^4 e^x \, dx = x^4 e^x - 4 \int x^3 e^x \, dx = x^4 e^x - 4 \left(x^3 - 3x^2 + 6x - 6 \right) e^x + C \quad \text{(by Exercise 10)}$$

$$= e^x \left(x^4 - 4x^3 + 12x^2 - 24x + 24 \right) + C$$

Or: Instead of using Exercise 10, apply Exercise 38 with $n = 3$, then $n = 2$, then $n = 1$.

41. Since $v(t) > 0$ for all t, the desired distance is $s(t) = \int_0^t v(w)\,dw = \int_0^t w^2 e^{-w}\,dw$.

First let $u = w^2$, $dv = e^{-w}\,dw$ $\Rightarrow$ $du = 2w\,dw$, $v = -e^{-w}$. Then $s(t) = \left[-w^2 e^{-w}\right]_0^t + 2\int_0^t we^{-w}\,dw$.

Next let $U = w$, $dV = e^{-w}\,dw$ $\Rightarrow$ $dU = dw$, $V = -e^{-w}$. Then

$$s(t) = -t^2 e^{-t} + 2\left(\left[-we^{-w}\right]_0^t + \int_0^t e^{-w}\,dw\right) = -t^2 e^{-t} + 2\left(-te^{-t} + 0 + \left[-e^{-w}\right]_0^t\right)$$

$$= -t^2 e^{-t} + 2\left(-te^{-t} - e^{-t} + 1\right) = -t^2 e^{-t} - 2te^{-t} - 2e^{-t} + 2$$

$$= 2 - e^{-t}\left(t^2 + 2t + 2\right) \text{ meters}$$

42. The rocket will have height $H = \int_0^{60} v(t)\,dt$ after 60 seconds.

$$H = \int_0^{60}\left[-gt - v_e \ln\left(\frac{m - rt}{m}\right)\right]\,dt = -g\left[\tfrac{1}{2}t^2\right]_0^{60} - v_e\left[\int_0^{60} \ln(m - rt)\,dt - \int_0^{60} \ln m\,dt\right]$$

$$= -g(1800) + v_e(\ln m)(60) - v_e\int_0^{60}\ln(m - rt)\,dt$$

Let $u = \ln(m - rt)$, $dv = dt$ $\Rightarrow$ $du = \dfrac{1}{m - rt}(-r)\,dt$, $v = t$. Then

$$\int_0^{60}\ln(m - rt)\,dt = [t\ln(m - rt)]_0^{60} + \int_0^{60}\frac{rt}{m - rt}\,dt = 60\ln(m - 60r) + \int_0^{60}\left(-1 + \frac{m}{m - rt}\right)\,dt$$

$$= 60\ln(m - 60r) + \left[-t - \frac{m}{r}\ln(m - rt)\right]_0^{60}$$

$$= 60\ln(m - 60r) - 60 - \frac{m}{r}\ln(m - 60r) + \frac{m}{r}\ln m$$

So $H = -1800g + 60v_e \ln m - 60v_e \ln(m - 60r) + 60v_e + \dfrac{m}{r}v_e \ln(m - 60r) - \dfrac{m}{r}v_e \ln m$. Substituting

$g = 9.8$, $m = 30{,}000$, $r = 160$, and $v_e = 3000$ gives us $H \approx 14{,}844$ m.

43. Take $g(x) = x$ and $g'(x) = 1$ in Equation 1.

44. (a) By Exercise 43, $\int_a^b f(x)\,dx = bf(b) - af(a) - \int_a^b xf'(x)\,dx$.

Now let $y = f(x)$, so that $x = f^{-1}(y)$ and $dy = f'(x)\,dx$. Then

$\int_a^b xf'(x)\,dx = \int_{f(a)}^{f(b)} f^{-1}(y)\,dy$. The result follows:

$\int_a^b f(x)\,dx = bf(b) - af(a) - \int_{f(a)}^{f(b)} f^{-1}(y)\,dy$.

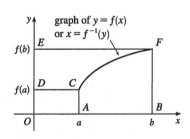

graph of $y = f(x)$
or $x = f^{-1}(y)$

(b) Part (a) says that the area of region $ABFC$ is

(area of rectangle $OBFE$) − (area of rectangle $OACD$) − (area of region $DCFE$)

45. Suppose $f(0) = g(0) = 0$ and let $u = f(x)$, $dv = g''(x)\,dx$ $\Rightarrow$ $du = f'(x)\,dx$, $v = g'(x)$.

Then $\int_0^a f(x)g''(x)\,dx = [f(x)g'(x)]_0^a - \int_0^a f'(x)g'(x)\,dx = f(a)g'(a) - \int_0^a f'(x)g'(x)\,dx$.

Now let $U = f'(x)$, $dV = g'(x)\,dx$ $\Rightarrow$ $dU = f''(x)\,dx$ and $V = g(x)$, so

$\int_0^a f'(x)g'(x)\,dx = [f'(x)g(x)]_0^a - \int_0^a f''(x)g(x)\,dx = f'(a)g(a) - \int_0^a f''(x)g(x)\,dx$. Combining the two

results, we get $\int_0^a f(x)g''(x)\,dx = f(a)g'(a) - f'(a)g(a) + \int_0^a f''(x)g(x)\,dx$.

46. (a) We note that for $0 \le x \le \frac{\pi}{2}$, $0 \le \sin x \le 1$, so $\sin^{2n+2} x \le \sin^{2n+1} x \le \sin^{2n} x$. So by the second

Comparison Property of the Integral, $I_{2n+2} \le I_{2n+1} \le I_{2n}$.

(b) Substituting directly into the result from Exercise 36, we get

$$\frac{I_{2n+2}}{I_{2n}} = \frac{\dfrac{1\cdot3\cdot5\cdot\cdots\cdot[2(n+1)-1]}{2\cdot4\cdot6\cdot\cdots\cdot[2(n+1)]}\dfrac{\pi}{2}}{\dfrac{1\cdot3\cdot5\cdot\cdots\cdot(2n-1)}{2\cdot4\cdot6\cdot\cdots\cdot(2n)}\dfrac{\pi}{2}} = \frac{2(n+1)-1}{2(n+1)} = \frac{2n+1}{2n+2}$$

(c) We divide the result from part (a) by I_{2n}. The inequalities are preserved since I_{2n} is positive:

$\dfrac{I_{2n+2}}{I_{2n}} \le \dfrac{I_{2n+1}}{I_{2n}} \le \dfrac{I_{2n}}{I_{2n}}$. Now from part (b), the left term is equal to $\dfrac{2n+1}{2n+2}$, so the expression becomes

$\dfrac{2n+1}{2n+2} \le \dfrac{I_{2n+1}}{I_{2n}} \le 1$. Now $\lim\limits_{n\to\infty}\dfrac{2n+1}{2n+2} = \lim\limits_{n\to\infty} 1 = 1$, so by the Squeeze Theorem, $\lim\limits_{n\to\infty}\dfrac{I_{2n+1}}{I_{2n}} = 1$.

(d) We substitute the results from Exercises 35 and 36 into the result from part (c):

$$1 = \lim_{n\to\infty}\frac{I_{2n+1}}{I_{2n}} = \lim_{n\to\infty}\frac{\dfrac{2\cdot4\cdot6\cdot\cdots\cdot(2n)}{3\cdot5\cdot7\cdot\cdots\cdot(2n+1)}}{\dfrac{1\cdot3\cdot5\cdot\cdots\cdot(2n-1)}{2\cdot4\cdot6\cdot\cdots\cdot(2n)}\dfrac{\pi}{2}}$$

$$= \lim_{n\to\infty}\left[\frac{2\cdot4\cdot6\cdot\cdots\cdot(2n)}{3\cdot5\cdot7\cdot\cdots\cdot(2n+1)}\right]\left[\frac{2\cdot4\cdot6\cdot\cdots\cdot(2n)}{1\cdot3\cdot5\cdot\cdots\cdot(2n-1)}\left(\frac{2}{\pi}\right)\right]$$

$$= \lim_{n\to\infty}\frac{2}{1}\cdot\frac{2}{3}\cdot\frac{4}{3}\cdot\frac{4}{5}\cdot\frac{6}{5}\cdot\frac{6}{7}\cdot\cdots\cdot\frac{2n}{2n-1}\cdot\frac{2n}{2n+1}\cdot\frac{2}{\pi}\qquad\text{[rearrange terms]}$$

Multiplying both sides by $\frac{\pi}{2}$ gives us the *Wallis product*:

$$\frac{\pi}{2} = \frac{2}{1}\cdot\frac{2}{3}\cdot\frac{4}{3}\cdot\frac{4}{5}\cdot\frac{6}{5}\cdot\frac{6}{7}\cdot\cdots$$

(e) The area of the kth rectangle is k. At the $2n$th step, the area is increased from $2n-1$ to $2n$ by multiplying the width by $\dfrac{2n}{2n-1}$, and at the $(2n+1)$th step, the area is increased from $2n$ to $2n+1$ by multiplying the height by $\dfrac{2n+1}{2n}$. These two steps multiply the ratio of width to height by $\dfrac{2n}{2n-1}$ and $\dfrac{1}{(2n+1)/(2n)} = \dfrac{2n}{2n+1}$ respectively. So, by part (d), the limiting ratio is $\dfrac{2}{1}\cdot\dfrac{2}{3}\cdot\dfrac{4}{3}\cdot\dfrac{4}{5}\cdot\dfrac{6}{5}\cdot\dfrac{6}{7}\cdot\cdots = \dfrac{\pi}{2}$.

5.7 Additional Techniques of Integration · · · · · · · · ·

The symbols $\overset{s}{=}$ and $\overset{c}{=}$ indicate the use of the substitutions $\{u = \sin x,\ du = \cos x\,dx\}$ and $\{u = \cos x,\ du = -\sin x\,dx\}$, respectively.

1. $\int \sin^3 x \cos^2 x\,dx = \int \sin^2 x \cos^2 x \sin x\,dx = \int(1-\cos^2 x)\cos^2 x \sin x\,dx \overset{c}{=} \int(1-u^2)u^2(-du)$

$\qquad = \int(u^2-1)u^2\,du = \int(u^4-u^2)\,du = \frac{1}{5}u^5 - \frac{1}{3}u^3 + C = \frac{1}{5}\cos^5 x - \frac{1}{3}\cos^3 x + C$

2. $\int_0^{\pi/2} \cos^5 x\,dx = \int_0^{\pi/2}(\cos^2 x)^2\cos x\,dx = \int_0^{\pi/2}(1-\sin^2 x)^2\cos x\,dx \overset{s}{=} \int_0^1(1-u^2)^2\,du$

$\qquad = \int_0^1(1-2u^2+u^4)\,du = \left[u - \frac{2}{3}u^3 + \frac{1}{5}u^5\right]_0^1 = \left(1 - \frac{2}{3} + \frac{1}{5}\right) - 0 = \frac{8}{15}$

3. $\int_{\pi/2}^{3\pi/4} \sin^5 x \cos^3 x\,dx = \int_{\pi/2}^{3\pi/4} \sin^5 x \cos^2 x \cos x\,dx = \int_{\pi/2}^{3\pi/4} \sin^5 x (1-\sin^2 x)\cos x\,dx$

$\qquad \overset{s}{=} \int_1^{\sqrt{2}/2} u^5(1-u^2)\,du = \int_1^{\sqrt{2}/2}(u^5-u^7)\,du = \left[\frac{1}{6}u^6 - \frac{1}{8}u^8\right]_1^{\sqrt{2}/2}$

$\qquad = \left(\frac{1/8}{6} - \frac{1/16}{8}\right) - \left(\frac{1}{6} - \frac{1}{8}\right) = -\frac{11}{384}$

4. $\int \sin^3 mx \, dx = \int (1 - \cos^2 mx) \sin mx \, dx = -\frac{1}{m} \int (1 - u^2) \, du$ $[u = \cos mx, \; du = -m \sin mx \, dx]$

$\qquad = -\frac{1}{m}\left(u - \frac{1}{3}u^3\right) + C = -\frac{1}{m}\left(\cos mx - \frac{1}{3}\cos^3 mx\right) + C$

$\qquad = \frac{1}{3m}\cos^3 mx - \frac{1}{m}\cos mx + C$

5. $\int \cos^4 t \, dt = \int (\cos^2 t)^2 \, dt = \int \left[\frac{1}{2}(1 + \cos 2t)\right]^2 dt = \frac{1}{4}\int (1 + 2\cos 2t + \cos^2 2t) \, dt$

$\qquad = \frac{1}{4}t + \frac{1}{4}\sin 2t + \frac{1}{4}\int \frac{1}{2}(1 + \cos 4t) \, dt = \frac{1}{4}\left[t + \sin 2t + \frac{1}{2}t + \frac{1}{8}\sin 4t\right] + C$

$\qquad = \frac{1}{4}\left(\frac{3}{2}t + \sin 2t + \frac{1}{8}\sin 4t\right) + C = \frac{3}{8}t + \frac{1}{4}\sin 2t + \frac{1}{32}\sin 4t + C$

6. $\int_0^{\pi/2} \sin^2 x \cos^2 x \, dx = \int_0^{\pi/2} \frac{1}{4}(4\sin^2 x \cos^2 x) \, dx = \int_0^{\pi/2} \frac{1}{4}(2\sin x \cos x)^2 dx = \frac{1}{4}\int_0^{\pi/2} \sin^2 2x \, dx$

$\qquad = \frac{1}{4}\int_0^{\pi/2} \frac{1}{2}(1 - \cos 4x) \, dx = \frac{1}{8}\int_0^{\pi/2}(1 - \cos 4x) \, dx = \frac{1}{8}\left[x - \frac{1}{4}\sin 4x\right]_0^{\pi/2}$

$\qquad = \frac{1}{8}\left(\frac{\pi}{2}\right) = \frac{\pi}{16}$

7. Let $u = \sec x$. Then $du = \sec x \tan x \, dx$, so

$\qquad \int \tan^3 x \sec x \, dx = \int (\tan^2 x)(\tan x \sec x) \, dx = \int (\sec^2 x - 1)(\sec x \tan x \, dx)$

$\qquad\qquad = \int (u^2 - 1) \, du = \frac{1}{3}u^3 - u + C = \frac{1}{3}\sec^3 x - \sec x + C$

8. Let $u = \tan x$. Then $du = \sec^2 x \, dx$, so

$\qquad \int_0^{\pi/4} \tan^2 x \sec^4 x \, dx = \int_0^{\pi/4} \tan^2 x \sec^2 x (\sec^2 x \, dx) = \int_0^{\pi/4} \tan^2 x (1 + \tan^2 x)(\sec^2 x \, dx)$

$\qquad\qquad = \int_0^1 u^2 (1 + u^2) \, du = \int_0^1 (u^2 + u^4) \, du$

$\qquad\qquad = \left[\frac{1}{3}u^3 + \frac{1}{5}u^5\right]_0^1 = \frac{1}{3} + \frac{1}{5} = \frac{8}{15}$

9. $x = 3\sin\theta$, where $-\pi/2 \le \theta \le \pi/2$. Then $dx = 3\cos\theta \, d\theta$ and

$\sqrt{9 - x^2} = \sqrt{9 - 9\sin^2\theta} = \sqrt{9\cos^2\theta} = 3\,|\cos\theta| = 3\cos\theta$. (Note that $\cos\theta \ge 0$ because

$-\pi/2 \le \theta \le \pi/2$.) Thus, substitution gives

$$\int \frac{\sqrt{9 - x^2}}{x^2} \, dx = \int \frac{3\cos\theta}{9\sin^2\theta} 3\cos\theta \, d\theta = \int \frac{\cos^2\theta}{\sin^2\theta} \, d\theta = \int \cot^2\theta \, d\theta$$

$$= \int (\csc^2\theta - 1) \, d\theta = -\cot\theta - \theta + C$$

Since this is an indefinite integral, we must return to the original
variable x. This can be done either by using trigonometric identities to
express $\cot\theta$ in terms of $\sin\theta = x/3$ or by drawing a diagram, as
shown, where θ is interpreted as an angle of a right triangle.

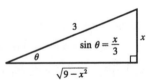

Since $\sin\theta = x/3$, we label the opposite side and the hypotenuse as having lengths x and 3. Then the Pythagorean
Theorem gives the length of the adjacent side as $\sqrt{9 - x^2}$, so we can simply read the value of $\cot\theta$ from the figure:

$\cot\theta = \dfrac{\sqrt{9 - x^2}}{x}$. (Although $\theta > 0$ in the diagram, this expression for $\cot\theta$ is valid even when $\theta < 0$.) Since

$\sin\theta = x/3$, we have $\theta = \sin^{-1}(x/3)$ and so $\displaystyle\int \frac{\sqrt{9 - x^2}}{x^2} \, dx = -\frac{\sqrt{9 - x^2}}{x} - \sin^{-1}\left(\frac{x}{3}\right) + C$.

10. $x = \sec\theta$, where $0 \le \theta < \pi/2$ or $\pi \le \theta < 3\pi/2$. Then

$dx = \sec\theta\,\tan\theta\,d\theta$ and

$\sqrt{x^2 - 1} = \sqrt{\sec^2\theta - 1} = \sqrt{\tan^2\theta} = |\tan\theta| = \tan\theta$ (since

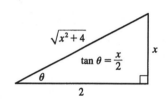

$\sec\theta = \dfrac{x}{1}$

$\tan\theta \ge 0$ for the specified values of θ). Thus, substitution gives

$$\int \frac{\sqrt{x^2-1}}{x^4}\,dx = \int \frac{\tan\theta}{\sec^4\theta}\sec\theta\,\tan\theta\,d\theta = \int \frac{\tan^2\theta}{\sec^3\theta}\,d\theta = \int \frac{\sin^2\theta}{\cos^2\theta}\cdot\cos^3\theta\,d\theta$$

$$= \int \sin^2\theta\,\cos\theta\,d\theta = \int u^2\,du \quad [u = \sin\theta,\, du = \cos\theta\,d\theta]$$

$$= \frac{1}{3}u^3 + C = \frac{1}{3}\sin^3\theta + C = \frac{1}{3}\left(\frac{\sqrt{x^2-1}}{x}\right)^3 + C = \frac{(x^2-1)^{3/2}}{3x^3} + C$$

11. $x = 2\tan\theta$, where $-\pi/2 < \theta < \pi/2$. Then $dx = 2\sec^2\theta\,d\theta$ and

$\sqrt{x^2+4} = \sqrt{(2\tan\theta)^2 + 4} = \sqrt{4\tan^2\theta + 4}$

$\qquad = \sqrt{4(\tan^2\theta + 1)} = 2\sqrt{\sec^2\theta} = 2|\sec\theta|$

$\qquad = 2\sec\theta$ (since $\sec\theta \ge 0$ for $-\pi/2 < \theta < \pi/2$).

$\sqrt{x^2+4}$, $\tan\theta = \dfrac{x}{2}$

Thus, substitution gives

$$\int \frac{1}{x^2\sqrt{x^2+4}}\,dx = \int \frac{1}{4\tan^2\theta\,(2\sec\theta)}(2\sec^2\theta\,d\theta) = \frac{1}{4}\int \frac{\sec\theta}{\tan^2\theta}\,d\theta = \frac{1}{4}\int \frac{1}{\cos\theta}\cdot\frac{\cos^2\theta}{\sin^2\theta}\,d\theta$$

$$= \frac{1}{4}\int \frac{\cos\theta}{\sin^2\theta}\,d\theta = \frac{1}{4}\int \frac{1}{u^2}\,du \quad [u = \sin\theta,\, du = \cos\theta\,d\theta]$$

$$= \frac{1}{4}\left(-\frac{1}{u}\right) + C = -\frac{1}{4}\frac{1}{\sin\theta} + C = -\frac{1}{4}\cdot\frac{\sqrt{x^2+4}}{x} + C = -\frac{\sqrt{x^2+4}}{4x} + C$$

12. (a) $\dfrac{d}{d\theta}\left[\frac{1}{2}(\sec\theta\,\tan\theta + \ln|\sec\theta + \tan\theta|) + C\right]$

$$= \frac{1}{2}\left(\sec\theta\cdot\sec^2\theta + \tan\theta\cdot\sec\theta\,\tan\theta + \frac{1}{\sec\theta + \tan\theta}\cdot\sec\theta\,\tan\theta + \sec^2\theta\right) + 0$$

$$= \frac{1}{2}\left[\sec\theta\,(\sec^2\theta + \tan^2\theta) + \frac{\sec\theta\,(\tan\theta + \sec\theta)}{\sec\theta + \tan\theta}\right]$$

$$= \frac{1}{2}\left[\sec\theta\,(\sec^2\theta + \sec^2\theta - 1) + \sec\theta\right] = \frac{1}{2}\sec\theta\left[(2\sec^2\theta - 1) + 1\right]$$

$$= \frac{1}{2}\sec\theta\,(2\sec^2\theta) = \sec^3\theta.$$

Thus, $\int \sec^3\theta\,d\theta = \frac{1}{2}(\sec\theta\,\tan\theta + \ln|\sec\theta + \tan\theta|) + C$.

(b) As in Exercise 11, we use the substitution $x = \tan\theta$, where $-\pi/2 < \theta < \pi/2$. Then $dx = \sec^2\theta\,d\theta$ and

$\sqrt{x^2+1} = \sqrt{\tan^2\theta + 1} = \sqrt{\sec^2\theta} = |\sec\theta| = \sec\theta$ (since $\sec\theta \ge 0$ for $-\pi/2 < \theta < \pi/2$). When $x = 0$,

$\tan\theta = 0 \;\Rightarrow\; \theta = 0$, and when $x = 1$, $\tan\theta = 1 \;\Rightarrow\; \theta = \frac{\pi}{4}$. Thus, substitution gives

$$\int_0^1 \sqrt{x^2+1}\,dx = \int_0^{\pi/4} \sec\theta\,(\sec^2\theta\,d\theta) = \int_0^{\pi/4} \sec^3\theta\,d\theta = \left[\frac{1}{2}(\sec\theta\,\tan\theta + \ln|\sec\theta + \tan\theta|)\right]_0^{\pi/4}$$

$$= \frac{1}{2}\left[(\sqrt{2}\cdot 1 + \ln|\sqrt{2}+1|) - (1\cdot 0 + \ln|1 + 0|)\right]$$

$$= \frac{1}{2}\left[\sqrt{2} + \ln(\sqrt{2}+1)\right]$$

13. The radicand has the form (variable)^2 − (constant)^2, so we'll use the substitution from Exercise 10; that is,
$t = \sec\theta$, where $0 \le \theta < \pi/2$ or $\pi \le \theta < 3\pi/2$. Then $dt = \sec\theta\tan\theta\,d\theta$ and
$\sqrt{x^2 - 1} = \sqrt{\sec^2\theta - 1} = \sqrt{\tan^2\theta} = |\tan\theta| = \tan\theta$ (since $\tan\theta \ge 0$ for the specified values of θ).
When $t = \sqrt{2}$, $\theta = \frac{\pi}{4}$; when $t = 2$, $\theta = \frac{\pi}{3}$. Thus,

$$\int_{\sqrt{2}}^{2} \frac{1}{t^3\sqrt{t^2 - 1}}\,dt = \int_{\pi/4}^{\pi/3} \frac{1}{\sec^3\theta\,\tan\theta}\,\sec\theta\,\tan\theta\,d\theta = \int_{\pi/4}^{\pi/3} \frac{1}{\sec^2\theta}\,d\theta = \int_{\pi/4}^{\pi/3} \cos^2\theta\,d\theta$$

$$= \int_{\pi/4}^{\pi/3} \tfrac{1}{2}(1 + \cos 2\theta)\,d\theta = \tfrac{1}{2}\left[\theta + \tfrac{1}{2}\sin 2\theta\right]_{\pi/4}^{\pi/3}$$

$$= \tfrac{1}{2}\left[\left(\tfrac{\pi}{3} + \tfrac{1}{2}\cdot\tfrac{\sqrt{3}}{2}\right) - \left(\tfrac{\pi}{4} + \tfrac{1}{2}\cdot 1\right)\right] = \tfrac{1}{2}\left(\tfrac{\pi}{12} + \tfrac{\sqrt{3}}{4} - \tfrac{1}{2}\right) = \tfrac{\pi}{24} + \tfrac{\sqrt{3}}{8} - \tfrac{1}{4}$$

14. Let $x = 4\sin\theta$, where $-\pi/2 \le \theta \le \pi/2$. Then $dx = 4\cos\theta\,d\theta$ and
$\sqrt{16 - x^2} = \sqrt{16 - 16\sin^2\theta} = \sqrt{16\cos^2\theta} = 4\,|\cos\theta| = 4\cos\theta$. When $x = 0$, $4\sin\theta = 0 \;\Rightarrow\; \theta = 0$, and
when $x = 2\sqrt{3}$, $4\sin\theta = 2\sqrt{3} \;\Rightarrow\; \sin\theta = \frac{\sqrt{3}}{2} \;\Rightarrow\; \theta = \frac{\pi}{3}$. Thus, substitution gives

$$\int_{0}^{2\sqrt{3}} \frac{x^3}{\sqrt{16 - x^2}}\,dx = \int_{0}^{\pi/3} \frac{4^3\sin^3\theta}{4\cos\theta}\,4\cos\theta\,d\theta = 4^3\int_{0}^{\pi/3} \sin^3\theta\,d\theta$$

$$= 4^3\int_{0}^{\pi/3}(1 - \cos^2\theta)\sin\theta\,d\theta$$

$$\overset{c}{=} -4^3\int_{1}^{1/2}(1 - u^2)\,du = -64\left[u - \tfrac{1}{3}u^3\right]_{1}^{1/2}$$

$$= -64\left[\left(\tfrac{1}{2} - \tfrac{1}{24}\right) - \left(1 - \tfrac{1}{3}\right)\right] = -64\left(-\tfrac{5}{24}\right) = \tfrac{40}{3}$$

Or: Let $u = 16 - x^2$, $x^2 = 16 - u$, $du = -2x\,dx$.

15. (a) $\dfrac{2}{x^2 + 3x - 4} = \dfrac{2}{(x+4)(x-1)} = \dfrac{A}{x+4} + \dfrac{B}{x-1}$

(b) $x^2 + x + 1$ is irreducible, so $\dfrac{x^2}{(x-1)(x^2+x+1)} = \dfrac{A}{x-1} + \dfrac{Bx+C}{x^2+x+1}$.

16. (a) $\dfrac{x-1}{x^3+x^2} = \dfrac{x-1}{x^2(x+1)} = \dfrac{A}{x} + \dfrac{B}{x^2} + \dfrac{C}{x+1}$

(b) $\dfrac{x-1}{x^3+x} = \dfrac{x-1}{x(x^2+1)} = \dfrac{A}{x} + \dfrac{Bx+C}{x^2+1}$

17. $\dfrac{x-9}{(x+5)(x-2)} = \dfrac{A}{x+5} + \dfrac{B}{x-2}$. Multiply both sides by $(x+5)(x-2)$ to get
$x - 9 = A(x-2) + B(x+5)(*)$, or equivalently, $x - 9 = (A+B)x - 2A + 5B$. Equating coefficients of x on
each side of the equation gives us $1 = A + B$ **(1)** and equating constants gives us $-9 = -2A + 5B$ **(2)**. Adding
two times **(1)** to **(2)** gives us $-7 = 7B \;\Leftrightarrow\; B = -1$ and hence, $A = 2$. [Alternatively, to find the coefficients A
and B, we may use substitution as follows: substitute -2 for x in (*) to get $-7 = 7B \;\Leftrightarrow\;$
$B = -1$, then substitute -5 for x in (*) to get $-14 = -7A \;\Leftrightarrow\; A = 2$.] Thus,

$$\int \frac{x-9}{(x+5)(x-2)}\,dx = \int\left(\frac{2}{x+5} + \frac{-1}{x-2}\right)dx = 2\ln|x+5| - \ln|x-2| + C.$$

To find the constants in problems involving partial fractions, we may use the coefficient comparison method or the substitution method (as in the solution for Exercise 17) or a combination of both methods.

18. $\dfrac{x-1}{x^2+3x+2} = \dfrac{A}{x+1} + \dfrac{B}{x+2}$. Multiply both sides by $(x+1)(x+2)$ to get $x-1 = A(x+2) + B(x+1)$.

Substituting -2 for x gives $-3 = -B \quad \Leftrightarrow \quad B = 3$. Substituting -1 for x gives $-2 = A$. Thus,

$$\int_0^1 \frac{x-1}{x^2+3x+2}\,dx = \int_0^1 \left(\frac{-2}{x+1} + \frac{3}{x+2}\right) dx = \left[-2\ln|x+1| + 3\ln|x+2|\right]_0^1$$

$$= (-2\ln 2 + 3\ln 3) - (-2\ln 1 + 3\ln 2) = 3\ln 3 - 5\ln 2 \quad \left[\text{or } \ln\tfrac{27}{32}\right]$$

19. $\dfrac{1}{x^2-1} = \dfrac{1}{(x+1)(x-1)} = \dfrac{A}{x+1} + \dfrac{B}{x-1}$. Multiply both sides by $(x+1)(x-1)$ to get

$1 = A(x-1) + B(x+1)$. Substituting 1 for x gives $1 = 2B \quad \Leftrightarrow \quad B = \tfrac{1}{2}$.

Substituting -1 for x gives $1 = -2A \quad \Leftrightarrow \quad A = -\tfrac{1}{2}$. Thus,

$$\int_2^3 \frac{1}{x^2-1}\,dx = \int_2^3 \left(\frac{-1/2}{x+1} + \frac{1/2}{x-1}\right) dx = \left[-\tfrac{1}{2}\ln|x+1| + \tfrac{1}{2}\ln|x-1|\right]_2^3$$

$$= \left(-\tfrac{1}{2}\ln 4 + \tfrac{1}{2}\ln 2\right) - \left(-\tfrac{1}{2}\ln 3 + \tfrac{1}{2}\ln 1\right) = \tfrac{1}{2}(\ln 2 + \ln 3 - \ln 4) \quad \left[\text{or } \tfrac{1}{2}\ln\tfrac{3}{2}\right]$$

20. $\dfrac{x^2+2x-1}{x^3-x} = \dfrac{3x^2-1}{x(x+1)(x-1)} = \dfrac{A}{x} + \dfrac{B}{x+1} + \dfrac{C}{x-1}$. Multiply both sides by $x(x+1)(x-1)$ to get

$x^2+2x-1 = A(x+1)(x-1) + Bx(x-1) + Cx(x+1)$. Substituting 0 for x gives $-1 = -A \quad \Leftrightarrow \quad A = 1$.

Substituting -1 for x gives $-2 = 2B \quad \Leftrightarrow \quad B = -1$. Substituting 1 for x gives $2 = 2C \quad \Leftrightarrow \quad C = 1$. Thus,

$$\int \frac{x^2+2x-1}{x^3-x}\,dx = \int \left(\frac{1}{x} - \frac{1}{x+1} + \frac{1}{x-1}\right) dx = \ln|x| - \ln|x+1| + \ln|x-1| + C = \ln\left|\frac{x(x-1)}{x+1}\right| + C.$$

21. $\dfrac{10}{(x-1)(x^2+9)} = \dfrac{A}{x-1} + \dfrac{Bx+C}{x^2+9}$. Multiply both sides by $(x-1)(x^2+9)$ to get

$10 = A(x^2+9) + (Bx+C)(x-1)$ $(\star)$. Substituting 1 for x gives $10 = 10A \quad \Leftrightarrow \quad A = 1$. Substituting 0 for x

gives $10 = 9A - C \quad \Rightarrow \quad C = 9(1) - 10 = -1$. The coefficients of the x^2-terms in $(\star)$ must be equal, so

$0 = A + B \quad \Rightarrow \quad B = -1$. Thus,

$$\int \frac{10}{(x-1)(x^2+9)}\,dx = \int \left(\frac{1}{x-1} + \frac{-x-1}{x^2+9}\right) dx = \int \left(\frac{1}{x-1} - \frac{x}{x^2+9} - \frac{1}{x^2+9}\right) dx$$

$$= \ln|x-1| - \tfrac{1}{2}\ln(x^2+9) \ \left[\text{let } u = x^2+9\right] - \tfrac{1}{3}\tan^{-1}\left(\tfrac{x}{3}\right) \ \left[\text{Formula 1}\right] + C$$

22. $\dfrac{2x^2+5}{(x^2+1)(x^2+4)} = \dfrac{Ax+B}{x^2+1} + \dfrac{Cx+D}{x^2+4}$. Multiply both sides by $(x^2+1)(x^2+4)$ to get

$2x^2+5 = (Ax+B)(x^2+4) + (Cx+D)(x^2+1) \quad \Leftrightarrow$

$2x^2+5 = (Ax^3+Bx^2+4Ax+4B) + (Cx^3+Dx^2+Cx+D) \quad \Leftrightarrow$

$2x^2+5 = (A+C)x^3 + (B+D)x^2 + (4A+C)x + (4B+D)$. Comparing coefficients gives us $A+C = 0$,

$B+D = 2$, $4A+C = 0$, and $4B+D = 5$. Solving gives us $A = C = 0$ and $B = D = 1$. Thus,

$$\int \frac{2x^2+5}{(x^2+1)(x^2+4)}\,dx = \int \left(\frac{1}{x^2+1} + \frac{1}{x^2+4}\right) dx = \tan^{-1}x + \tfrac{1}{2}\tan^{-1}\left(\tfrac{x}{2}\right) + C.$$

23. $\dfrac{x^3 + x^2 + 2x + 1}{(x^2 + 1)(x^2 + 2)} = \dfrac{Ax + B}{x^2 + 1} + \dfrac{Cx + D}{x^2 + 2}$. Multiply both sides by $(x^2 + 1)(x^2 + 2)$ to get

$x^3 + x^2 + 2x + 1 = (Ax + B)(x^2 + 2) + (Cx + D)(x^2 + 1)$ $\Leftrightarrow$

$x^3 + x^2 + 2x + 1 = (Ax^3 + Bx^2 + 2Ax + 2B) + (Cx^3 + Dx^2 + Cx + D)$ $\Leftrightarrow$

$x^3 + x^2 + 2x + 1 = (A + C)x^3 + (B + D)x^2 + (2A + C)x + (2B + D)$. Comparing coefficients gives us the

following system of equations:

$$A + C = 1 \quad \text{(1)} \qquad B + D = 1 \quad \text{(2)}$$
$$2A + C = 2 \quad \text{(3)} \qquad 2B + D = 1 \quad \text{(4)}$$

Subtracting equation **(1)** from equation **(3)** gives us $A = 1$, so $C = 0$. Subtracting equation **(2)** from equation **(4)**

gives us $B = 0$, so $D = 1$. Thus, $I = \displaystyle\int \dfrac{x^3 + x^2 + 2x + 1}{(x^2 + 1)(x^2 + 2)}\,dx = \int \left(\dfrac{x}{x^2 + 1} + \dfrac{1}{x^2 + 2} \right) dx$. For $\displaystyle\int \dfrac{x}{x^2 + 1}\,dx$,

let $u = x^2 + 1$ so $du = 2x\,dx$ and then $\displaystyle\int \dfrac{x}{x^2 + 1}\,dx = \dfrac{1}{2}\int \dfrac{1}{u}\,du = \dfrac{1}{2}\ln|u| + C = \dfrac{1}{2}\ln(x^2 + 1) + C$. For

$\displaystyle\int \dfrac{1}{x^2 + 2}\,dx$, use Formula 1 with $a = \sqrt{2}$. So $\displaystyle\int \dfrac{1}{x^2 + 2}\,dx = \int \dfrac{1}{x^2 + (\sqrt{2})^2}\,dx = \dfrac{1}{\sqrt{2}}\tan^{-1}\dfrac{x}{\sqrt{2}} + C$. Thus,

$I = \dfrac{1}{2}\ln(x^2 + 1) + \dfrac{1}{\sqrt{2}}\tan^{-1}\dfrac{x}{\sqrt{2}} + C$.

24. $\dfrac{x^2 - x + 6}{x^3 + 3x} = \dfrac{x^2 - x + 6}{x(x^2 + 3)} = \dfrac{A}{x} + \dfrac{Bx + C}{x^2 + 3}$. Multiply by $x(x^2 + 3)$ to get

$x^2 - x + 6 = A(x^2 + 3) + (Bx + C)x$. Substituting 0 for x gives $6 = 3A$ $\Leftrightarrow$ $A = 2$. The coefficients of the

x^2-terms must be equal, so $1 = A + B$ $\Rightarrow$ $B = 1 - 2 = -1$. The coefficients of the x-terms must be equal, so

$-1 = C$. Thus,

$$\int \dfrac{x^2 - x + 6}{x^3 + 3x}\,dx = \int \left(\dfrac{2}{x} + \dfrac{-x - 1}{x^2 + 3} \right) dx = \int \left(\dfrac{2}{x} - \dfrac{x}{x^2 + 3} - \dfrac{1}{x^2 + 3} \right) dx$$
$$= 2\ln|x| - \dfrac{1}{2}\ln(x^2 + 3) - \dfrac{1}{\sqrt{3}}\tan^{-1}\dfrac{x}{\sqrt{3}} + C$$

25.

$$\begin{array}{r} x - 1 \\ x + 1\ \overline{\smash{\big)}\ x^2 } \\ \underline{x^2 + x} \\ -x \\ \underline{-x - 1} \\ 1 \end{array}$$

By long division, $\dfrac{x^2}{x + 1} = x - 1 + \dfrac{1}{x + 1}$. Thus,

$$\int \dfrac{x^2}{x + 1}\,dx = \int \left(x - 1 + \dfrac{1}{x + 1} \right) dx$$
$$= \tfrac{1}{2}x^2 - x + \ln|x + 1| + C$$

26. $\displaystyle\int \dfrac{y}{y + 2}\,dy = \int \left(1 - \dfrac{2}{y + 2} \right) dy = y - 2\ln|y + 2| + C$

27.

$$\begin{array}{r} x \\ x^2 + 1\ \overline{\smash{\big)}\ x^3 } \\ \underline{x^3 + x} \\ -x \end{array}$$

By long division, $\dfrac{x^3}{x^2 + 1} = x - \dfrac{x}{x^2 + 1}$. Thus,

$$\int_0^1 \dfrac{x^3}{x^2 + 1}\,dx = \int_0^1 x\,dx - \int_0^1 \dfrac{x\,dx}{x^2 + 1}$$
$$= \left[\tfrac{1}{2}x^2 \right]_0^1 - \dfrac{1}{2}\int_1^2 \dfrac{1}{u}\,du \quad \text{[where } u = x^2 + 1,\ du = 2x\,dx\text{]}$$
$$= \tfrac{1}{2} - \left[\tfrac{1}{2}\ln u \right]_1^2 = \tfrac{1}{2} - \tfrac{1}{2}\ln 2 = \tfrac{1}{2}(1 - \ln 2)$$

28. $\dfrac{x^3 + x^2 - 12x + 1}{x^2 + x - 12} = x + \dfrac{1}{x^2 + x - 12} = x + \dfrac{1}{(x-3)(x+4)}$. Multiply $\dfrac{1}{(x-3)(x+4)} = \dfrac{A}{x-3} + \dfrac{B}{x+4}$ by $(x-3)(x+4)$ to get $1 = A(x+4) + B(x-3)$. Equating coefficients we get $A + B = 0$ and $4A - 3B = 1$.

Solving gives us $A = \frac{1}{7}$ and $B = -\frac{1}{7}$, so $\dfrac{x^3 + x^2 - 12x + 1}{x^2 + x - 12} = x + \dfrac{1/7}{x-3} - \dfrac{1/7}{x+4}$. Thus,

$$\int_0^2 \frac{x^3 + x^2 - 12x + 1}{x^2 + x - 12}\,dx = \left[\tfrac{1}{2}x^2 + \tfrac{1}{7}(\ln|x-3| - \ln|x+4|)\right]_0^2$$

$$= \left[2 + \tfrac{1}{7}(\ln 1 - \ln 6)\right] - \left[0 + \tfrac{1}{7}(\ln 3 - \ln 4)\right]$$

$$= 2 + \tfrac{1}{7}(\ln 4 - \ln 6 - \ln 3) = 2 + \tfrac{1}{7}\ln\tfrac{4}{18} = 2 + \tfrac{1}{7}\ln\tfrac{2}{9}$$

29. Let $u = \sqrt{x}$, so $u^2 = x$ and $dx = 2u\,du$. Thus,

$$\int_9^{16} \frac{\sqrt{x}}{x-4}\,dx = \int_3^4 \frac{u}{u^2 - 4}\,2u\,du = 2\int_3^4 \frac{u^2}{u^2 - 4}\,du = 2\int_3^4 \left(1 + \frac{4}{u^2 - 4}\right)du \quad \text{[by long division]}$$

$$= 2 + 8\int_3^4 \frac{du}{(u+2)(u-2)}.$$

Multiply $\dfrac{1}{(u+2)(u-2)} = \dfrac{A}{u+2} + \dfrac{B}{u-2}$ by $(u+2)(u-2)$ to get $1 = A(u-2) + B(u+2)$. Equating

coefficients we get $A + B = 0$ and $-2A + 2B = 1$. Solving gives us $B = \frac{1}{4}$ and $A = -\frac{1}{4}$, so

$\dfrac{1}{(u+2)(u-2)} = \dfrac{-1/4}{u+2} + \dfrac{1/4}{u-2}$ and the last integral is

$$2 + 8\int_3^4 \left(\frac{-1/4}{u+2} + \frac{1/4}{u-2}\right)du = 2 + 8\left[-\tfrac{1}{4}\ln|u+2| + \tfrac{1}{4}\ln|u-2|\right]_3^4$$

$$= 2 + [2\ln|u-2| - 2\ln|u+2|]_3^4 = 2 + 2\left[\ln\left|\frac{u-2}{u+2}\right|\right]_3^4$$

$$= 2 + 2\left(\ln\tfrac{2}{6} - \ln\tfrac{1}{5}\right) = 2 + 2\ln\tfrac{2/6}{1/5}$$

$$= 2 + 2\ln\tfrac{5}{3} \quad \text{or} \quad 2 + \ln\left(\tfrac{5}{3}\right)^2 = 2 + \ln\tfrac{25}{9}$$

30. Let $u = \sqrt{x+2}$. Then $x = u^2 - 2$, $dx = 2u\,du$ $\Rightarrow$

$$I = \int \frac{dx}{x - \sqrt{x+2}} = \int \frac{2u\,du}{u^2 - 2 - u} = 2\int \frac{u\,du}{u^2 - u - 2} \quad \text{and} \quad \frac{u}{u^2 - u - 2} = \frac{A}{u-2} + \frac{B}{u+1} \quad \Rightarrow$$

$u = A(u+1) + B(u-2)$. Substituting -1 for u gives $-1 = -3B \Leftrightarrow B = \frac{1}{3}$ and substituting 2 for u gives

$2 = 3A \Leftrightarrow A = \frac{2}{3}$. Thus,

$$I = \frac{2}{3}\int \left[\frac{2}{u-2} + \frac{1}{u+1}\right]du = \frac{2}{3}(2\ln|u-2| + \ln|u+1|) + C$$

$$= \frac{2}{3}\left[2\ln|\sqrt{x+2} - 2| + \ln(\sqrt{x+2} + 1)\right] + C$$

31. $x^2 + x + 1 = x^2 + x + \frac{1}{4} + 1 - \frac{1}{4}$ [add and subtract the square of one-half the
coefficient of x to complete the square]

$$= x^2 + x + \frac{1}{4} + \frac{3}{4} = \left(x + \frac{1}{2}\right)^2 + \left(\frac{\sqrt{3}}{2}\right)^2$$

So $I = \displaystyle\int \frac{dx}{x^2 + x + 1} = \int \frac{1}{\left(x + \frac{1}{2}\right)^2 + \left(\frac{\sqrt{3}}{2}\right)^2}\, dx$. Now let $u = x + \frac{1}{2}$ $\Rightarrow$ $du = dx$ and

$$I = \int \frac{1}{u^2 + \left(\frac{\sqrt{3}}{2}\right)^2}\, du = \frac{1}{\frac{\sqrt{3}}{2}} \tan^{-1} \frac{u}{\frac{\sqrt{3}}{2}} + C = \frac{2}{\sqrt{3}} \tan^{-1} \frac{2\left(x + \frac{1}{2}\right)}{\sqrt{3}} + C = \frac{2}{\sqrt{3}} \tan^{-1} \frac{2x + 1}{\sqrt{3}} + C.$$

32. $3 - 2x - x^2 = 3 - \left(x^2 + 2x\right) = 3 - \left(x^2 + 2x + 1 - 1\right) = 4 - \left(x + 1\right)^2.$

$I = \displaystyle\int \frac{x}{\sqrt{3 - 2x - x^2}}\, dx = \int \frac{x}{\sqrt{4 - (x+1)^2}}\, dx$. Let $x + 1 = 2\sin\theta$, where

$-\pi/2 \le \theta \le \pi/2$, so $dx = 2\cos\theta\, d\theta$ and

$\sqrt{4 - (x+1)^2} = \sqrt{4 - 4\sin^2\theta} = 2\sqrt{\cos^2\theta} = 2\,|\cos\theta| = 2\cos\theta$. Thus,

(Figure: right triangle with hypotenuse 2, vertical side $x+1$, with $\sin\theta = \dfrac{x+1}{2}$ and horizontal side $\sqrt{4-(x+1)^2} = \sqrt{3-2x-x^2}$)

$$I = \int \frac{2\sin\theta - 1}{2\cos\theta}(2\cos\theta\, d\theta) = \int (2\sin\theta - 1)\, d\theta = -2\cos\theta - \theta + C$$

$$= -2\,\frac{\sqrt{3 - 2x - x^2}}{2} - \sin^{-1}\frac{x+1}{2} + C = -\sqrt{3 - 2x - x^2} - \sin^{-1}\frac{x+1}{2} + C$$

5.8 Integration Using Tables and Computer Algebra Systems · ·

Keep in mind that there are several ways to approach many of these exercises, and different methods can lead to different forms
of the answer.

1. Using long division, $\dfrac{x^3 - x^2 + x - 1}{x^2 + 9} = x - 1 - 8\,\dfrac{x - 1}{x^2 + 9}.$

$I = \displaystyle\int \left(x - 1 - 8\,\frac{x-1}{x^2 + 9}\right) dx = \int (x - 1)\, dx - 8\left[\int \frac{x}{x^2 + 9}\, dx - \int \frac{1}{x^2 + 9}\, dx\right].$

Using Formula 17 with $a = 3$, we have

$I \overset{17}{=} \frac{1}{2}x^2 - x - 8 \cdot \frac{1}{2}\ln\left(x^2 + 9\right) + 8 \cdot \frac{1}{3}\tan^{-1}(x/3) + C = \frac{1}{2}x^2 - x - 4\ln\left(x^2 + 9\right) + \frac{8}{3}\tan^{-1}(x/3) + C.$

2. $\displaystyle\int e^{2\theta}\sin 3\theta\, d\theta \overset{98}{=} \frac{e^{2\theta}}{2^2 + 3^2}(2\sin 3\theta - 3\cos 3\theta) + C = \frac{2}{13}e^{2\theta}\sin 3\theta - \frac{3}{13}e^{2\theta}\cos 3\theta + C$

3. Let $u = \pi x$ $\Rightarrow$ $du = \pi\, dx$, so

$$\int \sec^3(\pi x)\, dx = \frac{1}{\pi}\int \sec^3 u\, du \overset{71}{=} \frac{1}{\pi}\left(\frac{1}{2}\sec u\tan u + \frac{1}{2}\ln\left|\sec u + \tan u\right|\right) + C$$

$$= \frac{1}{2\pi}\sec \pi x \tan \pi x + \frac{1}{2\pi}\ln\left|\sec \pi x + \tan \pi x\right| + C$$

4. $\displaystyle\int_2^3 \frac{1}{x^2\sqrt{4x^2-7}}\,dx = \int_4^6 \frac{1}{\left(\frac{1}{2}u\right)^2\sqrt{u^2-7}}\left(\frac{1}{2}\,du\right)$ $[u=2x,\ du=2\,dx]$

$$= 2\int_4^6 \frac{du}{u^2\sqrt{u^2-7}} \overset{45}{=} 2\left[\frac{\sqrt{u^2-7}}{7u}\right]_4^6$$

$$= 2\left(\frac{\sqrt{29}}{42}-\frac{3}{28}\right) = \frac{\sqrt{29}}{21}-\frac{3}{14}$$

5. Let $u=3x$. Then $du=3\,dx$, so

$$\int \frac{\sqrt{9x^2-1}}{x^2}\,dx = \int \frac{\sqrt{u^2-1}}{u^2/9}\frac{du}{3} = 3\int \frac{\sqrt{u^2-1}}{u^2}\,du \overset{42}{=} 3\left(-\frac{\sqrt{u^2-1}}{u}+\ln\left|u+\sqrt{u^2-1}\right|+C\right)$$

$$= -\frac{\sqrt{9x^2-1}}{x}+3\ln\left|3x+\sqrt{9x^2-1}\right|+C$$

6. $\displaystyle I = \int \frac{x^2+x+5}{\sqrt{x^2+1}}\,dx = \int \frac{x^2\,dx}{\sqrt{x^2+1}} + \int \frac{x\,dx}{\sqrt{x^2+1}} + \int \frac{5\,dx}{\sqrt{x^2+1}} = I_1+I_2+I_3.$

$$I_1 \overset{26}{=} \frac{x}{2}\sqrt{x^2+1} - \frac{1}{2}\ln\left(x+\sqrt{x^2+1}\right)+C$$

$$I_2 = \frac{1}{2}\int \frac{du}{\sqrt{u}}\ \ [u=x^2+1,\ du=2x\,dx] \ = \frac{1}{2}\left(2u^{1/2}\right)+C = \sqrt{x^2+1}+C$$

$$I_3 \overset{25}{=} 5\ln\left(x+\sqrt{x^2+1}\right)+C$$

So $I = \frac{1}{2}x\sqrt{x^2+1}+\sqrt{x^2+1}+\frac{9}{2}\ln\left(x+\sqrt{x^2+1}\right)+C.$

7. $\int x^3 \sin x\,dx \overset{84}{=} -x^3\cos x + 3\int x^2\cos x\,dx,\ \int x^2\cos x\,dx \overset{85}{=} x^2\sin x - 2\int x\sin x\,dx,$ and

$\int x\sin x\,dx \overset{82}{=} \sin x - x\cos x + C.$ Substituting, we get

$\int x^3 \sin x\,dx = -x^3\cos x + 3\left[x^2\sin x - 2(\sin x - x\cos x)\right] + C$

$$= -x^3\cos x + 3x^2\sin x - 6\sin x + 6x\cos x + C.$$

So $\int_0^\pi x^3\sin x\,dx = \left[-x^3\cos x + 3x^2\sin x - 6\sin x + 6x\cos x\right]_0^\pi$

$$= \left(-\pi^3\cdot -1 + 6\pi\cdot -1\right) - (0) = \pi^3 - 6\pi.$$

8. Let $u=e^x$. Then $du=e^x\,dx$, so

$$\int \frac{e^{2x}}{\sqrt{2+e^x}}\,dx = \int \frac{e^x}{\sqrt{2+e^x}}(e^x\,dx) = \int \frac{u}{\sqrt{2+u}}\,du \overset{55}{=} \frac{2}{3}(u-2\cdot 2)\sqrt{2+u}+C$$

$$= \frac{2}{3}(e^x-4)\sqrt{2+e^x}+C.$$

Another method: Let $u=2+e^x$. Then $du=e^x\,dx$, so

$$\int \frac{e^{2x}}{\sqrt{2+e^x}}\,dx = \int \frac{e^x}{\sqrt{2+e^x}}(e^x\,dx) = \int \frac{u-2}{\sqrt{u}}\,du = \int \left(u^{1/2}-2u^{-1/2}\right)du = \frac{2}{3}u^{3/2}-2\left(2u^{1/2}\right)+C$$

$$= \frac{2}{3}(2+e^x)^{3/2}-4(2+e^x)^{1/2}+C.$$

9. Let $u=x^2$. Then $du=2x\,dx$, so

$$\int x\sin^{-1}(x^2)\,dx = \frac{1}{2}\int \sin^{-1}u\,du \overset{87}{=} \frac{1}{2}\left(u\sin^{-1}u + \sqrt{1-u^2}\right)+C$$

$$= \frac{1}{2}\left[x^2\sin^{-1}(x^2)+\sqrt{1-x^4}\right]+C$$

10. Let $u = x^2$. Then $du = 2x\,dx$, so

$$\int x^3 \sin^{-1}(x^2)\,dx = \tfrac{1}{2}\int u \sin^{-1} u\,du \overset{90}{=} \tfrac{1}{2}\left(\frac{2u^2-1}{4}\sin^{-1}u + \frac{u\sqrt{1-u^2}}{4} + C\right)$$

$$= \frac{2x^4-1}{8}\sin^{-1}(x^2) + \frac{x^2\sqrt{1-x^4}}{8} + C.$$

11. $\int_{-2}^{1}\sqrt{5-4x-x^2}\,dx = \int_{-2}^{1}\sqrt{5-(x^2+4x)}\,dx = \int_{-2}^{1}\sqrt{5+4-(x^2+4x+4)}\,dx$

$$= \int_{-2}^{1}\sqrt{9-(x+2)^2}\,dx = \int_{0}^{3}\sqrt{3^2-u^2}\,du \quad [u = x+2,\ du = dx]$$

$$\overset{30}{=} \left[\tfrac{u}{2}\sqrt{9-u^2} + \tfrac{9}{2}\sin^{-1}\left(\tfrac{u}{3}\right)\right]_0^3 = \left[\left(0 + \tfrac{9}{2}\cdot\tfrac{\pi}{2}\right) - (0+0)\right] = \frac{9\pi}{4}$$

12. Let $u = e^x$. Then $x = \ln u$, $dx = du/u$, so

$$\int \frac{dx}{e^x(1+2e^x)} = \int \frac{du/u}{u(1+2u)} = \int \frac{du}{u^2(1+2u)} \overset{50}{=} -\frac{1}{u} + 2\ln\left|\frac{1+2u}{u}\right| + C = -e^{-x} + 2\ln(e^{-x}+2) + C.$$

13. Let $u = \sin x$. Then $du = \cos x\,dx$, so

$$\int \sin^2 x \cos x \ln(\sin x)\,dx = \int u^2 \ln u\,du \overset{101}{=} \frac{u^{2+1}}{(2+1)^2}[(2+1)\ln u - 1] + C = \tfrac{1}{9}u^3(3\ln u - 1) + C$$

$$= \tfrac{1}{9}\sin^3 x[3\ln(\sin x) - 1] + C.$$

14. Let $u = 3\theta$. Then $du = 3\,d\theta$, so $I = \int_0^{\pi}\cos^4(3\theta)\,d\theta = \tfrac{1}{3}\int_0^{3\pi}\cos^4 u\,du$. Now

$$\int \cos^4 u\,du \overset{74}{=} \tfrac{1}{4}\cos^3 u \sin u + \tfrac{3}{4}\int \cos^2 u\,du \text{ and } \int \cos^2 u\,du \overset{64}{=} \tfrac{1}{2}u + \tfrac{1}{4}\sin 2u + C. \text{ So}$$

$$I = \tfrac{1}{3}\left[\tfrac{1}{4}\cos^3 u \sin u + \tfrac{3}{4}\left(\tfrac{1}{2}u + \tfrac{1}{4}\sin 2u\right)\right]_0^{3\pi}$$

$$= \left[\tfrac{1}{12}\cos^3 u \sin u + \tfrac{1}{8}u + \tfrac{1}{16}\sin 2u\right]_0^{3\pi} = \tfrac{3\pi}{8} - 0 = \tfrac{3\pi}{8}.$$

15. $\int_0^{\pi/2}\cos^5 x\,dx \overset{74}{=} \tfrac{1}{5}\left[\cos^4 x \sin x\right]_0^{\pi/2} + \tfrac{4}{5}\int_0^{\pi/2}\cos^3 x\,dx \overset{68}{=} 0 + \tfrac{4}{5}\left[\tfrac{1}{3}(2+\cos^2 x)\sin x\right]_0^{\pi/2} = \tfrac{4}{15}(2-0) = \tfrac{8}{15}$

16. $\displaystyle\int \frac{x\,dx}{\sqrt{x^2-4x}} = \int \frac{x\,dx}{\sqrt{(x^2-4x+4)-4}} = \int \frac{x\,dx}{\sqrt{(x-2)^2-4}} = \int \frac{u+2}{\sqrt{u^2-4}}\,du \quad [u = x-2,\ du = dx]$

$$= \int \frac{u\,du}{\sqrt{u^2-4}} + 2\int \frac{du}{\sqrt{u^2-4}}$$

$$= \tfrac{1}{2}\int v^{-1/2}\,dv \quad [v = u^2-4,\ dv = 2u\,du] + 2\int \frac{du}{\sqrt{u^2-4}}$$

$$\overset{2,43}{=} v^{1/2} + 2\ln\left|u + \sqrt{u^2-4}\right| + C = \sqrt{x^2-4x} + 2\ln\left|x-2 + \sqrt{x^2-4x}\right| + C$$

17. $\displaystyle\int \frac{x^4\,dx}{\sqrt{x^{10}-2}} = \int \frac{x^4\,dx}{\sqrt{(x^5)^2-2}} = \tfrac{1}{5}\int \frac{du}{\sqrt{u^2-2}} \quad [u = x^5,\ du = 5x^4\,dx]$

$$\overset{43}{=} \tfrac{1}{5}\ln\left|u + \sqrt{u^2-2}\right| + C = \tfrac{1}{5}\ln\left|x^5 + \sqrt{x^{10}-2}\right| + C$$

18. $\int x^4 e^{-x}\,dx \overset{97}{=} -x^4 e^{-x} + 4\int x^3 e^{-x}\,dx \overset{97}{=} -x^4 e^{-x} + 4(-x^3 e^{-x} + 3\int x^2 e^{-x}\,dx)$

$$\overset{97}{=} -(x^4 + 4x^3)e^{-x} + 12(-x^2 e^{-x} + 2\int xe^{-x}\,dx)$$

$$\overset{96}{=} -(x^4 + 4x^3 + 12x^2)e^{-x} + 24[(-x-1)e^{-x}] + C$$

$$= -(x^4 + 4x^3 + 12x^2 + 24x + 24)e^{-x} + C$$

So $\int_0^1 x^4 e^{-x}\,dx = \left[-(x^4 + 4x^3 + 12x^2 + 24x + 24)e^{-x}\right]_0^1$

$$= -(1 + 4 + 12 + 24 + 24)e^{-1} + 24e^0 = 24 - 65e^{-1}.$$

19. Let $u = 1 + e^x$, so $du = e^x\, dx$. Then

$$\int e^x \ln(1 + e^x)\, dx = \int \ln u\, du \overset{100}{=} u \ln u - u + C$$
$$= (1 + e^x) \ln(1 + e^x) - e^x - 1 + C$$
$$= (1 + e^x) \ln(1 + e^x) - e^x + C_1, \text{ where } C_1 = C - 1$$

20. $\displaystyle\int x^2 \tan^{-1} x\, dx \overset{95}{=} \frac{1}{3}\left[x^3 \tan^{-1} x - \int \frac{x^3\, dx}{1 + x^2} \right] = \frac{x^3}{3} \tan^{-1} x - \frac{1}{3} \int \left(x - \frac{x}{x^2 + 1} \right) dx$

$$= \frac{x^3}{3} \tan^{-1} x - \frac{1}{3}\frac{x^2}{2} + \frac{1}{6} \int \frac{du}{u} \quad [u = x^2 + 1, \, du = 2x\, dx]$$
$$= \tfrac{1}{3} x^3 \tan^{-1} x - \tfrac{1}{6} x^2 + \tfrac{1}{6} \ln(1 + x^2) + C$$

21. Let $u = e^x$. Then $x = \ln u$, $dx = du/u$, so

$$\int \sqrt{e^{2x} - 1}\, dx = \int \frac{\sqrt{u^2 - 1}}{u}\, du \overset{41}{=} \sqrt{u^2 - 1} - \cos^{-1}(1/u) + C = \sqrt{e^{2x} - 1} - \cos^{-1}(e^{-x}) + C.$$

22. Let $u = \alpha t - 3$ and assume that $\alpha \neq 0$. Then $du = \alpha\, dt$ and

$$\int e^t \sin(\alpha t - 3)dt = \frac{1}{\alpha} \int e^{(u+3)/\alpha} \sin u\, du = \frac{1}{\alpha} e^{3/\alpha} \int e^{(1/\alpha)u} \sin u\, du$$

$$\overset{98}{=} \frac{1}{\alpha} e^{3/\alpha} \frac{e^{(1/\alpha)u}}{(1/\alpha)^2 + 1^2} \left(\frac{1}{\alpha} \sin u - \cos u \right) + C$$

$$= \frac{1}{\alpha} e^{3/\alpha} e^{(1/\alpha)u} \frac{\alpha^2}{1 + \alpha^2} \left(\frac{1}{\alpha} \sin u - \cos u \right) + C$$

$$= \frac{1}{1 + \alpha^2} e^{(u+3)/\alpha} (\sin u - \alpha \cos u) + C$$

$$= \frac{1}{1 + \alpha^2} e^t \left[\sin(\alpha t - 3) - \alpha \cos(\alpha t - 3) \right] + C$$

23. (a) $\displaystyle\frac{d}{du} \left[\frac{1}{b^3} \left(a + bu - \frac{a^2}{a + bu} - 2a \ln|a + bu| \right) + C \right] = \frac{1}{b^3} \left[b + \frac{ba^2}{(a + bu)^2} - \frac{2ab}{(a + bu)} \right]$

$$= \frac{1}{b^3} \left[\frac{b(a + bu)^2 + ba^2 - (a + bu)2ab}{(a + bu)^2} \right] = \frac{1}{b^3} \left[\frac{b^3 u^2}{(a + bu)^2} \right] = \frac{u^2}{(a + bu)^2}$$

(b) Let $t = a + bu \;\Rightarrow\; dt = b\, du$. Note that $u = \dfrac{t - a}{b}$ and $du = \dfrac{1}{b}\, dt$.

$$\int \frac{u^2\, du}{(a + bu)^2} = \frac{1}{b^3} \int \frac{(t - a)^2}{t^2}\, dt = \frac{1}{b^3} \int \frac{t^2 - 2at + a^2}{t^2}\, dt$$

$$= \frac{1}{b^3} \int \left(1 - \frac{2a}{t} + \frac{a^2}{t^2} \right) dt = \frac{1}{b^3} \left(t - 2a \ln|t| - \frac{a^2}{t} \right) + C$$

$$= \frac{1}{b^3} \left(a + bu - \frac{a^2}{a + bu} - 2a \ln|a + bu| \right) + C$$

24. (a) $\dfrac{d}{du}\left[\dfrac{u}{8}\left(2u^2 - a^2\right)\sqrt{a^2 - u^2} + \dfrac{a^4}{8}\sin^{-1}\dfrac{u}{a} + C\right]$

$= \dfrac{u}{8}\left(2u^2 - a^2\right)\dfrac{-u}{\sqrt{a^2 - u^2}} + \sqrt{a^2 - u^2}\left[\dfrac{u}{8}(4u) + \left(2u^2 - a^2\right)\tfrac{1}{8}\right] + \dfrac{a^4}{8}\dfrac{1/a}{\sqrt{1 - u^2/a^2}}$

$= -\dfrac{u^2\left(2u^2 - a^2\right)}{8\sqrt{a^2 - u^2}} + \sqrt{a^2 - u^2}\left[\dfrac{u^2}{2} + \dfrac{2u^2 - a^2}{8}\right] + \dfrac{a^4}{8\sqrt{a^2 - u^2}}$

$= \tfrac{1}{2}\left(a^2 - u^2\right)^{-1/2}\left[-\dfrac{u^2}{4}\left(2u^2 - a^2\right) + u^2\left(a^2 - u^2\right) + \tfrac{1}{4}\left(a^2 - u^2\right)\left(2u^2 - a^2\right) + \dfrac{a^4}{4}\right]$

$= \tfrac{1}{2}\left(a^2 - u^2\right)^{-1/2}\left[2u^2 a^2 - 2u^4\right] = \dfrac{u^2\left(a^2 - u^2\right)}{\sqrt{a^2 - u^2}} = u^2\sqrt{a^2 - u^2}$

(b) Let $u = a\sin\theta \;\Rightarrow\; du = a\cos\theta\,d\theta$. Then

$\displaystyle\int u^2\sqrt{a^2 - u^2}\,du = \int a^2\sin^2\theta\,a\sqrt{1 - \sin^2\theta}\,a\cos\theta\,d\theta = a^4\int\sin^2\theta\cos^2\theta\,d\theta$

$= a^4\int\tfrac{1}{2}(1 + \cos 2\theta)\tfrac{1}{2}(1 - \cos 2\theta)d\theta = \tfrac{1}{4}a^4\int\left(1 - \cos^2 2\theta\right)d\theta$

$= \tfrac{1}{4}a^4\int\left[1 - \tfrac{1}{2}(1 + \cos 4\theta)\right]d\theta = \tfrac{1}{4}a^4\left(\tfrac{1}{2}\theta - \tfrac{1}{8}\sin 4\theta\right) + C$

$= \tfrac{1}{4}a^4\left(\tfrac{1}{2}\theta - \tfrac{1}{8}2\sin 2\theta\cos 2\theta\right) + C = \tfrac{1}{4}a^4\left[\tfrac{1}{2}\theta - \tfrac{1}{2}\sin\theta\cos\theta\left(1 - 2\sin^2\theta\right)\right] + C$

$= \dfrac{a^4}{8}\left[\sin^{-1}\dfrac{u}{a} - \dfrac{u}{a}\dfrac{\sqrt{a^2 - u^2}}{a}\left(1 - \dfrac{2u^2}{a^2}\right)\right] + C$

$= \dfrac{a^4}{8}\left[\sin^{-1}\dfrac{u}{a} - \dfrac{u}{a}\dfrac{\sqrt{a^2 - u^2}}{a}\dfrac{a^2 - 2u^2}{a^2}\right] + C$

$= \dfrac{u}{8}\left(2u^2 - a^2\right)\sqrt{a^2 - u^2} + \dfrac{a^4}{8}\sin^{-1}\dfrac{u}{a} + C$

25. Maple, Mathematica and Derive all give $\int x^2\sqrt{5 - x^2}\,dx = -\tfrac{1}{4}x\left(5 - x^2\right)^{3/2} + \tfrac{5}{8}x\sqrt{5 - x^2} + \tfrac{25}{8}\sin^{-1}\left(\tfrac{1}{\sqrt{5}}x\right)$.

Using Formula 31, we get $\int x^2\sqrt{5 - x^2}\,dx = \tfrac{1}{8}x\left(2x^2 - 5\right)\sqrt{5 - x^2} + \tfrac{1}{8}\left(5^2\right)\sin^{-1}\left(\tfrac{1}{\sqrt{5}}x\right) + C$. But

$-\tfrac{1}{4}x\left(5 - x^2\right)^{3/2} + \tfrac{5}{8}x\sqrt{5 - x^2} = \tfrac{1}{8}x\sqrt{5 - x^2}\left[5 - 2\left(5 - x^2\right)\right] = \tfrac{1}{8}x\left(2x^2 - 5\right)\sqrt{5 - x^2}$, and the $\sin^{-1}$ terms are the same in each expression, so the answers are equivalent.

26. Maple and Mathematica both give $\int x^2\left(1 + x^3\right)^4 dx = \tfrac{1}{15}x^{15} + \tfrac{1}{3}x^{12} + \tfrac{2}{3}x^9 + \tfrac{2}{3}x^6 + \tfrac{1}{3}x^3$, while Derive gives $\int x^2\left(1 + x^3\right)^4 dx = \tfrac{1}{15}\left(x^3 + 1\right)^5$. Using the substitution $u = 1 + x^3 \;\Rightarrow\; du = 3x^2\,dx$, we get $\int x^2\left(1 + x^3\right)^4 dx = \int u^4\left(\tfrac{1}{3}\,du\right) = \tfrac{1}{15}u^5 + C = \tfrac{1}{15}\left(1 + x^3\right)^5 + C$. We can use the Binomial Theorem or a CAS to expand this expression, and we get $\tfrac{1}{15}\left(1 + x^3\right)^5 + C = \tfrac{1}{15} + \tfrac{1}{3}x^3 + \tfrac{2}{3}x^6 + \tfrac{2}{3}x^9 + \tfrac{1}{3}x^{12} + \tfrac{1}{15}x^{15} + C$.

27. Maple and Derive both give $\int\sin^3 x\cos^2 x\,dx = -\tfrac{1}{5}\sin^2 x\cos^3 x - \tfrac{2}{15}\cos^3 x$ (although Derive factors the expression), and Mathematica gives $\int\sin^3 x\cos^2 x\,dx = -\tfrac{1}{8}\cos x - \tfrac{1}{48}\cos 3x + \tfrac{1}{80}\cos 5x$. We can use a CAS to show that both of these expressions are equal to $-\tfrac{1}{3}\cos^3 x + \tfrac{1}{5}\cos^5 x$. Using Formula 86, we write

$\displaystyle\int\sin^3 x\cos^2 x\,dx = -\tfrac{1}{5}\sin^2 x\cos^3 x + \tfrac{2}{5}\int\sin x\cos^2 x\,dx = -\tfrac{1}{5}\sin^2 x\cos^3 x + \tfrac{2}{5}\left(-\tfrac{1}{3}\cos^3 x\right) + C$

$= -\tfrac{1}{5}\sin^2 x\cos^3 x - \tfrac{2}{15}\cos^3 x + C$

28. Maple gives $\int \tan^2 x \sec^4 dx = \dfrac{1}{5} \dfrac{\sin^3 x}{\cos^5 x} + \dfrac{2}{15} \dfrac{\sin^3 x}{\cos^3 x}$,

Mathematica gives $\int \tan^2 x \sec^4 dx = -\frac{1}{120} \sec^5 x \left(-20 \sin x + 5 \sin 3x + \sin 5x\right)$, and

Derive gives $\int \tan^2 x \sec^4 dx = -\frac{2}{15} \tan x - \dfrac{\sin x}{15 \cos^3 x} + \dfrac{\sin x}{5 \cos^5 x}$. All of these expressions can be "simplified"

to $-\dfrac{1}{15} \dfrac{\sin x \left(\cos^2 x - 2\cos^4 x - 3\right)}{\cos^5 x}$ using Maple. Using the identity $1 + \tan^2 x = \sec^2 x$, we write

$\int \tan^2 x \sec^4 x \, dx = \int \tan^2 x \left(1 + \tan^2 x\right) \sec^2 x \, dx = \int \left(\tan^2 x + \tan^4 x\right) \sec^2 x \, dx$.

Now we substitute $u = \tan x \;\Rightarrow\; du = \sec^2 x \, dx$, and the integral becomes

$\int \left(u^2 + u^4\right) du = \frac{1}{3} u^3 + \frac{1}{5} u^5 + C = \frac{1}{3} \tan^3 x + \frac{1}{5} \tan^5 x + C$. If we write

$\sin^5 x = \sin^3 x \left(1 - \cos^2 x\right)$ and substitute into the numerator of the $\tan^5 x$ term, this becomes

$\dfrac{1}{3} \dfrac{\sin^3 x}{\cos^3 x} + \dfrac{1}{5} \dfrac{\sin^3 x \left(1 - \cos^2 x\right)}{\cos^5 x} + C = \dfrac{1}{5} \dfrac{\sin^3 x}{\cos^5 x} + \left(\dfrac{1}{3} - \dfrac{1}{5}\right) \dfrac{\sin^3 x}{\cos^3 x} + C = \dfrac{1}{5} \dfrac{\sin^3 x}{\cos^5 x} + \dfrac{2}{15} \dfrac{\sin^3 x}{\cos^3 x} + C$, which

is the same as Maple's expression.

29. Maple gives $\int x \sqrt{1 + 2x} \, dx = \frac{1}{10}(1 + 2x)^{5/2} - \frac{1}{6}(1 + 2x)^{3/2}$, Mathematica gives $\sqrt{1 + 2x}\left(\frac{2}{5}x^2 + \frac{1}{15}x - \frac{1}{15}\right)$,

and Derive gives $\frac{1}{15}(1 + 2x)^{3/2}(3x - 1)$. The first two expressions can be simplified to Derive's result. If we use

Formula 54, we get

$$\int x\sqrt{1 + 2x} \, dx = \tfrac{2}{15(2)^2}(3 \cdot 2x - 2 \cdot 1)(1 + 2x)^{3/2} + C = \tfrac{1}{30}(6x - 2)(1 + 2x)^{3/2} + C$$

$$= \tfrac{1}{15}(3x - 1)(1 + 2x)^{3/2}$$

30. Maple and Derive both give $\int \sin^4 x \, dx = -\frac{1}{4} \sin^3 x \cos x - \frac{3}{8} \cos x \sin x + \frac{3}{8} x$, while Mathematica gives

$\frac{1}{32}(12x - 8 \sin 2x + \sin 4x)$, which can be expanded and simplified to give the other expression. Now

$$\int \sin^4 x \, dx \overset{73}{=} -\tfrac{1}{4} \sin^3 x \cos x + \tfrac{3}{4} \int \sin^2 x \, dx \overset{63}{=} -\tfrac{1}{4} \sin^3 x \cos x + \tfrac{3}{4}\left(\tfrac{1}{2}x - \tfrac{1}{4} \sin 2x\right) + C$$

$$= -\tfrac{1}{4} \sin^3 x \cos x - \tfrac{3}{8} \sin x \cos x + \tfrac{3}{8} x + C \text{ since } \sin 2x = 2 \sin x \cos x$$

31. Maple gives $\int \tan^5 x \, dx = \frac{1}{4} \tan^4 x - \frac{1}{2} \tan^2 x + \frac{1}{2} \ln\left(1 + \tan^2 x\right)$, Mathematica

gives $\int \tan^5 x \, dx = \frac{1}{4}[-1 - 2\cos(2x)] \sec^4 x - \ln(\cos x)$, and Derive gives

$\int \tan^5 x \, dx = \frac{1}{4} \tan^4 x - \frac{1}{2} \tan^2 x - \ln(\cos x)$. These expressions are equivalent, and none includes absolute

value bars or a constant of integration. Note that Mathematica's and Derive's expressions suggest that the integral is

undefined where $\cos x < 0$, which is not the case.

Using Formula 75, $\int \tan^5 x \, dx = \frac{1}{5-1} \tan^{5-1} x - \int \tan^{5-2} x \, dx = \frac{1}{4} \tan^4 x - \int \tan^3 x \, dx$. Using Formula 69,

$\int \tan^3 x \, dx = \frac{1}{2} \tan^2 x + \ln|\cos x| + C$, so $\int \tan^5 x \, dx = \frac{1}{4} \tan^4 x - \frac{1}{2} \tan^2 x - \ln|\cos x| + C$.

32. Maple gives $\int x^5\sqrt{x^2+1}\,dx = \frac{1}{35}x^4\sqrt{1+x^2} - \frac{4}{105}x^2\sqrt{1+x^2} + \frac{8}{105}\sqrt{1+x^2} + \frac{1}{7}x^6\sqrt{1+x^2}$. When we use

the `factor` command on this expression, it becomes $\frac{1}{105}\left(1+x^2\right)^{3/2}\left(15x^4 - 12x^2 + 8\right)$. Mathematica gives

$\sqrt{1+x^2}\left(\frac{8}{105} - \frac{4}{105}x^2 + \frac{1}{35}x^4 + \frac{1}{7}x^6\right)$, which again factors to give the above expression, and Derive gives the

factored form immediately. If we substitute $u = \sqrt{x^2+1} \;\Rightarrow\; x^4 = \left(u^2 - 1\right)^2$, $x\,dx = u\,du$, then the integral

becomes

$$\int\left(u^2-1\right)^2 u(u\,du) = \int\left(u^4 - 2u^2 + 1\right)u^2\,du = \tfrac{1}{7}u^7 - \tfrac{2}{5}u^5 + \tfrac{1}{3}u^3 + C$$

$$= \left(x^2+1\right)^{3/2}\left[\tfrac{1}{7}\left(x^2+1\right)^2 - \tfrac{2}{5}\left(x^2+1\right) + \tfrac{1}{3}\right] + C$$

$$= \tfrac{1}{105}\left(x^2+1\right)^{3/2}\left[15\left(x^2+1\right)^2 - 42\left(x^2+1\right) + 35\right] + C$$

$$= \tfrac{1}{105}\left(x^2+1\right)^{3/2}\left(15x^4 - 12x^2 + 8\right) + C$$

33. Derive gives $I = \int 2^x\sqrt{4^x - 1}\,dx = \dfrac{2^{x-1}\sqrt{2^{2x} - 1}}{\ln 2} - \dfrac{\ln\left(\sqrt{2^{2x} - 1} + 2^x\right)}{2\ln 2}$ immediately. Neither Maple nor

Mathematica is able to evaluate I in its given form. However, if we instead write I as $\int 2^x\sqrt{(2^x)^2 - 1}\,dx$, both

systems give the same answer as Derive (after minor simplification). Our trick works because the CAS now

recognizes 2^x as a promising substitution.

34. None of Maple, Mathematica and Derive is able to evaluate $\int(1+\ln x)\sqrt{1+(x\ln x)^2}\,dx$. However, if we let

$u = x\ln x$, then $du = (1+\ln x)\,dx$ and the integral is simply $\int\sqrt{1+u^2}\,du$, which any CAS can evaluate. The

antiderivative is $\tfrac{1}{2}\ln\left(x\ln x + \sqrt{1+(x\ln x)^2}\right) + \tfrac{1}{2}x\ln x\sqrt{1+(x\ln x)^2} + C$.

35. Maple gives the antiderivative

$$F(x) = \int \frac{x^2-1}{x^4+x^2+1}\,dx = -\tfrac{1}{2}\ln\left(x^2+x+1\right) + \tfrac{1}{2}\ln\left(x^2-x+1\right).$$

We can see that at 0, this antiderivative is 0. From the graphs, it appears

that F has a maximum at $x = -1$ and a minimum at $x = 1$ [since

$F'(x) = f(x)$ changes sign at these x-values], and that F has inflection

points at $x \approx -1.7$, $x = 0$, and $x \approx 1.7$ [since $f(x)$ has extrema at these

x-values].

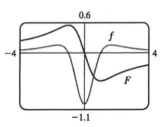

36. Maple gives the antiderivative which, after we use the `simplify` command, becomes

$\int xe^{-x}\sin x\,dx = -\tfrac{1}{2}e^{-x}(\cos x + x\cos x + x\sin x)$. At $x = 0$, this antiderivative has the value $-\tfrac{1}{2}$, so we use

$F(x) = -\tfrac{1}{2}e^{-x}(\cos x + x\cos x + x\sin x) + \tfrac{1}{2}$ to make $F(0) = 0$.

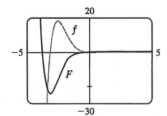

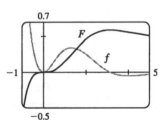

From the graphs, it appears that F has a minimum at $x \approx -3.1$ and a maximum at $x \approx 3.1$ [note that $f(x) = 0$ at

$x = \pm\pi$], and that F has inflection points where f' changes sign, at $x \approx -2.5$, $x = 0$, $x \approx 1.3$ and $x \approx 4.1$.

37. Since f is everywhere positive, we know that its antiderivative F is increasing. Maple gives $\int \sin^4 x \cos^6 x \, dx = -\frac{1}{10} \sin^3 x \cos^7 x - \frac{3}{80} \sin x \cos^7 x + \frac{1}{160} \cos^5 x \sin x + \frac{1}{128} \cos^3 x \sin x + \frac{3}{256} \cos x \sin x + \frac{3}{256} x$ and this expression is 0 at $x = 0$.

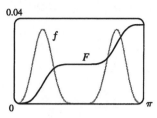

38. From the graph of $f(x) = \dfrac{x^3 - x}{x^6 + 1}$, we can see that F has a maximum at $x = 0$, and minima at $x \approx \pm 1$. The antiderivative given by Maple is $F(x) = -\frac{1}{3} \ln\left(x^2 + 1\right) + \frac{1}{6} \ln\left(x^4 - x^2 + 1\right)$, and $F(0) = 0$. Note that f is odd, and its antiderivative F is even.

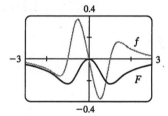

Discovery Project	**Patterns in Integrals**

1. (a) The CAS results are listed. Note that the absolute value symbols are missing, as is the familiar "$+ C$".

(i) $\displaystyle\int \frac{1}{(x+2)(x+3)}\, dx = \ln(x+2) - \ln(x+3)$

(ii) $\displaystyle\int \frac{1}{(x+1)(x+5)}\, dx = \frac{\ln(x+1)}{4} - \frac{\ln(x+5)}{4}$

(iii) $\displaystyle\int \frac{1}{(x+2)(x-5)}\, dx = \frac{\ln(x-5)}{7} - \frac{\ln(x+2)}{7}$

(iv) $\displaystyle\int \frac{1}{(x+2)^2}\, dx = -\frac{1}{x+2}$

(b) If $a \neq b$, it appears that $\ln(x+a)$ is divided by $b - a$ and $\ln(x+b)$ is divided by $a - b$, so we guess that

$$\int \frac{1}{(x+a)(x+b)}\, dx = \frac{\ln(x+a)}{b-a} + \frac{\ln(x+b)}{a-b} + C$$

If $a = b$, as in part (a)(iv), it appears that

$$\int \frac{1}{(x+a)^2}\, dx = -\frac{1}{x+a} + C$$

(c) The CAS verifies our guesses.

Proof by partial fractions:

Now

$$\frac{1}{(x+a)(x+b)} = \frac{A}{x+a} + \frac{B}{x+b} \quad \Rightarrow \quad 1 = A(x+b) + B(x+a)$$

Setting $x = -b$ gives $B = 1/(a-b)$ and setting $x = -a$ gives $A = 1/(b-a)$. So

$$\int \frac{1}{(x+a)(x+b)}\, dx = \int \left[\frac{1/(b-a)}{x+a} + \frac{1/(a-b)}{x+b} \right] dx = \frac{\ln|x+a|}{b-a} + \frac{\ln|x+b|}{a-b} + C$$

and our guess for $a \neq b$ is correct.

If $a = b$, then $\dfrac{1}{(x+a)(x+b)} = \dfrac{1}{(x+a)^2} = (x+a)^{-2}$. Letting $u = x + a$, $du = dx$, gives us

$\int (x+a)^{-2}\, dx = \int u^{-2}\, du = -\dfrac{1}{u} + C = -\dfrac{1}{x+a} + C$, and our guess for $a = b$ is also correct.

Proof by differentiation:

$$\frac{d}{dx} \left[\frac{\ln(x+a)}{b-a} + \frac{\ln(x+b)}{a-b} \right] = \frac{1}{b-a} \cdot \frac{1}{x+a} + \frac{1}{a-b} \cdot \frac{1}{x+b}$$

$$= \frac{1}{(b-a)(x+a)} - \frac{1}{(b-a)(x+b)}$$

$$= \frac{(x+b) - (x+a)}{(b-a)(x+a)(x+b)} = \frac{b-a}{(b-a)(x+a)(x+b)}$$

$$= \frac{1}{(x+a)(x+b)}$$

and

$$\frac{d}{dx}\left[-\frac{1}{x+a}\right] = \frac{d}{dx}\left[-1(x+a)^{-1}\right]$$

$$= 1(x+a)^{-2}$$

$$= \frac{1}{(x+a)^2}$$

2. (a) (i) $\int \sin x \cos 2x \, dx = \dfrac{\cos x}{2} - \dfrac{\cos 3x}{6}$

(ii) $\int \sin 3x \cos 7x \, dx = \dfrac{\cos 4x}{8} - \dfrac{\cos 10x}{20}$

(iii) $\int \sin 8x \cos 3x \, dx = -\dfrac{\cos 11x}{22} - \dfrac{\cos 5x}{10}$

(b) Looking at the sums and differences of a and b in part (a), we guess that

$$\int \sin ax \cos bx \, dx = \frac{\cos((a-b)x)}{2(b-a)} - \frac{\cos((a+b)x)}{2(a+b)} + C$$

Note that $\cos((a-b)x) = \cos((b-a)x)$.

(c) The CAS verifies our guess. Again, we can prove that the guess is correct by differentiating:

$$\frac{d}{dx}\left[\frac{\cos((a-b)x)}{2(b-a)} - \frac{\cos((a+b)x)}{2(a+b)}\right]$$

$$= \frac{1}{2(b-a)}\left[-\sin((a-b)x)\right](a-b) - \frac{1}{2(a+b)}\left[-\sin((a+b)x)\right](a+b)$$

$$= \tfrac{1}{2}\sin(ax-bx) + \tfrac{1}{2}\sin(ax+bx)$$

$$= \tfrac{1}{2}(\sin ax \cos bx - \cos ax \sin bx) + \tfrac{1}{2}(\sin ax \cos bx + \cos ax \sin bx)$$

$$= \sin ax \cos bx$$

Our formula is valid for $a \ne b$.

3. (a) (i) $\int \ln x \, dx = x \ln x - x$

(ii) $\int x \ln x \, dx = \tfrac{1}{2}x^2 \ln x - \tfrac{1}{4}x^2$

(iii) $\int x^2 \ln x \, dx = \tfrac{1}{3}x^3 \ln x - \tfrac{1}{9}x^3$

(iv) $\int x^3 \ln x \, dx = \tfrac{1}{4}x^4 \ln x - \tfrac{1}{16}x^4$

(v) $\int x^7 \ln x \, dx = \tfrac{1}{8}x^8 \ln x - \tfrac{1}{64}x^8$

(b) We guess that $\int x^n \ln x \, dx = \dfrac{1}{n+1}x^{n+1} \ln x - \dfrac{1}{(n+1)^2}x^{n+1}$.

(c) Let $u = \ln x$, $dv = x^n \, dx$ $\Rightarrow$ $du = \dfrac{dx}{x}$, $v = \dfrac{1}{n+1}x^{n+1}$.

Then

$$\int x^n \ln x \, dx = \frac{1}{n+1}x^{n+1} \ln x - \frac{1}{n+1}\int x^n \, dx$$

$$= \frac{1}{n+1}x^{n+1} \ln x - \frac{1}{n+1} \cdot \frac{1}{n+1}x^{n+1},$$

which verifies our guess. We must have $n+1 \ne 0$ $\Leftrightarrow$ $n \ne -1$.

4. (a) (i) $\int xe^x \, dx = e^x(x-1)$

(ii) $\int x^2 e^x \, dx = e^x(x^2 - 2x + 2)$

(iii) $\int x^3 e^x \, dx = e^x(x^3 - 3x^2 + 6x - 6)$

(iv) $\int x^4 e^x \, dx = e^x(x^4 - 4x^3 + 12x^2 - 24x + 24)$

(v) $\int x^5 e^x \, dx = e^x(x^5 - 5x^4 + 20x^3 - 60x^2 + 120x - 120)$

(b) Notice from part (a) that we can write

$$\int x^4 e^x \, dx = e^x(x^4 - 4x^3 + 4 \cdot 3x^2 - 4 \cdot 3 \cdot 2x + 4 \cdot 3 \cdot 2 \cdot 1)$$

and

$$\int x^5 e^x \, dx = e^x(x^5 - 5x^4 + 5 \cdot 4x^3 - 5 \cdot 4 \cdot 3x^2 + 5 \cdot 4 \cdot 3 \cdot 2x - 5 \cdot 4 \cdot 3 \cdot 2 \cdot 1)$$

So we guess that

$$\int x^6 e^x \, dx = e^x(x^6 - 6x^5 + 6 \cdot 5x^4 - 6 \cdot 5 \cdot 4x^3 + 6 \cdot 5 \cdot 4 \cdot 3x^2 - 6 \cdot 5 \cdot 4 \cdot 3 \cdot 2x + 6 \cdot 5 \cdot 4 \cdot 3 \cdot 2 \cdot 1)$$
$$= e^x(x^6 - 6x^5 + 30x^4 - 120x^3 + 360x^2 - 720x + 720)$$

The CAS verifies our guess.

(c) From the results in part (a), as well as our prediction in part (b), we speculate that

$$\int x^n e^x \, dx = e^x \left[x^n - nx^{n-1} + n(n-1)x^{n-2} - n(n-1)(n-2)x^{n-3} + \cdots \pm n!x \mp n! \right]$$

$$= e^x \sum_{i=0}^{n} (-1)^{n-i} \frac{n!}{i!} x^i$$

(We have reversed the order of the polynomial's terms.)

(d) Let S_n be the statement that $\int x^n e^x \, dx = e^x \sum_{i=0}^{n} (-1)^{n-i} \frac{n!}{i!} x^i$.

S_1 is true by part (a)(i). Suppose S_k is true for some k, and consider S_{k+1}. Integrating by parts with $u = x^{k+1}$, $dv = e^x \, dx \implies du = (k+1)x^k \, dx, v = e^x$, we get

$$\int x^{k+1} e^x \, dx = x^{k+1} e^x - (k+1) \int x^k e^x \, dx$$

$$= x^{k+1} e^x - (k+1) \left[e^x \sum_{i=0}^{k} (-1)^{k-i} \frac{k!}{i!} x^i \right]$$

$$= e^x \left[x^{k+1} - (k+1) \sum_{i=0}^{k} (-1)^{k-i} \frac{k!}{i!} x^i \right]$$

$$= e^x \left[x^{k+1} + \sum_{i=0}^{k} (-1)^{k-i+1} \frac{(k+1)k!}{i!} x^i \right]$$

$$= e^x \sum_{i=0}^{k+1} (-1)^{(k+1)-i} \frac{(k+1)!}{i!} x^i$$

This verifies S_n for $n = k+1$. Thus, by mathematical induction, S_n is true for all n, where n is a positive integer.

5.9 Approximate Integration • • • • • • • • • • •

1. (a) $\Delta x = (b-a)/n = (4-0)/2 = 2$

$$L_2 = \sum_{i=1}^{2} f(x_{i-1})\,\Delta x = f(x_0)\cdot 2 + f(x_1)\cdot 2 = 2\,[f(0) + f(2)] = 2(0.5 + 2.5) = 6$$

$$R_2 = \sum_{i=1}^{2} f(x_i)\,\Delta x = f(x_1)\cdot 2 + f(x_2)\cdot 2 = 2\,[f(2) + f(4)] = 2(2.5 + 3.5) = 12$$

$$M_2 = \sum_{i=1}^{2} f(\overline{x}_i)\,\Delta x = f(\overline{x}_1)\cdot 2 + f(\overline{x}_2)\cdot 2 = 2\,[f(1) + f(3)] \approx 2(1.6 + 3.2) = 9.6$$

(b)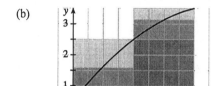

L_2 is an underestimate, since the area under the small rectangles is less than the area under the curve, and R_2 is an overestimate, since the area under the large rectangles is greater than the area under the curve. It appears that M_2 is an overestimate, though it is fairly close to I. See the solution to Exercise 33 for a proof of the fact that if f is concave down on $[a, b]$, then the Midpoint Rule is an overestimate of $\int_a^b f(x)\,dx$.

(c) $T_2 = \left(\frac{1}{2}\Delta x\right)[f(x_0) + 2f(x_1) + f(x_2)] = \frac{2}{2}[f(0) + 2f(2) + f(4)] = 0.5 + 2(2.5) + 3.5 = 9$.
This approximation is an underestimate, since the graph is concave down. Thus, $T_2 = 9 < I$. See the solution to Exercise 33 for a general proof of this conclusion.

(d) For any n, we will have $L_n < T_n < I < M_n < R_n$.

2.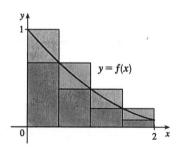

The diagram shows that $L_4 > T_4 > \int_0^2 f(x)\,dx > R_4$, and it appears that M_4 is a bit less than $\int_0^2 f(x)\,dx$. In fact, for any function that is concave upward, it can be shown that
$$L_n > T_n > \int_0^2 f(x)\,dx > M_n > R_n.$$
(a) Since $0.9540 > 0.8675 > 0.8632 > 0.7811$, it follows that
$$L_n = 0.9540,\ T_n = 0.8675,\ M_n = 0.8632,\ \text{and}\ R_n = 0.7811.$$
(b) Since $M_n < \int_0^2 f(x)\,dx < T_n$, we have
$$0.8632 < \int_0^2 f(x)\,dx < 0.8675.$$

3. $f(x) = \cos\left(x^2\right)$, $\Delta x = \frac{1-0}{4} = \frac{1}{4}$

(a) $T_4 = \frac{1}{4\cdot 2}\left[f(0) + 2f\left(\frac{1}{4}\right) + 2f\left(\frac{2}{4}\right) + 2f\left(\frac{3}{4}\right) + f(1)\right] \approx 0.895759$

(b) $M_4 = \frac{1}{4}\left[f\left(\frac{1}{8}\right) + f\left(\frac{3}{8}\right) + f\left(\frac{5}{8}\right) + f\left(\frac{7}{8}\right)\right] \approx 0.908907$

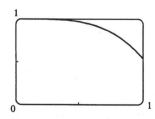

The graph shows that f is concave down on $[0, 1]$. So T_4 is an underestimate and M_4 is an overestimate. We can conclude that
$$0.895759 < \int_0^1 \cos\left(x^2\right)\,dx < 0.908907.$$

4.

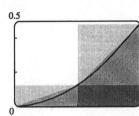

(a) Since f is increasing on $[0, 1]$, L_2 will underestimate I (since the area of the darkest rectangle is less than the area under the curve), and R_2 will overestimate I. Since f is concave upward on $[0, 1]$, M_2 will underestimate I and T_2 will overestimate I (the area under the straight line segments is greater than the area under the curve).

(b) For any n, we will have $L_n < M_n < I < T_n < R_n$.

(c) $L_5 = \sum_{i=1}^{5} f(x_{i-1}) \, \Delta x = \frac{1}{5}[f(0.0) + f(0.2) + f(0.4) + f(0.6) + f(0.8)] \approx 0.1187$

$R_5 = \sum_{i=1}^{5} f(x_i) \, \Delta x = \frac{1}{5}[f(0.2) + f(0.4) + f(0.6) + f(0.8) + f(1)] \approx 0.2146$

$M_5 = \sum_{i=1}^{5} f(\overline{x}_i) \, \Delta x = \frac{1}{5}[f(0.1) + f(0.3) + f(0.5) + f(0.7) + f(0.9)] \approx 0.1622$

$T_5 = \left(\frac{1}{2}\, \Delta x\right)[f(0) + 2f(0.2) + 2f(0.4) + 2f(0.6) + 2f(0.8) + f(1)] \approx 0.1666$

From the graph, it appears that the Midpoint Rule gives the best approximation. (This is in fact the case, since $I \approx 0.16371405$.)

5. $f(x) = x^2 \sin x$, $\Delta x = \dfrac{b - a}{n} = \dfrac{\pi - 0}{8} = \dfrac{\pi}{8}$

(a) $M_8 = \frac{\pi}{8}\left[f\left(\frac{\pi}{16}\right) + f\left(\frac{3\pi}{16}\right) + f\left(\frac{5\pi}{16}\right) + \cdots + f\left(\frac{15\pi}{16}\right)\right] \approx 5.932957$

(b) $S_8 = \frac{\pi}{8 \cdot 3}\left[f(0) + 4f\left(\frac{\pi}{8}\right) + 2f\left(\frac{2\pi}{8}\right) + 4f\left(\frac{3\pi}{8}\right) + 2f\left(\frac{4\pi}{8}\right) + 4f\left(\frac{5\pi}{8}\right) + 2f\left(\frac{6\pi}{8}\right) + 4f\left(\frac{7\pi}{8}\right) + f(\pi)\right]$
≈ 5.869247

Actual: $\int_0^\pi x^2 \sin x \, dx \overset{84}{=} \left[-x^2 \cos x\right]_0^\pi + 2\int_0^\pi x \cos x \, dx \overset{83}{=} \left[-\pi^2(-1) - 0\right] + 2[\cos x + x \sin x]_0^\pi$
$= \pi^2 + 2[(-1 + 0) - (1 + 0)] = \pi^2 - 4 \approx 5.869604$

Errors: $E_M = \text{actual} - M_8 = \int_0^\pi x^2 \sin x \, dx - M_8 \approx -0.063353$
$E_S = \text{actual} - S_8 = \int_0^\pi x^2 \sin x \, dx - S_8 \approx 0.000357$

6. $f(x) = e^{-\sqrt{x}}$, $\Delta x = \dfrac{b - a}{n} = \dfrac{1 - 0}{6} = \dfrac{1}{6}$

(a) $M_6 = \frac{1}{6}\left[f\left(\frac{1}{12}\right) + f\left(\frac{3}{12}\right) + f\left(\frac{5}{12}\right) + f\left(\frac{7}{12}\right) + f\left(\frac{9}{12}\right) + f\left(\frac{11}{12}\right)\right] \approx 0.525100$

(b) $S_6 = \frac{1}{6 \cdot 3}\left[f(0) + 4f\left(\frac{1}{6}\right) + 2f\left(\frac{2}{6}\right) + 4f\left(\frac{3}{6}\right) + 2f\left(\frac{4}{6}\right) + 4f\left(\frac{5}{6}\right) + f(1)\right] \approx 0.533979$

Actual: $\int_0^1 e^{-\sqrt{x}}\, dx = \int_0^{-1} e^u 2u \, du \qquad [u = -\sqrt{x},\ u^2 = x,\ 2u\,du = dx]$
$\overset{96}{=} 2[(u - 1)e^u]_0^{-1} = 2[-2e^{-1} - (-1e^0)] = 2 - 4e^{-1} \approx 0.528482$

Errors: $E_M = \text{actual} - M_6 = \int_0^1 e^{-\sqrt{x}}\, dx - M_6 \approx 0.003382$
$E_S = \text{actual} - S_6 = \int_0^1 e^{-\sqrt{x}}\, dx - S_6 \approx -0.005497$

7. $f(x) = e^{-x^2}$, $\Delta x = \dfrac{1 - 0}{10} = \dfrac{1}{10}$

(a) $T_{10} = \frac{1}{10 \cdot 2}[f(0) + 2f(0.1) + 2f(0.2) + \cdots + 2f(0.8) + 2f(0.9) + f(1)] \approx 0.746211$

(b) $M_{10} = \frac{1}{10}[f(0.05) + f(0.15) + f(0.25) + \cdots + f(0.75) + f(0.85) + f(0.95)] \approx 0.747131$

(c) $S_{10} = \frac{1}{10 \cdot 3}[f(0) + 4f(0.1) + 2f(0.2) + 4f(0.3) + 2f(0.4) + 4f(0.5)$
$\qquad\qquad + 2f(0.6) + 4f(0.7) + 2f(0.8) + 4f(0.9) + f(1)] \approx 0.746825$

8. $f(x) = \dfrac{1}{\sqrt{1+x^3}}$, $\Delta x = \dfrac{2-0}{10} = \dfrac{1}{5}$

(a) $T_{10} = \frac{1}{5 \cdot 2}[f(0) + 2f(0.2) + 2f(0.4) + \cdots + 2f(1.6) + 2f(1.8) + f(2)] \approx 1.401435$

(b) $M_{10} = \frac{1}{5}[f(0.1) + f(0.3) + f(0.5) + \cdots + f(1.7) + f(1.9)] \approx 1.402558$

(c) $S_{10} = \frac{1}{5 \cdot 3}[f(0) + 4f(0.2) + 2f(0.4) + 4f(0.6) + 2f(0.8) + 4f(1)$
$$\qquad\qquad\qquad + 2f(1.2) + 4f(1.4) + 2f(1.6) + 4f(1.8) + f(2)] \approx 1.402206$$

9. $f(x) = e^{1/x}$, $\Delta x = \dfrac{2-1}{4} = \dfrac{1}{4}$

(a) $T_4 = \frac{1}{4 \cdot 2}[f(1) + 2f(1.25) + 2f(1.5) + 2f(1.75) + f(2)] \approx 2.031893$

(b) $M_4 = \frac{1}{4}[f(1.125) + f(1.375) + f(1.625) + f(1.875)] \approx 2.014207$

(c) $S_4 = \frac{1}{4 \cdot 3}[f(1) + 4f(1.25) + 2f(1.5) + 4f(1.75) + f(2)] \approx 2.020651$

10. $f(x) = \ln(1 + e^x)$, $\Delta x = \dfrac{1-0}{8} = \dfrac{1}{8}$

(a) $T_8 = \frac{1}{8 \cdot 2}\left[f(0) + 2f\left(\frac{1}{8}\right) + 2f\left(\frac{2}{8}\right) + 2f\left(\frac{3}{8}\right) + 2f\left(\frac{4}{8}\right) + 2f\left(\frac{5}{8}\right) + 2f\left(\frac{6}{8}\right) + 2f\left(\frac{7}{8}\right) + f(1)\right]$
$$\approx 0.984120$$

(b) $M_8 = \frac{1}{8}\left[f\left(\frac{1}{16}\right) + f\left(\frac{3}{16}\right) + f\left(\frac{5}{16}\right) + f\left(\frac{7}{16}\right) + \cdots + f\left(\frac{15}{16}\right)\right] \approx 0.983669$

(c) $S_8 = \frac{1}{8 \cdot 3}\left[f(0) + 4f\left(\frac{1}{8}\right) + 2f\left(\frac{2}{8}\right) + 4f\left(\frac{3}{8}\right) + 2f\left(\frac{4}{8}\right) + 4f\left(\frac{5}{8}\right) + 2f\left(\frac{6}{8}\right) + 4f\left(\frac{7}{8}\right) + f(1)\right]$
$$\approx 0.983819$$

11. $f(t) = \sin\left(e^{t/2}\right)$, $\Delta t = \dfrac{1/2 - 0}{8} = \dfrac{1}{16}$

(a) $T_8 = \frac{1}{16 \cdot 2}\left[f(0) + 2f\left(\frac{1}{16}\right) + 2f\left(\frac{2}{16}\right) + \cdots + 2f\left(\frac{7}{16}\right) + f\left(\frac{1}{2}\right)\right] \approx 0.451948$

(b) $M_8 = \frac{1}{16}\left[f\left(\frac{1}{32}\right) + f\left(\frac{3}{32}\right) + f\left(\frac{5}{32}\right) + \cdots + f\left(\frac{13}{32}\right) + f\left(\frac{15}{32}\right)\right] \approx 0.451991$

(c) $S_8 = \frac{1}{16 \cdot 3}\left[f(0) + 4f\left(\frac{1}{16}\right) + 2f\left(\frac{2}{16}\right) + \cdots + 4f\left(\frac{7}{16}\right) + f\left(\frac{1}{2}\right)\right] \approx 0.451976$

12. $f(x) = \sqrt{x}\sin x$, $\Delta x = \dfrac{4-0}{8} = \dfrac{1}{2}$

(a) $T_8 = \frac{1}{2 \cdot 2}\left\{f(0) + 2\left[f\left(\frac{1}{2}\right) + f(1) + f\left(\frac{3}{2}\right) + f(2) + f\left(\frac{5}{2}\right) + f(3) + f\left(\frac{7}{2}\right)\right] + f(4)\right\} \approx 1.732865$

(b) $M_8 = \frac{1}{2}\left[f\left(\frac{1}{4}\right) + f\left(\frac{3}{4}\right) + f\left(\frac{5}{4}\right) + f\left(\frac{7}{4}\right) + \cdots + f\left(\frac{13}{4}\right) + f\left(\frac{15}{4}\right)\right] \approx 1.787427$

(c) $S_8 = \frac{1}{2 \cdot 3}\left[f(0) + 4f\left(\frac{1}{2}\right) + 2f(1) + 4f\left(\frac{3}{2}\right) + 2f(2) + 4f\left(\frac{5}{2}\right) + 2f(3) + 4f\left(\frac{7}{2}\right) + f(4)\right] \approx 1.772142$

13. $f(y) = \dfrac{1}{1+y^5}$, $\Delta y = \dfrac{3-0}{6} = \dfrac{1}{2}$

(a) $T_6 = \frac{1}{2 \cdot 2}\left[f(0) + 2f\left(\frac{1}{2}\right) + 2f\left(\frac{2}{2}\right) + 2f\left(\frac{3}{2}\right) + 2f\left(\frac{4}{2}\right) + 2f\left(\frac{5}{2}\right) + f(3)\right] \approx 1.064275$

(b) $M_6 = \frac{1}{2}\left[f\left(\frac{1}{4}\right) + f\left(\frac{3}{4}\right) + f\left(\frac{5}{4}\right) + f\left(\frac{7}{4}\right) + f\left(\frac{9}{4}\right) + f\left(\frac{11}{4}\right)\right] \approx 1.067416$

(c) $S_6 = \frac{1}{2 \cdot 3}\left[f(0) + 4f\left(\frac{1}{2}\right) + 2f\left(\frac{2}{2}\right) + 4f\left(\frac{3}{2}\right) + 2f\left(\frac{4}{2}\right) + 4f\left(\frac{5}{2}\right) + f(3)\right] \approx 1.074915$

14. $f(x) = \dfrac{e^x}{x}$, $\Delta x = \dfrac{4-2}{10} = \dfrac{1}{5}$

(a) $T_{10} = \frac{1}{5 \cdot 2}\{f(2) + 2[f(2.2) + f(2.4) + f(2.6) + \cdots + f(3.8)] + f(4)\} \approx 14.704592$

(b) $M_{10} = \frac{1}{5}[f(2.1) + f(2.3) + f(2.5) + f(2.7) + \cdots + f(3.7) + f(3.9)] \approx 14.662669$

(c) $S_{10} = \frac{1}{5 \cdot 3}[f(2) + 4f(2.2) + 2f(2.4) + 4f(2.6) + \cdots + 2f(3.6) + 4f(3.8) + f(4)] \approx 14.676696$

15. $f(x) = e^{-x^2}$, $\Delta x = \dfrac{2-0}{10} = \dfrac{1}{5}$

(a) $T_{10} = \frac{1}{5 \cdot 2}\{f(0) + 2[f(0.2) + f(0.4) + \cdots + f(1.8)] + f(2)\} \approx 0.881839$

$M_{10} = \frac{1}{5}[f(0.1) + f(0.3) + f(0.5) + \cdots + f(1.7) + f(1.9)] \approx 0.882202$

(b) $f(x) = e^{-x^2}$, $f'(x) = -2xe^{-x^2}$, $f''(x) = (4x^2 - 2)e^{-x^2}$, $f'''(x) = 4x(3 - 2x^2)e^{-x^2}$. $f'''(x) = 0$ $\Leftrightarrow$

$x = 0$ or $x = \pm\sqrt{\frac{3}{2}}$. So to find the maximum value of $|f''(x)|$ on $[0,2]$, we need only consider its values at

$x = 0$, $x = 2$, and $x = \sqrt{\frac{3}{2}}$. $|f''(0)| = 2$, $|f''(2)| \approx 0.2564$ and $\left|f''\left(\sqrt{\frac{3}{2}}\right)\right| \approx 0.8925$. Thus, taking $K = 2$,

$a = 0$, $b = 2$, and $n = 10$ in Theorem 3, we get $|E_T| \leq 2 \cdot 2^3/(12 \cdot 10^2) = \frac{1}{75} = 0.01\overline{3}$, and

$|E_M| \leq |E_T|/2 \leq 0.00\overline{6}$.

(c) Take $K = 2$ [as in part (b)] in Theorem 3. $|E_T| \leq \dfrac{K(b-a)^3}{12n^2} \leq 10^{-5}$ $\Leftrightarrow$ $\dfrac{2(2-0)^3}{12n^2} \leq 10^{-5}$ $\Leftrightarrow$

$\frac{3}{4}n^2 \geq 10^5$ $\Leftrightarrow$ $n \geq 365.1\ldots$ $\Leftrightarrow$ $n \geq 366$. Take $n = 366$ for T_n. For E_M, again take $K = 2$ in

Theorem 3 to get $|E_M| \leq 10^{-5}$ $\Leftrightarrow$ $\frac{3}{2}n^2 \geq 10^5$ $\Leftrightarrow$ $n \geq 258.2$ $\Rightarrow$ $n \geq 259$. Take $n = 259$ for M_n.

16. (a) $T_8 = \frac{1}{8 \cdot 2}\{f(0) + 2[f(\frac{1}{8}) + f(\frac{2}{8}) + \cdots + f(\frac{7}{8})] + f(1)\} \approx 0.902333$

$M_8 = \frac{1}{8}[f(\frac{1}{16}) + f(\frac{3}{16}) + f(\frac{5}{16}) + \cdots + f(\frac{15}{16})] = 0.905620$

(b) $f(x) = \cos(x^2)$, $f'(x) = -2x\sin(x^2)$, $f''(x) = -2\sin(x^2) - 4x^2\cos(x^2)$. For $0 \leq x \leq 1$, sin and cos are

positive, so $|f''(x)| = 2\sin(x^2) + 4x^2\cos(x^2) \leq 2 \cdot 1 + 4 \cdot 1 \cdot 1 = 6$ since $\sin(x^2) \leq 1$ and $\cos(x^2) \leq 1$ for

all x, and $x^2 \leq 1$ for $0 \leq x \leq 1$. So for $n = 8$, we take $K = 6$, $a = 0$, and $b = 1$ in Theorem 3, to get

$|E_T| \leq 6 \cdot 1^3/(12 \cdot 8^2) = \frac{1}{128} = 0.0078125$ and $|E_M| \leq \frac{1}{256} = 0.00390625$. [A better estimate is obtained

by noting from a graph of f'' that $|f''(x)| \leq 4$ for $0 \leq x \leq 1$.]

(c) Using $K = 6$ as in part (b), we have $|E_T| \leq 6 \cdot 1^3/(12n^2) = 1/(2n^2) \leq 10^{-5}$ $\Rightarrow$ $2n^2 \geq 10^5$ $\Rightarrow$

$n \geq \sqrt{\frac{1}{2} \cdot 10^5}$ or $n \geq 224$. To guarantee that $|E_M| \leq 0.00001$, we need $6 \cdot 1^3/(24n^2) \leq 10^{-5}$ $\Rightarrow$

$4n^2 \geq 10^5$ $\Rightarrow$ $n \geq \sqrt{\frac{1}{4} \cdot 10^5}$ or $n \geq 159$.

17. (a) $T_{10} = \frac{1}{10 \cdot 2}\{f(0) + 2[f(0.1) + f(0.2) + \cdots + f(0.9)] + f(1)\} \approx 1.71971349$

$S_{10} = \frac{1}{10 \cdot 3}[f(0) + 4f(0.1) + 2f(0.2) + 4f(0.3) + \cdots + 4f(0.9) + f(1)] \approx 1.71828278$

Since $I = \int_0^1 e^x\,dx = [e^x]_0^1 = e - 1 \approx 1.71828183$, $E_T = I - T_{10} \approx -0.00143166$ and

$E_S = I - S_{10} \approx -0.00000095$.

(b) $f(x) = e^x$ $\Rightarrow$ $f''(x) = e^x \leq e$ for $0 \leq x \leq 1$. Taking $K = e$, $a = 0$, $b = 1$, and $n = 10$ in Theorem 3, we

get $|E_T| \leq e(1)^3/(12 \cdot 10^2) \approx 0.002265 > 0.00143166$ [actual $|E_T|$ from (a)]. $f^{(4)}(x) = e^x < e$ for

$0 \leq x \leq 1$. Using Theorem 4, we have $|E_S| \leq e(1)^5/(180 \cdot 10^4) \approx 0.0000015 > 0.00000095$ [actual $|E_S|$

from (a)]. We see that the actual errors are about two-thirds the size of the error estimates.

(c) From part (b), we take $K = e$ to get $|E_T| \leq \dfrac{K(b-a)^3}{12n^2} \leq 0.00001$ $\Rightarrow$ $n^2 \geq \dfrac{e(1^3)}{12(0.00001)}$ $\Rightarrow$

$n \geq 150.5$. Take $n = 151$ for T_n. Now $|E_M| \leq \dfrac{K(b-a)^3}{24n^2} \leq 0.00001$ $\Rightarrow$ $n \geq 106.4$. Take $n = 107$ for

M_n. Finally, $|E_S| \leq \dfrac{K(b-a)^5}{180n^4} \leq 0.00001$ $\Rightarrow$ $n^4 \geq \dfrac{e(1^5)}{180(0.00001)}$ $\Rightarrow$ $n \geq 6.23$. Take $n = 8$ for S_n

(since n has to be even for Simpson's Rule).

18. From Example 7(b), we take $K = 76e$ to get $|E_S| \leq 76e(1)^5/(180n^4) \leq 0.00001$ $\Rightarrow$

$n^4 \geq 76e/[180(0.00001)]$ $\Rightarrow$ $n \geq 18.4$. Take $n = 20$ (since n must be even).

19. (a) Using a CAS, we differentiate $f(x) = e^{\cos x}$ twice, and find that

$f''(x) = e^{\cos x}(\sin^2 x - \cos x)$. From the graph, we see that the

maximum value of $|f''(x)|$ occurs at the endpoints of the

interval $[0, 2\pi]$. Since $f''(0) = -e$, we can use $K = e$ or $K = 2.8$.

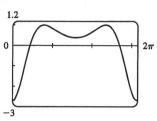

(b) A CAS gives $M_{10} \approx 7.954926518$. (In Maple, use `student[middlesum]`.)

(c) Using Theorem 3 for the Midpoint Rule, with $K = e$, we get $|E_M| \leq \dfrac{e(2\pi - 0)^3}{24 \cdot 10^2} \approx 0.280945995$. With

$K = 2.8$, we get $|E_M| \leq \dfrac{2.8(2\pi - 0)^3}{24 \cdot 10^2} = 0.289391916$.

(d) A CAS gives $I \approx 7.954926521$.

(e) The actual error is only about 3×10^{-9}, much less than the estimate in part (c).

(f) We use the CAS to differentiate twice more, and then graph

$f^{(4)}(x) = e^{\cos x}(\sin^4 x - 6\sin^2 x \cos x + 3 - 7\sin^2 x + \cos x)$.

From the graph, we see that the maximum value of $\left| f^{(4)}(x) \right|$ occurs

at the endpoints of the interval $[0, 2\pi]$. Since $f^{(4)}(0) = 4e$, we can use

$K = 4e$ or $K = 10.9$.

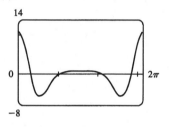

(g) A CAS gives $S_{10} \approx 7.953789422$. (In Maple, use `student[simpson]`.)

(h) Using Theorem 4 with $K = 4e$, we get $|E_S| \leq \dfrac{4e(2\pi - 0)^5}{180 \cdot 10^4} \approx 0.059153618$. With $K = 10.9$, we get

$|E_S| \leq \dfrac{10.9(2\pi - 0)^5}{180 \cdot 10^4} = 0.059299814$.

(i) The actual error is about $7.954926521 - 7.953789422 \approx 0.00114$. This is quite a bit smaller than the estimate in part (h), though the difference is not nearly as great as it was in the case of the Midpoint Rule.

(j) To ensure that $|E_S| \leq 0.0001$, we use Theorem 4: $|E_S| \leq \dfrac{4e(2\pi)^5}{180 \cdot n^4} \leq 0.0001$ $\Rightarrow$ $\dfrac{4e(2\pi)^5}{180 \cdot 0.0001} \leq n^4$ $\Rightarrow$

$n^4 \geq 5{,}915{,}362$ $\Leftrightarrow$ $n \geq 49.3$. So we must take $n \geq 50$ to ensure that $|I - S_n| \leq 0.0001$. ($K = 10.9$ leads to the same value of n.)

20. (a) Using the CAS, we differentiate $f(x) = \sqrt{4 - x^3}$ twice,

and find that $f''(x) = -\dfrac{9x^4}{4(4 - x^3)^{3/2}} - \dfrac{3x}{(4 - x^3)^{1/2}}$.

From the graph, we see that $|f''(x)| < 2.2$ on $[-1, 1]$.

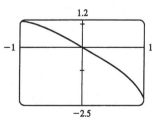

(b) A CAS gives $M_{10} \approx 3.995804152$. (In Maple, use `student[middlesum]`.)

(c) Using Theorem 3 for the Midpoint Rule, with $K = 2.2$, we get $|E_M| \leq \dfrac{2.2\,[1 - (-1)]^3}{24 \cdot 10^2} \approx 0.00733$.

(d) A CAS gives $I \approx 3.995487677$.

(e) The actual error is about -0.0003165, much less than the estimate in part (c).

(f) We use the CAS to differentiate twice more, and then graph $f^{(4)}(x) = \dfrac{9}{16} \dfrac{x^2 \left(x^6 - 224x^3 - 1280 \right)}{\left(4 - x^3 \right)^{7/2}}$.

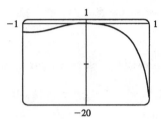

From the graph, we see that $\left| f^{(4)}(x) \right| < 18.1$ on $[-1, 1]$.

(g) A CAS gives $S_{10} \approx 3.995449790$. (In Maple, use `student[simpson]`.)

(h) Using Theorem 4 with $K = 18.1$, we get $|E_S| \leq \dfrac{18.1 \left[1 - (-1) \right]^5}{180 \cdot 10^4} \approx 0.000322$.

(i) The actual error is about $3.995487677 - 3.995449790 \approx 0.0000379$. This is quite a bit smaller than the estimate in part (h).

(j) To ensure that $|E_S| \leq 0.0001$, we use Theorem 4: $|E_S| \leq \dfrac{18.1(2)^5}{180 \cdot n^4} \leq 0.0001 \quad \Rightarrow \quad \dfrac{18.1(2)^5}{180 \cdot 0.0001} \leq n^4 \quad \Rightarrow$

$n^4 \geq 32{,}178 \quad \Rightarrow n \geq 13.4$. So we must take $n \geq 14$ to ensure that $|I - S_n| \leq 0.0001$.

21. $I = \int_0^1 x^3 \, dx = \left[\frac{1}{4} x^4 \right]_0^1 = 0.25$. $f(x) = x^3$.

$n = 4$: $\quad L_4 = \frac{1}{4} \left[0^3 + \left(\frac{1}{4} \right)^3 + \left(\frac{2}{4} \right)^3 + \left(\frac{3}{4} \right)^3 \right] = 0.140625$

$\qquad R_4 = \frac{1}{4} \left[\left(\frac{1}{4} \right)^3 + \left(\frac{2}{4} \right)^3 + \left(\frac{3}{4} \right)^3 + 1^3 \right] = 0.390625$

$\qquad T_4 = \frac{1}{4 \cdot 2} \left[0^3 + 2 \left(\frac{1}{4} \right)^3 + 2 \left(\frac{2}{4} \right)^3 + 2 \left(\frac{3}{4} \right)^3 + 1^3 \right] = 0.265625,$

$\qquad M_4 = \frac{1}{4} \left[\left(\frac{1}{8} \right)^3 + \left(\frac{3}{8} \right)^3 + \left(\frac{5}{8} \right)^3 + \left(\frac{7}{8} \right)^3 \right] = 0.2421875,$

$\qquad E_L = I - L_4 = \frac{1}{4} - 0.140625 = 0.109375, \ E_R = \frac{1}{4} - 0.390625 = -0.140625,$

$\qquad E_T = \frac{1}{4} - 0.265625 = -0.015625, \ E_M = \frac{1}{4} - 0.2421875 = 0.0078125$

$n = 8$: $\quad L_8 = \frac{1}{8} \left[f(0) + f \left(\frac{1}{8} \right) + f \left(\frac{2}{8} \right) + \cdots + f \left(\frac{7}{8} \right) \right] \approx 0.191406$

$\qquad R_8 = \frac{1}{8} \left[f \left(\frac{1}{8} \right) + f \left(\frac{2}{8} \right) + \cdots + f \left(\frac{7}{8} \right) + f(1) \right] \approx 0.316406$

$\qquad T_8 = \frac{1}{8 \cdot 2} \left\{ f(0) + 2 \left[f \left(\frac{1}{8} \right) + f \left(\frac{2}{8} \right) + \cdots + f \left(\frac{7}{8} \right) \right] + f(1) \right\} \approx 0.253906$

$\qquad M_8 = \frac{1}{8} \left[f \left(\frac{1}{16} \right) + f \left(\frac{3}{16} \right) + \cdots + f \left(\frac{13}{16} \right) + f \left(\frac{15}{16} \right) \right] = 0.248047$

$\qquad E_L \approx \frac{1}{4} - 0.191406 \approx 0.058594, \ E_R \approx \frac{1}{4} - 0.316406 \approx -0.066406,$

$\qquad E_T \approx \frac{1}{4} - 0.253906 \approx -0.003906, \ E_M \approx \frac{1}{4} - 0.248047 \approx 0.001953.$

$n = 16$: $L_{16} = \frac{1}{16}\left[f(0) + f\left(\frac{1}{16}\right) + f\left(\frac{2}{16}\right) + \cdots + f\left(\frac{15}{16}\right)\right] \approx 0.219727$

$R_{16} = \frac{1}{16}\left[f\left(\frac{1}{16}\right) + f\left(\frac{2}{16}\right) + \cdots + f\left(\frac{15}{16}\right) + f(1)\right] \approx 0.282227$

$T_{16} = \frac{1}{16 \cdot 2}\left\{f(0) + 2\left[f\left(\frac{1}{16}\right) + f\left(\frac{2}{16}\right) + \cdots + f\left(\frac{15}{16}\right)\right] + f(1)\right\} \approx 0.250977$

$M_{16} = \frac{1}{16}\left[f\left(\frac{1}{32}\right) + f\left(\frac{3}{32}\right) + \cdots + f\left(\frac{31}{32}\right)\right] \approx 0.249512$

$E_L \approx \frac{1}{4} - 0.219727 \approx 0.030273,\ E_R \approx \frac{1}{4} - 0.282227 \approx -0.032227,$

$E_T \approx \frac{1}{4} - 0.250977 \approx -0.000977,\ E_M \approx \frac{1}{4} - 0.249512 \approx 0.000488.$

n	L_n	R_n	T_n	M_n
4	0.140625	0.390625	0.265625	0.242188
8	0.191406	0.316406	0.253906	0.248047
16	0.219727	0.282227	0.250977	0.249512

n	E_L	E_R	E_T	E_M
4	0.109375	−0.140625	−0.015625	0.007813
8	0.058594	−0.066406	−0.003906	0.001953
16	0.030273	−0.032227	−0.000977	0.000488

Observations:

1. E_L and E_R are always opposite in sign, as are E_T and E_M.

2. As n is doubled, E_L and E_R are decreased by about a factor of 2, and E_T and E_M are decreased by a factor of about 4.

3. The Midpoint approximation is about twice as accurate as the Trapezoidal approximation.

4. All the approximations become more accurate as the value of n increases.

5. The Midpoint and Trapezoidal approximations are much more accurate than the endpoint approximations.

22. $I = \int_{-1}^{2} xe^x dx = [xe^x - e^x]_{-1}^{2} = e^2 + 2/e \approx 8.124815.\ f(x) = xe^x.$

$n = 6$: $\Delta x = [2 - (-1)]/6 = \frac{1}{2}$

$T_6 = \frac{1}{2 \cdot 2}\{f(-1) + 2[f(-0.5) + f(0) + \cdots + f(1.5)] + f(2)\} \approx 8.583514$

$M_6 = \frac{1}{2}[f(-0.75) + f(-0.25) + \cdots + f(1.75)] \approx 7.896632$

$S_6 = \frac{1}{2 \cdot 3}[f(-1) + 4f(-0.5) + 2f(0) + 4f(0.5) + 2f(1) + 4f(1.5) + f(2)] \approx 8.136885$

$E_T \approx I - 8.583514 \approx -0.458699,\ E_M \approx I - 7.896632 \approx 0.228183,$

$E_S \approx I - 8.136885 \approx -0.012070.$

$n = 12$: $\Delta x = [2 - (-1)]/12 = \frac{1}{4}$

$T_{12} = \frac{1}{4 \cdot 2}\{f(-1) + 2[f(-0.75) + f(-0.5) + \cdots + f(1.75)] + f(2)\} \approx 8.240073$

$M_{12} = \frac{1}{4}\left[f\left(-\frac{7}{8}\right) + f\left(-\frac{5}{8}\right) + \cdots + f\left(\frac{13}{8}\right) + f\left(\frac{15}{8}\right)\right] \approx 8.067259$

$S_{12} = \frac{1}{4 \cdot 3}[f(-1) + 4f(-0.75) + 2f(-0.5) + \cdots + 2f(1.5) + 4f(1.75) + f(2)] \approx 8.125593$

$E_T \approx I - 8.240073 \approx -0.115258,\ E_M \approx I - 8.067259 \approx 0.057556,$

$E_S \approx I - 8.125593 \approx -0.000778$

n	T_n	M_n	S_n
6	8.583514	7.896632	8.136885
12	8.240073	8.067259	8.125593

n	E_T	E_M	E_S
6	−0.458699	0.228183	−0.012070
12	−0.115258	0.057556	−0.000778

Observations:

1. E_T and E_M are opposite in sign and decrease by a factor of about 4 as n is doubled.

2. The Simpson's approximation is much more accurate than the Midpoint and Trapezoidal approximations, and seems to decrease by a factor of about 16 as n is doubled.

23. $\Delta x = (4-0)/4 = 1$

(a) $T_4 = \frac{1}{2}[f(0) + 2f(1) + 2f(2) + 2f(3) + f(4)] \approx \frac{1}{2}[0 + 2(3) + 2(5) + 2(3) + 1] = 11.5$

(b) $M_4 = 1 \cdot [f(0.5) + f(1.5) + f(2.5) + f(3.5)] \approx 1 + 4.5 + 4.5 + 2 = 12$

(c) $S_4 = \frac{1}{3}[f(0) + 4f(1) + 2f(2) + 4f(3) + f(4)] \approx \frac{1}{3}[0 + 4(3) + 2(5) + 4(3) + 1] = 11.\overline{6}$

24. We use Simpson's Rule with $n = 10$ and $\Delta x = \frac{1}{2}$:

$$\text{distance} = \int_0^5 v(t)\,dt \approx S_{10} = \frac{1}{2 \cdot 3}[f(0) + 4f(0.5) + 2f(1) + \cdots + 4f(4.5) + f(5)]$$

$$= \frac{1}{6}[0 + 4(4.67) + 2(7.34) + 4(8.86) + 2(9.73) + 4(10.22)$$
$$+ 2(10.51) + 4(10.67) + 2(10.76) + 4(10.81) + 10.81]$$
$$= \frac{1}{6}(268.41) = 44.735 \text{ m}$$

25. By the Total Change Theorem, the increase in velocity is equal to $\int_0^6 a(t)\,dt$. We use Simpson's Rule with $n = 6$ and $\Delta t = (6-0)/6 = 1$ to estimate this integral:

$$\int_0^6 a(t)\,dt \approx S_6 = \frac{1}{3}[a(0) + 4a(1) + 2a(2) + 4a(3) + 2a(4) + 4a(5) + a(6)]$$

$$\approx \frac{1}{3}[0 + 4(0.5) + 2(4.1) + 4(9.8) + 2(12.9) + 4(9.5) + 0] = \frac{1}{3}(113.2) = 37.7\overline{3} \text{ ft/s}$$

26. By the Total Change Theorem, the amount of water leaked is equal to $\int_0^4 r(t)\,dt$. We use Simpson's Rule with $n = 4$ and $\Delta t = (4-0)/4 = 1$ to estimate this integral:

$$\int_0^4 r(t)\,dt \approx S_4 = \frac{1}{3}[r(0) + 4r(1) + 2r(2) + 4r(3) + r(4)]$$

$$\approx \frac{1}{3}[6 + 4(5.7) + 2(5.1) + 4(4.1) + 3] = \frac{1}{3}(58.4) = 19.4\overline{6} \text{ L}$$

27. By the Total Change Theorem, the energy used is equal to $\int_0^6 P(t)\,dt$. We use Simpson's Rule with $n = 12$ and $\Delta t = (6-0)/12 = \frac{1}{2}$ to estimate this integral:

$$\int_0^6 P(t)\,dt \approx S_{12} = \frac{1/2}{3}[P(0) + 4P(0.5) + 2P(1) + 4P(1.5) + 2P(2) + 4P(2.5)$$
$$+ 2P(3) + 4P(3.5) + 2P(4) + 4P(4.5) + 2P(5) + 4P(5.5) + P(6)]$$

$$= \frac{1}{6}[1814 + 4(1735) + 2(1686) + 4(1646) + 2(1637) + 4(1609) + 2(1604)$$
$$+ 4(1611) + 2(1621) + 4(1666) + 2(1745) + 4(1886) + 2052]$$

$$= \frac{1}{6}(61{,}064) = 10{,}177.\overline{3} \text{ megawatt-hours.}$$

28. By the Total Change Theorem, the total amount of data transmitted is equal to $\int_0^8 D(t)\,dt \times 3600$ [since $D(t)$ is measured in megabits per second and t is in hours]. We use Simpson's Rule with $n = 8$ and $\Delta t = (8-0)/8 = 1$ to estimate this integral:

$$\int_0^8 D(t)\,dt \approx S_8 = \frac{1}{3}[D(0) + 4D(1) + 2D(2) + 4D(3) + 2D(4) + 4D(5) + 2D(6) + 4D(7) + D(8)]$$

$$\approx \frac{1}{3}[0.35 + 4(0.32) + 2(0.41) + 4(0.50) + 2(0.51) + 4(0.56) + 2(0.56) + 4(0.83) + 0.88]$$

$$= \frac{1}{3}(13.03) = 4.34\overline{3}$$

Now multiply by 3600 to obtain 15,636 megabits.

29. (a) We are given the function values at the endpoints of 8 intervals of length 0.4, so we'll use the Midpoint Rule with $n = 8/2 = 4$ and $\Delta x = (3.2 - 0)/4 = 0.8$.

$$\int_0^{3.2} f(x)\, dx \approx M_4 = 0.8[f(0.4) + f(1.2) + f(2.0) + f(2.8)]$$
$$= 0.8[6.5 + 6.4 + 7.6 + 8.8]$$
$$= 0.8(29.3) = 23.44$$

(b) $-4 \le f''(x) \le 1 \;\Rightarrow\; |f''(x)| \le 4$, so use $K = 4$, $a = 0$, $b = 3.2$, and $n = 4$ in Theorem 3. So

$$|E_M| \le \frac{4(3.2 - 0)^3}{24(4)^2} = \frac{128}{375} = 0.341\overline{3}.$$

30. Using Simpson's Rule with $n = 10$, $\Delta x = \frac{\pi/2}{10}$, $L = 1$, $\theta_0 = \frac{42\pi}{180}$ radians, $g = 9.8$ m/s^2, $k^2 = \sin^2\left(\frac{1}{2}\theta_0\right)$, and $f(x) = 1/\sqrt{1 - k^2 \sin^2 x}$, we get

$$T = 4\sqrt{\frac{L}{g}} \int_0^{\pi/2} \frac{dx}{\sqrt{1 - k^2 \sin^2 x}} \approx 4\sqrt{\frac{L}{g}}\, S_{10}$$

$$= 4\sqrt{\tfrac{1}{9.8}}\left(\tfrac{\pi/2}{10\cdot 3}\right)\left[f(0) + 4f\left(\tfrac{\pi}{20}\right) + 2f\left(\tfrac{2\pi}{20}\right) + \cdots + 4f\left(\tfrac{9\pi}{20}\right) + f\left(\tfrac{\pi}{2}\right)\right] \approx 2.07665$$

31. $I(\theta) = \dfrac{N^2 \sin^2 k}{k^2}$, where $k = \dfrac{\pi N d \sin \theta}{\lambda}$, $N = 10{,}000$, $d = 10^{-4}$, and $\lambda = 632.8 \times 10^{-9}$. So

$I(\theta) = \dfrac{(10^4)^2 \sin^2 k}{k^2}$, where $k = \dfrac{\pi(10^4)(10^{-4})\sin\theta}{632.8 \times 10^{-9}}$. Now $n = 10$ and $\Delta\theta = \dfrac{10^{-6} - (-10^{-6})}{10} = 2 \times 10^{-7}$,

so $M_{10} = 2 \times 10^{-7}[I(-0.0000009) + I(-0.0000007) + \cdots + I(0.0000009)] \approx 59.4$.

32. $f(x) = \cos(\pi x)$, $\Delta x = \frac{20 - 0}{10} = 2 \;\Rightarrow$

$$T_{10} = \tfrac{2}{2}\{f(0) + 2[f(2) + f(4) + \cdots + f(18)] + f(20)\}$$
$$= 1[\cos 0 + 2(\cos 2\pi + \cos 4\pi + \cdots + \cos 18\pi) + \cos 20\pi]$$
$$= 1 + 2(1 + 1 + 1 + 1 + 1 + 1 + 1 + 1 + 1) + 1 = 20$$

The actual value is $\int_0^{20} \cos(\pi x)\, dx = \frac{1}{\pi}[\sin \pi x]_0^{20} = \frac{1}{\pi}(\sin 20\pi - \sin 0) = 0$. The discrepancy is due to the fact that the function is sampled only at points of the form $2n$, where its value is $f(2n) = \cos(2n\pi) = 1$.

33. Since the Trapezoidal and Midpoint approximations on the interval $[a, b]$ are the sums of the Trapezoidal and Midpoint approximations on the subintervals $[x_{i-1}, x_i]$, $i = 1, 2, \ldots, n$, we can focus our attention on one such interval. The condition $f''(x) < 0$ for $a \le x \le b$ means that the graph of f is concave down as in Figure 5. In that figure, T_n is the area of the trapezoid $AQRD$, $\int_a^b f(x)\, dx$ is the area of the region $AQPRD$, and M_n is the area of the trapezoid $ABCD$, so $T_n < \int_a^b f(x)\, dx < M_n$. In general, the condition $f'' < 0$ implies that the graph of f on $[a, b]$ lies above the chord joining the points $(a, f(a))$ and $(b, f(b))$. Thus, $\int_a^b f(x)\, dx > T_n$. Since M_n is the area under a tangent to the graph, and since $f'' < 0$ implies that the tangent lies above the graph, we also have $M_n > \int_a^b f(x)\, dx$. Thus, $T_n < \int_a^b f(x)\, dx < M_n$.

34. Let f be a polynomial of degree ≤ 3; say $f(x) = Ax^3 + Bx^2 + Cx + D$. It will suffice to show that Simpson's estimate is exact when there are two subintervals ($n = 2$), because for a larger even number of subintervals the sum of exact estimates is exact. As in the derivation of Simpson's Rule, we can assume that $x_0 = -h$, $x_1 = 0$, and $x_2 = h$. Then Simpson's approximation is

$$\int_{-h}^{h} f(x)\,dx \approx \tfrac{1}{3}h[f(-h) + 4f(0) + f(h)]$$
$$= \tfrac{1}{3}h\left[(-Ah^3 + Bh^2 - Ch + D) + 4D + (Ah^3 + Bh^2 + Ch + D)\right]$$
$$= \tfrac{1}{3}h\left[2Bh^2 + 6D\right] = \tfrac{2}{3}Bh^3 + 2Dh$$

The exact value of the integral is

$$\int_{-h}^{h}(Ax^3 + Bx^2 + Cx + D)\,dx = 2\int_0^h (Bx^2 + D)\,dx \quad \text{[by Theorem 5.5.6(a) and (b)]}$$
$$= 2\left[\tfrac{1}{3}Bx^3 + Dx\right]_0^h = \tfrac{2}{3}Bh^3 + 2Dh$$

Thus, Simpson's Rule is exact.

35. $T_n = \frac{1}{2}\Delta x\left[f(x_0) + 2f(x_1) + \cdots + 2f(x_{n-1}) + f(x_n)\right]$ and

$M_n = \Delta x\left[f(\overline{x}_1) + f(\overline{x}_2) + \cdots + f(\overline{x}_{n-1}) + f(\overline{x}_n)\right]$, where $\overline{x}_i = \frac{1}{2}(x_{i-1} + x_i)$. Now

$$T_{2n} = \tfrac{1}{2}\left(\tfrac{1}{2}\Delta x\right)[f(x_0) + 2f(\overline{x}_1) + 2f(x_1) + 2f(\overline{x}_2) + 2f(x_2) + \cdots$$
$$+ 2f(\overline{x}_{n-1}) + 2f(x_{n-1}) + 2f(\overline{x}_n) + f(x_n)]$$

so $\quad \frac{1}{2}(T_n + M_n) = \frac{1}{2}T_n + \frac{1}{2}M_n$

$$= \tfrac{1}{4}\Delta x\left[f(x_0) + 2f(x_1) + \cdots + 2f(x_{n-1}) + f(x_n)\right]$$
$$+ \tfrac{1}{4}\Delta x\left[2f(\overline{x}_1) + 2f(\overline{x}_2) + \cdots + 2f(\overline{x}_{n-1}) + 2f(\overline{x}_n)\right]$$

$$= T_{2n}$$

36. $T_n = \dfrac{\Delta x}{2}\left[f(x_0) + 2\displaystyle\sum_{i=1}^{n-1} f(x_i) + f(x_n)\right]$ and $M_n = \Delta x \displaystyle\sum_{i=1}^{n} f\left(x_i - \dfrac{\Delta x}{2}\right)$, so

$$\tfrac{1}{3}T_n + \tfrac{2}{3}M_n = \tfrac{1}{3}(T_n + 2M_n) = \dfrac{\Delta x}{3\cdot 2}\left[f(x_0) + 2\sum_{i=1}^{n-1} f(x_i) + f(x_n) + 4\sum_{i=1}^{n} f\left(x_i - \dfrac{\Delta x}{2}\right)\right]$$

where $\Delta x = \dfrac{b-a}{n}$. Let $\delta x = \dfrac{b-a}{2n}$. Then $\Delta x = 2\delta x$, so

$$\tfrac{1}{3}T_n + \tfrac{2}{3}M_n = \dfrac{\delta x}{3}\left[f(x_0) + 2\sum_{i=1}^{n-1} f(x_i) + f(x_n) + 4\sum_{i=1}^{n} f(x_i - \delta x)\right]$$
$$= \tfrac{1}{3}\delta x[f(x_0) + 4f(x_1 - \delta x) + 2f(x_1) + 4f(x_2 - \delta x)$$
$$+ 2f(x_2) + \cdots + 2f(x_{n-1}) + 4f(x_n - \delta x) + f(x_n)]$$

Since $x_0, x_1 - \delta x, x_1, x_2 - \delta x, x_2, \ldots, x_{n-1}, x_n - \delta x, x_n$ are the subinterval endpoints for S_{2n}, and since $\delta x = \dfrac{b-a}{2n}$ is the width of the subintervals for S_{2n}, the last expression for $\frac{1}{3}T_n + \frac{2}{3}M_n$ is the usual expression for S_{2n}. Therefore, $\frac{1}{3}T_n + \frac{2}{3}M_n = S_{2n}$.

Improper Integrals · · · · · · · · · · · · · · ·

1. (a) Since $\int_1^\infty x^4 e^{-x^4}\,dx$ has an infinite interval of integration, it is an improper integral of Type I.

(b) Since $y = \sec x$ has an infinite discontinuity at $x = \frac{\pi}{2}$, $\int_0^{\pi/2} \sec x\,dx$ is a Type II improper integral.

(c) Since $y = \dfrac{x}{(x-2)(x-3)}$ has an infinite discontinuity at $x = 2$, $\displaystyle\int_0^2 \dfrac{x}{x^2-5x+6}\,dx$ is a Type II improper integral.

(d) Since $\displaystyle\int_{-\infty}^0 \dfrac{1}{x^2+5}\,dx$ has an infinite interval of integration, it is an improper integral of Type I.

2. (a) Since $y = 1/(2x-1)$ is defined and continuous on $[1,2]$, the integral is proper.

(b) Since $y = \dfrac{1}{2x-1}$ has an infinite discontinuity at $x = \frac{1}{2}$, $\displaystyle\int_0^1 \dfrac{1}{2x-1}\,dx$ is a Type II improper integral.

(c) Since $\displaystyle\int_{-\infty}^\infty \dfrac{\sin x}{1+x^2}\,dx$ has an infinite interval of integration, it is an improper integral of Type I.

(d) Since $y = \ln(x-1)$ has an infinite discontinuity at $x = 1$, $\int_1^2 \ln(x-1)\,dx$ is a Type II improper integral.

3. The area under the graph of $y = 1/x^3 = x^{-3}$ between $x = 1$ and $x = t$ is
$A(t) = \int_1^t x^{-3}\,dx = \left[-\frac{1}{2}x^{-2}\right]_1^t = -\frac{1}{2}t^{-2} - \left(-\frac{1}{2}\right) = \frac{1}{2} - 1/(2t^2)$. So the area for $1 \le x \le 10$ is
$A(10) = 0.5 - 0.005 = 0.495$, the area for $1 \le x \le 100$ is $A(100) = 0.5 - 0.00005 = 0.49995$, and the area for
$1 \le x \le 1000$ is $A(1000) = 0.5 - 0.0000005 = 0.4999995$. The total area under the curve for $x \ge 1$ is
$\displaystyle\lim_{t\to\infty} A(t) = \lim_{t\to\infty} \left[\frac{1}{2} - 1/(2t^2)\right] = \frac{1}{2}$.

4. (a)

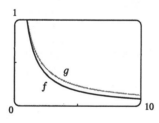 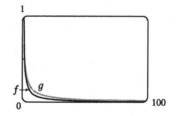

(b) The area under the graph of f from $x = 1$ to $x = t$ is

$F(t) = \int_1^t f(x)\,dx = \int_1^t x^{-1.1}\,dx = \left[-\frac{1}{0.1}x^{-0.1}\right]_1^t$

$= -10\left(t^{-0.1} - 1\right) = 10\left(1 - t^{-0.1}\right)$

and the area under the graph of g is

$G(t) = \int_1^t g(x)\,dx = \int_1^t x^{-0.9}\,dx = \left[\frac{1}{0.1}x^{0.1}\right]_1^t$

$= 10\left(t^{0.1} - 1\right)$

t	$F(t)$	$G(t)$
10	2.06	2.59
100	3.69	5.85
10^4	6.02	15.12
10^6	7.49	29.81
10^{10}	9	90
10^{20}	9.9	990

(c) The total area under the graph of f is $\displaystyle\lim_{t\to\infty} F(t) = \lim_{t\to\infty} 10\left(1 - t^{-0.1}\right) = 10$.

The total area under the graph of g does not exist, since $\displaystyle\lim_{t\to\infty} G(t) = \lim_{t\to\infty} 10\left(t^{0.1} - 1\right) = \infty$.

5. $I = \int_1^\infty \dfrac{1}{(3x+1)^2}\, dx = \lim\limits_{t\to\infty} \int_1^t \dfrac{1}{(3x+1)^2}\, dx$. Now

$\int \dfrac{1}{(3x+1)^2}\, dx = \dfrac{1}{3} \int \dfrac{1}{u^2}\, du \quad [u = 3x+1,\ du = 3\,dx]$

$\qquad = -\dfrac{1}{3u} + C = -\dfrac{1}{3(3x+1)} + C,$

so $I = \lim\limits_{t\to\infty} \left[-\dfrac{1}{3(3x+1)} \right]_1^t = \lim\limits_{t\to\infty} \left[-\dfrac{1}{3(3t+1)} + \dfrac{1}{12} \right] = 0 + \dfrac{1}{12} = \dfrac{1}{12}$. Convergent

6. $\int_2^\infty \dfrac{dx}{(x+3)^{3/2}} = \lim\limits_{t\to\infty} \int_2^t \dfrac{dx}{(x+3)^{3/2}} = \lim\limits_{t\to\infty} \left[\dfrac{-2}{\sqrt{x+3}} \right]_2^t = \lim\limits_{t\to\infty} \left[\dfrac{-2}{\sqrt{t+3}} + \dfrac{2}{\sqrt{5}} \right] = \dfrac{2}{\sqrt{5}}$. Convergent

7. $\int_0^\infty e^{-x}\, dx = \lim\limits_{t\to\infty} \int_0^t e^{-x}\, dx = \lim\limits_{t\to\infty} \left[-e^{-x} \right]_0^t = \lim\limits_{t\to\infty} (-e^{-t} + 1) = 1$. Convergent

8. $\int_{-\infty}^0 \dfrac{1}{2x-5}\, dx = \lim\limits_{t\to-\infty} \int_t^0 \dfrac{1}{2x-5}\, dx = \lim\limits_{t\to-\infty} \left[\tfrac{1}{2} \ln|2x-5| \right]_t^0 = \lim\limits_{t\to\infty} \left[\tfrac{1}{2} \ln 5 - \tfrac{1}{2} \ln|2t-5| \right] = -\infty$.

Divergent

9. $\int_{-\infty}^{-1} \dfrac{1}{\sqrt{2-w}}\, dw = \lim\limits_{t\to-\infty} \int_t^{-1} \dfrac{1}{\sqrt{2-w}}\, dw = \lim\limits_{t\to-\infty} \left[-2\sqrt{2-w} \right]_t^{-1} \quad [u = 2-w,\ du = -dw]$

$\qquad = \lim\limits_{t\to-\infty} \left[-2\sqrt{3} + 2\sqrt{2-t} \right] = \infty$. Divergent

10. $\int_{-\infty}^{-1} e^{-2t}\, dt = \lim\limits_{x\to-\infty} \int_x^{-1} e^{-2t}\, dt = \lim\limits_{x\to-\infty} \left[-\tfrac{1}{2} e^{-2t} \right]_x^{-1} = \lim\limits_{x\to-\infty} \left[-\tfrac{1}{2} e^2 + \tfrac{1}{2} e^{-2x} \right] = \infty$. Divergent

11. $I = \int_{-\infty}^\infty x^3\, dx = I_1 + I_2 = \int_{-\infty}^0 x^3\, dx + \int_0^\infty x^3\, dx$, but $I_1 = \lim\limits_{t\to-\infty} \left[\tfrac{1}{4} x^4 \right]_t^0 = \lim\limits_{t\to-\infty} (-\tfrac{1}{4} t^4) = -\infty$. Since I_1

is divergent, I is divergent, and there is no need to evaluate I_2. Divergent

12. $I = \int_{-\infty}^\infty (2 - v^4)\, dv = I_1 + I_2 = \int_{-\infty}^0 (2 - v^4)\, dv + \int_0^\infty (2 - v^4)\, dv$, but

$I_1 = \lim\limits_{t\to-\infty} \left[2v - \tfrac{1}{5} v^5 \right]_t^0 = \lim\limits_{t\to-\infty} (-2t + \tfrac{1}{5} t^5) = -\infty$. Since I_1 is divergent, I is divergent, and there is no need

to evaluate I_2. Divergent

13. $\int_{-\infty}^\infty x e^{-x^2}\, dx = \int_{-\infty}^0 x e^{-x^2}\, dx + \int_0^\infty x e^{-x^2}\, dx$.

$\int_{-\infty}^0 x e^{-x^2}\, dx = \lim\limits_{t\to-\infty} (-\tfrac{1}{2}) \left[e^{-x^2} \right]_t^0 = \lim\limits_{t\to-\infty} (-\tfrac{1}{2})(1 - e^{-t^2}) = -\tfrac{1}{2} \cdot 1 = -\tfrac{1}{2}$, and

$\int_0^\infty x e^{-x^2}\, dx = \lim\limits_{t\to\infty} (-\tfrac{1}{2}) \left[e^{-x^2} \right]_0^t = \lim\limits_{t\to\infty} (-\tfrac{1}{2})(e^{-t^2} - 1) = -\tfrac{1}{2} \cdot (-1) = \tfrac{1}{2}$.

Therefore, $\int_{-\infty}^\infty x e^{-x^2}\, dx = -\tfrac{1}{2} + \tfrac{1}{2} = 0$. Convergent

14. $\int_{-\infty}^\infty x^2 e^{-x^3}\, dx = \int_{-\infty}^0 x^2 e^{-x^3}\, dx + \int_0^\infty x^2 e^{-x^3}\, dx$, and

$\int_{-\infty}^0 x^2 e^{-x^3}\, dx = \lim\limits_{t\to-\infty} \left[-\tfrac{1}{3} e^{-x^3} \right]_t^0 = -\tfrac{1}{3} + \tfrac{1}{3} \left(\lim\limits_{t\to-\infty} e^{-t^3} \right) = \infty$. Divergent

15. $\int_0^\infty \cos x\, dx = \lim\limits_{t\to\infty} \left[\sin x \right]_0^t = \lim\limits_{t\to\infty} \sin t$, which does not exist. Divergent

16. $\int_{-\infty}^{\pi/2} \sin 2\theta\, d\theta = \lim\limits_{t\to-\infty} \int_t^{\pi/2} \sin 2\theta\, d\theta = \lim\limits_{t\to-\infty} \left[-\tfrac{1}{2} \cos 2\theta \right]_t^{\pi/2} = \lim\limits_{t\to-\infty} \left(\tfrac{1}{2} + \tfrac{1}{2} \cos 2t \right)$. This limit does not

exist, so the integral is divergent.

17. $\int_{-\infty}^{1} xe^{2x}\,dx = \lim\limits_{t\to-\infty} \int_{t}^{1} xe^{2x}\,dx = \lim\limits_{t\to-\infty} \left[\frac{1}{2}xe^{2x} - \frac{1}{4}e^{2x}\right]_{t}^{1}$ (by parts with $u = x$ and $dv = e^{2x}\,dx$)

$$= \lim\limits_{t\to-\infty} \left[\frac{1}{2}e^2 - \frac{1}{4}e^2 - \frac{1}{2}te^{2t} + \frac{1}{4}e^{2t}\right] = \frac{1}{4}e^2 - 0 + 0 = \frac{1}{4}e^2$$

since $\lim\limits_{t\to-\infty} te^{2t} = \lim\limits_{t\to-\infty} \dfrac{t}{e^{-2t}} \overset{\text{H}}{=} \lim\limits_{t\to-\infty} \dfrac{1}{-2e^{-2t}} = \lim\limits_{t\to-\infty} -\frac{1}{2}e^{2t} = 0$. Convergent

18. $\int_{0}^{\infty} xe^{-x}\,dx = \lim\limits_{t\to\infty} \left[-xe^{-x} - e^{-x}\right]_{0}^{t}$ (by parts with $u = x$ and $dv = e^{-x}\,dx$)

$$= \lim\limits_{t\to\infty} \left[-te^{-t} - e^{-t} + 1\right] = 0 - 0 + 1 = 1,$$

since $\lim\limits_{t\to\infty} \left(te^{-t}\right) = \lim\limits_{t\to\infty} \dfrac{t}{e^t} \overset{\text{H}}{=} \lim\limits_{t\to\infty} \dfrac{1}{e^t} = 0$. Convergent

19. $\int_{1}^{\infty} \dfrac{\ln x}{x}\,dx = \lim\limits_{t\to\infty} \left[\dfrac{(\ln x)^2}{2}\right]_{1}^{t}$ (by substitution with $u = \ln x$, $du = dx/x$) $= \lim\limits_{t\to\infty} \dfrac{(\ln t)^2}{2} = \infty$. Divergent

20. Since $f(r) = \dfrac{1}{r^2 + 4}$ is even,

$$I = \int_{-\infty}^{\infty} f(r)\,dr = 2\int_{0}^{\infty} f(r)\,dr = 2\lim\limits_{t\to\infty} \int_{0}^{t} \dfrac{1}{r^2 + 4}\,dr = 2\lim\limits_{t\to\infty} \left[\dfrac{1}{2}\arctan\dfrac{r}{2}\right]_{0}^{t}$$

$$= \lim\limits_{t\to\infty} \left(\arctan\dfrac{t}{2} - 0\right) = \dfrac{\pi}{2}. \quad \text{Convergent}$$

21. Integrate by parts with $u = \ln x$, $dv = dx/x^2 \;\Rightarrow\; du = dx/x$, $v = -1/x$.

$$\int_{1}^{\infty} \dfrac{\ln x}{x^2}\,dx = \lim\limits_{t\to\infty} \int_{1}^{t} \dfrac{\ln x}{x^2}\,dx = \lim\limits_{t\to\infty} \left[-\dfrac{\ln x}{x} - \dfrac{1}{x}\right]_{1}^{t} = \lim\limits_{t\to\infty} \left(-\dfrac{\ln t}{t} - \dfrac{1}{t} + 0 + 1\right)$$

$$= -0 - 0 + 0 + 1 = 1$$

since $\lim\limits_{t\to\infty} \dfrac{\ln t}{t} \overset{\text{H}}{=} \lim\limits_{t\to\infty} \dfrac{1/t}{1} = 0$. Convergent

22. Integrate by parts with $u = \ln x$, $dv = dx/x^3 \;\Rightarrow\; du = dx/x$, $v = -1/\left(2x^2\right)$.

$$\int_{1}^{\infty} \dfrac{\ln x}{x^3}\,dx = \lim\limits_{t\to\infty} \int_{1}^{t} \dfrac{\ln x}{x^3}\,dx = \lim\limits_{t\to\infty} \left(\left[-\dfrac{1}{2x^2}\ln x\right]_{1}^{t} + \dfrac{1}{2}\int_{1}^{t} \dfrac{1}{x^3}\,dx\right)$$

$$= \lim\limits_{t\to\infty} \left(-\dfrac{1}{2}\dfrac{\ln t}{t^2} + 0 - \dfrac{1}{4t^2} + \dfrac{1}{4}\right) = \dfrac{1}{4}$$

since $\lim\limits_{t\to\infty} \dfrac{\ln t}{t^2} \overset{\text{H}}{=} \lim\limits_{t\to\infty} \dfrac{1/t}{2t} = \lim\limits_{t\to\infty} \dfrac{1}{2t^2} = 0$. Convergent

23. There is an infinite discontinuity at the left endpoint of $[0, 3]$.

$$\int_{0}^{3} \dfrac{dx}{\sqrt{x}} = \lim\limits_{t\to0^+} \int_{t}^{3} \dfrac{dx}{\sqrt{x}} = \lim\limits_{t\to0^+} \left[2\sqrt{x}\right]_{t}^{3} = \lim\limits_{t\to0^+} \left(2\sqrt{3} - 2\sqrt{t}\right) = 2\sqrt{3}. \quad \text{Convergent}$$

24. There is an infinite discontinuity at the left endpoint of $[0, 3]$.

$$\int_{0}^{3} \dfrac{dx}{x\sqrt{x}} = \lim\limits_{t\to0^+} \int_{t}^{3} \dfrac{dx}{x^{3/2}} = \lim\limits_{t\to0^+} \left[\dfrac{-2}{\sqrt{x}}\right]_{t}^{3} = \dfrac{-2}{\sqrt{3}} + \lim\limits_{t\to0^+} \dfrac{2}{\sqrt{t}} = \infty. \quad \text{Divergent}$$

25. There is an infinite discontinuity at the right endpoint of $[-1, 0]$.

$$\int_{-1}^{0} \dfrac{dx}{x^2} = \lim\limits_{t\to0^-} \int_{-1}^{t} \dfrac{dx}{x^2} = \lim\limits_{t\to0^-} \left[\dfrac{-1}{x}\right]_{-1}^{t} = \lim\limits_{t\to0^-} \left[-\dfrac{1}{t} + \dfrac{1}{-1}\right] = \infty. \quad \text{Divergent}$$

26. $\int_1^9 \frac{dx}{\sqrt[3]{x-9}} = \lim_{t \to 9-} \int_1^t \frac{dx}{\sqrt[3]{x-9}} = \lim_{t \to 9-} \left[\frac{3}{2}(x-9)^{2/3}\right]_1^t = \lim_{t \to 9-} \left[\frac{3}{2}(t-9)^{2/3} - \frac{3}{2}(4)\right] = 0 - 6 = -6.$
Convergent

27. $\int_0^{\pi/4} \csc^2 t\, dt = \lim_{s \to 0+} \int_s^{\pi/4} \csc^2 t\, dt = \lim_{s \to 0+} \left[-\cot t\right]_s^{\pi/4} = \lim_{s \to 0+} \left[-\cot \frac{\pi}{4} + \cot s\right] = \infty.$ Divergent

28. $f(y) = 1/(4y-1)$ has an infinite discontinuity at $y = \frac{1}{4}$.

$$\int_{1/4}^1 \frac{1}{4y-1}\, dy = \lim_{t \to (1/4)+} \int_t^1 \frac{1}{4y-1}\, dy = \lim_{t \to (1/4)+} \left[\frac{1}{4}\ln|4y-1|\right]_t^1$$

$$= \lim_{t \to (1/4)+} \left[\frac{1}{4}\ln 3 - \frac{1}{4}\ln(4t-1)\right] = \infty$$

so $\int_{1/4}^1 \frac{1}{4y-1}\, dy$ diverges, and hence, $\int_0^1 \frac{1}{4y-1}\, dy$ diverges. Divergent

29. $\int_{-2}^3 \frac{dx}{x^4} = \int_{-2}^0 \frac{dx}{x^4} + \int_0^3 \frac{dx}{x^4}$, but $\int_{-2}^0 \frac{dx}{x^4} = \lim_{t \to 0-} \left[-\frac{x^{-3}}{3}\right]_{-2}^t = \lim_{t \to 0-} \left[-\frac{1}{3t^3} - \frac{1}{24}\right] = \infty.$ Divergent

30. $\int_0^4 \frac{dx}{x^2 + x - 6} = \int_0^4 \frac{dx}{(x+3)(x-2)} = \int_0^2 \frac{dx}{(x-2)(x+3)} + \int_2^4 \frac{dx}{(x-2)(x+3)}$, and

$$\int_0^2 \frac{dx}{(x-2)(x+3)} = \lim_{t \to 2-} \int_0^t \left[\frac{1/5}{x-2} - \frac{1/5}{x+3}\right] dx \text{ (partial fractions)} = \lim_{t \to 2-} \left[\frac{1}{5}\ln\left|\frac{x-2}{x+3}\right|\right]_0^t$$

$$= \lim_{t \to 2-} \frac{1}{5}\left[\ln\left|\frac{t-2}{t+3}\right| - \ln\frac{2}{3}\right] = -\infty. \text{ Divergent}$$

31. $I = \int_0^2 z^2 \ln z\, dz = \lim_{t \to 0+} \int_t^2 z^2 \ln z\, dz \overset{101}{=} \lim_{t \to 0+} \left[\frac{z^3}{3^2}(3\ln z - 1)\right]_t^2$

$= \lim_{t \to 0+} \left[\frac{8}{9}(3\ln 2 - 1) - \frac{1}{9}t^3(3\ln t - 1)\right] = \frac{8}{3}\ln 2 - \frac{8}{9} - \frac{1}{9}\lim_{t \to 0+} \left[t^3(3\ln t - 1)\right] = \frac{8}{3}\ln 2 - \frac{8}{9} - \frac{1}{9}L.$

Now $L = \lim_{t \to 0+} \left[t^3(3\ln t - 1)\right] = \lim_{t \to 0+} \frac{3\ln t - 1}{t^{-3}} \overset{\text{H}}{=} \lim_{t \to 0+} \frac{3/t}{-3/t^4} = \lim_{t \to 0+} (-t^3) = 0.$ Thus, $L = 0$ and
$I = \frac{8}{3}\ln 2 - \frac{8}{9}.$ Convergent

32. Integrate by parts with $u = \ln x$, $dv = dx/\sqrt{x} \quad \Rightarrow \quad du = dx/x$, $v = 2\sqrt{x}$.

$$\int_0^1 \frac{\ln x}{\sqrt{x}}\, dx = \lim_{t \to 0+} \int_t^1 \frac{\ln x}{\sqrt{x}}\, dx = \lim_{t \to 0+} \left(\left[2\sqrt{x}\ln x\right]_t^1 - 2\int_t^1 \frac{dx}{\sqrt{x}}\right) = \lim_{t \to 0+} \left(-2\sqrt{t}\ln t - 4\left[\sqrt{x}\right]_t^1\right)$$

$$= \lim_{t \to 0+} \left(-2\sqrt{t}\ln t - 4 + 4\sqrt{t}\right) = -4$$

since $\lim_{t \to 0+} \sqrt{t}\ln t = \lim_{t \to 0+} \frac{\ln t}{t^{-1/2}} \overset{\text{H}}{=} \lim_{t \to 0+} \frac{1/t}{-t^{-3/2}/2} = \lim_{t \to 0+} (-2\sqrt{t}) = 0.$ Convergent

33.

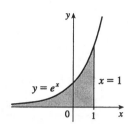

$$\text{Area} = \int_{-\infty}^{1} e^x \, dx = \lim_{t \to -\infty} [e^x]_t^1$$

$$= e - \lim_{t \to -\infty} e^t = e$$

34.

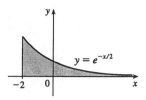

$$\text{Area} = \int_{-2}^{\infty} e^{-x/2} \, dx = -2 \lim_{t \to \infty} \left[e^{-x/2} \right]_{-2}^{t}$$

$$= -2 \lim_{t \to \infty} e^{-t/2} + 2e = 2e$$

35.

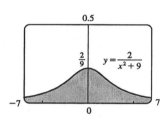

$$\text{Area} = \int_{-\infty}^{\infty} \frac{2}{x^2 + 9} \, dx = 2 \cdot 2 \int_{0}^{\infty} \frac{1}{x^2 + 9} \, dx$$

$$= 4 \lim_{t \to \infty} \int_{0}^{t} \frac{1}{x^2 + 9} \, dx = 4 \lim_{t \to \infty} \left[\frac{1}{3} \tan^{-1} \frac{x}{3} \right]_0^t$$

$$= \frac{4}{3} \lim_{t \to \infty} \left[\tan^{-1} \frac{t}{3} - 0 \right] = \frac{4}{3} \cdot \frac{\pi}{2} = \frac{2\pi}{3}$$

36.

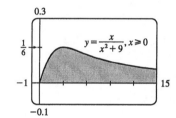

$$\text{Area} = \int_{0}^{\infty} \frac{x}{x^2 + 9} \, dx = \lim_{t \to \infty} \int_{0}^{t} \frac{x}{x^2 + 9} \, dx$$

$$= \lim_{t \to \infty} \left[\frac{1}{2} \ln(x^2 + 9) \right]_0^t$$

$$= \frac{1}{2} \lim_{t \to \infty} \left[\ln(t^2 + 9) - \ln 9 \right] = \infty$$

Infinite area

37.

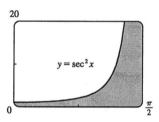

$$\text{Area} = \int_{0}^{\pi/2} \sec^2 x \, dx = \lim_{t \to (\pi/2)^-} \int_{0}^{t} \sec^2 x \, dx$$

$$= \lim_{t \to (\pi/2)^-} [\tan x]_0^t = \lim_{t \to (\pi/2)^-} (\tan t - 0) = \infty$$

Infinite area

38.

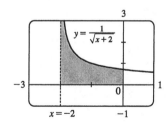

$$\text{Area} = \int_{-2}^{0} \frac{1}{\sqrt{x + 2}} \, dx$$

$$= \lim_{t \to -2^+} \int_{t}^{0} \frac{1}{\sqrt{x + 2}} \, dx$$

$$= \lim_{t \to -2^+} \left[2\sqrt{x + 2} \right]_t^0$$

$$= \lim_{t \to -2^+} \left(2\sqrt{2} - 2\sqrt{t + 2} \right)$$

$$= 2\sqrt{2} - 0 = 2\sqrt{2}$$

39. (a)

t	$\int_1^t g(x)\,dx$
2	0.447453
5	0.577101
10	0.621306
100	0.668479
1000	0.672957
10,000	0.673407

$g(x) = \dfrac{\sin^2 x}{x^2}$. It appears that the integral is convergent.

(c)

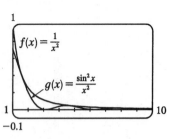

Since $\int_1^\infty f(x)\,dx$ is finite and the area under $g(x)$ is less than the area under $f(x)$ on any interval $[1, t]$, $\int_1^\infty g(x)\,dx$ must be finite; that is, the integral is convergent.

(b) $-1 \le \sin x \le 1 \;\Rightarrow\; 0 \le \sin^2 x \le 1 \;\Rightarrow\; 0 \le \dfrac{\sin^2 x}{x^2} \le \dfrac{1}{x^2}$. Since $\displaystyle\int_1^\infty \dfrac{1}{x^2}\,dx$ is convergent (Equation 2 with $p = 2 > 1$), $\displaystyle\int_1^\infty \dfrac{\sin^2 x}{x^2}\,dx$ is convergent by the Comparison Theorem.

40. (a)

t	$\int_2^t g(x)\,dx$
5	3.830327
10	6.801200
100	23.328769
1000	69.023361
10,000	208.124560

$g(x) = \dfrac{1}{\sqrt{x}-1}$. It appears that the integral is divergent.

(c)

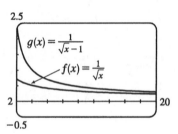

Since $\int_2^\infty f(x)\,dx$ is infinite and the area under $g(x)$ is greater than the area under $f(x)$ on any interval $[2, t]$, $\int_2^\infty g(x)\,dx$ must be infinite; that is, the integral is divergent.

(b) For $x \ge 2$, $\sqrt{x} > \sqrt{x} - 1 \;\Rightarrow\; \dfrac{1}{\sqrt{x}} < \dfrac{1}{\sqrt{x}-1}$. Since $\displaystyle\int_2^\infty \dfrac{1}{\sqrt{x}}\,dx$ is divergent (Equation 2 with $p = \tfrac{1}{2} \le 1$), $\displaystyle\int_2^\infty \dfrac{1}{\sqrt{x}-1}\,dx$ is divergent by the Comparison Theorem.

41. For $x \ge 1$, $\dfrac{\cos^2 x}{1 + x^2} \le \dfrac{1}{1 + x^2} < \dfrac{1}{x^2}$. $\displaystyle\int_1^\infty \dfrac{1}{x^2}\,dx$ is convergent by Equation 2 with $p = 2 > 1$, so $\displaystyle\int_1^\infty \dfrac{\cos^2 x}{1 + x^2}\,dx$ is convergent by the Comparison Theorem.

42. For $x \ge 1$, $\dfrac{1}{\sqrt{x^3 + 1}} \le \dfrac{1}{x^{3/2}}$. $\displaystyle\int_1^\infty \dfrac{1}{x^{3/2}}\,dx$ is convergent by Equation 2 with $p = \tfrac{3}{2} > 1$, so $\displaystyle\int_1^\infty \dfrac{1}{\sqrt{x^3 + 1}}\,dx$ is convergent by the Comparison Theorem.

43. For $x \geq 1$, $x + e^{2x} > e^{2x} > 0$ $\Rightarrow$ $\dfrac{1}{x + e^{2x}} \leq \dfrac{1}{e^{2x}} = e^{-2x}$ on $[1, \infty)$.

$$\int_1^\infty e^{-2x}\, dx = \lim_{t \to \infty} \left[-\frac{1}{2} e^{-2x} \right]_1^t = \lim_{t \to \infty} \left[-\frac{1}{2} e^{-2t} + \frac{1}{2} e^{-2} \right] = \frac{1}{2} e^{-2}.$$ Therefore, $\displaystyle\int_1^\infty e^{-2x}\, dx$ is convergent,

and by the Comparison Theorem, $\displaystyle\int_1^\infty \dfrac{dx}{x + e^{2x}}$ is also convergent.

44. $\dfrac{\sqrt{1 + \sqrt{x}}}{\sqrt{x}} > \dfrac{1}{\sqrt{x}}$ on $[1, \infty)$. $\displaystyle\int_1^\infty \dfrac{1}{\sqrt{x}}\, dx$ is divergent by Equation 2 with $p = \frac{1}{2} \leq 1$, so $\displaystyle\int_1^\infty \dfrac{\sqrt{1 + \sqrt{x}}}{\sqrt{x}}\, dx$ is divergent by the Comparison Theorem.

45. $\dfrac{1}{x \sin x} \geq \dfrac{1}{x}$ on $\left(0, \frac{\pi}{2}\right]$ since $0 \leq \sin x \leq 1$. $\displaystyle\int_0^{\pi/2} \dfrac{dx}{x} = \lim_{t \to 0^+} \int_t^{\pi/2} \dfrac{dx}{x} = \lim_{t \to 0^+} \big[\ln x \big]_t^{\pi/2}$.

But $\ln t \to -\infty$ as $t \to 0^+$, so $\displaystyle\int_0^{\pi/2} \dfrac{dx}{x}$ is divergent, and by the Comparison Theorem, $\displaystyle\int_0^{\pi/2} \dfrac{dx}{x \sin x}$ is also divergent.

46. For $0 \leq x \leq 1$, $e^{-x} \leq 1$ $\Rightarrow$ $\dfrac{e^{-x}}{\sqrt{x}} \leq \dfrac{1}{\sqrt{x}}$.

$$\int_0^1 \dfrac{1}{\sqrt{x}}\, dx = \lim_{t \to 0^+} \int_t^1 \dfrac{1}{\sqrt{x}}\, dx = \lim_{t \to 0^+} \big[2\sqrt{x} \big]_t^1 = \lim_{t \to 0^+} \left(2 - 2\sqrt{t} \right) = 2$$ is convergent. Therefore, $\displaystyle\int_0^1 \dfrac{e^{-x}}{\sqrt{x}}\, dx$

is convergent by the Comparison Theorem.

47. $\displaystyle\int_0^\infty \dfrac{dx}{\sqrt{x}\,(1 + x)} = \int_0^1 \dfrac{dx}{\sqrt{x}\,(1 + x)} + \int_1^\infty \dfrac{dx}{\sqrt{x}\,(1 + x)} = \lim_{t \to 0^+} \int_t^1 \dfrac{dx}{\sqrt{x}\,(1 + x)} + \lim_{t \to \infty} \int_1^t \dfrac{dx}{\sqrt{x}\,(1 + x)}$. Now

$$\int \dfrac{dx}{\sqrt{x}\,(1 + x)} = \int \dfrac{2u\, du}{u(1 + u^2)} \quad [u = \sqrt{x}, x = u^2, dx = 2u\, du]$$

$$= 2 \int \dfrac{du}{1 + u^2} = 2 \tan^{-1} u + C = 2 \tan^{-1} \sqrt{x} + C,$$

so $\displaystyle\int_0^\infty \dfrac{dx}{\sqrt{x}\,(1 + x)} = \lim_{t \to 0^+} \big[2 \tan^{-1} \sqrt{x} \big]_t^1 + \lim_{t \to \infty} \big[2 \tan^{-1} \sqrt{x} \big]_1^t$

$$= \lim_{t \to 0^+} \big[2 \big(\tfrac{\pi}{4} \big) - 2 \tan^{-1} \sqrt{t} \big] + \lim_{t \to \infty} \big[2 \tan^{-1} \sqrt{t} - 2 \big(\tfrac{\pi}{4} \big) \big] = \tfrac{\pi}{2} - 0 + 2 \big(\tfrac{\pi}{2} \big) - \tfrac{\pi}{2} = \pi.$$

48. $\displaystyle\int_2^\infty \dfrac{dx}{x \sqrt{x^2 - 4}} = \int_2^3 \dfrac{dx}{x \sqrt{x^2 - 4}} + \int_3^\infty \dfrac{dx}{x \sqrt{x^2 - 4}} = \lim_{t \to 2^+} \int_t^3 \dfrac{dx}{x \sqrt{x^2 - 4}} + \lim_{t \to \infty} \int_3^t \dfrac{dx}{x \sqrt{x^2 - 4}}$. Now

$$\int \dfrac{dx}{x \sqrt{x^2 - 4}} = \int \dfrac{2 \sec \theta \tan \theta\, d\theta}{2 \sec \theta\, 2 \tan \theta} \quad [x = 2 \sec \theta, \text{ where } 0 \leq \theta < \pi/2 \text{ or } \pi \leq \theta < 3\pi/2]$$

$$= \tfrac{1}{2} \theta + C = \tfrac{1}{2} \sec^{-1} \big(\tfrac{1}{2} x \big) + C, \text{ so}$$

$$\int_2^\infty \dfrac{dx}{x \sqrt{x^2 - 4}} = \lim_{t \to 2^+} \big[\tfrac{1}{2} \sec^{-1} \big(\tfrac{1}{2} x \big) \big]_t^3 + \lim_{t \to \infty} \big[\tfrac{1}{2} \sec^{-1} \big(\tfrac{1}{2} x \big) \big]_3^t$$

$$= \tfrac{1}{2} \sec^{-1} \big(\tfrac{3}{2} \big) - 0 + \tfrac{1}{2} \big(\tfrac{\pi}{2} \big) - \tfrac{1}{2} \sec^{-1} \big(\tfrac{3}{2} \big) = \tfrac{\pi}{4}$$

49. If $p = 1$, then $\int_0^1 \frac{dx}{x^p} = \lim_{t \to 0^+} \int_t^1 \frac{dx}{x} = \lim_{t \to 0^+} [\ln x]_t^1 = \infty$. Divergent.

If $p \neq 1$, then $\int_0^1 \frac{dx}{x^p} = \lim_{t \to 0^+} \int_t^1 \frac{dx}{x^p}$ (note that the integral is not improper if $p < 0$)

$$= \lim_{t \to 0^+} \left[\frac{x^{-p+1}}{-p+1} \right]_t^1 = \lim_{t \to 0^+} \frac{1}{1-p} \left[1 - \frac{1}{t^{p-1}} \right]$$

If $p > 1$, then $p - 1 > 0$, so $\frac{1}{t^{p-1}} \to \infty$ as $t \to 0^+$, and the integral diverges.

If $p < 1$, then $p - 1 < 0$, so $\frac{1}{t^{p-1}} \to 0$ as $t \to 0^+$ and $\int_0^1 \frac{dx}{x^p} = \frac{1}{1-p} \left[\lim_{t \to 0^+} (1 - t^{1-p}) \right] = \frac{1}{1-p}$.

Thus, the integral converges if and only if $p < 1$, and in that case its value is $\frac{1}{1-p}$.

50. (a) $n = 0$: $\int_0^\infty x^n e^{-x}\,dx = \lim_{t \to \infty} \int_0^t e^{-x}\,dx = \lim_{t \to \infty} \left[-e^{-x} \right]_0^t$

$$= \lim_{t \to \infty} \left[-e^{-t} + 1 \right] = 0 + 1 = 1$$

$n = 1$: $\int_0^\infty x^n e^{-x}\,dx = \lim_{t \to \infty} \int_0^t x e^{-x}\,dx$. To evaluate $\int x e^{-x}\,dx$, we'll use integration by parts

with $u = x$, $dv = e^{-x}\,dx$ $\Rightarrow$ $du = dx$, $v = -e^{-x}$.

So $\int x e^{-x}\,dx = -xe^{-x} - \int -e^{-x}\,dx = -xe^{-x} - e^{-x} + C = (-x - 1)e^{-x} + C$ and

$$\lim_{t \to \infty} \int_0^t x e^{-x}\,dx = \lim_{t \to \infty} \left[(-x - 1)e^{-x} \right]_0^t$$

$$= \lim_{t \to \infty} \left[(-t - 1)e^{-t} + 1 \right] = \lim_{t \to \infty} \left[-te^{-t} - e^{-t} + 1 \right]$$

$$= 0 - 0 + 1 \quad \text{[use l'Hospital's Rule]} \quad = 1$$

$n = 2$: $\int_0^\infty x^n e^{-x}\,dx = \lim_{t \to \infty} \int_0^t x^2 e^{-x}\,dx$. To evaluate $\int x^2 e^{-x}\,dx$, we could use integration by parts

again or Formula 97. Thus,

$$\lim_{t \to \infty} \int_0^t x^2 e^{-x}\,dx = \lim_{t \to \infty} \left[-x^2 e^{-x} \right]_0^t + 2 \lim_{t \to \infty} \int_0^t x e^{-x}\,dx$$

$$= 0 + 0 + 2(1) \quad \text{[use l'Hospital's Rule and the result for } n = 1 \text{]} \quad = 2$$

$n = 3$: $\int_0^\infty x^n e^{-x}\,dx = \lim_{t \to \infty} \int_0^t x^3 e^{-x}\,dx \overset{97}{=} \lim_{t \to \infty} \left[-x^3 e^{-x} \right]_0^t + 3 \lim_{t \to \infty} \int_0^t x^2 e^{-x}\,dx$

$$= 0 + 0 + 3(2) \quad \text{[use l'Hospital's Rule and the result for } n = 2 \text{]} \quad = 6$$

(b) For $n = 1, 2$, and 3, we have $\int_0^\infty x^n e^{-x}\,dx = 1, 2,$ and 6. The values for the integral are equal to the factorials

for n, so we guess $\int_0^\infty x^n e^{-x}\,dx = n!$.

(c) Suppose that $\int_0^\infty x^k e^{-x}\,dx = k!$ for some positive integer k. Then $\int_0^\infty x^{k+1} e^{-x}\,dx = \lim_{t \to \infty} \int_0^t x^{k+1} e^{-x}\,dx$.

To evaluate $\int x^{k+1} e^{-x}\,dx$, we use parts with $u = x^{k+1}$, $dv = e^{-x}\,dx$ $\Rightarrow$ $du = (k+1)x^k\,dx$, $v = -e^{-x}$.

So $\int x^{k+1}e^{-x}\,dx = -x^{k+1}e^{-x} - \int -(k+1)x^k e^{-x}\,dx = -x^{k+1}e^{-x} + (k+1)\int x^k e^{-x}\,dx$ and

$$\lim_{t\to\infty}\int_0^t x^{k+1}e^{-x}\,dx = \lim_{t\to\infty}\left[-x^{k+1}e^{-x}\right]_0^t + (k+1)\lim_{t\to\infty}\int_0^t x^k e^{-x}\,dx$$

$$= \lim_{t\to\infty}\left[-t^{k+1}e^{-t} + 0\right] + (k+1)k! = 0 + 0 + (k+1)! = (k+1)!,$$

so the formula holds for $k+1$. By induction, the formula holds for all positive integers. (Since $0! = 1$, the formula holds for $n = 0$, too.)

51. (a) $I = \int_{-\infty}^{\infty} x\,dx = \int_{-\infty}^{0} x\,dx + \int_0^{\infty} x\,dx$, and

$\int_0^{\infty} x\,dx = \lim_{t\to\infty}\int_0^t x\,dx = \lim_{t\to\infty}\left[\frac{1}{2}x^2\right]_0^t = \lim_{t\to\infty}\left[\frac{1}{2}t^2 - 0\right] = \infty$, so I is divergent.

(b) $\int_{-t}^{t} x\,dx = \left[\frac{1}{2}x^2\right]_{-t}^{t} = \frac{1}{2}t^2 - \frac{1}{2}t^2 = 0$, so $\lim_{t\to\infty}\int_{-t}^{t} x\,dx = 0$. Therefore, $\int_{-\infty}^{\infty} x\,dx \neq \lim_{t\to\infty}\int_{-t}^{t} x\,dx$.

52. Assume without loss of generality that $a < b$. Then

$$\int_{-\infty}^{a} f(x)\,dx + \int_{a}^{\infty} f(x)\,dx = \lim_{t\to-\infty}\int_{t}^{a} f(x)\,dx + \lim_{u\to\infty}\int_{a}^{u} f(x)\,dx$$

$$= \lim_{t\to-\infty}\int_{t}^{a} f(x)\,dx + \lim_{u\to\infty}\left[\int_{a}^{b} f(x)\,dx + \int_{b}^{u} f(x)\,dx\right]$$

$$= \lim_{t\to-\infty}\int_{t}^{a} f(x)\,dx + \int_{a}^{b} f(x)\,dx + \lim_{u\to\infty}\int_{b}^{u} f(x)\,dx$$

$$= \lim_{t\to-\infty}\left[\int_{t}^{a} f(x)\,dx + \int_{a}^{b} f(x)\,dx\right] + \int_{b}^{\infty} f(x)\,dx$$

$$= \lim_{t\to-\infty}\int_{t}^{b} f(x)\,dx + \int_{b}^{\infty} f(x)\,dx$$

$$= \int_{-\infty}^{b} f(x)\,dx + \int_{b}^{\infty} f(x)\,dx$$

53. (a) We would expect a small percentage of bulbs to burn out in the first few hundred hours, most of the bulbs to burn out after close to 700 hours, and a few overachievers to burn on and on.

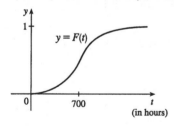

(b) $r(t) = F'(t)$ is the rate at which the fraction $F(t)$ of burnt-out bulbs increases as t increases. This could be interpreted as a fractional burnout rate.

(c) $\int_0^{\infty} r(t)\,dt = \lim_{x\to\infty} F(x) = 1$, since all of the bulbs will eventually burn out.

54. Let $k = \dfrac{M}{2RT}$ so that $\bar{v} = \dfrac{4}{\sqrt{\pi}}k^{3/2}\displaystyle\int_0^{\infty} v^3 e^{-kv^2}\,dv$. Let I denote the integral and use parts to integrate I. Let

$\alpha = v^2,\ d\beta = ve^{-kv^2}\,dv \quad \Rightarrow \quad d\alpha = 2v\,dv,\ \beta = -\dfrac{1}{2k}e^{-kv^2}$:

$$I = \lim_{t\to\infty}\left[-\frac{1}{2k}v^2 e^{-kv^2}\right]_0^t + \frac{1}{k}\int_0^{\infty} ve^{-kv^2}\,dv = -\frac{1}{2k}\lim_{t\to\infty}\left(t^2 e^{-kt^2}\right) + \frac{1}{k}\lim_{t\to\infty}\left[-\frac{1}{2k}e^{-kv^2}\right]_0^t$$

$$\overset{H}{=} -\frac{1}{2k}\cdot 0 - \frac{1}{2k^2}(0-1) = \frac{1}{2k^2}$$

Thus, $\bar{v} = \dfrac{4}{\sqrt{\pi}}k^{3/2}\cdot\dfrac{1}{2k^2} = \dfrac{2}{(k\pi)^{1/2}} = \dfrac{2}{[\pi M/(2RT)]^{1/2}} = \dfrac{2\sqrt{2}\sqrt{RT}}{\sqrt{\pi M}} = \sqrt{\dfrac{8RT}{\pi M}}$.

55. $I = \displaystyle\int_0^\infty te^{kt}\,dt = \lim_{s\to\infty}\left[\frac{1}{k^2}(kt-1)e^{kt}\right]_0^s$ (Formula 96, or parts) $= \lim_{s\to\infty}\left[\left(\frac{1}{k}se^{ks}-\frac{1}{k^2}e^{ks}\right)-\left(-\frac{1}{k^2}\right)\right]$.

Since $k < 0$ the first two terms approach 0 (you can verify that the first term does so with l'Hospital's Rule), so the limit is equal to $1/k^2$. Thus, $M = -kI = -k\left(1/k^2\right) = -1/k = -1/(-0.000121) \approx 8264.5$ years.

56. $y(s) = \displaystyle\int_s^R \frac{2r}{\sqrt{r^2-s^2}}\,x(r)\,dr$ and $x(r) = \frac{1}{2}(R-r)^2$ $\Rightarrow$

$$y(s) = \lim_{t\to s^+}\int_t^R \frac{r(R-r)^2}{\sqrt{r^2-s^2}}\,dr = \lim_{t\to s^+}\int_t^R \frac{r^3-2Rr^2+R^2r}{\sqrt{r^2-s^2}}\,dr$$

$$= \lim_{t\to s^+}\left[\int_t^R \frac{r^3\,dr}{\sqrt{r^2-s^2}} - 2R\int_t^R \frac{r^2\,dr}{\sqrt{r^2-s^2}} + R^2\int_t^R \frac{r\,dr}{\sqrt{r^2-s^2}}\right]$$

$$= \lim_{t\to s^+}\left(I_1 - 2RI_2 + R^2 I_3\right) = L$$

For I_1: Let $u = \sqrt{r^2-s^2}$ $\Rightarrow$ $u^2 = r^2-s^2, r^2 = u^2+s^2, 2r\,dr = 2u\,du$, so, omitting limits and constant of integration,

$$I_1 = \int \frac{\left(u^2+s^2\right)u}{u}\,du = \int\left(u^2+s^2\right)du = \frac{1}{3}u^3 + s^2u = \frac{1}{3}u\left(u^2+3s^2\right)$$

$$= \frac{1}{3}\sqrt{r^2-s^2}\left(r^2-s^2+3s^2\right) = \frac{1}{3}\sqrt{r^2-s^2}\left(r^2+2s^2\right)$$

For I_2: Using Formula 44, $I_2 = \dfrac{r}{2}\sqrt{r^2-s^2} + \dfrac{s^2}{2}\ln\left|r+\sqrt{r^2-s^2}\right|$.

For I_3: Let $u = r^2-s^2$ $\Rightarrow$ $du = 2r\,dr$. Then $I_3 = \dfrac{1}{2}\displaystyle\int\frac{du}{\sqrt{u}} = \frac{1}{2}\cdot 2\sqrt{u} = \sqrt{r^2-s^2}$.

Thus,

$$L = \lim_{t\to s^+}\left[\frac{1}{3}\sqrt{r^2-s^2}\left(r^2+2s^2\right) - 2R\left(\frac{r}{2}\sqrt{r^2-s^2}+\frac{s^2}{2}\ln\left|r+\sqrt{r^2-s^2}\right|\right) + R^2\sqrt{r^2-s^2}\right]_t^R$$

$$= \lim_{t\to s^+}\left[\frac{1}{3}\sqrt{R^2-s^2}\left(R^2+2s^2\right) - 2R\left(\frac{R}{2}\sqrt{R^2-s^2}+\frac{s^2}{2}\ln\left|R+\sqrt{R^2-s^2}\right|\right) + R^2\sqrt{R^2-s^2}\right]$$

$$-\lim_{t\to s^+}\left[\frac{1}{3}\sqrt{t^2-s^2}\left(t^2+2s^2\right) - 2R\left(\frac{t}{2}\sqrt{t^2-s^2}+\frac{s^2}{2}\ln\left|t+\sqrt{t^2-s^2}\right|\right) + R^2\sqrt{t^2-s^2}\right]$$

$$= \left[\frac{1}{3}\sqrt{R^2-s^2}\left(R^2+2s^2\right) - Rs^2\ln\left|R+\sqrt{R^2-s^2}\right|\right] - \left[-Rs^2\ln|s|\right]$$

$$= \frac{1}{3}\sqrt{R^2-s^2}\left(R^2+2s^2\right) - Rs^2\ln\left(\frac{R+\sqrt{R^2-s^2}}{s}\right)$$

57. $I = \displaystyle\int_a^\infty \frac{1}{x^2+1}\,dx = \lim_{t\to\infty}\int_a^t \frac{1}{x^2+1}\,dx = \lim_{t\to\infty}\left[\tan^{-1}x\right]_a^t = \lim_{t\to\infty}\left(\tan^{-1}t - \tan^{-1}a\right) = \frac{\pi}{2} - \tan^{-1}a$.

$I < 0.001$ $\Rightarrow$ $\frac{\pi}{2} - \tan^{-1}a < 0.001$ $\Rightarrow$ $\tan^{-1}a > \frac{\pi}{2} - 0.001$ $\Rightarrow$ $a > \tan\left(\frac{\pi}{2} - 0.001\right) \approx 1000$.

58. $f(x) = e^{-x^2}$ and $\Delta x = \frac{4-0}{8} = \frac{1}{2}$.

$$\int_0^4 f(x)\,dx \approx S_8 = \frac{1}{2\cdot 3}[f(0) + 4f(0.5) + 2f(1) + \cdots + 2f(3) + 4f(3.5) + f(4)]$$

$$\approx \frac{1}{6}(5.31717808) \approx 0.8862$$

Now $x > 4$ $\Rightarrow$ $-x\cdot x < -x\cdot 4$ $\Rightarrow$ $e^{-x^2} < e^{-4x}$ $\Rightarrow$ $\int_4^\infty e^{-x^2}\,dx < \int_4^\infty e^{-4x}\,dx$.

$\int_4^\infty e^{-4x}\,dx = \lim_{t\to\infty}\left[-\frac{1}{4}e^{-4x}\right]_4^t = -\frac{1}{4}\left(0 - e^{-16}\right) = 1/\left(4e^{16}\right) \approx 0.0000000281 < 0.0000001$, as desired.

59. We use integration by parts: let $u = x$, $dv = xe^{-x^2}\,dx \Rightarrow du = dx$, $v = -\frac{1}{2}e^{-x^2}$. So

$$\int_0^\infty x^2 e^{-x^2}\,dx = \lim_{t\to\infty}\left[-\frac{1}{2}xe^{-x^2}\right]_0^t + \frac{1}{2}\int_0^\infty e^{-x^2}\,dx$$

$$= \lim_{t\to\infty}\left[-t\Big/\left(2e^{t^2}\right)\right] + \frac{1}{2}\int_0^\infty e^{-x^2}\,dx = \frac{1}{2}\int_0^\infty e^{-x^2}\,dx$$

(The limit is 0 by l'Hospital's Rule.)

60. $\int_0^\infty e^{-x^2}\,dx$ is the area under the curve $y = e^{-x^2}$ for $0 \le x < \infty$ and $0 < y \le 1$. Solving $y = e^{-x^2}$ for x, we get

$y = e^{-x^2} \Rightarrow \ln y = -x^2 \Rightarrow -\ln y = x^2 \Rightarrow x = \pm\sqrt{-\ln y}$. Since x is positive, choose $x = \sqrt{-\ln y}$,

and the area is represented by $\int_0^1 \sqrt{-\ln y}\,dy$. Therefore, each integral represents the same area, so the integrals are equal.

61. For the first part of the integral, let $x = 2\tan\theta \Rightarrow dx = 2\sec^2\theta\,d\theta$.

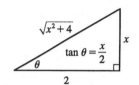

$$\int \frac{1}{\sqrt{x^2+4}}\,dx = \int \frac{2\sec^2\theta}{2\sec\theta}\,d\theta = \int \sec\theta\,d\theta = \ln|\sec\theta + \tan\theta|.\ \text{From the}$$

figure, $\tan\theta = \dfrac{x}{2}$, and $\sec\theta = \dfrac{\sqrt{x^2+4}}{2}$. So

$$I = \int_0^\infty \left(\frac{1}{\sqrt{x^2+4}} - \frac{C}{x+2}\right)dx = \lim_{t\to\infty}\left[\ln\left|\frac{\sqrt{x^2+4}}{2} + \frac{x}{2}\right| - C\ln|x+2|\right]_0^t$$

$$= \lim_{t\to\infty}\left[\ln\frac{\sqrt{t^2+4}+t}{2} - C\ln(t+2) - (\ln 1 - C\ln 2)\right]$$

$$= \lim_{t\to\infty}\left[\ln\left(\frac{\sqrt{t^2+4}+t}{2(t+2)^C}\right) + \ln 2^C\right]$$

$$= \ln\left(\lim_{t\to\infty}\frac{t+\sqrt{t^2+4}}{(t+2)^C}\right) + \ln 2^{C-1}$$

Now $L = \lim\limits_{t\to\infty}\dfrac{t+\sqrt{t^2+4}}{(t+2)^C} \overset{\text{H}}{=} \lim\limits_{t\to\infty}\dfrac{1+t/\sqrt{t^2+4}}{C(t+2)^{C-1}} = \dfrac{2}{C\lim\limits_{t\to\infty}(t+2)^{C-1}}$.

If $C < 1$, $L = \infty$ and I diverges. If $C = 1$, $L = 2$ and I converges to $\ln 2 + \ln 2^0 = \ln 2$. If $C > 1$, $L = 0$ and I diverges to $-\infty$.

62. $I = \displaystyle\int_0^\infty \left(\frac{x}{x^2+1} - \frac{C}{3x+1}\right)dx = \lim_{t\to\infty}\left[\frac{1}{2}\ln(x^2+1) - \frac{1}{3}C\ln(3x+1)\right]_0^t$

$$= \lim_{t\to\infty}\left[\ln(t^2+1)^{1/2} - \ln(3t+1)^{C/3}\right]$$

$$= \lim_{t\to\infty}\left(\ln\frac{(t^2+1)^{1/2}}{(3t+1)^{C/3}}\right) = \ln\left(\lim_{t\to\infty}\frac{\sqrt{t^2+1}}{(3t+1)^{C/3}}\right)$$

For $C \le 0$, the integral diverges. For $C > 0$, we have

$$L = \lim_{t\to\infty}\frac{\sqrt{t^2+1}}{(3t+1)^{C/3}} \overset{\text{H}}{=} \lim_{t\to\infty}\frac{t/\sqrt{t^2+1}}{C(3t+1)^{(C/3)-1}} = \frac{1}{C}\lim_{t\to\infty}\frac{1}{(3t+1)^{(C/3)-1}}.$$

For $C/3 < 1 \Leftrightarrow C < 3$, $L = \infty$ and I diverges. For $C = 3$, $L = \frac{1}{3}$ and $I = \ln\frac{1}{3}$. For $C > 3$, $L = 0$ and I diverges to $-\infty$.

Review

1. (a) $\sum_{i=1}^{n} f(x_i^*) \, \Delta x$ is an expression for a Riemann sum of a function f.

x_i^* is a point in the ith subinterval $[x_{i-1}, x_i]$ and Δx is the length of the subintervals.

(b) See Figure 1 in Section 5.2.

(c) In Section 5.2, see Figure 3 and the paragraph above it.

2. (a) See Definition 5.2.2.

(b) See Figure 2 in Section 5.2.

(c) In Section 5.2, see Figure 4 and the paragraph above it.

3. (a) See the Evaluation Theorem at the beginning of Section 5.3.

(b) See the Total Change Theorem after Example 6 in Section 5.3.

4. $\int_{t_1}^{t_2} r(t) \, dt$ represents the change in the amount of water in the reservoir between time t_1 and time t_2.

5. (a) $\int_{60}^{120} v(t) \, dt$ represents the change in position of the particle from $t = 60$ to $t = 120$ seconds.

(b) $\int_{60}^{120} |v(t)| \, dt$ represents the total distance traveled by the particle from $t = 60$ to 120 seconds.

(c) $\int_{60}^{120} a(t) \, dt$ represents the change in the velocity of the particle from $t = 60$ to $t = 120$ seconds.

6. (a) $\int f(x) \, dx$ is the family of functions $\{ F \mid F' = f \}$. Any two such functions differ by a constant.

(b) The connection is given by the Evaluation Theorem: $\int_a^b f(x) \, dx = \left[\int f(x) \, dx \right]_a^b$ if f is continuous.

7. See the Fundamental Theorem of Calculus after Example 5 in Section 5.4.

8. (a) See the Substitution Rule (5.5.4). This says that it is permissible to operate with the dx after an integral sign as if it were a differential.

(b) See Formula 5.6.1 or 5.6.2. We try to choose $u = f(x)$ to be a function that becomes simpler when differentiated (or at least not more complicated) as long as $dv = g'(x) \, dx$ can be readily integrated to give v.

9. See the Midpoint Rule, the Trapezoidal Rule, and Simpson's Rule, as well as their associated error bounds, all in Section 5.9. We would expect the best estimate to be given by Simpson's Rule.

10. See Definitions 1(a), (b), and (c) in Section 5.10.

11. See Definitions 3(b), (a), and (c) in Section 5.10.

12. See the Comparison Theorem after Example 8 in Section 5.10.

13. The precise version of this statement is given by the Fundamental Theorem of Calculus. See the statement of this theorem and the paragraph that follows it in Section 5.4.

───────────────── ▲ TRUE–FALSE QUIZ ▲ ─────────────────

1. True by Property 2 of the Integral in Section 5.2.

2. False. Try $a = 0$, $b = 2$, $f(x) = g(x) = 1$ as a counterexample.

3. True by Property 3 of the Integral in Section 5.2.

4. False. You can't take a variable outside the integral sign. For example, using $f(x) = 1$ on $[0, 1]$,

$\int_0^1 x\, f(x)\, dx = \int_0^1 x\, dx = \left[\frac{1}{2}x^2\right]_0^1 = \frac{1}{2}$ (a constant) while $x \int_0^1 1\, dx = x\,[x]_0^1 = x \cdot 1 = x$ (a variable).

5. False. For example, let $f(x) = x^2$. Then $\int_0^1 \sqrt{x^2}\, dx = \int_0^1 x\, dx = \frac{1}{2}$, but $\sqrt{\int_0^1 x^2\, dx} = \sqrt{\frac{1}{3}} = \frac{1}{\sqrt{3}}$.

6. True by the Total Change Theorem.

7. True by Comparison Property 7 of the Integral in Section 5.2.

8. False. For example, let $a = 0$, $b = 1$, $f(x) = 3$, $g(x) = x$. $f(x) > g(x)$ for each x in $(0, 1)$, but
$f'(x) = 0 < 1 = g'(x)$ for $x \in (0, 1)$.

9. True. The integrand is an odd function that is continuous on $[-1, 1]$, so the result follows from Equation 5.5.6(b).

10. True. $\int_{-5}^5 \left(ax^2 + bx + c\right) dx = \int_{-5}^5 \left(ax^2 + c\right) dx + \int_{-5}^5 bx\, dx$

$\qquad\qquad = 2\int_0^5 \left(ax^2 + c\right) dx$ [by 5.5.6(a)] $+\, 0$ [by 5.5.6(b)]

11. False. This is an improper integral, since the denominator vanishes at $x = 1$.

$\int_0^4 \frac{x}{x^2 - 1}\, dx = \int_0^1 \frac{x}{x^2 - 1}\, dx + \int_1^4 \frac{x}{x^2 - 1}\, dx$ and

$\int_0^1 \frac{x}{x^2 - 1}\, dx = \lim_{t \to 1^-} \int_0^t \frac{x}{x^2 - 1}\, dx = \lim_{t \to 1^-} \left[\frac{1}{2}\ln\left|x^2 - 1\right|\right]_0^t = \lim_{t \to 1^-} \frac{1}{2}\ln\left|t^2 - 1\right| = \infty$

So the integral diverges.

12. True by Theorem 5.10.2 with $p = \sqrt{2} > 1$.

13. False. See the remarks and Figure 4 before Example 1 in Section 5.2, and notice that $y = x - x^3 < 0$ for
$1 < x \le 2$.

14. True by FTC1.

15. False. For example, the function $y = |x|$ is continuous on $\mathbb{R}$, but has no derivative at $x = 0$.

16. False. For example, with $n = 1$ the Trapezoidal Rule is much more accurate
than the Midpoint Rule for the function in the diagram.

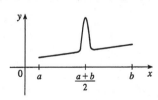

17. False. See Exercise 51 in Section 5.10.

18. False. $\int_0^\infty f(x)\, dx$ could converge or diverge. For example, if $g(x) = 1$, then $\int_0^\infty f(x)\, dx$ diverges if $f(x) = 1$
and converges if $f(x) = 0$.

◆ **EXERCISES** ◆

1. (a)

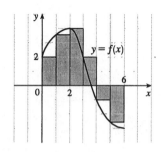

$$L_6 = \sum_{i=1}^{6} f(x_{i-1})\, \Delta x \quad [\Delta x = \tfrac{6-0}{6} = 1]$$

$$= f(x_0) \cdot 1 + f(x_1) \cdot 1 + f(x_2) \cdot 1$$
$$+ f(x_3) \cdot 1 + f(x_4) \cdot 1 + f(x_5) \cdot 1$$
$$\approx 2 + 3.5 + 4 + 2 + (-1) + (-2.5) = 8$$

The Riemann sum represents the sum of the areas of the four rectangles above the x-axis minus the sum of the areas of the two rectangles below the x-axis.

(b)

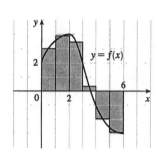

$$M_6 = \sum_{i=1}^{6} f(\overline{x}_i)\, \Delta x \quad [\Delta x = \tfrac{6-0}{6} = 1]$$

$$= f(\overline{x}_1) \cdot 1 + f(\overline{x}_2) \cdot 1 + f(\overline{x}_3) \cdot 1$$
$$+ f(\overline{x}_4) \cdot 1 + f(\overline{x}_5) \cdot 1 + f(\overline{x}_6) \cdot 1$$
$$= f(0.5) + f(1.5) + f(2.5) + f(3.5) + f(4.5) + f(5.5)$$
$$\approx 3 + 3.9 + 3.4 + 0.3 + (-2) + (-2.9) = 5.7$$

The Riemann sum represents the sum of the areas of the four rectangles above the x-axis minus the sum of the areas of the two rectangles below the x-axis.

2. (a)

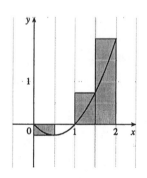

$$f(x) = x^2 - x \text{ and } \Delta x = \tfrac{2-0}{4} = 0.5 \quad \Rightarrow$$

$$R_4 = 0.5f(0.5) + 0.5f(1) + 0.5f(1.5) + 0.5f(2)$$
$$= 0.5(-0.25 + 0 + 0.75 + 2) = 1.25$$

The Riemann sum represents the sum of the areas of the two rectangles above the x-axis minus the area of the rectangle below the x-axis. (The second rectangle vanishes.)

(b) $\int_0^2 (x^2 - x)\, dx = \lim\limits_{n \to \infty} \sum\limits_{i=1}^{n} f(x_i)\, \Delta x \quad [\Delta x = 2/n \text{ and } x_i = 2i/n]$

$$= \lim_{n \to \infty} \sum_{i=1}^{n} \left(\frac{4i^2}{n^2} - \frac{2i}{n} \right)\left(\frac{2}{n} \right) = \lim_{n \to \infty} \frac{2}{n} \left[\frac{4}{n^2} \sum_{i=1}^{n} i^2 - \frac{2}{n} \sum_{i=1}^{n} i \right]$$

$$= \lim_{n \to \infty} \left[\frac{8}{n^3} \cdot \frac{n(n+1)(2n+1)}{6} - \frac{4}{n^2} \cdot \frac{n(n+1)}{2} \right]$$

$$= \lim_{n \to \infty} \left[\frac{4}{3} \cdot \frac{n+1}{n} \cdot \frac{2n+1}{n} - 2 \cdot \frac{n+1}{n} \right]$$

$$= \lim_{n \to \infty} \left[\frac{4}{3} \left(1 + \frac{1}{n} \right)\left(2 + \frac{1}{n} \right) - 2\left(1 + \frac{1}{n} \right) \right] = \tfrac{4}{3} \cdot 1 \cdot 2 - 2 \cdot 1 = \tfrac{2}{3}$$

(c) $\int_0^2 (x^2 - x)\, dx = \left[\tfrac{1}{3}x^3 - \tfrac{1}{2}x^2 \right]_0^2 = \left(\tfrac{8}{3} - 2 \right) = \tfrac{2}{3}$

(d)

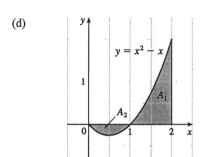

$\int_0^2 (x^2 - x)\, dx = A_1 - A_2$, where A_1 and A_2 are the areas shown in the diagram.

3. $\int_0^1 \left(x + \sqrt{1 - x^2}\right) dx = \int_0^1 x\, dx + \int_0^1 \sqrt{1 - x^2}\, dx = I_1 + I_2$.

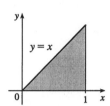 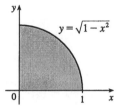

I_1 can be interpreted as the area of the triangle shown in the figure and I_2 can be interpreted as the area of the quarter-circle. Area $= \frac{1}{2}(1)(1) + \frac{1}{4}(\pi)(1)^2 = \frac{1}{2} + \frac{\pi}{4}$.

4. On $[0, \pi]$, $\displaystyle\lim_{n \to \infty} \sum_{i=1}^{n} \sin x_i\, \Delta x = \int_0^\pi \sin x\, dx = [-\cos x]_0^\pi = -(-1) - (-1) = 2$.

5. $\int_0^6 f(x)\, dx = \int_0^4 f(x)\, dx + \int_4^6 f(x)\, dx \;\;\Rightarrow\;\; 10 = 7 + \int_4^6 f(x)\, dx \;\;\Rightarrow\;\; \int_4^6 f(x)\, dx = 10 - 7 = 3$

6. (a) $f(x) = e^{3x}$, $\Delta x = (2 - 0)/n = 2/n$, and $x_i = 2i/n \;\;\Rightarrow$

$$\int_0^2 e^{3x}\, dx = \lim_{n \to \infty} \sum_{i=1}^{n} f\left(\frac{2i}{n}\right)\left(\frac{2}{n}\right) = \lim_{n \to \infty} \sum_{i=1}^{n} e^{3(2i/n)}\left(\frac{2}{n}\right)$$

$$\overset{\text{CAS}}{=} \lim_{n \to \infty} \frac{2e^{6/n}\left(e^6 - 1\right)}{n(e^{6/n} - 1)} \overset{\text{CAS}}{=} \frac{e^6 - 1}{3} \approx 134.14$$

(b) $\int_0^2 e^{3x}\, dx = \left[\frac{1}{3}e^{3x}\right]_0^2 = \frac{1}{3}\left(e^6 - 1\right)$, as in part (a).

7. First note that either a or b must be the graph of $\int_0^x f(t)\, dt$, since $\int_0^0 f(t)\, dt = 0$, and $c(0) \neq 0$. Now notice that $b > 0$ when c is increasing, and that $c > 0$ when a is increasing. It follows that c is the graph of $f(x)$, b is the graph of $f'(x)$, and a is the graph of $\int_0^x f(t)\, dt$.

8. (a) By the Evaluation Theorem (FTC2), $\displaystyle\int_0^1 \frac{d}{dx}\left(e^{\arctan x}\right) dx = \left[e^{\arctan x}\right]_0^1 = e^{\pi/4} - 1$

(b) $\dfrac{d}{dx} \displaystyle\int_0^1 e^{\arctan x}\, dx = 0$ since this is the derivative of a constant.

(c) By FTC1, $\dfrac{d}{dx} \displaystyle\int_0^x e^{\arctan t}\, dt = e^{\arctan x}$.

9. $\int_1^2 (8x^3 + 3x^2)\, dx = \left[\frac{8}{4}x^4 + \frac{3}{3}x^3\right]_1^2 = (2 \cdot 2^4 + 2^3) - (2 + 1) = 40 - 3 = 37$

10. $\displaystyle\int_0^T (x^4 - 8x + 7)\, dx = \left[\frac{1}{5}x^5 - 4x^2 + 7x\right]_0^T = \left(\frac{1}{5}T^5 - 4T^2 + 7T\right) - 0 = \frac{1}{5}T^5 - 4T^2 + 7T$

11. $\int_0^1 (1 - x^9)\, dx = \left[x - \frac{1}{10}x^{10}\right]_0^1 = \left(1 - \frac{1}{10}\right) - 0 = \frac{9}{10}$

12. Let $u = 1 - x$. Then $du = -dx$, so $\int_0^1 (1-x)^9\, dx = \int_1^0 u^9(-du) = \int_0^1 u^9\, du = \frac{1}{10}\left[u^{10}\right]_0^1 = \frac{1}{10}(1-0) = \frac{1}{10}$.

13. $\int_1^8 \sqrt[3]{x}\,(x-1)\, dx = \int_1^8 \left(x^{4/3} - x^{1/3}\right) dx = \left[\frac{3}{7}x^{7/3} - \frac{3}{4}x^{4/3}\right]_1^8 = \left(\frac{3}{7}\cdot 128 - \frac{3}{4}\cdot 16\right) - \left(\frac{3}{7} - \frac{3}{4}\right) = \frac{1209}{28}$

14. $\displaystyle\int_1^4 \frac{x^2 - x + 1}{\sqrt{x}}\, dx = \int_1^4 \left(x^{3/2} - x^{1/2} + x^{-1/2}\right) dx = \left[\frac{2}{5}x^{5/2} - \frac{2}{3}x^{3/2} + 2x^{1/2}\right]_1^4$

$$= \left(\tfrac{2}{5}\cdot 32 - \tfrac{2}{3}\cdot 8 + 4\right) - \left(\tfrac{2}{5} - \tfrac{2}{3} + 2\right) = \tfrac{146}{15}$$

15. $u = x^2 + 1$, $du = 2x\, dx$, so $\displaystyle\int_0^1 \frac{x}{x^2+1}\, dx = \int_1^2 \frac{1}{u}\left(\frac{1}{2}\, du\right) = \frac{1}{2}\left[\ln u\right]_1^2 = \frac{1}{2}\ln 2$.

16. $\displaystyle\int_0^1 \frac{1}{x^2+1}\, dx = \left[\tan^{-1} x\right]_0^1 = \tan^{-1} 1 - \tan^{-1} 0 = \frac{\pi}{4} - 0 = \frac{\pi}{4}$

17. Let $u = 1 + 2x^3$. Then $du = 6x^2\, dx$, so
$\int_0^2 x^2\left(1 + 2x^3\right)^3 dx = \int_1^{17} u^3\left(\frac{1}{6}\, du\right) = \left[\frac{1}{24}u^4\right]_1^{17} = \frac{1}{24}\left(17^4 - 1\right) = 3480$.

18. Let $u = 16 - 3x$. Then $x = \frac{1}{3}(16 - u)$, $dx = -\frac{1}{3}\, du$, so

$$\int_0^4 x\sqrt{16-3x}\, dx = \int_{16}^4 u^{1/2}\left(\frac{16-u}{3}\right)\left(-\frac{1}{3}\, du\right) = \frac{1}{9}\int_4^{16}\left(16u^{1/2} - u^{3/2}\right) du$$

$$= \frac{1}{9}\left[16\cdot \frac{2}{3}u^{3/2} - \frac{2}{5}u^{5/2}\right]_4^{16} = \frac{1}{9}\left[\frac{32}{3}\cdot 64 - \frac{2}{5}\cdot 1024 - \frac{32}{3}\cdot 8 + \frac{2}{5}\cdot 32\right] = \frac{3008}{135}$$

19. $\int_0^1 e^{\pi t}\, dt = \left[\frac{1}{\pi}e^{\pi t}\right]_0^1 = \frac{1}{\pi}(e^{\pi} - 1)$

20. Integrate by parts with $u = \ln x$, $dv = x^3\, dx$ $\Rightarrow$ $du = dx/x$, $v = x^4/4$:
$\int_1^2 x^3 \ln x\, dx = \left[\frac{1}{4}x^4 \ln x\right]_1^2 - \frac{1}{4}\int_1^2 x^3\, dx = 4\ln 2 - \frac{1}{16}\left[x^4\right]_1^2 = 4\ln 2 - \frac{15}{16}$.

21. Integrate by parts with $u = x$, $dv = \sec x \tan x\, dx$ $\Rightarrow$ $du = dx$, $v = \sec x$:
$\int x \sec x \tan x\, dx = x \sec x - \int \sec x\, dx \overset{14}{=} x \sec x - \ln|\sec x + \tan x| + C$.

22. Let $u = 2 - 3x$. Then $du = -3\, dx$, so $\displaystyle\int_1^2 \frac{1}{2-3x}\, dx = -\frac{1}{3}\int_{-1}^{-4}\frac{du}{u} = \left[-\frac{\ln|u|}{3}\right]_{-1}^{-4} = -\frac{\ln 4}{3}$.

23. Let $u = \dfrac{1}{t}$. Then $du = -\dfrac{1}{t^2}\, dt$, so $\displaystyle\int \frac{\cos(1/t)}{t^2}\, dt = \int \cos u\,(-du) = -\sin u + C = -\sin\left(\frac{1}{t}\right) + C$.

24. Let $u = \cos x$. Then $du = -\sin x\, dx$, so
$\int \sin x \cos(\cos x)\, dx = -\int \cos u\, du = -\sin u + C = -\sin(\cos x) + C$.

25. Since the degree of the numerator is equal to the degree of the denominator, we first change the form of the integrand by using long division.
$$\int \frac{6x+1}{3x+2}\, dx = \int \left(2 - \frac{3}{3x+2}\right) dx = 2x - 3\cdot \frac{1}{3}\ln|3x+2| + C = 2x - \ln|3x+2| + C$$

26. Let $u = x$, $dv = \cos 3x\, dx$ $\Rightarrow$ $du = dx$, $v = \frac{1}{3}\sin 3x$. Then
$\int x \cos 3x\, dx = \frac{1}{3}x \sin 3x - \frac{1}{3}\int \sin 3x\, dx = \frac{1}{3}x \sin 3x + \frac{1}{9}\cos 3x + C$.

27. Integrate by parts with $u = x^2$, $dv = e^{-x} dx$ $\Rightarrow$ $du = 2x\,dx$, $v = -e^{-x}$:

$$I = \int x^2 e^{-x}\,dx = -x^2 e^{-x} + 2\int x e^{-x} dx$$

Now integrate by parts with $u = x$, $dv = e^{-x} dx$ $\Rightarrow$ $du = dx$, $v = -e^{-x}$:

$$\int x e^{-x}\,dx = -x e^{-x} + \int e^{-x} dx = -x e^{-x} - e^{-x} + C$$

Thus, $I = -x^2 e^{-x} + 2\left(-x e^{-x} - e^{-x} + C\right) = -x^2 e^{-x} - 2x e^{-x} - 2e^{-x} + C = -e^{-x}\left(x^2 + 2x + 2\right) + C$.

28. $\int \sin^4 \theta \cos^3 \theta\,d\theta = \int \sin^4 \theta \cos^2 \theta \cos \theta\,d\theta = \int \sin^4 \theta \left(1 - \sin^2 \theta\right)\cos \theta\,d\theta$

$\qquad = \int u^4 \left(1 - u^2\right) du$ $[u = \sin \theta,\ du = \cos \theta\,d\theta]$

$\qquad = \int \left(u^4 - u^6\right) du = \tfrac{1}{5} u^5 - \tfrac{1}{7} u^7 + C = \tfrac{1}{5} \sin^5 \theta - \tfrac{1}{7} \sin^7 \theta + C$

29. $\dfrac{1}{t^2 + 6t + 8} = \dfrac{1}{(t+2)(t+4)} = \dfrac{A}{t+2} + \dfrac{B}{t+4}$. Multiply both sides by $(t+2)(t+4)$

to get $1 = A(t+4) + B(t+2)$. Substituting -4 for t gives

$1 = -2B$ $\Leftrightarrow$ $B = -\tfrac{1}{2}$. Substituting -2 for t gives $1 = 2A$ $\Leftrightarrow$ $A = \tfrac{1}{2}$. Thus,

$$\int \frac{dt}{t^2 + 6t + 8} = \int \left(\frac{1/2}{t+2} - \frac{1/2}{t+4}\right) dt = \tfrac{1}{2}\ln|t+2| - \tfrac{1}{2}\ln|t+4| + C = \tfrac{1}{2}\ln\left|\frac{t+2}{t+4}\right| + C.$$

30. Let $u = x^2$. Then $du = 2x\,dx$, so $\displaystyle\int \frac{x}{\sqrt{1-x^4}}\,dx = \frac{1}{2}\int \frac{du}{\sqrt{1-u^2}} = \tfrac{1}{2}\sin^{-1} u + C = \tfrac{1}{2}\sin^{-1}\left(x^2\right) + C.$

31. Let $x = 3\sin \theta$, where $-\pi/2 \le \theta \le \pi/2$. Then $dx = 3\cos \theta\,d\theta$ and

$\sqrt{9 - x^2} = \sqrt{9 - 9\sin^2 \theta} = \sqrt{9\cos^2 \theta} = 3\,|\cos \theta| = 3\cos \theta$ since $\cos \theta \ge 0$ for $-\pi/2 \le \theta \le \pi/2$. When

$x = 0$, $3\sin \theta = 0$ $\Rightarrow$ $\theta = 0$ and when $x = 3$, $3\sin \theta = 3$ $\Rightarrow$ $\sin \theta = 1$ $\Rightarrow$ $\theta = \tfrac{\pi}{2}$. Thus,

$$\int_0^3 x^3 \sqrt{9 - x^2}\,dx = \int_0^{\pi/2} (3\sin \theta)^3 (3\cos \theta)(3\cos \theta\,d\theta) = 3^5 \int_0^{\pi/2} \sin^3 \theta \cos^2 \theta\,d\theta$$

$$= 3^5 \int_0^{\pi/2} \sin^2 \theta \cos^2 \theta(\sin \theta\,d\theta) = 3^5 \int_0^{\pi/2} \left(1 - \cos^2 \theta\right)\cos^2 \theta(\sin \theta\,d\theta) = I.$$

Now let $u = \cos \theta$ so that $du = -\sin \theta\,d\theta$. When $\theta = 0$, $u = 1$ and when $\theta = \tfrac{\pi}{2}$, $u = 0$. Substitution gives us

$$I = 3^5 \int_1^0 \left(1 - u^2\right)u^2 (-du) = 3^5 \int_0^1 \left(u^2 - u^4\right) du = 3^5 \left[\tfrac{1}{3}u^3 - \tfrac{1}{5}u^5\right]_0^1$$

$$= 3^5 \left(\tfrac{1}{3} - \tfrac{1}{5}\right) = 3^5 \left(\tfrac{2}{15}\right) = \tfrac{162}{5} = 32.4.$$

Another method: Let $u = 9 - x^2$. Then $du = -2x\,dx$ and $x^2 = 9 - u$, so

$$\int_0^3 x^3 \sqrt{9 - x^2}\,dx = \int_0^3 x^2 \sqrt{9 - x^2}\,(x\,dx) = \int_9^0 (9 - u)\sqrt{u}\left(-\tfrac{1}{2}\,du\right) = \frac{1}{2}\int_0^9 \left(9u^{1/2} - u^{3/2}\right) du$$

$$= \tfrac{1}{2}\left[6u^{3/2} - \tfrac{2}{5}u^{5/2}\right]_0^9 = \tfrac{1}{2}\left[\left(6 \cdot 27 - \tfrac{2}{5} \cdot 243\right) - 0\right] = \tfrac{1}{2}\left(\tfrac{324}{5}\right) = \tfrac{162}{5} = 32.4$$

32. Let $u = \tan^{-1} x$, $dv = dx$ $\Rightarrow$ $du = \dfrac{1}{1+x^2}\,dx$, $v = x$:

$$\int \tan^{-1} x\,dx = x\tan^{-1} x - \int \frac{x}{1+x^2}\,dx = x\tan^{-1} x - \tfrac{1}{2}\ln\left(1 + x^2\right) + C.$$

33. Let $u = 1 + \sec \theta$. Then $du = \sec \theta \tan \theta\,d\theta$, so

$$\int \frac{\sec \theta \tan \theta}{1 + \sec \theta}\,d\theta = \int \frac{1}{u}\,du = \ln |u| + C = \ln |1 + \sec \theta| + C$$

34. $\displaystyle\int_{-1}^1 \frac{\sin x}{1 + x^2}\,dx = 0$ by Theorem 5.5.6(b), since $f(x) = \dfrac{\sin x}{1 + x^2}$ is an odd function.

In Exercises 35 and 36, let $f(x)$ denote the integrand and $F(x)$ its antiderivative (with $C = 0$).

35. Let $u = 1 + \sin x$. Then $du = \cos x\, dx$, so

$$\int \frac{\cos x\, dx}{\sqrt{1 + \sin x}} = \int u^{-1/2}\, du = 2u^{1/2} + C = 2\sqrt{1 + \sin x} + C.$$

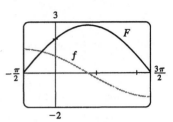

36. Let $u = x^2 + 1$. Then $x^2 = u - 1$ and $x\, dx = \frac{1}{2}\, du$, so

$$\int \frac{x^3}{\sqrt{x^2 + 1}}\, dx = \int \frac{(u - 1)}{\sqrt{u}} \left(\tfrac{1}{2}\, du\right) = \frac{1}{2} \int \left(u^{1/2} - u^{-1/2}\right) du$$

$$= \tfrac{1}{2}\left(\tfrac{2}{3}u^{3/2} - 2u^{1/2}\right) + C$$

$$= \tfrac{1}{3}\left(x^2 + 1\right)^{3/2} - \left(x^2 + 1\right)^{1/2} + C$$

$$= \tfrac{1}{3}\left(x^2 + 1\right)^{1/2} \left[\left(x^2 + 1\right) - 2\right] + C$$

$$= \tfrac{1}{3}\sqrt{x^2 + 1}\left(x^2 - 2\right) + C.$$

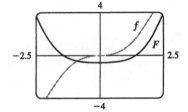

37. From the graph, it appears that the area under the curve $y = x\sqrt{x}$ between $x = 0$ and $x = 4$ is somewhat less than half the area of an 8×4 rectangle, so perhaps about 13 or 14. To find the exact value, we evaluate

$$\int_0^4 x\sqrt{x}\, dx = \int_0^4 x^{3/2}\, dx = \left[\tfrac{2}{5}x^{5/2}\right]_0^4 = \tfrac{2}{5}(4)^{5/2} = \tfrac{64}{5} = 12.8.$$

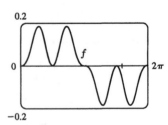

38. From the graph, it seems as though $\int_0^{2\pi} \cos^2 x\, \sin^3 x\, dx$ is equal to 0. To evaluate the integral, we write the integral as

$I = \int_0^{2\pi} \cos^2 x\left(1 - \cos^2 x\right)\sin x\, dx$ and let $u = \cos x \quad \Rightarrow$

$du = -\sin x\, dx$. Thus, $I = \int_1^1 u^2\left(1 - u^2\right)(-du) = 0$.

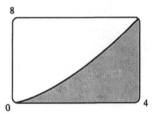

39. By FTC1, $F(x) = \int_1^x \sqrt{1 + t^4}\, dt \quad \Rightarrow \quad F'(x) = \sqrt{1 + x^4}$.

40. Let $u = \cos x$. Then $\dfrac{du}{dx} = -\sin x$. Also, $\dfrac{dg}{dx} = \dfrac{dg}{du}\dfrac{du}{dx}$, so

$$\frac{d}{dx}\int_1^{\cos x} \sqrt[3]{1 - t^2}\, dt = \frac{d}{du}\int_1^u \sqrt[3]{1 - t^2}\, dt \cdot \frac{du}{dx} = \sqrt[3]{1 - u^2}\left(-\sin x\right)$$

$$= \sqrt[3]{1 - \cos^2 x}\left(-\sin x\right) = -\sin x\sqrt[3]{\sin^2 x} = -(\sin x)^{5/3}$$

41. $y = \int_{\sqrt{x}}^{x} \frac{e^t}{t}\,dt = \int_{\sqrt{x}}^{1} \frac{e^t}{t}\,dt + \int_{1}^{x} \frac{e^t}{t}\,dt = -\int_{1}^{\sqrt{x}} \frac{e^t}{t}\,dt + \int_{1}^{x} \frac{e^t}{t}\,dt \Rightarrow$

$\dfrac{dy}{dx} = -\dfrac{d}{dx}\left(\displaystyle\int_{1}^{\sqrt{x}} \frac{e^t}{t}\,dt\right) + \dfrac{d}{dx}\left(\displaystyle\int_{1}^{x} \frac{e^t}{t}\,dt\right)$. Let $u = \sqrt{x}$. Then

$\dfrac{d}{dx}\displaystyle\int_{1}^{\sqrt{x}} \frac{e^t}{t}\,dt = \dfrac{d}{dx}\displaystyle\int_{1}^{u} \frac{e^t}{t}\,dt = \dfrac{d}{du}\left(\displaystyle\int_{1}^{u} \frac{e^t}{t}\,dt\right)\dfrac{du}{dx} = \dfrac{e^u}{u}\cdot\dfrac{1}{2\sqrt{x}} = \dfrac{e^{\sqrt{x}}}{\sqrt{x}}\cdot\dfrac{1}{2\sqrt{x}} = \dfrac{e^{\sqrt{x}}}{2x}$,

so $\dfrac{dy}{dx} = -\dfrac{e^{\sqrt{x}}}{2x} + \dfrac{e^x}{x}$.

42. $y = \int_{2x}^{3x+1} \sin(t^4)\,dt = \int_{2x}^{0} \sin(t^4)\,dt + \int_{0}^{3x+1} \sin(t^4)\,dt = \int_{0}^{3x+1} \sin(t^4)\,dt - \int_{0}^{2x} \sin(t^4)\,dt \Rightarrow$

$y' = \sin\left[(3x+1)^4\right]\cdot\dfrac{d}{dx}(3x+1) - \sin\left[(2x)^4\right]\cdot\dfrac{d}{dx}(2x) = 3\sin\left[(3x+1)^4\right] - 2\sin\left[(2x)^4\right]$

43. $u = e^x \Rightarrow du = e^x\,dx$, so

$\int e^x\sqrt{1-e^{2x}}\,dx = \int \sqrt{1-u^2}\,du \overset{30}{=} \tfrac{1}{2}u\sqrt{1-u^2} + \tfrac{1}{2}\sin^{-1}u + C = \tfrac{1}{2}\left[e^x\sqrt{1-e^{2x}} + \sin^{-1}(e^x)\right] + C$

44. $\int \csc^5 t\,dt \overset{78}{=} -\tfrac{1}{4}\cot t\,\csc^3 t + \tfrac{3}{4}\int \csc^3 t\,dt$

$\overset{72}{=} -\tfrac{1}{4}\cot t\,\csc^3 t + \tfrac{3}{4}\left[-\tfrac{1}{2}\csc t\cot t + \tfrac{1}{2}\ln|\csc t - \cot t|\right] + C$

$= -\tfrac{1}{4}\cot t\,\csc^3 t - \tfrac{3}{8}\csc t\cot t + \tfrac{3}{8}\ln|\csc t - \cot t| + C$

45. $\displaystyle\int \sqrt{x^2 + x + 1}\,dx = \int \sqrt{x^2 + x + \tfrac{1}{4} + \tfrac{3}{4}}\,dx = \int \sqrt{\left(x + \tfrac{1}{2}\right)^2 + \tfrac{3}{4}}\,dx$

$= \displaystyle\int \sqrt{u^2 + \left(\tfrac{\sqrt{3}}{2}\right)^2}\,du \quad [u = x + \tfrac{1}{2},\, du = dx]$

$\overset{21}{=} \tfrac{1}{2}u\sqrt{u^2 + \tfrac{3}{4}} + \tfrac{3}{8}\ln\left(u + \sqrt{u^2 + \tfrac{3}{4}}\right) + C$

$= \dfrac{2x+1}{4}\sqrt{x^2 + x + 1} + \tfrac{3}{8}\ln\left(x + \tfrac{1}{2} + \sqrt{x^2 + x + 1}\right) + C$

46. Let $u = \sin x$. Then $du = \cos x\,dx$, so

$\displaystyle\int \frac{\cot x\,dx}{\sqrt{1 + 2\sin x}} = \int \frac{du}{u\sqrt{1 + 2u}} \overset{\substack{57\text{ with}\\ a=1,\,b=2}}{=} \ln\left|\frac{\sqrt{1+2u}-1}{\sqrt{1+2u}+1}\right| + C = \ln\left|\frac{\sqrt{1+2\sin x}-1}{\sqrt{1+2\sin x}+1}\right| + C$

47. $f(x) = \sqrt{1 + x^4}$, $\Delta x = \dfrac{b-a}{n} = \dfrac{1-0}{10} = \dfrac{1}{10}$.

(a) $T_{10} = \dfrac{1}{10\cdot2}\{f(0) + 2\left[f(0.1) + f(0.2) + \cdots + f(0.9)\right] + f(1)\} \approx 1.090608$

(b) $M_{10} = \dfrac{1}{10}\left[f\left(\tfrac{1}{20}\right) + f\left(\tfrac{3}{20}\right) + f\left(\tfrac{5}{20}\right) + \cdots + f\left(\tfrac{19}{20}\right)\right] \approx 1.088840$

(c) $S_{10} = \dfrac{1}{10\cdot3}\left[f(0) + 4f(0.1) + 2f(0.2) + \cdots + 4f(0.9) + f(1)\right] \approx 1.089429$

f is concave upward, so the Trapezoidal Rule gives us an overestimate, the Midpoint Rule gives an underestimate, and we cannot tell whether Simpson's Rule gives us an overestimate or an underestimate.

48. $f(x) = \sqrt{\sin x}$, $\Delta x = \dfrac{\frac{\pi}{2} - 0}{10} = \dfrac{\pi}{20}$.

(a) $T_{10} = \dfrac{\pi}{20\cdot2}\{f(0) + 2\left[f\left(\tfrac{\pi}{20}\right) + f\left(\tfrac{2\pi}{20}\right) + \cdots + f\left(\tfrac{9\pi}{20}\right)\right] + f\left(\tfrac{\pi}{2}\right)\} \approx 1.185197$

(b) $M_{10} = \dfrac{\pi}{20}\left[f\left(\tfrac{\pi}{40}\right) + f\left(\tfrac{3\pi}{40}\right) + f\left(\tfrac{5\pi}{40}\right) + \cdots + f\left(\tfrac{17\pi}{40}\right) + f\left(\tfrac{19\pi}{40}\right)\right] \approx 1.201932$

(c) $S_{10} = \dfrac{\pi}{20\cdot3}\left[f(0) + 4f\left(\tfrac{\pi}{20}\right) + 2f\left(\tfrac{2\pi}{20}\right) + \cdots + 4f\left(\tfrac{9\pi}{20}\right) + f\left(\tfrac{\pi}{2}\right)\right] \approx 1.193089$

f is concave downward, so the Trapezoidal Rule gives us an underestimate, the Midpoint Rule gives an overestimate, and we cannot tell whether Simpson's Rule gives us an overestimate or an underestimate.

49. $f(x) = (1+x^4)^{1/2}$, $f'(x) = \frac{1}{2}(1+x^4)^{-1/2}(4x^3) = 2x^3(1+x^4)^{-1/2}$, $f''(x) = (2x^6 + 6x^2)(1+x^4)^{-3/2}$.

A graph of f'' on $[0, 1]$ shows that it has its maximum at $x = 1$, so $|f''(x)| \le f''(1) = \sqrt{8}$ on $[0, 1]$. By taking

$K = \sqrt{8}$, we find that the error in Exercise 47(a) is bounded by $\dfrac{K(b-a)^3}{12n^2} = \dfrac{\sqrt{8}}{1200} \approx 0.0024$, and in (b) by about

$\frac{1}{2}(0.0024) = 0.0012$.

Note: Another way to estimate K is to let $x = 1$ in the factor $2x^6 + 6x^2$ (maximizing the numerator) and let $x = 0$ in the factor $(1+x^4)^{-3/2}$ (minimizing the denominator). Doing so gives us $K = 8$ and errors of $0.00\overline{6}$ and $0.00\overline{3}$.

Using $K = 8$ for the Trapezoidal Rule, we have $|E_T| \le \dfrac{K(b-a)^3}{12n^2} \le 0.00001 \quad \Leftrightarrow \quad \dfrac{8(1-0)^3}{12n^2} \le \dfrac{1}{100{,}000}$

$\Leftrightarrow \quad n^2 \ge \dfrac{800{,}000}{12} \quad \Leftrightarrow \quad n \gtrsim 258.2$, so we should take $n = 259$.

For the Midpoint Rule, $|E_M| \le \dfrac{K(b-a)^3}{24n^2} \le 0.00001 \quad \Leftrightarrow \quad n^2 \ge \dfrac{800{,}000}{24} \quad \Leftrightarrow \quad n \gtrsim 182.6$, so we should

take $n = 183$.

50. $\displaystyle\int_1^4 \frac{e^x}{x}\, dx \approx S_6 = \dfrac{(4-1)/6}{3}[f(1) + 4f(1.5) + 2f(2) + 4f(2.5) + 2f(3) + 4f(3.5) + f(4)] \approx 17.739438$

51. (a) $f(x) = \sin(\sin x)$. A CAS gives

$$f^{(4)}(x) = \sin(\sin x)\left[\cos^4 x + 7\cos^2 x - 3\right]$$

$$+ \cos(\sin x)\left[6\cos^2 x \sin x + \sin x\right]$$

From the graph, we see that $\left|f^{(4)}(x)\right| < 3.8$ for $x \in [0, \pi]$.

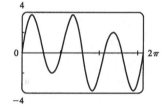

(b) We use Simpson's Rule with $f(x) = \sin(\sin x)$ and $\Delta x = \frac{\pi}{10}$:

$$\int_0^\pi f(x)\, dx \approx \tfrac{\pi}{10\cdot 3}\left[f(0) + 4f\!\left(\tfrac{\pi}{10}\right) + 2f\!\left(\tfrac{2\pi}{10}\right) + \cdots + 4f\!\left(\tfrac{9\pi}{10}\right) + f(\pi)\right] \approx 1.786721$$

From part (a), we know that $\left|f^{(4)}(x)\right| < 3.8$ on $[0, \pi]$, so we use Theorem 5.9.4 with $K = 3.8$, and estimate the

error as $|E_S| \le \dfrac{3.8(\pi - 0)^5}{180(10)^4} \approx 0.000646$.

(c) If we want the error to be less than 0.00001, we must have $|E_S| \le \frac{3.8\pi^5}{180n^4} \le 0.00001$, so

$n^4 \ge \frac{3.8\pi^5}{180(0.00001)} \approx 646{,}041.6 \quad \Rightarrow \quad n \ge 28.35$. Since n must be even for Simpson's Rule, we must have

$n \ge 30$ to ensure the desired accuracy.

52. (a) To evaluate $\int x^5 e^{-2x}\, dx$ by hand, we would integrate by parts repeatedly, always taking $dv = e^{-2x}$ and starting with $u = x^5$. Each time we would reduce the degree of the x-factor by 1.

(b) To evaluate the integral using tables, we would use Formula 97 (which is proved using integration by parts) until the exponent of x was reduced to 1, and then we would use Formula 96.

(d)

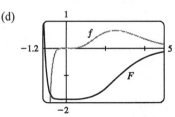

(c) $\int x^5 e^{-2x}\, dx$

$= -\tfrac{1}{8}e^{-2x}\left(4x^5 + 10x^4 + 20x^3 + 30x^2 + 30x + 15\right) + C$

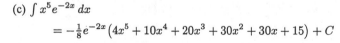

53. If $1 \leq x \leq 3$, then $\sqrt{1^2 + 3} \leq \sqrt{x^2 + 3} \leq \sqrt{3^2 + 3}$ $\Rightarrow$ $2 \leq \sqrt{x^2 + 3} \leq 2\sqrt{3}$, so
$2(3 - 1) \leq \int_1^3 \sqrt{x^2 + 3}\, dx \leq 2\sqrt{3}(3 - 1)$; that is, $4 \leq \int_1^3 \sqrt{x^2 + 3}\, dx \leq 4\sqrt{3}$.

54. On $[0, 1]$, $x^4 \geq x^4 \cos x$ (since $0 \leq \cos x \leq 1$), so by Property 7, $\int_0^1 x^4\, dx \geq \int_0^1 x^4 \cos x\, dx$. Also, $x^4 \cos x \geq 0$,
so by Property 6, $\int_0^1 x^4 \cos x\, dx \geq 0$. But $\int_0^1 x^4\, dx = \left[\frac{1}{5}x^5\right]_0^1 = \frac{1}{5} = 0.2$, so $0 \leq \int_0^1 x^4 \cos x\, dx \leq 0.2$.

55. $\displaystyle \int_1^\infty \frac{1}{(2x+1)^3}\, dx = \lim_{t \to \infty} \int_1^t \frac{1}{(2x+1)^3}\, dx = \lim_{t \to \infty} \int_1^t \frac{1}{2}(2x+1)^{-3}\, 2\, dx$

$\displaystyle = \lim_{t \to \infty} \left[-\frac{1}{4(2x+1)^2} \right]_1^t = -\frac{1}{4} \lim_{t \to \infty} \left[\frac{1}{(2t+1)^2} - \frac{1}{9} \right] = -\frac{1}{4}\left(0 - \frac{1}{9}\right) = \frac{1}{36}$

56. $\displaystyle I = \int_0^\infty \frac{\ln x}{x^4}\, dx = \int_0^1 \frac{\ln x}{x^4}\, dx + \int_1^\infty \frac{\ln x}{x^4}\, dx = I_1 + I_2$. Integrate by parts with $u = \ln x$, $dv = dx/x^4$ $\Rightarrow$
$du = dx/x$, $v = -1/\left(3x^3\right)$:

$$\int \frac{\ln x}{x^4}\, dx = -\frac{\ln x}{3x^3} + \frac{1}{3} \int \frac{1}{x^4}\, dx = -\frac{\ln x}{3x^3} + \frac{1}{3}\left(-\frac{1}{3x^3}\right) + C = -\frac{1}{9} \cdot \frac{3\ln x + 1}{x^3} + C$$

$$I_1 = \lim_{t \to 0^+} \int_t^1 \frac{\ln x}{x^4}\, dx = -\frac{1}{9} \lim_{t \to 0^+} \left[\frac{3\ln x + 1}{x^3} \right]_t^1 = -\frac{1}{9} \lim_{t \to 0^+} \left[1 - \frac{3\ln t + 1}{t^3} \right] = -\infty$$

So I_1 diverges and hence, I diverges. Divergent

57. $\displaystyle \int_{-\infty}^0 e^{-2x}\, dx = \lim_{t \to -\infty} \int_t^0 e^{-2x}\, dx = \lim_{t \to -\infty} \left[-\frac{1}{2}e^{-2x} \right]_t^0 = \lim_{t \to -\infty} \left(-\frac{1}{2} + \frac{1}{2}e^{-2t}\right) = \infty$. Divergent

58. Note that $f(x) = 1/(2 - 3x)$ has an infinite discontinuity at $x = \frac{2}{3}$. Now

$$\int_0^{2/3} \frac{1}{2 - 3x}\, dx = \lim_{t \to (2/3)^-} \int_0^t \frac{1}{2 - 3x}\, dx = \lim_{t \to (2/3)^-} \left[-\frac{1}{3}\ln|2 - 3x|\right]_0^t$$

$$= -\frac{1}{3} \lim_{t \to (2/3)^-} \left[\ln|2 - 3t| - \ln 2\right] = \infty$$

Since $\displaystyle \int_0^{2/3} \frac{1}{2 - 3x}\, dx$ diverges, so does $\displaystyle \int_0^1 \frac{1}{2 - 3x}\, dx$.

59. Let $u = \ln x$. Then $du = dx/x$, so $\displaystyle\int \frac{dx}{x\sqrt{\ln x}} = \int \frac{du}{\sqrt{u}} = 2\sqrt{u} + C = 2\sqrt{\ln x} + C.$

Thus, $\displaystyle\int_1^e \frac{dx}{x\sqrt{\ln x}} = \lim_{t\to 1^+} \int_t^e \frac{dx}{x\sqrt{\ln x}} = \lim_{t\to 1^+} \left[2\sqrt{\ln x}\right]_t^e = \lim_{t\to 1^+} \left(2\sqrt{\ln e} - 2\sqrt{\ln t}\right) = 2 \cdot 1 - 2 \cdot 0 = 2.$

60. Let $u = \sqrt{y-2}$. Then $y = u^2 + 2$ and $dy = 2u\,du$, so

$$\int \frac{y\,dy}{\sqrt{y-2}} = \int \frac{(u^2+2)\,2u\,du}{u} = 2\int (u^2 + 2)\,du = 2\left[\tfrac{1}{3}u^3 + 2u\right] + C$$

Thus, $\displaystyle\int_2^6 \frac{y\,dy}{\sqrt{y-2}} = \lim_{t\to 2^+} \int_t^6 \frac{y\,dy}{\sqrt{y-2}} = \lim_{t\to 2^+} \left[\tfrac{2}{3}(y-2)^{3/2} + 4\sqrt{y-2}\right]_t^6$

$= \displaystyle\lim_{t\to 2^+} \left[\tfrac{16}{3} + 8 - \tfrac{2}{3}(t-2)^{3/2} - 4\sqrt{t-2}\right] = \tfrac{40}{3}.$

61. $\dfrac{x^3}{x^5+2} \le \dfrac{x^3}{x^5} = \dfrac{1}{x^2}$ for x in $[1, \infty)$. $\displaystyle\int_1^\infty \frac{1}{x^2}\,dx$ is convergent by (5.10.2) with $p = 2 > 1$. Therefore,

$\displaystyle\int_1^\infty \frac{x^3}{x^5+2}\,dx$ is convergent by the Comparison Theorem.

62. $I = \displaystyle\int_0^\infty e^{ax}\cos x\,dx = \lim_{t\to\infty} \int_0^t e^{ax}\cos x\,dx \overset{\substack{99 \text{ with}\\ b=1}}{=} \lim_{t\to\infty} \left[\frac{e^{ax}}{a^2+1}(a\cos x + \sin x)\right]_0^t$

$= \displaystyle\lim_{t\to\infty} \left[\frac{e^{at}}{a^2+1}(a\cos t + \sin t) - \frac{1}{a^2+1}(a)\right] = \frac{1}{a^2+1}\lim_{t\to\infty}\left[e^{at}(a\cos t + \sin t) - a\right].$

For $a \ge 0$, the limit does not exist due to oscillation. For $a < 0$, $\displaystyle\lim_{t\to\infty}\left[e^{at}(a\cos t + \sin t)\right] = 0$ by the Squeeze

Theorem, because $\left|e^{at}(a\cos t + \sin t)\right| \le e^{at}(|a| + 1)$, so $I = \dfrac{1}{a^2+1}(-a) = -\dfrac{a}{a^2+1}.$

63. (a) displacement $= \displaystyle\int_0^5 (t^2 - t)\,dt = \left[\tfrac{1}{3}t^3 - \tfrac{1}{2}t^2\right]_0^5 = \tfrac{125}{3} - \tfrac{25}{2} = \tfrac{175}{6} = 29.1\overline{6}$ meters

(b) distance traveled $= \displaystyle\int_0^5 |t^2 - t|\,dt = \int_0^5 |t(t-1)|\,dt = \int_0^1 (t - t^2)\,dt + \int_1^5 (t^2 - t)\,dt$

$= \left[\tfrac{1}{2}t^2 - \tfrac{1}{3}t^3\right]_0^1 + \left[\tfrac{1}{3}t^3 - \tfrac{1}{2}t^2\right]_1^5$

$= \tfrac{1}{2} - \tfrac{1}{3} - 0 + \left(\tfrac{125}{3} - \tfrac{25}{2}\right) - \left(\tfrac{1}{3} - \tfrac{1}{2}\right) = \tfrac{177}{6} = 29.5$ meters

64. $\Delta t = \left(\tfrac{10}{60} - 0\right)/10 = \tfrac{1}{60}.$

Distance traveled $= \displaystyle\int_0^{10} v\,dt \approx S_{10} = \frac{1}{60 \cdot 3}[40 + 4(42) + 2(45) + 4(49) + 2(52)$

$+ 4(54) + 2(56) + 4(57) + 2(57) + 4(55) + 56]$

$= \tfrac{1}{180}(1544) = 8.5\overline{7}$ mi

65. Note that $r(t) = b'(t)$, where $b(t) = $ the number of barrels of oil consumed up to time t. So, by the Total Change Theorem, $\int_0^3 r(t)\,dt = b(3) - b(0)$ represents the number of barrels of oil consumed from Jan. 1, 2000, through Jan. 1, 2003.

66. We use Simpson's Rule with $n = 6$ and $\Delta t = \dfrac{24 - 0}{6} = 4$:

Increase in bee population $= \displaystyle\int_0^{24} r(t)\,dt \approx S_6$

$= \tfrac{4}{3}[r(0) + 4r(4) + 2r(8) + 4r(12) + 2r(16) + 4r(20) + r(24)]$

$= \tfrac{4}{3}[0 + 4(300) + 2(3000) + 4(11{,}000) + 2(4000) + 4(400) + 0]$

$= \tfrac{4}{3}(60{,}800) \approx 81{,}067$ bees

67. Both numerator and denominator approach 0 as $a \to 0$, so we use l'Hospital's Rule. (Note that we are differentiating *with respect to a*, since that is the quantity which is changing.) We also use FTC1:

$$\lim_{a \to 0} T(x, t) = \lim_{a \to 0} \frac{C \int_0^a e^{-(x-u)^2/(4kt)} \, du}{a\sqrt{4\pi kt}} \stackrel{\text{H}}{=} \lim_{a \to 0} \frac{Ce^{-(x-a)^2/(4kt)}}{\sqrt{4\pi kt}} = \frac{Ce^{-x^2/(4kt)}}{\sqrt{4\pi kt}}$$

68. (a) C is increasing on those intervals where C' is positive. By the Fundamental Theorem of Calculus,

$C'(x) = \frac{d}{dx} \left[\int_0^x \cos\left(\frac{\pi}{2}t^2\right) dt \right] = \cos\left(\frac{\pi}{2}x^2\right)$. This is positive when $\frac{\pi}{2}x^2$ is in the interval

$\left((2n - \frac{1}{2})\pi, (2n + \frac{1}{2})\pi\right)$, n any integer. This implies that $(2n - \frac{1}{2})\pi < \frac{\pi}{2}x^2 < (2n + \frac{1}{2})\pi$ $\Leftrightarrow$

$0 \le |x| \le 1$ or $\sqrt{4n-1} < |x| < \sqrt{4n+1}$, n any positive integer. So C is increasing on the intervals $[-1, 1]$,

$[\sqrt{3}, \sqrt{5}], [-\sqrt{5}, -\sqrt{3}], [\sqrt{7}, 3], [-3, -\sqrt{7}], \ldots$.

(b) C is concave upward on those intervals where $C'' > 0$. We differentiate C' to find C'': $C'(x) = \cos\left(\frac{\pi}{2}x^2\right)$

$\Rightarrow$ $C''(x) = -\sin\left(\frac{\pi}{2}x^2\right)\left(\frac{\pi}{2} \cdot 2x\right) = -\pi x \sin\left(\frac{\pi}{2}x^2\right)$. For $x > 0$, this is positive where

$(2n - 1)\pi < \frac{\pi}{2}x^2 < 2n\pi$, n any positive integer $\Leftrightarrow$ $\sqrt{2(2n - 1)} < x < 2\sqrt{n}$, n any positive integer.

Since there is a factor of $-x$ in C'', the intervals of upward concavity for $x < 0$ are $\left(-\sqrt{2(2n + 1)}, -2\sqrt{n}\right)$,

n any nonnegative integer. That is, C is concave upward on $(-\sqrt{2}, 0), (\sqrt{2}, 2), (-\sqrt{6}, -2), (\sqrt{6}, 2\sqrt{2}), \ldots$.

(c)

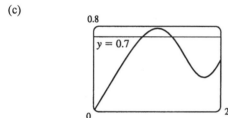
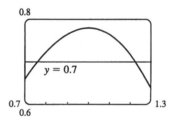

From the graphs, we can determine that $\int_0^x \cos\left(\frac{\pi}{2}t^2\right) dt = 0.7$ at $x \approx 0.76$ and $x \approx 1.22$.

(d)

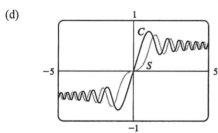

The graphs of $S(x)$ and $C(x)$ have similar shapes, except that S's flattens out near the origin, while C's does not. Note that for $x > 0$, C is increasing where S is concave up, and C is decreasing where S is concave down. Similarly, S is increasing where C is concave down, and S is decreasing where C is concave up. For $x < 0$, these relationships are reversed; that is, C is increasing where S is concave down, and S is increasing where C is concave up. See Example 5.4.4 and Exercise 5.4.21 for a discussion of $S(x)$.

69. Using FTC1, we differentiate both sides of the given equation, $\int_0^x f(t) \, dt = xe^{2x} + \int_0^x e^{-t}f(t) \, dt$, and get

$f(x) = e^{2x} + 2xe^{2x} + e^{-x}f(x)$ $\Rightarrow$ $f(x)(1 - e^{-x}) = e^{2x} + 2xe^{2x}$ $\Rightarrow$ $f(x) = \frac{e^{2x}(1 + 2x)}{1 - e^{-x}}$.

70. $2\int_a^x f(t) \, dt = 2\sin x - 1$ $\Rightarrow$ $\int_a^x f(t) \, dt = \sin x - \frac{1}{2}$. Differentiating both sides using FTC1 gives

$f(x) = \cos x$. We put $x = a$ into the last equation to get $0 = \sin a - \frac{1}{2}$, so $a = \frac{\pi}{6}$ satisfies the given equation.

71. Let $u = f(x)$ and $du = f'(x) \, dx$. So $2\int_a^b f(x)f'(x) \, dx = 2\int_{f(a)}^{f(b)} u \, du = \left[u^2\right]_{f(a)}^{f(b)} = [f(b)]^2 - [f(a)]^2$.

72. Integrate by parts with $u = (\ln x)^n$, $dv = dx$ $\Rightarrow$ $du = n(\ln x)^{n-1} \cdot \frac{1}{x}\, dx$, $v = x$:

$\int (\ln x)^n\, dx = x(\ln x)^n - \int x \cdot n(\ln x)^{n-1}(dx/x) = x(\ln x)^n - n\int (\ln x)^{n-1}\, dx$. Thus,

$\int_0^1 (\ln x)^n\, dx = \lim\limits_{t\to 0^+} \int_t^1 (\ln x)^n\, dx = \lim\limits_{t\to 0^+} [x(\ln x)^n]_t^1 - n \lim\limits_{t\to 0^+} \int_t^1 (\ln x)^{n-1}\, dx$

$\qquad = -\lim\limits_{t\to 0^+} \dfrac{(\ln t)^n}{1/t} - n\int_0^1 (\ln x)^{n-1}\, dx = -n\int_0^1 (\ln x)^{n-1}\, dx$,

by repeated application of l'Hospital's Rule. We want to prove that $\int_0^1 (\ln x)^n\, dx = (-1)^n n!$ for every positive

integer n. For $n = 1$, we have $\int_0^1 (\ln x)^1\, dx = (-1)\int_0^1 (\ln x)^0\, dx = -\int_0^1 dx = -1$ (or

$\int_0^1 \ln x\, dx = \lim\limits_{t\to 0^+} [x\ln x - x]_t^1 = -1$). Assuming that the formula holds for n, we find that

$\int_0^1 (\ln x)^{n+1}\, dx = -(n+1)\int_0^1 (\ln x)^n\, dx = -(n+1)(-1)^n n! = (-1)^{n+1}(n+1)!$.

This is the formula for $n + 1$. Thus, the formula holds for all positive integers n by induction.

73. By the Fundamental Theorem of Calculus,

$\int_0^\infty f'(x)\, dx = \lim\limits_{t\to\infty} \int_0^t f'(x)\, dx = \lim\limits_{t\to\infty} [f(t) - f(0)] = \lim\limits_{t\to\infty} f(t) - f(0) = 0 - f(0) = -f(0)$.

74. The area $A(t) = \int_0^t \sin(x^2)\, dx$, and the area $B(t) = \frac{1}{2}t\sin(t^2)$. Since $\lim\limits_{t\to 0^+} A(t) = 0 = \lim\limits_{t\to 0^+} B(t)$, we can use

l'Hospital's Rule:

$$\lim_{t\to 0^+} \frac{A(t)}{B(t)} \overset{H}{=} \lim_{t\to 0^+} \frac{\sin(t^2)}{\frac{1}{2}\sin(t^2) + \frac{1}{2}t\,[2t\cos(t^2)]} \quad \text{(by FTC1 and the Product Rule)}$$

$$\overset{H}{=} \lim_{t\to 0^+} \frac{2t\cos(t^2)}{t\cos(t^2) - 2t^3\sin(t^2) + 2t\cos(t^2)} = \lim_{t\to 0^+} \frac{2\cos(t^2)}{3\cos(t^2) - 2t^2\sin(t^2)}$$

$$= \frac{2}{3 - 0} = \frac{2}{3}$$

1.

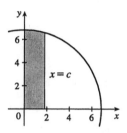

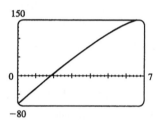

By symmetry, the problem can be reduced to finding the line $x = c$ such that the shaded area is one-third of the area of the quarter-circle. The equation of the circle is $y = \sqrt{49 - x^2}$, so we require that $\int_0^c \sqrt{49 - x^2}\, dx = \frac{1}{3} \cdot \frac{1}{4}\pi(7)^2$
$\Leftrightarrow$ $\left[\frac{1}{2}x\sqrt{49 - x^2} + \frac{49}{2}\sin^{-1}(x/7)\right]_0^c = \frac{49}{12}\pi$ (by Formula 30) $\Leftrightarrow$ $\frac{1}{2}c\sqrt{49 - c^2} + \frac{49}{2}\sin^{-1}(c/7) = \frac{49}{12}\pi$.
This equation would be difficult to solve exactly, so we plot the left-hand side as a function of c, and find that the equation holds for $c \approx 1.85$. So the cuts should be made at distances of about 1.85 inches from the center of the pizza.

2. (a)

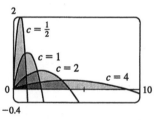

From the graph of $f(x) = \dfrac{2cx - x^2}{c^3}$, it appears that the areas are equal; that is, the area enclosed is independent of c.

(b) We first find the x-intercepts of the curve, to determine the limits of integration: $y = 0$ $\Leftrightarrow$ $2cx - x^2 = 0$
$\Leftrightarrow$ $x = 0$ or $x = 2c$. Now we integrate the function between these limits to find the enclosed area:
$$A = \int_0^{2c} \frac{2cx - x^2}{c^3}\, dx = \frac{1}{c^3}\left[cx^2 - \frac{1}{3}x^3\right]_0^{2c} = \frac{1}{c^3}\left[c(2c)^2 - \frac{1}{3}(2c)^3\right] = \frac{1}{c^3}\left[4c^3 - \frac{8}{3}c^3\right] = \frac{4}{3}, \text{ a constant.}$$

(c)

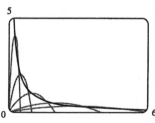

The vertices of the family of parabolas seem to determine a branch of a hyperbola.

(d) For a particular c, the vertex is the point where the maximum occurs. We have seen that the x-intercepts are 0 and $2c$, so by symmetry, the maximum occurs at $x = c$, and its value is $\dfrac{2c(c) - c^2}{c^3} = \dfrac{1}{c}$. So we are interested in

443

the curve consisting of all points of the form $\left(c, \dfrac{1}{c}\right)$, $c > 0$. This is the part of the hyperbola $y = 1/x$ lying in the first quadrant.

3. Differentiating both sides of the equation $x \sin \pi x = \int_0^{x^2} f(t)\, dt$ (using FTC1 and the Chain Rule for the right side) gives $\sin \pi x + \pi x \cos \pi x = 2xf\left(x^2\right)$. Letting $x = 2$ so that $f\left(x^2\right) = f(4)$, we obtain $\sin 2\pi + 2\pi \cos 2\pi = 4f(4)$, so $f(4) = \frac{1}{4}(0 + 2\pi \cdot 1) = \frac{\pi}{2}$.

4. If $f(x) = \int_0^x x^2 \sin\left(t^2\right) dt = x^2 \int_0^x \sin\left(t^2\right) dt$, then $f'(x) = x^2 \sin\left(x^2\right) + 2x \int_0^x \sin\left(t^2\right) dt$, by the Product Rule and FTC1.

5. By FTC2, $\int_0^1 f'(x)\, dx = f(1) - f(0) = 1 - 0 = 1$.

6.

Let x be the distance between the center of the disk and the surface of the liquid. The wetted circular region has area $\pi r^2 - \pi x^2$ while the unexposed wetted region (shaded in the diagram) has area $2 \int_x^r \sqrt{r^2 - t^2}\, dt$, so the exposed wetted region has area $A(x) = \pi r^2 - \pi x^2 - 2 \int_x^r \sqrt{r^2 - t^2}\, dt$, $0 \le x \le r$. By FTC1, we have $A'(x) = -2\pi x + 2\sqrt{r^2 - x^2}$, so $A'(x) = 0$ when $\pi x = \sqrt{r^2 - x^2} \Rightarrow \pi^2 x^2 = r^2 - x^2$ and hence $\left(1 + \pi^2\right)x^2 = r^2$, so $x = \dfrac{r}{\sqrt{1 + \pi^2}}$.

Now $A(0) = \pi r^2 - 2\left(\frac{1}{4}\pi r^2\right) = \frac{1}{2}\pi r^2$ and $A(r) = 0$, while

$A\left(\dfrac{r}{\sqrt{1+\pi^2}}\right) = \frac{1}{2}\pi r^2 + r^2 \sin^{-1} \dfrac{1}{\sqrt{1+\pi^2}}$ (after some simplification) $> \frac{1}{2}\pi r^2$, so there is an absolute maximum when $x = \dfrac{r}{\sqrt{1+\pi^2}}$.

7. By l'Hospital's Rule and the Fundamental Theorem, using the notation $\exp(y) = e^y$,

$$\lim_{x \to 0} \frac{\int_0^x (1 - \tan 2t)^{1/t}\, dt}{x} \stackrel{\text{H}}{=} \lim_{x \to 0} \frac{(1 - \tan 2x)^{1/x}}{1} = \exp\left(\lim_{x \to 0} \frac{\ln(1 - \tan 2x)}{x}\right)$$

$$\stackrel{\text{H}}{=} \exp\left(\lim_{x \to 0} \frac{-2\sec^2 2x}{1 - \tan 2x}\right) = \exp\left(\frac{-2 \cdot 1^2}{1 - 0}\right) = e^{-2}.$$

8. $f(x) = \displaystyle\int_0^{g(x)} \frac{1}{\sqrt{1+t^3}}\, dt$, where $g(x) = \int_0^{\cos x} \left[1 + \sin\left(t^2\right)\right] dt$. Using FTC1 and the Chain Rule (twice) we

have $f'(x) = \dfrac{1}{\sqrt{1 + [g(x)]^3}} g'(x) = \dfrac{1}{\sqrt{1 + [g(x)]^3}} \left[1 + \sin\left(\cos^2 x\right)\right](-\sin x)$. Now

$g\left(\frac{\pi}{2}\right) = \int_0^0 \left[1 + \sin\left(t^2\right)\right] dt = 0$, so $f'\left(\frac{\pi}{2}\right) = \frac{1}{\sqrt{1+0}}(1 + \sin 0)(-1) = 1 \cdot 1 \cdot (-1) = -1$.

9. Such a function cannot exist. $f'(x) > 3$ for all x means that f is differentiable (and hence continuous) for all x. So by Part 2 of the Fundamental Theorem, $\int_1^4 f'(x)\, dx = f(4) - f(1) = 7 - (-1) = 8$. However, if $f'(x) > 3$ for all x, then $\int_1^4 f'(x)\, dx \ge 3 \cdot (4 - 1) = 9$ by Comparison Property 8 in Section 5.2.

Another solution: By the Mean Value Theorem there exists a number $c \in (1, 4)$ such that

$f'(c) = \dfrac{f(4) - f(1)}{4 - 1} = \dfrac{7 - (-1)}{3} = \dfrac{8}{3} \Rightarrow 8 = 3f'(c)$. But $f'(x) > 3 \Rightarrow 3f'(c) > 9$, so such a function cannot exist.

10.

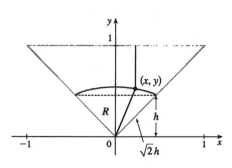

We restrict our attention to the triangle shown. A point in this triangle is closer to the side shown than to any other side, so if we find the area of the region R consisting of all points in the triangle that are closer to the center than to that side, we can multiply this area by 4 to find the total area. We find the equation of the set of points which are equidistant from the center and the side: the distance of the point (x, y) from the side is $1 - y$, and its distance from the center is $\sqrt{x^2 + y^2}$.

So the distances are equal if $\sqrt{x^2 + y^2} = 1 - y \iff x^2 + y^2 = 1 - 2y + y^2 \iff y = \frac{1}{2}(1 - x^2)$. Note that the area we are interested in is equal to the area of a triangle plus a crescent-shaped area. To find these areas, we have to find the y-coordinate h of the horizontal line separating them. From the diagram, $1 - h = \sqrt{2}h \iff$ $h = \frac{1}{1+\sqrt{2}} = \sqrt{2} - 1$. We calculate the areas in terms of h, and substitute afterward.

The area of the triangle is $\frac{1}{2}(2h)(h) = h^2$, and the area of the crescent-shaped section is

$\int_{-h}^{h} \left[\frac{1}{2}(1 - x^2) - h\right] dx = 2 \int_0^h \left(\frac{1}{2} - h - \frac{1}{2}x^2\right) dx = 2\left[\left(\frac{1}{2} - h\right)x - \frac{1}{6}x^3\right]_0^h = h - 2h^2 - \frac{1}{3}h^3$. So the area of the whole region is

$$4\left[(h - 2h^2 - \frac{1}{3}h^3) + h^2\right] = 4h\left(1 - h - \frac{1}{3}h^2\right) = 4\left(\sqrt{2} - 1\right)\left[1 - \left(\sqrt{2} - 1\right) - \frac{1}{3}\left(\sqrt{2} - 1\right)^2\right]$$

$$= 4\left(\sqrt{2} - 1\right)\left(1 - \frac{1}{3}\sqrt{2}\right) = \frac{4}{3}\left(4\sqrt{2} - 5\right)$$

11. $f(x) = 2 + x - x^2 = (-x + 2)(x + 1) = 0 \iff x = 2$ or $x = -1$. $f(x) \geq 0$ for $x \in [-1, 2]$ and $f(x) < 0$ everywhere else. The integral $\int_a^b (2 + x - x^2) \, dx$ has a maximum on the interval where the integrand is positive, which is $[-1, 2]$. So $a = -1$, $b = 2$. (Any larger interval gives a smaller integral since $f(x) < 0$ outside $[-1, 2]$. Any smaller interval also gives a smaller integral since $f(x) \geq 0$ in $[-1, 2]$.)

12. The shaded region has area $\int_0^1 f(x) \, dx = \frac{1}{3}$. The integral $\int_0^1 f^{-1}(y) \, dy$ gives the area of the unshaded region, which we know to be $1 - \frac{1}{3} = \frac{2}{3}$. So $\int_0^1 f^{-1}(y) \, dy = \frac{2}{3}$.

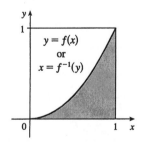

13. By FTC1, $\dfrac{d}{dx} \int_0^x \left(\int_1^{\sin t} \sqrt{1 + u^4} \, du\right) dt = \int_1^{\sin x} \sqrt{1 + u^4} \, du$. Again using FTC1,

$\dfrac{d^2}{dx^2} \int_0^x \left(\int_1^{\sin t} \sqrt{1 + u^4} \, du\right) dt = \dfrac{d}{dx} \int_1^{\sin x} \sqrt{1 + u^4} \, du = \sqrt{1 + \sin^4 x} \cos x$.

14. This sum can be interpreted as a Riemann sum, with the right endpoints of the subintervals as sample points and with $a = 0$, $b = 10{,}000$, and $f(x) = \sqrt{x}$. So we approximate

$$\sum_{i=1}^{10{,}000} \sqrt{i} \approx \lim_{n \to \infty} \frac{10{,}000}{n} \sum_{i=1}^{n} \sqrt{\frac{10{,}000i}{n}} = \int_{0}^{10{,}000} \sqrt{x}\, dx = \left[\tfrac{2}{3} x^{3/2} \right]_{0}^{10{,}000} = \tfrac{2}{3}(1{,}000{,}000) \approx 666{,}667.$$

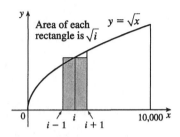

Alternate method: We can use graphical methods as follows:

From the figure we see that $\int_{i-1}^{i} \sqrt{x}\, dx < \sqrt{i} < \int_{i}^{i+1} \sqrt{x}\, dx$, so

$$\int_{0}^{10{,}000} \sqrt{x}\, dx < \sum_{i=1}^{10{,}000} \sqrt{i} < \int_{1}^{10{,}001} \sqrt{x}\, dx. \text{ Since}$$

$\int \sqrt{x}\, dx = \tfrac{2}{3} x^{3/2} + C$, we get $\int_{0}^{10{,}000} \sqrt{x}\, dx = 666{,}666.\overline{6}$ and

$\int_{1}^{10{,}001} \sqrt{x}\, dx = \tfrac{2}{3}\left[(10{,}001)^{3/2} - 1 \right] \approx 666{,}766.$

Hence, $666{,}666.\overline{6} < \displaystyle\sum_{i=1}^{10{,}000} \sqrt{i} < 666{,}766$. We can estimate the sum by averaging these bounds:

$$\sum_{i=1}^{10{,}000} \approx \frac{666{,}666.\overline{6} + 666{,}766}{2} \approx 666{,}716. \text{ The actual value is about } 666{,}716.46.$$

15. The given integral represents the difference of the shaded areas, which appears to be 0. It can be calculated by integrating with respect to either x or y, so we find x in terms of y for each curve:

$y = \sqrt[3]{1 - x^7} \quad \Rightarrow \quad x = \sqrt[7]{1 - y^3}$ and

$y = \sqrt[7]{1 - x^3} \quad \Rightarrow \quad x = \sqrt[3]{1 - y^7}$, so

$\int_{0}^{1} \left(\sqrt[7]{1 - y^7} - \sqrt[7]{1 - y^3} \right) dy = \int_{0}^{1} \left(\sqrt[7]{1 - x^3} - \sqrt[3]{1 - x^7} \right) dx.$ But

this equation is of the form $z = -z$. So

$\int_{0}^{1} \left(\sqrt[3]{1 - x^7} - \sqrt[7]{1 - x^3} \right) dx = 0.$

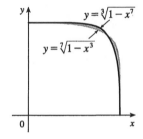

16. The problem can be reduced to finding the line which minimizes the shaded area in the diagram. The equation of the circle in the first quadrant is $y = \sqrt{1 - x^2}$, so if the equation of the line is $y = h$, then the circle and the line intersect where $h = \sqrt{1 - x^2} \quad \Rightarrow \quad x = \sqrt{1 - h^2}$. So the shaded area is

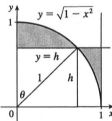

$A = \int_{0}^{\sqrt{1-h^2}} \left(\sqrt{1 - x^2} - h \right) dx + \int_{\sqrt{1-h^2}}^{1} \left(h - \sqrt{1 - x^2} \right)$

$\overset{\star}{=} [-hx]_{0}^{\sqrt{1-h^2}} + [hx]_{\sqrt{1-h^2}}^{1} + \int_{0}^{\sqrt{1-h^2}} \sqrt{1 - x^2}\, dx + \int_{1}^{\sqrt{1-h^2}} \sqrt{1 - x^2}\, dx$

$= -h\sqrt{1 - h^2} + h - h\sqrt{1 - h^2} + \int_{0}^{\sqrt{1-h^2}} \sqrt{1 - x^2}\, dx + \int_{1}^{\sqrt{1-h^2}} \sqrt{1 - x^2}\, dx$

$= h\left(1 - 2\sqrt{1 - h^2} \right) + \int_{0}^{\sqrt{1-h^2}} \sqrt{1 - x^2}\, dx + \int_{1}^{\sqrt{1-h^2}} \sqrt{1 - x^2}\, dx$

Note that at $(\star)$, we reversed the limits of integration and changed the sign in the last integral.

We are interested in the minimum of $A\left(h\right) = h\left(1 - 2\sqrt{1 - h^2}\right) + \int_0^{\sqrt{1-h^2}} \sqrt{1 - x^2}\, dx + \int_1^{\sqrt{1-h^2}} \sqrt{1 - x^2}\, dx$,
so we find dA/dh using FTC1 and the Chain Rule:

$$\frac{dA}{dh} = h\left(-2\frac{-h}{\sqrt{1 - h^2}}\right) + \left(1 - 2\sqrt{1 - h^2}\right) + 2\left[\sqrt{1 - \left(\sqrt{1 - h^2}\right)^2}\right]\frac{d}{dh}\left(\sqrt{1 - h^2}\right)$$

$$= \frac{1}{\sqrt{1 - h^2}}\left[2h^2 + \sqrt{1 - h^2} - 2\left(1 - h^2\right)\right] + 2h\frac{-h}{\sqrt{1 - h^2}}$$

This is 0 when $\sqrt{1 - h^2} - 2\left(1 - h^2\right) = 0 \quad \Leftrightarrow \quad u - 2u^2 = 0$ (where $u = \sqrt{1 - h^2}$) $\quad \Leftrightarrow \quad u = 0$ or $\frac{1}{2}$ $\quad \Leftrightarrow$

$h = 1$ or $\frac{\sqrt{3}}{2}$. By the First Derivative Test, $h = \frac{\sqrt{3}}{2}$ represents a minimum for $A(h)$, since $A'(h) = 1 - \dfrac{2}{\sqrt{1 - h^2}}$

goes from negative to positive at $h = \frac{\sqrt{3}}{2}$.

Another method: Use FTC2 to evaluate all of the integrals before differentiating.

Note: Another strategy is to use the angle θ as the variable (see diagram above) and show that
$A = \theta + \cos\theta - \frac{\pi}{4} - \frac{1}{2}\sin 2\theta$, which is minimized when $\theta = \frac{\pi}{6}$.

17. In accordance with the hint, we let $I_k = \int_0^1 \left(1 - x^2\right)^k dx$, and we find an expression for I_{k+1} in terms of I_k. We
integrate I_{k+1} by parts with $u = \left(1 - x^2\right)^{k+1}$, $dv = dx \quad \Rightarrow \quad du = (k + 1)\left(1 - x^2\right)^k(-2x)$, $v = x$, and then
split the remaining integral into identifiable quantities:

$$I_{k+1} = \left[x\left(1 - x^2\right)^{k+1}\right]_0^1 + 2(k + 1)\int_0^1 x^2\left(1 - x^2\right)^k dx$$

$$= (2k + 2)\int_0^1 \left(1 - x^2\right)^k\left[1 - \left(1 - x^2\right)\right] dx = (2k + 2)(I_k - I_{k+1})$$

So $I_{k+1}\left[1 + (2k + 2)\right] = (2k + 2)I_k \Rightarrow I_{k+1} = \dfrac{2k + 2}{2k + 3}I_k.$

Now to complete the proof, we use induction: $I_0 = 1 = \dfrac{2^0(0!)^2}{1!}$, so the formula holds for $n = 0$. Now suppose it
holds for $n = k$. Then

$$I_{k+1} = \frac{2k + 2}{2k + 3}I_k = \frac{2k + 2}{2k + 3}\left[\frac{2^{2k}(k!)^2}{(2k + 1)!}\right] = \frac{2(k + 1)2^{2k}(k!)^2}{(2k + 3)(2k + 1)!} = \frac{2(k + 1)2^{2k}(k!)^2}{(2k + 3)(2k + 1)!} \cdot \frac{2(k + 1)}{2k + 2}$$

$$= \frac{[2(k + 1)]^2\, 2^{2k}(k!)^2}{(2k + 3)(2k + 2)(2k + 1)!} = \frac{2^{2(k+1)}\,[(k + 1)!]^2}{[2(k + 1) + 1]!}$$

So by induction, the formula holds for all integers $n \geq 0$.

18.

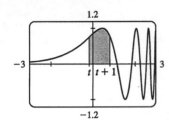

From the graph, it appears that the area under the graph of $f(x) = \sin(e^x)$ on the interval $[t, t+1]$ is greatest when $t \approx -0.2$. To find the exact value, we write the integral as $I = \int_t^{t+1} f(x)\,dx = \int_0^{t+1} f(x)\,dx - \int_0^t f(x)\,dx$, and use FTC1 to find $dI/dt = f(t+1) - f(t) = \sin(e^{t+1}) - \sin(e^t) = 0$ when $\sin(e^{t+1}) = \sin(e^t)$.

Now we have $\sin x = \sin y$ whenever $x - y = 2k\pi$ and also whenever x and y are the same distance from $(k + \frac{1}{2})\pi$, k any integer, since $\sin x$ is symmetric about the line $x = (k + \frac{1}{2})\pi$. The first possibility is the more obvious one, but if we calculate $e^{t+1} - e^t = 2k\pi$, we get $t = \ln(2k\pi/(e-1))$, which is about 1.3 for $k = 1$ (the least possible value of k). From the graph, this looks unlikely to give the maximum we are looking for. So instead we set $e^{t+1} - (k + \frac{1}{2})\pi = (k + \frac{1}{2})\pi - e^t \iff e^{t+1} + e^t = (2k+1)\pi \iff e^t(e+1) = (2k+1)\pi \iff t = \ln((2k+1)\pi/(e+1))$. Now $k = 0 \implies t = \ln(\pi/(e+1)) \approx -0.16853$, which does give the maximum value, as we have seen from the graph of f.

19. (a) The tangent to the curve $y = f(x)$ at $x = x_0$ has the equation $y - f(x_0) = f'(x_0)(x - x_0)$. The y-intercept of this tangent line is $f(x_0) - f'(x_0)x_0$. Thus, L is the distance from the point $(0, f(x_0) - f'(x_0)x_0)$ to the point $(x_0, f(x_0))$; that is, $L^2 = x_0^2 + [f'(x_0)]^2 x_0^2$, so $[f'(x_0)]^2 = \dfrac{L^2 - x_0^2}{x_0^2}$ and $f'(x_0) = -\dfrac{\sqrt{L^2 - x_0^2}}{x_0}$ for $0 < x_0 < L$.

(b) $\dfrac{dy}{dx} = -\dfrac{\sqrt{L^2 - x^2}}{x} \implies y = \int\left(-\dfrac{\sqrt{L^2 - x^2}}{x}\right)dx.$

Let $x = L\sin\theta$. Then $dx = L\cos\theta\,d\theta$ and

$$y = \int \frac{-L\cos\theta\, L\cos\theta\,d\theta}{L\sin\theta} = L\int\frac{\sin^2\theta - 1}{\sin\theta}\,d\theta$$

$$= L\int(\sin\theta - \csc\theta)\,d\theta$$

$$= -L\cos\theta - L\ln|\csc\theta - \cot\theta| + C$$

$$= -\sqrt{L^2 - x^2} - L\ln\left(\frac{L}{x} - \frac{\sqrt{L^2 - x^2}}{x}\right) + C.$$

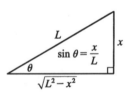

When $x = L$, $y = 0$, and $0 = -0 - L\ln(1-0) + C$, so $C = 0$. Therefore,

$$y = -\sqrt{L^2 - x^2} - L\ln\left(\frac{L - \sqrt{L^2 - x^2}}{x}\right)$$

20. Note that the graphs of $(x-c)^2$ and $[(x-c)-2]^2$ intersect when

$$|x-c| = |x-c-2| \quad \Leftrightarrow \quad c-x = x-c-2 \quad \Leftrightarrow \quad x = c+1.$$ The integration will proceed differently depending on the value of c.

Case 1: $-2 \le c < -1$ In this case, $f_c(x) = (x-c-2)^2$ for $x \in [0,1]$, so

$$g(c) = \int_0^1 (x-c-2)^2 \, dx = \frac{1}{3} \left[(x-c-2)^3\right]_0^1 = \frac{1}{3}\left[(-c-1)^3 - (-c-2)^3\right]$$

$$= \frac{1}{3}\left(3c^2 + 9c + 7\right) = c^2 + 3c + \frac{7}{3} = \left(c + \frac{3}{2}\right)^2 + \frac{1}{12}$$

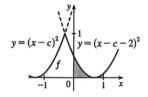

$y = (x-c)^2$ $y = (x-c-2)^2$

This is a parabola; its maximum for $-2 \le c < -1$ is $g(-2) = \frac{1}{3}$, and its minimum is $g\left(-\frac{3}{2}\right) = \frac{1}{12}$.

Case 2: $-1 \le c < 0$ In this case, $f_c(x) = \begin{cases} (x-c)^2 & \text{if } 0 \le x \le c+1 \\ (x-c-2)^2 & \text{if } c+1 < x \le 1 \end{cases}$ Therefore,

$$g(c) = \int_0^1 f_c(x) \, dx = \int_0^{c+1} (x-c)^2 \, dx + \int_{c+1}^1 (x-c-2)^2 \, dx$$

$$= \frac{1}{3}\left[(x-c)^3\right]_0^{c+1} + \frac{1}{3}\left[(x-c-2)^3\right]_{c+1}^1 = \frac{1}{3}\left[1 + c^3 + (-c-1)^3 - (-1)\right]$$

$$= -c^2 - c + \frac{1}{3} = -\left(c + \frac{1}{2}\right)^2 + \frac{7}{12}$$

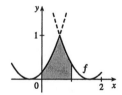

Again, this is a parabola, whose maximum for $-1 \le c < 0$ is $g\left(-\frac{1}{2}\right) = \frac{7}{12}$, and whose minimum on this c-interval is $g(-1) = \frac{1}{3}$.

Case 3: $0 \le c \le 2$ In this case, $f_c(x) = (x-c)^2$ for $x \in [0,1]$, so

$$g(c) = \int_0^1 (x-c)^2 \, dx = \frac{1}{3}\left[(x-c)^3\right]_0^1 = \frac{1}{3}\left[(1-c)^3 - (-c)^3\right] = c^2 - c + \frac{1}{3} = \left(c - \frac{1}{2}\right)^2 + \frac{1}{12}.$$

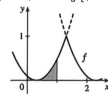

This parabola has a maximum of $g(2) = \frac{7}{3}$ and a minimum of $g\left(\frac{1}{2}\right) = \frac{1}{12}$.

We conclude that $g(c)$ has an absolute maximum of $g(2) = \frac{7}{3}$, and absolute minima of $g\left(-\frac{3}{2}\right) = g\left(\frac{1}{2}\right) = \frac{1}{12}$.

6 Applications of Integration

6.1 More about Areas • • • • • • • • • • • • • • • • •

1. $A = \int_{x=0}^{x=4} (y_T - y_B)\, dx = \int_0^4 \left[(5x - x^2) - x\right] dx = \int_0^4 (4x - x^2)\, dx$

$= \left[2x^2 - \tfrac{1}{3}x^3\right]_0^4 = \left(32 - \tfrac{64}{3}\right) - (0) = \tfrac{32}{3}$

2. $A = \int_0^2 \left(\sqrt{x+2} - \dfrac{1}{x+1}\right) dx = \left[\tfrac{2}{3}(x+2)^{3/2} - \ln(x+1)\right]_0^2$

$= \left[\tfrac{2}{3}(4)^{3/2} - \ln 3\right] - \left[\tfrac{2}{3}(2)^{3/2} - \ln 1\right] = \tfrac{16}{3} - \ln 3 - \tfrac{4}{3}\sqrt{2}$

3. $A = \int_{y=-1}^{y=1} (x_R - x_L)\, dy = \int_{-1}^1 \left[e^y - (y^2 - 2)\right] dy$

$= \int_{-1}^1 (e^y - y^2 + 2)\, dy = \left[e^y - \tfrac{1}{3}y^3 + 2y\right]_{-1}^1 = \left(e^1 - \tfrac{1}{3} + 2\right) - \left(e^{-1} + \tfrac{1}{3} - 2\right) = e - \dfrac{1}{e} + \dfrac{10}{3}$

4. $A = \int_0^3 \left[(2y - y^2) - (y^2 - 4y)\right] dy = \int_0^3 (-2y^2 + 6y)\, dy$

$= \left[-\tfrac{2}{3}y^3 + 3y^2\right]_0^3 = (-18 + 27) - 0 = 9$

5. $A = \int_{-1}^2 \left[(9 - x^2) - (x + 1)\right] dx$

$= \int_{-1}^2 (8 - x - x^2)\, dx$

$= \left[8x - \dfrac{x^2}{2} - \dfrac{x^3}{3}\right]_{-1}^2$

$= \left(16 - 2 - \tfrac{8}{3}\right) - \left(-8 - \tfrac{1}{2} + \tfrac{1}{3}\right)$

$= 22 - 3 + \tfrac{1}{2} = \tfrac{39}{2}$

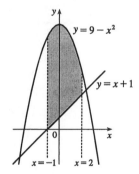
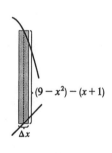

6. $A = \int_0^{\pi/2} (e^x - \sin x)\, dx$

$= \left[e^x + \cos x\right]_0^{\pi/2}$

$= \left(e^{\pi/2} + 0\right) - (1 + 1)$

$= e^{\pi/2} - 2$

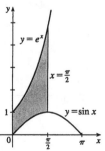
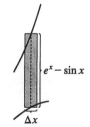

7. The curves intersect when $x = x^2 \Rightarrow x^2 - x = 0 \Leftrightarrow x(x-1) = 0 \Leftrightarrow x = 0, 1$.

$$A = \int_0^1 (x - x^2)\,dx$$

$$= \left[\tfrac{1}{2}x^2 - \tfrac{1}{3}x^3\right]_0^1$$

$$= \tfrac{1}{2} - \tfrac{1}{3}$$

$$= \tfrac{1}{6}$$

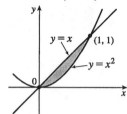
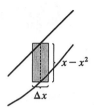

8. $1 + \sqrt{x} = \dfrac{3+x}{3} = 1 + \dfrac{x}{3} \Rightarrow \sqrt{x} = \dfrac{x}{3} \Rightarrow x = \dfrac{x^2}{9} \Rightarrow 9x - x^2 = 0 \Rightarrow x(9-x) = 0 \Rightarrow x = 0$

or 9, so

$$A = \int_0^9 \left[(1 + \sqrt{x}) - \left(\frac{3+x}{3}\right)\right] dx = \int_0^9 \left[(1 + \sqrt{x}) - \left(1 + \frac{x}{3}\right)\right] dx$$

$$= \int_0^9 \left(\sqrt{x} - \tfrac{1}{3}x\right) dx = \left[\tfrac{2}{3}x^{3/2} - \tfrac{1}{6}x^2\right]_0^9 = 18 - \tfrac{27}{2} = \tfrac{9}{2}$$

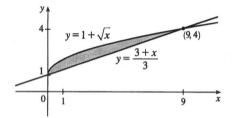
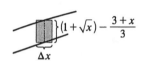

9. The curves intersect when $4x^2 = x^2 + 3 \Leftrightarrow 3x^2 = 3 \Leftrightarrow x^2 = 1 \Leftrightarrow x = \pm 1$.

$$A = \int_{-1}^1 \left[(x^2 + 3) - 4x^2\right] dx$$

$$= 2\int_0^1 (3 - 3x^2)\,dx$$

$$= 2\left[3x - x^3\right]_0^1 = 2(3 - 1) = 4$$

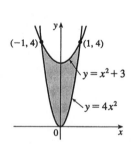
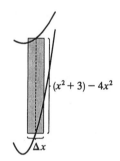

10. $A = \int_{-1}^1 \left[(1 - x^2) - (x^4 - x^2)\right] dx = 2\int_0^1 (1 - x^4)\,dx = 2\left[x - \tfrac{1}{5}x^5\right]_0^1 = 2\left(1 - \tfrac{1}{5}\right) = \tfrac{8}{5}$

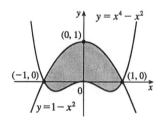
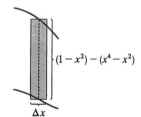

11. The curves intersect when $y^2 = 2y + 3 \Leftrightarrow y^2 - 2y - 3 = 0 \Leftrightarrow (y - 3)(y + 1) = 0 \Leftrightarrow y = -1, 3.$

$A = \int_{-1}^{3} \left[(2y + 3) - y^2\right] dy$

$= \left[y^2 + 3y - \tfrac{1}{3}y^3\right]_{-1}^{3}$

$= (9 + 9 - 9) - (1 - 3 + \tfrac{1}{3})$

$= \tfrac{32}{3}$

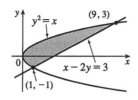

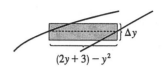

12. $A = \int_{-1}^{2} \left[(2 - y^2) - (-y)\right] dy$

$= \int_{-1}^{2} (-y^2 + y + 2) \, dy$

$= \left[-\tfrac{1}{3}y^3 + \tfrac{1}{2}y^2 + 2y\right]_{-1}^{2}$

$= (-\tfrac{8}{3} + 2 + 4) - (\tfrac{1}{3} + \tfrac{1}{2} - 2) = \tfrac{9}{2}$

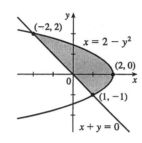

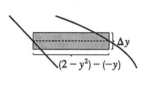

13. The curves intersect when $1 - y^2 = y^2 - 1 \Leftrightarrow 2 = 2y^2 \Leftrightarrow y^2 = 1 \Leftrightarrow y = \pm 1.$

$A = \int_{-1}^{1} \left[(1 - y^2) - (y^2 - 1)\right] dy$

$= \int_{-1}^{1} 2(1 - y^2) \, dy$

$= 2 \cdot 2 \int_{0}^{1} (1 - y^2) \, dy$

$= 4\left[y - \tfrac{1}{3}y^3\right]_{0}^{1} = 4(1 - \tfrac{1}{3}) = \tfrac{8}{3}$

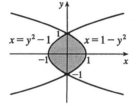

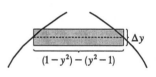

14. $A = \int_{-\pi/4}^{\pi/4} \left(\sec^2 x - \cos x\right) dx$

$= 2 \int_{0}^{\pi/4} \left(\sec^2 x - \cos x\right) dx$

$= 2[\tan x - \sin x]_{0}^{\pi/4}$

$= 2\left(1 - \tfrac{1}{\sqrt{2}}\right) = 2 - \sqrt{2} \approx 0.59$

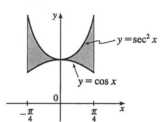

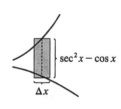

15. The curves intersect when $x^2 = \dfrac{2}{x^2 + 1} \Leftrightarrow x^4 + x^2 = 2 \Leftrightarrow x^4 + x^2 - 2 = 0 \Leftrightarrow$

$(x^2 + 2)(x^2 - 1) = 0 \Leftrightarrow x^2 = 1 \Leftrightarrow x = \pm 1.$

$A = \int_{-1}^{1} \left(\dfrac{2}{x^2 + 1} - x^2\right) dx$

$= 2 \int_{0}^{1} \left(\dfrac{2}{x^2 + 1} - x^2\right) dx$

$= 2\left[2 \tan^{-1} x - \tfrac{1}{3}x^3\right]_{0}^{1} = 2\left(2 \cdot \tfrac{\pi}{4} - \tfrac{1}{3}\right)$

$= \pi - \tfrac{2}{3} \approx 2.47$

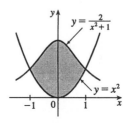

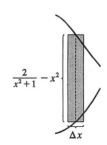

16. For $x > 0$, $x = x^2 - 2$ $\Rightarrow$ $0 = x^2 - x - 2$ $\Rightarrow$ $0 = (x - 2)(x + 1)$ $\Rightarrow$ $x = 2$. By symmetry,

$$\int_{-2}^{2} \left[|x| - (x^2 - 2)\right] dx = 2\int_{0}^{2} \left[x - (x^2 - 2)\right] dx = 2\int_{0}^{2} \left(x - x^2 + 2\right) dx = 2\left[\tfrac{1}{2}x^2 - \tfrac{1}{3}x^3 + 2x\right]_{0}^{2}$$
$$= 2\left(2 - \tfrac{8}{3} + 4\right) = \tfrac{20}{3}$$

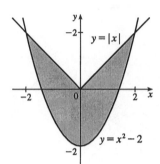
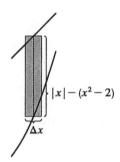

17.

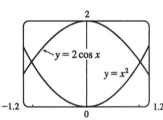

From the graph, we see that the curves intersect at $x = \pm a \approx \pm 1.02$, with $2\cos x > x^2$ on $(-a, a)$. So the area of the region bounded by the curves is

$$A = \int_{-a}^{a} \left(2\cos x - x^2\right) dx = 2\int_{0}^{a} \left(2\cos x - x^2\right) dx$$
$$= 2\left[2\sin x - \tfrac{1}{3}x^3\right]_{0}^{a} \approx 2.70$$

18.

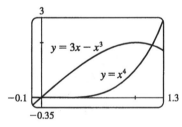

From the graph, we see that the curves intersect at $x = 0$ and at $x = a \approx 1.17$, with $3x - x^3 > x^4$ on $(0, a)$. So the area of the region bounded by the curves is

$$A = \int_{0}^{a} \left[(3x - x^3) - x^4\right] dx = \left[\tfrac{3}{2}x^2 - \tfrac{1}{4}x^4 - \tfrac{1}{5}x^5\right]_{0}^{a}$$
$$\approx 1.15$$

19.

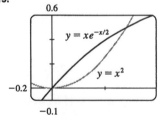

From the graph, we see that the curves intersect at $x = 0$ and $x = a \approx 0.70$, with $xe^{-x/2} > x^2$ on $(0, a)$. So the area of the region bounded by the curves is

$$A = \int_{0}^{a} \left(xe^{-x/2} - x^2\right) dx$$
$$= \left[4\left(-\tfrac{1}{2}x - 1\right)e^{-x/2} - \tfrac{1}{3}x^3\right]_{0}^{a} \quad \text{(Formula 96 with } a = -\tfrac{1}{2}\text{)}$$
$$\approx 0.08$$

20. From the graph, we see that the curves

intersect at $x = a \approx -1.32$ and

$x = b \approx 0.54$, with $2 - x^2 > e^x$ on

(a, b). So the area of the region bounded

by the curves is

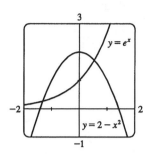

$$A = \int_a^b \left[(2 - x^2) - e^x \right] dx$$
$$= \left[2x - \tfrac{1}{3}x^3 - e^x \right]_a^b$$
$$\approx 1.45$$

21. As in Example 4, we approximate the distance between the two cars after ten seconds using Simpson's Rule with $\Delta t = 1\,\mathrm{s} = \frac{1}{3600}$ h.

$$\text{distance}_{\text{Kelly}} - \text{distance}_{\text{Chris}} = \int_0^{10} v_K \, dt - \int_0^{10} v_C \, dt = \int_0^{10} (v_K - v_C)\, dt \approx S_{10}$$

$$= \tfrac{1}{3 \cdot 3600}[(0 - 0) + 4(22 - 20) + 2(37 - 32) + 4(52 - 46) + 2(61 - 54) + 4(71 - 62)$$

$$+ 2(80 - 69) + 4(86 - 75) + 2(93 - 81) + 4(98 - 86) + (102 - 90)]$$

$$= \tfrac{1}{10,800}(242) = \tfrac{121}{5400} \text{ mi}$$

So after 10 seconds, Kelly's car is about $\dfrac{121}{5400}$ mi $\left(5280\dfrac{\text{ft}}{\text{mi}} \right) \approx 118$ ft ahead of Chris's.

22. We know that the area under curve A between $t = 0$ and $t = x$ is $\int_0^x v_A(t)\, dt = s_A(x)$, where $v_A(t)$ is the velocity of car A and s_A is its displacement. Similarly, the area under curve B between $t = 0$ and $t = x$ is $\int_0^x v_B(t)\, dt = s_B(x)$.

(a) After one minute, the area under curve A is greater than the area under curve B. So A is ahead after one minute.

(b) The area of the shaded region has numerical value $s_A(1) - s_B(1)$, which is the distance by which A is ahead of B after 1 minute.

(c) After two minutes, car B is traveling faster than car A and has gained some ground, but the area under curve A from $t = 0$ to $t = 2$ is still greater than the corresponding area for curve B, so car A is still ahead.

(d) From the graph, it appears that the area between curves A and B for $0 \le t \le 1$ (when car A is going faster), which corresponds to the distance by which car A is ahead, seems to be about 3 squares. Therefore, the cars will be side by side at the time x where the area between the curves for $1 \le t \le x$ (when car B is going faster) is the same as the area for $0 \le t \le 1$. From the graph, it appears that this time is $x \approx 2.2$. So the cars are side by side when $t \approx 2.2$ minutes.

23. If $x =$ distance from left end of pool and $w = w(x) =$ width at x, then Simpson's Rule with $n = 8$ and $\Delta x = 2$ gives

$$\text{Area} = \int_0^{16} w\, dx \approx \tfrac{2}{3}[0 + 4(6.2) + 2(7.2) + 4(6.8) + 2(5.6) + 4(5.0) + 2(4.8) + 4(4.8) + 0]$$
$$= \tfrac{2}{3}(126.4) \approx 84 \text{ m}^2$$

24. The area under $R'(x)$ from $x = 50$ to $x = 100$ represents the change in revenue, and the area under $C'(x)$ from $x = 50$ to $x = 100$ represents the change in cost. The shaded region represents the difference between these two values; that is, the increase in profit as the production level increases from 50 units to 100 units. We use the

Midpoint Rule with $n = 5$ and $\Delta x = 10$:

$$M_5 = \Delta x\{[R'(55) - C'(55)] + [R'(65) - C'(65)] + [R'(75) - C'(75)]$$

$$+ [R'(85) - C'(85)] + [R'(95) - C'(95)]\}$$

$$\approx 10(2.40 - 0.85 + 2.20 - 0.90 + 2.00 - 1.00 + 1.80 - 1.10 + 1.70 - 1.20)$$

$$= 10(5.05) = 50.5 \text{ thousand dollars}$$

Using M_1 would give us $50(2 - 1) = 50$ thousand dollars.

25. $\cos x = \sin 2x = 2 \sin x \cos x \Leftrightarrow 2 \sin x \cos x - \cos x = 0 \Leftrightarrow \cos x\,(2 \sin x - 1) = 0 \Leftrightarrow$
$2 \sin x = 1 \text{ or } \cos x = 0 \Leftrightarrow x = \frac{\pi}{6} \text{ or } \frac{\pi}{2}$.

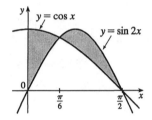

$$A = \int_0^{\pi/6}(\cos x - \sin 2x)\,dx + \int_{\pi/6}^{\pi/2}(\sin 2x - \cos x)\,dx$$

$$= \left[\sin x + \tfrac{1}{2}\cos 2x\right]_0^{\pi/6} + \left[-\tfrac{1}{2}\cos 2x - \sin x\right]_{\pi/6}^{\pi/2}$$

$$= \left(\tfrac{1}{2} + \tfrac{1}{2}\cdot\tfrac{1}{2}\right) - \left(0 + \tfrac{1}{2}\cdot 1\right)$$

$$+ \left[-\tfrac{1}{2}\cdot(-1) - 1\right] - \left(-\tfrac{1}{2}\cdot\tfrac{1}{2} - \tfrac{1}{2}\right)$$

$$= \tfrac{3}{4} - \tfrac{1}{2} - \tfrac{1}{2} + \tfrac{3}{4} = \tfrac{1}{2}$$

26. $A = \int_0^1 \left[(x^3 - 4x^2 + 3x) - (x^2 - x)\right]dx$

$$+ \int_1^4 \left[(x^2 - x) - (x^3 - 4x^2 + 3x)\right]dx$$

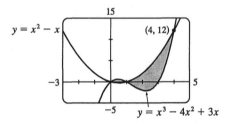

$$= \int_0^1 (x^3 - 5x^2 + 4x)\,dx + \int_1^4 (-x^3 + 5x^2 - 4x)\,dx$$

$$= \left[\tfrac{1}{4}x^4 - \tfrac{5}{3}x^3 + 2x^2\right]_0^1 + \left[-\tfrac{1}{4}x^4 + \tfrac{5}{3}x^3 - 2x^2\right]_1^4$$

$$= \left(\tfrac{1}{4} - \tfrac{5}{3} + 2\right) - 0$$

$$+ \left(-64 + \tfrac{320}{3} - 32\right) - \left(-\tfrac{1}{4} + \tfrac{5}{3} - 2\right)$$

$$= \tfrac{71}{6}$$

27. Let the equation of the large circle be $x^2 + y^2 = R^2$. Then the equation
of the small circle is $x^2 + (y - b)^2 = r^2$, where $b = \sqrt{R^2 - r^2}$ is the
distance between the centers of the circles. The desired area is

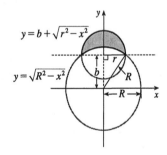

$$A = \int_{-r}^{r} \left[(b + \sqrt{r^2 - x^2}) - \sqrt{R^2 - x^2}\right]dx$$

$$= 2\int_0^r (b + \sqrt{r^2 - x^2} - \sqrt{R^2 - x^2})\,dx$$

$$= 2\int_0^r b\,dx + 2\int_0^r \sqrt{r^2 - x^2}\,dx - 2\int_0^r \sqrt{R^2 - x^2}\,dx$$

The first integral is just $2br = 2r\sqrt{R^2 - r^2}$. The second integral represents the area of a quarter-circle of radius r,
so its value is $\tfrac{1}{4}\pi r^2$. To evaluate the other integral, note that

$$\int \sqrt{a^2 - x^2}\,dx = \int a^2 \cos^2\theta\,d\theta \ \ (x = a\sin\theta,\ dx = a\cos\theta\,d\theta) \ = \left(\tfrac{1}{2}a^2\right)\int(1 + \cos 2\theta)\,d\theta$$

$$= \tfrac{1}{2}a^2\left(\theta + \tfrac{1}{2}\sin 2\theta\right) + C = \tfrac{1}{2}a^2(\theta + \sin\theta\cos\theta) + C$$

$$= \frac{a^2}{2}\arcsin\left(\frac{x}{a}\right) + \frac{a^2}{2}\left(\frac{x}{a}\right)\frac{\sqrt{a^2 - x^2}}{a} + C = \frac{a^2}{2}\arcsin\left(\frac{x}{a}\right) + \frac{x}{2}\sqrt{a^2 - x^2} + C$$

Thus, the desired area is

$$A = 2r\sqrt{R^2 - r^2} + 2\left(\tfrac{1}{4}\pi r^2\right) - \left[R^2 \arcsin(x/R) + x\sqrt{R^2 - x^2}\right]_0^r$$

$$= 2r\sqrt{R^2 - r^2} + \tfrac{1}{2}\pi r^2 - \left[R^2 \arcsin(r/R) + r\sqrt{R^2 - r^2}\right] = r\sqrt{R^2 - r^2} + \tfrac{\pi}{2}r^2 - R^2 \arcsin(r/R)$$

28. The inequality $x \geq 2y^2$ describes the region that lies on, or to the right of, the parabola $x = 2y^2$. The inequality $x \leq 1 - |y|$ describes the region that lies on, or to the left of, the curve $x = 1 - |y| = \begin{cases} 1 - y & \text{if } y \geq 0 \\ 1 + y & \text{if } y < 0 \end{cases}$. So the given region is the shaded region that lies between the curves. The graphs of $x = 1 - y$ and $x = 2y^2$ intersect when $1 - y = 2y^2$

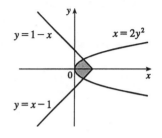

$\Leftrightarrow 2y^2 + y - 1 = 0 \Leftrightarrow (2y - 1)(y + 1) = 0 \Rightarrow$

$y = \tfrac{1}{2}$ (for $y \geq 0$). By symmetry,

$$A = 2\int_0^{1/2} \left[(1 - y) - 2y^2\right] dy = 2\left[-\tfrac{2}{3}y^3 - \tfrac{1}{2}y^2 + y\right]_0^{1/2}$$

$$= 2\left[\left(-\tfrac{1}{12} - \tfrac{1}{8} + \tfrac{1}{2}\right) - 0\right] = 2\left(\tfrac{7}{24}\right) = \tfrac{7}{12}$$

29. By symmetry of the ellipse about the x- and y-axes,

$$A = 4\int_0^a y\, dx = 4\int_{\pi/2}^0 b\sin\theta\, (-a\sin\theta)\, d\theta \qquad \begin{bmatrix} x = a\cos\theta = 0 & \Rightarrow & \theta = \tfrac{\pi}{2} \text{ and} \\ x = a\cos\theta = a & \Rightarrow & \theta = 0 \end{bmatrix}$$

$$= 4ab\int_0^{\pi/2} \sin^2\theta\, d\theta = 4ab\int_0^{\pi/2} \tfrac{1}{2}(1 - \cos 2\theta)\, d\theta$$

$$= 2ab\left[\theta - \tfrac{1}{2}\sin 2\theta\right]_0^{\pi/2} = 2ab\left(\tfrac{\pi}{2}\right) = \pi ab$$

Note that the formula for the area of a circle, $A = \pi r^2$, is just a special case of this formula with $a = b = r$.

30.

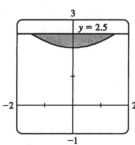

$y = 2.5 \Rightarrow t + 1/t = 2.5 \Leftrightarrow$

$t^2 - 2.5t + 1 = 0 \Rightarrow t = \tfrac{1}{2}$ or 2,

and for $\tfrac{1}{2} < t < 2$, we have $t + 1/t < 2.5$.

$x = -\tfrac{3}{2}$ when $t = \tfrac{1}{2}$ and $x = \tfrac{3}{2}$ when $t = 2$.

$$A = \int_{-3/2}^{3/2} (2.5 - y)\, dx = \int_{1/2}^2 \left(\tfrac{5}{2} - t - 1/t\right)(1 + 1/t^2)\, dt \quad [x = t - 1/t \Rightarrow dx = (1 + 1/t^2)\, dt]$$

$$= \int_{1/2}^2 \left(-t + \tfrac{5}{2} - 2t^{-1} + \tfrac{5}{2}t^{-2} - t^{-3}\right) dt = \left[\tfrac{-t^2}{2} + \tfrac{5t}{2} - 2\ln|t| - \tfrac{5}{2t} + \tfrac{1}{2t^2}\right]_{1/2}^2$$

$$= \left(-2 + 5 - 2\ln 2 - \tfrac{5}{4} + \tfrac{1}{8}\right) - \left(-\tfrac{1}{8} + \tfrac{5}{4} + 2\ln 2 - 5 + 2\right) \quad \left[\ln\tfrac{1}{2} = \ln 2^{-1} = -\ln 2\right]$$

$$= \tfrac{15}{4} - 4\ln 2$$

31.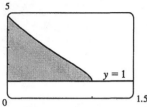

$x = \cos t,\ y = e^t,\ 0 \le t \le \frac{\pi}{2}$.

When $x = 0$, $t = \pi/2$; when $x = 1$, $t = 0$.

$A = \int_0^1 (y - 1)\,dx = \int_{\pi/2}^0 (e^t - 1)\,(-\sin t)\,dt$

$= \int_0^{\pi/2} (e^t \sin t - \sin t)\,dt$

By Example 4 in Section 5.6 or Integration Formula 98, $\int e^x \sin x\,dx = \frac{1}{2}e^x(\sin x - \cos x) + C$, so

$\int_0^{\pi/2} (e^t \sin t - \sin t)\,dt = \left[\frac{1}{2}e^t(\sin t - \cos t) + \cos t\right]_0^{\pi/2}$

$= \left[\frac{1}{2}e^{\pi/2}(1 - 0) + 0\right] - \left[\frac{1}{2}e^0(0 - 1) + 1\right]$

$= \frac{1}{2}e^{\pi/2} - \frac{1}{2} = \frac{1}{2}\left(e^{\pi/2} - 1\right)$

32.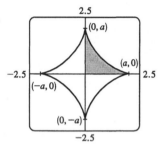

$x = a \cos^3 \theta,\ y = a \sin^3 \theta$. (In the diagram, $a = 2$.)

By symmetry,

$A = 4 \int_0^a y\,dx = 4 \int_{\pi/2}^0 a \sin^3 \theta\,\left(-3a \cos^2 \theta \sin \theta\right)\,d\theta$

$= 12a^2 \int_0^{\pi/2} \sin^4 \theta \cos^2 \theta\,d\theta \overset{\text{CAS}}{=} 12a^2\left(\frac{\pi}{32}\right) = \frac{3}{8}\pi a^2$

33. By symmetry, the area of the region enclosed by the loop is twice the area above the x-axis inside the loop. $y = 0 \iff t^3 - 3t = 0 \iff t(t^2 - 3) = 0 \iff t = 0, \pm\sqrt{3}$. The top half of the loop is described by $x = t^2$, $y = t^3 - 3t$, $-\sqrt{3} \le t \le 0$, so, using the Substitution Rule with $y = t^3 - 3t$ and $dx = 2t\,dt$, we find that

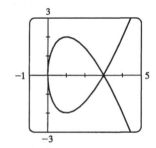

area $= 2\int_0^3 y\,dx = 2\int_0^{-\sqrt{3}} (t^3 - 3t)2t\,dt = 4\int_0^{-\sqrt{3}} (t^4 - 3t^2)\,dt$

$= 4\left[\frac{1}{5}t^5 - t^3\right]_0^{-\sqrt{3}} = 4\left[\frac{1}{5}\left(-3^{1/2}\right)^5 - \left(-3^{1/2}\right)^3\right]$

$= 4\left[\frac{1}{5}\left(-9\sqrt{3}\right) - \left(-3\sqrt{3}\right)\right] = \frac{24}{5}\sqrt{3} \approx 8.31$.

34. We plot the curve $x = t^3 - 12t$, $y = 3t^2 + 2t + 5$ in the parameter interval $t \in [-4, 3.5]$. In order to find the area of the loop, we need to estimate the two t-values corresponding to the point at which the curve crosses itself. By zooming in, we estimate the y-coordinate of the point of intersection to be 39.667, and so the two t-values at the point of intersection are approximately the two solutions of the

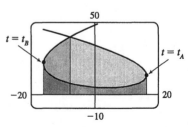

equation $y = 3t^2 + 2t + 5 = 39.667$, which are $t = -\frac{1}{3} \pm \frac{\sqrt{420.004}}{6} \approx -3.7490$ or 3.0823. We can evaluate the area of the loop simply by integrating $y \, dx$ between these two t-values, since this integral represents the area under the upper part of the loop for t between the first t-value and t_A, minus the area under the bottom part between t_A and t_B, plus the area under the top part between t_B and the final t-value. So since $dx = (3t^2 - 12) \, dt$, the area of the loop is $A \approx \int_{-3.7490}^{3.0823} (3t^2 + 2t + 5)(3t^2 - 12) \, dt \approx 743.85$.

35. We first assume that $c > 0$, since c can be replaced by $-c$ in both equations without changing the graphs, and if $c = 0$ the curves do not enclose a region. We see from the graph that the enclosed area A lies between $x = -c$ and $x = c$, and by symmetry, it is equal to four times the area in the first quadrant.
The enclosed area is

$$A = 4 \int_0^c (c^2 - x^2) \, dx = 4 \left[c^2 x - \tfrac{1}{3} x^3 \right]_0^c$$

$$= 4\left(c^3 - \tfrac{1}{3} c^3\right) = 4\left(\tfrac{2}{3} c^3\right) = \tfrac{8}{3} c^3$$

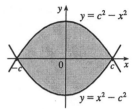

So $A = 576 \iff \tfrac{8}{3} c^3 = 576 \iff c^3 = 216 \iff c = \sqrt[3]{216} = 6$.
Note that $c = -6$ is another solution, since the graphs are the same.

36.

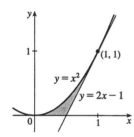

We start by finding the equation of the tangent line to $y = x^2$ at the point $(1, 1)$: $y' = 2x$, so the slope of the tangent is $2(1) = 2$, and its equation is $y - 1 = 2(x - 1)$, or $y = 2x - 1$. We would need two integrals to integrate with respect to x, but only one to integrate with respect to y.

$$A = \int_0^1 \left[\tfrac{1}{2}(y+1) - \sqrt{y} \right] dy = \left[\tfrac{1}{4} y^2 + \tfrac{1}{2} y - \tfrac{2}{3} y^{3/2} \right]_0^1$$

$$= \tfrac{1}{4} + \tfrac{1}{2} - \tfrac{2}{3} = \tfrac{1}{12}$$

37.

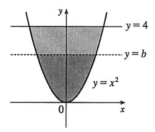

By the symmetry of the problem, we consider only the first quadrant, where $y = x^2 \implies x = \sqrt{y}$. We are looking for a number b such that $\int_0^b \sqrt{y} \, dy = \int_b^4 \sqrt{y} \, dy \implies \tfrac{2}{3} \left[y^{3/2} \right]_0^b = \tfrac{2}{3} \left[y^{3/2} \right]_b^4 \implies$
$b^{3/2} = 4^{3/2} - b^{3/2} \implies 2b^{3/2} = 8 \implies b^{3/2} = 4 \implies$
$b = 4^{2/3} \approx 2.52$.

38. (a) We want to choose a so that $\displaystyle\int_1^a \frac{1}{x^2} \, dx = \int_a^4 \frac{1}{x^2} \, dx \implies \left[\frac{-1}{x} \right]_1^a = \left[\frac{-1}{x} \right]_a^4 \implies -\frac{1}{a} + 1 = -\frac{1}{4} + \frac{1}{a}$

$\implies \dfrac{5}{4} = \dfrac{2}{a} \implies a = \dfrac{8}{5}$.

(b) The area under the curve $y = 1/x^2$ from $x = 1$ to $x = 4$ is $\tfrac{3}{4}$ [take $a = 4$ in the first integral in part (a)]. Now the line $y = b$ must intersect the curve $x = 1/\sqrt{y}$ and not the line $x = 4$, since the area under the line $y = 1/4^2$ from $x = 1$ to $x = 4$ is only $\tfrac{3}{16}$, which is less than half of $\tfrac{3}{4}$. We want to choose b so that the upper area in the diagram is half of the total area under the curve $y = \dfrac{1}{x^2}$ from $x = 1$ to $x = 4$. This implies that

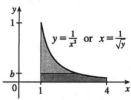

$\int_b^1 (1/\sqrt{y} - 1)\, dy = \frac{1}{2} \cdot \frac{3}{4}$ $\Rightarrow$ $[2\sqrt{y} - y]_b^1 = \frac{3}{8}$ $\Rightarrow$

$1 - 2\sqrt{b} + b = \frac{3}{8}$ $\Rightarrow$ $b - 2\sqrt{b} + \frac{5}{8} = 0$. Letting $c = \sqrt{b}$, we get

$c^2 - 2c + \frac{5}{8} = 0$ $\Rightarrow$ $8c^2 - 16c + 5 = 0$. Thus,

$c = \frac{16 \pm \sqrt{256 - 160}}{16} = 1 \pm \frac{\sqrt{6}}{4}$. But $c = \sqrt{b} < 1$ $\Rightarrow$ $c = 1 - \frac{\sqrt{6}}{4}$ $\Rightarrow$

$b = c^2 = 1 + \frac{3}{8} - \frac{\sqrt{6}}{2} = \frac{1}{8}\left(11 - 4\sqrt{6}\right) \approx 0.1503$.

39. The area under the graph of f from 0 to t is equal to $\int_0^t f(x)\, dx$, so the requirement is that $\int_0^t f(x)\, dx = t^3$ for all t. We differentiate both sides of this equation with respect to t (with the help of FTC1) to get $f(t) = 3t^2$. This function is positive and continuous, as required.

40.

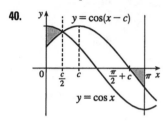

It appears from the diagram that the curves $y = \cos x$ and $y = \cos(x - c)$ intersect halfway between 0 and c, namely, when $x = c/2$. We can verify that this is indeed true by noting that $\cos(c/2 - c) = \cos(-c/2) = \cos(c/2)$. The point where $\cos(x - c)$ crosses the x-axis is $x = \frac{\pi}{2} + c$. So we require that

$\int_0^{c/2} [\cos x - \cos(x - c)]\, dx = -\int_{\pi/2+c}^{\pi} \cos(x - c)\, dx$ (the negative sign on the RHS is needed since the second area is beneath the x-axis) $\Leftrightarrow$

$[\sin x - \sin(x - c)]_0^{c/2} = -[\sin(x - c)]_{\pi/2+c}^{\pi}$ $\Rightarrow$

$[\sin(c/2) - \sin(-c/2)] - [-\sin(-c)] = -\sin(\pi - c) + \sin\left[\left(\frac{\pi}{2} + c\right) - c\right]$ $\Leftrightarrow$

$2\sin(c/2) - \sin c = -\sin c + 1$. [Here we have used the oddness of the sine function, and the fact that $\sin(\pi - c) = \sin c$]. So $2\sin(c/2) = 1$ $\Leftrightarrow$ $\sin(c/2) = \frac{1}{2}$ $\Leftrightarrow$ $c/2 = \frac{\pi}{6}$ $\Leftrightarrow$ $c = \frac{\pi}{3}$.

41. The curve and the line will determine a region when they intersect at two or more points. So we solve the equation

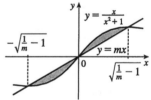

$x/(x^2 + 1) = mx$ $\Rightarrow$ $x = x(mx^2 + m)$ $\Rightarrow$

$x(mx^2 + m) - x = 0$ $\Rightarrow$ $x(mx^2 + m - 1) = 0$ $\Rightarrow$

$x = 0$ or $mx^2 + m - 1 = 0$ $\Rightarrow$ $x = 0$ or $x^2 = \dfrac{1 - m}{m}$ $\Rightarrow$

$x = 0$ or $x = \pm\sqrt{\dfrac{1}{m} - 1}$. Note that if $m = 1$, this has only

the solution $x = 0$, and no region is determined. But if $1/m - 1 > 0$ $\Leftrightarrow$ $1/m > 1$ $\Leftrightarrow$ $0 < m < 1$, then there are two solutions. [Another way of seeing this is to observe that the slope of the tangent to $y = x/(x^2 + 1)$ at the origin is $y' = 1$ and therefore we must have $0 < m < 1$.] Note that we cannot just integrate between the positive and negative roots, since the curve and the line cross at the origin. Since mx and $x/(x^2 + 1)$ are both odd functions, the total area is twice the area between the curves on the interval $\left[0, \sqrt{1/m - 1}\right]$. So the total area enclosed is

$$2\int_0^{\sqrt{1/m-1}} \left[\frac{x}{x^2 + 1} - mx\right] dx = 2\left[\frac{1}{2}\ln(x^2 + 1) - \frac{1}{2}mx^2\right]_0^{\sqrt{1/m-1}}$$

$$= [\ln(1/m - 1 + 1) - m(1/m - 1)] - (\ln 1 - 0)$$

$$= \ln(1/m) - 1 + m = m - \ln m - 1$$

6.2 Volumes · · · · · · · · · · · · · · · · · · ·

1. A cross-section is a disk with radius $1/x$, so its area is $A(x) = \pi(1/x)^2$.

$$V = \int_1^2 A(x)\,dx = \int_1^2 \pi\left(\frac{1}{x}\right)^2 dx = \pi \int_1^2 \frac{1}{x^2}\,dx = \pi\left[-\frac{1}{x}\right]_1^2 = \pi\left[-\frac{1}{2} - (-1)\right] = \frac{\pi}{2}$$

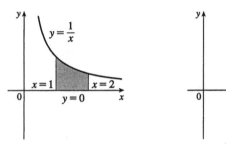
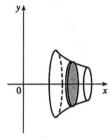

2. A cross-section is a disk with radius e^x, so its area is $A(x) = \pi(e^x)^2$.

$$V = \int_0^1 A(x)\,dx = \int_0^1 \pi(e^x)^2 dx = \pi \int_0^1 e^{2x}\,dx = \frac{1}{2}\pi\left[e^{2x}\right]_0^1 = \frac{\pi}{2}\left(e^2 - 1\right)$$

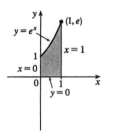
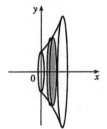

3. A cross-section is a disk with radius $\sqrt{y}$, so its area is $A(y) = \pi\left(\sqrt{y}\right)^2$.

$$V = \int_0^4 A(y)\,dy = \int_0^4 \pi\left(\sqrt{y}\right)^2 dy = \pi \int_0^4 y\,dy = \pi\left[\frac{1}{2}y^2\right]_0^4 = 8\pi$$

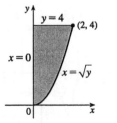
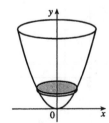

4. A cross-section is a disk with radius $y - y^2$, so its area is $A(y) = \pi(y - y^2)^2$.

$$V = \int_0^1 A(y)\,dy = \int_0^1 \pi(y - y^2)^2 dy = \pi \int_0^1 (y^4 - 2y^3 + y^2)\,dy = \pi\left[\tfrac{1}{5}y^5 - \tfrac{1}{2}y^4 + \tfrac{1}{3}y^3\right]_0^1$$
$$= \pi\left(\tfrac{1}{5} - \tfrac{1}{2} + \tfrac{1}{3}\right) = \tfrac{\pi}{30}$$

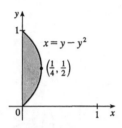

5. A cross-section is a washer (annulus) with inner radius x^2 and outer radius $\sqrt{x}$, so its area is
$A(x) = \pi(\sqrt{x})^2 - \pi(x^2)^2 = \pi(x - x^4)$.

$$V = \int_0^1 A(x)\,dx = \pi \int_0^1 (x - x^4)\,dx = \pi\left[\tfrac{1}{2}x^2 - \tfrac{1}{5}x^5\right]_0^1 = \pi\left(\tfrac{1}{2} - \tfrac{1}{5}\right) = \tfrac{3\pi}{10}$$

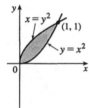
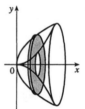

6. A cross-section is a washer with inner radius 1 and outer radius $\sec x$, so its area is
$A(x) = \pi(\sec x)^2 - \pi(1)^2 = \pi(\sec^2 x - 1)$.

$$V = \int_{-1}^{1} A(x)\,dx = \int_{-1}^{1} \pi(\sec^2 x - 1)\,dx = 2\pi \int_0^1 (\sec^2 x - 1)\,dx = 2\pi[\tan x - x]_0^1 = 2\pi(\tan 1 - 1)$$
$$\approx 3.5023$$

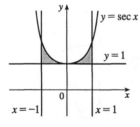
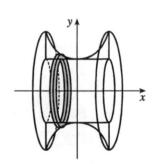

7. A cross-section is a washer with inner radius y^2 and outer radius $2y$, so its area is
$A(y) = \pi(2y)^2 - \pi(y^2)^2 = \pi(4y^2 - y^4)$.

$$V = \int_0^2 A(y)\,dy = \pi \int_0^2 (4y^2 - y^4)\,dy = \pi\left[\tfrac{4}{3}y^3 - \tfrac{1}{5}y^5\right]_0^2 = \pi\left(\tfrac{32}{3} - \tfrac{32}{5}\right) = \tfrac{64\pi}{15}$$

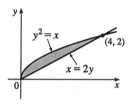
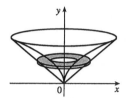

8. $y = x^{2/3} \quad\Leftrightarrow\quad x = y^{3/2}$, so a cross-section is a washer with inner radius $y^{3/2}$ and outer radius 1, and its area is
$A(y) = \pi(1)^2 - \pi\left(y^{3/2}\right)^2 = \pi(1 - y^3)$.

$$V = \int_0^1 A(y)\,dy = \pi \int_0^1 (1 - y^3)\,dy = \pi\left[y - \tfrac{1}{4}y^4\right]_0^1 = \tfrac{3}{4}\pi$$

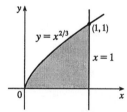
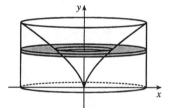

9. A cross-section is a washer with inner radius $1 - \sqrt{x}$ and outer radius $1 - x$, so its area is
$A(x) = \pi(1-x)^2 - \pi(1-\sqrt{x})^2 = \pi\left[(1 - 2x + x^2) - (1 - 2\sqrt{x} + x)\right] = \pi\left(-3x + x^2 + 2\sqrt{x}\right)$.

$$V = \int_0^1 A(x)\,dx = \pi \int_0^1 \left(-3x + x^2 + 2\sqrt{x}\right)dx$$
$$= \pi\left[-\tfrac{3}{2}x^2 + \tfrac{1}{3}x^3 + \tfrac{4}{3}x^{3/2}\right]_0^1 = \pi\left(-\tfrac{3}{2} + \tfrac{5}{3}\right) = \tfrac{\pi}{6}$$

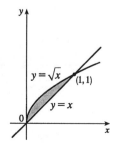
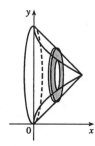

10. $V = \int_1^3 \pi \left\{ \left[\frac{1}{x} - (-1)\right]^2 - [0 - (-1)]^2 \right\} dx = \pi \int_1^3 \left[\left(\frac{1}{x} + 1\right)^2 - 1^2 \right] dx$

$\quad = \pi \int_1^3 \left(\frac{1}{x^2} + \frac{2}{x}\right) dx = \pi \left[-\frac{1}{x} + 2\ln x\right]_1^3$

$\quad = \pi\left[(-\frac{1}{3} + 2\ln 3) - (-1 + 0)\right] = \pi\left(2\ln 3 + \frac{2}{3}\right) = 2\pi\left(\ln 3 + \frac{1}{3}\right)$

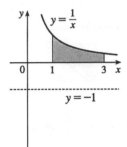 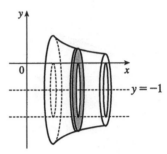

11. $y = x^2 \Rightarrow x = \sqrt{y}$ for $x \ge 0$. The outer radius is the distance from $x = -1$ to $x = \sqrt{y}$ and the inner radius is the distance from $x = -1$ to $x = y^2$.

$\quad V = \int_0^1 \pi \left\{ \left[\sqrt{y} - (-1)\right]^2 - \left[y^2 - (-1)\right]^2 \right\} dy = \pi \int_0^1 \left[\left(\sqrt{y} + 1\right)^2 - \left(y^2 + 1\right)^2 \right] dy$

$\quad = \pi \int_0^1 \left(y + 2\sqrt{y} + 1 - y^4 - 2y^2 - 1\right) dy = \pi \int_0^1 \left(y + 2\sqrt{y} - y^4 - 2y^2\right) dy$

$\quad = \pi \left[\frac{1}{2}y^2 + \frac{4}{3}y^{3/2} - \frac{1}{5}y^5 - \frac{2}{3}y^3\right]_0^1 = \pi\left(\frac{1}{2} + \frac{4}{3} - \frac{1}{5} - \frac{2}{3}\right) = \frac{29}{30}\pi$

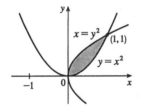 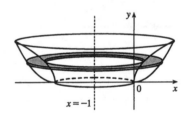

12. $y = \sqrt{x} \Rightarrow x = y^2$, so the outer radius is $2 - y^2$.

$\quad V = \int_0^1 \pi \left[\left(2 - y^2\right)^2 - (2 - y)^2\right] dy = \pi \int_0^1 \left[\left(4 - 4y^2 + y^4\right) - \left(4 - 4y + y^2\right)\right] dy$

$\quad = \pi \int_0^1 \left(y^4 - 5y^2 + 4y\right) dy = \pi\left[\frac{1}{5}y^5 - \frac{5}{3}y^3 + 2y^2\right]_0^1 = \pi\left(\frac{1}{5} - \frac{5}{3} + 2\right) = \frac{8}{15}\pi$

 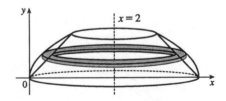

13. $y = \sqrt[3]{x} \iff x = y^3$

A cross-section is a washer with inner radius $8 - 4y$ and outer

radius $8 - y^3$, so its area is $A(y) = \pi \left(8 - y^3\right)^2 - \pi \left(8 - 4y\right)^2$.

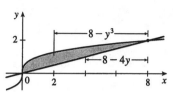

$V = \int_0^2 A(y)\,dy = \pi \int_0^2 \left[\left(8 - y^3\right)^2 - \left(8 - 4y\right)^2\right] dy = \pi \int_0^2 \left[\left(64 - 16y^3 + y^6\right) - \left(64 - 64y + 16y^2\right)\right] dy$

$\qquad = \pi \int_0^2 \left(-16y^3 + y^6 + 64y - 16y^2\right) dy = \pi \left[-4y^4 + \frac{1}{7}y^7 + 32y^2 - \frac{16}{3}y^3\right]_0^2$

$\qquad = \pi\left(-64 + \frac{128}{7} + 128 - \frac{128}{3}\right) = \frac{832}{21}\pi$

14. $x = 4y \iff y = \frac{1}{4}x$

A cross-section is a washer with inner radius $2 - \sqrt[3]{x}$ and outer

radius $2 - \frac{1}{4}x$, so its area is $A(x) = \pi\left(2 - \frac{1}{4}x\right)^2 - \pi(2 - \sqrt[3]{x})^2$.

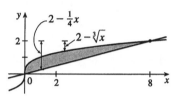

$V = \int_0^8 A(x)\,dx = \pi \int_0^8 \left[\left(2 - \frac{1}{4}x\right)^2 - \left(2 - \sqrt[3]{x}\right)^2\right] dx$

$\qquad = \pi \int_0^8 \left[\left(4 - x + \frac{1}{16}x^2\right) - \left(4 - 4\sqrt[3]{x} + x^{2/3}\right)\right] dx = \pi \int_0^8 \left(-x + \frac{1}{16}x^2 + 4x^{1/3} - x^{2/3}\right) dx$

$\qquad = \pi\left[-\frac{1}{2}x^2 + \frac{1}{48}x^3 + 3x^{4/3} - \frac{3}{5}x^{5/3}\right]_0^8 = \pi\left(-32 + \frac{32}{3} + 48 - \frac{96}{5}\right) = \frac{112}{15}\pi$

15.

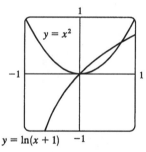

$y = x^2$ and $y = \ln(x + 1)$ intersect at $x = 0$ and

at $x = a \approx 0.747$.

$V = \pi \int_0^a \left\{[\ln(x + 1)]^2 - \left(x^2\right)^2\right\} dx \approx 0.132$

16.

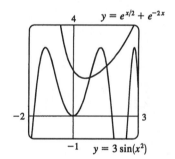

$y = 3\sin\left(x^2\right)$ and $y = e^{x/2} + e^{-2x}$ intersect at

$x = a \approx 0.772$ and at $x = b \approx 1.524$.

$V = \pi \int_a^b \left\{\left[3\sin\left(x^2\right)\right]^2 - \left(e^{x/2} + e^{-2x}\right)^2\right\} dx$

$\qquad \approx 7.519$

17. (a) $\pi \int_0^{\pi/2} \cos^2 x\,dx$ describes the volume of the solid obtained by rotating the region

$\mathcal{R} = \left\{(x, y) \mid 0 \le x \le \frac{\pi}{2}, 0 \le y \le \cos x\right\}$ of the xy-plane about the x-axis.

(b) $\pi \int_0^1 \left(y^4 - y^8\right) dy = \pi \int_0^1 \left[\left(y^2\right)^2 - \left(y^4\right)^2\right] dy$ describes the volume of the solid obtained by rotating the region

$\mathcal{R} = \left\{(x, y) \mid 0 \le y \le 1, y^4 \le x \le y^2\right\}$ of the xy-plane about the y-axis.

18. (a) $\pi \int_2^5 y\, dy = \pi \int_2^5 \left(\sqrt{y}\right)^2 dy$ describes the volume of the solid obtained by rotating the region

$\mathcal{R} = \{(x, y) \mid 2 \leq y \leq 5, 0 \leq x \leq \sqrt{y}\}$ of the xy-plane about the y-axis.

(b) $\pi \int_0^{\pi/2} \left[(1 + \cos x)^2 - 1^2\right] dx$ describes the volume of the solid obtained by rotating the region

$\mathcal{R} = \{(x, y) \mid 0 \leq x \leq \frac{\pi}{2}, 1 \leq y \leq 1 + \cos x\}$ of the xy-plane about the x-axis.

Or: The solid could be obtained by rotating the region $\mathcal{R}' = \{(x, y) \mid 0 \leq x \leq \frac{\pi}{2}, 0 \leq y \leq \cos x\}$ about the

line $y = -1$.

19. There are 10 subintervals over the 15-cm length, so we'll use $n = 10/2 = 5$ for the Midpoint Rule.

$V = \int_0^{15} A(x)\, dx \approx M_5 = \frac{15-0}{5}[A(1.5) + A(4.5) + A(7.5) + A(10.5) + A(13.5)]$

$= 3(18 + 79 + 106 + 128 + 39) = 3 \cdot 370 = 1110 \text{ cm}^3$

20. $V = \int_0^{10} A(x)\, dx \approx M_5 = \frac{10-0}{5}[A(1) + A(3) + A(5) + A(7) + A(9)]$

$= 2(0.65 + 0.61 + 0.59 + 0.55 + 0.50) = 2(2.90) = 5.80 \text{ m}^3$

21. We'll form a right circular cone with height h and base radius r by

revolving the line $y = \frac{r}{h}x$ about the x-axis.

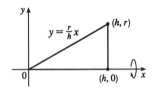

$V = \pi \int_0^h \left(\frac{r}{h}x\right)^2 dx = \pi \int_0^h \frac{r^2}{h^2} x^2\, dx = \pi \frac{r^2}{h^2}\left[\frac{1}{3}x^3\right]_0^h$

$= \pi \frac{r^2}{h^2}\left(\frac{1}{3}h^3\right) = \frac{1}{3}\pi r^2 h$

Another solution: Revolve $x = -\dfrac{r}{h}y + r$ about the y-axis.

$V = \pi \int_0^h \left(-\frac{r}{h}y + r\right)^2 dy \overset{*}{=} \pi \int_0^h \left[\frac{r^2}{h^2}y^2 - \frac{2r^2}{h}y + r^2\right] dy$

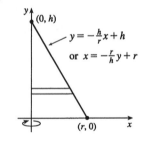

$= \pi \left[\frac{r^2}{3h^2}y^3 - \frac{r^2}{h}y^2 + r^2 y\right]_0^h = \pi\left(\frac{1}{3}r^2 h - r^2 h + r^2 h\right) = \frac{1}{3}\pi r^2 h$

* Or use substitution with $u = r - \dfrac{r}{h}y$ and $du = -\dfrac{r}{h}\, dy$ to get

$\pi \int_r^0 u^2 \left(-\frac{h}{r}\, du\right) = -\pi \frac{h}{r}\left[\frac{1}{3}u^3\right]_r^0 = -\pi \frac{h}{r}\left(-\frac{1}{3}r^3\right) = \frac{1}{3}\pi r^2 h.$

22. $V = \pi \int_0^h \left(R - \frac{R-r}{h}y\right)^2 dy$

$= \pi \int_0^h \left[R^2 - \frac{2R(R-r)}{h}y + \left(\frac{R-r}{h}\right)^2 y^2\right] dy$

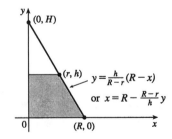

$= \pi \left[R^2 y - \frac{R(R-r)}{h}y^2 + \frac{1}{3}\left(\frac{R-r}{h}\right)^2 y^3\right]_0^h$

$= \pi \left[R^2 h - R(R-r)h + \frac{1}{3}(R-r)^2 h\right]$

$= \frac{1}{3}\pi h\left[3Rr + (R^2 - 2Rr + r^2)\right] = \frac{1}{3}\pi h(R^2 + Rr + r^2)$

Another solution: $\dfrac{H}{R} = \dfrac{H-h}{r}$ by similar triangles. Therefore,

$$Hr = HR - hR \quad \Rightarrow \quad hR = H(R - r) \quad \Rightarrow \quad H = \dfrac{hR}{R-r}. \text{ Now}$$

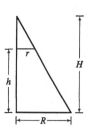

$$V = \tfrac{1}{3}\pi R^2 H - \tfrac{1}{3}\pi r^2(H - h) \quad \text{[by Exercise 21]}$$

$$= \tfrac{1}{3}\pi R^2 \dfrac{hR}{R-r} - \tfrac{1}{3}\pi r^2 \dfrac{rh}{R-r} \quad \left[H - h = \dfrac{rH}{R} = \dfrac{rhR}{R(R-r)} \right]$$

$$= \dfrac{1}{3}\pi h \dfrac{R^3 - r^3}{R - r} = \tfrac{1}{3}\pi h (R^2 + Rr + r^2)$$

$$= \tfrac{1}{3}\left[\pi R^2 + \pi r^2 + \sqrt{(\pi R^2)\,(\pi r^2)} \right] h = \tfrac{1}{3}\left(A_1 + A_2 + \sqrt{A_1 A_2} \right) h$$

where A_1 and A_2 are the areas of the bases of the frustum. (See Exercise 24 for a related result.)

23. $x^2 + y^2 = r^2 \quad \Leftrightarrow \quad x^2 = r^2 - y^2$

$$V = \pi \int_{r-h}^{r} (r^2 - y^2)\, dy = \pi \left[r^2 y - \dfrac{y^3}{3} \right]_{r-h}^{r}$$

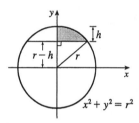

$$= \pi \left\{ \left[r^3 - \dfrac{r^3}{3} \right] - \left[r^2(r - h) - \dfrac{(r - h)^3}{3} \right] \right\}$$

$$= \pi \left\{ \tfrac{2}{3}r^3 - \tfrac{1}{3}(r - h)\left[3r^2 - (r - h)^2 \right] \right\}$$

$$= \tfrac{1}{3}\pi \left\{ 2r^3 - (r - h)\left[3r^2 - (r^2 - 2rh + h^2) \right] \right\}$$

$$= \tfrac{1}{3}\pi \left\{ 2r^3 - (r - h)\left[2r^2 + 2rh - h^2 \right] \right\}$$

$$= \tfrac{1}{3}\pi \left(2r^3 - 2r^3 - 2r^2 h + rh^2 + 2r^2 h + 2rh^2 - h^3 \right)$$

$$= \tfrac{1}{3}\pi \left(3rh^2 - h^3 \right) = \tfrac{1}{3}\pi h^2 (3r - h), \text{ or, equivalently, } \pi h^2 \left(r - \dfrac{h}{3} \right)$$

24. An equation of the line is $x = \dfrac{\Delta x}{\Delta y} y + (x\text{-intercept}) = \dfrac{a/2 - b/2}{h - 0} y + \dfrac{b}{2} = \dfrac{a - b}{2h} y + \dfrac{b}{2}.$

$$V = \int_0^h A(y)\, dy = \int_0^h (2x)^2\, dy = \int_0^h \left[2\left(\dfrac{a - b}{2h} y + \dfrac{b}{2} \right) \right]^2 dy$$

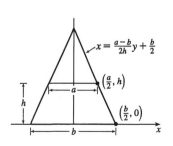

$$= \int_0^h \left[\dfrac{a - b}{h} y + b \right]^2 dy = \int_0^h \left[\dfrac{(a - b)^2}{h^2} y^2 + \dfrac{2b(a - b)}{h} y + b^2 \right] dy$$

$$= \left[\dfrac{(a - b)^2}{3h^2} y^3 + \dfrac{b(a - b)}{h} y^2 + b^2 y \right]_0^h$$

$$= \tfrac{1}{3}(a - b)^2 h + b(a - b)h + b^2 h = \tfrac{1}{3}\left(a^2 - 2ab + b^2 + 3ab \right) h$$

$$= \tfrac{1}{3}\left(a^2 + ab + b^2 \right) h$$

[Note that this can be written as $\tfrac{1}{3}\left(A_1 + A_2 + \sqrt{A_1 A_2} \right) h$, as in Exercise 22.]

25. For a cross-section at height y, we see from similar triangles that $\dfrac{a/2}{b/2} = \dfrac{h-y}{h}$, so $\alpha = b\left(1 - \dfrac{y}{h}\right)$.

Similarly, for cross-sections having $2b$ as their base and β replacing α, $\beta = 2b\left(1 - \dfrac{y}{h}\right)$. So

$$V = \int_0^h A(y)\,dy = \int_0^h \left[b\left(1 - \dfrac{y}{h}\right)\right]\left[2b\left(1 - \dfrac{y}{h}\right)\right]dy = \int_0^h 2b^2\left(1 - \dfrac{y}{h}\right)^2 dy$$

$$= 2b^2 \int_0^h \left(1 - \dfrac{2y}{h} + \dfrac{y^2}{h^2}\right)dy = 2b^2\left[y - \dfrac{y^2}{h} + \dfrac{y^3}{3h^2}\right]_0^h = 2b^2\left[h - h + \tfrac{1}{3}h\right]$$

$$= \tfrac{2}{3}b^2 h \quad \left[= \tfrac{1}{3}Bh \text{ where } B \text{ is the area of the base, as with any pyramid.}\right]$$

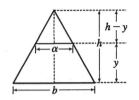

26. Consider the triangle consisting of two vertices of the base and the center of the base. This triangle is similar to the corresponding triangle at a height y, so $a/b = \alpha/\beta \ \Rightarrow \ \alpha = a\beta/b$. Also by similar triangles, $b/h = \beta/(h-y)$ $\Rightarrow \ \beta = b(h-y)/h$. These two equations imply that $\alpha = a(1 - y/h)$, and since the cross-section is an equilateral triangle, it has area

$$A(y) = \dfrac{1}{2} \cdot \alpha \cdot \dfrac{\sqrt{3}}{2}\alpha = \dfrac{a^2(1-y/h)^2}{4}\sqrt{3}, \text{ so}$$

$$V = \int_0^h A(y)\,dy = \dfrac{a^2\sqrt{3}}{4} \int_0^h \left(1 - \dfrac{y}{h}\right)^2 dy$$

$$= \dfrac{a^2\sqrt{3}}{4}\left[-\dfrac{h}{3}\left(1 - \dfrac{y}{h}\right)^3\right]_0^h = -\dfrac{\sqrt{3}}{12}a^2 h(-1) = \dfrac{\sqrt{3}}{12}a^2 h$$

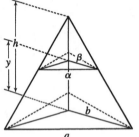

27. A cross-section at height z is a triangle similar to the base, so we'll multiply the legs of the base triangle, 3 and 4, by a proportionality factor of $(5 - z)/5$. Thus, the triangle at height z has area

$$A(z) = \dfrac{1}{2} \cdot 3\left(\dfrac{5-z}{5}\right) \cdot 4\left(\dfrac{5-z}{5}\right) = 6\left(1 - \dfrac{z}{5}\right)^2, \text{ so}$$

$$V = \int_0^5 A(z)\,dz = 6\int_0^5 (1 - z/5)^2\,dz$$

$$= 6\int_1^0 u^2(-5\,du) \quad \left[u = 1 - z/5,\ du = -\tfrac{1}{5}dz\right]$$

$$= -30\left[\tfrac{1}{3}u^3\right]_1^0 = -30\left(-\tfrac{1}{3}\right) = 10 \text{ cm}^3$$

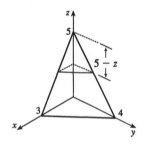

28. A cross-section is shaded in the diagram.

$$A(x) = (2y)^2 = \left(2\sqrt{r^2 - x^2}\right)^2, \text{ so}$$

$$V = \int_{-r}^r A(x)\,dx = 2\int_0^r 4\left(r^2 - x^2\right)dx = 8\left[r^2 x - \tfrac{1}{3}x^3\right]_0^r$$

$$= 8\left(\tfrac{2}{3}r^3\right) = \tfrac{16}{3}r^3$$

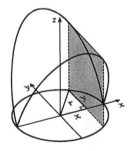

29. If l is a leg of the isosceles right triangle and $2y$ is the hypotenuse, then

$$l^2 + l^2 = (2y)^2 \quad \Rightarrow \quad 2l^2 = 4y^2 \quad \Rightarrow \quad l^2 = 2y^2.$$

$$V = \int_{-2}^{2} A(x)\, dx = 2\int_{0}^{2} A(x)\, dx = 2\int_{0}^{2} \tfrac{1}{2}(l)(l)\, dx = 2\int_{0}^{2} y^2\, dx$$

$$= 2\int_{0}^{2} \tfrac{1}{4}(36 - 9x^2)\, dx = \tfrac{9}{2}\int_{0}^{2}(4 - x^2)\, dx = \tfrac{9}{2}\left[4x - \tfrac{1}{3}x^3\right]_0^2$$

$$= \tfrac{9}{2}\left(8 - \tfrac{8}{3}\right) = 24$$

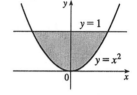

typical cross-section of length $2y = \sqrt{36 - 9x^2}$

30. The cross-section of the base corresponding to the coordinate y has length $2x = 2\sqrt{y}$. The corresponding equilateral triangle with side s has area

$$A(y) = s^2\left(\tfrac{\sqrt{3}}{4}\right) = (2x)^2\left(\tfrac{\sqrt{3}}{4}\right) = \left(2\sqrt{y}\right)^2\left(\tfrac{\sqrt{3}}{4}\right) = y\sqrt{3}. \text{ Therefore,}$$

$$V = \int_{0}^{1} A(y)\, dy = \int_{0}^{1} y\sqrt{3}\, dy = \sqrt{3}\left[\tfrac{1}{2}y^2\right]_0^1 = \tfrac{\sqrt{3}}{2}$$

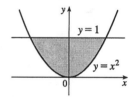

$y = 1$

$y = x^2$

31. The cross-section of the base corresponding to the coordinate y has length $2x = 2\sqrt{y}$. The square has area $A(y) = \left(2\sqrt{y}\right)^2 = 4y$, so

$$V = \int_{0}^{1} A(y)\, dy = \int_{0}^{1} 4y\, dy = \left[2y^2\right]_0^1 = 2.$$

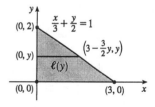

$y = 1$

$y = x^2$

32. A typical cross-section perpendicular to the y-axis in the base has length $\ell(y) = 3 - \tfrac{3}{2}y$. This length is the diameter of a cross-sectional semicircle in S, so

$$V = \int_{0}^{2} A(y)\, dy = \int_{0}^{2} \tfrac{\pi}{2}\left[\tfrac{\ell(y)}{2}\right]^2 dy = \tfrac{\pi}{8}\int_{0}^{2}\left(3 - \tfrac{3}{2}y\right)^2 dy$$

$$= \tfrac{\pi}{8}\int_{3}^{0} u^2\left(-\tfrac{2}{3}\, du\right) \quad \left[u = 3 - \tfrac{3}{2}y,\ du = -\tfrac{3}{2}\, dy\right]$$

$$= -\tfrac{\pi}{12}\left[\tfrac{1}{3}u^3\right]_3^0 = -\tfrac{\pi}{12}(-9) = \tfrac{3\pi}{4}$$

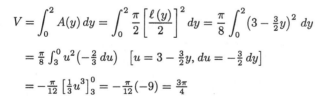

$(0, 2)$ $\tfrac{x}{3} + \tfrac{y}{2} = 1$

$(0, y)$ $\left(3 - \tfrac{3}{2}y, y\right)$

$\ell(y)$

$(0, 0)$ $(3, 0)$

33. A typical cross-section perpendicular to the y-axis in the base has length $\ell(y) = 3 - \tfrac{3}{2}y$. This length is the leg of an isosceles right triangle, so

$$A(y) = \tfrac{1}{2}\left[\ell(y)\right]^2 \quad \left[\tfrac{1}{2}bh \text{ with base} = \text{height}\right]$$

$$= \tfrac{1}{2}\left[3\left(1 - \tfrac{1}{2}y\right)\right]^2 = \tfrac{9}{2}\left(1 - \tfrac{1}{2}y\right)^2$$

Thus,

$$V = \int_{0}^{2} A(y)\, dy = \tfrac{9}{2}\int_{1}^{0} u^2(-2\, du) \quad \left[u = 1 - \tfrac{1}{2}y,\ du = -\tfrac{1}{2}\, dy\right]$$

$$= -9\left[\tfrac{1}{3}u^3\right]_1^0 = -9\left(-\tfrac{1}{3}\right) = 3$$

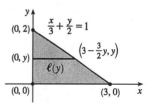

$(0, 2)$ $\tfrac{x}{3} + \tfrac{y}{2} = 1$

$(0, y)$ $\left(3 - \tfrac{3}{2}y, y\right)$

$\ell(y)$

$(0, 0)$ $(3, 0)$

34. (a) $V = \int_{-r}^{r} A(x)\,dx = 2\int_{0}^{r} A(x)\,dx = 2\int_{0}^{r} \frac{1}{2}h\left(2\sqrt{r^2-x^2}\right)dx = 2h\int_{0}^{r}\sqrt{r^2-x^2}\,dx$

(b) Observe that the integral represents one quarter of the area of a circle of radius r, so $V = 2h \cdot \frac{1}{4}\pi r^2 = \frac{1}{2}\pi h r^2$.

35. (a) The torus is obtained by rotating the circle $(x-R)^2 + y^2 = r^2$ about the
y-axis. Solving for x, we see that the right half of the circle is given by

$x = R + \sqrt{r^2-y^2} = f(y)$ and the left half by

$x = R - \sqrt{r^2-y^2} = g(y)$. So

$V = \pi\int_{-r}^{r}\left\{[f(y)]^2 - [g(y)]^2\right\}dy$

$\quad = 2\pi\int_{0}^{r}\left[\left(R^2 + 2R\sqrt{r^2-y^2} + r^2 - y^2\right) - \left(R^2 - 2R\sqrt{r^2-y^2} + r^2 - y^2\right)\right]dy$

$\quad = 2\pi\int_{0}^{r} 4R\sqrt{r^2-y^2}\,dy = 8\pi R\int_{0}^{r}\sqrt{r^2-y^2}\,dy$

(b) Observe that the integral represents a quarter of the area of a circle with radius r, so
$8\pi R\int_{0}^{r}\sqrt{r^2-y^2}\,dy = 8\pi R \cdot \frac{1}{4}\pi r^2 = 2\pi^2 r^2 R$.

36.

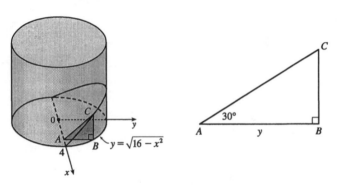

If we place the x-axis along the diameter where the planes meet, then the base of the solid is a semicircle with
equation $y = \sqrt{16-x^2}$, $-4 \leq x \leq 4$. A cross-section perpendicular to the x-axis at a distance x from the origin
is a triangle ABC, as shown in the figure, whose base is $y = \sqrt{16-x^2}$ and whose height is
$|BC| = y\tan 30° = \sqrt{16-x^2}/\sqrt{3}$. Thus, the cross-sectional area is

$A(x) = \frac{1}{2}\sqrt{16-x^2} \cdot \frac{1}{\sqrt{3}}\sqrt{16-x^2} = \frac{16-x^2}{2\sqrt{3}}$ and the volume is

$V = \int_{-4}^{4} A(x)\,dx = \int_{-4}^{4}\frac{16-x^2}{2\sqrt{3}}\,dx = \frac{1}{\sqrt{3}}\int_{0}^{4}(16-x^2)\,dx = \frac{1}{\sqrt{3}}\left[16x - \frac{1}{3}x^3\right]_{0}^{4} = \frac{128}{3\sqrt{3}}$.

Another method: The cross-sections perpendicular to the y-axis in the figure are rectangles. The rectangle
corresponding to the coordinate y has a base of length $2\sqrt{16-y^2}$ in the xy-plane and a height of $\frac{1}{\sqrt{3}}y$, since
$\angle BAC = 30°$ and $|BC| = \frac{1}{\sqrt{3}}|AB|$. Thus, $A(y) = \frac{2}{\sqrt{3}}y\sqrt{16-y^2}$ and

$V = \int_{0}^{4} A(y)\,dy = \frac{2}{\sqrt{3}}\int_{0}^{4}\sqrt{16-y^2}\,y\,dy = \frac{2}{\sqrt{3}}\int_{16}^{0} u^{1/2}\left(-\frac{1}{2}\,du\right) \quad \begin{bmatrix} u = 16 - y^2, \\ du = -2y\,dy \end{bmatrix}$

$\quad = \frac{1}{\sqrt{3}}\int_{0}^{16} u^{1/2}\,du = \frac{1}{\sqrt{3}}\frac{2}{3}\left[u^{3/2}\right]_{0}^{16} = \frac{2}{3\sqrt{3}}(64) = \frac{128}{3\sqrt{3}}$

37. (a) Volume$(S_1) = \int_0^h A(z)\, dz =$ Volume(S_2) since the cross-sectional area $A(z)$ at height z is the same for both solids.

(b) By Cavalieri's Principle, the volume of the cylinder in the figure is the same as that of a right circular cylinder with radius r and height h, that is, $\pi r^2 h$.

38. Each cross-section of the solid S in a plane perpendicular to the x-axis is a square (since the edges of the cut lie on the cylinders, which are perpendicular). One-quarter of this square and one-eighth of S are shown. The area of this quarter-square is $|PQ|^2 = r^2 - x^2$. Therefore, $A(x) = 4(r^2 - x^2)$ and the volume of S is

$$V = \int_{-r}^{r} A(x)\, dx = 4\int_{-r}^{r} (r^2 - x^2)\, dx$$

$$= 8\int_0^r (r^2 - x^2)\, dx = 8\left[r^2 x - \tfrac{1}{3}x^3\right]_0^r = \tfrac{16}{3}r^3$$

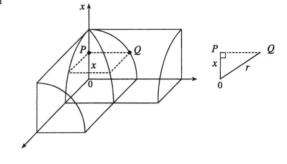

39. The volume is obtained by rotating the area common to two circles of radius r, as shown. The volume of the right half is

$$V_{\text{right}} = \pi \int_0^{r/2} y^2\, dx = \pi \int_0^{r/2} \left[r^2 - \left(\tfrac{1}{2}r + x\right)^2\right] dx$$

$$= \pi\left[r^2 x - \tfrac{1}{3}\left(\tfrac{1}{2}r + x\right)^3\right]_0^{r/2} = \pi\left[\left(\tfrac{1}{2}r^3 - \tfrac{1}{3}r^3\right) - \left(0 - \tfrac{1}{24}r^3\right)\right] = \tfrac{5}{24}\pi r^3$$

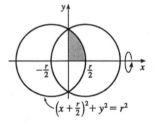

So by symmetry, the total volume is twice this, or $\tfrac{5}{12}\pi r^3$.

Another solution: We observe that the volume is the twice the volume of a cap of a sphere, so we can use the formula from Exercise 23 with $h = \tfrac{1}{2}r$: $V = 2 \cdot \tfrac{1}{3}\pi h^2 (3r - h) = \tfrac{2}{3}\pi\left(\tfrac{1}{2}r\right)^2\left(3r - \tfrac{1}{2}r\right) = \tfrac{5}{12}\pi r^3$.

40. We consider two cases: one in which the ball is not completely submerged and the other in which it is.

Case 1: $0 \le h \le 10$ The ball will not be completely submerged, and so a cross-section of the water parallel to the surface will be the shaded area shown in the first diagram. We can find the area of the cross-section at height x above the bottom of the bowl by using the Pythagorean Theorem: $R^2 = 15^2 - (15 - x)^2$ and $r^2 = 5^2 - (x - 5)^2$, so $A(x) = \pi(R^2 - r^2) = 20\pi x$. The volume of water when it has depth h is then

$$V(h) = \int_0^h A(x)\, dx = \int_0^h 20\pi x\, dx = \left[10\pi x^2\right]_0^h = 10\pi h^2 \text{ cm}^3,\ 0 \le h \le 10.$$

Case 2: $10 < h \le 15$ In this case we can find the volume by simply subtracting the volume displaced by the ball from the total volume inside the bowl underneath the surface of the water. The total volume underneath the surface is just the volume of a cap of the bowl, so we use the formula from Exercise 23:

$V_{\text{cap}}(h) = \tfrac{1}{3}\pi h^2 (45 - h)$. The volume of the small sphere is $V_{\text{ball}} = \tfrac{4}{3}\pi(5)^3 = \tfrac{500}{3}\pi$, so the total volume is

$V_{\text{cap}} - V_{\text{ball}} = \tfrac{1}{3}\pi\left(45h^2 - h^3 - 500\right) \text{ cm}^3.$

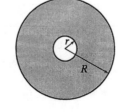

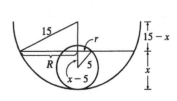

41. Take the x-axis to be the axis of the cylindrical hole of radius r.
A quarter of the cross-section through y, perpendicular to the
y-axis, is the rectangle shown. Using the Pythagorean Theorem
twice, we see that the dimensions of this rectangle are
$x = \sqrt{R^2 - y^2}$ and $z = \sqrt{r^2 - y^2}$, so
$\frac{1}{4}A(y) = xz = \sqrt{r^2 - y^2}\sqrt{R^2 - y^2}$, and

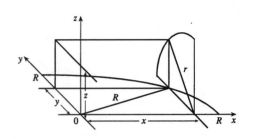

$$V = \int_{-r}^{r} A(y)\, dy = \int_{-r}^{r} 4\sqrt{r^2 - y^2}\sqrt{R^2 - y^2}\, dy$$

$$= 8\int_{0}^{r} \sqrt{r^2 - y^2}\sqrt{R^2 - y^2}\, dy$$

42. The line $y = r$ intersects the semicircle $y = \sqrt{R^2 - x^2}$ when $r = \sqrt{R^2 - x^2} \;\Rightarrow\; r^2 = R^2 - x^2 \;\Rightarrow\;$
$x^2 = R^2 - r^2 \;\Rightarrow\; x = \pm\sqrt{R^2 - r^2}$. Rotating the shaded region about the x-axis gives us

$$V = \int_{-\sqrt{R^2-r^2}}^{\sqrt{R^2-r^2}} \pi\left[\left(\sqrt{R^2-x^2}\right)^2 - r^2\right] dx$$

$$= 2\pi\int_{0}^{\sqrt{R^2-r^2}} \left(R^2 - x^2 - r^2\right) dx \quad \text{[by symmetry]}$$

$$= 2\pi\int_{0}^{\sqrt{R^2-r^2}} \left[(R^2 - r^2) - x^2\right] dx = 2\pi\left[(R^2 - r^2)x - \tfrac{1}{3}x^3\right]_0^{\sqrt{R^2-r^2}}$$

$$= 2\pi\left[(R^2 - r^2)^{3/2} - \tfrac{1}{3}(R^2 - r^2)^{3/2}\right]$$

$$= 2\pi\cdot\tfrac{2}{3}(R^2 - r^2)^{3/2} = \tfrac{4\pi}{3}(R^2 - r^2)^{3/2}$$

Our answer makes sense in
limiting cases. As $r \to 0$,
$V \to \frac{4}{3}\pi R^3$, which is the
volume of the full sphere. As
$r \to R$, $V \to 0$, which makes
sense because the hole's radius is
approaching that of the sphere.

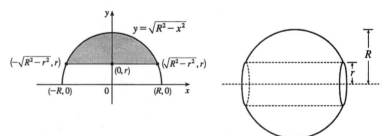

43.

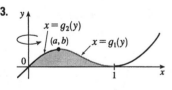

If we were to use the "washer method," we would first have to locate the
local maximum point (a, b) of $y = x(x - 1)^2$ using the methods of
Chapter 4. Then we would have to solve the equation $y = x(x - 1)^2$
for x in terms of y to obtain the functions $x = g_1(y)$ and $x = g_2(y)$
shown in the figure above. This step would be difficult because it
involves the cubic formula. Finally we would find the volume using

$$V = \pi\int_{0}^{b} \left\{[g_1(y)]^2 - [g_2(y)]^2\right\} dy.$$

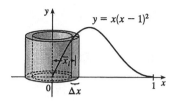

$y = x(x-1)^2$

Instead, we use cylindrical shells. As in Example 9, we rotate an approximating rectangle with width Δx about the y-axis, to get a cylindrical shell whose average radius is $\overline{x}_i$ and whose volume is

$$2\pi\overline{x}_i\left[\overline{x}_i(\overline{x}_i - 1)^2\right]\Delta x.$$

So the total volume is

$$V = \lim_{n\to\infty}\sum_{i=1}^{n} 2\pi\,\overline{x}_i\left[\overline{x}_i(\overline{x}_i - 1)^2\right]\Delta x = \int_0^1 2\pi x\left[x(x-1)^2\right]dx = 2\pi\int_0^1\left(x^4 - 2x^3 + x^2\right)dx$$

$$= 2\pi\left[\frac{x^5}{5} - 2\frac{x^4}{4} + \frac{x^3}{3}\right]_0^1 = 2\pi\left(\frac{1}{5} - \frac{1}{2} + \frac{1}{3}\right) = 2\pi\left(\frac{1}{30}\right) = \frac{\pi}{15}.$$

44.

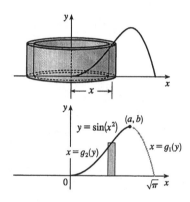

$y = \sin(x^2)$ (a, b)

$x = g_2(y)$ $x = g_1(y)$

$\sqrt{\pi}\ x$

A typical cylindrical shell has circumference $2\pi x$ and height $\sin(x^2)$. $V = \int_0^{\sqrt{\pi}} 2\pi x \sin(x^2)\,dx$. Let $u = x^2$. Then $du = 2x\,dx$, so $V = \pi\int_0^{\pi}\sin u\,du = \pi[-\cos u]_0^{\pi} = \pi[1 - (-1)] = 2\pi$.

For slicing, we would first have to locate the local maximum point (a, b) of $y = \sin(x^2)$ using the methods of Chapter 4. Then we would have to solve the equation $y = \sin(x^2)$ for x in terms of y to obtain the functions $x = g_1(y)$ and $x = g_2(y)$ shown in the second figure. Finally we would find the volume using $V = \pi\int_0^b\left\{[g_1(y)]^2 - [g_2(y)]^2\right\}dy$. Using shells is definitely preferable to slicing.

45. Let $y = f(x)$ denote the curve. Using cylindrical shells, $V = \int_2^{10} 2\pi x f(x)\,dx = 2\pi\int_2^{10} x f(x)\,dx = 2\pi I$. Now use Simpson's Rule to approximate I:

$$I \approx S_8 = \frac{10-2}{3(8)}\left[2f(2) + 4\cdot 3f(3) + 2\cdot 4f(4) + 4\cdot 5f(5) + 2\cdot 6f(6)\right.$$

$$\left. + 4\cdot 7f(7) + 2\cdot 8f(8) + 4\cdot 9f(9) + 10f(10)\right]$$

$$\approx \tfrac{1}{3}[2(0) + 12(1.5) + 8(1.9) + 20(2.2) + 12(3.0) + 28(3.8) + 16(4.0) + 36(3.1) + 10(0)]$$

$$= \tfrac{1}{3}(395.2)$$

Thus, $V \approx 2\pi \cdot \tfrac{1}{3}(395.2) \approx 827.7$ or 828 cubic units.

46.

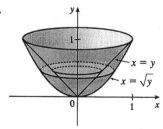

$x = y$

$x = \sqrt{y}$

The first figure shows a cross-section perpendicular to the y-axis. It is a washer with inner radius y and outer radius $\sqrt{y}$, so the volume by slicing is

$$V = \int_0^1 A(y)\,dy = \pi\int_0^1\left[(\sqrt{y})^2 - y^2\right]dy$$

$$= \pi\int_0^1\left(y - y^2\right)dy = \pi\left[\frac{y^2}{2} - \frac{y^3}{3}\right]_0^1 = \frac{\pi}{6}$$

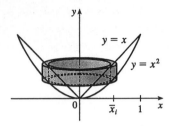

Next, we use cylindrical shells to find the volume. The height of a shell is $\overline{x}_i - \overline{x}_i^2$, so its volume is $2\pi \overline{x}_i (\overline{x}_i - \overline{x}_i^2) \Delta x$. Thus,

$$V = \lim_{n \to \infty} \sum_{i=1}^{n} 2\pi \overline{x}_i (\overline{x}_i - \overline{x}_i^2) \Delta x = \int_0^1 2\pi x(x - x^2) \, dx$$

$$= 2\pi \int_0^1 (x^2 - x^3) \, dx = 2\pi \left[\frac{x^3}{3} - \frac{x^4}{4} \right]_0^1 = 2\pi \left(\frac{1}{12} \right) = \frac{\pi}{6}$$

47.

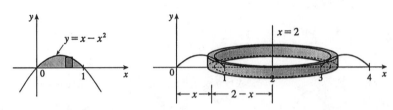

$$V = \int_0^1 \text{(circumference) (height) (thickness)} = \int_0^1 [2\pi(2 - x)] \, (x - x^2) \, dx$$

$$= 2\pi \int_0^1 (x^3 - 3x^2 + 2x) \, dx = 2\pi \left[\tfrac{1}{4}x^4 - x^3 + x^2 \right]_0^1 = 2\pi \left(\tfrac{1}{4} \right) = \tfrac{\pi}{2}$$

See the solution for Exercise 43 as to why the method of cylindrical shells is preferable to slicing.

48. (b) By symmetry, the volume of a napkin ring obtained by drilling a hole of radius r through a sphere with radius R is twice the volume obtained by rotating the area above the x-axis and below the curve $y = \sqrt{R^2 - x^2}$ (the equation of the top half of the cross-section of the sphere), between $x = r$ and $x = R$, about the y-axis. Using cylindrical shells, this is equal to

$$2 \int_{\text{inner radius}}^{\text{outer radius}} 2\pi r h \, dx = 2 \cdot 2\pi \int_r^R x \sqrt{R^2 - x^2} \, dx = 4\pi \left[-\tfrac{1}{3}(R^2 - x^2)^{3/2} \right]_r^R = \tfrac{4}{3}\pi(R^2 - r^2)^{3/2}. \text{ But by the}$$

Pythagorean Theorem, $R^2 - r^2 = \left(\tfrac{1}{2}h \right)^2$, so the volume of the napkin ring is $\tfrac{4}{3}\pi \left(\tfrac{1}{2}h \right)^3 = \tfrac{1}{6}\pi h^3$, which is independent of both R and r; that is, the amount of wood in a napkin ring of height h is the same regardless of the size of the sphere used.

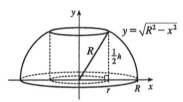

Another solution: The height of the missing cap is the radius of the sphere minus half the height of the cut-out cylinder, that is, $R - \tfrac{1}{2}h$. Using Exercise 23,

$$V_{\text{napkin ring}} = V_{\text{sphere}} - V_{\text{cylinder}} - 2V_{\text{cap}}$$

$$= \tfrac{4}{3}\pi R^3 - \pi r^2 h - 2 \cdot \tfrac{1}{3}\pi \left(R - \tfrac{1}{2}h \right)^2 \left[3R - \left(R - \tfrac{1}{2}h \right) \right]$$

$$= \tfrac{4}{3}\pi R^3 - \pi \left[R^2 - \left(\tfrac{1}{2}h \right)^2 \right] h - \tfrac{2}{3}\pi (R^2 - Rh + \tfrac{1}{4}h^2)[2R + \tfrac{1}{2}h]$$

$$= \tfrac{1}{3}\pi \left[4R^3 - 3h(R^2 - \tfrac{1}{4}h^2) - 2(2R^3 + \tfrac{1}{2}R^2 h - 2R^2 h - \tfrac{1}{2}Rh^2 + \tfrac{1}{2}Rh^2 + \tfrac{1}{8}h^3) \right]$$

$$= \tfrac{1}{3}\pi \left(4R^3 - 3R^2 h + \tfrac{3}{4}h^3 - 4R^3 - R^2 h + 4R^2 h + Rh^2 - Rh^2 - \tfrac{1}{4}h^3 \right)$$

$$= \tfrac{1}{3}\pi \left(\tfrac{1}{2}h^3 \right) = \tfrac{1}{6}\pi h^3$$

Discovery Project

Rotating on a Slant

1.

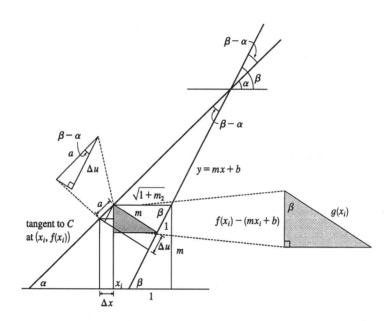

In the figure, the segment a lying above the interval $[x_i - \Delta x, x_i]$ along the tangent to C has length
$\Delta x \sec \alpha = \Delta x \sqrt{1 + \tan^2 \alpha} = \sqrt{1 + [f'(x_i)]^2} \, \Delta x$. The segment from $(x_i, f(x_i))$ drawn perpendicular to the line $y = mx + b$ has length

$$g(x_i) = [f(x_i) - mx_i - b] \cos \beta = \frac{f(x_i) - mx_i - b}{\sec \beta} = \frac{f(x_i) - mx_i - b}{\sqrt{1 + \tan^2 \beta}} = \frac{f(x_i) - mx_i - b}{\sqrt{1 + m^2}}$$

Also, $\cos(\beta - \alpha) = \dfrac{\Delta u}{\Delta x \sec \alpha} \quad \Rightarrow$

$$\Delta u = \Delta x \sec \alpha \cos(\beta - \alpha) = \Delta x \, \frac{\cos \beta \cos \alpha + \sin \beta \sin \alpha}{\cos \alpha} = \Delta x (\cos \beta + \sin \beta \tan \alpha)$$

$$= \Delta x \left[\frac{1}{\sqrt{1 + m^2}} + \frac{m}{\sqrt{1 + m^2}} f'(x_i) \right] = \frac{1 + m f'(x_i)}{\sqrt{1 + m^2}} \Delta x$$

Thus,

$$\text{Area}(\mathcal{R}) = \lim_{n \to \infty} \sum_{i=1}^{n} g(x_i) \, \Delta u = \lim_{n \to \infty} \sum_{i=1}^{n} \frac{f(x_i) - mx_i - b}{\sqrt{1 + m^2}} \cdot \frac{1 + m f'(x_i)}{\sqrt{1 + m^2}} \Delta x$$

$$= \frac{1}{1 + m^2} \int_{p}^{q} [f(x) - mx - b] \left[1 + m f'(x) \right] dx$$

2. From Problem 1 with $m = 1$, $f(x) = x + \sin x$, $mx + b = x - 2$, $p = 0$, and $q = 2\pi$,

$$\text{Area} = \tfrac{1}{1+1^2} \int_0^{2\pi} [x + \sin x - (x - 2)] [1 + 1(1 + \cos x)] \, dx = \tfrac{1}{2} \int_0^{2\pi} (\sin x + 2)(2 + \cos x) \, dx$$

$$= \tfrac{1}{2} \int_0^{2\pi} (2 \sin x + \sin x \cos x + 4 + 2 \cos x) \, dx = \tfrac{1}{2} \left[-2 \cos x + \tfrac{1}{2} \sin^2 x + 4x + 2 \sin x \right]_0^{2\pi}$$

$$= \tfrac{1}{2} [(-2 + 0 + 8\pi + 0) - (-2 + 0 + 0 + 0)] = \tfrac{1}{2}(8\pi) = 4\pi$$

3. $V = \lim\limits_{n \to \infty} \sum\limits_{i=1}^{n} \pi \left[g(x_i) \right]^2 \Delta u = \lim\limits_{n \to \infty} \sum\limits_{i=1}^{n} \pi \left[\dfrac{f(x_i) - mx_i - b}{\sqrt{1 + m^2}} \right]^2 \dfrac{1 + mf'(x_i)}{\sqrt{1 + m^2}} \Delta x$

$$= \dfrac{\pi}{(1 + m^2)^{3/2}} \int_p^q [f(x) - mx - b]^2 \left[1 + mf'(x) \right] \, dx$$

4. $V = \dfrac{\pi}{(1 + 1^2)^{3/2}} \displaystyle\int_0^{2\pi} (x + \sin x - x + 2)^2 (1 + 1 + \cos x) \, dx = \dfrac{\pi}{2\sqrt{2}} \int_0^{2\pi} (\sin x + 2)^2 (\cos x + 2) \, dx$

$$= \tfrac{\pi}{2\sqrt{2}} \int_0^{2\pi} (\sin^2 x + 4 \sin x + 4)(\cos x + 2) \, dx$$

$$= \tfrac{\pi}{2\sqrt{2}} \int_0^{2\pi} (\sin^2 x \cos x + 4 \sin x \cos x + 4 \cos x + 2 \sin^2 x + 8 \sin x + 8) \, dx$$

$$= \tfrac{\pi}{2\sqrt{2}} \left[\tfrac{1}{3} \sin^3 x + 2 \sin^2 x + 4 \sin x + x - \tfrac{1}{2} \sin 2x - 8 \cos x + 8x \right]_0^{2\pi} \quad [\text{since } 2 \sin^2 x = 1 - \cos 2x]$$

$$= \tfrac{\pi}{2\sqrt{2}} [(2\pi - 8 + 16\pi) - (-8)] = \tfrac{9\sqrt{2}}{2} \pi^2$$

◆ **6.3** ◆ **Arc Length** • • • • • • • • • • • • • • • • • •

1. $y = 2 - 3x \;\Rightarrow\; L = \int_{-2}^{1} \sqrt{1 + (dy/dx)^2} \, dx = \int_{-2}^{1} \sqrt{1 + (-3)^2} \, dx = \sqrt{10} \, [1 - (-2)] = 3\sqrt{10}.$
   The arc length can be calculated using the distance formula, since the curve is a line segment, so

$$L = [\text{distance from } (-2, 8) \text{ to } (1, -1)] = \sqrt{[1 - (-2)]^2 + [(-1) - 8]^2} = \sqrt{90} = 3\sqrt{10}$$

2. (a) $x = \cos t$, $y = \sin t$, $0 \le t \le 2\pi$. $\left(\dfrac{dx}{dt} \right)^2 + \left(\dfrac{dy}{dt} \right)^2 = (-\sin t)^2 + (\cos t)^2 = \sin^2 t + \cos^2 t = 1.$ So by
   formula (1), $L = \int_0^{2\pi} \sqrt{1} \, dt = \left[t \right]_0^{2\pi} = 2\pi$, as expected.

(b) $x = \sin 2t$, $y = \cos 2t$, $0 \le t \le 2\pi$.

$$\left(\dfrac{dx}{dt} \right)^2 + \left(\dfrac{dy}{dt} \right)^2 = (2 \cos 2t)^2 + (-2 \sin 2t)^2 = 4 \cos^2 2t + 4 \sin^2 2t = 4.$$

$L = \int_0^{2\pi} \sqrt{4} \, dt = 2 \left[t \right]_0^{2\pi} = 2(2\pi) = 4\pi.$ The discrepancy results from the fact that the unit circle is traversed
   twice with this parametrization.

3. $x = t - t^2$, $y = \tfrac{4}{3} t^{3/2}$, $1 \le t \le 2$. $dx/dt = 1 - 2t$ and $dy/dt = 2t^{1/2}$, so

$$(dx/dt)^2 + (dy/dt)^2 = (1 - 2t)^2 + \left(2t^{1/2} \right)^2 = 1 - 4t + 4t^2 + 4t = 1 + 4t^2 \text{ and}$$

$L = \int_a^b \sqrt{(dx/dt)^2 + (dy/dt)^2} \, dt = \int_1^2 \sqrt{1 + 4t^2} \, dt.$

4. $y = 2^x \;\Rightarrow\; dy/dx = (2^x) \ln 2 \;\Rightarrow\; L = \int_0^3 \sqrt{1 + (\ln 2)^2\, 2^{2x}}\, dx$

5. $x = e^t \cos t,\; y = e^t \sin t,\; 0 \le t \le \pi.$

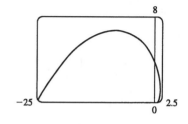

$$\left(\frac{dx}{dt}\right)^2 + \left(\frac{dy}{dt}\right)^2 = \left[e^t(\cos t - \sin t)\right]^2 + \left[e^t(\sin t + \cos t)\right]^2$$

$$= \left(e^t\right)^2 \left(\cos^2 t - 2\cos t \sin t + \sin^2 t\right)$$

$$+ \left(e^t\right)^2 \left(\sin^2 t + 2\sin t \cos t + \cos^2 t\right)$$

$$= e^{2t}\left(2\cos^2 t + 2\sin^2 t\right) = 2e^{2t}$$

Thus, $L = \int_0^\pi \sqrt{2e^{2t}}\, dt = \int_0^\pi \sqrt{2}\, e^t\, dt = \sqrt{2}\left[e^t\right]_0^\pi = \sqrt{2}\left(e^\pi - 1\right).$

6.

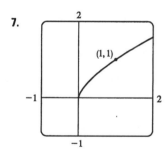

$x = e^t + e^{-t},\; y = 5 - 2t,\; 0 \le t \le 3.$
$dx/dt = e^t - e^{-t}$ and $dy/dt = -2$, so
$(dx/dt)^2 + (dy/dt)^2 = e^{2t} - 2 + e^{-2t} + 4 = e^{2t} + 2 + e^{-2t} = \left(e^t + e^{-t}\right)^2$
and
$L = \int_0^3 \left(e^t + e^{-t}\right) dt = \left[e^t - e^{-t}\right]_0^3 = e^3 - e^{-3} - (1 - 1) = e^3 - e^{-3}.$

7.

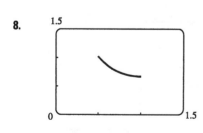

$x = y^{3/2} \;\Rightarrow\; 1 + (dx/dy)^2 = 1 + \left(\tfrac{3}{2}y^{1/2}\right)^2 = 1 + \tfrac{9}{4}y.$

$$L = \int_0^1 \sqrt{1 + \tfrac{9}{4}y}\; dy = \int_1^{13/4} \sqrt{u}\left(\tfrac{4}{9}\, du\right) \quad \left[u = 1 + \tfrac{9}{4}\, y,\; du = \tfrac{9}{4}\, dy\right]$$

$$= \tfrac{4}{9} \cdot \tfrac{2}{3}\left[u^{3/2}\right]_1^{13/4} = \tfrac{8}{27}\left(\tfrac{13\sqrt{13}}{8} - 1\right) = \tfrac{13\sqrt{13} - 8}{27}.$$

8.

$$y = \frac{x^3}{6} + \frac{1}{2x} \;\Rightarrow\; y' = \frac{x^2}{2} - \frac{x^{-2}}{2} \;\Rightarrow$$

$$1 + (y')^2 = 1 + \frac{x^4}{4} - \frac{1}{2} + \frac{x^{-4}}{4} = \frac{x^4}{4} + \frac{1}{2} + \frac{x^{-4}}{4} = \left(\frac{x^2}{2} + \frac{x^{-2}}{2}\right)^2$$

so, using the fact that the parenthetical expression is positive,

$$L = \int_{1/2}^1 \sqrt{\left(\frac{x^2}{2} + \frac{x^{-2}}{2}\right)^2}\, dx = \int_{1/2}^1 \left(\frac{x^2}{2} + \frac{x^{-2}}{2}\right) dx$$

$$= \left[\frac{x^3}{6} - \frac{1}{2x}\right]_{1/2}^1 = \left(\tfrac{1}{6} - \tfrac{1}{2}\right) - \left(\tfrac{1}{48} - 1\right) = \tfrac{31}{48}$$

9. $x = e^t - t,\ y = 4e^{t/2},\ -8 \le t \le 3.$

$$(dx/dt)^2 + (dy/dt)^2 = (e^t + 1)^2 + \left(2e^{t/2}\right)^2 = e^{2t} - 2e^t + 1 + 4e^t$$

$$= e^{2t} + 2e^t + 1 = (e^t + 1)^2$$

$$L = \int_{-8}^{3} \sqrt{(e^t + 1)^2}\, dt = \int_{-8}^{3}(e^t + 1)dt = \left[e^t + t\right]_{-8}^{3}$$

$$= (e^3 + 3) - (e^{-8} - 8) = e^3 - e^{-8} + 11$$

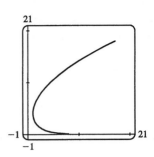

10. $x = a(\cos\theta + \theta\sin\theta),\ y = a(\sin\theta - \theta\cos\theta),\ 0 \le \theta \le \pi.$

$$(dx/d\theta)^2 + (dy/d\theta)^2 = a^2\left[(-\sin\theta + \theta\cos\theta + \sin\theta)^2 + (\cos\theta + \theta\sin\theta - \cos\theta)^2\right]$$

$$= a^2\theta^2\left(\cos^2\theta + \sin^2\theta\right) = (a\theta)^2$$

$$L = \int_0^\pi a\theta\, d\theta = a\left[\tfrac{1}{2}\theta^2\right]_0^\pi = \tfrac{1}{2}\pi^2 a$$

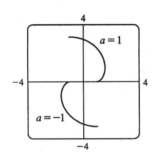

11. $x = \ln t$ and $y = e^{-t}$ $\Rightarrow$ $\dfrac{dx}{dt} = \dfrac{1}{t}$ and $\dfrac{dy}{dt} = -e^{-t}$ $\Rightarrow$ $L = \int_1^2 \sqrt{t^{-2} + e^{-2t}}\, dt.$

Using Simpson's Rule with $n = 10$, $\Delta x = (2 - 1)/10 = 0.1$ and $f(t) = \sqrt{t^{-2} + e^{-2t}}$ we get

$$L \approx \tfrac{0.1}{3}\left[f(1.0) + 4f(1.1) + 2f(1.2) + \cdots + 2f(1.8) + 4f(1.9) + f(2.0)\right] \approx 0.7314.$$

12. $y = \tan x$, $1 + (y')^2 = 1 + \sec^4 x$, $L = \int_0^{\pi/4} \sqrt{1 + \sec^4 x}\, dx.$ Let $g(x) = \sqrt{1 + \sec^4 x}.$ Then

$$L \approx \tfrac{\pi/40}{3}\left[g(0) + 4g\left(\tfrac{\pi}{40}\right) + 2g\left(\tfrac{2\pi}{40}\right) + 4g\left(\tfrac{3\pi}{40}\right) + 2g\left(\tfrac{4\pi}{40}\right) + 4g\left(\tfrac{5\pi}{40}\right)\right.$$

$$\left. + 2g\left(\tfrac{6\pi}{40}\right) + 4g\left(\tfrac{7\pi}{40}\right) + 2g\left(\tfrac{8\pi}{40}\right) + 4g\left(\tfrac{9\pi}{40}\right) + g\left(\tfrac{\pi}{4}\right)\right] \approx 1.278$$

13. $y = \sin x$, $1 + (dy/dx)^2 = 1 + \cos^2 x$, $L = \int_0^\pi \sqrt{1 + \cos^2 x}\, dx.$ Let $g(x) = \sqrt{1 + \cos^2 x}.$ Then

$$L \approx \tfrac{\pi/10}{3}\left[g(0) + 4g\left(\tfrac{\pi}{10}\right) + 2g\left(\tfrac{2\pi}{10}\right) + 4g\left(\tfrac{3\pi}{10}\right) + 2g\left(\tfrac{4\pi}{10}\right) + 4g\left(\tfrac{5\pi}{10}\right)\right.$$

$$\left. + 2g\left(\tfrac{6\pi}{10}\right) + 4g\left(\tfrac{7\pi}{10}\right) + 2g\left(\tfrac{8\pi}{10}\right) + 4g\left(\tfrac{9\pi}{10}\right) + g(\pi)\right] \approx 3.820$$

14. $x = 2a\cot\theta$ $\Rightarrow$ $dx/dt = -2a\csc^2\theta$ and $y = 2a\sin^2\theta$ $\Rightarrow$ $dy/dt = 4a\sin\theta\cos\theta = 2a\sin 2\theta.$

So $L = \int_{\pi/4}^{\pi/2} \sqrt{4a^2\csc^4\theta + 4a^2\sin^2 2\theta}\, d\theta = 2a\int_{\pi/4}^{\pi/2} \sqrt{\csc^4\theta + \sin^2 2\theta}\, d\theta.$ Using Simpson's

Rule with $n = 4$, $\Delta x = \tfrac{\pi/2 - \pi/4}{4} = \tfrac{\pi}{16}$ and $f(\theta) = \sqrt{\csc^4\theta + \sin^2 2\theta}$, we get

$$L \approx 2a \cdot S_4 = (2a)\tfrac{\pi}{16 \cdot 3}\left[f\left(\tfrac{\pi}{4}\right) + 4f\left(\tfrac{5\pi}{16}\right) + 2f\left(\tfrac{3\pi}{8}\right) + 4f\left(\tfrac{7\pi}{16}\right) + f\left(\tfrac{\pi}{2}\right)\right] \approx 2.2605a.$$

15. (a) Let $f(x) = y = x\sqrt[3]{4-x}$ with $0 \le x \le 4$.

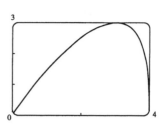

(b) The polygon with one side is just the line segment joining the points $(0, f(0)) = (0,0)$ and $(4, f(4)) = (4,0)$, and its length is 4. The polygon with two sides joins the points $(0,0)$, $(2, f(2)) = (2, 2\sqrt[3]{2})$ and $(4,0)$. Its length is

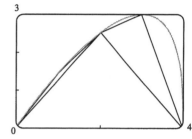

$$\sqrt{(2-0)^2 + \left(2\sqrt[3]{2}-0\right)^2} + \sqrt{(4-2)^2 + \left(0-2\sqrt[3]{2}\right)^2} = 2\sqrt{4+2^{8/3}} \approx 6.43$$

Similarly, the inscribed polygon with four sides joins the points $(0,0)$, $(1, \sqrt[3]{3})$, $(2, 2\sqrt[3]{2})$, $(3,3)$, and $(4,0)$, so its length is

$$\sqrt{1 + \left(\sqrt[3]{3}\right)^2} + \sqrt{1 + \left(2\sqrt[3]{2} - \sqrt[3]{3}\right)^2} + \sqrt{1 + \left(3 - 2\sqrt[3]{2}\right)^2} + \sqrt{1+9} \approx 7.50$$

(c) Using the arc length formula with

$$\frac{dy}{dx} = x\left[\tfrac{1}{3}(4-x)^{-2/3}(-1)\right] + \sqrt[3]{4-x} = \frac{-x + 3(4-x)}{3(4-x)^{2/3}} = \frac{12 - 4x}{3(4-x)^{2/3}}, \text{ the length of the curve is}$$

$$L = \int_0^4 \sqrt{1 + \left(\frac{dy}{dx}\right)^2}\,dx = \int_0^4 \sqrt{1 + \left[\frac{12 - 4x}{3(4-x)^{2/3}}\right]^2}\,dx.$$

(d) According to a CAS, the length of the curve is $L \approx 7.7988$. The actual value is larger than any of the approximations in part (b). This is always true, since any approximating straight line between two points on the curve is shorter than the length of the curve between the two points.

16. (a) Let $f(x) = y = x + \sin x$ with $0 \le x \le 2\pi$.

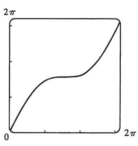

(b) The polygon with one side is just the line segment joining the points $(0, f(0)) = (0,0)$ and $(2\pi, f(2\pi)) = (2\pi, 2\pi)$, and its length is $\sqrt{(2\pi - 0)^2 + (2\pi - 0)^2} = 2\sqrt{2}\,\pi \approx 8.9$.

The polygon with two sides joins the points $(0,0)$, $(\pi, f(\pi)) = (\pi, \pi)$, and $(2\pi, 2\pi)$. Its length is

$$\sqrt{(\pi - 0)^2 + (\pi - 0)^2} + \sqrt{(2\pi - \pi)^2 + (2\pi - \pi)^2} = \sqrt{2}\,\pi + \sqrt{2}\,\pi = 2\sqrt{2}\,\pi \approx 8.9$$

Note from the diagram that the two approximations are the same because the sides of the 2-sided polygon are in fact on the same line, since $f(\pi) = \pi = \frac{1}{2}f(2\pi)$.

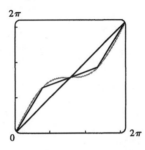

The four-sided polygon joins the points $(0,0)$, $\left(\frac{\pi}{2}, \frac{\pi}{2}+1\right)$, (π, π), $\left(\frac{3\pi}{2}, \frac{3\pi}{2}-1\right)$, and $(2\pi, 2\pi)$, so its length is

$$\sqrt{\left(\tfrac{\pi}{2}\right)^2 + \left(\tfrac{\pi}{2}+1\right)^2} + \sqrt{\left(\tfrac{\pi}{2}\right)^2 + \left(\tfrac{\pi}{2}-1\right)^2} + \sqrt{\left(\tfrac{\pi}{2}\right)^2 + \left(\tfrac{\pi}{2}-1\right)^2} + \sqrt{\left(\tfrac{\pi}{2}\right)^2 + \left(\tfrac{\pi}{2}+1\right)^2} \approx 9.4$$

(c) Using the arc length formula with $dy/dx = 1 + \cos x$, the length of the curve is

$$L = \int_0^{2\pi} \sqrt{1 + (1+\cos x)^2}\, dx = \int_0^{2\pi} \sqrt{2 + 2\cos x + \cos^2 x}\, dx$$

(d) The CAS approximates the integral as 9.5076. The actual length is larger than the approximations in part (b).

17. $x = t^3 \Rightarrow dx/dt = 3t^2$ and $y = t^4 \Rightarrow dy/dt = 4t^3$. So
$L = \int_0^1 \sqrt{9t^4 + 16t^6}\, dt = \int_0^1 \sqrt{t^4(9 + 16t^2)}\, dt = \int_0^1 t^2\sqrt{9 + 16t^2}\, dt.$
Now use Formula 22 from the table of integrals to evaluate L.

$$L = \int_0^4 \left(\tfrac{1}{4}u\right)^2 \sqrt{a^2 + u^2}\left(\tfrac{1}{4}u\right) \quad [a = 3,\ u = 4t,\ du = 4\, dt]$$

$$= \tfrac{1}{64}\int_0^4 u^2\sqrt{a^2 + u^2}\, du$$

$$= \tfrac{1}{64}\left[\tfrac{u}{8}\left(9 + 2u^2\right)\sqrt{9 + u^2} - \tfrac{81}{8}\ln\!\left(u + \sqrt{9 + u^2}\right)\right]_0^4$$

$$= \tfrac{1}{64}\left\{\left[\tfrac{1}{2}\cdot 41\cdot 5 - \tfrac{81}{8}\ln(4 + 5)\right] - \left[0 - \tfrac{81}{8}\ln 3\right]\right\}$$

$$= \tfrac{1}{64}\left[\tfrac{205}{2} - \tfrac{81}{8}(2\ln 3) + \tfrac{81}{8}\ln 3\right] \quad [\ln 9 = \ln 3^2 = 2\ln 3]$$

$$= \tfrac{1}{64}\left(\tfrac{205}{2} - \tfrac{81}{8}\ln 3\right) = \tfrac{205}{128} - \tfrac{81\ln 3}{512} \approx 1.428.$$

18. $x = \ln(1 - y^2) \Rightarrow \dfrac{dx}{dy} = \dfrac{-2y}{1 - y^2} \Rightarrow$

$$1 + \left(\frac{dx}{dy}\right)^2 = 1 + \frac{4y^2}{(1 - y^2)^2} = \frac{1 - 2y^2 + y^4 + 4y^2}{(1 - y^2)^2} = \frac{1 + 2y^2 + y^4}{(1 - y^2)^2} = \frac{(1 + y^2)^2}{(1 - y^2)^2}.\ \text{So}$$

$$L = \int_0^{1/2} \frac{1 + y^2}{1 - y^2}\, dy = \int_0^{1/2}\left(-1 + \frac{2}{1 - y^2}\right) dy \quad [\text{by dividing}]$$

$$\overset{19}{=} \left[-y + 2\cdot\tfrac{1}{2}\ln\left|\frac{y+1}{y-1}\right|\right]_0^{1/2} = \left(-\tfrac{1}{2} + \ln 3\right) - (-0 + \ln|-1|) = \ln 3 - \tfrac{1}{2} \approx 0.599.$$

19. $y = \ln(\cos x) \Rightarrow y' = \dfrac{1}{\cos x}(-\sin x) = -\tan x \Rightarrow 1 + (y')^2 = 1 + \tan^2 x = \sec^2 x.$

So $L = \int_0^{\pi/4} \sec x\, dx \overset{14}{=} \left[\ln|\sec x + \tan x|\right]_0^{\pi/4} = \ln(\sqrt{2} + 1) - \ln(1 + 0) = \ln(\sqrt{2} + 1) \approx 0.881.$

20. $y = e^x \implies y' = e^x \implies$

$L = \int_0^1 \sqrt{1 + e^{2x}}\, dx = -\ln\left((\sqrt{2} - 1)(\sqrt{e^2 + 1} + 1)\right) + \sqrt{e^2 + 1} - \sqrt{2} + 1 \approx 2.003$ (from Derive). Maple and Mathematica give the form $\tanh^{-1}\sqrt{e^2 + 1} + \tanh^{-1}\sqrt{2} + \sqrt{e^2 + 1} - \sqrt{2}$, which is equivalent to Derive's answer.

21. The prey hits the ground when $y = 0 \iff 180 - \frac{1}{45}x^2 = 0 \iff x^2 = 45 \cdot 180 \implies x = \sqrt{8100} = 90$, since x must be positive. $y' = -\frac{2}{45}x \implies 1 + (y')^2 = 1 + \frac{4}{45^2}x^2$, so the distance traveled by the prey is

$$L = \int_0^{90} \sqrt{1 + \frac{4}{45^2}x^2}\, dx = \int_0^4 \sqrt{1 + u^2}\left(\frac{45}{2}\, du\right) \quad [u = \frac{2}{45}x,\ du = \frac{2}{45}\, dx]$$

$$\overset{21}{=} \frac{45}{2}\left[\frac{1}{2}u\sqrt{1 + u^2} + \frac{1}{2}\ln\left(u + \sqrt{1 + u^2}\right)\right]_0^4$$

$$= \frac{45}{2}\left[2\sqrt{17} + \frac{1}{2}\ln\left(4 + \sqrt{17}\right)\right] = 45\sqrt{17} + \frac{45}{4}\ln\left(4 + \sqrt{17}\right) \approx 209.1\ \text{m}$$

22. $y = 150 - \frac{1}{40}(x - 50)^2 \implies y' = -\frac{1}{20}(x - 50) \implies 1 + (y')^2 = 1 + \frac{1}{20^2}(x - 50)^2$, so the distance traveled by the kite is

$$L = \int_0^{80} \sqrt{1 + \frac{1}{20^2}(x - 50)^2}\, dx = \int_{-5/2}^{3/2} \sqrt{1 + u^2}\,(20\, du) \quad [u = \frac{1}{20}(x - 50),\ du = \frac{1}{20}\, dx]$$

$$\overset{21}{=} 20\left[\frac{1}{2}u\sqrt{1 + u^2} + \frac{1}{2}\ln\left(u + \sqrt{1 + u^2}\right)\right]_{-5/2}^{3/2}$$

$$= 10\left[\frac{3}{2}\sqrt{\frac{13}{4}} + \ln\left(\frac{3}{2} + \sqrt{\frac{13}{4}}\right) + \frac{5}{2}\sqrt{\frac{29}{4}} - \ln\left(-\frac{5}{2} + \sqrt{\frac{29}{4}}\right)\right]$$

$$= \frac{15}{2}\sqrt{13} + \frac{25}{2}\sqrt{29} + 10\ln\left(\frac{3 + \sqrt{13}}{-5 + \sqrt{29}}\right) \approx 122.8\ \text{ft}$$

23. The sine wave has amplitude 1 and period 14, since it goes through two periods in a distance of 28 in., so its equation is $y = 1\sin\left(\frac{2\pi}{14}x\right) = \sin\left(\frac{\pi}{7}x\right)$. The width w of the flat metal sheet needed to make the panel is the arc length of the sine curve from $x = 0$ to $x = 28$. We set up the integral to evaluate w using the arc length formula with $\frac{dy}{dx} = \frac{\pi}{7}\cos\left(\frac{\pi}{7}x\right)$: $L = \int_0^{28} \sqrt{1 + \left[\frac{\pi}{7}\cos\left(\frac{\pi}{7}x\right)\right]^2}\, dx = 2\int_0^{14} \sqrt{1 + \left[\frac{\pi}{7}\cos\left(\frac{\pi}{7}x\right)\right]^2}\, dx$. This integral would be very difficult to evaluate exactly, so we use a CAS, and find that $L \approx 29.36$ inches.

24. $x = a\cos^3\theta$, $y = a\sin^3\theta$.

$$(dx/d\theta)^2 + (dy/d\theta)^2 = \left(-3a\cos^2\theta\,\sin\theta\right)^2 + \left(3a\sin^2\theta\,\cos\theta\right)^2$$

$$= 9a^2\cos^4\theta\,\sin^2\theta + 9a^2\sin^4\theta\,\cos^2\theta$$

$$= 9a^2\sin^2\theta\,\cos^2\theta\left(\cos^2\theta + \sin^2\theta\right) = 9a^2\sin^2\theta\,\cos^2\theta.$$

The graph has four-fold symmetry and the curve in the first quadrant

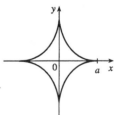

corresponds to $0 \le \theta \le \pi/2$. Thus, $L = 4\int_0^{\pi/2} 3a\sin\theta\,\cos\theta\, d\theta$ [since $a > 0$ and $\sin\theta$ and $\cos\theta$ are positive for $0 \le \theta \le \pi/2$]

$$= \left[12a\frac{1}{2}\sin^2\theta\right]_0^{\pi/2} = 6a.$$

25. $x = a \sin \theta,\ y = b \cos \theta,\ 0 \le \theta \le 2\pi$.

$$\left(\frac{dx}{d\theta}\right)^2 + \left(\frac{dy}{d\theta}\right)^2 = (a \cos \theta)^2 + (-b \sin \theta)^2 = a^2 \cos^2 \theta + b^2 \sin^2 \theta = a^2 \left(1 - \sin^2 \theta\right) + b^2 \sin^2 \theta$$

$$= a^2 - \left(a^2 - b^2\right) \sin^2 \theta = a^2 - c^2 \sin^2 \theta = a^2 \left(1 - \frac{c^2}{a^2} \sin^2 \theta\right) = a^2 \left(1 - e^2 \sin^2 \theta\right)$$

So $L = 4 \int_0^{\pi/2} \sqrt{a^2 \left(1 - e^2 \sin^2 \theta\right)}\, d\theta$ [by symmetry] $= 4a \int_0^{\pi/2} \sqrt{1 - e^2 \sin^2 \theta}\, d\theta$.

26. By symmetry, the length of the curve in each quadrant is the same, so we'll find the length in the first quadrant and multiply by 4.

$$x^{2k} + y^{2k} = 1 \quad \Rightarrow \quad y^{2k} = 1 - x^{2k} \quad \Rightarrow \quad y = \left(1 - x^{2k}\right)^{1/(2k)}$$

(in the first quadrant), so we use the arc length formula with

$$\frac{dy}{dx} = \frac{1}{2k} \left(1 - x^{2k}\right)^{1/(2k)-1} \left(-2kx^{2k-1}\right)$$

$$= -x^{2k-1} \left(1 - x^{2k}\right)^{1/(2k)-1}$$

The total length is therefore

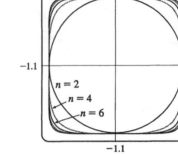

1.1

-1.1   1.1

$n = 2$

$n = 4$

$n = 6$

-1.1

$$L_{2k} = 4 \int_0^1 \sqrt{1 + \left[-x^{2k-1} \left(1 - x^{2k}\right)^{1/(2k)-1}\right]^2}\, dx = 4 \int_0^1 \sqrt{1 + x^{2(2k-1)} \left(1 - x^{2k}\right)^{1/k-2}}\, dx$$

Now from the graph, we see that as k increases, the "corners" of these fat circles get closer to the points $(\pm 1, \pm 1)$ and $(\pm 1, \mp 1)$, and the "edges" of the fat circles approach the lines joining these four points. It seems plausible that as $k \to \infty$, the total length of the fat circle with $n = 2k$ will approach the length of the perimeter of the square with sides of length 2. This is supported by taking the limit as $k \to \infty$ of the equation of the fat circle in the first quadrant: $\lim_{k \to \infty} \left(1 - x^{2k}\right)^{1/(2k)} = 1$ for $0 \le x < 1$. So we guess that $\lim_{k \to \infty} L_{2k} = 4 \cdot 2 = 8$.

27. (a) Notice that $0 \le t \le 2\pi$ does not give the complete curve because $x(0) \ne x(2\pi)$. In fact, we must take $t \in [0, 4\pi]$ in order to obtain the complete curve, since the first term in each of the parametric equations has period 2π and the second has period $\frac{2\pi}{11/2} = \frac{4\pi}{11}$, and the least common integer multiple of these two numbers is 4π.

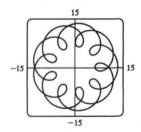

15

-15   15

-15

(b) We use the CAS to find the derivatives dx/dt and dy/dt, and then use Formula 1 to find the arc length. Recent versions of Maple express the integral $\int_0^{4\pi} \sqrt{(dx/dt)^2 + (dy/dt)^2}\, dt$ as $88E\left(2\sqrt{2}\,i\right)$, where $E(x)$ is the elliptic integral $\int_0^1 \frac{\sqrt{1 - x^2 t^2}}{\sqrt{1 - t^2}}\, dt$ and i is the imaginary number $\sqrt{-1}$. Some earlier versions of Maple (as well as Mathematica) cannot do the integral exactly, so we use the command `evalf(Int(sqrt(diff(x,t)^2+diff(y,t)^2),t=0..4*Pi));` to estimate the length, and find that the arc length is approximately 294.03. Derive's `Para_arc_length` function in the utility file `Int_apps` simplifies the integral to $11 \int_0^{4\pi} \sqrt{-4 \cos t\, \cos\left(\frac{11t}{2}\right) - 4 \sin t\, \sin\left(\frac{11t}{2}\right) + 5}\, dt$.

28. (a) It appears that as $t \to \infty$, $(x, y) \to \left(\frac{1}{2}, \frac{1}{2}\right)$, and

as $t \to -\infty$, $(x, y) \to \left(-\frac{1}{2}, -\frac{1}{2}\right)$.

(b) By the Fundamental Theorem of Calculus,

$dx/dt = \cos\left(\frac{\pi}{2}t^2\right)$ and $dy/dt = \sin\left(\frac{\pi}{2}t^2\right)$, so

by Formula 1, the length of the curve from the

origin to the point with parameter value t is

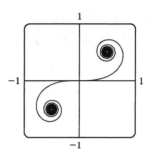

$$L = \int_0^t \sqrt{(dx/du)^2 + (dy/du)^2}\, du = \int_0^t \sqrt{\cos^2\left(\frac{\pi}{2}u^2\right) + \sin^2\left(\frac{\pi}{2}u^2\right)}\, du$$

$$= \int_0^t 1\, du = t \quad [\text{or } -t \text{ if } t < 0]$$

We have used u as the dummy variable so as not to confuse it with the upper limit of integration.

Discovery Project | **Arc Length Contest**

For advice on how to run the contest and a list of student entries, see the article "Arc Length Contest" by Larry Riddle in *The College Mathematics Journal*, Volume 29, No. 4, September 1998, pages 314–320.

 Average Value of a Function • • • • • • • • • •

1. $g_{\text{ave}} = \frac{1}{\pi/2 - 0} \int_0^{\pi/2} \cos x\, dx = \frac{2}{\pi}[\sin x]_0^{\pi/2} = \frac{2}{\pi}(1 - 0) = \frac{2}{\pi}$

2. $g_{\text{ave}} = \frac{1}{4-1} \int_1^4 \sqrt{x}\, dx = \frac{1}{3}\left[\frac{2}{3}x^{3/2}\right]_1^4 = \frac{2}{9}\left[x^{3/2}\right]_1^4 = \frac{2}{9}(8 - 1) = \frac{14}{9}$

3. $f_{\text{ave}} = \frac{1}{5-0} \int_0^5 te^{-t^2}\, dt = \frac{1}{5}\int_0^{-25} e^u\left(-\frac{1}{2}\, du\right) \quad [u = -t^2, du = -2t\, dt, t\, dt = -\frac{1}{2}\, du]$

$= -\frac{1}{10}[e^u]_0^{-25} = -\frac{1}{10}\left(e^{-25} - 1\right) = \frac{1}{10}\left(1 - e^{-25}\right)$

4. $h_{\text{ave}} = \frac{1}{6-1} \int_1^6 \frac{3}{(1+r)^2}\, dr = \frac{1}{5}\int_2^7 3u^{-2}\, du \quad [u = 1 + r, du = dr]$

$= -\frac{3}{5}\left[u^{-1}\right]_2^7 = -\frac{3}{5}\left(\frac{1}{7} - \frac{1}{2}\right) = \frac{3}{5}\left(\frac{1}{2} - \frac{1}{7}\right) = \frac{3}{5} \cdot \frac{5}{14} = \frac{3}{14}$

5. (a) $f_{\text{ave}} = \frac{1}{2-0} \int_0^2 (4 - x^2)\, dx$

$= \frac{1}{2}\left[4x - \frac{1}{3}x^3\right]_0^2$

$= \frac{1}{2}\left(8 - \frac{8}{3}\right) = \frac{8}{3}$

(b) $f_{\text{ave}} = f(c) \iff \frac{8}{3} = 4 - c^2 \iff c^2 = \frac{4}{3}$

$\iff c = \frac{2}{\sqrt{3}} \approx 1.15$

(c)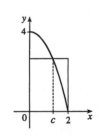

6. (a) $f_{ave} = \frac{1}{3-1}\int_1^3 \ln x \, dx = \frac{1}{2}[x\ln x - x]_1^3$ [by parts]

$= \frac{1}{2}[(3\ln 3 - 3) - (\ln 1 - 1)] = \frac{1}{2}(3\ln 3 - 2)$

$= \frac{3}{2}\ln 3 - 1$

(b) $f_{ave} = f(c) \iff \frac{3}{2}\ln 3 - 1 = \ln c \iff c = e^{(3/2)\ln 3 - 1}$

or $c = 3\sqrt{3}/e \approx 1.91$

(c)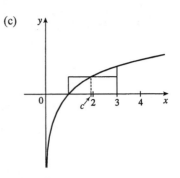

7. (a) $f_{ave} = \frac{1}{2-0}\int_0^2 (x^3 - x + 1)\, dx$

$= \frac{1}{2}[\frac{1}{4}x^4 - \frac{1}{2}x^2 + x]_0^2$

$= \frac{1}{2}(4 - 2 + 2) = 2$

(b) From the graph, $f(x) = 2$ at $x \approx 1.32$.

(c)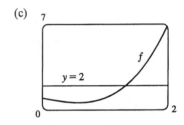

8. (a) $f_{ave} = \frac{1}{\sqrt{\pi}-0}\int_0^{\sqrt{\pi}} [x\sin(x^2)]\, dx$

$= \frac{1}{\sqrt{\pi}}[-\frac{1}{2}\cos(x^2)]_0^{\sqrt{\pi}}$

$= -\frac{1}{2\sqrt{\pi}}(\cos\pi - \cos 0) = \frac{1}{\sqrt{\pi}} \approx 0.56$

(b) From the graph, $f(x) = \frac{1}{\sqrt{\pi}}$ at $x \approx 0.85$ and at $x \approx 1.67$.

(c)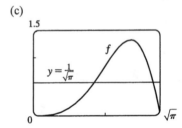

9. f is continuous on $[1,3]$, so by the Mean Value Theorem for Integrals there exists a number c in $[1,3]$ such that $\int_1^3 f(x)\, dx = f(c)(3-1) \Rightarrow 8 = 2f(c)$; that is, there is a number c such that $f(c) = \frac{8}{2} = 4$.

10. The requirement is that $\dfrac{1}{b-0}\displaystyle\int_0^b f(x)\, dx = 3$. The LHS of this equation is equal to

$\frac{1}{b}\int_0^b (2 + 6x - 3x^2)\, dx = \frac{1}{b}[2x + 3x^2 - x^3]_0^b = 2 + 3b - b^2$, so we solve the equation $2 + 3b - b^2 = 3 \iff$

$b^2 - 3b + 1 = 0 \iff b = \dfrac{3 \pm \sqrt{(-3)^2 - 4\cdot 1\cdot 1}}{2\cdot 1} = \dfrac{3 \pm \sqrt{5}}{2}$. Both roots are valid since they are positive.

11. Let $t = 0$ and $t = 12$ correspond to 9 A.M. and 9 P.M., respectively.

$T_{ave} = \frac{1}{12-0}\int_0^{12} [50 + 14\sin\frac{1}{12}\pi t]\, dt = \frac{1}{12}[50t - 14 \cdot \frac{12}{\pi}\cos\frac{1}{12}\pi t]_0^{12}$

$= \frac{1}{12}[50\cdot 12 + 14\cdot\frac{12}{\pi} + 14\cdot\frac{12}{\pi}] = (50 + \frac{28}{\pi})\,°F \approx 59\,°F$

12. (a) $v_{\text{ave}} = \frac{1}{12-0} \int_0^{12} v(t)\, dt = \frac{1}{12} I$. Use Simpson's Rule with $n = 6$ and $\Delta t = (12-0)/6 = 2$ to estimate I.

$$I \approx S_6 = \tfrac{2}{3}[v(0) + 4v(2) + 2v(4) + 4v(6) + 2v(8) + 4v(10) + v(12)]$$
$$= \tfrac{2}{3}[0 + 4(21) + 2(38) + 4(50) + 2(60) + 4(66) + 70]$$
$$= \tfrac{2}{3}(814) = \tfrac{1628}{3}$$

Thus, $v_{\text{ave}} \approx \frac{1}{12} \cdot \frac{1628}{3} = \frac{407}{9} = 45.\overline{2}$ km/h.

(b) Estimating from the graph, $v(t) = 45.\overline{2}$ when $t \approx 5.2$ s.

13. (a) We want to calculate the square root of the average value of $[E(t)]^2 = [155\sin(120\pi t)]^2 = 155^2 \sin^2(120\pi t)$.
First, we calculate the average value itself, by integrating $[E(t)]^2$ over one cycle (between $t = 0$ and $t = \frac{1}{60}$, since there are 60 cycles per second) and dividing by $\left(\frac{1}{60} - 0\right)$:

$$[E(t)]^2_{\text{ave}} = \tfrac{1}{1/60} \int_0^{1/60} [155^2 \sin^2(120\pi t)]\, dt = 60 \cdot 155^2 \int_0^{1/60} \tfrac{1}{2}[1 - 2\cos(240\pi t)]\, dt$$
$$= 60 \cdot 155^2 \left(\tfrac{1}{2}\right)\left[t - 2 \cdot \tfrac{1}{240\pi}\sin(240\pi t)\right]_0^{1/60} = 60 \cdot 155^2 \left(\tfrac{1}{2}\right)\left[\left(\tfrac{1}{60} - 0\right) - (0 - 0)\right] = \tfrac{155^2}{2}$$

The RMS value is just the square root of this quantity, which is $\frac{155}{\sqrt{2}} \approx 110$ V.

(b) $220 = \sqrt{[E(t)]^2_{\text{ave}}} \quad \Rightarrow$

$$220^2 = [E(t)]^2_{\text{ave}} = \tfrac{1}{1/60} \int_0^{1/60} A^2 \sin^2(120\pi t)\, dt = 60A^2 \int_0^{1/60} \tfrac{1}{2}[1 - 2\cos(240\pi t)]\, dt$$
$$= 30A^2 \left[t - \tfrac{2}{240\pi}\sin(240\pi t)\right]_0^{1/60} = 30A^2 \left[\left(\tfrac{1}{60} - 0\right) - (0 - 0)\right] = \tfrac{1}{2}A^2$$

Thus, $220^2 = \tfrac{1}{2}A^2 \quad \Rightarrow \quad A = 220\sqrt{2} \approx 311$ V.

14. $s(t) = \tfrac{1}{2}gt^2 \quad \Rightarrow \quad v(t) = s'(t) = gt \quad \Rightarrow \quad v_T = v(T) = gT$, and $s(T) = \tfrac{1}{2}gT^2$. Also,
$s'(t) = gt = g\sqrt{2s/g} = \sqrt{2gs} = v(s)$. The average of the velocities with respect to time t during the interval

$[0, T]$ is $v_{\text{ave}} = \dfrac{1}{T} \displaystyle\int_0^T v(t)\, dt = \dfrac{1}{T}[s(T) - s(0)]$ [by FTC] $= \dfrac{1}{T} \cdot \dfrac{1}{2}gT^2 = \tfrac{1}{2}gT = \tfrac{1}{2}v_T$. But with respect to s,

$$v_{\text{ave}} = \dfrac{1}{s(T)} \int_0^{s(T)} v(s)\, ds = \dfrac{1}{s(T)} \int_0^{s(T)} \sqrt{2gs}\, ds = \dfrac{2}{gT^2}\sqrt{2g} \int_0^{s(T)} s^{1/2}\, ds$$
$$= \dfrac{2\sqrt{2}}{\sqrt{g}\, T^2}\left(\tfrac{2}{3}\right)\left[s^{3/2}\right]_0^{gT^2/2} = \dfrac{4\sqrt{2}}{3\sqrt{g}\, T^2}\left(\tfrac{1}{2}gT^2\right)^{3/2} = \dfrac{4\sqrt{2}}{3\sqrt{g}\, T^2} \cdot \dfrac{g^{3/2}T^3}{2\sqrt{2}} = \tfrac{2}{3}gT = \tfrac{2}{3}v_T$$

15. $V_{\text{ave}} = \tfrac{1}{5}\int_0^5 V(t)\, dt = \tfrac{1}{5}\int_0^5 \tfrac{5}{4\pi}\left[1 - \cos\left(\tfrac{2}{5}\pi t\right)\right] dt = \tfrac{1}{4\pi}\int_0^5 \left[1 - \cos\left(\tfrac{2}{5}\pi t\right)\right] dt$

$= \tfrac{1}{4\pi}\left[t - \tfrac{5}{2\pi}\sin\left(\tfrac{2}{5}\pi t\right)\right]_0^5 = \tfrac{1}{4\pi}[(5-0) - 0] = \tfrac{5}{4\pi} \approx 0.4$ L

16. $v_{\text{ave}} = \dfrac{1}{R-0}\displaystyle\int_0^R v(r)\, dr = \dfrac{1}{R}\int_0^R \dfrac{P}{4\eta l}(R^2 - r^2)\, dr = \dfrac{P}{4\eta l R}\left[R^2 r - \tfrac{1}{3}r^3\right]_0^R = \dfrac{P}{4\eta l R}\left(\tfrac{2}{3}\right)R^3 = \dfrac{PR^2}{6\eta l}$.

Since $v(r)$ is decreasing on $(0, R]$, $v_{\max} = v(0) = \dfrac{PR^2}{4\eta l}$. Thus, $v_{\text{ave}} = \tfrac{2}{3}v_{\max}$.

17. Let $F(x) = \int_a^x f(t)\, dt$ for x in $[a, b]$. Then F is continuous on $[a, b]$ and differentiable on (a, b), so by the Mean Value Theorem there is a number c in (a, b) such that $F(b) - F(a) = F'(c)(b - a)$. But $F'(x) = f(x)$ by the Fundamental Theorem of Calculus. Therefore, $\int_a^b f(t)\, dt - 0 = f(c)(b - a)$.

18. $f_{\text{ave}}\,[a,b] = \dfrac{1}{b-a}\displaystyle\int_a^b f(x)\,dx = \dfrac{1}{b-a}\int_a^c f(x)\,dx + \dfrac{1}{b-a}\int_c^b f(x)\,dx$

$\qquad = \dfrac{c-a}{b-a}\left[\dfrac{1}{c-a}\displaystyle\int_a^c f(x)\,dx\right] + \dfrac{b-c}{b-a}\left[\dfrac{1}{b-c}\int_c^b f(x)\,dx\right] = \dfrac{c-a}{b-a}f_{\text{ave}}\,[a,c] + \dfrac{b-c}{b-a}f_{\text{ave}}\,[c,b]$

Applied Project	Where to Sit at the Movies

1.

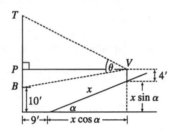

$|VP| = 9 + x\cos\alpha$, $|PT| = 35 - (4 + x\sin\alpha) = 31 - x\sin\alpha$, and

$|PB| = (4 + x\sin\alpha) - 10 = x\sin\alpha - 6$. So using the Pythagorean Theorem, we have

$|VT| = \sqrt{|VP|^2 + |PT|^2} = \sqrt{(9 + x\cos\alpha)^2 + (31 - x\sin\alpha)^2} = a$, and

$|VB| = \sqrt{|VP|^2 + |PB|^2} = \sqrt{(9 + x\cos\alpha)^2 + (x\sin\alpha - 6)^2} = b$. Using the Law of Cosines on $\triangle VBT$, we

get $25^2 = a^2 + b^2 - 2ab\cos\theta \;\Leftrightarrow\; \cos\theta = \dfrac{a^2 + b^2 - 625}{2ab} \;\Leftrightarrow\; \theta = \arccos\left(\dfrac{a^2 + b^2 - 625}{2ab}\right)$, as required.

2. From the graph of θ, it appears that the value of x which maximizes θ is $x \approx 8.25$ ft. Assuming that the first row is at $x = 0$, the row closest to this value of x is the fourth row, at $x = 9$ ft, and from the graph, the viewing angle in this row seems to be about 0.85 radians, or about $49°$.

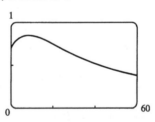

3. With a CAS, we type in the definition of θ, substitute in the proper values of a and b in terms of x and $\alpha = 20° = \frac{\pi}{9}$ radians, and then use the differentiation command to find the derivative. We use a numerical root finder and find that the root of the equation $d\theta/dx = 0$ is $x \approx 8.253062$, as approximated in Problem 2.

4. From the graph in Problem 2, it seems that the average value of the function on the interval $[0, 60]$ is about 0.6. We can use a CAS to approximate $\frac{1}{60}\int_0^{60}\theta(x)\,dx \approx 0.625 \approx 36°$. (The calculation is much faster if we reduce the number of digits of accuracy required.) The minimum value is $\theta(60) \approx 0.38$ and, from Problem 2, the maximum value is about 0.85.

6.5 **Applications to Physics and Engineering** • • • • • • •

1. $W = \int_a^b f(x)\, dx = \int_0^9 \frac{10}{(1+x)^2}\, dx = 10 \int_1^{10} \frac{1}{u^2}\, du$ $[u = 1+x,\ du = dx]$

$= 10 \left[-\frac{1}{u} \right]_1^{10} = 10(-\frac{1}{10} + 1) = 9$ ft-lb

2. $W = \int_1^2 \cos\left(\frac{1}{3}\pi x\right) dx = \frac{3}{\pi} \left[\sin\left(\frac{1}{3}\pi x\right) \right]_1^2 = \frac{3}{\pi}\left(\frac{\sqrt{3}}{2} - \frac{\sqrt{3}}{2} \right) = 0$ N-m $= 0$ J.

Interpretation: From $x = 1$ to $x = \frac{3}{2}$, the force does work equal to $\int_1^{3/2} \cos\left(\frac{1}{3}\pi x\right) dx = \frac{3}{\pi}\left(1 - \frac{\sqrt{3}}{2}\right)$ J in

accelerating the particle and increasing its kinetic energy. From $x = \frac{3}{2}$ to $x = 2$, the force opposes the motion of the particle, decreasing its kinetic energy. This is negative work, equal in magnitude but opposite in sign to the work done from $x = 1$ to $x = \frac{3}{2}$.

3. $10 = f(x) = kx = \frac{1}{3}k$ [4 inches $= \frac{1}{3}$ foot], so $k = 30$ lb/ft and $f(x) = 30x$. Now 6 inches $= \frac{1}{2}$ foot, so

$W = \int_0^{1/2} 30x\, dx = \left[15x^2 \right]_0^{1/2} = \frac{15}{4}$ ft-lb.

4. $25 = f(x) = kx = k(0.1)$ [10 cm $= 0.1$ m], so $k = 250$ N/m and $f(x) = 250x$. Now 5 cm $= 0.05$ m, so

$W = \int_0^{0.05} 250x\, dx = \left[125x^2 \right]_0^{0.05} = 125(0.0025) = 0.3125 \approx 0.31$ J.

5. (a) If $\int_0^{0.12} kx\, dx = 2$ J, then $2 = \left[\frac{1}{2}kx^2 \right]_0^{0.12} = \frac{1}{2}k(0.0144) = 0.0072k$ and

$k = \frac{2}{0.0072} = \frac{2500}{9} \approx 277.78$. Thus, the work needed to stretch the spring from 35 cm to 40 cm is

$\int_{0.05}^{0.10} \frac{2500}{9} x\, dx = \left[\frac{1250}{9}x^2 \right]_{1/20}^{1/10} = \frac{1250}{9}\left(\frac{1}{100} - \frac{1}{400} \right) = \frac{25}{24} \approx 1.04$ J.

(b) $f(x) = kx$, so $30 = \frac{2500}{9}x$ and $x = \frac{270}{2500}$ m $= 10.8$ cm

6. Let L be the natural length of the spring in meters. Then

$6 = \int_{0.10-L}^{0.12-L} kx\, dx = \left[\frac{1}{2}kx^2 \right]_{0.10-L}^{0.12-L} = \frac{1}{2}k\left[(0.12 - L)^2 - (0.10 - L)^2 \right]$ and

$10 = \int_{0.12-L}^{0.14-L} kx\, dx = \left[\frac{1}{2}kx^2 \right]_{0.12-L}^{0.14-L} = \frac{1}{2}k\left[(0.14 - L)^2 - (0.12 - L)^2 \right]$. Simplifying gives us

$12 = k(0.0044 - 0.04L)$ and $20 = k(0.0052 - 0.04L)$. Subtracting the first equation from the second gives

$8 = 0.0008k$, so $k = 10{,}000$. Now the second equation becomes $20 = 52 - 400L$, so $L = \frac{32}{400}$ m $= 8$ cm.

In Exercises 7–12, n is the number of subintervals of length Δx, and x_i^* is a sample point in the ith subinterval $[x_{i-1}, x_i]$.

7. The portion of the rope from x ft to $(x + \Delta x)$ ft below the top of the building weighs $\frac{1}{2}\Delta x$ lb and must be lifted

x_i^* ft, so its contribution to the total work is $\frac{1}{2}x_i^*\, \Delta x$ ft-lb. The total work is

$$W = \lim_{n \to \infty} \sum_{i=1}^n \frac{1}{2}x_i^*\, \Delta x = \int_0^{50} \frac{1}{2}x\, dx = \left[\frac{1}{4}x^2 \right]_0^{50} = \frac{2500}{4} = 625 \text{ ft-lb}$$

Notice that the exact height of the building does not matter (as long as it is more than 50 ft).

8. Each part of the top 10 ft of cable is lifted a distance x_i^* equal to its distance from the top. The cable weighs

$\frac{60}{40} = 1.5$ lb/ft, so the work done on the ith subinterval is $\frac{3}{2}x_i^*\, \Delta x$. The remaining 30 ft of cable is lifted 10 ft.

Thus,

$$W = \lim_{n \to \infty} \sum_{i=1}^n \left(\frac{3}{2}x_i^*\, \Delta x + \frac{3}{2} \cdot 10\, \Delta x \right) = \int_0^{10} \frac{3}{2}x\, dx + \int_{10}^{40} \frac{3}{2} \cdot 10\, dx = \left[\frac{3}{4}x^2 \right]_0^{10} + \left[15x \right]_{10}^{40}$$

$$= \frac{3}{4}(100) + 15(30) = 75 + 450 = 525 \text{ ft-lb}$$

9. The work needed to lift the cable is $\lim\limits_{n\to\infty} \sum_{i=1}^{n} 2x_i^* \, \Delta x = \int_0^{500} 2x \, dx = \left[x^2\right]_0^{500} = 250{,}000$ ft-lb. The work needed to lift the coal is $800 \text{ lb} \cdot 500 \text{ ft} = 400{,}000$ ft-lb. Thus, the total work required is $250{,}000 + 400{,}000 = 650{,}000$ ft-lb.

10. The work needed to lift the bucket itself is $4 \text{ lb} \cdot 80 \text{ ft} = 320$ ft-lb. At time t (in seconds) the bucket is $x_i^* = 2t$ ft above its original 80 ft depth, but it now holds only $(40 - 0.2t)$ lb of water. In terms of distance, the bucket holds $\left[40 - 0.2\left(\frac{1}{2}x_i^*\right)\right]$ lb of water when it is x_i^* ft above its original 80 ft depth. Moving this amount of water a distance Δx requires $\left(40 - \frac{1}{10}x_i^*\right)\Delta x$ ft-lb of work. Thus, the work needed to lift the water is

$$W = \lim_{n\to\infty} \sum_{i=1}^{n} \left(40 - \tfrac{1}{10}x_i^*\right)\Delta x = \int_0^{80}\left(40 - \tfrac{1}{10}x\right)dx = \left[40x - \tfrac{1}{20}x^2\right]_0^{80} = (3200 - 320) \text{ ft-lb}$$

Adding the work of lifting the bucket gives a total of 3200 ft-lb of work.

11. A "slice" of water Δx m thick and lying at a depth of x_i^* m (where $0 \le x_i^* \le \frac{1}{2}$) has volume $(2 \times 1 \times \Delta x)$ m^3, a mass of $2000 \, \Delta x$ kg, weighs about $(9.8)(2000 \, \Delta x) = 19{,}600 \, \Delta x$ N, and thus requires about $19{,}600 x_i^* \, \Delta x$ J of work for its removal. So

$$W = \lim_{n\to\infty} \sum_{i=1}^{n} 19{,}600 x_i^* \, \Delta x = \int_0^{1/2} 19{,}600 x \, dx = \left[9800 x^2\right]_0^{1/2} = 2450 \text{ J}$$

12. A horizontal cylindrical slice of water Δx ft thick has a volume of $\pi r^2 h = \pi \cdot 12^2 \cdot \Delta x$ ft^3 and weighs about $\left(62.5 \text{ lb/ft}^3\right)\left(144\pi \, \Delta x \text{ ft}^3\right) = 9000\pi \, \Delta x$ lb. If the slice lies x_i^* ft below the edge of the pool (where $1 \le x_i^* \le 5$), then the work needed to pump it out is about $9000\pi x_i^* \, \Delta x$. Thus,

$$W = \lim_{n\to\infty} \sum_{i=1}^{n} 9000\pi x_i^* \, \Delta x = \int_1^5 9000\pi x \, dx = \left[4500\pi x^2\right]_1^5 = 4500\pi(25 - 1) = 108{,}000\pi \text{ ft-lb}$$

13. (a) A rectangular "slice" of water Δx m thick and lying x ft above the bottom has width x ft and volume $8x\Delta x$ m^3. It weighs about $(9.8 \times 1000)(8x \, \Delta x)$ N, and must be lifted $(5 - x)$ m by the pump, so the work needed is about $\left(9.8 \times 10^3\right)(5 - x)(8x \, \Delta x)$J. The total work required is

$$W \approx \int_0^3 \left(9.8 \times 10^3\right)(5 - x)8x \, dx = \left(9.8 \times 10^3\right)\int_0^3 \left(40x - 8x^2\right)dx = \left(9.8 \times 10^3\right)\left[20x^2 - \tfrac{8}{3}x^3\right]_0^3$$

$$= \left(9.8 \times 10^3\right)(180 - 72) = \left(9.8 \times 10^3\right)(108) = 1058.4 \times 10^3 \approx 1.06 \times 10^6 \text{ J}$$

(b) If only 4.7×10^5 J of work is done, then only the water above a certain level (call it h) will be pumped out. So we use the same formula as in part (a), except that the work is fixed, and we are trying to find the lower limit of integration: $4.7 \times 10^5 \approx \int_h^3 \left(9.8 \times 10^3\right)(5 - x)8x \, dx = \left(9.8 \times 10^3\right)\left[20x^2 - \tfrac{8}{3}x^3\right]_h^3 \Leftrightarrow$

$\frac{4.7}{9.8} \times 10^2 \approx 48 = \left(20 \cdot 3^2 - \tfrac{8}{3} \cdot 3^3\right) - \left(20h^2 - \tfrac{8}{3}h^3\right) \Leftrightarrow$

$2h^3 - 15h^2 + 45 = 0$. To find the solution of this equation, we plot $2h^3 - 15h^2 + 45$ between $h = 0$ and $h = 3$. We see that the equation is satisfied for $h \approx 2.0$. So the depth of water remaining in the tank is about 2.0 m.

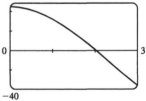

14. Let x be depth in feet, so that $0 \le x \le 5$. Then $\Delta W = (62.5)\pi \left(\sqrt{5^2 - x^2}\right)^2 \Delta x \cdot x$ ft-lb and

$$W \approx 62.5\pi \int_0^5 x\left(25 - x^2\right) dx = 62.5\pi\left[\tfrac{25}{2}x^2 - \tfrac{1}{4}x^4\right]_0^5 = 62.5\pi\left(\tfrac{625}{2} - \tfrac{625}{4}\right) = 62.5\pi\left(\tfrac{625}{4}\right)$$

$$\approx 3.07 \times 10^4 \text{ ft-lb}$$

15. $V = \pi r^2 x$, so V is a function of x and P can also be regarded as a function of x. If $V_1 = \pi r^2 x_1$ and $V_2 = \pi r^2 x_2$, then

$W = \int_{x_1}^{x_2} F(x)\, dx = \int_{x_1}^{x_2} \pi r^2 P(V(x))\, dx = \int_{x_1}^{x_2} P(V(x))\, dV(x)$ [Let $V(x) = \pi r^2 x$, so $dV(x) = \pi r^2\, dx$.]

$= \int_{V_1}^{V_2} P(V)\, dV$ by the Substitution Rule.

16. $160\ \text{lb/in}^2 = 160 \cdot 144\ \text{lb/ft}^2$, $100\ \text{in}^3 = \frac{100}{1728}\ \text{ft}^3$, and $800\ \text{in}^3 = \frac{800}{1728}\ \text{ft}^3$.

$k = PV^{1.4} = (160 \cdot 144)\left(\frac{100}{1728}\right)^{1.4} = 23{,}040\left(\frac{25}{432}\right)^{1.4} \approx 426.5$. Therefore, $P \approx 426.5V^{-1.4}$ and

$W = \int_{100/1728}^{800/1728} 426.5V^{-1.4}\, dV = 426.5\left[\frac{1}{-0.4}V^{-0.4}\right]_{25/432}^{25/54} = (426.5)(2.5)\left[\left(\frac{432}{25}\right)^{0.4} - \left(\frac{54}{25}\right)^{0.4}\right]$

$\approx 1.88 \times 10^3\ \text{ft-lb}$

17. (a) $W = \int_a^b F(r)\, dr = \int_a^b G\frac{m_1 m_2}{r^2}\, dr = Gm_1 m_2\left[\frac{-1}{r}\right]_a^b = Gm_1 m_2\left(\frac{1}{a} - \frac{1}{b}\right)$

(b) By part (a), $W = GMm\left(\dfrac{1}{R} - \dfrac{1}{R + 1{,}000{,}000}\right)$ where $M =$ mass of earth in kg, $R =$ radius of earth in m, and $m =$ mass of satellite in kg. (Note that $1000\ \text{km} = 1{,}000{,}000$ m.) Thus,

$W = \left(6.67 \times 10^{-11}\right)\left(5.98 \times 10^{24}\right)(1000) \times \left(\dfrac{1}{6.37 \times 10^6} - \dfrac{1}{7.37 \times 10^6}\right) \approx 8.50 \times 10^9\ \text{J}.$

18. (a) $W = \int_R^\infty \dfrac{GMm}{r^2}\, dr = \lim_{t \to \infty} \int_R^t \dfrac{GMm}{r^2}\, dr = \lim_{t \to \infty} GMm\left[\dfrac{-1}{r}\right]_R^t = GMm \lim_{t \to \infty}\left(\dfrac{-1}{t} + \dfrac{1}{R}\right)$

$= \dfrac{GMm}{R}$, where $M =$ mass of earth $= 5.98 \times 10^{24}$ kg, $m =$ mass of satellite $= 10^3$ kg,

$R =$ radius of earth $= 6.37 \times 10^6$ m, and $G =$ gravitational constant $= 6.67 \times 10^{-11}\ \text{N·m}^2/\text{kg}^2$. Therefore,

$\text{work} = \dfrac{6.67 \times 10^{-11} \cdot 5.98 \times 10^{24} \cdot 10^3}{6.37 \times 10^6} \approx 6.26 \times 10^{10}\ \text{J}.$

(b) From part (a), $W = \dfrac{GMm}{R}$. The initial kinetic energy supplies the needed work, so

$\frac{1}{2}mv_0^2 = \dfrac{GMm}{R} \quad \Rightarrow \quad v_0 = \sqrt{\dfrac{2GM}{R}}.$

In Exercises 19–21, n is the number of subintervals of length Δx and x_i^* is a sample point in the ith subinterval $[x_{i-1}, x_i]$.

19. In the middle of the figure in the text, draw a vertical x-axis that increases in the downward direction. Since

$x^2 + y^2 = 10^2$, $y = \sqrt{100 - x^2}$, and the width of the ith rectangular strip is $2y = 2\sqrt{100 - (x_i^*)^2}$. The area of

the ith rectangular strip is $2\sqrt{100 - (x_i^*)^2}\,\Delta x$ and the pressure on the strip is $\rho g x_i^*$ [$\rho = 1000\ \text{kg/m}^3$ and

$g = 9.8\ \text{m/s}^2$]. Thus, the hydrostatic force on the ith strip is the product $\rho g x_i^* 2\sqrt{100 - (x_i^*)^2}\,\Delta x$.

$F = \lim_{n \to \infty} \sum_{i=1}^n \rho g x_i^* 2\sqrt{100 - (x_i^*)^2}\,\Delta x = \int_0^{10} \rho g x \cdot 2\sqrt{100 - x^2}\, dx = 9.8 \times 10^3 \int_0^{10} \sqrt{100 - x^2}\, 2x\, dx$

$= 9.8 \times 10^3 \int_{100}^0 u^{1/2}(-du)$ [$u = 100 - x^2$, $du = -2x\, dx$]

$= 9.8 \times 10^3 \int_0^{100} u^{1/2}\, du = 9.8 \times 10^3 \left[\frac{2}{3}u^{3/2}\right]_0^{100} = \frac{2}{3} \cdot 9.8 \times 10^6 \approx 6.5 \times 10^6\ \text{N}$

20. This is like Exercise 19, except that the pressure on the strip is $\rho g(x_i^* - 5)$.

$$F = \lim_{n \to \infty} \sum_{i=1}^{n} \rho g(x_i^* - 5)2\sqrt{100 - (x_i^*)^2}\,\Delta x = \int_5^{10} \rho g(x - 5) \cdot 2\sqrt{100 - x^2}\,dx$$

$$= \rho g \int_5^{10} 2x\sqrt{100 - x^2}\,dx - 10\rho g \int_5^{10} \sqrt{100 - x^2}\,dx$$

$$\overset{30}{=} -\rho g\left[\tfrac{2}{3}(100 - x^2)^{3/2}\right]_5^{10} - 10\rho g\left[\tfrac{1}{2}x\sqrt{100 - x^2} + 50\sin^{-1}(x/10)\right]_5^{10}$$

$$= \tfrac{2}{3}\rho g(75)^{3/2} - 10\rho g\left[50(\tfrac{\pi}{2}) - \tfrac{5}{2}\sqrt{75} - 50(\tfrac{\pi}{6})\right] = 250\rho g\left(\tfrac{3\sqrt{3}}{2} - \tfrac{2\pi}{3}\right) \approx 1.23 \times 10^6\text{ N}$$

21. Using similar triangles, $\dfrac{4\text{ ft wide}}{8\text{ ft high}} = \dfrac{a\text{ ft wide}}{x_i^*\text{ ft high}}$, so $a = \tfrac{1}{2}x_i^*$ and the width

of the ith rectangular strip is $12 + 2a = 12 + x_i^*$. The area of the strip is

$(12 + x_i^*)\,\Delta x$. The pressure on the strip is δx_i^*.

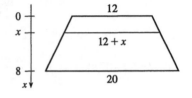

$$F = \lim_{n \to \infty} \sum_{i=1}^{n} \delta x_i^*(12 + x_i^*)\,\Delta x = \int_0^8 \delta x \cdot (12 + x)\,dx$$

$$= \delta \int_0^8 (12x + x^2)\,dx = \delta\left[6x^2 + \tfrac{x^3}{3}\right]_0^8 = \delta\left(384 + \tfrac{512}{3}\right)$$

$$= (62.5)\tfrac{1664}{3} \approx 3.47 \times 10^4\text{ lb}$$

22. The area of the ith rectangular strip is $2\sqrt{2y_i^*}\,\Delta y$ and the pressure

on it is $\delta d_i = \delta(8 - y_i^*)$.

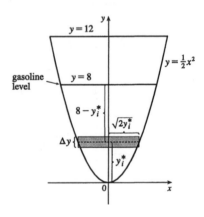

$$F = \int_0^8 \delta(8 - y)2\sqrt{2y}\,dy = 42 \cdot 2 \cdot \sqrt{2}\int_0^8 (8 - y)y^{1/2}\,dy$$

$$= 84\sqrt{2}\int_0^8 \left(8y^{1/2} - y^{3/2}\right)\,dy = 84\sqrt{2}\left[8 \cdot \tfrac{2}{3}y^{3/2} - \tfrac{2}{5}y^{5/2}\right]_0^8$$

$$= 84\sqrt{2}\left[8 \cdot \tfrac{2}{3} \cdot 16\sqrt{2} - \tfrac{2}{5} \cdot 128\sqrt{2}\right]$$

$$= 84\sqrt{2} \cdot 256\sqrt{2}(\tfrac{1}{3} - \tfrac{1}{5}) = 43,008 \cdot \tfrac{2}{15} = 5734.4\text{ lb}$$

23. (a) The area of a strip is $20\,\Delta x$ and the pressure on it is δx_i.

$$F = \int_0^3 \delta x 20\,dx = 20\delta\left[\tfrac{1}{2}x^2\right]_0^3 = 20\delta \cdot \tfrac{9}{2} = 90\delta = 90(62.5) = 5625\text{ lb} \approx 5.63 \times 10^3\text{ lb.}$$

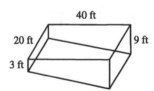

(b) $F = \int_0^9 \delta x 20\,dx = 20\delta\left[\tfrac{1}{2}x^2\right]_0^9 = 20\delta \cdot \tfrac{81}{2} = 810\delta = 810(62.5) = 50,625\text{ lb} \approx 5.06 \times 10^4\text{ lb.}$

(c) For the first 3 ft, the length of the side is constant at 40 ft. For $3 < x \le 9$, we can use similar triangles to find the

length a: $\dfrac{a}{40} = \dfrac{9-x}{6} \quad \Rightarrow \quad a = 40 \cdot \dfrac{9-x}{6}$.

$$F = \int_0^3 \delta x 40 \, dx + \int_3^9 \delta x (40) \tfrac{9-x}{6} \, dx = 40\delta \left[\tfrac{1}{2}x^2\right]_0^3 + \tfrac{20}{3}\delta \int_3^9 (9x - x^2) \, dx$$

$$= 180\delta + \tfrac{20}{3}\delta \left[\tfrac{9}{2}x^2 - \tfrac{1}{3}x^3\right]_3^9 = 180\delta + \tfrac{20}{3}\delta \left[\left(\tfrac{729}{2} - 243\right) - \left(\tfrac{81}{2} - 9\right)\right]$$

$$= 180\delta + 600\delta = 780\delta = 780(62.5) = 48{,}750 \text{ lb} = 780(62.5) \approx 4.88 \times 10^4 \text{ lb}$$

(d) For any right triangle with hypotenuse on the bottom,

$$\csc\theta = \frac{\Delta x}{\text{hypotenuse}} \quad \Rightarrow$$

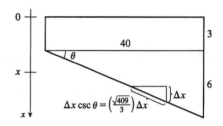

$$\text{hypotenuse} = \Delta x \csc\theta = \Delta x \, \frac{\sqrt{40^2 + 6^2}}{6} = \frac{\sqrt{409}}{3} \Delta x.$$

$$F = \int_3^9 \delta x 20 \frac{\sqrt{409}}{3} \, dx = \tfrac{1}{3}\left(20\sqrt{409}\right)\delta \left[\tfrac{1}{2}x^2\right]_3^9$$

$$= \tfrac{1}{3} \cdot 10\sqrt{409}\,\delta(81 - 9)$$

$$\approx 303{,}356 \text{ lb} \approx 3.03 \times 10^5 \text{ lb}$$

24. $F = \int_0^2 \rho g \, (10 - x) \, 2\sqrt{4 - x^2} \, dx$

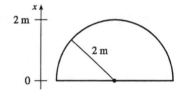

$$= 20\rho g \int_0^2 \sqrt{4 - x^2} \, dx - \rho g \int_0^2 \sqrt{4 - x^2} \, 2x \, dx$$

$$= 20\rho g \tfrac{1}{4}\pi \left(2^2\right) - \rho g \int_0^4 u^{1/2} \, du \quad [u = 4 - x^2, \, du = -2x \, dx]$$

$$= 20\pi \rho g - \tfrac{2}{3}\rho g \left[u^{3/2}\right]_0^4 = 20\pi \rho g - \tfrac{16}{3}\rho g = \rho g \left(20\pi - \tfrac{16}{3}\right)$$

$$= (1000)(9.8)\left(20\pi - \tfrac{16}{3}\right) \approx 5.63 \times 10^5 \text{ N}$$

25. $m_1 = 4$, $m_2 = 8$; $P_1(-1, 2)$, $P_2(2, 4)$. The total mass of the system is $m = \displaystyle\sum_{i=1}^{2} m_i = m_1 + m_2 = 12$. The

moment of the system about the x-axis is $M_x = \displaystyle\sum_{i=1}^{2} m_i y_i = 4 \cdot 2 + 8 \cdot 4 = 40$. The moment of the system about

the y-axis is $M_y = \displaystyle\sum_{i=1}^{2} m_i x_i = 4 \cdot (-1) + 8 \cdot 2 = 12$. $\overline{x} = \dfrac{M_y}{m} = \dfrac{12}{12} = 1$ and $\overline{y} = \dfrac{M_x}{m} = \dfrac{40}{12} = \dfrac{10}{3}$, so the

center of mass of the system is $(\overline{x}, \overline{y}) = \left(1, \tfrac{10}{3}\right)$.

26. $M_x = \displaystyle\sum_{i=1}^{4} m_i y_i = 6(-2) + 5(4) + 1(-7) + 4(-1) = -3$, $M_y = \displaystyle\sum_{i=1}^{4} m_i x_i = 6(1) + 5(3) + 1(-3) + 4(6) = 42$,

and $m = \displaystyle\sum_{i=1}^{4} m_i = 16$, so $\overline{x} = \dfrac{M_y}{m} = \dfrac{42}{16} = \dfrac{21}{8}$ and $\overline{y} = \dfrac{M_x}{m} = -\dfrac{3}{16}$; the center of mass is $(\overline{x}, \overline{y}) = \left(\tfrac{21}{8}, -\tfrac{3}{16}\right)$.

27. $A = \int_0^2 x^2 \, dx = \left[\frac{1}{3}x^3\right]_0^2 = \frac{8}{3}$,

$\bar{x} = \frac{1}{A} \int_0^2 x f(x) \, dx = \frac{1}{A} \int_0^2 x \cdot x^2 \, dx = \frac{3}{8} \left[\frac{1}{4}x^4\right]_0^2 = \frac{3}{8} \cdot 4 = \frac{3}{2}$,

$\bar{y} = \frac{1}{A} \int_0^2 \frac{1}{2}[f(x)]^2 \, dx = \frac{1}{A} \int_0^2 \frac{1}{2}(x^2)^2 \, dx = \frac{3}{8} \cdot \frac{1}{2}\left[\frac{1}{5}x^5\right]_0^2 = \frac{3}{16} \cdot \frac{32}{5} = \frac{6}{5}$.

Centroid $(\bar{x}, \bar{y}) = \left(\frac{3}{2}, \frac{6}{5}\right) = (1.5, 1.2)$.

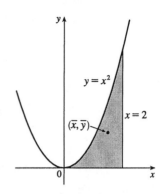

28. $A = \int_0^9 \sqrt{x} \, dx = \left[\frac{2}{3}x^{3/2}\right]_0^9 = \frac{2}{3} \cdot 27 = 18$,

$\bar{x} = \frac{1}{A} \int_0^9 x \sqrt{x} \, dx = \frac{1}{18}\left[\frac{2}{5}x^{5/2}\right]_0^9 = \frac{1}{18} \cdot \frac{2}{5} \cdot 243 = \frac{27}{5}$,

$\bar{y} = \frac{1}{A} \int_0^9 \frac{1}{2}(\sqrt{x})^2 \, dx = \frac{1}{18} \cdot \frac{1}{2}\left[\frac{1}{2}x^2\right]_0^9 = \frac{81}{72} = \frac{9}{8}$.

Centroid $(\bar{x}, \bar{y}) = \left(\frac{27}{5}, \frac{9}{8}\right) = (5.4, 1.125)$.

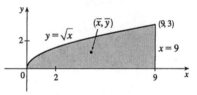

29. $A = \int_0^1 e^x \, dx = [e^x]_0^1 = e - 1$,

$\bar{x} = \frac{1}{A} \int_0^1 x e^x \, dx = \frac{1}{e-1}[xe^x - e^x]_0^1$ [by parts]

$= \frac{1}{e-1}[0 - (-1)] = \frac{1}{e-1}$,

$\bar{y} = \frac{1}{A} \int_0^1 \frac{1}{2}(e^x)^2 \, dx = \frac{1}{e-1} \cdot \frac{1}{4}\left[e^{2x}\right]_0^1 = \frac{1}{4(e-1)}(e^2 - 1) = \frac{e+1}{4}$.

Centroid $(\bar{x}, \bar{y}) = \left(\frac{1}{e-1}, \frac{e+1}{4}\right) \approx (0.58, 0.93)$.

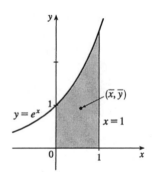

30. $A = \int_1^2 \frac{1}{x} \, dx = [\ln x]_1^2 = \ln 2$, $\bar{x} = \frac{1}{A} \int_1^2 x \cdot \frac{1}{x} \, dx = \frac{1}{A}[x]_1^2 = \frac{1}{A} = \frac{1}{\ln 2}$,

$\bar{y} = \frac{1}{A} \int_1^2 \frac{1}{2}\left(\frac{1}{x}\right)^2 \, dx = \frac{1}{2A} \int_1^2 x^{-2} \, dx = \frac{1}{2A}\left[-\frac{1}{x}\right]_1^2$

$= \frac{1}{2\ln 2}\left(-\frac{1}{2} + 1\right) = \frac{1}{4\ln 2}$.

Centroid $(\bar{x}, \bar{y}) = \left(\frac{1}{\ln 2}, \frac{1}{4\ln 2}\right) \approx (1.44, 0.36)$.

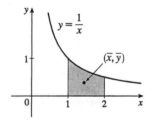

31. By symmetry, $M_y = 0$ and $\bar{x} = 0$. $A = \frac{1}{2}bh = \frac{1}{2} \cdot 2 \cdot 2 = 2$.

$M_x = \rho \int_{-1}^1 \frac{1}{2}(2 - 2x)^2 \, dx = 2\rho \int_0^1 \frac{1}{2}(2 - 2x)^2 \, dx$

$= \left(2 \cdot 1 \cdot \frac{1}{2} \cdot 2^2\right) \int_0^1 (1 - x)^2 \, dx$

$= 4 \int_1^0 u^2(-du)$ $[u = 1 - x, \, du = -dx]$

$= -4\left[\frac{1}{3}u^3\right]_1^0 = -4\left(-\frac{1}{3}\right) = \frac{4}{3}$

$\bar{y} = \frac{1}{m}M_x = \frac{1}{\rho A}M_x = \frac{1}{1 \cdot 2} \cdot \frac{4}{3} = \frac{2}{3}$. $(\bar{x}, \bar{y}) = \left(0, \frac{2}{3}\right)$.

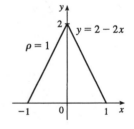

32. By symmetry about the line $y = x$, we expect that $\overline{x} = \overline{y}$. $A = \frac{1}{4}\pi r^2$, so $m = \rho A = 2A = \frac{1}{2}\pi r^2$.

$$M_x = \rho \int_0^r \frac{1}{2}\left(\sqrt{r^2 - x^2}\right)^2 dx = 2 \cdot \frac{1}{2}\int_0^r (r^2 - x^2)\,dx = \left[r^2 x - \frac{1}{3}x^3\right]_0^r = \frac{2}{3}r^3.$$

$$M_y = \rho \int_0^r x\sqrt{r^2 - x^2}\,dx = \int_0^r (r^2 - x^2)^{1/2} 2x\,dx = \int_0^{r^2} u^{1/2}\,du \; [u = r^2 - x^2] = \left[\frac{2}{3}u^{3/2}\right]_0^{r^2} = \frac{2}{3}r^3.$$

$$\overline{x} = \frac{1}{m}M_y = \frac{2}{\pi r^2}\left(\frac{2}{3}r^3\right) = \frac{4}{3\pi}r; \; \overline{y} = \frac{1}{m}M_x = \frac{2}{\pi r^2}\left(\frac{2}{3}r^3\right) = \frac{4}{3\pi}r. \quad (\overline{x},\overline{y}) = \left(\frac{4}{3\pi}r, \frac{4}{3\pi}r\right).$$

33. (a)

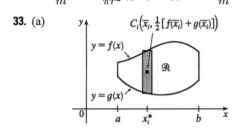

Suppose the region lies between two curves $y = f(x)$ and $y = g(x)$ where $f(x) \geq g(x)$, as illustrated in the figure. Use n subintervals determined by points x_i with $a = x_0 < x_1 < \cdots < x_n = b$ and choose $x_i^* = \overline{x}_i$ to be the midpoint of the ith subinterval; that is, $\overline{x}_i = \frac{1}{2}(x_{i-1} + x_i)$. Then the centroid of the ith approximating rectangle R_i is its center $C_i = \left(\overline{x}_i, \frac{1}{2}[f(\overline{x}_i) + g(\overline{x}_i)]\right)$. Its area is $[f(\overline{x}_i) - g(\overline{x}_i)]\,\Delta x$, so its mass is $\rho[f(\overline{x}_i) - g(\overline{x}_i)]\,\Delta x$.

Thus, $M_y(R_i) = \rho[f(\overline{x}_i) - g(\overline{x}_i)]\,\Delta x \cdot \overline{x}_i = \rho\overline{x}_i[f(\overline{x}_i) - g(\overline{x}_i)]\,\Delta x$ and

$M_x(R_i) = \rho[f(\overline{x}_i) - g(\overline{x}_i)]\,\Delta x \cdot \frac{1}{2}[f(\overline{x}_i) + g(\overline{x}_i)] = \rho \cdot \frac{1}{2}\left\{[f(\overline{x}_i)]^2 - [g(\overline{x}_i)]^2\right\}\Delta x$. Summing over i and

taking the limit as $n \to \infty$, we get $M_y = \lim\limits_{n\to\infty}\sum\limits_{i=1}^n \rho\overline{x}_i[f(\overline{x}_i) - g(\overline{x}_i)]\,\Delta x = \rho\int_a^b x[f(x) - g(x)]\,dx$ and

$M_x = \lim\limits_{n\to\infty}\sum\limits_{i=1}^n \rho \cdot \frac{1}{2}\left[f(\overline{x}_i)^2 - g(\overline{x}_i)^2\right]\Delta x = \rho\int_a^b \frac{1}{2}\left\{[f(x)]^2 - [g(x)]^2\right\}dx$. Thus,

$$\overline{x} = \frac{M_y}{m} = \frac{M_y}{\rho A} = \frac{1}{A}\int_a^b x[f(x) - g(x)]\,dx \text{ and } \overline{y} = \frac{M_x}{m} = \frac{M_x}{\rho A} = \frac{1}{A}\int_a^b \frac{1}{2}\left\{[f(x)]^2 - [g(x)]^2\right\}dx.$$

(b)

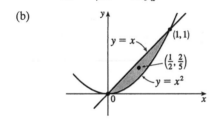

The region is sketched in the figure. We take $f(x) = x$, $g(x) = x^2$, $a = 0$, and $b = 1$ in the formulas in part (a). First we note that the area of the region is

$$A = \int_0^1 (x - x^2)\,dx = \left[\frac{1}{2}x^2 - \frac{1}{3}x^3\right]_0^1 = \frac{1}{6}$$

Therefore,

$$\overline{x} = \frac{1}{A}\int_0^1 x[f(x) - g(x)]\,dx = \frac{1}{1/6}\int_0^1 x(x - x^2)\,dx = 6\int_0^1 (x^2 - x^3)\,dx = 6\left[\frac{1}{3}x^3 - \frac{1}{4}x^4\right]_0^1 = \frac{1}{2} \text{ and}$$

$$\overline{y} = \frac{1}{A}\int_0^1 \frac{1}{2}\left\{[f(x)]^2 - [g(x)]^2\right\}dx = \frac{1}{1/6}\int_0^1 \frac{1}{2}(x^2 - x^4)\,dx = 3\left[\frac{1}{3}x^3 - \frac{1}{5}x^5\right]_0^1 = \frac{2}{5}.$$

The centroid is $\left(\frac{1}{2}, \frac{2}{5}\right)$.

34. (a) Let $0 \leq x \leq 1$. If $n < m$, then $x^n > x^m$; that is, raising x to a larger power produces a smaller number.

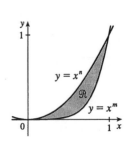

(b) Using Formulas 11 and the fact that the area of $\mathcal{R}$ is

$$A = \int_0^1 (x^n - x^m)\, dx = \frac{1}{n+1} - \frac{1}{m+1} = \frac{m-n}{(n+1)(m+1)}, \text{ we get}$$

$$\bar{x} = \frac{(n+1)(m+1)}{m-n} \int_0^1 x[x^n - x^m]\, dx = \frac{(n+1)(m+1)}{m-n} \int_0^1 (x^{n+1} - x^{m+1})\, dx$$

$$= \frac{(n+1)(m+1)}{m-n} \left[\frac{1}{n+2} - \frac{1}{m+2} \right] = \frac{(n+1)(m+1)}{(n+2)(m+2)}$$

and

$$\bar{y} = \frac{(n+1)(m+1)}{m-n} \int_0^1 \frac{1}{2} \left[(x^n)^2 - (x^m)^2 \right] dx = \frac{(n+1)(m+1)}{2(m-n)} \int_0^1 (x^{2n} - x^{2m})\, dx$$

$$= \frac{(n+1)(m+1)}{2(m-n)} \left[\frac{1}{2n+1} - \frac{1}{2m+1} \right] = \frac{(n+1)(m+1)}{(2n+1)(2m+1)}$$

(c) If we take $n = 3$ and $m = 4$, then

$$(\bar{x}, \bar{y}) = \left(\frac{4\cdot5}{5\cdot6}, \frac{4\cdot5}{7\cdot9} \right) = \left(\frac{2}{3}, \frac{20}{63} \right)$$

which lies outside $\mathcal{R}$ since $\left(\frac{2}{3}\right)^3 = \frac{8}{27} < \frac{20}{63}$. This is the simplest of many possibilities.

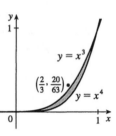

6.6 Applications to Economics and Biology • • • • • • •

1. $C(2000) = C(0) + \int_0^{2000} C'(x)\, dx = 1{,}500{,}000 + \int_0^{2000} (0.006x^2 - 1.5x + 8)\, dx$

$$= 1{,}500{,}000 + \left[0.002x^3 - 0.75x^2 + 8x \right]_0^{2000} = \$14{,}516{,}000$$

2. $R'(x) = 90 - 0.02x$ and $R(100) = \$8800$, so

$$R(200) = R(100) + \int_{100}^{200} R'(x)\, dx = 8800 + \int_{100}^{200} (90 - 0.02x)\, dx = 8800 + \left[90x - 0.01x^2 \right]_{100}^{200}$$

$$= 8800 + (18{,}000 - 400) - (9000 - 100) = \$17{,}500$$

3. If the production level is raised from 1200 units to 1600 units, then the increase in cost is

$$C(1600) - C(1200) = \int_{1200}^{1600} C'(x)\, dx = \int_{1200}^{1600} (74 + 1.1x - 0.002x^2 + 0.00004x^3)\, dx$$

$$= \left[74x + 0.55x^2 - \frac{0.002}{3}x^3 + 0.00001x^4 \right]_{1200}^{1600}$$

$$= 64{,}331{,}733.33 - 20{,}464{,}800 = \$43{,}866{,}933.33$$

4. Consumer surplus $= \int_0^{30} [p(x) - p(30)]\, dx$

$$= \int_0^{30} \left[5 - \tfrac{1}{10}x - \left(5 - \tfrac{30}{10} \right) \right] dx$$

$$= \left[3x - \tfrac{1}{20}x^2 \right]_0^{30} = 90 - 45 = \$45$$

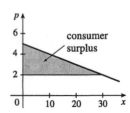

5. $p(x) = 10 \implies \dfrac{450}{x+8} = 10 \implies x+8 = 45 \implies x = 37.$

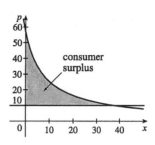

$\text{Consumer surplus} = \displaystyle\int_0^{37} [p(x) - 10]\, dx = \int_0^{37} \left(\dfrac{450}{x+8} - 10 \right) dx$

$= [450 \ln (x+8) - 10x]_0^{37}$

$= (450 \ln 45 - 370) - 450 \ln 8$

$= 450 \ln \left(\frac{45}{8} \right) - 370 \approx \$407.25$

6. $p_S(x) = 3 + 0.01x^2.\ P = p_S(10) = 3 + 1 = 4.$

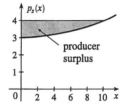

$\text{Producer surplus} = \displaystyle\int_0^{10} [P - p_S(x)]\, dx$

$= \displaystyle\int_0^{10} \left[4 - 3 - 0.01x^2 \right] dx = \left[x - \frac{0.01}{3} x^3 \right]_0^{10}$

$\approx 10 - 3.33 = \$6.67$

7. $P = p_S(x) = 10 = 5 + \frac{1}{10}\sqrt{x} \implies 50 = \sqrt{x} \implies x = 2500.$

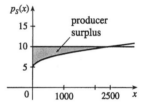

$\text{Producer surplus} = \displaystyle\int_0^{2500} [P - p_S(x)]\, dx$

$= \displaystyle\int_0^{2500} \left(10 - 5 - \tfrac{1}{10}\sqrt{x} \right) dx$

$= \left[5x - \tfrac{1}{15} x^{3/2} \right]_0^{2500} \approx \$4166.67$

8. $p = 50 - \frac{1}{20}x$ and $p = 20 + \frac{1}{10}x$ intersect at $p = 40$ and $x = 200.$

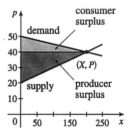

$\text{Consumer surplus} = \displaystyle\int_0^{200} \left(50 - \tfrac{1}{20}x - 40 \right) dx$

$= \left[10x - \tfrac{1}{40} x^2 \right]_0^{200} = \$1000$

$\text{Producer surplus} = \displaystyle\int_0^{200} \left(40 - 20 - \tfrac{1}{10}x \right) dx$

$= \left[20x - \tfrac{1}{20} x^2 \right]_0^{200} = \$2000$

9. $p(x) = \dfrac{800{,}000 e^{-x/5000}}{x + 20{,}000} = 16 \implies x = x_1 \approx 3727.04.$

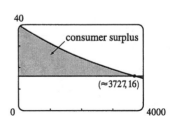

$\text{Consumer surplus} = \displaystyle\int_0^{x_1} [p(x) - 16]\, dx \approx \$37{,}753$

10. The demand function is linear with slope $\frac{-0.5}{35} = -\frac{1}{70}$ and $p(400) = 7.5$, so an equation is

$p - 7.5 = -\frac{1}{70}(x - 400)$ or $p = -\frac{1}{70}x + \frac{185}{14}$. A selling price of \$6 implies that $6 = -\frac{1}{70}x + \frac{185}{14}$ $\Rightarrow$

$\frac{1}{70}x = \frac{185}{14} - \frac{84}{14} = \frac{101}{14}$ $\Rightarrow$ $x = 505$.

Consumer surplus $= \int_0^{505} \left(-\frac{1}{70}x + \frac{185}{14} - 6\right) dx = \left[-\frac{1}{140}x^2 + \frac{101}{14}x\right]_0^{505} \approx \$1821.61$

11. $f(8) - f(4) = \int_4^8 f'(t)\, dt = \int_4^8 \sqrt{t}\, dt = \left[\frac{2}{3}t^{3/2}\right]_4^8 = \frac{2}{3}\left(16\sqrt{2} - 8\right) \approx \$9.75$ million

12. $n(9) - n(5) = \int_5^9 (2200 + 10e^{0.8t})\, dt = \left[2200t + \dfrac{10e^{0.8t}}{0.8}\right]_5^9 = [2200t]_5^9 + \frac{25}{2}\left[e^{0.8t}\right]_5^9$

$= 2200(9 - 5) + 12.5\left(e^{7.2} - e^4\right) \approx 24{,}860$

13. $F = \dfrac{\pi P R^4}{8\eta l} = \dfrac{\pi(4000)(0.008)^4}{8(0.027)(2)} \approx 1.19 \times 10^{-4}\ \text{cm}^3/\text{s}$

14. If the flux remains constant, then $\dfrac{\pi P_0 R_0^4}{8\eta l} = \dfrac{\pi P R^4}{8\eta l}$ $\Rightarrow$ $P_0 R_0^4 = P R^4$ $\Rightarrow$ $\dfrac{P}{P_0} = \left(\dfrac{R_0}{R}\right)^4$.

$R = \frac{3}{4}R_0$ $\Rightarrow$ $\dfrac{P}{P_0} = \left(\dfrac{R_0}{\frac{3}{4}R_0}\right)^4$ $\Rightarrow$ $P = P_0\left(\frac{4}{3}\right)^4 \approx 3.1605 P_0 > 3P_0$; that is, the blood pressure is more

than tripled.

15. $\int_0^{12} c(t)\, dt = \int_0^{12} \frac{1}{4}t(12 - t)\, dt = \int_0^{12}\left(3t - \frac{1}{4}t^2\right) dt = \left[\frac{3}{2}t^2 - \frac{1}{12}t^3\right]_0^{12} = (216 - 144) = 72\ \text{mg} \cdot \text{s/L}$.

Thus, the cardiac output is $F = \dfrac{A}{\int_0^{12} c(t)\, dt} = \dfrac{8\ \text{mg}}{72\ \text{mg} \cdot \text{s/L}} = \frac{1}{9}\ \text{L/s} = \frac{60}{9}\ \text{L/min}$.

16. As in Example 2, we will estimate the cardiac output using Simpson's Rule with $\Delta t = 2$.

$\int_0^{20} c(t)\, dt \approx \frac{2}{3}[1(0) + 4(2.4) + 2(5.1) + 4(7.8) + 2(7.6)$

$+ 4(5.4) + 2(3.9) + 4(2.3) + 2(1.6) + 4(0.7) + 1(0)]$

$= \frac{2}{3}(110.8) \approx 73.87\ \text{mg} \cdot \text{s/L}$

Therefore, $F \approx \dfrac{A}{73.87} = \dfrac{8}{73.87} \approx 0.1083\ \text{L/s}$ or $6.498\ \text{L/min}$.

6.7 Probability · · · · · · · · · · · · · · · · ·

1. (a) $\displaystyle\int_{30{,}000}^{40{,}000} f(x)\, dx$ is the probability that a randomly chosen tire will have a lifetime between 30,000 and 40,000 miles.

(b) $\displaystyle\int_{25{,}000}^{\infty} f(x)\, dx$ is the probability that a randomly chosen tire will have a lifetime of at least 25,000 miles.

2. (a) The probability that you drive to school in less than 15 minutes is $\int_0^{15} f(t)\, dt$.

(b) The probability that it takes you more than half an hour to get to school is $\int_{30}^{\infty} f(t)\, dt$.

3. (a) In general, we must satisfy the two conditions that are mentioned before Example 1—namely, (1) $f(x) \geq 0$ for

all x, and (2) $\int_{-\infty}^{\infty} f(x)\, dx = 1$. Since $f(x) = 0$ or $f(x) = 0.1$, condition (1) is satisfied. For condition (2), we

see that $\int_{-\infty}^{\infty} f(x)\, dx = \int_0^{10} 0.1\, dx = \left[\frac{1}{10}x\right]_0^{10} = 1$. Thus, $f(x)$ is a probability density function for the

spinner's values.

(b) Since all the numbers between 0 and 10 are equally likely to be selected, we expect the mean to be halfway between the endpoints of the interval; that is, $x = 5$.

$\mu = \int_{-\infty}^{\infty} x f(x)\, dx = \int_0^{10} x(0.1)\, dx = \left[\frac{1}{20}x^2\right]_0^{10} = \frac{100}{20} = 5$, as expected.

4. (a) As in the preceding exercise, (1) $f(x) \geq 0$ and

(2) $\int_{-\infty}^{\infty} f(x)\, dx = \int_0^{10} f(x)\, dx = \frac{1}{2}(10)(0.2)$ [area of a triangle] $= 1$. So $f(x)$ is a probability density function.

(b) (i) $P(X < 3) = \int_0^3 f(x)\, dx = \frac{1}{2}(3)(0.1) = \frac{3}{20} = 0.15$

(ii) We first compute $P(X > 8)$ and then subtract that value and our answer in (i) from 1 (the total probability).

$P(X > 8) = \int_8^{10} f(x)\, dx = \frac{1}{2}(2)(0.1) = \frac{2}{20} = 0.10$. So $P(3 \leq X \leq 8) = 1 - 0.15 - 0.10 = 0.75$.

(c) We find equations of the lines from $(0,0)$ to $(6, 0.2)$ and from $(6, 0.2)$ to $(10, 0)$, and find that

$$f(x) = \begin{cases} \frac{1}{30}x & \text{if } 0 \leq x < 6 \\ -\frac{1}{20}x + \frac{1}{2} & \text{if } 6 \leq x < 10 \\ 0 & \text{otherwise} \end{cases}$$

$\mu = \int_{-\infty}^{\infty} x f(x)\, dx = \int_0^6 x\left(\frac{1}{30}x\right) dx + \int_6^{10} x\left(-\frac{1}{20}x + \frac{1}{2}\right) dx = \left[\frac{1}{90}x^3\right]_0^6 + \left[-\frac{1}{60}x^3 + \frac{1}{4}x^2\right]_6^{10}$

$= \frac{216}{90} + \left(-\frac{1000}{60} + \frac{100}{4}\right) - \left(-\frac{216}{60} + \frac{36}{4}\right) = \frac{16}{3} = 5.\overline{3}$

5. We need to find m so that $\int_m^{\infty} f(t)\, dt = \frac{1}{2}$ $\Rightarrow$ $\lim_{x \to \infty} \int_m^x \frac{1}{5}e^{-t/5}\, dt = \frac{1}{2}$ $\Rightarrow$ $\lim_{x \to \infty}\left[\frac{1}{5}(-5)e^{-t/5}\right]_m^x = \frac{1}{2}$ $\Rightarrow$

$(-1)\left(0 - e^{-m/5}\right) = \frac{1}{2}$ $\Rightarrow$ $e^{-m/5} = \frac{1}{2}$ $\Rightarrow$ $-m/5 = \ln\frac{1}{2}$ $\Rightarrow$ $m = -5\ln\frac{1}{2} = 5\ln 2 \approx 3.47$ min.

6. (a) $\mu = 1000$ $\Rightarrow$ $f(t) = \begin{cases} 0 & \text{if } t < 0 \\ \frac{1}{1000}e^{-t/1000} & \text{if } t \geq 0 \end{cases}$

(i) $P(0 \leq X \leq 200) = \int_0^{200} \frac{1}{1000}e^{-t/1000}\, dt = \left[-e^{-t/1000}\right]_0^{200} = -e^{-1/5} + 1 \approx 0.181$

(ii) $P(X > 800) = \int_{800}^{\infty} \frac{1}{1000}e^{-t/1000}\, dt = \lim_{x \to \infty}\left[-e^{-t/1000}\right]_{800}^x = 0 + e^{-4/5} \approx 0.449$

(b) We need to find m so that $\int_m^{\infty} f(t)\, dt = \frac{1}{2}$ $\Rightarrow$ $\lim_{x \to \infty} \int_m^x \frac{1}{1000}e^{-t/1000}\, dt = \frac{1}{2}$ $\Rightarrow$

$\lim_{x \to \infty}\left[-e^{-t/1000}\right]_m^x = \frac{1}{2}$ $\Rightarrow$ $0 + e^{-m/1000} = \frac{1}{2}$ $\Rightarrow$ $-m/1000 = \ln\frac{1}{2}$ $\Rightarrow$

$m = -1000\ln\frac{1}{2} = 1000\ln 2 \approx 693.1$ h.

7. We use an exponential density function with $\mu = 2.5$ min.

(a) $P(X > 4) = \int_4^{\infty} f(t)\, dt = \lim_{x \to \infty} \int_4^x \frac{1}{2.5}e^{-t/2.5}\, dt = \lim_{x \to \infty}\left[-e^{-t/2.5}\right]_4^x = 0 + e^{-4/2.5} \approx 0.202$

(b) $P(0 \leq X \leq 2) = \int_0^2 f(t)\, dt = \left[-e^{-t/2.5}\right]_0^2 = -e^{-2/2.5} + 1 \approx 0.551$

(c) We need to find a value a so that $P(X \geq a) = 0.02$, or, equivalently, $P(0 \leq X \leq a) = 0.98$ $\Leftrightarrow$

$\int_0^a f(t)\, dt = 0.98$ $\Leftrightarrow$ $\left[-e^{-t/2.5}\right]_0^a = 0.98$ $\Leftrightarrow$ $-e^{-a/2.5} + 1 = 0.98$ $\Leftrightarrow$ $e^{-a/2.5} = 0.02$ $\Leftrightarrow$

$-a/2.5 = \ln 0.02$ $\Leftrightarrow$ $a = -2.5\ln\frac{1}{50} = 2.5\ln 50 \approx 9.78$ min ≈ 10 min. The ad should say that if you aren't served within 10 minutes, you get a free hamburger.

8. (a) With $\mu = 69$ and $\sigma = 2.8$, we have $P(65 \leq X \leq 73) = \int_{65}^{73} \frac{1}{2.8\sqrt{2\pi}} \exp\left(-\frac{(x-69)^2}{2 \cdot 2.8^2}\right) dx \approx 0.847$ (using
a calculator or computer to estimate the integral).

(b) $P(X > 6 \text{ feet}) = P(X > 72 \text{ inches}) = 1 - P(0 \leq X \leq 72) \approx 1 - 0.858 = 0.142$, so 14.2% of the adult
male population is more than 6 feet tall.

9. $P(X \geq 10) = \int_{10}^{\infty} \frac{1}{4.2\sqrt{2\pi}} \exp\left(-\frac{(x-9.4)^2}{2 \cdot 4.2^2}\right) dx$. To avoid the improper integral we approximate it by the

integral from 10 to 100. Thus, $P(X \geq 10) \approx \int_{10}^{100} \frac{1}{4.2\sqrt{2\pi}} \exp\left(-\frac{(x-9.4)^2}{2 \cdot 4.2^2}\right) dx \approx 0.443$ (using a calculator
or computer to estimate the integral), so about 44 percent of the households throw out at least 10 lb of paper a week.
Note: We can't evaluate $1 - P(0 \leq X \leq 10)$ for this problem since a significant amount of area lies to the left of
$X = 0$.

10. (a) $P(0 \leq X \leq 480) = \int_{0}^{480} \frac{1}{12\sqrt{2\pi}} \exp\left(-\frac{(x-500)^2}{2 \cdot 12^2}\right) dx \approx 0.0478$ (using a calculator or computer to
estimate the integral), so there is about a 4.78% chance that a particular box contains less than 480 g of cereal.

(b) We need to find μ so that $P(0 \leq X < 500) = 0.05$. Using our calculator or computer to find $P(0 \leq X \leq 500)$
for various values of μ, we find that if $\mu = 519.73$, $P = 0.05007$; and if $\mu = 519.74$, $P = 0.04998$. So a good
target weight is at least 519.74 g.

11. $P(\mu - 2\sigma \leq X \leq \mu + 2\sigma) = \int_{\mu-2\sigma}^{\mu+2\sigma} \frac{1}{\sigma\sqrt{2\pi}} \exp\left(-\frac{(x-\mu)^2}{2\sigma^2}\right) dx$. Substituting $t = \frac{x-\mu}{\sigma}$ and $dt = \frac{1}{\sigma} dx$
gives us

$$\int_{-2}^{2} \frac{1}{\sigma\sqrt{2\pi}} e^{-t^2/2}(\sigma\, dt) = \frac{1}{\sqrt{2\pi}} \int_{-2}^{2} e^{-t^2/2}\, dt \approx 0.9545$$

12. Let $f(x) = \begin{cases} 0 & \text{if } x < 0 \\ ce^{-cx} & \text{if } x \geq 0 \end{cases}$ where $c = 1/\mu$. By using parts, tables, or a CAS, we find that

(1): $\int xe^{bx}\, dx = \left(e^{bx}/b^2\right)(bx - 1)$
(2): $\int x^2 e^{bx}\, dx = \left(e^{bx}/b^3\right)\left(b^2x^2 - 2bx + 2\right)$
Now

$$\sigma^2 = \int_{-\infty}^{\infty}(x-\mu)^2 f(x)\, dx = \int_{-\infty}^{0}(x-\mu)^2 f(x)\, dx + \int_{0}^{\infty}(x-\mu)^2 f(x)\, dx$$

$$= 0 + \lim_{t\to\infty} c\int_{0}^{t}(x-\mu)^2 e^{-cx}\, dx = c \cdot \lim_{t\to\infty} \int_{0}^{t}\left(x^2 e^{-cx} - 2x\mu e^{-cx} + \mu^2 e^{-cx}\right) dx$$

Next we use (2) and (1) with $b = -c$ to get

$$\sigma^2 = c\lim_{t\to\infty}\left[-\frac{e^{-cx}}{c^3}(c^2 x^2 + 2cx + 2) - 2\mu\frac{e^{-cx}}{c^2}(-cx - 1) + \mu^2\frac{e^{-cx}}{-c}\right]_{0}^{t}$$

Using l'Hospital's Rule several times, along with the fact that $\mu = 1/c$, we get

$$\sigma^2 = c\left[0 - \left(-\frac{2}{c^3} + \frac{2}{c}\cdot\frac{1}{c^2} + \frac{1}{c^2}\cdot\frac{1}{-c}\right)\right] = c\left(\frac{1}{c^3}\right) = \frac{1}{c^2} \quad\Rightarrow\quad \sigma = \frac{1}{c} = \mu$$

13. (a) First $p(r) = \frac{4}{a_0^3}r^2 e^{-2r/a_0} \geq 0$ for $r \geq 0$. Next,

$$\int_{-\infty}^{\infty} p(r)\, dr = \int_{0}^{\infty} \frac{4}{a_0^3}r^2 e^{-2r/a_0}\, dr = \frac{4}{a_0^3}\lim_{t\to\infty}\int_{0}^{t} r^2 e^{-2r/a_0}\, dr$$

As in Exercise 12, we use (2) from that solution (with $b = -2/a_0$) and l'Hospital's Rule to get

$\frac{4}{a_0^3}\left[\frac{a_0^3}{-8}(-2)\right] = 1$. This satisfies the second condition for a function to be a probability density function.

(b) Using l'Hospital's Rule, $\frac{4}{a_0^3}\lim\limits_{r\to\infty}\frac{r^2}{e^{2r/a_0}} = \frac{4}{a_0^3}\lim\limits_{r\to\infty}\frac{2r}{(2/a_0)e^{2r/a_0}} = \frac{2}{a_0^2}\lim\limits_{r\to\infty}\frac{2}{(2/a_0)e^{2r/a_0}} = 0$.

To find the maximum of p, we differentiate:

$$p'(r) = \frac{4}{a_0^3}\left[r^2 e^{-2r/a_0}\left(-\frac{2}{a_0}\right) + e^{-2r/a_0}(2r)\right] = \frac{4}{a_0^3}e^{-2r/a_0}(2r)\left(-\frac{r}{a_0}+1\right)$$

$p'(r) = 0 \iff r = 0$ or $1 = \frac{r}{a_0} \iff r = a_0$ [$a_0 \approx 5.59 \times 10^{-11}$ m]. $p'(r)$ changes from positive to

negative at $r = a_0$, so $p(r)$ has its maximum value at $r = a_0$.

(c) It is fairly difficult to find a viewing rectangle, but knowing the
maximum value from part (b) helps.

$$p(a_0) = \frac{4}{a_0^3}a_0^2 e^{-2a_0/a_0} = \frac{4}{a_0}e^{-2} \approx 9{,}684{,}098{,}979$$

With a maximum of nearly 10 billion and a total area under the curve
of 1, we know that the "hump" in the graph must be extremely
narrow.

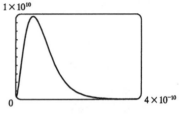

(d) $P(r) = \displaystyle\int_0^r \frac{4}{a_0^3}s^2 e^{-2s/a_0}\,ds \implies P(4a_0) = \int_0^{4a_0}\frac{4}{a_0^3}s^2 e^{-2s/a_0}\,ds$. Using (2) from the solution to

Exercise 12 (with $b = -2/a_0$),

$$P(4a_0) = \frac{4}{a_0^3}\left[\frac{e^{-2s/a_0}}{-8/a_0^3}\left(\frac{4}{a_0^2}s^2 + \frac{4}{a_0}s + 2\right)\right]_0^{4a_0} = \frac{4}{a_0^3}\left(\frac{a_0^3}{-8}\right)\left[e^{-8}(64+16+2) - 1(2)\right]$$

$$= -\tfrac{1}{2}\left(82e^{-8} - 2\right) = 1 - 41e^{-8} \approx 0.986$$

(e) $\mu = \displaystyle\int_{-\infty}^{\infty} rp(r)\,dr = \frac{4}{a_0^3}\lim\limits_{t\to\infty}\int_0^t r^3 e^{-2r/a_0}\,dr$. Integrating by parts three times or using a CAS, we find that

$\displaystyle\int x^3 e^{bx}\,dx = \frac{e^{bx}}{b^4}\left(b^3 x^3 - 3b^2 x^2 + 6bx - 6\right)$. So with $b = -\frac{2}{a_0}$, we use l'Hospital's Rule, and get

$$\mu = \frac{4}{a_0^3}\left[\frac{a_0^4}{16}(-6)\right] = \tfrac{3}{2}a_0.$$

6 **Review**

────────────────────── • **CONCEPT CHECK** • ──────────────────────

1. (a) See Section 6.1, Figure 2 and Equations 6.1.1 and 6.1.2.

   (b) Instead of using "top minus bottom" and integrating from left to right, we use "right minus left" and integrate from bottom to top. See Figures 9 and 10 in Section 6.1.

2. The numerical value of the area represents the number of meters by which Sue is ahead of Kathy after 1 minute.

3. (a) See the discussion in Section 6.2, near Figures 2 and 3, ending in the Definition of Volume.

   (b) See the discussion between Examples 5 and 6 in Section 6.2. If the cross-section is a disk, find the radius in terms of x or y and use $A = \pi(\text{radius})^2$. If the cross-section is a washer, find the inner radius r_{in} and outer radius r_{out} and use $A = \pi\left(r_{out}^2\right) - \pi\left(r_{in}^2\right)$.

4. (a) The length of a curve is defined to be the limit of the lengths of the inscribed polygons, as described near Figure 3 in Section 6.3.

   (b) See Equation 6.3.1.

   (c) See Equations 6.3.2 and 6.3.3.

5. (a) See the boxed equation preceding Example 1 in Section 6.4.

   (b) The Mean Value Theorem for Integrals says that there is a number c at which the value of f is exactly equal to the average value of the function, that is, $f(c) = f_{ave}$. For a geometric interpretation of the Mean Value Theorem for Integrals, see Figure 2 in Section 6.4 and the discussion that accompanies it.

6. $\int_0^6 f(x)\,dx$ represents the amount of work done. Its units are newton-meters, or joules.

7. Let $c(x)$ be the cross-sectional length of the wall (measured parallel to the surface of the fluid) at depth x. Then the hydrostatic force against the wall is given by $F = \int_a^b \delta x c(x)\,dx$, where a and b are the lower and upper limits for x at points of the wall and δ is the weight density of the fluid.

8. (a) The center of mass is the point at which the plate balances horizontally.

   (b) See Equations 6.5.11.

9. See Figure 3 in Section 6.6, and the discussion which precedes it.

10. (a) See the definition before Figure 6 in Section 6.6.

    (b) See the discussion after Figure 6 in Section 6.6.

11. A probability density function f is a function on the domain of a continuous random variable X such that $\int_a^b f(x)\,dx$ measures the probability that X lies between a and b. Such a function f has nonnegative values and satisfies the relation $\int_D f(x)\,dx = 1$, where D is the domain of the corresponding random variable X. If $D = \mathbb{R}$, or if we define $f(x) = 0$ for real numbers $x \notin D$, then $\int_{-\infty}^{\infty} f(x)\,dx = 1$. (Of course, to work with f in this way, we must assume that the integrals of f exist.)

12. (a) $\int_0^{100} f(x)\,dx$ represents the probability that the weight of a randomly chosen female college student is less than 100 pounds.

    (b) $\mu = \int_{-\infty}^{\infty} x f(x)\,dx = \int_0^{\infty} x f(x)\,dx$

    (c) The median of f is the number m such that $\int_m^{\infty} f(x)\,dx = \frac{1}{2}$.

◆ **EXERCISES** ◆

1. $A = \int_0^1 \left[(e^x - 1) - (x^2 - x) \right] dx$

$= \int_0^1 (e^x - 1 - x^2 + x) \, dx = \left[e^x - x - \frac{1}{3}x^3 + \frac{1}{2}x^2 \right]_0^1$

$= \left(e - 1 - \frac{1}{3} + \frac{1}{2} \right) - (1 - 0 - 0 + 0) = e - \frac{11}{6}$

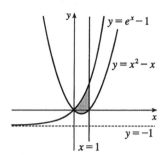

2. $A = \int_1^7 \left[(2y - 7) - (y^2 - 6y) \right] dy$

$= \int_1^7 (-y^2 + 8y - 7) \, dy$

$= \left[-\frac{1}{3}y^3 + 4y^2 - 7y \right]_1^7$

$= \left(-\frac{343}{3} + 196 - 49 \right) - \left(-\frac{1}{3} + 4 - 7 \right) = 36$

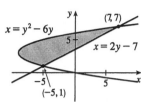

3. $x = 2\theta - \sin\theta \;\Rightarrow\; dx = (2 - \cos\theta) \, d\theta$

$A = \int_0^{2\pi} y \, dx = \int_0^{2\pi} \left[(2 - \cos\theta)(2 - \cos\theta) \right] d\theta$

$= \int_0^{2\pi} (4 - 4\cos\theta + \cos^2\theta) \, d\theta$

$= \int_0^{2\pi} \left(4 - 4\cos\theta + \frac{1}{2} + \frac{1}{2}\cos 2\theta \right) d\theta$

$= \left[4\theta - 4\sin\theta + \frac{1}{2}\theta + \frac{1}{4}\sin 2\theta \right]_0^{2\pi}$

$= (8\pi - 0 + \pi + 0) - (0) = 9\pi$

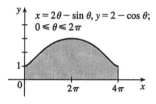

4. $V = \int_0^1 \pi \left[(1 + x)^2 - \left(e^{-2x} \right)^2 \right] dx = \pi \int_0^1 \left(1 + 2x + x^2 - e^{-4x} \right) dx$

$= \pi \left[x + x^2 + \frac{1}{3}x^3 + \frac{1}{4}e^{-4x} \right]_0^1 = \pi \left(1 + 1 + \frac{1}{3} + \frac{1}{4}e^{-4} - \frac{1}{4} \right)$

$= \pi \left(\dfrac{25}{12} + \dfrac{1}{4e^4} \right)$

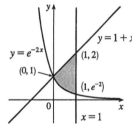

5. (a) Using the Midpoint Rule on $[0, 1]$ with $f(x) = \tan(x^2)$ and $n = 4$, we estimate

$$A = \int_0^1 \tan(x^2) \, dx \approx \frac{1}{4} \left[\tan\left(\left(\tfrac{1}{8} \right)^2 \right) + \tan\left(\left(\tfrac{3}{8} \right)^2 \right) + \tan\left(\left(\tfrac{5}{8} \right)^2 \right) + \tan\left(\left(\tfrac{7}{8} \right)^2 \right) \right] \approx \frac{1}{4}(1.53) \approx 0.38$$

(b) Using the Midpoint Rule on $[0, 1]$ with $f(x) = \pi \tan^2(x^2)$ (for disks) and $n = 4$, we estimate

$$V = \int_0^1 f(x) \, dx \approx \frac{1}{4}\pi \left[\tan^2\left(\left(\tfrac{1}{8} \right)^2 \right) + \tan^2\left(\left(\tfrac{3}{8} \right)^2 \right) + \tan^2\left(\left(\tfrac{5}{8} \right)^2 \right) + \tan^2\left(\left(\tfrac{7}{8} \right)^2 \right) \right] \approx \frac{\pi}{4}(1.114) \approx 0.87$$

6. (a) $A = \int_0^1 (2x - x^2 - x^3) \, dx = \left[x^2 - \frac{1}{3}x^3 - \frac{1}{4}x^4 \right]_0^1 = 1 - \frac{1}{3} - \frac{1}{4} = \frac{5}{12}$

(b) A cross-section is a washer with inner radius x^3 and outer radius $2x - x^2$, so its area is $\pi (2x - x^2)^2 - \pi (x^3)^2$.

$$V = \int_0^1 A(x) \, dx = \int_0^1 \pi \left[(2x - x^2)^2 - (x^3)^2 \right] dx = \int_0^1 \pi (4x^2 - 4x^3 + x^4 - x^6) \, dx$$

$$= \pi \left[\tfrac{4}{3}x^3 - x^4 + \tfrac{1}{5}x^5 - \tfrac{1}{7}x^7 \right]_0^1 = \pi \left(\tfrac{4}{3} - 1 + \tfrac{1}{5} - \tfrac{1}{7} \right) = \frac{41\pi}{105}$$

(c) Using the method of cylindrical shells,

$$V = \int_0^1 2\pi x (2x - x^2 - x^3)\, dx = \int_0^1 2\pi (2x^2 - x^3 - x^4)\, dx = 2\pi \left[\tfrac{2}{3}x^3 - \tfrac{1}{4}x^4 - \tfrac{1}{5}x^5\right]_0^1$$
$$= 2\pi \left(\tfrac{2}{3} - \tfrac{1}{4} - \tfrac{1}{5}\right) = \tfrac{13\pi}{30}.$$

7. (a) A cross-section is a washer with inner radius x^2 and outer radius x.

$$V = \int_0^1 \pi \left[(x)^2 - (x^2)^2\right] dx = \int_0^1 \pi (x^2 - x^4)\, dx = \pi \left[\tfrac{1}{3}x^3 - \tfrac{1}{5}x^5\right]_0^1 = \pi \left[\tfrac{1}{3} - \tfrac{1}{5}\right] = \tfrac{2\pi}{15}$$

(b) A cross-section is a washer with inner radius y and outer radius $\sqrt{y}$.

$$V = \int_0^1 \pi \left[\left(\sqrt{y}\right)^2 - y^2\right] dy = \int_0^1 \pi (y - y^2)\, dy = \pi \left[\tfrac{1}{2}y^2 - \tfrac{1}{3}y^3\right]_0^1 = \pi \left[\tfrac{1}{2} - \tfrac{1}{3}\right] = \tfrac{\pi}{6}$$

(c) A cross-section is a washer with inner radius $2 - x$ and outer radius $2 - x^2$.

$$V = \int_0^1 \pi \left[(2 - x^2)^2 - (2 - x)^2\right] dx = \int_0^1 \pi (x^4 - 5x^2 + 4x)\, dx = \pi \left[\tfrac{1}{5}x^5 - \tfrac{5}{3}x^3 + 2x^2\right]_0^1$$
$$= \pi \left[\tfrac{1}{5} - \tfrac{5}{3} + 2\right] = \tfrac{8\pi}{15}$$

8. (a)

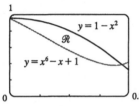

From the graph, we see that the curves intersect at $x = 0$ and at $x = a \approx 0.75$, with $1 - x^2 > x^6 - x + 1$ on $(0, a)$.

(b) The area of $\mathcal{R}$ is

$$A = \int_0^a \left[(1 - x^2) - (x^6 - x + 1)\right] dx = \left[-\tfrac{1}{3}x^3 - \tfrac{1}{7}x^7 + \tfrac{1}{2}x^2\right]_0^a \approx 0.12$$

(c) Using disks, the volume generated when $\mathcal{R}$ is rotated about the x-axis is

$$V = \pi \int_0^a \left[(1 - x^2)^2 - (x^6 - x + 1)^2\right] dx = \pi \int_0^a (-x^{12} + 2x^7 - 2x^6 + x^4 - 3x^2 + 2x)\, dx$$
$$= \pi \left[-\tfrac{1}{13}x^{13} + \tfrac{1}{4}x^8 - \tfrac{2}{7}x^7 + \tfrac{1}{5}x^5 - x^3 + x^2\right]_0^a \approx 0.54$$

(d) Using shells, the volume generated when $\mathcal{R}$ is rotated about the y-axis is

$$V = \int_0^a 2\pi x \left[(1 - x^2) - (x^6 - x + 1)\right] dx = 2\pi \int_0^a (-x^3 - x^7 + x^2)\, dx$$
$$= 2\pi \left[-\tfrac{1}{4}x^4 - \tfrac{1}{8}x^8 + \tfrac{1}{3}x^3\right]_0^a \approx 0.31$$

9. (a) The solid is obtained by rotating the region $\mathcal{R} = \left\{(x, y) \mid 0 \le x \le \tfrac{\pi}{2}, 0 \le y \le \sqrt{2}\cos x\right\}$ about the x-axis.

(b) The solid is obtained by rotating the region $\mathcal{R} = \left\{(x, y) \mid 0 \le x \le 1, 2 - \sqrt{x} \le y \le 2 - x^2\right\}$ about the x-axis.

Or: The solid is obtained by rotating the region $\mathcal{R} = \left\{(x, y) \mid 0 \le x \le 1, x^2 \le y \le \sqrt{x}\right\}$ about the line $y = 2$.

10. With an x-axis in the normal position, at $x = 7$ we have $C = 2\pi r = 45 \;\Rightarrow\; r(7) = \tfrac{2\pi}{45}$. Using Simpson's Rule with $n = 4$ and $\Delta x = 7$, we have

$$V = \int_0^{28} \pi [r(x)]^2\, dx \approx S_4 = \tfrac{7}{3}\left[0 + 4\pi \left(\tfrac{45}{2\pi}\right)^2 + 2\pi \left(\tfrac{53}{2\pi}\right)^2 + 4\pi \left(\tfrac{45}{2\pi}\right)^2 + 0\right] = \tfrac{7}{3}\left(\tfrac{21{,}818}{4\pi}\right) \approx 4051\ \text{cm}^3$$

11. Take the base to be the disk $x^2 + y^2 \le 9$. Then $V = \int_{-3}^{3} A(x)\, dx$, where $A(x_0)$ is the area of the isosceles right triangle whose hypotenuse lies along the line $x = x_0$ in the xy-plane. The length of the hypotenuse is $2\sqrt{9 - x^2}$ and the length of each leg is $\sqrt{2}\sqrt{9 - x^2}$. $A(x) = \tfrac{1}{2}\left(\sqrt{2}\sqrt{9 - x^2}\right)^2 = 9 - x^2$, so

$$V = 2\int_0^3 A(x)\, dx = 2\int_0^3 (9 - x^2)\, dx = 2\left[9x - \tfrac{1}{3}x^3\right]_0^3 = 2(27 - 9) = 36.$$

12. $V = \int_{-1}^{1} A(x)\, dx = 2\int_0^1 A(x)\, dx = 2\int_0^1 \left[(2-x^2)-x^2\right]^2 dx = 2\int_0^1 \left[2(1-x^2)\right]^2 dx$

$\qquad = 8\int_0^1 (1-2x^2+x^4)\, dx = 8\left[x - \frac{2}{3}x^3 + \frac{1}{5}x^5\right]_0^1 = 8\left(1 - \frac{2}{3} + \frac{1}{5}\right) = \frac{64}{15}$

13. Equilateral triangles with sides measuring $\frac{1}{4}x$ meters have height $\frac{1}{4}x\sin 60° = \frac{\sqrt{3}}{8}x$. Therefore,

$\quad A(x) = \frac{1}{2}\cdot\frac{1}{4}x\cdot\frac{\sqrt{3}}{8}x = \frac{\sqrt{3}}{64}x^2.\ \ V = \int_0^{20} A(x)\, dx = \frac{\sqrt{3}}{64}\int_0^{20} x^2\, dx = \frac{\sqrt{3}}{64}\left[\frac{1}{3}x^3\right]_0^{20} = \frac{8000\sqrt{3}}{64\cdot 3} = \frac{125\sqrt{3}}{3}\ \text{m}^3.$

14. (a) By the symmetry of the problem, we consider only the solid to the right of the origin. The semicircular
cross-sections perpendicular to the x-axis have radius $1-x$, so $A(x) = \frac{1}{2}\pi(1-x)^2$. Now we can calculate

$\qquad V = 2\int_0^1 A(x)\, dx = 2\int_0^1 \frac{1}{2}\pi(1-x)^2\, dx = \int_0^1 \pi(1-x)^2\, dx = -\frac{\pi}{3}\left[(1-x)^3\right]_0^1 = \frac{\pi}{3}.$

(b) Cut the solid with a plane perpendicular to the x-axis and passing through the y-axis. Fold the half of the solid in
the region $x \le 0$ under the xy-plane so that the point $(-1, 0)$ comes around and touches the point $(1, 0)$. The
resulting solid is a right circular cone of radius 1 with vertex at $(x, y, z) = (1, 0, 0)$ and with its base in the
yz-plane, centered at the origin. The volume of this cone is $\frac{1}{3}\pi r^2 h = \frac{1}{3}\pi\cdot 1^2\cdot 1 = \frac{\pi}{3}.$

15. $x = 3t^2,\ y = 2t^3,\ 0 \le t \le 2.$

$\quad L = \int_0^2 \sqrt{(dx/dt)^2 + (dy/dt)^2}\, dt = \int_0^2 \sqrt{(6t)^2 + (6t^2)^2}\, dt = \int_0^2 \sqrt{36t^2 + 36t^4}\, dt = 6\int_0^2 t\sqrt{1+t^2}\, dt$

$\qquad = 6\int_1^5 \sqrt{u}\left(\frac{1}{2}du\right)\ \left[u = 1+t^2,\, du = 2t\, dt\right]\ = 3\left[\frac{2}{3}u^{3/2}\right]_1^5 = 2(5\sqrt{5}-1)$

16. $y = \dfrac{1}{x^2},\ 1 \le x \le 2.\ \ \dfrac{dy}{dx} = -\dfrac{2}{x^3},$ so $1 + \left(\dfrac{dy}{dx}\right)^2 = 1 + \dfrac{4}{x^6}\ \Rightarrow\ f(x) = \sqrt{1 + 4/x^6}$

$\quad$ and $L = \int_1^2 \sqrt{1 + 4/x^6}\, dx$. By Simpson's Rule with $n = 10$,

$\quad L \approx \frac{1/10}{3}[f(1) + 4f(1.1) + 2f(1.2) + 4f(1.3) + \cdots + 2f(1.8) + 4f(1.9) + f(2)] \approx 1.297.$

17. $f(x) = kx\ \Rightarrow\ 30\,\text{N} = k(15-12)\,\text{cm}\ \Rightarrow\ k = 10\,\text{N/cm} = 1000\,\text{N/m}.\ \ 20\,\text{cm} - 12\,\text{cm} = 0.08\,\text{m}\ \Rightarrow$

$\quad W = \int_0^{0.08} kx\, dx = 1000\int_0^{0.08} x\, dx = 500\left[x^2\right]_0^{0.08} = 500(0.08)^2 = 3.2\,\text{N-m} = 3.2\,\text{J}.$

18. The work needed to raise the elevator alone is $1600\,\text{lb} \times 30\,\text{ft} = 48{,}000\,\text{ft-lb}$. The work needed to raise the bottom
170 ft of cable is $170\,\text{ft} \times 10\,\text{lb/ft} \times 30\,\text{ft} = 51{,}000\,\text{ft-lb}$. The work needed to raise the top 30 ft of cable is
$\int_0^{30} 10x\, dx = \left[5x^2\right]_0^{30} = 5\cdot 900 = 4500\,\text{ft-lb}$. Adding these, we see that the total work needed is
$48{,}000 + 51{,}000 + 4{,}500 = 103{,}500\,\text{ft-lb}.$

19. (a) The parabola has equation $y = ax^2$ with vertex at the origin and passing

$\quad$ through $(4, 4)$. $4 = a\cdot 4^2\ \Rightarrow\ a = \frac{1}{4}\ \Rightarrow\ y = \frac{1}{4}x^2\ \Rightarrow\ x^2 = 4y$

$\quad \Rightarrow\ x = 2\sqrt{y}$. Each circular disk has radius $2\sqrt{y}$ and is moved $4-y$ ft.

$\qquad W = \int_0^4 \pi\left(2\sqrt{y}\right)^2 62.5\,(4-y)\, dy = 250\pi\int_0^4 y(4-y)\, dy$

$\qquad = 250\pi\left[2y^2 - \frac{1}{3}y^3\right]_0^4 = 250\pi\left(32 - \frac{64}{3}\right) = \frac{8000\pi}{3} \approx 8378\,\text{ft-lb}$

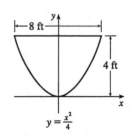

(b) In part (a) we knew the final water level (0) but not the amount of work done. Here we use the same equation, except with the work fixed, and the lower limit of integration (that is, the final water level — call it h)

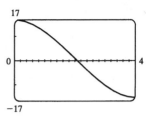

unknown: $W = 4000 \iff 250\pi\left[2y^2 - \frac{1}{3}y^3\right]_h^4 = 4000 \iff$

$\frac{16}{\pi} = \left[(32 - \frac{64}{3}) - (2h^2 - \frac{1}{3}h^3)\right] \iff h^3 - 6h^2 + 32 - \frac{48}{\pi} = 0.$

We graph the function $f(h) = h^3 - 6h^2 + 32 - \frac{48}{\pi}$ on the interval $[0, 4]$ to see where it is 0. From the graph, $f(h) = 0$ for $h \approx 2.1$. So the depth of water remaining is about 2.1 ft.

20. $F = \int_0^4 \delta(4 - y)2\left(2\sqrt{y}\right)dy = 4\delta\int_0^4\left(4y^{1/2} - y^{3/2}\right)dy$

$= 4\delta\left[\frac{8}{3}y^{3/2} - \frac{2}{5}y^{5/2}\right]_0^4 = 4\delta\left(\frac{64}{3} - \frac{64}{5}\right)$

$= 256\delta\left(\frac{1}{3} - \frac{1}{5}\right) = \frac{512}{15}\delta$

≈ 2133.3 lb $\quad[\delta \approx 62.5 \text{ lb/ft}^3]$

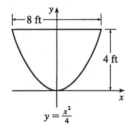

$y = \frac{x^2}{4}$

21. As in Example 4 of Section 6.5, $\dfrac{a}{2 - x} = \dfrac{1}{2} \Rightarrow 2a = 2 - x$ and

$w = 2(1.5 + a) = 3 + 2a = 3 + 2 - x = 5 - x$. Thus,

$F = \int_0^2 \rho gx(5 - x)\,dx = \rho g\left[\frac{5}{2}x^2 - \frac{1}{3}x^3\right]_0^2 = \rho g\left(10 - \frac{8}{3}\right) = \frac{22}{3}\delta \ [\rho g = \delta] \ \approx \frac{22}{3} \cdot 62.5 \approx 458$ lb.

22. An equation of the line passing through $(0, 0)$ and $(3, 2)$ is $y = \frac{2}{3}x$. $A = \frac{1}{2} \cdot 3 \cdot 2 = 3$. Therefore, using Equations

6.5.11, $\bar{x} = \frac{1}{3}\int_0^3 x\left(\frac{2}{3}x\right)dx = \frac{2}{27}\left[x^3\right]_0^3 = 2$, and $\bar{y} = \frac{1}{3}\int_0^3 \frac{1}{2}\left(\frac{2}{3}x\right)^2 dx = \frac{2}{81}\left[x^3\right]_0^3 = \frac{2}{3}$. $(\bar{x}, \bar{y}) = \left(2, \frac{2}{3}\right)$.

23. $x = 100 \Rightarrow P = 2000 - 0.1(100) - 0.01(100)^2 = 1890$

Consumer surplus $= \int_0^{100}[p(x) - P]\,dx = \int_0^{100}\left(2000 - 0.1x - 0.01x^2 - 1890\right)dx$

$= \left[110x - 0.05x^2 - \frac{0.01}{3}x^3\right]_0^{100} = 11,000 - 500 - \frac{10,000}{3} \approx \$7166.67$

24. $f_{\text{ave}} = \frac{1}{2 - 0}\int_0^2 x^2\sqrt{1 + x^3}\,dx = \frac{1}{2} \cdot \frac{1}{3}\int_1^9 \sqrt{u}\,du \quad [u = 1 + x^3,\ du = 3x^2\,dx]$

$= \frac{1}{6}\left[\frac{2}{3}u^{3/2}\right]_1^9 = \frac{1}{9}\left(9^{3/2} - 1^{3/2}\right) = \frac{1}{9}(27 - 1) = \frac{26}{9}$

25. $\displaystyle\lim_{h\to 0} f_{\text{ave}} = \lim_{h\to 0}\frac{1}{(x + h) - x}\int_x^{x+h} f(t)\,dt = \lim_{h\to 0}\frac{F(x + h) - F(x)}{h}$, where $F(x) = \int_a^x f(t)\,dt$. But we

recognize this limit as being $F'(x)$ by the definition of a derivative. Therefore, $\displaystyle\lim_{h\to 0} f_{\text{ave}} = F'(x) = f(x)$

by FTC1.

26. $\int_0^{24} c(t)\,dt \approx S_{12} = \frac{24 - 0}{12 \cdot 3}[1(0) + 4(1.9) + 2(3.3) + 4(5.1) + 2(7.6) + 4(7.1) + 2(5.8)$

$+ 4(4.7) + 2(3.3) + 4(2.1) + 2(1.1) + 4(0.5) + 1(0)]$

$= \frac{2}{3}(127.8) = 85.2$ mg $\cdot$ s/L

Therefore, $F \approx A/85.2 = 6/85.2 \approx 0.0704$ L/s or 4.225 L/min.

27. $f(x) = \begin{cases} \frac{\pi}{20}\sin\left(\frac{\pi}{10}x\right) & \text{if } 0 \le x \le 10 \\ 0 & \text{if } x < 0 \text{ or } x > 10 \end{cases}$

(a) $f(x) \geq 0$ for all real numbers x and

$\int_{-\infty}^{\infty} f(x)\,dx = \int_{0}^{10} \frac{\pi}{20}\sin\left(\frac{\pi}{10}x\right)\,dx = \frac{\pi}{20}\cdot\frac{10}{\pi}\left[-\cos\left(\frac{\pi}{10}x\right)\right]_0^{10} = \frac{1}{2}(-\cos\pi + \cos 0) = \frac{1}{2}(1+1) = 1.$

Therefore, f is a probability density function.

(b) $P(X < 4) = \int_{-\infty}^{4} f(x)\,dx = \int_0^4 \frac{\pi}{20}\sin\left(\frac{\pi}{10}x\right)\,dx = \frac{1}{2}\left[-\cos\left(\frac{\pi}{10}x\right)\right]_0^4 = \frac{1}{2}\left(-\cos\frac{2\pi}{5} + \cos 0\right)$

$\approx \frac{1}{2}(-0.309017 + 1) \approx 0.3455$

(c) $\mu = \int_{-\infty}^{\infty} xf(x)\,dx = \int_0^{10} \frac{\pi}{20}x\sin\left(\frac{\pi}{10}x\right)\,dx$

$= \int_0^{\pi} \frac{\pi}{20}\cdot\frac{10}{\pi}u(\sin u)\left(\frac{10}{\pi}\right)\,du \quad [u = \frac{\pi}{10}x,\ du = \frac{\pi}{10}\,dx]$

$= \frac{5}{\pi}\int_0^{\pi} u\sin u\,du \overset{82}{=} \frac{5}{\pi}\left[\sin u - u\cos u\right]_0^{\pi} = \frac{5}{\pi}[0 - \pi(-1)] = 5$

This answer is expected because the graph of f is symmetric about

the line $x = 5$.

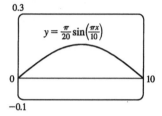

28. $P(250 \leq X \leq 280) = \int_{250}^{280} \frac{1}{15\sqrt{2\pi}}\exp\left(\frac{-(x-268)^2}{2\cdot 15^2}\right)\,dx \approx 0.673.$ Thus, the percentage of pregnancies that last between 250 and 280 days is about 67.3%.

29. (a) The probability density function is $f(t) = \begin{cases} 0 & \text{if } t < 0 \\ \frac{1}{8}e^{-t/8} & \text{if } t \geq 0 \end{cases}$

$P(0 \leq X \leq 3) = \int_0^3 \frac{1}{8}e^{-t/8}\,dt = \left[-e^{-t/8}\right]_0^3 = -e^{-3/8} + 1 \approx 0.3127$

(b) $P(X > 10) = \int_{10}^{\infty} \frac{1}{8}e^{-t/8}\,dt = \lim_{x\to\infty}\left[-e^{-t/8}\right]_{10}^{x} = \lim_{x\to\infty}\left(-e^{-x/8} + e^{-10/8}\right) = 0 + e^{-5/4} \approx 0.2865$

(c) We need to find m such that $P(X \geq m) = \frac{1}{2} \Rightarrow \int_m^{\infty} \frac{1}{8}e^{-t/8}\,dt = \frac{1}{2} \Rightarrow \lim_{x\to\infty}\left[-e^{-t/8}\right]_m^{x} = \frac{1}{2} \Rightarrow$

$\lim_{x\to\infty}\left(-e^{-x/8} + e^{-m/8}\right) = \frac{1}{2} \Rightarrow e^{-m/8} = \frac{1}{2} \Rightarrow -m/8 = \ln\frac{1}{2} \Rightarrow$

$m = -8\ln\frac{1}{2} = 8\ln 2 \approx 5.55$ minutes.

Focus on Problem Solving

1. $x^2 + y^2 \leq 4y \Leftrightarrow x^2 + (y-2)^2 \leq 4$, so S is part of a circle, as shown in the diagram. The area of S is

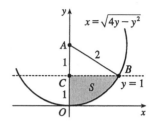

$$\int_0^1 \sqrt{4y - y^2}\, dy \overset{113}{=} \left[\frac{y-2}{2}\sqrt{4y-y^2} + 2\cos^{-1}\left(\frac{2-y}{2}\right)\right]_0^1 \quad [a=2]$$

$$= -\tfrac{1}{2}\sqrt{3} + 2\cos^{-1}\left(\tfrac{1}{2}\right) - 2\cos^{-1} 1$$

$$= -\tfrac{\sqrt{3}}{2} + 2\left(\tfrac{\pi}{3}\right) - 2(0) = \tfrac{2\pi}{3} - \tfrac{\sqrt{3}}{2}$$

Another method (without calculus): Note that $\theta = \angle CAB = \frac{\pi}{3}$, so the area is

$$(\text{area of sector } OAB) - (\text{area of } \triangle ABC) = \tfrac{1}{2}(2^2)\tfrac{\pi}{3} - \tfrac{1}{2}(1)\sqrt{3} = \tfrac{2\pi}{3} - \tfrac{\sqrt{3}}{2}$$

2. The total area of the region bounded by the parabola

$y = x - x^2 = x(1-x)$ and the x-axis is

$\int_0^1 (x - x^2)\, dx = \left[\tfrac{1}{2}x^2 - \tfrac{1}{3}x^3\right]_0^1 = \tfrac{1}{6}$.

Let the slope of the line we are looking for be m. Then the area above this line but below the parabola is $\int_0^a \left[(x - x^2) - mx\right] dx$, where a is the x-coordinate of the point of intersection of the line and the parabola. We find the point of intersection by solving the equation $x - x^2 = mx \Leftrightarrow 1 - x = m \Leftrightarrow x = 1 - m$. So the value of a is $1 - m$, and

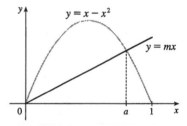

$$\int_0^{1-m} \left[(x - x^2) - mx\right] dx = \int_0^{1-m} \left[(1-m)x - x^2\right] dx = \left[\tfrac{1}{2}(1-m)x^2 - \tfrac{1}{3}x^3\right]_0^{1-m}$$

$$= \tfrac{1}{2}(1-m)(1-m)^2 - \tfrac{1}{3}(1-m)^3 = \tfrac{1}{6}(1-m)^3$$

We want this to be half of $\tfrac{1}{6}$, so $\tfrac{1}{6}(1-m)^3 = \tfrac{1}{12} \Leftrightarrow (1-m)^3 = \tfrac{6}{12} \Leftrightarrow$

$1 - m = \sqrt[3]{\tfrac{1}{2}} \Leftrightarrow m = 1 - \tfrac{1}{\sqrt[3]{2}}$. So the slope of the required line is $1 - \tfrac{1}{\sqrt[3]{2}} \approx 0.206$.

3. (a) Stacking disks along the y-axis gives us $V = \int_0^h \pi \left[f(y)\right]^2 dy$.

(b) Using the Chain Rule, $\dfrac{dV}{dt} = \dfrac{dV}{dh} \cdot \dfrac{dh}{dt} = \pi \left[f(h)\right]^2 \dfrac{dh}{dt}$.

(c) $kA\sqrt{h} = \pi[f(h)]^2 \dfrac{dh}{dt}$. Set $\dfrac{dh}{dt} = C$: $\pi[f(h)]^2 C = kA\sqrt{h} \Rightarrow [f(h)]^2 = \dfrac{kA}{\pi C}\sqrt{h} \Rightarrow$

$f(h) = \sqrt{\dfrac{kA}{\pi C}}\, h^{1/4}$; that is, $f(y) = \sqrt{\dfrac{kA}{\pi C}}\, y^{1/4}$. The advantage of having $\dfrac{dh}{dt} = C$ is that the markings on the container are equally spaced.

4. Let a and b be the x-coordinates of the points where the line intersects the curve. From the figure,

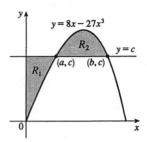

$$R_1 = R_2 \quad \Rightarrow$$

$$\int_0^a \left[c - (8x - 27x^3)\right] dx = \int_a^b \left[(8x - 27x^3) - c\right] dx$$

$$\left[cx - 4x^2 + \tfrac{27}{4}x^4\right]_0^a = \left[4x^2 - \tfrac{27}{4}x^4 - cx\right]_a^b$$

$$ac - 4a^2 + \tfrac{27}{4}a^4 = \left(4b^2 - \tfrac{27}{4}b^4 - bc\right) - \left(4a^2 - \tfrac{27}{4}a^4 - ac\right)$$

$$0 = 4b^2 - \tfrac{27}{4}b^4 - bc = 4b^2 - \tfrac{27}{4}b^4 - b\left(8b - 27b^3\right)$$

$$= 4b^2 - \tfrac{27}{4}b^4 - 8b^2 + 27b^4 = \tfrac{81}{4}b^4 - 4b^2$$

$$= b^2 \left(\tfrac{81}{4}b^2 - 4\right)$$

So for $b > 0$, $b^2 = \frac{16}{81} \Rightarrow b = \frac{4}{9}$. Thus, $c = 8b - 27b^3 = 8\left(\frac{4}{9}\right) - 27\left(\frac{64}{729}\right) = \frac{32}{9} - \frac{64}{27} = \frac{32}{27}$.

5. The volume generated from $x = 0$ to $x = b$ is $\int_0^b \pi[f(x)]^2\, dx$. Hence, we are given that $b^2 = \int_0^b \pi[f(x)]^2\, dx$ for all $b > 0$. Differentiating both sides of this equation with respect to b using the Fundamental Theorem of Calculus gives $2b = \pi[f(b)]^2 \Rightarrow f(b) = \sqrt{2b/\pi}$, since f is positive. Therefore, $f(x) = \sqrt{2x/\pi}$.

6. (a) Take slices perpendicular to the line through the center C of the bottom of the glass and the point P where the top surface of the water meets the bottom of the glass.

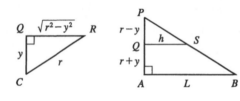

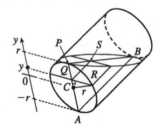

A typical rectangular cross-section y units above the axis of the graph has width $2\,|QR| = 2\sqrt{r^2 - y^2}$ and length $h = |QS| = \dfrac{L}{2r}(r - y)$. [Triangles PQS and PAB are similar, so $\dfrac{h}{L} = \dfrac{|PQ|}{|PA|} = \dfrac{r - y}{2r}$.] Thus,

$$V = \int_{-r}^{r} 2\sqrt{r^2 - y^2} \cdot \frac{L}{2r}(r - y)\, dy = L\int_{-r}^{r}\left(1 - \frac{y}{r}\right)\sqrt{r^2 - y^2}\, dy$$

$$= L\int_{-r}^{r}\sqrt{r^2 - y^2}\, dy - \frac{L}{r}\int_{-r}^{r} y\sqrt{r^2 - y^2}\, dy$$

$$= L \cdot \frac{\pi r^2}{2} - \frac{L}{r}\cdot 0 \quad \begin{bmatrix} \text{the first integral is the area of a semicircle of radius } r, \\ \text{and the second has an odd integrand} \end{bmatrix} = \frac{\pi r^2 L}{2}$$

(b) Slice parallel to the plane through the axis of the glass and the point of contact P. (This is the plane determined by P, B, and C in the figure.) $STUV$ is a typical trapezoidal slice. With respect to an x-axis with origin at C as shown, if S and V have x-coordinate x, then $|SV| = 2\sqrt{r^2 - x^2}$. Projecting the trapezoid $STUV$ onto the

plane of the triangle PAB, we see that $|AP| = 2r$, $|SV| = 2\sqrt{r^2 - x^2}$, and
$|SP| = |VA| = \frac{1}{2}(|AP| - |SV|) = r - \sqrt{r^2 - x^2}$.

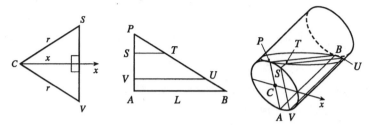

By similar triangles, $\dfrac{|ST|}{|SP|} = \dfrac{|AB|}{|AP|}$, so $|ST| = \left(r - \sqrt{r^2 - x^2}\right) \cdot \dfrac{L}{2r}$. In the same way, we find that

$\dfrac{|VU|}{|VP|} = \dfrac{|AB|}{|AP|}$, so $|VU| = |VP| \cdot \dfrac{L}{2r} = (|AP| - |VA|) \cdot \dfrac{L}{2r} = \left(r + \sqrt{r^2 - x^2}\right) \cdot \dfrac{L}{2r}$.

The area $A(x)$ of the trapezoid $STUV$ is $\frac{1}{2}|SV| \cdot (|ST| + |VU|)$; that is,

$A(x) = \frac{1}{2} \cdot 2\sqrt{r^2 - x^2} \cdot \left[\left(r - \sqrt{r^2 - x^2}\right) \cdot \dfrac{L}{2r} + \left(r + \sqrt{r^2 - x^2}\right) \cdot \dfrac{L}{2r}\right] = L\sqrt{r^2 - x^2}$. Thus,

$V = \int_{-r}^{r} A(x)\, dx = L \int_{-r}^{r} \sqrt{r^2 - x^2}\, dx = L \cdot \dfrac{\pi r^2}{2} = \dfrac{\pi r^2 L}{2}$.

(c) See the computation of V in part (a) or part (b).

(d) The volume of the water is exactly half the volume of the cylindrical glass, so $V = \frac{1}{2}\pi r^2 L$.

(e)

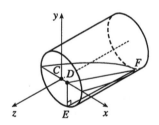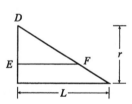

Choose x-, y-, and z-axes as shown in the figure. Then slices perpendicular to the x-axis are triangular, slices perpendicular to the y-axis are rectangular, and slices perpendicular to the z-axis are segments of circles. Using triangular slices, we find that the area $A(x)$ of a typical slice DEF, where D has x-coordinate x, is given by

$A(x) = \frac{1}{2}|DE| \cdot |EF| = \frac{1}{2}|DE| \cdot \left(\dfrac{L}{r}|DE|\right) = \dfrac{L}{2r}|DE|^2 = \dfrac{L}{2r}(r^2 - x^2)$. Thus,

$V = \int_{-r}^{r} A(x)\, dx = \dfrac{L}{2r} \int_{-r}^{r} (r^2 - x^2)\, dx = \dfrac{L}{r} \int_{0}^{r} (r^2 - x^2)\, dx = \dfrac{L}{r}\left[r^2 x - \dfrac{x^3}{3}\right]_0^r$

$= \dfrac{L}{r}\left(r^3 - \dfrac{r^3}{3}\right) = \dfrac{L}{r} \cdot \frac{2}{3}r^3 = \frac{2}{3}r^2 L$ [This is $2/(3\pi) \approx 0.21$ of the volume of the glass.]

7. (a) $V = \pi h^2(r - h/3) = \frac{1}{3}\pi h^2(3r - h)$. See the solution to Exercise 6.2.23.

(b) The smaller segment has height $h = 1 - x$ and so by part (a) its volume is

$V = \frac{1}{3}\pi(1-x)^2[3(1) - (1-x)] = \frac{1}{3}\pi(x-1)^2(x+2)$. This volume must be $\frac{1}{3}$ of the total volume of the

sphere, which is $\frac{4}{3}\pi(1)^3$. So $\frac{1}{3}\pi(x-1)^2(x+2) = \frac{1}{3}\left(\frac{4}{3}\pi\right) \Rightarrow (x^2 - 2x + 1)(x + 2) = \frac{4}{3} \Rightarrow$

$x^3 - 3x + 2 = \frac{4}{3} \Rightarrow 3x^3 - 9x + 2 = 0$. Using Newton's method with $f(x) = 3x^3 - 9x + 2$,

$f'(x) = 9x^2 - 9$, we get $x_{n+1} = x_n - \dfrac{3x_n^3 - 9x_n + 2}{9x_n^2 - 9}$. Taking $x_1 = 0$, we get $x_2 \approx 0.2222$, and

$x_3 \approx 0.2261 \approx x_4$, so, correct to four decimal places, $x \approx 0.2261$.

(c) With $r = 0.5$ and $s = 0.75$, the equation $x^3 - 3rx^2 + 4r^3 s = 0$ becomes $x^3 - 3(0.5)x^2 + 4(0.5)^3(0.75) = 0$

$\Rightarrow x^3 - \frac{3}{2}x^2 + 4\left(\frac{1}{8}\right)\frac{3}{4} = 0 \Rightarrow 8x^3 - 12x^2 + 3 = 0$. We use Newton's method with

$f(x) = 8x^3 - 12x^2 + 3$, $f'(x) = 24x^2 - 24x$, so $x_{n+1} = x_n - \dfrac{8x_n^3 - 12x_n^2 + 3}{24x_n^2 - 24x_n}$. Take $x_1 = 0.5$. Then

$x_2 \approx 0.6667$, and $x_3 \approx 0.6736 \approx x_4$. So to four decimal places the depth is 0.6736 m.

(d) (i) From part (a) with $r = 5$ in., the volume of water in the bowl is

$V = \frac{1}{3}\pi h^2(3r - h) = \frac{1}{3}\pi h^2(15 - h) = 5\pi h^2 - \frac{1}{3}\pi h^3$. We are given that $\dfrac{dV}{dt} = 0.2$ m^3/s and we want to

find $\dfrac{dh}{dt}$ when $h = 3$. Now $\dfrac{dV}{dt} = 10\pi h \dfrac{dh}{dt} - \pi h^2 \dfrac{dh}{dt}$, so $\dfrac{dh}{dt} = \dfrac{0.2}{\pi(10h - h^2)}$. When $h = 3$, we have

$\dfrac{dh}{dt} = \dfrac{0.2}{\pi(10 \cdot 3 - 3^2)} = \dfrac{1}{105\pi} \approx 0.003$ in/s.

(ii) From part (a), the volume of water required to fill the bowl from the instant that the water is 4 in. deep is

$V = \frac{1}{2} \cdot \frac{4}{3}\pi(5)^3 - \frac{1}{3}\pi(4)^2(15 - 4) = \frac{2}{3} \cdot 125\pi - \frac{16}{3} \cdot 11\pi = \frac{74}{3}\pi$. To find the time required to fill the

bowl we divide this volume by the rate: Time $= \dfrac{74\pi/3}{0.2} = \dfrac{370\pi}{3} \approx 387$ s ≈ 6.5 min

8. (a) The volume above the surface is $\int_0^{L-h} A(y)\,dy = \int_{-h}^{L-h} A(y)\,dy - \int_{-h}^0 A(y)\,dy$. So the proportion of volume

above the surface is $\dfrac{\int_0^{L-h} A(y)\,dy}{\int_{-h}^{L-h} A(y)\,dy} = \dfrac{\int_{-h}^{L-h} A(y)\,dy - \int_{-h}^0 A(y)\,dy}{\int_{-h}^{L-h} A(y)\,dy}$. Now by Archimedes' Principle, we

have $F = W \Rightarrow \rho_f g \int_{-h}^0 A(y)\,dy = \rho_0 g \int_{-h}^{L-h} A(y)\,dy$, so $\int_{-h}^0 A(y)\,dy = (\rho_0/\rho_f)\int_{-h}^{L-h} A(y)\,dy$.

Therefore, $\dfrac{\int_0^{L-h} A(y)\,dy}{\int_{-h}^{L-h} A(y)\,dy} = \dfrac{\int_{-h}^{L-h} A(y)\,dy - (\rho_0/\rho_f)\int_{-h}^{L-h} A(y)\,dy}{\int_{-h}^{L-h} A(y)\,dy} = \dfrac{\rho_f - \rho_0}{\rho_f}$, so the percentage of

volume above the surface is $100\left(\dfrac{\rho_f - \rho_0}{\rho_f}\right)$%.

(b) For an iceberg, the percentage of volume above the surface is $100\left(\dfrac{1030 - 917}{1030}\right)\% \approx 11\%$.

(c) No, the water does not overflow. Let V_i be the volume of the ice cube, and let V_w be the volume of the water
which results from the melting. Then by the formula derived in part (a), the volume of ice above the surface of
the water is $[(\rho_f - \rho_0)/\rho_f]V_i$, so the volume below the surface is $V_i - [(\rho_f - \rho_0)/\rho_f]V_i = (\rho_0/\rho_f)V_i$.
Now the mass of the ice cube is the same as the mass of the water which is created when it melts, namely
$m = \rho_0 V_i = \rho_f V_w \Rightarrow V_w = (\rho_0/\rho_f)V_i$. So when the ice cube melts, the volume of the resulting water is
the same as the underwater volume of the ice cube, and so the water does not overflow.

(d)

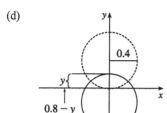

The figure shows the instant when the height of the exposed part of the ball is y. Using the formula in part (a) with $r = 0.4$ and $h = 0.8 - y$, we see that the volume of the submerged part of the sphere is $\frac{1}{3}\pi(0.8 - y)^2[1.2 - (0.8 - y)]$, so its weight is $1000g \cdot \frac{1}{3}\pi s^2(1.2 - s)$, where $s = 0.8 - y$. Then the work done to submerge the sphere is

$$W = g\tfrac{1000}{3}\pi s^2(1.2 - s)\, ds = g\tfrac{1000}{3}\pi \int_0^{0.8} (1.2s^2 - s^3)\, ds$$

$$= g\tfrac{1000}{3}\pi\left[0.4s^3 - \tfrac{1}{4}s^4\right]_0^{0.8} = g\tfrac{1000}{3}\pi(0.2048 - 0.1024)$$

$$= 9.8\,\tfrac{1000}{3}\,\pi(0.1024) \approx 1.05 \times 10^3 \text{ joules}$$

9. We are given that the rate of change of the volume of water is $\dfrac{dV}{dt} = -kA(x)$, where k is some positive constant and $A(x)$ is the area of the surface when the water has depth x. Now we are concerned with the rate of change of the depth of the water with respect to time, that is, $\dfrac{dx}{dt}$. But by the Chain Rule, $\dfrac{dV}{dt} = \dfrac{dV}{dx}\dfrac{dx}{dt}$, so the first equation can be written $\dfrac{dV}{dx}\dfrac{dx}{dt} = -kA(x)$ $(\star)$. Also, we know that the total volume of water up to a depth x is $V(x) = \int_0^x A(s)\, ds$, where $A(s)$ is the area of a cross-section of the water at a depth s. Differentiating this equation with respect to x, we get $dV/dx = A(x)$. Substituting this into equation $\star$, we get $A(x)(dx/dt) = -kA(x)$ $\Rightarrow$ $dx/dt = -k$, a constant.

10. A typical sphere of radius r is shown in the figure. We wish to maximize the shaded volume V, which can be thought of as the volume of a hemisphere of radius r minus the volume of the spherical cap with height $h = 1 - \sqrt{1 - r^2}$ and radius 1.

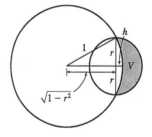

$$V = \tfrac{1}{2}\cdot\tfrac{4}{3}\pi r^3 - \tfrac{1}{3}\pi\left(1 - \sqrt{1-r^2}\right)^2\left[3(1) - \left(1 - \sqrt{1-r^2}\right)\right] \quad \text{[by Problem 7(a)]}$$

$$= \tfrac{1}{3}\pi\left[2r^3 - \left(2 - 2\sqrt{1-r^2} - r^2\right)\left(2 + \sqrt{1-r^2}\right)\right]$$

$$= \tfrac{1}{3}\pi\left[2r^3 - 2 + (r^2 + 2)\sqrt{1-r^2}\right]$$

$$V' = \tfrac{1}{3}\pi\left[6r^2 + \frac{(r^2+2)(-r)}{\sqrt{1-r^2}} + \sqrt{1-r^2}(2r)\right] = \tfrac{1}{3}\pi\left[\frac{6r^2\sqrt{1-r^2} - r(r^2+2) + 2r(1-r^2)}{\sqrt{1-r^2}}\right]$$

$$= \tfrac{1}{3}\pi\left(\frac{6r^2\sqrt{1-r^2} - 3r^3}{\sqrt{1-r^2}}\right) = \frac{\pi r^2\left(2\sqrt{1-r^2} - r\right)}{\sqrt{1-r^2}}$$

$V'(r) = 0 \Leftrightarrow 2\sqrt{1-r^2} = r \Leftrightarrow 4 - 4r^2 = r^2 \Leftrightarrow r^2 = \tfrac{4}{5} \Leftrightarrow r = \tfrac{2}{\sqrt{5}} \approx 0.89$. Since $V'(r) > 0$ for $0 < r < \tfrac{2}{\sqrt{5}}$ and $V'(r) < 0$ for $\tfrac{2}{\sqrt{5}} < r < 1$, we know that V attains a maximum at $r = \tfrac{2}{\sqrt{5}}$.

11. (a) Choose a vertical x-axis pointing downward with its origin at the surface. In order to calculate the pressure at depth z, consider n subintervals of the interval $[0, z]$ by points x_i and choose a point $x_i^* \in [x_{i-1}, x_i]$ for each i. The thin layer of water lying between depth x_{i-1} and depth x_i has a density of approximately $\rho(x_i^*)$, so the weight of a piece of that layer with unit cross-sectional area is $\rho(x_i^*)g\,\Delta x$. The total weight of a column of water extending from the surface to depth z (with unit cross-sectional area) would be approximately $\sum_{i=1}^{n}\rho(x_i^*)g\,\Delta x$. The estimate becomes exact if we take the limit as $n \to \infty$; weight (or force) per unit area at depth z is $W = \lim\limits_{n\to\infty} \sum\limits_{i=1}^{n} \rho(x_i^*)g\,\Delta x$. In other words, $P(z) = \int_0^z \rho(x)g\,dx$. More generally, if we make no

assumptions about the location of the origin, then $P(z) = P_0 + \int_0^z \rho(x)g\,dx$, where P_0 is the pressure at $x = 0$.

Differentiating, we get $dP/dz = \rho(z)g$.

(b)

$$F = \int_{-r}^{r} P(L+x) \cdot 2\sqrt{r^2 - x^2}\,dx$$

$$= \int_{-r}^{r} \left(P_0 + \int_0^{L+x} \rho_0 e^{z/H} g\,dz\right) \cdot 2\sqrt{r^2 - x^2}\,dx$$

$$= P_0 \int_{-r}^{r} 2\sqrt{r^2 - x^2}\,dx + \rho_0 gH \int_{-r}^{r} \left(e^{(L+x)/H} - 1\right) \cdot 2\sqrt{r^2 - x^2}\,dx$$

$$= (P_0 - \rho_0 gH)\int_{-r}^{r} 2\sqrt{r^2 - x^2}\,dx + \rho_0 gH \int_{-r}^{r} e^{(L+x)/H} \cdot 2\sqrt{r^2 - x^2}\,dx$$

$$= (P_0 - \rho_0 gH)(\pi r^2) + \rho_0 gH e^{L/H} \int_{-r}^{r} e^{x/H} \cdot 2\sqrt{r^2 - x^2}\,dx$$

12. The problem can be reduced to finding the line which minimizes the shaded area in the diagram. The equation of the circle in the first quadrant is $y = \sqrt{1 - x^2}$, so if the equation of the line is $y = h$, then the circle and the line intersect where $h = \sqrt{1 - x^2} \;\Rightarrow\; x = \sqrt{1 - h^2}$. So the shaded area is

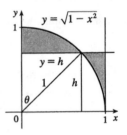

$$A = \int_0^{\sqrt{1-h^2}} \left(\sqrt{1 - x^2} - h\right) dx + \int_{\sqrt{1-h^2}}^{1} \left(h - \sqrt{1 - x^2}\right) dx$$

$$\overset{\star}{=} \left[-hx\right]_0^{\sqrt{1-h^2}} + \left[hx\right]_{\sqrt{1-h^2}}^{1} + \int_0^{\sqrt{1-h^2}} \sqrt{1 - x^2}\,dx + \int_1^{\sqrt{1-h^2}} \sqrt{1 - x^2}\,dx$$

$$= -h\sqrt{1 - h^2} + h - h\sqrt{1 - h^2} + \int_0^{\sqrt{1-h^2}} \sqrt{1 - x^2}\,dx + \int_1^{\sqrt{1-h^2}} \sqrt{1 - x^2}\,dx$$

$$= h\left(1 - 2\sqrt{1 - h^2}\right) + \int_0^{\sqrt{1-h^2}} \sqrt{1 - x^2}\,dx + \int_1^{\sqrt{1-h^2}} \sqrt{1 - x^2}\,dx$$

Note that at $(\star)$, we reversed the limits of integration and changed the sign in the last integral.

We are interested in the minimum of $A(h) = h\left(1 - 2\sqrt{1 - h^2}\right) + \int_0^{\sqrt{1-h^2}} \sqrt{1 - x^2}\,dx + \int_1^{\sqrt{1-h^2}} \sqrt{1 - x^2}\,dx$,

so we find dA/dh using FTC1 and the Chain Rule:

$$\frac{dA}{dh} = h\left(-2\frac{-h}{\sqrt{1 - h^2}}\right) + \left(1 - 2\sqrt{1 - h^2}\right) + 2\left[\sqrt{1 - \left(\sqrt{1 - h^2}\right)^2}\right]\frac{d}{dh}\left(\sqrt{1 - h^2}\right)$$

$$= \frac{1}{\sqrt{1 - h^2}}\left[2h^2 + \sqrt{1 - h^2} - 2(1 - h^2)\right] + 2h\frac{-h}{\sqrt{1 - h^2}}$$

This is 0 when $\sqrt{1-h^2} - 2(1-h^2) = 0 \Leftrightarrow u - 2u^2 = 0$ (where $u = \sqrt{1-h^2}$) $\Leftrightarrow u = 0$ or $\frac{1}{2}$ $\Leftrightarrow$

$h = 1$ or $\frac{\sqrt{3}}{2}$. By the First Derivative Test, $h = \frac{\sqrt{3}}{2}$ represents a minimum for $A(h)$, since $A'(h) = 1 - \dfrac{2}{\sqrt{1-h^2}}$

goes from negative to positive at $h = \frac{\sqrt{3}}{2}$.

Another method: Use FTC2 to evaluate all of the integrals before differentiating.

Note: Another strategy is to use the angle θ as the variable (see diagram above) and show that

$A = \theta + \cos\theta - \frac{\pi}{4} - \frac{1}{2}\sin 2\theta$, which is minimized when $\theta = \frac{\pi}{6}$.

13. To find the height of the pyramid, we use similar triangles. The first figure shows a cross-section of the pyramid passing through the top and through two opposite corners of the square base. Now $|BD| = b$, since it is a radius of the sphere, which has diameter $2b$ since it is tangent to the opposite sides of the square base. Also, $|AD| = b$ since $\triangle ADB$ is isosceles. So the height is $|AB| = \sqrt{b^2 + b^2} = \sqrt{2}b$.

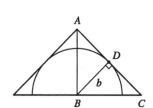  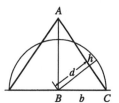

We first observe that the shared volume is equal to half the volume of the sphere, minus the sum of the four equal volumes (caps of the sphere) cut off by the triangular faces of the pyramid. See Exercise 6.2.23 for a derivation of the formula for the volume of a cap of a sphere. To use the formula, we need to find the perpendicular distance h of each triangular face from the surface of the sphere. We first find the distance d from the center of the sphere to one of the triangular faces. The third figure shows a cross-section of the pyramid through the top and through the midpoints of opposite sides of the square base. From similar triangles we find that

$$\frac{d}{b} = \frac{|AB|}{|AC|} = \frac{\sqrt{2}b}{\sqrt{b^2 + \left(\sqrt{2}b\right)^2}} \quad \Rightarrow \quad d = \frac{\sqrt{2}b^2}{\sqrt{3b^2}} = \frac{\sqrt{6}}{3}b$$

So $h = b - d = b - \frac{\sqrt{6}}{3}b = \frac{3-\sqrt{6}}{3}b$. So, using the formula $V = \pi h^2(r - h/3)$

from Exercise 6.2.23 with $r = b$, we find that the volume of each of the caps is

$\pi\left(\frac{3-\sqrt{6}}{3}b\right)^2\left(b - \frac{3-\sqrt{6}}{3\cdot 3}b\right) = \frac{15-6\sqrt{6}}{9}\cdot\frac{6+\sqrt{6}}{9}\pi b^3 = \left(\frac{2}{3} - \frac{7}{27}\sqrt{6}\right)\pi b^3$. So, using our first observation, the

shared volume is $V = \frac{1}{2}\left(\frac{4}{3}\pi b^3\right) - 4\left(\frac{2}{3} - \frac{7}{27}\sqrt{6}\right)\pi b^3 = \left(\frac{28}{27}\sqrt{6} - 2\right)\pi b^3$.

14. We want to find the volume of that part of the sphere which is below the
surface of the water. As we can see from the diagram, this region is a cap of
a sphere with radius r and height $r + d$. If we can find an expression for d in
terms of h, r and θ, then we can determine the volume of the region [see
Problem 7(a)], and then differentiate with respect to r to find the maximum.
We see that $\sin \theta = \dfrac{r}{h-d}$ $\Leftrightarrow$ $h - d = \dfrac{r}{\sin \theta}$ $\Leftrightarrow$ $d = h - r \csc \theta$.

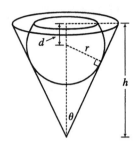

Now we can use the formula from Problem 7(a) to find the volume of water displaced:

$$V = \tfrac{1}{3}\pi h^2(3r - h) = \tfrac{1}{3}\pi(r + d)^2 \left[3r - (r + d)\right] = \tfrac{1}{3}\pi(r + h - r \csc \theta)^2(2r - h + r \csc \theta)$$

$$= \tfrac{\pi}{3}[r(1 - \csc \theta) + h]^2[r(2 + \csc \theta) - h]$$

Now we differentiate with respect to r:

$$dV/dr = \tfrac{\pi}{3}\left([r(1 - \csc \theta) + h]^2(2 + \csc \theta) + 2[r(1 - \csc \theta) + h](1 - \csc \theta)^2[r(2 + \csc \theta) - h]\right)$$

$$= \tfrac{\pi}{3}[r(1 - \csc \theta) + h]\left([r(1 - \csc \theta) + h](2 + \csc \theta) + 2(1 - \csc \theta)^2[r(2 + \csc \theta) - h]\right)$$

$$= \tfrac{\pi}{3}[r(1 - \csc \theta) + h](3(2 + \csc \theta)(1 - \csc \theta)r + [(2 + \csc \theta) - 2(1 - \csc \theta)]h)$$

$$= \tfrac{\pi}{3}[r(1 - \csc \theta) + h][3(2 + \csc \theta)(1 - \csc \theta)r + 3h \csc \theta]$$

This is 0 when $r = \dfrac{h}{\csc \theta - 1}$ and when $r = \dfrac{h \csc \theta}{(\csc \theta + 2)(\csc \theta - 1)}$. Now since $V\left(\dfrac{h}{\csc \theta - 1}\right) = 0$
(the first factor vanishes; this corresponds to $d = -r$), the maximum volume of water is displaced when
$r = \dfrac{h \csc \theta}{(\csc \theta - 1)(\csc \theta + 2)}$. (Our intuition tells that a maximum value does exist, and it must occur at a critical
number.) Multiplying numerator and denominator by $\sin^2 \theta$, we get an alternative form of the answer:
$r = \dfrac{h \sin \theta}{\sin \theta + \cos 2\theta}$.

15. $x = \displaystyle\int_1^t \dfrac{\cos u}{u}\, du$, $y = \displaystyle\int_1^t \dfrac{\sin u}{u}\, du$, so by FTC1, we have $\dfrac{dx}{dt} = \dfrac{\cos t}{t}$ and $\dfrac{dy}{dt} = \dfrac{\sin t}{t}$. Vertical tangent lines
occur when $dx/dt = 0$ $\Leftrightarrow$ $\cos t = 0$ $\Leftrightarrow$ $t = \tfrac{\pi}{2} + n\pi$. The parameter value corresponding to the origin,
$(x, y) = (0, 0)$, is $t = 1$, so the nearest vertical tangent occurs when $t = \tfrac{\pi}{2}$. Therefore, the arc length between these

points is $L = \displaystyle\int_1^{\pi/2} \sqrt{\left(\dfrac{dx}{dt}\right)^2 + \left(\dfrac{dy}{dt}\right)^2}\, dt = \int_1^{\pi/2} \sqrt{\dfrac{\cos^2 t}{t^2} + \dfrac{\sin^2 t}{t^2}}\, dt = \int_1^{\pi/2} \dfrac{dt}{t} = \big[\ln t\big]_1^{\pi/2} = \ln \tfrac{\pi}{2}$.

16. (a) Place the round flat tortilla on an xy-coordinate system as shown in the first figure. An equation of the circle is $x^2 + y^2 = 4^2$ and the height of a cross-section is $2\sqrt{16 - x^2}$.

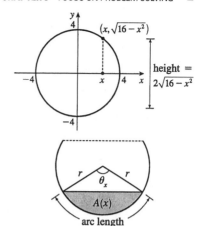

Now look at a cross-section with central angle θ_x as shown in the second figure (r is the radius of the circular cylinder). The filled area $A(x)$ is equal to the area $A_1(x)$ of the sector minus the area $A_2(x)$ of the triangle.

$$A(x) = A_1(x) - A_2(x)$$
$$= \tfrac{1}{2}r^2\theta_x - \tfrac{1}{2}r^2 \sin\theta_x \quad \text{[area formulas from trigonometry]}$$
$$= \tfrac{1}{2}r(r\theta_x) - \tfrac{1}{2}r^2 \sin\left(\frac{s}{r}\right) \quad \text{[arc length } s = r\theta_x \quad \Rightarrow \quad \theta_x = s/r\text{]}$$
$$= \tfrac{1}{2}r \cdot 2\sqrt{16 - x^2} - \tfrac{1}{2}r^2 \sin\left(\frac{2\sqrt{16 - x^2}}{r}\right) \quad [s = 2\sqrt{16 - x^2}\,]$$
$$= r\sqrt{16 - x^2} - \tfrac{1}{2}r^2 \sin\left(\frac{2}{r}\sqrt{16 - x^2}\right) \quad (*)$$

Note that the central angle θ_x will be small near the ends of the tortilla; that is, when $|x| \approx 4$. But near the center of the tortilla (when $|x| \approx 0$), the central angle θ_x may exceed $180°$. Thus, the sine of θ_x will be negative and the second term in $(*)$ will be positive (actually adding area to the area of the sector). The volume of the taco can be found by integrating the cross-sectional areas from $x = -4$ to $x = 4$. Thus,

$$V(x) = \int_{-4}^{4} A(x)\,dx = \int_{-4}^{4} \left[r\sqrt{16 - x^2} - \tfrac{1}{2}r^2 \sin\left(\frac{2}{r}\sqrt{16 - x^2}\right) \right] dx$$

(b) To find the value of r that maximizes the volume of the taco, we can define the function

$$V(r) = \int_{-4}^{4} \left[r\sqrt{16 - x^2} - \tfrac{1}{2}r^2 \sin\left(\frac{2}{r}\sqrt{16 - x^2}\right) \right] dx$$

The third figure shows a graph of $y = V(r)$ and $y = V'(r)$. The maximum volume of about 52.94 occurs when $r \approx 2.2912$.

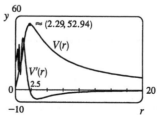

17.

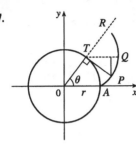

The coordinates of T are $(x_1, y_1) = (r \cos \theta, r \sin \theta)$. Since TP was

unwound from arc TA, TP has length $r\theta$. Also

$\angle PTQ = \angle PTR - \angle QTR = \frac{1}{2}\pi - \theta$, so P has coordinates

$x = x_1 + |TP| \cos \angle PTQ = r \cos \theta + r\theta \cos\left(\frac{1}{2}\pi - \theta\right) = r(\cos \theta + \theta \sin \theta)$,

$y = y_1 + |TP| \sin \angle PTQ = r \sin \theta - r\theta \sin\left(\frac{1}{2}\pi - \theta\right) = r(\sin \theta - \theta \cos \theta)$.

18. If the cow walks with the rope taut, it traces out the portion of the involute in Problem 17 corresponding to the range

$0 \le \theta \le \pi$, arriving at the point $(-r, \pi r)$ when $\theta = \pi$. With the rope now fully extended, the cow walks in a

semicircle of radius πr, arriving at $(-r, -\pi r)$. Finally, the cow traces out another portion of the involute, namely

the reflection about the x-axis of the initial involute path. (This corresponds to the range $-\pi \le \theta \le 0$.)

Referring to the figure, we see that the total grazing area is

$2(A_1 + A_3)$. A_3 is $\frac{1}{4}$ of the area of a circle of radius πr, so

$A_3 = \frac{1}{4}\pi(\pi r)^2 = \frac{1}{4}\pi^3 r^2$. We will compute $A_1 + A_2$ and

then subtract $A_2 = \frac{1}{2}\pi r^2$ to obtain A_1. To find $A_1 + A_2$,

first note that the rightmost point of the involute is $\left(\frac{\pi}{2}r, r\right)$.

[To see this, note that $dx/d\theta = 0$ when $\theta = 0$ or $\frac{\pi}{2}$. $\theta = 0$

corresponds to the cusp at $(r, 0)$ and $\theta = \frac{\pi}{2}$ corresponds to

$\left(\frac{\pi}{2}r, r\right)$.] The leftmost point of the involute is $(-r, \pi r)$.

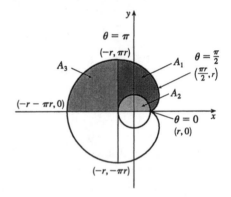

Thus, $A_1 + A_2 = \int_{\theta=\pi}^{\pi/2} y \, dx - \int_{\theta=0}^{\pi/2} y \, dx = \int_{\theta=\pi}^{0} y \, dx$.

Now $y \, dx = r(\sin \theta - \theta \cos \theta) \, r\theta \cos \theta \, d\theta = r^2 \left(\theta \sin \theta \, \cos \theta - \theta^2 \cos^2 \theta\right) d\theta$.

Integrate: $(1/r^2) \int y \, dx = -\theta \cos^2 \theta - \frac{1}{2}\left(\theta^2 - 1\right) \sin \theta \, \cos \theta - \frac{1}{6}\theta^3 + \frac{1}{2}\theta + C$. This enables us to compute

$A_1 + A_2 = r^2 \left[-\theta \cos^2 \theta - \frac{1}{2}\left(\theta^2 - 1\right) \sin \theta \, \cos \theta - \frac{1}{6}\theta^3 + \frac{1}{2}\theta\right]_{\pi}^{0}$

$= r^2 \left[0 - \left(-\pi - \frac{\pi^3}{6} + \frac{\pi}{2}\right)\right] = r^2 \left(\frac{\pi}{2} + \frac{\pi^3}{6}\right)$.

Therefore, $A_1 = (A_1 + A_2) - A_2 = \frac{1}{6}\pi^3 r^2$, so the grazing area is $2(A_1 + A_3) = 2\left(\frac{1}{6}\pi^3 r^2 + \frac{1}{4}\pi^3 r^2\right) = \frac{5}{6}\pi^3 r^2$.

19. If $h = L$, then

$$P = \frac{\text{area under } y = L \sin \theta}{\text{area of rectangle}} = \frac{\int_0^\pi L \sin \theta \, d\theta}{\pi L} = \frac{[-\cos \theta]_0^\pi}{\pi} = \frac{-(-1) + 1}{\pi} = \frac{2}{\pi}$$

If $h = L/2$, then

$$P = \frac{\text{area under } y = \frac{1}{2}L \sin \theta}{\text{area of rectangle}} = \frac{\int_0^\pi \frac{1}{2}L \sin \theta \, d\theta}{\pi L} = \frac{[-\cos \theta]_0^\pi}{2\pi} = \frac{2}{2\pi} = \frac{1}{\pi}$$

20. (a) The total set of possibilities can be identified with the rectangular region $\mathcal{R} = \{(\theta, y) \mid 0 \le y < L, 0 \le \theta < \pi\}$. Even when $h > L$, the needle intersects at least one line if and only if $y \le h \sin \theta$. Let $\mathcal{R}_1 = \{(\theta, y) \mid 0 \le y \le h \sin \theta, 0 \le \theta < \pi\}$. When $h \le L$, $\mathcal{R}_1$ is contained in $\mathcal{R}$, but that is no longer true when $h > L$. Thus, the probability that the needle intersects a line becomes

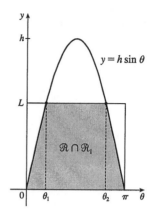

$$P = \frac{\text{area}(\mathcal{R} \cap \mathcal{R}_1)}{\text{area}(\mathcal{R})} = \frac{\text{area}(\mathcal{R} \cap \mathcal{R}_1)}{\pi L}$$

When $h > L$, the curve $y = h \sin \theta$ intersects the line $y = L$ twice — at $\left(\sin^{-1}(L/h), L\right)$ and at $\left(\pi - \sin^{-1}(L/h), L\right)$. Set $\theta_1 = \sin^{-1}(L/h)$ and $\theta_2 = \pi - \theta_1$. Then

$$\text{area}(\mathcal{R} \cap \mathcal{R}_1) = \int_0^{\theta_1} h \sin \theta \, d\theta + \int_{\theta_1}^{\theta_2} L \, d\theta + \int_{\theta_2}^{\pi} h \sin \theta \, d\theta$$

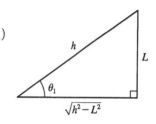

$$= 2 \int_0^{\theta_1} h \sin \theta \, d\theta + L(\theta_2 - \theta_1) = 2h \left[-\cos \theta\right]_0^{\theta_1} + L(\pi - 2\theta_1)$$

$$= 2h(1 - \cos \theta_1) + L(\pi - 2\theta_1)$$

$$= 2h \left(1 - \frac{\sqrt{h^2 - L^2}}{h}\right) + L \left[\pi - 2 \sin^{-1}\left(\frac{L}{h}\right)\right]$$

$$= 2h - 2\sqrt{h^2 - L^2} + \pi L - 2L \sin^{-1}\left(\frac{L}{h}\right)$$

We are told that $L = 4$ and $h = 7$, so $\text{area}(\mathcal{R} \cap \mathcal{R}_1) = 14 - 2\sqrt{33} + 4\pi - 8 \sin^{-1}\left(\frac{4}{7}\right) \approx 10.21128$ and $P = \frac{1}{4\pi} \text{area}(\mathcal{R} \cap \mathcal{R}_1) \approx 0.812588$. (By comparison, $P = \frac{2}{\pi} \approx 0.636620$ when $h = L$, as shown in the solution to Problem 19.)

(b) The needle intersects at least two lines when $y + L \le h \sin \theta$; that is, when $y \le h \sin \theta - L$. Set $\mathcal{R}_2 = \{(\theta, y) \mid 0 \le y \le h \sin \theta - L, 0 \le \theta < \pi\}$. Then the probability that the needle intersects at least two lines is

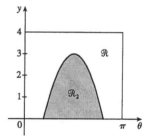

$$P_2 = \frac{\text{area}(\mathcal{R} \cap \mathcal{R}_2)}{\text{area}(\mathcal{R})} = \frac{\text{area}(\mathcal{R} \cap \mathcal{R}_2)}{\pi L}. \text{ When } L = 4 \text{ and } h = 7, \mathcal{R}_2$$

is contained in $\mathcal{R}$ (see the figure). Thus,

$$P_2 = \frac{1}{4\pi} \text{area}(\mathcal{R}_2) = \frac{1}{4\pi} \int_{\sin^{-1}(4/7)}^{\pi - \sin^{-1}(4/7)} (7 \sin \theta - 4) \, d\theta = \frac{1}{4\pi} \cdot 2 \int_{\sin^{-1}(4/7)}^{\pi/2} (7 \sin \theta - 4) \, d\theta$$

$$= \frac{1}{2\pi} \left[-7 \cos \theta - 4\theta\right]_{\sin^{-1}(4/7)}^{\pi/2} = \frac{1}{2\pi} \left[0 - 2\pi + 7 \frac{\sqrt{33}}{7} + 4 \sin^{-1}(4/7)\right]$$

$$= \frac{\sqrt{33} + 4 \sin^{-1}(4/7) - 2\pi}{2\pi} \approx 0.301497$$

(c) The needle intersects at least three lines when $y + 2L \le h \sin \theta$: that is, when $y \le h \sin \theta - 2L$. Set $\mathcal{R}_3 = \{(\theta, y) \mid 0 \le y \le h \sin \theta - 2L, 0 \le \theta < \pi\}$. Then the probability that the needle intersects at least three lines is $P_3 = \dfrac{\text{area}(\mathcal{R} \cap \mathcal{R}_3)}{\text{area}(\mathcal{R})} = \dfrac{\text{area}(\mathcal{R} \cap \mathcal{R}_3)}{\pi L}$. (At this point, the generalization to P_n, n any positive integer, should be clear.) Under the given assumption,

$$P_3 = \frac{1}{\pi L} \text{area}(\mathcal{R}_3) = \frac{1}{\pi L} \int_{\sin^{-1}(2L/h)}^{\pi - \sin^{-1}(2L/h)} (h \sin \theta - 2L) \, d\theta$$

$$= \frac{2}{\pi L} \int_{\sin^{-1}(2L/h)}^{\pi/2} (h \sin \theta - 2L) \, d\theta$$

$$= \frac{2}{\pi L} [-h \cos \theta - 2L\theta]_{\sin^{-1}(2L/h)}^{\pi/2}$$

$$= \frac{2}{\pi L} \left[-\pi L + \sqrt{h^2 - 4L^2} + 2L \sin^{-1}(2L/h) \right]$$

Note that the probability that a needle touches exactly one line is $P_1 - P_2$, the probability that it touches exactly two lines is $P_2 - P_3$, and so on.

7 Differential Equations

7.1 Modeling with Differential Equations

1. $y = x - x^{-1} \;\Rightarrow\; y' = 1 + x^{-2}$. To show that y is a solution of the differential equation, we will substitute the expressions for y and y' in the left-hand side of the equation and show that the left-hand side is equal to the right-hand side.

$$\text{LHS} = xy' + y = x\left(1 + x^{-2}\right) + \left(x - x^{-1}\right) = x + x^{-1} + x - x^{-1} = 2x = \text{RHS}$$

2. $y = \sin x \cos x - \cos x \;\Rightarrow\; y' = \sin x\,(-\sin x) + \cos x\,(\cos x) - (-\sin x) = \cos^2 x - \sin^2 x + \sin x.$

$$\text{LHS} = y' + (\tan x)y = \cos^2 x - \sin^2 x + \sin x + (\tan x)(\sin x \cos x - \cos x)$$
$$= \cos^2 x - \sin^2 x + \sin x + \sin^2 x - \sin x = \cos^2 x = \text{RHS},$$

so y is a solution of the differential equation. Also, $y(0) = \sin 0 \cos 0 - \cos 0 = 0 \cdot 1 - 1 = -1$, so the initial condition is satisfied.

3. (a) $y = \sin kt \;\Rightarrow\; y' = k\cos kt \;\Rightarrow\; y'' = -k^2 \sin kt$. $y'' + 9y = 0 \;\Rightarrow\; -k^2 \sin kt + 9\sin kt = 0 \;\Rightarrow\;$
$\left(9 - k^2\right)\sin kt = 0$ [for all t] $\;\Rightarrow\; 9 - k^2 = 0 \;\Rightarrow\; k = \pm 3$

(b) $y = A\sin kt + B\cos kt \;\Rightarrow\; y' = Ak\cos kt - Bk\sin kt \;\Rightarrow\; y'' = -Ak^2 \sin kt - Bk^2 \cos kt$.
Thus, $y'' + 9y = 0 \;\Rightarrow\; -Ak^2 \sin kt - Bk^2 \cos kt + 9(A\sin kt + B\cos kt) = 0 \;\Rightarrow\;$
$\left(9 - k^2\right)A\sin kt + \left(9 - k^2\right)B\cos kt = 0$. The last equation is true for all values of A and B if $k = \pm 3$.

4. $y = e^{rt} \;\Rightarrow\; y' = re^{rt} \;\Rightarrow\; y'' = r^2 e^{rt}$. $y'' + y' - 6y = 0 \;\Rightarrow\; r^2 e^{rt} + re^{rt} - 6e^{rt} = 0 \;\Rightarrow\;$
$\left(r^2 + r - 6\right)e^{rt} = 0 \;\Rightarrow\; (r+3)(r-2) = 0 \;\Rightarrow\; r = -3 \text{ or } 2$

5. (a) $y = e^t \;\Rightarrow\; y' = e^t \;\Rightarrow\; y'' = e^t$. $\text{LHS} = y'' + 2y' + y = e^t + 2e^t + e^t = 4e^t \ne 0$, so $y = e^t$ is not a solution of the differential equation.

(b) $y = e^{-t} \;\Rightarrow\; y' = -e^{-t} \;\Rightarrow\; y'' = e^{-t}$. $\text{LHS} = y'' + 2y' + y = e^{-t} - 2e^{-t} + e^{-t} = 0 = \text{RHS}$, so $y = e^{-t}$ is a solution.

(c) $y = te^{-t} \;\Rightarrow\; y' = t(-e^{-t}) + e^{-t}(1) = e^{-t}(1 - t) \;\Rightarrow\; y'' = e^{-t}(t - 2)$.

$$\text{LHS} = y'' + 2y' + y = e^{-t}(t - 2) + 2e^{-t}(1 - t) + te^{-t}$$
$$= e^{-t}\left[(t - 2) + 2(1 - t) + t\right] = e^{-t}(0) = 0 = \text{RHS},$$

so $y = te^{-t}$ is a solution.

(d) $y = t^2 e^{-t} \;\Rightarrow\; y' = te^{-t}(2 - t) \;\Rightarrow\; y'' = e^{-t}\left(t^2 - 4t + 2\right)$.

$$\text{LHS} = y'' + 2y' + y = e^{-t}\left(t^2 - 4t + 2\right) + 2te^{-t}(2 - t) + t^2 e^{-t}$$
$$= e^{-t}\left[\left(t^2 - 4t + 2\right) + 2t(2 - t) + t^2\right] = e^{-t}(2) \ne 0,$$

so $y = t^2 e^{-t}$ is not a solution.

6. (a) $y = Ce^{x^2/2} \Rightarrow y' = Ce^{x^2/2}(2x/2) = xCe^{x^2/2} = xy.$

(b)

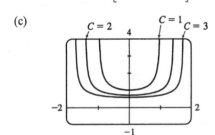

$C = 2$ $C = 3$ $C = 1$
10
-3 3
$C = -1$ $C = -3$ -10 $C = -2$

(c) $y(0) = 5 \Rightarrow Ce^0 = 5 \Rightarrow C = 5$, so the solution is

$y = 5e^{x^2/2}$.

(d) $y(1) = 2 \Rightarrow Ce^{1/2} = 2 \Rightarrow C = 2e^{-1/2}$, so the solution is

$y = 2e^{-1/2}e^{x^2/2} = 2e^{(x^2-1)/2}$.

7. (a) Since the derivative $y' = -y^2$ is always negative (or 0 if $y = 0$), the function y must be decreasing (or equal to 0) on any interval on which it is defined.

(b) $y = \dfrac{1}{x+C} \Rightarrow y' = -\dfrac{1}{(x+C)^2}$. LHS $= y' = -\dfrac{1}{(x+C)^2} = -\left(\dfrac{1}{x+C}\right)^2 = -y^2 =$ RHS

(c) $y = 0$ is a solution of $y' = -y^2$ that is not a member of the family in part (b).

(d) If $y(x) = \dfrac{1}{x+C}$, then $y(0) = \dfrac{1}{0+C} = \dfrac{1}{C}$. Since $y(0) = 0.5$, $\dfrac{1}{C} = \dfrac{1}{2} \Rightarrow C = 2$, so $y = \dfrac{1}{x+2}$.

8. (a) If x is close to 0, then xy^3 is close to 0, and hence, y' is close to 0. Thus, the graph of y must have a tangent line that is nearly horizontal. If x is large, then xy^3 is large, and the graph of y must have a tangent line that is nearly vertical. (In both cases, we assume reasonable values for y.)

(b) $y = (C - x^2)^{-1/2} \Rightarrow y' = x(C - x^2)^{-3/2}$.

RHS $= xy^3 = x\left[(C - x^2)^{-1/2}\right]^3 = x(C - x^2)^{-3/2} = y' =$ LHS

(c)

$C = 2$ $C = 1$ $C = 3$
4
-2 2
-1

When x is close to 0, y' is also close to 0.

As x gets larger, so does $|y'|$.

(d) $y(0) = (C - 0)^{-1/2} = 1/\sqrt{C}$ and $y(0) = 2 \Rightarrow \sqrt{C} = \frac{1}{2} \Rightarrow C = \frac{1}{4}$, so $y = \left(\frac{1}{4} - x^2\right)^{-1/2}$.

9. (a) $\dfrac{dP}{dt} = 1.2P\left(1 - \dfrac{P}{4200}\right)$. Now $\dfrac{dP}{dt} > 0 \Rightarrow 1 - \dfrac{P}{4200} > 0$ [assuming that $P > 0$] $\Rightarrow \dfrac{P}{4200} < 1 \Rightarrow$

$P < 4200 \Rightarrow$ the population is increasing for $0 < P < 4200$.

(b) $\dfrac{dP}{dt} < 0 \Rightarrow P > 4200$

(c) $\dfrac{dP}{dt} = 0 \Rightarrow P = 4200$ or $P = 0$

10. (a) $y = k \ \Rightarrow \ y' = 0$, so $\dfrac{dy}{dt} = y^4 - 6y^3 + 5y^2 \ \Rightarrow \ 0 = k^4 - 6k^3 + 5k^2 \ \Rightarrow \ k^2\left(k^2 - 6k + 5\right) = 0 \ \Rightarrow$

$k^2(k-1)(k-5) = 0 \ \Rightarrow \ k = 0, 1, \text{ or } 5$

(b) y is increasing $\ \Leftrightarrow \ \dfrac{dy}{dt} > 0 \ \Leftrightarrow \ y^2(y-1)(y-5) > 0 \ \Leftrightarrow \ y \in (-\infty, 0) \cup (0, 1) \cup (5, \infty)$

(c) y is decreasing $\ \Leftrightarrow \ \dfrac{dy}{dt} < 0 \ \Leftrightarrow \ y \in (1, 5)$

11. First graph: This function is increasing *and* also decreasing. But $dy/dt = e^t(y-1)^2 \geq 0$ for all t,
   implying that the graph of the solution of the differential equation cannot be decreasing on any interval.
   Second graph: When $y = 1$, $dy/dt = 0$, but the graph does not have a horizontal tangent line.

12. The correct graph for this exercise is shown in the figure at the right.

A. $y' = 1 + xy > 1$ for points in the first quadrant, but we can
   see that $y' < 0$ for some points in the first quadrant.

B. $y' = -2xy = 0$ when $x = 0$, but we can see that $y' > 0$ for $x = 0$.

Thus, equations A and B are incorrect, so the correct equation is C.

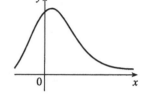

C. $y' = 1 - 2xy$ seems reasonable since:

   (1) When $x = 0$, y' could be 1.

   (2) When $x < 0$, y' could be greater than 1.

   (3) Solving $y' = 1 - 2xy$ for y gives us $y = \dfrac{1 - y'}{2x}$. If y' takes on small negative values, then as $x \to \infty$,
   $y \to 0^+$, as shown in the figure.

13. (a) P increases most rapidly at the beginning, since there are usually
   many simple, easily-learned sub-skills associated with learning a
   skill. As t increases, we would expect dP/dt to remain positive, but
   decrease. This is because as time progresses, the only points left to
   learn are the more difficult ones.

(b) $\dfrac{dP}{dt} = k(M - P)$ is always positive, so the level of performance P is
   increasing. As P gets close to M, dP/dt gets close to 0; that is, the
   performance levels off, as explained in part (a).

(c)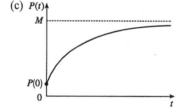

14. (a) The coffee cools most quickly as soon as it is removed from the heat
   source. The rate of cooling decreases toward 0 since the coffee
   approaches room temperature.

(b) $\dfrac{dy}{dt} = k(y - R)$, where k is a proportionality constant, y is the
   temperature of the coffee, and R is the room temperature. The initial
   condition is $y(0) = 95\,°C$. The answer and the model support each
   other because as y approaches R, dy/dt approaches 0, so the model
   seems appropriate.

(c)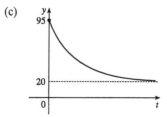

7.2 Direction Fields and Euler's Method • • • • • • • •

1. (a)

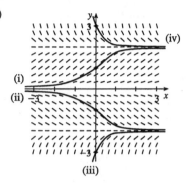

(b) It appears that the constant functions $y = 0$, $y = -2$, and $y = 2$ are equilibrium solutions. Note that these three values of y satisfy the given differential equation $y' = y\left(1 - \frac{1}{4}y^2\right)$.

2. (a)

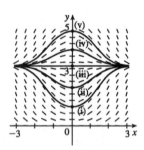

(b) From the figure, it appears that $y = \pi$ is an equilibrium solution. From the equation $y' = x \sin y$, we see that $y = n\pi$ (n an integer) describes all the equilibrium solutions.

3. $y' = y - 1$. The slopes at each point are independent of x, so the slopes are the same along each line parallel to the x-axis. Thus, IV is the direction field for this equation. Note that for $y = 1$, $y' = 0$.

4. $y' = y - x = 0$ on the line $y = x$, when $x = 0$ the slope is y, and when $y = 0$ the slope is $-x$. Direction field II satisfies these conditions. [Looking at the slope at the point $(0, 2)$, II looks more like it has a slope of 2 than does direction field I.]

5. $y' = y^2 - x^2 = 0 \implies y = \pm x$. There are horizontal tangents on these lines only in graph III, so this equation corresponds to direction field III.

6. $y' = y^3 - x^3 = 0$ on the line $y = x$, when $x = 0$ the slope is y^3, and when $y = 0$ the slope is $-x^3$. The graph is similar to the graph for Exercise 4, but the segments must get steeper very rapidly as they move away from the origin, because x and y are raised to the third power. This is the case in direction field I.

7. (a) $y(0) = 1$ (b) $y(0) = 0$ (c) $y(0) = -1$

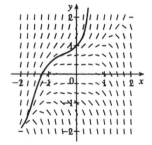 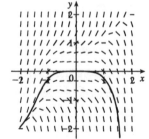 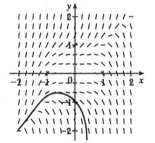

8. (a) $y(0) = 1$ (b) $y(0) = 0$ (c) $y(0) = -1$

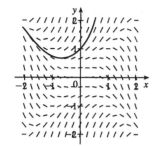 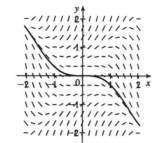 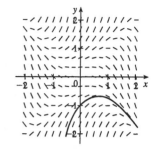

9. 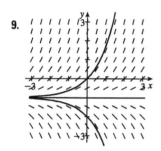   **10.** 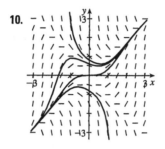   **11.**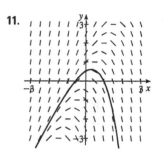

12. 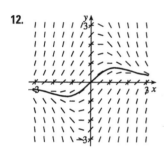   **13.** 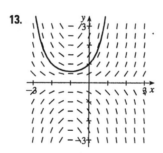   **14.**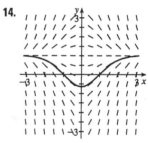

15. In Maple, we can use either `directionfield` (in Maple's share library) or `plots[fieldplot]` to plot the direction field. To plot the solution, we can either use the initial-value option in `directionfield`, or actually solve the equation. In Mathematica, we use `PlotVectorField` for the direction field, and the `Plot[Evaluate[...]]` construction to plot the solution, which is $y = e^{(1-\cos 2x)/2}$. In Derive, use `Direction_Field` (in utility file ODE_APPR) to plot the direction field. Then use `DSOLVE1(-y*SIN(2*x),1,x,y,0,1)` (in utility file ODE1) to solve the equation. Simplify each result.

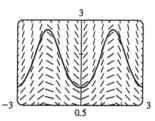

16. See Exercise 15 for specific CAS directions. The exact solution is

$$y = -x - 2\arctan \frac{2 + x - \dfrac{2}{1 + \tan(1/2)}}{x - \dfrac{2}{1 + \tan(1/2)}}$$

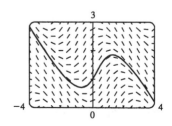

17.

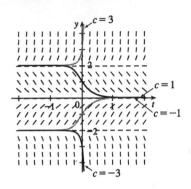

$L = \lim_{t \to \infty} y(t)$ exists for $-2 \le c \le 2$; $L = \pm 2$ for $c = \pm 2$ and $L = 0$ for $-2 < c < 2$. For other values of c, L does not exist.

18.

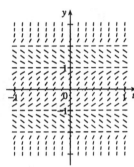

Note that when $f(y) = 0$ on the graph in the text, we have $y' = f(y) = 0$; so we get horizontal segments at $y = \pm 1, \pm 2$. We get segments with negative slopes only for $1 < |y| < 2$. All other segments have positive slope. For the limiting behavior of solutions:

- If $y(0) > 2$, then $\lim_{t \to \infty} y = \infty$ and $\lim_{t \to -\infty} y = 2$.
- If $1 < y(0) < 2$, then $\lim_{t \to \infty} y = 1$ and $\lim_{t \to -\infty} y = 2$.
- If $-1 < y(0) < 1$, then $\lim_{t \to \infty} y = 1$ and $\lim_{t \to -\infty} y = -1$.
- If $-2 < y(0) < -1$, then $\lim_{t \to \infty} y = -2$ and $\lim_{t \to -\infty} y = -1$.
- If $y < -2$, then $\lim_{t \to \infty} y = -2$ and $\lim_{t \to -\infty} y = -\infty$.

19. (a) $y' = F(x, y) = y$ and $y(0) = 1 \quad \Rightarrow \quad x_0 = 0, y_0 = 1$.

(i) $h = 0.4$ and $y_1 = y_0 + hF(x_0, y_0) \quad \Rightarrow \quad y_1 = 1 + 0.4 \cdot 1 = 1.4$. $x_1 = x_0 + h = 0 + 0.4 = 0.4$, so $y_1 = y(0.4) = 1.4$.

(ii) $h = 0.2 \quad \Rightarrow \quad x_1 = 0.2$ and $x_2 = 0.4$, so we need to find y_2.
$y_1 = y_0 + hF(x_0, y_0) = 1 + 0.2y_0 = 1 + 0.2 \cdot 1 = 1.2$,
$y_2 = y_1 + hF(x_1, y_1) = 1.2 + 0.2y_1 = 1.2 + 0.2 \cdot 1.2 = 1.44$.

(iii) $h = 0.1 \quad \Rightarrow \quad x_4 = 0.4$, so we need to find y_4. $y_1 = y_0 + hF(x_0, y_0) = 1 + 0.1y_0 = 1 + 0.1 \cdot 1 = 1.1$,
$y_2 = y_1 + hF(x_1, y_1) = 1.1 + 0.1y_1 = 1.1 + 0.1 \cdot 1.1 = 1.21$,
$y_3 = y_2 + hF(x_2, y_2) = 1.21 + 0.1y_2 = 1.21 + 0.1 \cdot 1.21 = 1.331$,
$y_4 = y_3 + hF(x_3, y_3) = 1.331 + 0.1y_3 = 1.331 + 0.1 \cdot 1.331 = 1.4641$.

(b)

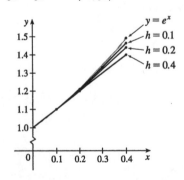

We see that the estimates are underestimates since they are all below the graph of $y = e^x$.

(c) (i) For $h = 0.4$: (exact value) − (approximate value) $= e^{0.4} − 1.4 \approx 0.091$

 (ii) For $h = 0.2$: (exact value) − (approximate value) $= e^{0.4} − 1.44 \approx 0.0518$

 (iii) For $h = 0.1$: (exact value) − (approximate value) $= e^{0.4} − 1.4641 \approx 0.0277$

Each time the step size is halved, the error estimate also appears to be halved (approximately).

20.

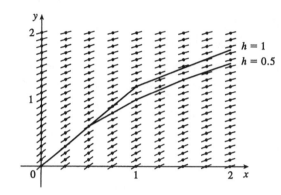

As x increases, the slopes decrease and all of the estimates are above the true values. Thus, all of the estimates are overestimates.

21. $h = 0.5$, $x_0 = 1$, $y_0 = 0$, and $F(x, y) = y − 2x$.

Note that $x_1 = x_0 + h = 1 + 0.5 = 1.5$, $x_2 = 2$, and $x_3 = 2.5$.

$y_1 = y_0 + hF(x_0, y_0) = 0 + 0.5F(1, 0) = 0.5[0 − 2(1)] = −1$.

$y_2 = y_1 + hF(x_1, y_1) = −1 + 0.5F(1.5, −1) = −1 + 0.5[−1 − 2(1.5)] = −3$.

$y_3 = y_2 + hF(x_2, y_2) = −3 + 0.5F(2, −3) = −3 + 0.5[−3 − 2(2)] = −6.5$.

$y_4 = y_3 + hF(x_3, y_3) = −6.5 + 0.5F(2.5, −6.5) = −6.5 + 0.5[−6.5 − 2(2.5)] = −12.25$.

22. $h = 0.2$, $x_0 = 0$, $y_0 = 0$, and $F(x, y) = 1 − xy$.

Note that $x_1 = x_0 + h = 0 + 0.2 = 0.2$, $x_2 = 0.4$, $x_3 = 0.6$, and $x_4 = 0.8$.

$y_1 = y_0 + hF(x_0, y_0) = 0 + 0.2F(0, 0) = 0.2[1 − (0)(0)] = 0.2$.

$y_2 = y_1 + hF(x_1, y_1) = 0.2 + 0.2F(0.2, 0.2) = 0.2 + 0.2[1 − (0.2)(0.2)] = 0.392$.

$y_3 = y_2 + hF(x_2, y_2) = 0.392 + 0.2F(0.4, 0.392) = 0.392 + 0.2[1 − (0.4)(0.392)] = 0.56064$.

$y_4 = y_3 + hF(x_3, y_3) = 0.56064 + 0.2[1 − (0.6)(0.56064)] = 0.6933632$.

$y_5 = y_4 + hF(x_4, y_4) = 0.6933632 + 0.2[1 − (0.8)(0.6933632)] = 0.782425088$.

Thus, $y(1) \approx 0.7824$.

23. $h = 0.1$, $x_0 = 0$, $y_0 = 1$, and $F(x, y) = y + xy$.

Note that $x_1 = x_0 + h = 0 + 0.1 = 0.1$, $x_2 = 0.2$, $x_3 = 0.3$, and $x_4 = 0.4$.

$y_1 = y_0 + hF(x_0, y_0) = 1 + 0.1F(0, 1) = 1 + 0.1[1 + (0)(1)] = 1.1$.

$y_2 = y_1 + hF(x_1, y_1) = 1.1 + 0.1F(0.1, 1.1) = 1.1 + 0.1[1.1 + (0.1)(1.1)] = 1.221$.

$y_3 = y_2 + hF(x_2, y_2) = 1.221 + 0.1F(0.2, 1.221) = 1.221 + 0.1[1.221 + (0.2)(1.221)] = 1.36752$.

$y_4 = y_3 + hF(x_3, y_3) = 1.36752 + 0.1F(0.3, 1.36752) = 1.36752 + 0.1[1.36752 + (0.3)(1.36752]$

$\qquad\qquad = 1.5452976$.

$y_5 = y_4 + hF(x_4, y_4) = 1.5452976 + 0.1F(0.4, 1.5452976)$

$\qquad\qquad = 1.5452976 + 0.1[1.5452976 + (0.4)(1.5452976)] = 1.761639264$.

Thus, $y(0.5) \approx 1.7616$.

24. (a) $h = 0.2$, $x_0 = 1$, $y_0 = 0$, and $F(x, y) = x - xy$.

We need to find y_2, because $x_1 = 1.2$ and $x_2 = 1.4$.

$y_1 = y_0 + hF(x_0, y_0) = 0 + 0.2F(1, 0) = 0.2[1 - (1)(0)] = 0.2$.

$y_2 = y_1 + hF(x_1, y_1) = 0.2 + 0.2F(1.2, 0.2) = 0.2 + 0.2[1.2 - (1.2)(0.2)] = 0.392 \approx y(1.4)$.

(b) Now $h = 0.1$, so we need to find y_4.

$y_1 = 0 + 0.1[1 - (1)(0)] = 0.1$,

$y_2 = 0.1 + 0.1[1.1 - (1.1)(0.1)] = 0.199$,

$y_3 = 0.199 + 0.1[1.2 - (1.2)(0.199)] = 0.29512$, and

$y_4 = 0.29512 + 0.1[1.3 - (1.3)(0.29512)] = 0.3867544 \approx y(1.4)$.

25. (a) $dy/dx + 3x^2 y = 6x^2 \Rightarrow y' = 6x^2 - 3x^2 y$. Store this expression in Y_1 and use the following simple program to evaluate $y(1)$ for each part, using $H = h = 1$ and $N = 1$ for part (i), $H = 0.1$ and $N = 10$ for part (ii), and so forth.

$h \to H: 0 \to X: 3 \to Y$:

For(I, 1, N): $Y + H \times Y_1 \to Y: X + H \to X$:

End(loop):

Display Y. [To see all iterations, include this statement in the loop.]

(i) $H = 1, N = 1 \Rightarrow y(1) = 3$ | (ii) $H = 0.1, N = 10 \Rightarrow y(1) \approx 2.3928$

(iii) $H = 0.01, N = 100 \Rightarrow y(1) \approx 2.3701$ | (iv) $H = 0.001, N = 1000 \Rightarrow y(1) \approx 2.3681$

(b) $y = 2 + e^{-x^3} \Rightarrow y' = -3x^2 e^{-x^3}$

$$\text{LHS} = y' + 3x^2 y = -3x^2 e^{-x^3} + 3x^2 \left(2 + e^{-x^3}\right) = -3x^2 e^{-x^3} + 6x^2 + 3x^2 e^{-x^3} = 6x^2 = \text{RHS}$$

$$y(0) = 2 + e^{-0} = 2 + 1 = 3$$

(c) The exact value of $y(1)$ is $2 + e^{-1^3} = 2 + e^{-1}$.

(i) For $h = 1$: (exact value) − (approximate value) $= 2 + e^{-1} - 3 \approx -0.6321$

(ii) For $h = 0.1$: (exact value) − (approximate value) $= 2 + e^{-1} - 2.3928 \approx -0.0249$

(iii) For $h = 0.01$: (exact value) − (approximate value) $= 2 + e^{-1} - 2.3701 \approx -0.0022$

(iv) For $h = 0.001$: (exact value) − (approximate value) $= 2 + e^{-1} - 2.3681 \approx -0.0002$

In (ii)–(iv), it seems that when the step size is divided by 10, the error estimate is also divided by 10 (approximately).

26. (a) We use the program from the solution to Exercise 25 with $Y_1 = x^3 - y^3$, $H = 0.01$, and $N = \frac{2-0}{0.01} = 200$. With $(x_0, y_0) = (0, 1)$, we get $y(2) \approx 1.9000$.

(b)

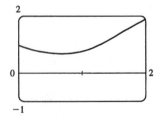

Notice from the graph that $y(2) \approx 1.9$, which serves as a check on our calculation in part (a).

27. (a) $R\dfrac{dQ}{dt} + \dfrac{1}{C}Q = E(t)$ becomes

$5Q' + \dfrac{1}{0.05}Q = 60$ or $Q' + 4Q = 12$.

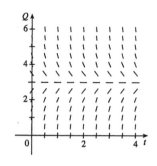

(b) From the graph, it appears that the limiting value of the charge Q is about 3.

(c) If $Q' = 0$, then $4Q = 12 \Rightarrow Q = 3$ is an equilibrium solution.

(d)

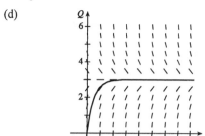

(e) $Q' + 4Q = 12 \Rightarrow Q' = 12 - 4Q$. Now $Q(0) = 0$, so $t_0 = 0$ and $Q_0 = 0$.

$$Q_1 = Q_0 + hF(t_0, Q_0) = 0 + 0.1(12 - 4 \cdot 0) = 1.2$$
$$Q_2 = Q_1 + hF(t_1, Q_1) = 1.2 + 0.1(12 - 4 \cdot 1.2) = 1.92$$
$$Q_3 = Q_2 + hF(t_2, Q_2) = 1.92 + 0.1(12 - 4 \cdot 1.92) = 2.352$$
$$Q_4 = Q_3 + hF(t_3, Q_3) = 2.352 + 0.1(12 - 4 \cdot 2.352) = 2.6112$$
$$Q_5 = Q_4 + hF(t_4, Q_4) = 2.6112 + 0.1(12 - 4 \cdot 2.6112) = 2.76672$$

Thus, $Q_5 = Q(0.5) \approx 2.77$ C.

28. (a) From Exercise 7.1.14, we have $dy/dt = k(y - R)$. We are given that $R = 20\,°\text{C}$ and $dy/dt = -1\,°\text{C/min}$ when $y = 70\,°\text{C}$. Thus, $-1 = k(70 - 20) \Rightarrow k = -\frac{1}{50}$ and the differential equation becomes $dy/dt = -\frac{1}{50}(y - 20)$.

(b)

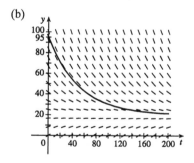

The limiting value of the temperature is $20\,°\text{C}$; that is, the temperature of the room.

(c) From part (a), $dy/dt = -\frac{1}{50}(y - 20)$. With $t_0 = 0$, $y_0 = 95$, and $h = 2$ min, we get

$y_1 = y_0 + hF(t_0, y_0) = 95 + 2\left[-\frac{1}{50}(95 - 20)\right] = 92$

$y_2 = y_1 + hF(t_1, y_1) = 92 + 2\left[-\frac{1}{50}(92 - 20)\right] = 89.12$

$y_3 = y_2 + hF(t_2, y_2) = 89.12 + 2\left[-\frac{1}{50}(89.12 - 20)\right]$
$\quad = 86.3552$

$y_4 = y_3 + hF(t_3, y_3) = 86.3552 + 2\left[-\frac{1}{50}(86.3552 - 20)\right]$
$\quad = 83.700992$

$y_5 = y_4 + hF(t_4, y_4) = 83.700992 + 2\left[-\frac{1}{50}(83.700992 - 20)\right]$
$\quad = 81.15295232$

Thus, $y(10) \approx 81.15\,°\text{C}$.

7.3 **Separable Equations** • • • • • • • • • • • • •

1. $\dfrac{dy}{dx} = y^2$ $\Rightarrow$ $\dfrac{dy}{y^2} = dx$ $[y \neq 0]$ $\Rightarrow$ $\displaystyle\int \dfrac{dy}{y^2} = \int dx$ $\Rightarrow$ $-\dfrac{1}{y} = x + C$ $\Rightarrow$ $-y = \dfrac{1}{x+C}$ $\Rightarrow$

$y = \dfrac{-1}{x+C}$, and $y = 0$ is also a solution.

2. $\dfrac{dy}{dx} = \dfrac{e^{2x}}{4y^3}$ $\Rightarrow$ $4y^3\,dy = e^{2x}\,dx$ $\Rightarrow$ $\int 4y^3\,dy = \int e^{2x}\,dx$ $\Rightarrow$ $y^4 = \tfrac{1}{2}e^{2x} + C$ $\Rightarrow$

$y = \pm\sqrt[4]{\tfrac{1}{2}e^{2x} + C}$

3. $yy' = x$ $\Rightarrow$ $y\dfrac{dy}{dx} = x$ $\Rightarrow$ $\int y\,dy = \int x\,dx$ $\Rightarrow$ $\tfrac{1}{2}y^2 = \tfrac{1}{2}x^2 + C_1$ $\Rightarrow$ $y^2 = x^2 + 2C_1$ $\Rightarrow$

$x^2 - y^2 = C$ (where $C = -2C_1$). This represents a family of hyperbolas.

4. $y' = xy$ $\Rightarrow$ $\displaystyle\int \dfrac{dy}{y} = \int x\,dx$ $[y \neq 0]$ $\Rightarrow$ $\ln|y| = \dfrac{x^2}{2} + C$ $\Rightarrow$ $|y| = e^C e^{x^2/2}$ $\Rightarrow$ $y = Ke^{x^2/2}$,

where $K = \pm e^C$ is a constant. (In our derivation, K was nonzero, but we can restore the excluded case $y = 0$ by allowing K to be zero.)

5. $\dfrac{dy}{dt} = \dfrac{te^t}{y\sqrt{1+y^2}}$ $\Rightarrow$ $y\sqrt{1+y^2}\,dy = te^t\,dt$ $\Rightarrow$ $\int y\sqrt{1+y^2}\,dy = \int te^t\,dt$ $\Rightarrow$

$\tfrac{1}{3}(1+y^2)^{3/2} = te^t - e^t + C$ [where the first integral is evaluated by substitution and the second by parts] $\Rightarrow$

$1 + y^2 = [3(te^t - e^t + C)]^{2/3}$ $\Rightarrow$ $y = \pm\sqrt{[3(te^t - e^t + C)]^{2/3} - 1}$

6. $y' = \dfrac{xy}{2\ln y}$ $\Rightarrow$ $\dfrac{2\ln y}{y}\,dy = x\,dx$ $\Rightarrow$ $\displaystyle\int \dfrac{2\ln y}{y}\,dy = \int x\,dx$ $\Rightarrow$ $(\ln y)^2 = \dfrac{x^2}{2} + C$ $\Rightarrow$

$\ln y = \pm\sqrt{x^2/2 + C}$ $\Rightarrow$ $y = e^{\pm\sqrt{x^2/2+C}}$

7. $\dfrac{du}{dt} = 2 + 2u + t + tu$ $\Rightarrow$ $\dfrac{du}{dt} = (1+u)(2+t)$ $\Rightarrow$ $\displaystyle\int \dfrac{du}{1+u} = \int (2+t)dt$ $[u \neq -1]$ $\Rightarrow$

$\ln|1+u| = \tfrac{1}{2}t^2 + 2t + C$ $\Rightarrow$ $|1+u| = e^{t^2/2+2t+C} = Ke^{t^2/2+2t}$, where $K = e^C$ $\Rightarrow$

$1 + u = \pm Ke^{t^2/2+2t}$ $\Rightarrow$ $u = -1 \pm Ke^{t^2/2+2t}$ where $K > 0$. $u = -1$ is also a solution, so

$u = -1 + Ae^{t^2/2+2t}$, where A is an arbitrary constant.

8. $\dfrac{dz}{dt} + e^{t+z} = 0$ $\Rightarrow$ $\dfrac{dz}{dt} = -e^t e^z$ $\Rightarrow$ $\int e^{-z}\,dz = -\int e^t\,dt$ $\Rightarrow$ $-e^{-z} = -e^t + C$ $\Rightarrow$ $e^{-z} = e^t - C$

$\Rightarrow$ $\dfrac{1}{e^z} = e^t - C$ $\Rightarrow$ $e^z = \dfrac{1}{e^t - C}$ $\Rightarrow$ $z = \ln\left(\dfrac{1}{e^t - C}\right)$ $\Rightarrow$ $z = -\ln(e^t - C)$

9. $\dfrac{dy}{dx} = y^2 + 1$, $y(1) = 0$. $\displaystyle\int \dfrac{dy}{y^2+1} = \int dx$ $\Rightarrow$ $\tan^{-1} y = x + C$. $y = 0$ when $x = 1$, so

$1 + C = \tan^{-1} 0 = 0$ $\Rightarrow$ $C = -1$. Thus, $\tan^{-1} y = x - 1$ and $y = \tan(x-1)$.

10. $\dfrac{dy}{dx} = \dfrac{y\cos x}{1+y^2}$, $y(0) = 1$. $(1+y^2)\,dy = y\cos x\,dx$ $\Rightarrow$ $\dfrac{1+y^2}{y}\,dy = \cos x\,dx$ $\Rightarrow$

$\int \left(\tfrac{1}{y} + y\right)dy = \int \cos x\,dx$ $\Rightarrow$ $\ln|y| + \tfrac{1}{2}y^2 = \sin x + C$. $y(0) = 1$ $\Rightarrow$ $\ln 1 + \tfrac{1}{2} = \sin 0 + C$ $\Rightarrow$

$C = \tfrac{1}{2}$, so $\ln|y| + \tfrac{1}{2}y^2 = \sin x + \tfrac{1}{2}$. We cannot solve explicitly for y.

11. $xe^{-t}\dfrac{dx}{dt} = t$, $x(0) = 1$. $\int x\,dx = \int te^t\,dt \Rightarrow \frac{1}{2}x^2 = (t-1)e^t + C$ [by parts]. $x(0) = 1$, so
$\frac{1}{2} = (0-1)e^0 + C$ and $C = \frac{3}{2}$. Thus, $\frac{1}{2}x^2 = (t-1)e^t + \frac{3}{2} \Rightarrow x^2 = 2(t-1)e^t + 3 \Rightarrow$
$x = \sqrt{2(t-1)e^t + 3}$ [use the positive square root since $x(0) = +1$].

12. $x + 2y\sqrt{x^2+1}\,\dfrac{dy}{dx} = 0$, $y(0) = 1$. $x\,dx + 2y\sqrt{x^2+1}\,dy = 0 \Rightarrow \displaystyle\int 2y\,dy = -\int \dfrac{x\,dx}{\sqrt{x^2+1}} \Rightarrow$
$y^2 = -\sqrt{x^2+1} + C$. $y(0) = 1 \Rightarrow 1 = -1 + C \Rightarrow C = 2$, so $y^2 = 2 - \sqrt{x^2+1}$ and
$y = \sqrt{2 - \sqrt{x^2+1}}$.

13. $\dfrac{du}{dt} = \dfrac{2t + \sec^2 t}{2u}$, $u(0) = -5$. $\int 2u\,du = \int (2t + \sec^2 t)\,dt \Rightarrow u^2 = t^2 + \tan t + C$, where
$[u(0)]^2 = 0^2 + \tan 0 + C \Rightarrow C = (-5)^2 = 25$. Therefore, $u^2 = t^2 + \tan t + 25$, so $u = \pm\sqrt{t^2 + \tan t + 25}$.
Since $u(0) = -5$, we must have $u = -\sqrt{t^2 + \tan t + 25}$.

14. $\dfrac{dy}{dt} = te^y$, $y(1) = 0$. $\int e^{-y}\,dy = \int t\,dt \Rightarrow -e^{-y} = \frac{1}{2}t^2 + C$. Since $y(1) = 0$, $-e^0 = \frac{1}{2} \cdot 1^2 + C$. Therefore,
$C = -1 - \frac{1}{2} = -\frac{3}{2}$ and $-e^{-y} = \frac{1}{2}t^2 - \frac{3}{2}$. So $e^{-y} = \frac{3}{2} - \frac{1}{2}t^2 = \dfrac{3 - t^2}{2} \Rightarrow e^y = \dfrac{2}{3 - t^2} \Rightarrow$
$y = \ln 2 - \ln(3 - t^2)$ for $|t| < \sqrt{3}$.

15. $\dfrac{dy}{dx} = 4x^3 y$, $y(0) = 7$. $\dfrac{dy}{y} = 4x^3\,dx$ [if $y \ne 0$] $\Rightarrow \displaystyle\int \dfrac{dy}{y} = \int 4x^3\,dx \Rightarrow \ln|y| = x^4 + C \Rightarrow$
$e^{\ln|y|} = e^{x^4 + C} \Rightarrow |y| = e^{x^4}e^C \Rightarrow y = Ae^{x^4}$; $y(0) = 7 \Rightarrow A = 7 \Rightarrow y = 7e^{x^4}$.

16. $\dfrac{dy}{dx} = \dfrac{y^2}{x^3}$, $y(1) = 1$. $\displaystyle\int \dfrac{dy}{y^2} = \int \dfrac{dx}{x^3} \Rightarrow -\dfrac{1}{y} = -\dfrac{1}{2x^2} + C$. $y(1) = 1 \Rightarrow -1 = -\frac{1}{2} + C \Rightarrow$
$C = -\frac{1}{2}$. So $\dfrac{1}{y} = \dfrac{1}{2x^2} + \dfrac{1}{2} = \dfrac{2 + 2x^2}{2 \cdot 2x^2} \Rightarrow y = \dfrac{2x^2}{x^2 + 1}$.

17. (a) $y' = 2x\sqrt{1 - y^2} \Rightarrow \dfrac{dy}{dx} = 2x\sqrt{1 - y^2} \Rightarrow \dfrac{dy}{\sqrt{1 - y^2}} = 2x\,dx \Rightarrow \displaystyle\int \dfrac{dy}{\sqrt{1 - y^2}} = \int 2x\,dx \Rightarrow$
$\sin^{-1} y = x^2 + C$ for $-\frac{\pi}{2} \le x^2 + C \le \frac{\pi}{2}$.

(b) $y(0) = 0 \Rightarrow \sin^{-1} 0 = 0^2 + C \Rightarrow C = 0$, so $\sin^{-1} y = x^2$
and $y = \sin(x^2)$ for $-\sqrt{\pi/2} \le x \le \sqrt{\pi/2}$.

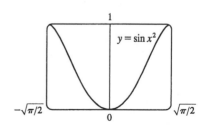

(c) For $\sqrt{1 - y^2}$ to be a real number, we must have $-1 \le y \le 1$; that is, $-1 \le y(0) \le 1$. Thus, the initial-value
problem $y' = 2x\sqrt{1 - y^2}$, $y(0) = 2$ does *not* have a solution.

18. $e^{-y}y' + \cos x = 0 \quad \Leftrightarrow \quad \int e^{-y}\, dy = -\int \cos x\, dx \quad \Leftrightarrow \quad -e^{-y} = -\sin x + C_1 \quad \Leftrightarrow \quad y = -\ln(\sin x + C)$.
The solution is periodic, with period 2π. Note that for $C > 1$, the domain of the solution is $\mathbb{R}$, but for $-1 < C \le 1$
it is only defined on the intervals where $\sin x + C > 0$, and it is meaningless for $C \le -1$, since then
$\sin x + C \le 0$, and the logarithm is undefined.

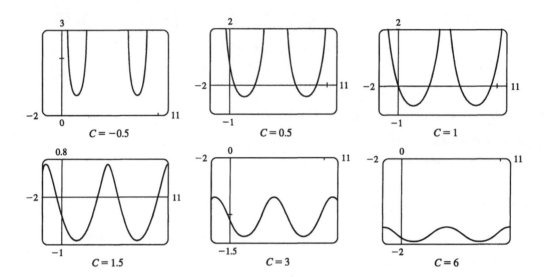

For $-1 < C < 1$, the solution curve consists of concave-up pieces separated by intervals on which the solution is
not defined (where $\sin x + C \le 0$). For $C = 1$, the solution curve consists of concave-up pieces separated by
vertical asymptotes at the points where $\sin x + C = 0 \Leftrightarrow \sin x = -1$. For $C > 1$, the curve is continuous, and
as C increases, the graph moves downward, and the amplitude of the oscillations decreases.

19. $\dfrac{dy}{dx} = \dfrac{\sin x}{\sin y}$, $y(0) = \dfrac{\pi}{2}$. So $\int \sin y\, dy = \int \sin x\, dx \quad \Leftrightarrow$

$-\cos y = -\cos x + C \quad \Leftrightarrow \quad \cos y = \cos x - C$. From the initial

condition, we need $\cos \dfrac{\pi}{2} = \cos 0 - C \Rightarrow 0 = 1 - C \Rightarrow C = 1$,

so the solution is $\cos y = \cos x - 1$. Note that we cannot take $\cos^{-1}$ of

both sides, since that would unnecessarily restrict the solution to the case

where $-1 \le \cos x - 1 \quad \Leftrightarrow \quad 0 \le \cos x$, as $\cos^{-1}$ is defined only on

$[-1, 1]$. Instead we plot the graph using Maple's

`plots[implicitplot]` or Mathematica's `Plot[Evaluate[⋯]]`.

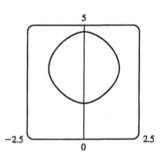

20. $\dfrac{dy}{dx} = \dfrac{x\sqrt{x^2 + 1}}{ye^y} \quad \Leftrightarrow \quad \int ye^y\, dy = \int x\sqrt{x^2 + 1}\, dx$. We use parts on the LHS with $u = y$, $dv = e^y\, dy$, and on

the RHS we use the substitution $z = x^2 + 1$, so $dz = 2x\, dx$. The equation becomes $ye^y - \int e^y\, dy = \frac{1}{2}\int \sqrt{z}\, dz$

$\Leftrightarrow \quad e^y(y - 1) = \frac{1}{3}(x^2 + 1)^{3/2} + C$, so we see that the curves are symmetric about the y-axis. Every point (x, y)

in the plane lies on one of the curves, namely the one for which $C = (y - 1)e^y - \frac{1}{3}(x^2 + 1)^{3/2}$. For example, along the y-axis, $C = (y-1)e^y - \frac{1}{3}$, so the origin lies on the curve with $C = -\frac{4}{3}$. We use Maple's `plots[implicitplot]` command or `Plot[Evaluate[···]]` in Mathematica to plot the solution curves for various values of C.

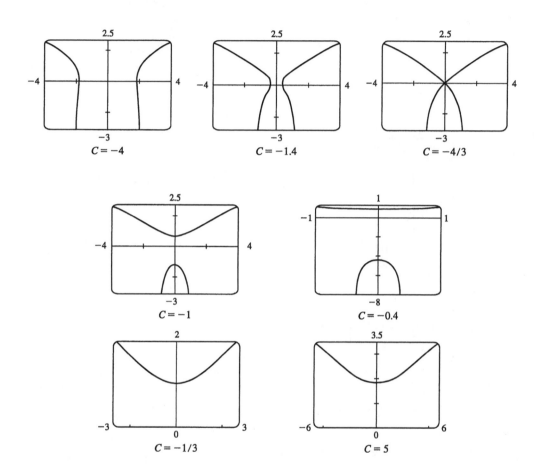

It seems that the transitional values of C are $-\frac{4}{3}$ and $-\frac{1}{3}$. For $C < -\frac{4}{3}$, the graph consists of left and right branches. At $C = -\frac{4}{3}$, the two branches become connected at the origin, and as C increases, the graph splits into top and bottom branches. At $C = -\frac{1}{3}$, the bottom half disappears. As C increases further, the graph moves upward, but doesn't change shape much.

21. (a)

x	y	$y' = 1/y$	x	y	$y' = 1/y$
0	0.5	2	0	−2	−0.5
0	−0.5	−2	0	4	0.25
0	1	1	0	3	$0.\overline{3}$
0	−1	−1	0	0.25	4
0	2	0.5	0	$0.\overline{3}$	3

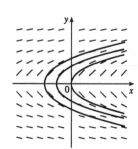

(b) $y' = 1/y \Rightarrow dy/dx = 1/y \Rightarrow$

$y\,dy = dx \Rightarrow \int y\,dy = \int dx \Rightarrow$

$\frac{1}{2}y^2 = x + c \Rightarrow y^2 = 2(x + c)$

or $y = \pm\sqrt{2(x + c)}$.

(c)

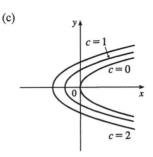

22. (a)

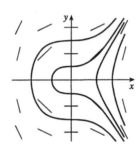

x	y	$y' = x^2/y$
1	1	1
-1	1	1
-1	-1	-1
1	-1	-1
1	2	0.5
2	1	4
2	2	2
1	0.5	2
0.5	1	0.25
2	0.5	8

(b) $y' = x^2/y \Rightarrow y\,dy = x^2\,dx$,

so $\frac{1}{2}y^2 = \frac{1}{3}x^3 + c_1$, or

$y = \pm\left(\frac{2}{3}x^3 + c\right)^{1/2}$.

(c)

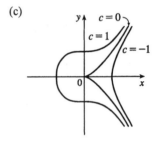

23. The curves $y = kx^2$ form a family of parabolas with axis the y-axis. Differentiating gives $y' = 2kx$, but $k = y/x^2$, so $y' = 2y/x$. Thus, the slope of the tangent line at any point (x, y) on one of the parabolas is $y' = 2y/x$, so the orthogonal trajectories must satisfy $y' = -x/(2y)$ $\Leftrightarrow 2y\,dy = -x\,dx \Leftrightarrow y^2 = -x^2/2 + C_1 \Leftrightarrow x^2 + 2y^2 = C$. This is a family of ellipses.

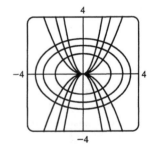

24. The curves $x^2 - y^2 = k$ form a family of hyperbolas. Differentiating gives $2x - 2y\,(dy/dx) = 0$ or $y' = x/y$, the slope of the tangent line at (x, y) on one of the hyperbolas. Thus, the orthogonal trajectories must satisfy $y' = -y/x \Leftrightarrow dy/y = -dx/x \Leftrightarrow \ln|y| = -\ln|x| + C_1 \Leftrightarrow \ln|x| + \ln|y| = C_1 \Leftrightarrow \ln|xy| = C_1 \Leftrightarrow |xy| = e^{C_1} \Leftrightarrow xy = C$. This is a family of hyperbolas.

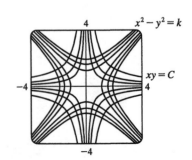

25. Differentiating $y = (x+k)^{-1}$ gives $y' = -\dfrac{1}{(x+k)^2}$, but $k = \dfrac{1}{y} - x$, so

$y' = -\dfrac{1}{(1/y)^2} = -y^2$. Thus, the orthogonal trajectories must satisfy

$y' = -\dfrac{1}{-y^2} = \dfrac{1}{y^2} \iff y^2\,dy = dx \iff \dfrac{y^3}{3} = x + C$ or

$y = [3(x+C)]^{1/3}$

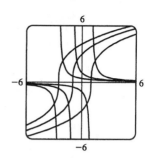

26. Differentiating $y = ke^{-x}$ gives $y' = -ke^{-x}$, but $k = ye^x$, so $y' = -y$.

Thus, the orthogonal trajectories must satisfy $y' = -1/(-y) = 1/y \iff$

$y\,dy = dx \iff \frac{1}{2}y^2 = x + C \iff y = \pm[2(C+x)]^{1/2}$. This is a

family of parabolas with axis the x-axis.

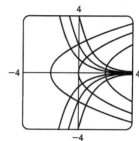

27. From Exercise 7.2.27, $\dfrac{dQ}{dt} = 12 - 4Q \iff \displaystyle\int \dfrac{dQ}{12 - 4Q} = \int dt \iff -\frac{1}{4}\ln|12 - 4Q| = t + C \iff$

$\ln|12 - 4Q| = -4t - 4C \iff |12 - 4Q| = e^{-4t-4C} \iff 12 - 4Q = Ke^{-4t} \ [K = \pm e^{-4C}] \iff$

$4Q = 12 - Ke^{-4t} \iff Q = 3 - Ae^{-4t} \ [A = K/3]. \ Q(0) = 0 \iff 0 = 3 - A \iff A = 3 \iff$

$Q(t) = 3 - 3e^{-4t}$. As $t \to \infty$, $Q(t) \to 3 - 0 = 3$ (the limiting value).

28. From Exercise 7.2.28, $\dfrac{dy}{dt} = -\frac{1}{50}(y - 20) \iff \displaystyle\int \dfrac{dy}{y - 20} = \int \left(-\frac{1}{50}\right) dt \iff \ln|y - 20| = -\frac{1}{50}t + C \iff$

$y - 20 = Ke^{-t/50} \iff y(t) = Ke^{-t/50} + 20. \ y(0) = 95 \iff 95 = K + 20 \iff K = 75 \iff$

$y(t) = 75e^{-t/50} + 20.$

29. $\dfrac{dP}{dt} = k(M - P) \iff \displaystyle\int \dfrac{dP}{P - M} = \int (-k)\,dt \iff \ln|P - M| = -kt + C \iff |P - M| = e^{-kt+C}$

$\iff P - M = Ae^{-kt} \ [A = \pm e^C] \iff P = M + Ae^{-kt}$. If we assume that performance is at level 0 when

$t = 0$, then $P(0) = 0 \iff 0 = M + A \iff A = -M \iff P(t) = M - Me^{-kt}$.

$\displaystyle\lim_{t\to\infty} P(t) = M - M \cdot 0 = M.$

30. (a) $\dfrac{dx}{dt} = k(a - x)(b - x), \ a \neq b$. Using partial fractions, $\dfrac{1}{(a - x)(b - x)} = \dfrac{1/(b - a)}{a - x} - \dfrac{1/(b - a)}{b - x}$, so

$\displaystyle\int \dfrac{dx}{(a - x)(b - x)} = \int k\,dt \ \Rightarrow \ \dfrac{1}{b - a}(-\ln|a - x| + \ln|b - x|) = kt + C \ \Rightarrow$

$\ln\left|\dfrac{b - x}{a - x}\right| = (b - a)(kt + C)$. The concentrations $[A] = a - x$ and $[B] = b - x$ cannot be negative, so

$\dfrac{b - x}{a - x} \geq 0$ and $\left|\dfrac{b - x}{a - x}\right| = \dfrac{b - x}{a - x}$. We now have $\ln\left(\dfrac{b - x}{a - x}\right) = (b - a)(kt + C)$. Since $x(0) = 0$, we get

$\ln\left(\dfrac{b}{a}\right) = (b - a)C$. Hence, $\ln\left(\dfrac{b - x}{a - x}\right) = (b - a)kt + \ln\left(\dfrac{b}{a}\right) \ \Rightarrow \ \dfrac{b - x}{a - x} = \dfrac{b}{a}e^{(b-a)kt} \ \Rightarrow$

$x = \dfrac{b\left[e^{(b-a)kt} - 1\right]}{be^{(b-a)kt}/a - 1} = \dfrac{ab\left[e^{(b-a)kt} - 1\right]}{be^{(b-a)kt} - a}$ moles/L.

(b) If $b = a$, then $\dfrac{dx}{dt} = k(a-x)^2$, so $\displaystyle\int \dfrac{dx}{(a-x)^2} = \int k\,dt$ and $\dfrac{1}{a-x} = kt + C$. Since $x(0) = 0$, we get

$C = \dfrac{1}{a}$. Thus, $a - x = \dfrac{1}{kt + 1/a}$ and $x = a - \dfrac{a}{akt + 1} = \dfrac{a^2 kt}{akt + 1} \dfrac{\text{moles}}{\text{L}}$.

Suppose $x = [C] = a/2$ when $t = 20$. Then $x(20) = a/2 \ \Rightarrow \ \dfrac{a}{2} = \dfrac{20a^2 k}{20ak + 1} \ \Rightarrow \ 40a^2 k = 20a^2 k + a$

$\Rightarrow \ 20a^2 k = a \ \Rightarrow \ k = \dfrac{1}{20a}$, so $x = \dfrac{a^2 t/(20a)}{1 + at/(20a)} = \dfrac{at/20}{1 + t/20} = \dfrac{at}{t + 20} \dfrac{\text{moles}}{\text{L}}$.

31. (a) If $a = b$, then $\dfrac{dx}{dt} = k(a-x)(b-x)^{1/2}$ becomes $\dfrac{dx}{dt} = k(a-x)^{3/2}$. $(a-x)^{-3/2}dx = k\,dt \ \Rightarrow$

$\displaystyle\int(a-x)^{-3/2}dx = \int k\,dt \ \Rightarrow \ 2(a-x)^{-1/2} = kt + C$ ([by substitution] $\ \Rightarrow \ \dfrac{2}{kt + C} = \sqrt{a-x} \ \Rightarrow$

$\left(\dfrac{2}{kt + C}\right)^2 = a - x \ \Rightarrow \ x(t) = a - \dfrac{4}{(kt + C)^2}$. The initial concentration of HBr is 0, so $x(0) = 0 \ \Rightarrow$

$0 = a - \dfrac{4}{C^2} \ \Rightarrow \ \dfrac{4}{C^2} = a \ \Rightarrow \ C^2 = \dfrac{4}{a} \ \Rightarrow \ C = 2/\sqrt{a}$ (C is positive since

$kt + C = 2(a-x)^{-1/2} > 0$). Thus, $x(t) = a - \dfrac{4}{(kt + 2/\sqrt{a})^2}$.

(b) $\dfrac{dx}{dt} = k(a-x)(b-x)^{1/2} \ \Rightarrow \ \dfrac{dx}{(a-x)\sqrt{b-x}} = k\,dt \ \Rightarrow \ \displaystyle\int \dfrac{dx}{(a-x)\sqrt{b-x}} = \int k\,dt$ ($\star$). From the

hint, $u = \sqrt{b-x} \ \Rightarrow \ u^2 = b - x \ \Rightarrow \ 2u\,du = -dx$, so $\displaystyle\int \dfrac{dx}{(a-x)\sqrt{b-x}} = \int \dfrac{-2u\,du}{[a - (b - u^2)]u} =$

$-2\displaystyle\int \dfrac{du}{a - b + u^2} = -2\int \dfrac{du}{(\sqrt{a-b})^2 + u^2} \stackrel{17}{=} -2\left(\dfrac{1}{\sqrt{a-b}} \tan^{-1}\dfrac{u}{\sqrt{a-b}}\right)$. So ($\star$) becomes

$\dfrac{-2}{\sqrt{a-b}} \tan^{-1}\dfrac{\sqrt{b-x}}{\sqrt{a-b}} = kt + C$. Now $x(0) = 0 \ \Rightarrow \ C = \dfrac{-2}{\sqrt{a-b}} \tan^{-1}\dfrac{\sqrt{b}}{\sqrt{a-b}}$

and we have $\dfrac{-2}{\sqrt{a-b}} \tan^{-1}\dfrac{\sqrt{b-x}}{\sqrt{a-b}} = kt - \dfrac{2}{\sqrt{a-b}} \tan^{-1}\dfrac{\sqrt{b}}{\sqrt{a-b}} \ \Rightarrow$

$\dfrac{2}{\sqrt{a-b}}\left(\tan^{-1}\sqrt{\dfrac{b}{a-b}} - \tan^{-1}\sqrt{\dfrac{b-x}{a-b}}\right) = kt \ \Rightarrow$

$t(x) = \dfrac{2}{k\sqrt{a-b}}\left(\tan^{-1}\sqrt{\dfrac{b}{a-b}} - \tan^{-1}\sqrt{\dfrac{b-x}{a-b}}\right)$.

32. If $S = \dfrac{dT}{dr}$, then $\dfrac{dS}{dr} = \dfrac{d^2 T}{dr^2}$. The differential equation $\dfrac{d^2 T}{dr^2} + \dfrac{2}{r}\dfrac{dT}{dr} = 0$ can be written as $\dfrac{dS}{dr} + \dfrac{2}{r}S = 0$. Thus,

$\dfrac{dS}{dr} = \dfrac{-2S}{r} \ \Rightarrow \ \dfrac{dS}{S} = -\dfrac{2}{r}\,dr \ \Rightarrow \ \displaystyle\int \dfrac{1}{S}\,dS = \int -\dfrac{2}{r}\,dr \ \Rightarrow \ \ln|S| = -2\ln|r| + C$. Assuming

$S = dT/dr > 0$ and $r > 0$, we have $S = e^{-2\ln r + C} = e^{\ln r^{-2}}e^C = r^{-2}k \ [k = e^C] \ \Rightarrow \ S = \dfrac{1}{r^2}k \ \Rightarrow$

$\dfrac{dT}{dr} = \dfrac{1}{r^2}k \ \Rightarrow \ dT = \dfrac{1}{r^2}k\,dr \ \Rightarrow \ \displaystyle\int dT = \int \dfrac{1}{r^2}k\,dr \ \Rightarrow \ T(r) = -\dfrac{k}{r} + A$.

$T(1) = 15 \ \Rightarrow \ 15 = -k + A$ **(1)** and $T(2) = 25 \ \Rightarrow \ 25 = -\frac{1}{2}k + A$ **(2)**.

Now solve for k and A: $-2\textbf{(2)} + \textbf{(1)} \ \Rightarrow \ -35 = -A$, so $A = 35$ and $k = 20$, and $T(r) = -20/r + 35$.

33. (a) $\dfrac{dC}{dt} = r - kC \ \Rightarrow \ \dfrac{dC}{dt} = -(kC - r) \ \Rightarrow \ \displaystyle\int \dfrac{dC}{kC - r} = \int -dt \ \Rightarrow \ (1/k)\ln|kC - r| = -t + M_1$

$\Rightarrow \ \ln|kC - r| = -kt + M_2 \ \Rightarrow \ |kC - r| = e^{-kt + M_2} \ \Rightarrow \ kC - r = M_3 e^{-kt} \ \Rightarrow$

$kC = M_3 e^{-kt} + r \;\Rightarrow\; C(t) = M_4 e^{-kt} + r/k.$ $C(0) = C_0 \;\Rightarrow\; C_0 = M_4 + r/k \;\Rightarrow$
$M_4 = C_0 - r/k \;\Rightarrow\; C(t) = (C_0 - r/k)e^{-kt} + r/k.$

(b) If $C_0 < r/k$, then $C_0 - r/k < 0$ and the formula for $C(t)$ shows that $C(t)$ increases and $\lim\limits_{t \to \infty} C(t) = r/k$.
As t increases, the formula for $C(t)$ shows how the role of C_0 steadily diminishes as that of r/k increases.

34. (a) Use 1 billion dollars as the x-unit and 1 day as the t-unit. Initially, there is \$10 billion of old currency in
circulation, so all of the \$50 million returned to the banks is old. At time t, the amount of new currency is
$x(t)$ billion dollars, so $10 - x(t)$ billion dollars of currency is old. The fraction of circulating money that
is old is $[10 - x(t)]/10$, and the amount of old currency being returned to the banks each day is
$\dfrac{10 - x(t)}{10}0.05$ billion dollars. This amount of new currency per day is introduced into circulation, so
$\dfrac{dx}{dt} = \dfrac{10 - x}{10} \cdot 0.05 = 0.005(10 - x)$ billion dollars per day.

(b) $\dfrac{dx}{10 - x} = 0.005\,dt \;\Rightarrow\; \dfrac{-dx}{10 - x} = -0.005\,dt \;\Rightarrow\; \ln(10 - x) = -0.005t + c \;\Rightarrow$
$10 - x = Ce^{-0.005t}$, where $C = e^c \;\Rightarrow\; x(t) = 10 - Ce^{-0.005t}$. From $x(0) = 0$, we get $C = 10$, so
$x(t) = 10\left(1 - e^{-0.005t}\right)$.

(c) The new bills make up 90% of the circulating currency when $x(t) = 0.9 \cdot 10 = 9$ billion dollars.
$9 = 10\left(1 - e^{-0.005t}\right) \;\Rightarrow\; 0.9 = 1 - e^{-0.005t} \;\Rightarrow\; e^{-0.005t} = 0.1 \;\Rightarrow\; -0.005t = -\ln 10 \;\Rightarrow$
$t = 200\ln 10 \approx 460.517$ days ≈ 1.26 years.

35. (a) Let $y(t)$ be the amount of salt (in kg) after t minutes. Then $y(0) = 15$. The amount of liquid in the tank is
1000 L at all times, so the concentration at time t (in minutes) is $y(t)/1000$ kg/L and
$\dfrac{dy}{dt} = -\left[\dfrac{y(t)}{1000}\dfrac{\text{kg}}{\text{L}}\right]\left(10\dfrac{\text{L}}{\text{min}}\right) = -\dfrac{y(t)}{100}\dfrac{\text{kg}}{\text{min}}.$ $\displaystyle\int \dfrac{dy}{y} = -\dfrac{1}{100}\int dt \;\Rightarrow\; \ln y = -\dfrac{t}{100} + C,$ and
$y(0) = 15 \;\Rightarrow\; \ln 15 = C$, so $\ln y = \ln 15 - \dfrac{t}{100}$. It follows that $\ln\!\left(\dfrac{y}{15}\right) = -\dfrac{t}{100}$ and $\dfrac{y}{15} = e^{-t/100}$, so
$y = 15e^{-t/100}$ kg.

(b) After 20 minutes, $y = 15e^{-20/100} = 15e^{-0.2} \approx 12.3$ kg.

36. (a) If $y(t)$ is the amount of salt (in kg) after t minutes, then $y(0) = 0$ and the total amount of liquid in the tank
remains constant at 1000 L.
$$\dfrac{dy}{dt} = \left(0.05\,\dfrac{\text{kg}}{\text{L}}\right)\left(5\,\dfrac{\text{L}}{\text{min}}\right) + \left(0.04\,\dfrac{\text{kg}}{\text{L}}\right)\left(10\,\dfrac{\text{L}}{\text{min}}\right) - \left(\dfrac{y(t)}{1000}\,\dfrac{\text{kg}}{\text{L}}\right)\left(15\,\dfrac{\text{L}}{\text{min}}\right)$$
$$= 0.25 + 0.40 - 0.015y = 0.65 - 0.015y = \dfrac{130 - 3y}{200}\,\dfrac{\text{kg}}{\text{min}}$$
so $\displaystyle\int \dfrac{dy}{130 - 3y} = \int \dfrac{dt}{200}$ and $-\tfrac{1}{3}\ln|130 - 3y| = \tfrac{1}{200}t + C$; since $y(0) = 0$, we have $-\tfrac{1}{3}\ln 130 = C$, so
$-\tfrac{1}{3}\ln|130 - 3y| = \tfrac{1}{200}t - \tfrac{1}{3}\ln 130 \;\Rightarrow\; \ln|130 - 3y| = -\tfrac{3}{200}t + \ln 130 = \ln\!\left(130e^{-3t/200}\right)$, and
$|130 - 3y| = 130e^{-3t/200}$. Since y is continuous, $y(0) = 0$, and the right-hand side is never zero, we deduce
that $130 - 3y$ is always positive. Thus, $130 - 3y = 130e^{-3t/200}$ and $y = \tfrac{130}{3}\left(1 - e^{-3t/200}\right)$ kg.

(b) After one hour, $y = \tfrac{130}{3}\left(1 - e^{-3 \cdot 60/200}\right) = \tfrac{130}{3}\left(1 - e^{-0.9}\right) \approx 25.7$ kg.
Note: As $t \to \infty$, $y(t) \to \tfrac{130}{3} = 43\tfrac{1}{3}$ kg.

37. Assume that the raindrop begins at rest, so that $v(0) = 0$. $dm/dt = km$ and $(mv)' = gm$ $\Rightarrow$

$mv' + vm' = gm$ $\Rightarrow$ $mv' + v(km) = gm$ $\Rightarrow$ $v' + vk = g$ $\Rightarrow$ $dv/dt = g - kv$ $\Rightarrow$

$\displaystyle\int \frac{dv}{g - kv} = \int dt$ $\Rightarrow$ $-(1/k)\ln|g - kv| = t + C$ $\Rightarrow$ $\ln|g - kv| = -kt - kC$ $\Rightarrow$ $g - kv = Ae^{-kt}$.

$v(0) = 0$ $\Rightarrow$ $A = g$. So $kv = g - ge^{-kt}$ $\Rightarrow$ $v = (g/k)(1 - e^{-kt})$. Since $k > 0$, as $t \to \infty$, $e^{-kt} \to 0$

and therefore, $\displaystyle\lim_{t\to\infty} v(t) = g/k$.

38. (a) $m\dfrac{dv}{dt} = -kv$ $\Rightarrow$ $\dfrac{dv}{v} = -\dfrac{k}{m}\,dt$ $\Rightarrow$ $\ln|v| = -\dfrac{k}{m}t + C$. Since $v(0) = v_0$, $\ln|v_0| = C$. Therefore,

$\ln\left|\dfrac{v}{v_0}\right| = -\dfrac{k}{m}t$ $\Rightarrow$ $\left|\dfrac{v}{v_0}\right| = e^{-kt/m}$ $\Rightarrow$ $v(t) = \pm v_0 e^{-kt/m}$. The sign is $+$ when $t = 0$, and we assume

v is continuous, so that the sign is $+$ for all t. Thus, $v(t) = v_0 e^{-kt/m}$. $ds/dt = v_0 e^{-kt/m}$ $\Rightarrow$

$s(t) = -\dfrac{mv_0}{k}e^{-kt/m} + C'$. From $s(0) = s_0$, we get $s_0 = -\dfrac{mv_0}{k} + C'$, so $C' = s_0 + \dfrac{mv_0}{k}$ and

$s(t) = s_0 + \dfrac{mv_0}{k}\left(1 - e^{-kt/m}\right)$. The distance traveled from time 0 to time t is $s(t) - s_0$, so the total distance

traveled is $\displaystyle\lim_{t\to\infty}[s(t) - s_0] = \dfrac{mv_0}{k}$.

Note: In finding the limit, we use the fact that $k > 0$ to conclude that $\displaystyle\lim_{t\to\infty} e^{-kt/m} = 0$.

(b) $m\dfrac{dv}{dt} = -kv^2$ $\Rightarrow$ $\dfrac{dv}{v^2} = -\dfrac{k}{m}\,dt$ $\Rightarrow$ $\dfrac{-1}{v} = -\dfrac{kt}{m} + C$ $\Rightarrow$ $\dfrac{1}{v} = \dfrac{kt}{m} - C$. Since $v(0) = v_0$, $C = -\dfrac{1}{v_0}$

and $\dfrac{1}{v} = \dfrac{kt}{m} + \dfrac{1}{v_0}$. Therefore, $v(t) = \dfrac{1}{kt/m + 1/v_0} = \dfrac{mv_0}{kv_0 t + m}$. $\dfrac{ds}{dt} = \dfrac{mv_0}{kv_0 t + m}$ $\Rightarrow$

$s(t) = \dfrac{m}{k}\displaystyle\int \dfrac{kv_0\,dt}{kv_0 t + m} = \dfrac{m}{k}\ln|kv_0 t + m| + C'$. Since $s(0) = s_0$, we get $s_0 = \dfrac{m}{k}\ln m + C'$ $\Rightarrow$

$C' = s_0 - \dfrac{m}{k}\ln m$ $\Rightarrow$ $s(t) = s_0 + \dfrac{m}{k}(\ln|kv_0 t + m| - \ln m) = s_0 + \dfrac{m}{k}\ln\left|\dfrac{kv_0 t + m}{m}\right|$. We can rewrite

the formulas for $v(t)$ and $s(t)$ as $v(t) = \dfrac{v_0}{1 + (kv_0/m)t}$ and $s(t) = s_0 + \dfrac{m}{k}\ln\left|1 + \dfrac{kv_0}{m}t\right|$.

Remarks: This model of horizontal motion through a resistive medium was designed to handle the case in which

$v_0 > 0$. Then the term $-kv^2$ representing the resisting force causes the object to decelerate. The absolute value

in the expression for $s(t)$ is unnecessary (since k, v_0, and m are all positive), and $\displaystyle\lim_{t\to\infty} s(t) = \infty$. In other

words, the object travels infinitely far. However, $\displaystyle\lim_{t\to\infty} v(t) = 0$. When $v_0 < 0$, the term $-kv^2$ increases the

magnitude of the object's negative velocity. According to the formula for $s(t)$, the position of the object

approaches $-\infty$ as t approaches $m/k(-v_0)$: $\displaystyle\lim_{t\to -m/(kv_0)} s(t) = -\infty$. Again the object travels infinitely far,

but this time the feat is accomplished in a finite amount of time. Notice also that $\displaystyle\lim_{t\to -m/(kv_0)} v(t) = -\infty$ when

$v_0 < 0$, showing that the speed of the object increases without limit.

39. (a) The rate of growth of the area is jointly proportional to $\sqrt{A(t)}$ and $M - A(t)$; that is, the rate is proportional to

the product of those two quantities. So for some constant k, $dA/dt = k\sqrt{A}\,(M - A)$. We are interested in the

maximum of the function dA/dt (when the tissue grows the fastest), so we differentiate, using the Chain Rule

and then substituting for dA/dt from the differential equation:

$$\frac{d}{dt}\left(\frac{dA}{dt}\right) = k\left[\sqrt{A}\,(-1)\frac{dA}{dt} + (M - A)\cdot\tfrac{1}{2}A^{-1/2}\frac{dA}{dt}\right] = \tfrac{1}{2}kA^{-1/2}\frac{dA}{dt}[-2A + (M - A)]$$

$$= \tfrac{1}{2}kA^{-1/2}\left[k\sqrt{A}(M - A)\right][M - 3A] = \tfrac{1}{2}k^2(M - A)(M - 3A)$$

This is 0 when $M - A = 0$ [this situation never actually occurs, since the graph of $A(t)$ is asymptotic to the line $y = M$, as in the logistic model] and when $M - 3A = 0$ ⇔ $A(t) = M/3$. This represents a maximum by the First Derivative Test, since $\dfrac{d}{dt}\left(\dfrac{dA}{dt}\right)$ goes from positive to negative when $A(t) = M/3$.

(b) From the CAS, we get $A(t) = M\left(\dfrac{Ce^{\sqrt{M}kt} - 1}{Ce^{\sqrt{M}kt} + 1}\right)^2$. To get C in terms of the initial area A_0 and the maximum

area M, we substitute $t = 0$ and $A = A_0 = A(0)$: $A_0 = M\left(\dfrac{C-1}{C+1}\right)^2$ ⇔ $(C+1)\sqrt{A_0} = (C-1)\sqrt{M}$

⇔ $C\sqrt{A_0} + \sqrt{A_0} = C\sqrt{M} - \sqrt{M}$ ⇔ $\sqrt{M} + \sqrt{A_0} = C\sqrt{M} - C\sqrt{A_0}$ ⇔

$\sqrt{M} + \sqrt{A_0} = C\left(\sqrt{M} - \sqrt{A_0}\right)$ ⇔ $C = \dfrac{\sqrt{M} + \sqrt{A_0}}{\sqrt{M} - \sqrt{A_0}}$. (Notice that if $A_0 = 0$, then $C = 1$.)

40. (a) According to the hint we use the Chain Rule: $m\dfrac{dv}{dt} = m\dfrac{dv}{dx} \cdot \dfrac{dx}{dt} = mv\dfrac{dv}{dx} = -\dfrac{mgR^2}{(x+R)^2}$ ⇒

$\displaystyle\int v \, dv = \int \dfrac{-gR^2 \, dx}{(x+R)^2}$ ⇒ $\dfrac{v^2}{2} = \dfrac{gR^2}{x+R} + C$. When $x = 0$, $v = v_0$, so $\dfrac{v_0^2}{2} = \dfrac{gR^2}{0+R} + C$ ⇒

$C = \frac{1}{2}v_0^2 - gR$ ⇒ $\frac{1}{2}v^2 - \frac{1}{2}v_0^2 = \dfrac{gR^2}{x+R} - gR$. Now at the top of its flight, the rocket's velocity will be 0,

and its height will be $x = h$. Solving for v_0: $-\frac{1}{2}v_0^2 = \dfrac{gR^2}{h+R} - gR$ ⇒

$\dfrac{v_0^2}{2} = g\left[-\dfrac{R^2}{R+h} + \dfrac{R(R+h)}{R+h}\right] = \dfrac{gRh}{R+h}$ ⇒ $v_0 = \sqrt{\dfrac{2gRh}{R+h}}$.

(b) $v_e = \lim_{h \to \infty} v_0 = \lim_{h \to \infty} \sqrt{\dfrac{2gRh}{R+h}} = \lim_{h \to \infty} \sqrt{\dfrac{2gR}{(R/h)+1}} = \sqrt{2gR}$

(c) $v_e = \sqrt{2 \cdot 32 \text{ ft/s}^2 \cdot 3960 \text{ mi} \cdot 5280 \text{ ft/mi}} \approx 36{,}581 \text{ ft/s} \approx 6.93 \text{ mi/s}$

41. (a) $V = \pi r^2 y$ ⇒ $\dfrac{dV}{dt} = \pi r^2 \dfrac{dy}{dt}$ [implicit differentiation] ⇒

$$\dfrac{dy}{dt} = \dfrac{1}{\pi r^2}\dfrac{dV}{dt} = \dfrac{1}{\pi r^2}\left(-a\sqrt{2gy}\right) = \dfrac{1}{\pi 2^2}\left[-\pi\left(\tfrac{1}{12}\right)^2\sqrt{2 \cdot 32}\sqrt{y}\right] = -\tfrac{1}{72}\sqrt{y}$$

(b) $\dfrac{dy}{dt} = -\tfrac{1}{72}\sqrt{y}$ ⇒ $y^{-1/2}\, dy = -\tfrac{1}{72}\, dt$ ⇒ $2\sqrt{y} = -\tfrac{1}{72}t + C$.

$y(0) = 6$ ⇒ $2\sqrt{6} = 0 + C$ ⇒ $C = 2\sqrt{6}$ ⇒ $y(t) = \left(-\tfrac{1}{144}t + \sqrt{6}\right)^2$.

(c) We want to find t when $y = 0$, so we set $y = 0 = \left(-\tfrac{1}{144}t + \sqrt{6}\right)^2$ ⇒ $t = 144\sqrt{6} \approx 5 \text{ min } 53 \text{ s}$.

42. (a) If the radius of the circular cross-section at height y is r, then the Pythagorean Theorem gives $r^2 = 2^2 - (2-y)^2$ since the radius of the tank is 2 m. So $A(y) = \pi r^2 = \pi\left[4 - (2-y)^2\right] = \pi(4y - y^2)$.

Thus, $A(y)\dfrac{dy}{dt} = -a\sqrt{2gy}$ ⇒ $\pi(4y - y^2)\dfrac{dy}{dt} = -\pi(0.01)^2\sqrt{2 \cdot 10y}$ ⇒

$(4y - y^2)\dfrac{dy}{dt} = -0.0001\sqrt{20y}$.

(b) From part (a) we have $\left(4y^{1/2} - y^{3/2}\right)dy = \left(-0.0001\sqrt{20}\,\right)dt \;\Rightarrow\; \frac{8}{3}y^{3/2} - \frac{2}{5}y^{5/2} = \left(-0.0001\sqrt{20}\,\right)t + C.$

$y(0) = 2 \;\Rightarrow\; \frac{8}{3}(2)^{3/2} - \frac{2}{5}(2)^{5/2} = C \;\Rightarrow\; C = \left(\frac{16}{3} - \frac{8}{5}\right)\sqrt{2} = \frac{56}{15}\sqrt{2}.$ To find out how long it will take

to drain all the water we evaluate t when $y = 0$: $0 = \left(-0.0001\sqrt{20}\,\right)t + C \;\Rightarrow$

$$t = \frac{C}{0.0001\sqrt{20}} = \frac{56\sqrt{2}/15}{0.0001\sqrt{20}} = \frac{11,200\sqrt{10}}{3} \approx 11,806 \text{ s} \approx 3 \text{ h } 17 \text{ min}.$$

Applied Project	**Which Is Faster, Going Up or Coming Down?**

1. $mv' = -pv - mg \;\Rightarrow\; m\dfrac{dv}{dt} = -(pv + mg) \;\Rightarrow\; \displaystyle\int \frac{dv}{pv + mg} = \int -\frac{1}{m}\,dt \;\Rightarrow$

$\dfrac{1}{p}\ln(pv + mg) = -\dfrac{1}{m}t + C$ $[pv + mg > 0]$. At $t = 0$, $v = v_0$, so $C = \dfrac{1}{p}\ln(pv_0 + mg)$. Thus,

$\dfrac{1}{p}\ln(pv + mg) = -\dfrac{1}{m}t + \dfrac{1}{p}\ln(pv_0 + mg) \;\Rightarrow\; \ln(pv + mg) = -\dfrac{p}{m}t + \ln(pv_0 + mg) \;\Rightarrow$

$pv + mg = e^{-pt/m}(pv_0 + mg) \;\Rightarrow\; pv = (pv_0 + mg)e^{-pt/m} - mg \;\Rightarrow$

$v(t) = \left(v_0 + \dfrac{mg}{p}\right)e^{-pt/m} - \dfrac{mg}{p}.$

2. $y(t) = \int v(t)\,dt = \displaystyle\int \left[\left(v_0 + \dfrac{mg}{p}\right)e^{-pt/m} - \dfrac{mg}{p}\right]dt = \left(v_0 + \dfrac{mg}{p}\right)e^{-pt/m}\left(-\dfrac{m}{p}\right) - \dfrac{mg}{p}t + C$

At $t = 0$, $y = 0$, so $C = \left(v_0 + \dfrac{mg}{p}\right)\dfrac{m}{p}.$ Thus,

$$y(t) = \left(v_0 + \frac{mg}{p}\right)\frac{m}{p} - \left(v_0 + \frac{mg}{p}\right)\frac{m}{p}e^{-pt/m} - \frac{mgt}{p} = \left(v_0 + \frac{mg}{p}\right)\frac{m}{p}\left(1 - e^{-pt/m}\right) - \frac{mgt}{p}$$

3. $y'(t) = \left(v_0 + \dfrac{mg}{p}\right)\dfrac{m}{p}\left(\dfrac{p}{m}e^{-pt/m}\right) - \dfrac{mg}{p}$, so $y'(t) = 0 \;\Rightarrow\; \dfrac{mg}{p} = \left(v_0 + \dfrac{mg}{p}\right)e^{-pt/m} \;\Rightarrow$

$e^{pt/m} = \dfrac{pv_0}{mg} + 1 \;\Rightarrow\; \dfrac{pt}{m} = \ln\left(\dfrac{pv_0}{mg} + 1\right) \;\Rightarrow\; t_1 = \dfrac{m}{p}\ln\left(\dfrac{mg + pv_0}{mg}\right).$ With $m = 1$, $v_0 = 20$, $p = \frac{1}{10}$,

and $g = 9.8$, we have $t_1 = 10\ln\left(\frac{11.8}{9.8}\right) \approx 1.86$ s.

4.

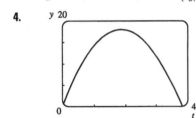

y 20

0   4
       t

The figure shows the graph of $y = 1180\left(1 - e^{-0.1t}\right) - 98t$. The zeros are at $t = 0$ and $t_2 \approx 3.84$. Thus, $t_1 - 0 \approx 1.86$ and $t_2 - t_1 \approx 1.98$. So the time it takes to come down is about 0.12 s longer than the time it takes to go up; hence, going up is faster.

5. $y(2t_1) = \left(v_0 + \dfrac{mg}{p}\right)\dfrac{m}{p}\left(1 - e^{-2pt_1/m}\right) - \dfrac{mg}{p}\cdot 2t_1$

$\qquad = \left(\dfrac{pv_0 + mg}{p}\right)\dfrac{m}{p}\left[1 - \left(e^{pt_1/m}\right)^{-2}\right] - \dfrac{mg}{p}\cdot 2\dfrac{m}{p}\ln\left(\dfrac{pv_0 + mg}{mg}\right)$

Substituting $x = e^{pt_1/m} = \dfrac{pv_0}{mg} + 1 = \dfrac{pv_0 + mg}{mg}$ (from Problem 3), we get

$$y\left(2t_1\right) = \left(x \cdot \frac{mg}{p}\right)\frac{m}{p}\left(1 - x^{-2}\right) - \frac{m^2g}{p^2} \cdot 2\ln x = \frac{m^2g}{p^2}\left(x - \frac{1}{x} - 2\ln x\right). \text{ Now } p > 0, m > 0, t_1 > 0 \;\Rightarrow$$

$$x = e^{pt_1/m} > e^0 = 1. \; f(x) = x - \frac{1}{x} - 2\ln x \;\Rightarrow\; f'(x) = 1 + \frac{1}{x^2} - \frac{2}{x} = \frac{x^2 - 2x + 1}{x^2} = \frac{(x-1)^2}{x^2} > 0 \text{ for}$$

$x > 1 \;\Rightarrow\; f(x)$ is increasing for $x > 1$. Since $f(1) = 0$, it follows that $f(x) > 0$ for every $x > 1$. Therefore,

$y(2t_1) = \dfrac{m^2g}{p^2}f(x)$ is positive, which means that the ball has not yet reached the ground at time $2t_1$. This tells us

that the time spent going up is always less than the time spent coming down, so *ascent is faster*.

Exponential Growth and Decay • • • • • • • • • •

1. The relative growth rate is $\dfrac{1}{P}\dfrac{dP}{dt} = 0.7944$, so $\dfrac{dP}{dt} = 0.7944P$ and, by Theorem 2,

$P(t) = P(0)e^{0.7944t} = 2e^{0.7944t}$. Thus, $P(6) = 2e^{0.7944(6)} \approx 234.99$ or about 235 members.

2. (a) By Theorem 2, $P(t) = P(0)e^{kt} = 60e^{kt}$. In 20 minutes ($\frac{1}{3}$ hour), there are 120 cells, so

$$P\left(\tfrac{1}{3}\right) = 60e^{k/3} = 120 \;\Rightarrow\; e^{k/3} = 2 \;\Rightarrow\; k/3 = \ln 2 \;\Rightarrow\; k = 3\ln 2 = \ln\left(2^3\right) = \ln 8.$$

(b) $P(t) = 60e^{(\ln 8)t} = 60 \cdot 8^t$

(c) $P(8) = 60 \cdot 8^8 = 60 \cdot 2^{24} = 1{,}006{,}632{,}960$

(d) $dP/dt = kP \;\Rightarrow\; P'(8) = kP(8) = (\ln 8)P(8) \approx 2.093$ billion cells/h

(e) $P(t) = 20{,}000 \;\Rightarrow\; 60 \cdot 8^t = 20{,}000 \;\Rightarrow\; 8^t = 1000/3 \;\Rightarrow\; t\ln 8 = \ln(1000/3) \;\Rightarrow$

$t = \dfrac{\ln(1000/3)}{\ln 8} \approx 2.79$ h

3. (a) By Theorem 2, $y(t) = y(0)e^{kt} = 500e^{kt}$. Now $y(3) = 500e^{k(3)} = 8000 \;\Rightarrow\; e^{3k} = \frac{8000}{500} \;\Rightarrow$

$3k = \ln 16 \;\Rightarrow\; k = (\ln 16)/3$. So $y(t) = 500e^{(\ln 16)t/3} = 500 \cdot 16^{t/3}$

(b) $y(4) = 500 \cdot 16^{4/3} \approx 20{,}159$

(c) $dy/dt = ky \;\Rightarrow\; y'(4) = ky(4) = \frac{1}{3}\ln 16\left(500 \cdot 16^{4/3}\right)$ [from part (a)] $\approx 18{,}631$ cells/h

(d) $y(t) = 500 \cdot 16^{t/3} = 30{,}000 \;\Rightarrow\; 16^{t/3} = 60 \;\Rightarrow\; \frac{1}{3}t\ln 16 = \ln 60 \;\Rightarrow\; t = 3(\ln 60)/(\ln 16) \approx 4.4$ h

4. (a) $y(t) = y(0)e^{kt} \;\Rightarrow\; y(2) = y(0)e^{2k} = 600, y(8) = y(0)e^{8k} = 75{,}000$. Dividing these equations, we get

$e^{8k}/e^{2k} = 75{,}000/600 \;\Rightarrow\; e^{6k} = 125 \;\Rightarrow\; 6k = \ln 125 = \ln 5^3 = 3\ln 5 \;\Rightarrow\; k = \frac{3}{6}\ln 5 = \frac{1}{2}\ln 5$.

Thus, $y(0) = 600/e^{2k} = 600/e^{\ln 5} = \frac{600}{5} = 120$.

(b) $y(t) = y(0)e^{kt} = 120e^{(\ln 5)t/2}$ or $y = 120 \cdot 5^{t/2}$

(c) $y(5) = 120 \cdot 5^{5/2} = 120 \cdot 25\sqrt{5} = 3000\sqrt{5} \approx 6708$ bacteria.

(d) $y(t) = 120 \cdot 5^{t/2} \;\Rightarrow\; y'(t) = 120 \cdot 5^{t/2} \cdot \ln 5 \cdot \frac{1}{2} = 60 \cdot \ln 5 \cdot 5^{t/2}$.

$y'(5) = 60 \cdot \ln 5 \cdot 5^{5/2} = 60 \cdot \ln 5 \cdot 25\sqrt{5} \approx 5398$ bacteria/hour.

(e) $y(t) = 200{,}000 \;\Leftrightarrow\; 120e^{(\ln 5)t/2} = 200{,}000 \;\Leftrightarrow\; e^{(\ln 5)t/2} = \frac{5000}{3} \;\Leftrightarrow\; (\ln 5)t/2 = \ln\frac{5000}{3} \;\Leftrightarrow$

$t = \left(2\ln\frac{5000}{3}\right)/\ln 5 \approx 9.2$ h.

5. (a) Let the population (in millions) in the year t be $P(t)$. Since the initial time is the year 1750, we substitute
$t - 1750$ for t in Theorem 2, so the exponential model gives $P(t) = P(1750)e^{k(t-1750)}$. Then
$P(1800) = 980 = 790e^{k(1800-1750)}$ $\Rightarrow$ $\frac{980}{790} = e^{k(50)}$ $\Rightarrow$ $\ln\frac{980}{790} = 50k$ $\Rightarrow$
$k = \frac{1}{50}\ln\frac{980}{790} \approx 0.0043104$. So with this model, we have $P(1900) = 790e^{k(1900-1750)} \approx 1508$ million, and
$P(1950) = 790e^{k(1950-1750)} \approx 1871$ million. Both of these estimates are much too low.

(b) In this case, the exponential model gives $P(t) = P(1850)e^{k(t-1850)}$ $\Rightarrow$
$P(1900) = 1650 = 1260e^{k(1900-1850)}$ $\Rightarrow$ $\ln\frac{1650}{1260} = k(50)$ $\Rightarrow$ $k = \frac{1}{50}\ln\frac{1650}{1260} \approx 0.005393$. So with
this model, we estimate $P(1950) = 1260e^{k(1950-1850)} \approx 2161$ million. This is still too low, but closer than the
estimate of $P(1950)$ in part (a).

(c) The exponential model gives $P(t) = P(1900)e^{k(t-1900)}$ $\Rightarrow$ $P(1950) = 2560 = 1650e^{k(1950-1900)}$ $\Rightarrow$
$\ln\frac{2560}{1650} = k(50)$ $\Rightarrow$ $k = \frac{1}{50}\ln\frac{2560}{1650} \approx 0.008785$. With this model, we estimate
$P(2000) = 1650e^{k(2000-1900)} \approx 3972$ million. This is much too low. The discrepancy is explained by the fact
that the world birth rate (average yearly number of births per person) is about the same as always, whereas the
mortality rate (especially the infant mortality rate) is much lower, owing mostly to advances in medical science
and to the wars in the first part of the twentieth century. The exponential model assumes, among other things,
that the birth and mortality rates will remain constant.

6. (a) Let $P(t)$ be the population (in millions) in the year t. Since the initial time is the year 1900, we substitute
$t - 1900$ for t in Theorem 2, and find that the exponential model gives $P(t) = P(1900)e^{k(t-1900)}$ $\Rightarrow$
$P(1910) = 92 = 76e^{k(1910-1900)}$ $\Rightarrow$ $k = \frac{1}{10}\ln\frac{92}{76} \approx 0.0191$. With this model, we estimate
$P(2000) = 76e^{k(2000-1900)} \approx 514$ million. This estimate is much too high. The discrepancy is explained by
the fact that, between the years 1900 and 1910, an enormous number of immigrants (compared to the total
population) came to the United States. Since that time, immigration (as a proportion of total population) has
been much lower. Also, the birth rate in the United States has declined since the turn of the century. So our
calculation of the constant k was based partly on factors which no longer exist.

(b) Substituting $t - 1980$ for t in Theorem 2, we find that the exponential model gives $P(t) = P(1980)e^{k(t-1980)}$
$\Rightarrow$ $P(1990) = 250 = 227e^{k(1990-1980)}$ $\Rightarrow$ $k = \frac{1}{10}\ln\frac{250}{227} \approx 0.00965$. With this model, we estimate
$P(2000) = 227e^{k(2000-1980)} \approx 275.3$ million. This is quite accurate. The further estimates are
$P(2010) = 227e^{30k} \approx 303$ million and $P(2020) = 227e^{40k} \approx 334$ million.

(c)

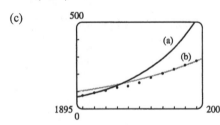

The model in part (a) is quite inaccurate after 1910 (off
by 5 million in 1920 and 12 million in 1930). The model in
part (b) is more accurate (which is not surprising, since it is
based on more recent information).

7. (a) If $y = [N_2O_5]$ then by Theorem 2, $\frac{dy}{dt} = -0.0005y$ $\Rightarrow$ $y(t) = y(0)e^{-0.0005t} = Ce^{-0.0005t}$.

(b) $y(t) = Ce^{-0.0005t} = 0.9C$ $\Rightarrow$ $e^{-0.0005t} = 0.9$ $\Rightarrow$ $-0.0005t = \ln 0.9$ $\Rightarrow$
$t = -2000\ln 0.9 \approx 211$ s

8. (a) The mass remaining after t days is

$y(t) = y(0)e^{kt} = 800e^{kt}$. Since the half-life is 5.0 days,

$y(5) = 800e^{5k} = 400 \;\Rightarrow\; e^{5k} = \frac{1}{2} \;\Rightarrow\;$

$5k = \ln\frac{1}{2} \;\Rightarrow\; k = -(\ln 2)/5$, so

$y(t) = 800e^{-(\ln 2)t/5} = 800 \cdot 2^{-t/5}$.

(b) $y(30) = 800 \cdot 2^{-30/5} = 12.5$ mg

(c) $800e^{-(\ln 2)t/5} = 1 \;\Leftrightarrow\; -(\ln 2)\frac{t}{5} = \ln\frac{1}{800} = -\ln 800$

$\Leftrightarrow\; t = 5\frac{\ln 800}{\ln 2} \approx 48$ days

(d)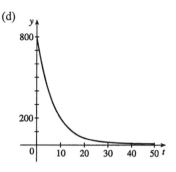

9. (a) If $y(t)$ is the mass remaining after t days, then $y(t) = y(0)e^{kt} = 100e^{kt}$. $y(30) = 100e^{30k} = \frac{1}{2}(100) \;\Rightarrow\;$
$e^{30k} = \frac{1}{2} \;\Rightarrow\; k = -(\ln 2)/30 \;\Rightarrow\; y(t) = 100e^{-(\ln 2)t/30} = 100 \cdot 2^{-t/30}$

(b) $y(100) = 100 \cdot 2^{-100/30} \approx 9.92$ mg

(c) $100e^{-(\ln 2)t/30} = 1 \;\Rightarrow\; -(\ln 2)t/30 = \ln\frac{1}{100} \;\Rightarrow\; t = -30\frac{\ln 0.01}{\ln 2} \approx 199.3$ years

10. (a) If $y(t)$ is the mass after t days and $y(0) = A$, then $y(t) = Ae^{kt}$. $y(3) = Ae^{3k} = 0.58A \;\Rightarrow\;$
$e^{3k} = 0.58 \;\Rightarrow\; 3k = \ln 0.58 \;\Rightarrow\; k = \frac{1}{3}\ln 0.58$. Then $Ae^{\ln(0.58)t/3} = \frac{1}{2}A \;\Leftrightarrow\;$

$\ln e^{\ln(0.58)t/3} = \ln\frac{1}{2} \;\Leftrightarrow\; \dfrac{\ln(0.58)t}{3} = \ln\frac{1}{2}$, so the half-life is $t = -\dfrac{3\ln 2}{\ln 0.58} \approx 3.82$ days.

(b) $Ae^{\ln(0.58)t/3} = 0.10A \;\Leftrightarrow\; \dfrac{\ln(0.58)t}{3} = \ln\frac{1}{10} \;\Leftrightarrow\; t = -\dfrac{3\ln 10}{\ln 0.58} \approx 12.68$ days

11. Let $y(t)$ be the level of radioactivity. Thus, $y(t) = y(0)e^{-kt}$ and k is determined by using the half-life:

$y(5730) = \frac{1}{2}y(0) \;\Rightarrow\; y(0)e^{-k(5730)} = \frac{1}{2}y(0) \;\Rightarrow\; e^{-5730k} = \frac{1}{2} \;\Rightarrow\;$

$-5730k = \ln\frac{1}{2} \;\Rightarrow\; k = -\dfrac{\ln\frac{1}{2}}{5730} = \dfrac{\ln 2}{5730}$. If 74% of the ^{14}C remains, then we know that $y(t) = 0.74y(0)$

$\Rightarrow\; 0.74 = e^{-t(\ln 2)/5730} \;\Rightarrow\; \ln 0.74 = -\dfrac{t\ln 2}{5730} \;\Rightarrow\; t = -\dfrac{5730(\ln 0.74)}{\ln 2} \approx 2489 \approx 2500$ years.

12. From the information given, we know that $\dfrac{dy}{dx} = 2y \;\Rightarrow\; y = Ce^{2x}$ by Theorem 2. To calculate C we use the
point $(0, 5)$: $5 = Ce^{2(0)} \;\Rightarrow\; C = 5$. Thus, the equation of the curve is $y = 5e^{2x}$.

13. (a) If $y = u - 75$, $u(0) = 185 \;\Rightarrow\; y(0) = 185 - 75 = 110$, and the initial-value problem is $dy/dt = ky$ with
$y(0) = 110$. So the solution is $y(t) = 110e^{kt}$.

(b) $y(30) = 110e^{30k} = 150 - 75 \;\Rightarrow\; e^{30k} = \frac{75}{110} = \frac{15}{22} \;\Rightarrow\; k = \frac{1}{30}\ln\frac{15}{22}$, so $y(t) = 110e^{\frac{1}{30}t\ln\left(\frac{15}{22}\right)}$ and
$y(45) = 110e^{\frac{45}{30}\ln\left(\frac{15}{22}\right)} \approx 62\,°$F. Thus, $u(45) \approx 62 + 75 = 137\,°$F.

(c) $u(t) = 100 \;\Rightarrow\; y(t) = 25$. $y(t) = 110e^{\frac{1}{30}t\ln\left(\frac{15}{22}\right)} = 25 \;\Rightarrow\; e^{\frac{1}{30}t\ln\left(\frac{15}{22}\right)} = \frac{25}{110} \;\Rightarrow\;$

$\frac{1}{30}t\ln\frac{15}{22} = \ln\frac{25}{110} \;\Rightarrow\; t = \dfrac{30\ln\frac{25}{110}}{\ln\frac{15}{22}} \approx 116$ min.

14. (a) Let $y(t)$ = temperature after t minutes. Newton's Law of Cooling implies that $\dfrac{dy}{dt} = k(y-5)$. Let

$u(t) = y(t) - 5$. Then $\dfrac{du}{dt} = ku$, so $u(t) = u(0)e^{kt} = (20-5)e^{kt} \Rightarrow y(t) = 5 + 15e^{kt} \Rightarrow$

$y(1) = 5 + 15e^k = 12 \Rightarrow e^k = \frac{7}{15} \Rightarrow k = \ln\frac{7}{15}$, so $y(t) = 5 + 15e^{\ln(7/15)t}$ and

$y(2) = 5 + 15e^{2\ln(7/15)} \approx 8.3\,^{\circ}\text{C}$.

(b) $5 + 15e^{\ln(7/15)t} = 6$ when $e^{\ln(7/15)t} = \frac{1}{15} \Rightarrow \ln\left(\frac{7}{15}\right)t = \ln\frac{1}{15} \Rightarrow t = \dfrac{\ln\frac{1}{15}}{\ln\frac{7}{15}} \approx 3.6$ min.

15. (a) Let $P(h)$ be the pressure at altitude h. Then $dP/dh = kP \Rightarrow P(h) = P(0)e^{kh} = 101.3e^{kh}$.

$P(1000) = 101.3e^{1000k} = 87.14 \Rightarrow 1000k = \ln\left(\frac{87.14}{101.3}\right) \Rightarrow$

$k = \frac{1}{1000}\ln\left(\frac{87.14}{101.3}\right) \Rightarrow P(h) = 101.3\,e^{\frac{1}{1000}h\ln\left(\frac{87.14}{101.3}\right)}$, so $P(3000) = 101.3e^{3\ln\left(\frac{87.14}{101.3}\right)} \approx 64.5$ kPa.

(b) $P(6187) = 101.3\,e^{\frac{6187}{1000}\ln\left(\frac{87.14}{101.3}\right)} \approx 39.9$ kPa

16. (a) Using $A = A_0\left(1 + \dfrac{r}{n}\right)^{nt}$ with $A_0 = 500$, $r = 0.14$, and $t = 2$,

(b)

we have:

(i) Annually: $n = 1$; $A = 500\left(1 + \frac{0.14}{1}\right)^{1\cdot2} = \$649.80$

(ii) Quarterly: $n = 4$; $A = 500\left(1 + \frac{0.14}{4}\right)^{4\cdot2} = \$658.40$

(iii) Monthly: $n = 12$; $A = 500\left(1 + \frac{0.14}{12}\right)^{12\cdot2} = \$660.49$

(iv) Daily: $n = 365$; $A = 500\left(1 + \frac{0.14}{365}\right)^{365\cdot2} = \$661.53$

(v) Hourly: $n = 365\cdot24$; $A = 500\left(1 + \frac{0.14}{365\cdot24}\right)^{365\cdot24\cdot2} = \$661.56$

(vi) Continuously: $A = 500e^{(0.14)2} = \$661.56$

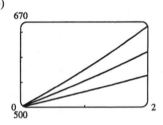

$A_{0.14}(2) = \$661.56$,

$A_{0.10}(2) = \$610.70$, and

$A_{0.06}(2) = \$563.75$.

17. (a) Using $A = A_0\left(1 + \dfrac{r}{n}\right)^{nt}$ with $A_0 = 3000$, $r = 0.05$, and $t = 5$, we have:

(i) Annually: $n = 1$; $A = 3000\left(1 + \frac{0.05}{1}\right)^{1\cdot5} = \$3828.84$

(ii) Semiannually: $n = 2$; $A = 3000\left(1 + \frac{0.05}{2}\right)^{2\cdot5} = \$3840.25$

(iii) Monthly: $n = 12$; $A = 3000\left(1 + \frac{0.05}{12}\right)^{12\cdot5} = \$3850.08$

(iv) Weekly: $n = 52$; $A = 3000\left(1 + \frac{0.05}{52}\right)^{52\cdot5} = \$3851.61$

(v) Daily: $n = 365$; $A = 3000\left(1 + \frac{0.05}{365}\right)^{365\cdot5} = \$3852.01$

(vi) Continuously: $A = 3000e^{(0.05)5} = \$3852.08$

(b) $dA/dt = 0.05A$ and $A(0) = 3000$.

18. (a) $A_0e^{0.06t} = 2A_0 \Leftrightarrow e^{0.06t} = 2 \Leftrightarrow 0.06t = \ln 2 \Leftrightarrow t = \frac{50}{3}\ln 2 \approx 11.55$, so the investment will

double in about 11.55 years.

(b) The annual interest rate in $A = A_0(1+r)^t$ is r. From part (a), we have $A = A_0e^{0.06t}$. These amounts must be

equal, so $(1+r)^t = e^{0.06t} \Rightarrow 1 + r = e^{0.06} \Rightarrow r = e^{0.06} - 1 \approx 0.0618 = 6.18\%$, which is the

equivalent annual interest rate.

19. (a) $\frac{dP}{dt} = kP - m = k\left(P - \frac{m}{k}\right)$. Let $y = P - \frac{m}{k}$, so $\frac{dy}{dt} = \frac{dP}{dt}$ and the differential equation becomes

$\frac{dy}{dt} = ky$. The solution is $y = y_0 e^{kt}$ $\Rightarrow$ $P - \frac{m}{k} = \left(P_0 - \frac{m}{k}\right)e^{kt}$ $\Rightarrow$ $P(t) = \frac{m}{k} + \left(P_0 - \frac{m}{k}\right)e^{kt}$.

(b) There will be an exponential expansion $\Leftrightarrow$ $P_0 - \frac{m}{k} > 0$ $\Leftrightarrow$ $m < kP_0$.

(c) The population will be constant if $P_0 - \frac{m}{k} = 0$ $\Leftrightarrow$ $m = kP_0$. It will decline if $P_0 - \frac{m}{k} < 0$ $\Leftrightarrow$ $m > kP_0$.

(d) $P_0 = 8{,}000{,}000$, $k = \alpha - \beta = 0.016$, $m = 210{,}000$ $\Rightarrow$ $m > kP_0 (= 128{,}000)$, so by part (c), the population was declining.

20. (a) $\frac{dy}{dt} = ky^{1+c}$ $\Rightarrow$ $y^{-1-c}\,dy = k\,dt$ $\Rightarrow$ $\frac{y^{-c}}{-c} = kt + C$. Since $y(0) = y_0$, we have $C = \frac{y_0^{-c}}{-c}$. Thus,

$\frac{y^{-c}}{-c} = kt + \frac{y_0^{-c}}{-c}$, or $y^{-c} = y_0^{-c} - ckt$. So $y^c = \frac{1}{y_0^{-c} - ckt} = \frac{y_0^c}{1 - cy_0^c kt}$ and $y(t) = \frac{y_0}{(1 - cy_0^c kt)^{1/c}}$.

(b) $y(t) \to \infty$ as $1 - cy_0^c kt \to 0$, that is, as $t \to \frac{1}{cy_0^c k}$. Define $T = \frac{1}{cy_0^c k}$. Then $\lim\limits_{t \to T^-} y(t) = \infty$.

(c) According to the data given, we have $c = 0.01$, $y(0) = 2$, and $y(3) = 16$, where the time t is given in months. Thus, $y_0 = 2$ and $16 = y(3) = \frac{y_0}{(1 - cy_0^c k \cdot 3)^{1/c}}$. Since $T = \frac{1}{cy_0^c k}$, we will solve for $cy_0^c k$.

$16 = \frac{2}{(1 - 3cy_0^c k)^{100}}$ $\Rightarrow$ $1 - 3cy_0^c k = \left(\frac{1}{8}\right)^{0.01} = 8^{-0.01}$ $\Rightarrow$ $cy_0^c k = \frac{1}{3}\left(1 - 8^{-0.01}\right)$. Thus, doomsday

occurs when $t = T = \frac{1}{cy_0^c k} = \frac{3}{1 - 8^{-0.01}} \approx 145.77$ months or 12.15 years.

Applied Project | **Calculus and Baseball**

1. (a) $F = ma = m\frac{dv}{dt}$, so by the Substitution Rule we have

$$\int_{t_0}^{t_1} F(t)\,dt = \int_{t_0}^{t_1} m\left(\frac{dv}{dt}\right)dt = m\int_{v_0}^{v_1} dv = [mv]_{v_0}^{v_1} = mv_1 - mv_0 = p(t_1) - p(t_0)$$

(b) (i) We have $v_1 = 110$ mi/h $= \frac{110(5280)}{3600}$ ft/s $= 161.\overline{3}$ ft/s, $v_0 = -90$ mi/h $= -132$ ft/s, and the mass of the baseball is $m = \frac{w}{g} = \frac{5/16}{32} = \frac{5}{512}$. So the change in momentum is

$p(t_1) - p(t_0) = mv_1 - mv_0 = \frac{5}{512}\left[161.\overline{3} - (-132)\right] \approx 2.86$ slug-ft/s.

(ii) From part (a) and part (b)(i), we have $\int_0^{0.001} F(t)dt = p(0.001) - p(0) \approx 2.86$, so the average force over the interval $[0, 0.001]$ is $\frac{1}{0.001}\int_0^{0.001} F(t)\,dt \approx \frac{1}{0.001}(2.86) = 2860$ lb.

2. (a) $W = \int_{s_0}^{s_1} F(s)\,ds$, where $F(s) = m\frac{dv}{dt} = m\frac{dv}{ds}\frac{ds}{dt} = mv\frac{dv}{ds}$ and so, by the Substitution Rule,

$$W = \int_{s_0}^{s_1} F(s)\,ds = \int_{s_0}^{s_1} mv\frac{dv}{ds}\,ds = \int_{v(s_0)}^{v(s_1)} mv\,dv = \left[\tfrac{1}{2}mv^2\right]_{v_0}^{v_1} = \tfrac{1}{2}mv_1^2 - \tfrac{1}{2}mv_0^2$$

(b) From part (b)(i), 90 mi/h $= 132$ ft/s. Assume $v_0 = v(s_0) = 0$ and $v_1 = v(s_1) = 132$ ft/s (note that s_1 is the point of release of the baseball). $m = \frac{5}{512}$, so the work done is

$$W = \tfrac{1}{2}mv_1^2 - \tfrac{1}{2}mv_0^2 = \tfrac{1}{2} \cdot \tfrac{5}{512} \cdot (132)^2 \approx 85 \text{ ft-lb}$$

3. (a) Here we have a differential equation of the form $dv/dt = kv$, so by Theorem 7.4.2, the solution is $v(t) = v(0)e^{kt}$. In this case $k = -\frac{1}{10}$ and $v(0) = 100$ ft/s, so $v(t) = 100e^{-t/10}$. We are interested in the time t that the ball takes to travel 280 ft, so we find the distance function

$$s(t) = \int_0^t v(x)\, dx = \int_0^t 100e^{-x/10}\, dx = 100\left[-10e^{-x/10}\right]_0^t = -1000\left(e^{-t/10} - 1\right)$$

$$= 1000\left(1 - e^{-t/10}\right)$$

Now we set $s(t) = 280$ and solve for t: $280 = 1000\left(1 - e^{-t/10}\right) \;\Rightarrow\; 1 - e^{-t/10} = \frac{7}{25} \;\Rightarrow\;$
$-\frac{1}{10}t = \ln\left(1 - \frac{7}{25}\right) \;\Rightarrow\; t \approx 3.285$ seconds.

(b) Let x be the distance of the shortstop from home plate. We calculate the time for the ball to reach home plate as a function of x, then differentiate with respect to x to find the value of x which corresponds to the minimum time. The total time that it takes the ball to reach home is the sum of the times of the two throws, plus the relay time ($\frac{1}{2}$ s). The distance from the fielder to the shortstop is $280 - x$, so to find the time t_1 taken by the first throw, we solve the equation $s_1(t_1) = 280 - x \;\Leftrightarrow\; 1 - e^{-t_1/10} = \dfrac{280 - x}{1000} \;\Leftrightarrow\; t_1 = -10\ln\dfrac{720 + x}{1000}$.

We find the time t_2 taken by the second throw if the shortstop throws with velocity w, since we see that this velocity varies in the rest of the problem. We use $v = we^{-t/10}$ and isolate t_2 in the equation

$$s(t_2) = 10w\left(1 - e^{-t_2/10}\right) = x \;\Leftrightarrow\; e^{-t_2/10} = 1 - \frac{x}{10w} \;\Leftrightarrow\; t_2 = -10\ln\frac{10w - x}{10w}, \text{ so the total time is}$$

$$t_w(x) = \frac{1}{2} - 10\left[\ln\frac{720 + x}{1000} + \ln\frac{10w - x}{10w}\right]. \text{ To find the minimum, we differentiate:}$$

$$\frac{dt_w}{dx} = -10\left[\frac{1}{720 + x} - \frac{1}{10w - x}\right], \text{ which changes from negative to positive when } 720 + x = 10w - x \;\Leftrightarrow\;$$
$x = 5w - 360$. By the First Derivative Test, t_w has a minimum at this distance from the shortstop to home plate. So if the shortstop throws at $w = 105$ ft/s from a point $x = 5(105) - 360 = 165$ ft from home plate, the minimum time is $t_{105}(165) = \frac{1}{2} - 10\left(\ln\frac{720 + 165}{1000} + \ln\frac{1050 - 165}{1050}\right) \approx 3.431$ seconds. This is longer than the time taken in part (a), so in this case the manager should encourage a direct throw.

If $w = 115$ ft/s, then $x = 215$ ft from home, and the minimum time is
$t_{115}(215) = \frac{1}{2} - 10\left(\ln\frac{720 + 215}{1000} + \ln\frac{1150 - 215}{1150}\right) \approx 3.242$ seconds. This is less than the time taken in part (a), so in this case, the manager should encourage a relayed throw.

(c) In general, the minimum time is

$$t_w(5w - 360) = \frac{1}{2} - 10\left[\ln\frac{360 + 5w}{1000} + \ln\frac{360 + 5w}{10w}\right]$$

$$= \frac{1}{2} - 10\ln\frac{(w + 72)^2}{400w}$$

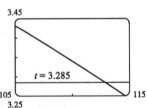

We want to find out when this is about 3.285 seconds, the same time as the direct throw. From the graph, we estimate that this is the case for $w \approx 112.8$ ft/s. So if the shortstop can throw the ball with this velocity, then a relayed throw takes the same time as a direct throw.

7.5 The Logistic Equation • • • • • • • • • • • • •

1. (a) $dP/dt = 0.05P - 0.0005P^2 = 0.05P(1 - 0.01P) = 0.05P(1 - P/100)$. Comparing to Equation 1,
$dP/dt = kP(1 - P/K)$, we see that the carrying capacity is $K = 100$ and the value of k is 0.05.

(b) The slopes close to 0 occur where P is near 0 or 100. The largest slopes appear to be on the line $P = 50$. The
solutions are increasing for $0 < P_0 < 100$ and decreasing for $P_0 > 100$.

(c)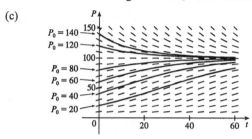

All of the solutions approach $P = 100$ as t increases. As
in part (b), the solutions differ since for $0 < P_0 < 100$
they are increasing, and for $P_0 > 100$ they are decreasing.
Also, some have an IP and some don't. It appears that the
solutions which have $P_0 = 20$ and $P_0 = 40$ have
inflection points at $P = 50$.

(d) The equilibrium solutions are $P = 0$ (trivial solution) and $P = 100$. The increasing solutions move away from
$P = 0$ and all nonzero solutions approach $P = 100$ as $t \to \infty$.

2. (a) $K = 6000$ and $k = 0.0015 \Rightarrow dP/dt = 0.0015P(1 - P/6000)$.

(b)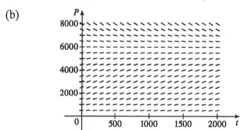

All of the solution curves approach 6000 as $t \to \infty$.

(c)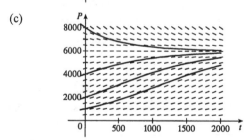

The curves with $P_0 = 1000$ and $P_0 = 2000$ appear to be
concave upward at first and then concave downward. The
curve with $P_0 = 4000$ appears to be concave downward
everywhere. The curve with $P_0 = 8000$ appears to be
concave upward everywhere. The inflection points are
where the population grows the fastest.

(d) See the solution to Exercise 7.2.25 for a possible program to calculate $P(50)$. [In this case, we use $X = 0$,
$H = 1$, $N = 50$, $Y_1 = 0.0015y(1 - y/6000)$, and $Y = 1000$.] We find that $P(50) \approx 1064$.

(e) Using Equation 4 with $K = 6000$, $k = 0.0015$, and $P_0 = 1000$, we

have $P(t) = \dfrac{K}{1 + Ae^{-kt}} = \dfrac{6000}{1 + Ae^{-0.0015t}}$, where

$A = \dfrac{K - P_0}{P_0} = \dfrac{6000 - 1000}{1000} = 5$. Thus,

$P(50) = \dfrac{6000}{1 + 5e^{-0.0015(50)}} \approx 1064.1$, which is extremely close to

the estimate obtained in part (d).

(f)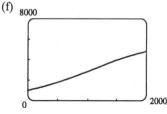

The curves are very similar.

3. (a) $\frac{dy}{dt} = ky\left(1 - \frac{y}{K}\right) \Rightarrow y(t) = \frac{K}{1 + Ae^{-kt}}$ with $A = \frac{K - y(0)}{y(0)}$. With $K = 8 \times 10^7$, $k = 0.71$, and

$y(0) = 2 \times 10^7$, we get the model $y(t) = \frac{8 \times 10^7}{1 + 3e^{-0.71t}}$, so $y(1) = \frac{8 \times 10^7}{1 + 3e^{-0.71}} \approx 3.23 \times 10^7$ kg.

(b) $y(t) = 4 \times 10^7 \Rightarrow \frac{8 \times 10^7}{1 + 3e^{-0.71t}} = 4 \times 10^7 \Rightarrow 2 = 1 + 3e^{-0.71t} \Rightarrow e^{-0.71t} = \frac{1}{3} \Rightarrow$

$-0.71t = \ln\frac{1}{3} \Rightarrow t = \frac{\ln 3}{0.71} \approx 1.55$ years

4. (a)

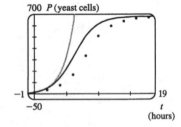

P (yeast cells)

700

100

0   5   10   15 t
(hours)

From the graph, we estimate the carrying capacity
K for the yeast population to be 680.

(b) An estimate of the initial relative growth rate is

$$\frac{1}{P_0}\frac{dP}{dt} = \frac{1}{18} \cdot \frac{39 - 18}{2 - 0} = \frac{7}{12} = 0.58\overline{3}.$$

(c) An exponential model is $P(t) = 18e^{7t/12}$. A

logistic model is $P(t) = \frac{680}{1 + Ae^{-7t/12}}$, where

$A = \frac{680 - 18}{18} = \frac{331}{9}$.

(d)

Time in Hours	Observed Values	Exponential Model	Logistic Model
0	18	18	18
2	39	58	55
4	80	186	149
6	171	596	322
8	336	1914	505
10	509	6147	614
12	597	19,739	658
14	640	63,389	673
16	664	203,558	678
18	672	653,679	679

700 P (yeast cells)

−1   19
−50 t
(hours)

The exponential model is a poor fit
for anything beyond the first two
observed values.
The logistic model varies more for
the middle values than it does for
the values at either end, but provides
a good general fit, as shown in the
figure.

(e) $P(7) = \frac{680}{1 + \frac{331}{9}e^{-7(7/12)}} \approx 420$ yeast cells

5. (a) We will assume that the difference in the birth and death rates is 20 million/year. Let $t = 0$ correspond to the

year 1990 and use a unit of 1 billion for all calculations. $k \approx \frac{1}{P}\frac{dP}{dt} = \frac{1}{5.3}(0.02) = \frac{1}{265}$, so

$$\frac{dP}{dt} = kP\left(1 - \frac{P}{K}\right) = \frac{1}{265}P\left(1 - \frac{P}{100}\right), P \text{ in billions}$$

(b) $A = \frac{K - P_0}{P_0} = \frac{100 - 5.3}{5.3} = \frac{947}{53} \approx 17.8679.$ $P(t) = \frac{K}{1 + Ae^{-kt}} = \frac{100}{1 + \frac{947}{53}e^{-(1/265)t}}$, so

$P(10) \approx 5.49$ billion.

(c) $P(110) \approx 7.81$, and $P(510) \approx 27.72$. The predictions are 7.81 billion in the year 2100 and 27.72 billion in 2500.

(d) If $K = 50$, then $P(t) = \dfrac{50}{1 + \frac{447}{53}e^{-(1/265)t}}$. So $P(10) \approx 5.48$, $P(110) \approx 7.61$, and $P(510) \approx 22.41$. The predictions become 5.48 billion in the year 2000, 7.61 billion in 2100, and 22.41 billion in the year 2500.

6. (a) If we assume that the carrying capacity for the world population is 100 billion, it would seem reasonable that the carrying capacity for the U.S. is 3–5 billion by using current populations and simple proportions. We will use $K = 4$ billion or 4000 million. With $t = 0$ corresponding to 1980, we have

$$P(t) = \frac{4000}{1 + \left(\frac{4000 - 250}{250}\right)e^{-kt}} = \frac{4000}{1 + 15e^{-kt}}$$

(b) $P(10) = 275 \ \Rightarrow \ \dfrac{4000}{1 + 15e^{-10k}} = 275 \ \Rightarrow \ 1 + 15e^{-10k} = \frac{4000}{275} \ \Rightarrow \ e^{-10k} = \dfrac{\frac{160}{11} - 1}{15} \ \Rightarrow$

$-10k = \ln \frac{149}{165} \ \Rightarrow \ k = -\frac{1}{10}\ln \frac{149}{165} \approx 0.01019992$.

(c) $2100 - 1990 = 110$ and $P(110) \approx 680$ million.

$2200 - 1990 = 210$ and $P(210) \approx 1449$ million, or about 1.4 billion.

(d) $P(t) = 300 \ \Rightarrow \ \dfrac{4000}{1 + 15e^{-kt}} = 300 \ \Rightarrow \ 1 + 15e^{-kt} = \frac{40}{3} \ \Rightarrow \ e^{-kt} = \frac{37}{3} \cdot \frac{1}{15} \ \Rightarrow \ -kt = \ln \frac{37}{45}$

$\Rightarrow \ t = 10\,\dfrac{\ln \frac{37}{45}}{\ln \frac{149}{165}} \approx 19.19 \approx 19$. So we predict that the U.S. population will exceed 300 million in the year

$1990 + 19 = 2009$.

7. (a) Our assumption is that $\dfrac{dy}{dt} = ky(1 - y)$, where y is the fraction of the population that has heard the rumor.

(b) Using the logistic equation (1), $\dfrac{dP}{dt} = kP\left(1 - \dfrac{P}{K}\right)$, we substitute $y = \dfrac{P}{K}$, $P = Ky$, and $\dfrac{dP}{dt} = K\dfrac{dy}{dt}$, to

obtain $K\dfrac{dy}{dt} = k(Ky)(1 - y) \ \Leftrightarrow \ \dfrac{dy}{dt} = ky(1 - y)$, our equation in part (a). Now the solution to (1) is

$P(t) = \dfrac{K}{1 + Ae^{-kt}}$, where $A = \dfrac{K - P_0}{P_0}$. We use the same substitution to obtain $Ky = \dfrac{K}{1 + \dfrac{K - Ky_0}{Ky_0}e^{-kt}}$

$\Rightarrow \ y = \dfrac{y_0}{y_0 + (1 - y_0)e^{-kt}}$.

Alternatively, we could use the same steps as outlined in "The Analytic Solution," following Example 2.

(c) Let t be the number of hours since 8 A.M. Then $y_0 = y(0) = \frac{80}{1000} = 0.08$ and $y(4) = \frac{1}{2}$, so

$\dfrac{1}{2} = y(4) = \dfrac{0.08}{0.08 + 0.92e^{-4k}}$. Thus, $0.08 + 0.92e^{-4k} = 0.16$, $e^{-4k} = \frac{0.08}{0.92} = \frac{2}{23}$, and $e^{-k} = \left(\frac{2}{23}\right)^{1/4}$, so

$y = \dfrac{0.08}{0.08 + 0.92(2/23)^{t/4}} = \dfrac{2}{2 + 23(2/23)^{t/4}}$. Solving this equation for t, we get

$2y + 23y\left(\dfrac{2}{23}\right)^{t/4} = \dfrac{2 - 2y}{23y} \ \Rightarrow \ \left(\dfrac{2}{23}\right)^{t/4} = \dfrac{2}{23} \cdot \dfrac{1 - y}{y} \ \Rightarrow \ \left(\dfrac{2}{23}\right)^{t/4-1} = \dfrac{1 - y}{y}$. It follows that

$\dfrac{t}{4} - 1 = \dfrac{\ln[(1 - y)/y]}{\ln \frac{2}{23}}$, so $t = 4\left[1 + \dfrac{\ln((1 - y)/y)}{\ln \frac{2}{23}}\right]$. When $y = 0.9$, $\dfrac{1 - y}{y} = \frac{1}{9}$, so

$t = 4\left(1 - \dfrac{\ln 9}{\ln \frac{2}{23}}\right) \approx 7.6$ h or 7 h 36 min. Thus, 90% of the population will have heard the rumor by 3:36 P.M.

8. (a) $P(0) = P_0 = 400$, $P(1) = 1200$ and $K = 10{,}000$. From the solution to the logistic differential equation

$$P(t) = \frac{P_0 K}{P_0 + (K - P_0)e^{-kt}}, \text{ we get } P = \frac{400\,(10{,}000)}{400 + (9600)e^{-kt}} = \frac{10{,}000}{1 + 24e^{-kt}}. \quad P(1) = 1200 \implies$$

$$1 + 24e^{-k} = \tfrac{100}{12} \implies e^k = \tfrac{288}{88} \implies k = \ln\tfrac{36}{11}. \text{ So } P = \frac{10{,}000}{1 + 24e^{-t\ln(36/11)}} = \frac{10{,}000}{1 + 24 \cdot (11/36)^t}.$$

(b) $5000 = \dfrac{10{,}000}{1 + 24(11/36)^t} \implies 24\left(\tfrac{11}{36}\right)^t = 1 \implies t\ln\tfrac{11}{36} = \ln\tfrac{1}{24} \implies t \approx 2.68$ years.

9. (a) $\dfrac{dP}{dt} = k(P)\left(1 - \dfrac{P}{K}\right) \implies$

$$\frac{d^2P}{dt^2} = k\left[P\left(-\frac{1}{K}\frac{dP}{dt}\right) + \left(1 - \frac{P}{K}\right)\frac{dP}{dt}\right] = k\frac{dP}{dt}\left(-\frac{P}{K} + 1 - \frac{P}{K}\right)$$

$$= k\left[kP\left(1 - \frac{P}{K}\right)\right]\left(1 - \frac{2P}{K}\right) = k^2 P\left(1 - \frac{P}{K}\right)\left(1 - \frac{2P}{K}\right)$$

(b) P grows fastest when P' has a maximum, that is, when $P'' = 0$. From part (a), $P'' = 0 \iff P = 0, P = K$, or $P = K/2$. Since $0 < P < K$, we see that $P'' = 0 \iff P = K/2$.

10.

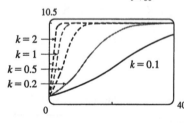

First we keep k constant (at 0.1, say) and change P_0 in the function $P = \dfrac{10P_0}{P_0 + (10 - P_0)e^{-0.1t}}$. (Notice that P_0 is the P-intercept.) If $P_0 = 0$, the function is 0 everywhere. For $0 < P_0 < 5$, the curve has an inflection point, which moves to the right as P_0 decreases. If $5 < P_0 < 10$, the graph is concave down everywhere. (We are considering only $t \geq 0$.) If $P_0 = 10$, the function is the constant function $P = 10$, and if $P_0 > 10$, the function decreases. For all $P_0 \neq 0$, $\lim\limits_{t\to\infty} P = 10$.

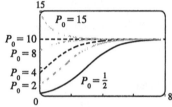

Now we instead keep P_0 constant (at $P_0 = 1$) and change k in the function $P = \dfrac{10}{1 + 9e^{-kt}}$. It seems that as k increases, the graph approaches the line $P = 10$ more and more quickly. (Note that the only difference in the shape of the curves is in the horizontal scaling; if we choose suitable x-scales, the graphs all look the same.)

11. (a) The term -15 represents a harvesting of fish at a constant rate—in this case, 15 fish/week. This is the rate at which fish are caught.

(b)

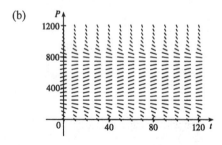

(c) From the graph in part (b), it appears that $P(t) = 250$ and $P(t) = 750$ are the equilibrium solutions. We confirm this analytically by solving the equation $dP/dt = 0$ as follows:

$0.08P(1 - P/1000) - 15 = 0 \implies$

$0.08P - 0.00008P^2 - 15 = 0 \implies$

$-0.00008\left(P^2 - 1000P + 187{,}500\right) = 0 \implies$

$(P - 250)(P - 750) = 0 \implies P = 250$ or 750.

(d)

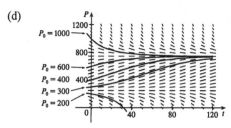

For $0 < P_0 < 250$, $P(t)$ decreases to 0. For $P_0 = 250$, $P(t)$ remains constant. For $250 < P_0 < 750$, $P(t)$ increases and approaches 750. For $P_0 = 750$, $P(t)$ remains constant. For $P_0 > 750$, $P(t)$ decreases and approaches 750.

(e) $\dfrac{dP}{dt} = 0.08P\left(1 - \dfrac{P}{1000}\right) - 15$ $\Leftrightarrow$ $-\dfrac{100,000}{8} \cdot \dfrac{dP}{dt} = (0.08P - 0.00008P^2 - 15) \cdot \left(-\dfrac{100,000}{8}\right)$ $\Leftrightarrow$

$-12,500\dfrac{dP}{dt} = P^2 - 1000P + 187,500$ $\Leftrightarrow$ $\dfrac{dP}{(P - 250)(P - 750)} = -\dfrac{1}{12,500}\,dt$ $\Leftrightarrow$

$\displaystyle\int\left(\dfrac{-1/500}{P - 250} + \dfrac{1/500}{P - 750}\right)dP = -\dfrac{1}{12,500}\,dt$ $\Leftrightarrow$ $\displaystyle\int\left(\dfrac{1}{P - 250} - \dfrac{1}{P - 750}\right)dP = \dfrac{1}{25}\,dt$ $\Leftrightarrow$

$\ln|P - 250| - \ln|P - 750| = \dfrac{1}{25}t + C$ $\Leftrightarrow$ $\ln\left|\dfrac{P - 250}{P - 750}\right| = \dfrac{1}{25}t + C$ $\Leftrightarrow$

$\left|\dfrac{P - 250}{P - 750}\right| = e^{t/25+C} = ke^{t/25}$ $\Leftrightarrow$ $\dfrac{P - 250}{P - 750} = ke^{t/25}$ $\Leftrightarrow$ $P - 250 = Pke^{t/25} - 750ke^{t/25}$ $\Leftrightarrow$

$P - Pke^{t/25} = 250 - 750ke^{t/25}$ $\Leftrightarrow$

$P(t) = \dfrac{250 - 750ke^{t/25}}{1 - ke^{t/25}}$. If $t = 0$ and $P = 200$, then

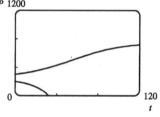

$200 = \dfrac{250 - 750k}{1 - k}$ $\Leftrightarrow$ $200 - 200k = 250 - 750k$ $\Leftrightarrow$ $550k = 50$

$\Leftrightarrow$ $k = \dfrac{1}{11}$. Similarly, if $t = 0$ and $P = 300$, then $k = -\dfrac{1}{9}$. Simplifying P with these two values of k gives us

$P(t) = \dfrac{250\left(3e^{t/25} - 11\right)}{e^{t/25} - 11}$ and $P(t) = \dfrac{750\left(e^{t/25} + 3\right)}{e^{t/25} + 9}$.

12. (a)

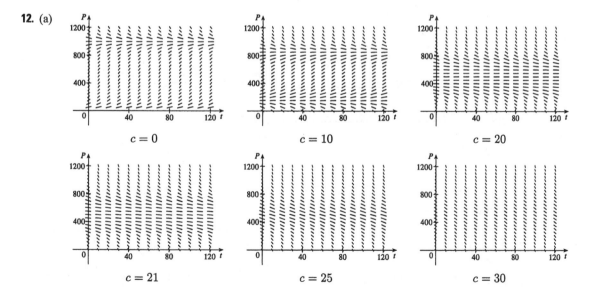

(b) For $0 \le c \le 20$, there is at least one equilibrium solution. For $c > 20$, the population always dies out.

(c) $\dfrac{dP}{dt} = 0.08P - 0.00008P^2 - c$. $\dfrac{dP}{dt} = 0 \;\Leftrightarrow\; P = \dfrac{-0.08 \pm \sqrt{(0.08)^2 - 4(-0.00008)(-c)}}{2(-0.00008)}$, which has at

least one solution when the discriminant is nonnegative $\Rightarrow$ $0.0064 - 0.00032c \geq 0 \;\Leftrightarrow\; c \leq 20$. For
$0 \leq c \leq 20$, there is at least one value of P such that $dP/dt = 0$ and hence, at least one equilibrium solution.
For $c > 20$, $dP/dt < 0$ and the population always dies out.

(d) The weekly catch should be less than 20 fish per week.

13. (a) $\dfrac{dP}{dt} = (kP)\left(1 - \dfrac{P}{K}\right)\left(1 - \dfrac{m}{P}\right)$. If $m < P < K$, then $dP/dt = (+)(+)(+) = + \;\Rightarrow\; P$ is increasing.

If $0 < P < m$, then $dP/dt = (+)(+)(-) = - \;\Rightarrow\; P$ is decreasing.

(b)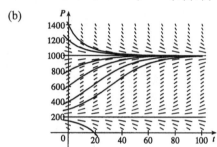

$k = 0.08$, $K = 1000$, and $m = 200 \;\Rightarrow$

$$\frac{dP}{dt} = 0.08P\left(1 - \frac{P}{1000}\right)\left(1 - \frac{200}{P}\right)$$

For $0 < P_0 < 200$, the population dies out. For $P_0 = 200$, the
population is steady. For $200 < P_0 < 1000$, the population
increases and approaches 1000. For $P_0 > 1000$, the population
decreases and approaches 1000.

The equilibrium solutions are $P(t) = 200$ and $P(t) = 1000$.

(c) $\dfrac{dP}{dt} = kP\left(1 - \dfrac{P}{K}\right)\left(1 - \dfrac{m}{P}\right) = kP\left(\dfrac{K - P}{K}\right)\left(\dfrac{P - m}{P}\right) = \dfrac{k}{K}(K - P)(P - m) \;\Leftrightarrow\;$

$\displaystyle\int \dfrac{dP}{(K - P)(P - m)} = \int \dfrac{k}{K}\, dt.$

By partial fractions, $\dfrac{1}{(K - P)(P - m)} = \dfrac{A}{K - P} + \dfrac{B}{P - m}$, so $A(P - m) + B(K - P) = 1$.

If $P = m$, $B = \dfrac{1}{K - m}$; if $P = K$, $A = \dfrac{1}{K - m}$, so $\dfrac{1}{K - m}\displaystyle\int\left(\dfrac{1}{K - P} + \dfrac{1}{P - m}\right) dP = \int \dfrac{k}{K}\, dt \;\Rightarrow\;$

$\dfrac{1}{K - m}\left(-\ln|K - P| + \ln|P - m|\right) = \dfrac{k}{K}t + M.$

But $m < P < K$, so $\dfrac{1}{K - m}\ln\dfrac{P - m}{K - P} = \dfrac{k}{K}t + M \;\Rightarrow\; \ln\dfrac{P - m}{K - P} = (K - m)\dfrac{k}{K}t + M_1 \;\Leftrightarrow\;$

$\dfrac{P - m}{K - P} = De^{(K-m)(k/K)t}$ $(D = e^{M_1})$. Let $t = 0$: $\dfrac{P_0 - m}{K - P_0} = D$. So $\dfrac{P - m}{K - P} = \dfrac{P_0 - m}{K - P_0}e^{(K-m)(k/K)t}$.

Solving for P, we get $P(t) = \dfrac{m(K - P_0) + K(P_0 - m)e^{(K-m)(k/K)t}}{K - P_0 + (P_0 - m)e^{(K-m)(k/K)t}}$.

(d) If $P_0 < m$, then $P_0 - m < 0$. Let $N(t)$ be the numerator of the expression for $P(t)$ in part (c). Then
$N(0) = P_0(K - m) > 0$, and $P_0 - m < 0 \;\Leftrightarrow\; \displaystyle\lim_{t\to\infty} K(P_0 - m)e^{(K-m)(k/K)t} = -\infty \;\Rightarrow\;$
$\displaystyle\lim_{t\to\infty} N(t) = -\infty$. Since N is continuous, there is a number t such that $N(t) = 0$ and thus $P(t) = 0$. So the
species will become extinct.

14. (a) $\dfrac{dP}{dt} = c\ln\left(\dfrac{K}{P}\right)P \;\Rightarrow\; \displaystyle\int \dfrac{dP}{P\ln(K/P)} = \int c\, dt$. Let $u = \ln\left(\dfrac{K}{P}\right) = \ln K - \ln P \;\Rightarrow\; du = -\dfrac{dP}{P}$

$\Rightarrow\; \displaystyle\int -\dfrac{du}{u} = ct + D \;\Rightarrow\; \ln|u| = -ct - D \;\Rightarrow\; |u| = e^{-(ct+D)} \;\Rightarrow\; |\ln(K/P)| = e^{-(ct+D)} \;\Rightarrow\;$

$\ln(K/P) = e^{-(ct+D)}$ [we know that $\ln(K/P) \geq 0$ since $K \geq P$]. Letting $t = 0$, we get $\ln(K/P_0) = e^{-D}$,

so $\ln(K/P) = e^{-ct-D} = e^{-ct}e^{-D} = \ln(K/P_0)\,e^{-ct} \Rightarrow K/P = e^{\ln(K/P_0)e^{-ct}} \Rightarrow$
$P(t) = Ke^{-\ln(K/P_0)e^{-ct}}, c \neq 0.$

(b) $\lim\limits_{t\to\infty} P(t) = \lim\limits_{t\to\infty} Ke^{-\ln(K/P_0)e^{-ct}} = Ke^{-\ln(K/P_0)\cdot 0} = Ke^0 = K$

(c)

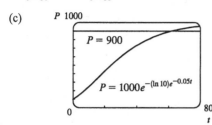

P 1000
$P = 900$
$P = 1000e^{-(\ln 10)e^{-0.05t}}$
0
80
t

The graphs look very similar. For the Gompertz function, $P(40) \approx 732$, nearly the same as the logistic function. The Gompertz function reaches $P = 900$ at $t \approx 61.7$ and its value at $t = 80$ is about 959, so it doesn't increase quite as fast as the logistic curve.

(d) $\dfrac{dP}{dt} = c\ln\left(\dfrac{K}{P}\right)P = cP(\ln K - \ln P) \Rightarrow$

$$\frac{d^2P}{dt^2} = c\left[P\left(-\frac{1}{P}\frac{dP}{dt}\right) + (\ln K - \ln P)\frac{dP}{dt}\right] = c\frac{dP}{dt}\left[-1 + \ln\left(\frac{K}{P}\right)\right]$$

$$= c\left[c\ln(K/P)\,P\right]\left[\ln(K/P) - 1\right] = c^2 P\ln(K/P)\left[\ln(K/P) - 1\right]$$

Since $0 < P < K$, $P'' = 0 \Leftrightarrow \ln(K/P) = 1 \Leftrightarrow K/P = e \Leftrightarrow P = K/e$. $P'' > 0$ for $0 < P < K/e$ and $P'' < 0$ for $K/e < P < K$, so P' is a maximum (and P grows fastest) when $P = K/e$.

15. (a) $dP/dt = kP\cos(rt - \phi) \Rightarrow (dP)/P = k\cos(rt - \phi)\,dt \Rightarrow \int (dP)/P = k\int \cos(rt - \phi)\,dt \Rightarrow$
$\ln P = (k/r)\sin(rt - \phi) + C$. (Since this is a growth model, $P > 0$ and we can write $\ln P$ instead of $\ln|P|$.)
Since $P(0) = P_0$, we obtain $\ln P_0 = (k/r)\sin(-\phi) + C = -(k/r)\sin\phi + C \Rightarrow$
$C = \ln P_0 + (k/r)\sin\phi$. Thus, $\ln P = (k/r)\sin(rt - \phi) + \ln P_0 + (k/r)\sin\phi$, which we can rewrite as
$\ln(P/P_0) = (k/r)[\sin(rt - \phi) + \sin\phi]$ or, after exponentiation, $P(t) = P_0 e^{(k/r)[\sin(rt-\phi)+\sin\phi]}$.

(b) As k increases, the amplitude increases, but the minimum value stays the same.

As r increases, the amplitude and the period decrease.

A change in ϕ produces slight adjustments in the phase shift and amplitude.

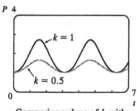

P 4
$k = 1$
$k = 0.5$
0
7
t
Comparing values of k with $P_0 = 1$, $r = 2$, and $\phi = \pi/2$

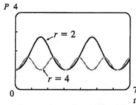

P 4
$r = 2$
$r = 4$
0
7
t
Comparing values of r with $P_0 = 1$, $k = 1$, and $\phi = \pi/2$

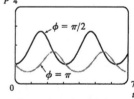

P 4
$\phi = \pi/2$
$\phi = \pi$
0
7
t
Comparing values of ϕ with $P_0 = 1$, $k = 1$, and $r = 2$

$P(t)$ oscillates between $P_0 e^{(k/r)(1+\sin\phi)}$ and $P_0 e^{(k/r)(-1+\sin\phi)}$ (the extreme values are attained when $rt - \phi$ is an odd multiple of $\frac{\pi}{2}$), so $\lim\limits_{t\to\infty} P(t)$ does not exist.

16. (a) $dP/dt = kP\cos^2(rt - \phi) \Rightarrow (dP)/P = k\cos^2(rt - \phi)\,dt \Rightarrow \int (dP)/P = k\int \cos^2(rt - \phi)\,dt \Rightarrow$
$\ln P = k\displaystyle\int \frac{1 + \cos(2(rt - \phi))}{2}\,dt = \frac{k}{2}t + \frac{k}{4r}\sin(2(rt - \phi)) + C$. From $P(0) = P_0$, we get
$\ln P_0 = \dfrac{k}{4r}\sin(-2\phi) + C = C - \dfrac{k}{4r}\sin 2\phi$, so $C = \ln P_0 + \dfrac{k}{4r}\sin 2\phi$ and

$\ln P = \dfrac{k}{2}t + \dfrac{k}{4r}\sin(2(rt - \phi)) + \ln P_0 + \dfrac{k}{4r}\sin 2\phi$. Simplifying, we get

$\ln \dfrac{P}{P_0} = \dfrac{k}{2}t + \dfrac{k}{4r}[\sin(2(rt - \phi)) + \sin 2\phi] = f(t)$, or $P(t) = P_0 e^{f(t)}$.

(b) An increase in k stretches the graph of P vertically while maintaining $P(0) = P_0$.

An increase in r compresses the graph of P horizontally—similar to changing the period in Exercise 15.

As in Exercise 15, a change in ϕ only makes slight adjustments in the growth of P, as shown in the figure.

Comparing values of k with $P_0 = 1$, $r = 2$, and $\phi = \pi/2$

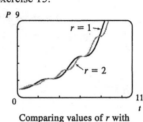

Comparing values of r with $P_0 = 1$, $k = 0.5$, and $\phi = \pi/2$

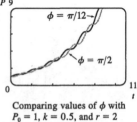

Comparing values of ϕ with $P_0 = 1$, $k = 0.5$, and $r = 2$

$f'(t) = k/2 + [k/(4r)][2r\cos(2(rt - \phi))] = (k/2)[1 + \cos(2(rt - \phi))] \geq 0$. Since $P(t) = P_0 e^{f(t)}$, we have $P'(t) = P_0 f'(t)e^{f(t)} \geq 0$, with equality only when $\cos(2(rt - \phi)) = -1$; that is, when $rt - \phi$ is an odd multiple of $\frac{\pi}{2}$. Therefore, $P(t)$ is an increasing function on $(0, \infty)$. P can also be written as $P(t) = P_0 e^{kt/2}e^{(k/4r)[\sin(2(rt-\phi))+\sin 2\phi]}$. The second exponential oscillates between $e^{(k/4r)(1+\sin 2\phi)}$ and $e^{(k/4r)(-1+\sin 2\phi)}$, while the first one, $e^{kt/2}$, grows without bound. So $\lim\limits_{t\to\infty} P(t) = \infty$.

7.6 Predator-Prey Systems • • • • • • • • • • • • •

1. (a) $dx/dt = -0.05x + 0.0001xy$. If $y = 0$, we have $dx/dt = -0.05x$, which indicates that in the absence of y, x declines at a rate proportional to itself. So x represents the predator population and y represents the prey population. The growth of the prey population, $0.1y$ (from $dy/dt = 0.1y - 0.005xy$), is restricted only by encounters with predators (the term $-0.005xy$). The predator population increases only through the term $0.0001xy$; that is, by encounters with the prey and not through additional food sources.

(b) $dy/dt = -0.015y + 0.00008xy$. If $x = 0$, we have $dy/dt = -0.015y$, which indicates that in the absence of x, y would decline at a rate proportional to itself. So y represents the predator population and x represents the prey population. The growth of the prey population, $0.2x$ (from $dx/dt = 0.2x - 0.0002x^2 - 0.006xy = 0.2x(1 - 0.001x) - 0.006xy$), is restricted by a carrying capacity of 1000 [from the term $1 - 0.001x = 1 - x/1000$] and by encounters with predators (the term $-0.006xy$). The predator population increases only through the term $0.00008xy$; that is, by encounters with the prey and not through additional food sources.

2. (a) $dx/dt = 0.12x - 0.0006x^2 + 0.00001xy$. $dy/dt = 0.08y + 0.00004xy$.

The xy terms represent encounters between the two species x and y. An increase in y makes dx/dt (the growth rate of x) larger due to the positive term $0.00001xy$. An increase in x makes dy/dt (the growth rate of y) larger due to the positive term $0.00004xy$. Hence, the system describes a cooperation model.

(b) $dx/dt = 0.15x - 0.0002x^2 - 0.0006xy = 0.15x(1 - x/750) - 0.0006xy.$

$dy/dt = 0.2y - 0.00008y^2 - 0.0002xy = 0.2y(1 - y/2500) - 0.0002xy.$

The system shows that x and y have carrying capacities of 750 and 2500. An increase in x reduces the growth rate of y due to the negative term $-0.0002xy$. An increase in y reduces the growth rate of x due to the negative term $-0.0006xy$. Hence, the system describes a competition model.

3. (a) At $t = 0$, there are about 300 rabbits and 100 foxes. At $t = t_1$, the number of foxes reaches a minimum of about 20 while the number of rabbits is about 1000. At $t = t_2$, the number of rabbits reaches a maximum of about 2400, while the number of foxes rebounds to 100. At $t = t_3$, the number of rabbits decreases to about 1000 and the number of foxes reaches a maximum of about 315. As t increases, the number of foxes decreases greatly to 100, and the number of rabbits decreases to 300 (the initial populations), and the cycle starts again.

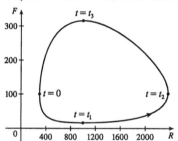

(b)

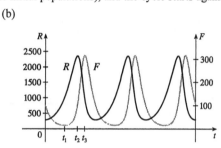

4. (a) At $t = 0$, there are about 600 rabbits and 160 foxes. At $t = t_1$, the number of rabbits reaches a minimum of about 80 and the number of foxes is also 80. At $t = t_2$, the number of foxes reaches a minimum of about 25 while the number of rabbits rebounds to 1000. At $t = t_3$, the number of foxes has increased to 40 and the rabbit population has reached a maximum of about 1750. The curve ends at $t = t_4$, where the number of foxes has increased to 65 and the number of rabbits has decreased to about 950.

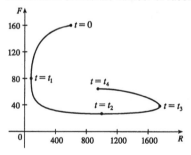

(b)

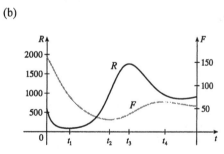

5.

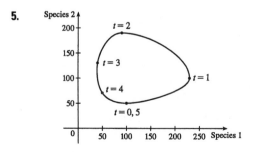

6.

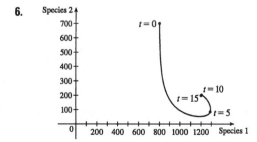

7. $\dfrac{dW}{dR} = \dfrac{-0.02W + 0.00002RW}{0.08R - 0.001RW}$ ⟺ $(0.08 - 0.001W)R\,dW = (-0.02 + 0.00002R)W\,dR$ ⟺

$\dfrac{0.08 - 0.001W}{W}\,dW = \dfrac{-0.02 + 0.00002R}{R}\,dR$ ⟺ $\displaystyle\int\left(\dfrac{0.08}{W} - 0.001\right)dW = \int\left(-\dfrac{0.02}{R} + 0.00002\right)dR$

⟺ $0.08\ln|W| - 0.001W = -0.02\ln|R| + 0.00002R + K$ ⟺

$0.08\ln W + 0.02\ln R = 0.001W + 0.00002R + K$ ⟺ $\ln\left(W^{0.08}R^{0.02}\right) = 0.00002R + 0.001W + K$ ⟺

$W^{0.08}R^{0.02} = e^{0.00002R + 0.001W + K}$ ⟺ $R^{0.02}W^{0.08} = Ce^{0.00002R}e^{0.001W}$ ⟺ $\dfrac{R^{0.02}W^{0.08}}{e^{0.00002R}e^{0.001W}} = C.$

In general, if $\dfrac{dy}{dx} = \dfrac{-ry + bxy}{kx - axy}$, then $C = \dfrac{x^r y^k}{e^{bx}e^{ay}}.$

8. (a) A and L are constant $\Rightarrow A' = 0$ and $L' = 0 \Rightarrow \begin{cases} 0 = 2A - 0.01AL \\ 0 = -0.5L + 0.0001AL \end{cases} \Rightarrow \begin{cases} 0 = A(2 - 0.01L) \\ 0 = L(-0.5 + 0.0001A) \end{cases}$

So either $A = L = 0$ or $L = \frac{2}{0.01} = 200$ and $A = \frac{0.5}{0.0001} = 5000$. The trivial solution $A = L = 0$ just says
that if there aren't any aphids or ladybugs, then the populations will not change. The non-trivial solution,
$L = 200$ and $A = 5000$, indicates the population sizes needed so that there are no changes in either the number
of aphids or the number of ladybugs.

(b) $\dfrac{dL}{dA} = \dfrac{dL/dt}{dA/dt} = \dfrac{-0.5L + 0.0001AL}{2A - 0.01AL}$

(c) The solution curves (phase trajectories) are all closed curves
that have the equilibrium point $(5000, 200)$ inside them.

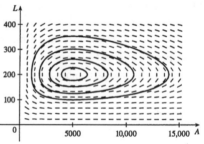

(d)

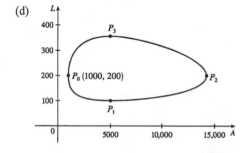

At $P_0(1000, 200)$, $dA/dt = 0$ and $dL/dt = -80 < 0$, so the
number of ladybugs is decreasing and hence, we are
proceeding in a counterclockwise direction. At P_0, there aren't
enough aphids to support the ladybug population, so the
number of ladybugs decreases and the number of aphids begins
to increase. The ladybug population reaches a minimum at
$P_1(5000, 100)$ while the aphid population increases in a
dramatic way, reaching its maximum at $P_2(14,250, 200)$.

Meanwhile, the ladybug population is increasing from P_1 to $P_3(5000, 355)$, and as we pass through P_2, the
increasing number of ladybugs starts to deplete the aphid population. At P_3 the ladybugs reach a maximum
population, and start to decrease due to the reduced aphid population. Both populations then decrease until P_0,
where the cycle starts over again.

(e) Both graphs have the same period and the graph
of L peaks about a quarter of a cycle after the
graph of A.

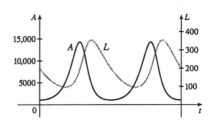

9. (a) Letting $W = 0$ gives us $dR/dt = 0.08R(1 - 0.0002R)$. $dR/dt = 0 \Leftrightarrow R = 0$ or 5000. Since $dR/dt > 0$
for $0 < R < 5000$, we would expect the rabbit population to *increase* to 5000 for these values of R. Since
$dR/dt < 0$ for $R > 5000$, we would expect the rabbit population to *decrease* to 5000 for these values of R.
Hence, in the absence of wolves, we would expect the rabbit population to stabilize at 5000.

(b) R and W are constant $\Rightarrow R' = 0$ and $W' = 0 \Rightarrow$

$$\left. \begin{cases} 0 = 0.08R(1 - 0.0002R) - 0.001RW \\ 0 = -0.02W + 0.00002RW \end{cases} \right\} \Rightarrow \begin{cases} 0 = R[0.08(1 - 0.0002R) - 0.001W] \\ 0 = W(-0.02 + 0.00002R) \end{cases}$$

The second equation is true if $W = 0$ or $R = \frac{0.02}{0.00002} = 1000$. If $W = 0$ in the first equation, then either $R = 0$
or $R = \frac{1}{0.0002} = 5000$ [as in part (a)]. If $R = 1000$, then $0 = 1000[0.08(1 - 0.0002 \cdot 1000) - 0.001W] \Leftrightarrow$
$0 = 80(1 - 0.2) - W \Leftrightarrow W = 64$.
Case (i): $W = 0$, $R = 0$: both populations are zero
Case (ii): $W = 0$, $R = 5000$: see part (a)
Case (iii): $R = 1000$, $W = 64$: the predator/prey interaction balances and the populations are stable.

(c) The populations of wolves and rabbits fluctuate
around 64 and 1000, respectively, and eventually
stabilize at those values.

(d)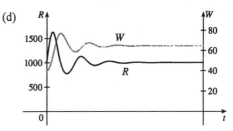

10. (a) If $L = 0$, $dA/dt = 2A(1 - 0.0001A)$, so $dA/dt = 0 \Leftrightarrow A = 0$ or $A = \frac{1}{0.0001} = 10{,}000$. Since
$dA/dt > 0$ for $0 < A < 10{,}000$, we expect the aphid population to *increase* to 10,000 for these values of A.
Since $dA/dt < 0$ for $A > 10{,}000$, we expect the aphid population to *decrease* to 10,000 for these values of A.
Hence, in the absence of ladybugs we expect the aphid population to stabilize at 10,000.

(b) A and L are constant $\Rightarrow A' = 0$ and $L' = 0 \Rightarrow$

$$\left. \begin{cases} 0 = 2A(1 - 0.0001A) - 0.01AL \\ 0 = -0.5L + 0.0001AL \end{cases} \right\} \Rightarrow \begin{cases} 0 = A[2(1 - 0.0001A) - 0.01L] \\ 0 = L(-0.5 + 0.0001A) \end{cases}$$

The second equation is true if $L = 0$ or $A = \frac{0.5}{0.0001} = 5000$. If $L = 0$ in the first equation, then either $A = 0$ or
$A = \frac{1}{0.0001} = 10{,}000$. If $A = 5000$, then $0 = 5000[2(1 - 0.0001 \cdot 5000) - 0.01L] \Leftrightarrow$
$0 = 10{,}000(1 - 0.5) - 50L \Leftrightarrow 50L = 5000 \Leftrightarrow L = 100$. The equilibrium solutions are:
(i) $L = 0$, $A = 0$ (ii) $L = 0$, $A = 10{,}000$ (iii) $A = 5000$, $L = 100$

(c) $\dfrac{dL}{dA} = \dfrac{dL/dt}{dA/dt} = \dfrac{-0.5L + 0.0001AL}{2A(1 - 0.0001A) - 0.01AL}$

(d)

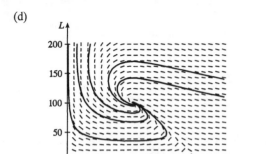

(e)

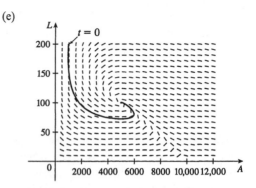

All of the phase trajectories spiral tightly around the equilibrium solution $(5000, 100)$.

(f)

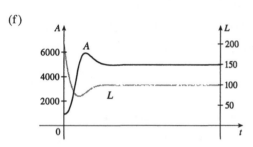

The graph of A peaks just after the graph of L has a minimum.

At $t = 0$, the ladybug population decreases rapidly and the aphid population decreases slightly before beginning to increase. As the aphid population continues to increase, the ladybug population reaches a minimum at about $(5000, 75)$. The ladybug population starts to increase and quickly stabilizes at 100, while the aphid population stabilizes at 5000.

7 Review

— • CONCEPT CHECK • —

1. (a) A differential equation is an equation that contains an unknown function and one or more of its derivatives.

   (b) The order of a differential equation is the order of the highest derivative that occurs in the equation.

   (c) An initial condition is a condition of the form $y(t_0) = y_0$.

2. $y' = x^2 + y^2 \geq 0$ for all x and y. $y' = 0$ only at the origin, so there is a horizontal tangent at $(0, 0)$, but nowhere else. The graph of the solution is increasing on every interval.

3. See the paragraph preceding Example 1 in Section 7.2.

4. See the paragraph after Figure 14 in Section 7.2.

5. A separable equation is a first-order differential equation in which the expression for dy/dx can be factored as a function of x times a function of y, that is, $dy/dx = g(x)f(y)$. We can solve the equation by integrating both sides of the equation $dy/f(y) = g(x)dx$ and solving for y.

6. (a) $dy/dt = ky$

(b) The equation in part (a) is an appropriate model for population growth, assuming that there is enough room and nutrition to support the growth.

(c) If $y(0) = y_0$, then the solution is $y(t) = y_0 e^{kt}$.

7. (a) $dP/dt = kP(1 - P/K)$, where K is the carrying capacity.

(b) The equation in part (a) is an appropriate model for population growth, assuming that the population grows at a rate proportional to the size of the population in the beginning, but eventually levels off and approaches its carrying capacity because of limited resources.

8. (a) $dF/dt = kF - aFS$ and $dS/dt = -rS + bFS$.

(b) In the absence of sharks, an ample food supply would support exponential growth of the fish population, that is, $dF/dt = kF$, where k is a positive constant. In the absence of fish, we assume that the shark population would decline at a rate proportional to itself, that is, $dS/dt = -rS$, where r is a positive constant.

──────────────── ▲ **TRUE–FALSE QUIZ** ▲ ────────────────

1. True. Since $y^4 \geq 0$, $y' = -1 - y^4 < 0$ and the solutions are decreasing functions.

2. True. $y = \dfrac{\ln x}{x} \;\Rightarrow\; y' = \dfrac{1 - \ln x}{x^2}$.

LHS $= x^2 y' + xy = x^2 \cdot \dfrac{1 - \ln x}{x^2} + x \cdot \dfrac{\ln x}{x} = (1 - \ln x) + \ln x = 1 =$ RHS, so $y = \dfrac{\ln x}{x}$ is a solution of $x^2 y' + xy = 1$.

3. False. $x + y$ cannot be written in the form $g(x) f(y)$.

4. True. $y' = 3y - 2x + 6xy - 1 = 6xy - 2x + 3y - 1 = 2x(3y - 1) + 1(3y - 1) = (2x + 1)(3y - 1)$, so y' can be written in the form $g(x) f(y)$.

5. True. By comparing $\dfrac{dy}{dt} = 2y\left(1 - \dfrac{y}{5}\right)$ with the logistic differential equation (7.5.1), we see that the carrying capacity is 5; that is, $\lim\limits_{t \to \infty} y = 5$.

──────────────── ◆ **EXERCISES** ◆ ────────────────

1. (a)

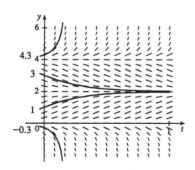

(b) $\lim\limits_{t \to \infty} y(t)$ appears to be finite for $0 \leq c \leq 4$. In fact $\lim\limits_{t \to \infty} y(t) = 4$ for $c = 4$, $\lim\limits_{t \to \infty} y(t) = 2$ for $0 < c < 4$, and $\lim\limits_{t \to \infty} y(t) = 0$ for $c = 0$. The equilibrium solutions are $y(t) = 0$, $y(t) = 2$, and $y(t) = 4$.

2. (a)

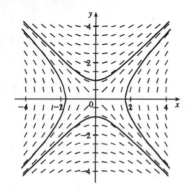

We sketch the direction field and four solution curves, as shown. Note that the slope $y' = x/y$ is not defined on the line $y = 0$.

(b) $y' = x/y \;\Leftrightarrow\; y\,dy = x\,dx \;\Leftrightarrow\; y^2 = x^2 + C$. For $C = 0$, this is the pair of lines $y = \pm x$. For $C \neq 0$, it is the hyperbola $x^2 - y^2 = -C$.

3. (a)

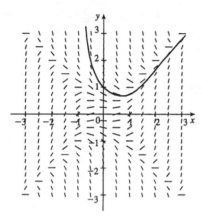

We estimate that when $x = 0.3$, $y = 0.8$, so $y(0.3) \approx 0.8$.

(b) $h = 0.1$, $x_0 = 0$, $y_0 = 1$ and $F(x, y) = x^2 - y^2$. So $y_n = y_{n-1} + 0.1\left(x_{n-1}^2 - y_{n-1}^2\right)$. Thus,

$y_1 = 1 + 0.1\left(0^2 - 1^2\right) = 0.9$,

$y_2 = 0.9 + 0.1\left(0.1^2 - 0.9^2\right) = 0.82$,

$y_3 = 0.82 + 0.1\left(0.2^2 - 0.82^2\right) = 0.75676$. This is close to our graphical estimate of $y(0.3) \approx 0.8$.

(c) The centers of the horizontal line segments of the direction field are located on the lines $y = x$ and $y = -x$. When a solution curve crosses one of these lines, it has a local maximum or minimum.

4. (a) $h = 0.2$, $x_0 = 0$, $y_0 = 1$ and $F(x, y) = 2xy^2$. We need y_2.

$y_1 = 1 + 0.2\left(2 \cdot 0 \cdot 1^2\right) = 1$, $y_2 = 1 + 0.2\left(2 \cdot 0.2 \cdot 1^2\right) = 1.08 \approx y(0.4)$.

(b) $h = 0.1$ now, so $y_1 = 1 + 0.1\left(2 \cdot 0 \cdot 1^2\right) = 1$, $y_2 = 1 + 0.1\left(2 \cdot 0.1 \cdot 1^2\right) = 1.02$,

$y_3 = 1.02 + 0.1\left(2 \cdot 0.2 \cdot 1.02^2\right) \approx 1.06162$, $y_4 = 1.06162 + 0.1\left(2 \cdot 0.3 \cdot 1.06162^2\right) \approx 1.1292 \approx y(0.4)$.

(c) The equation is separable, so we write $\dfrac{dy}{y^2} = 2x\,dx \;\Rightarrow\; \displaystyle\int \dfrac{dy}{y^2} = \int 2x\,dx \;\Leftrightarrow\; -\dfrac{1}{y} = x^2 + C$, but

$y(0) = 1$, so $C = -1$ and $y(x) = \dfrac{1}{1 - x^2} \;\Leftrightarrow\; y(0.4) = \dfrac{1}{1 - 0.16} \approx 1.1905$. From this we see that the approximation was greatly improved by increasing the number of steps, but the approximations were still far off.

5. $(3y^2 + 2y)\,y' = x\cos x \;\Rightarrow\; (3y^2 + 2y)\,dy = (x\cos x)\,dx \;\Rightarrow\; \int(3y^2 + 2y)\,dy = \int(x\cos x)\,dx \;\Rightarrow\;$
$y^3 + y^2 = \cos x + x\sin x + C$. For the last step, use integration by parts or Formula 83 in the Table of Integrals.

6. $\dfrac{dx}{dt} = 1 - t + x - tx = 1(1 - t) + x(1 - t) = (1 + x)(1 - t) \;\Rightarrow\; \dfrac{dx}{1 + x} = (1 - t)\,dt \;\Rightarrow\;$

$\displaystyle\int \dfrac{dx}{1 + x} = \int(1 - t)\,dt \;\Rightarrow\; \ln|1 + x| = t - \tfrac{1}{2}t^2 + C \;\Rightarrow\; |1 + x| = e^{t - t^2/2 + C} \;\Rightarrow\;$

$1 + x = \pm e^{t - t^2/2} \cdot e^C \;\Rightarrow\; x = -1 + K e^{t - t^2/2}$, where K is any nonzero constant.

7. $xyy' = \ln x \;\Rightarrow\; y\,dy = \dfrac{\ln x}{x}\,dx \;\Rightarrow\; \displaystyle\int y\,dy = \int \dfrac{\ln x}{x}\,dx$ (Make the substitution $u = \ln x$; then

$du = dx/x$.) So $\int y\,dy = \int u\,du \;\Rightarrow\; \frac{1}{2}y^2 = \frac{1}{2}u^2 + C \;\Rightarrow\; \frac{1}{2}y^2 = \frac{1}{2}(\ln x)^2 + C.$ $y(1) = 2 \;\Rightarrow\;$

$\frac{1}{2}2^2 = \frac{1}{2}(\ln 1)^2 + C = C \;\Leftrightarrow\; C = 2.$ Therefore, $\frac{1}{2}y^2 = \frac{1}{2}(\ln x)^2 + 2$, or $y = \sqrt{(\ln x)^2 + 4}$. The negative

square root is inadmissible, since $y(1) > 0$.

8. $1 + x = 2xyy' \;\Rightarrow\; y' = \dfrac{1+x}{2xy} \;\Leftrightarrow\; y\,dy = \dfrac{1+x}{2x}\,dx \;\Rightarrow\; \dfrac{y^2}{2} = \dfrac{\ln|x|}{2} + \dfrac{x}{2} + c_1.$ But $x > 0$, so

$y^2 = \ln x + x + c \;\Leftrightarrow\; y(x) = \pm\sqrt{c + x + \ln x}$. But $-2 = y(1)$ so choose the negative square root and

$-2 = -\sqrt{c+1}$ so $c = 3$. Thus, the solution is $y(x) = -\sqrt{3 + x + \ln x}$.

9. The curves $kx^2 + y^2 = 1$ form a family of ellipses for $k > 0$, a family of hyperbolas for $k < 0$, and two parallel

lines $y = \pm 1$ for $k = 0$. Solving $kx^2 + y^2 = 1$ for k gives $k = \dfrac{1 - y^2}{x^2}$. Differentiating gives $2kx + 2yy' = 0 \;\Leftrightarrow\;$

$y' = -\dfrac{kx}{y} = -\left(1 - y^2\right)\dfrac{x}{yx^2} = \dfrac{y^2 - 1}{xy}$. Thus, for $k \ne 0$ the orthogonal trajectories must satisfy $y' = -\dfrac{xy}{y^2 - 1}$

$\Rightarrow \dfrac{y^2 - 1}{y}\,dy = -x\,dx \;\Rightarrow\; \dfrac{y^2}{2} - \ln|y| = \dfrac{-x^2}{2} + K \;\Rightarrow\; y^2 - 2\ln|y| + x^2 = C.$ For $k = 0$, the

orthogonal trajectories are given by $x = C_1$ for C_1 an arbitrary constant.

10. Differentiating both sides of $y = \dfrac{k}{1 + x^2}$ gives $y' = -\dfrac{2kx}{(1 + x^2)^2} = -2xy\dfrac{1 + x^2}{(1 + x^2)^2} = -\dfrac{2xy}{1 + x^2}$. Thus, for

$k \ne 0$ the orthogonal trajectories must satisfy $y' = \dfrac{1 + x^2}{2xy} \;\Rightarrow\; 2y\,dy = \left(\dfrac{1}{x} + x\right)dx \;\Rightarrow\;$

$y^2 = \dfrac{x^2}{2} + \ln|x| + C.$ For $k = 0$, the orthogonal trajectories are given by $x = C_2$ for C_2 an arbitrary constant.

11. (a) $y(t) = y(0)e^{kt} = 1000e^{kt} \;\Rightarrow\; y(2) = 1000e^{2k} = 9000 \;\Rightarrow\; e^{2k} = 9 \;\Rightarrow\; 2k = \ln 9 \;\Rightarrow\;$

$\quad\; k = \frac{1}{2}\ln 9 = \ln 3 \;\Rightarrow\; y(t) = 1000e^{(\ln 3)t} = 1000 \cdot 3^t$

(b) $y(3) = 1000 \cdot 3^3 = 27{,}000$

(c) $y'(t) = 1000 \cdot 3^t \cdot \ln 3$, so $y'(3) = 27{,}000\ln 3 \approx 29{,}663$ bacteria per hour

(d) $1000 \cdot 3^t = 2 \cdot 1000 \;\Rightarrow\; 3^t = 2 \;\Rightarrow\; t\ln 3 = \ln 2 \;\Rightarrow\; t = (\ln 2)/\ln 3 \approx 0.63$ h

12. (a) If $y(t)$ is the mass remaining after t years, then $y(t) = y(0)e^{kt} = 18e^{kt}$. $y(25) = 18e^{25k} = \frac{1}{2} \cdot 18 \;\Rightarrow\;$

$\quad\; e^{25k} = \frac{1}{2} \;\Rightarrow\; 25k = -\ln 2 \;\Rightarrow\; k = -\frac{1}{25}\ln 2 \;\Rightarrow\; y(t) = 18\,e^{-(\ln 2)t/25} = 18 \cdot 2^{-t/25}.$

(b) $18 \cdot 2^{-t/25} = 2 \;\Rightarrow\; 2^{-t/25} = \frac{1}{9} \;\Rightarrow\; -\frac{1}{25}t\ln 2 = -\ln 9 \;\Rightarrow\; t = 25\,\frac{\ln 9}{\ln 2} \approx 79$ years

13. (a) $C'(t) = -kC(t) \;\Rightarrow\; C(t) = C(0)e^{-kt}$ by Theorem 7.4.2. But $C(0) = C_0$, so $C(t) = C_0e^{-kt}$.

(b) $C(30) = \frac{1}{2}C_0$ since the concentration is reduced by half. Thus, $\frac{1}{2}C_0 = C_0e^{-30k} \;\Rightarrow\; \ln\frac{1}{2} = -30k \;\Rightarrow\;$

$\quad\; k = -\frac{1}{30}\ln\frac{1}{2} = \frac{1}{30}\ln 2.$ Since 10% of the original concentration remains if 90% is eliminated, we want the

value of t such that $C(t) = \frac{1}{10}C_0$. Therefore, $\frac{1}{10}C_0 = C_0e^{-t(\ln 2)/30} \;\Rightarrow\; \ln 0.1 = -t(\ln 2)/30 \;\Rightarrow\;$

$\quad\; t = -\frac{30}{\ln 2}\ln 0.1 \approx 100$ h.

14. (a) Let $t = 0$ correspond to 1990 so that $P(t) = 5.28e^{kt}$ is a starting point for the model. When $t = 10$, $P = 6.07$.

$\quad\;$ So $6.07 = 5.28e^{10k} \;\Rightarrow\; 10k = \ln\frac{6.07}{5.28} \;\Rightarrow\; k = \frac{1}{10}\ln\frac{6.07}{5.28} \approx 0.01394.$ For the year 2020, $t = 30$, and

$\quad\; P(30) = 5.28e^{30k} \approx 8.02$ billion.

(b) $P = 10 \Rightarrow 5.28e^{kt} = 10 \Rightarrow \frac{10}{5.28} = e^{kt} \Rightarrow kt = \ln\frac{10}{5.28} \Rightarrow t = 10\frac{\ln\frac{10}{5.28}}{\ln\frac{6.07}{5.28}} \approx 45.8$ years; that is,

in $1990 + 45 = 2035$.

(c) $P(t) = \dfrac{K}{1 + Ae^{-kt}} = \dfrac{100}{1 + Ae^{-kt}}$, where $A = \dfrac{100 - 5.28}{5.28} \approx 17.94$. Using $k = \dfrac{1}{10}\ln\dfrac{6.07}{5.28}$ from part (a), a

model is $P(t) \approx \dfrac{100}{1 + 17.94e^{-0.01394t}}$ and $P(30) \approx 7.81$ billion, slightly lower than our estimate of

8.02 billion in part (a).

(d) $P = 10 \Rightarrow 1 + Ae^{-kt} = \frac{100}{10} \Rightarrow Ae^{-kt} = 9 \Rightarrow e^{-kt} = 9/A \Rightarrow -kt = \ln(9/A) \Rightarrow$

$t = -\dfrac{1}{k}\ln\dfrac{9}{A} \approx 49.47$ years (that is, in 2039), which is later than the prediction of 2035 in part (b).

15. (a) $\dfrac{dL}{dt} \propto L_\infty - L \Rightarrow \dfrac{dL}{dt} = k(L_\infty - L) \Rightarrow \displaystyle\int \dfrac{dL}{L_\infty - L} = \int k\,dt \Rightarrow -\ln|L_\infty - L| = kt + C \Rightarrow$

$\ln|L_\infty - L| = -kt - C \Rightarrow |L_\infty - L| = e^{-kt - C} \Rightarrow L_\infty - L = Ae^{-kt} \Rightarrow L = L_\infty - Ae^{-kt}$.

At $t = 0$, $L = L(0) = L_\infty - A \Rightarrow A = L_\infty - L(0) \Rightarrow L(t) = L_\infty - [L_\infty - L(0)]e^{-kt}$.

(b) $L_\infty = 53$ cm, $L(0) = 10$ cm, and $k = 0.2 \Rightarrow L(t) = 53 - (53 - 10)e^{-0.2t} = 53 - 43e^{-0.2t}$.

16. Denote the amount of salt in the tank (in kg) by y. $y(0) = 0$ since initially there is only water in the tank. The rate
at which y increases is equal to the rate at which salt flows into the tank minus the rate at which it flows out. That

rate is $\dfrac{dy}{dt} = 0.1\dfrac{\text{kg}}{\text{L}} \times 10\dfrac{\text{L}}{\text{min}} - \dfrac{y}{100}\dfrac{\text{kg}}{\text{L}} \times 10\dfrac{\text{L}}{\text{min}} = 1 - \dfrac{y}{10}\dfrac{\text{kg}}{\text{min}} \Rightarrow \displaystyle\int \dfrac{dy}{10 - y} = \int \dfrac{1}{10}\,dt \Rightarrow$

$-\ln|10 - y| = \frac{1}{10}t + C \Rightarrow 10 - y = Ae^{-t/10}$. $y(0) = 0 \Rightarrow 10 = A \Rightarrow y = 10(1 - e^{-t/10})$.

At $t = 6$ minutes, $y = 10\left(1 - e^{-6/10}\right) \approx 4.512$ kg.

17. Let P be the population and I be the number of infected people. The rate of spread dI/dt is jointly proportional to

I and to $P - I$, so for some constant k, $dI/dt = kI(P - I) \Rightarrow I = \dfrac{I_0 P}{I_0 + (P - I_0)e^{-kPt}}$ (from the

discussion of logistic growth in Section 7.5).

Now, measuring t in days, we substitute $t = 7$, $P = 5000$, $I_0 = 160$ and $I(7) = 1200$ to find k:

$1200 = \dfrac{160 \cdot 5000}{160 + (5000 - 160)e^{-5000 \cdot 7 \cdot k}} \Leftrightarrow k \approx 0.00006448$. So, putting $I = 5000 \times 80\% = 4000$, we solve

for t: $4000 = \dfrac{160 \cdot 5000}{160 + (5000 - 160)e^{-0.00006448 \cdot 5000 \cdot t}} \Leftrightarrow 160 + 4840e^{-0.3224t} = 200 \Leftrightarrow$

$-0.3224t = \ln\frac{40}{4840} \Leftrightarrow t \approx 14.9$. So it takes about 15 days for 80% of the population to be infected.

18. $\dfrac{1}{R}\dfrac{dR}{dt} = \dfrac{k}{S}\dfrac{dS}{dt} \Rightarrow \dfrac{d}{dt}(\ln R) = \dfrac{d}{dt}(k\ln S) \Rightarrow \ln R = k\ln S + C \Rightarrow$

$R = e^{k\ln S + C} = e^C\left(e^{\ln S}\right)^k \Rightarrow R = AS^k$, where $A = e^C$ is a positive constant.

19. $\dfrac{dh}{dt} = -\dfrac{R}{V}\left(\dfrac{h}{k+h}\right) \Rightarrow \displaystyle\int \dfrac{k+h}{h}\,dh = \int\left(-\dfrac{R}{V}\right)dt \Rightarrow \int\left(1 + \dfrac{k}{h}\right)dh = -\dfrac{R}{V}\int 1\,dt \Rightarrow$

$h + k\ln h = -\dfrac{R}{V}t + C$. This equation gives a relationship between h and t, but it is not possible to isolate h and
express it in terms of t.

20. $dx/dt = 0.4x - 0.002xy$, $dy/dt = -0.2y + 0.000008xy$

(a) The xy terms represent encounters between the birds and the insects. Since the y-population increases from
these terms and the x-population decreases, we expect y to represent the birds and x the insects.

(b) x and y are constant $\Rightarrow$ $x' = 0$ and $y' = 0$ $\Rightarrow$

$$\left.\begin{cases} 0 = 0.4x - 0.002xy \\ 0 = -0.2y + 0.000008xy \end{cases}\right\} \Rightarrow \begin{cases} 0 = 0.4x(1 - 0.005y) \\ 0 = -0.2y(1 - 0.00004x) \end{cases} \Rightarrow \quad y = 0 \text{ and } x = 0 \text{ (zero populations)}$$

or $y = \frac{1}{0.005} = 200$ and $x = \frac{1}{0.00004} = 25{,}000$. The non-trivial solution represents the population sizes needed so that there are no changes in either the number of birds or the number of insects.

(c) $\dfrac{dy}{dx} = \dfrac{dy/dt}{dx/dt} = \dfrac{-0.2y + 0.000008xy}{0.4x - 0.002xy}$

(d)

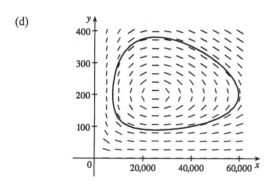

At $(x, y) = (40{,}000, 100)$, $dx/dt = 8000 > 0$, so as t increases we are proceeding in a counterclockwise direction. The populations increase to approximately $(59{,}646, 200)$, at which point the insect population starts to decrease. The birds attain a maximum population of about 380 when the insect population is 25,000. The populations decrease to about $(7370, 200)$, at which point the insect population starts to increase. The birds attain a minimum population of about 88 when the insect population is 25,000, and then the cycle repeats.

(e)

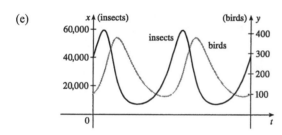

Both graphs have the same period and the bird population peaks about a quarter-cycle after the insect population.

21. (a) $dx/dt = 0.4x(1 - 0.000005x) - 0.002xy$, $dy/dt = -0.2y + 0.000008xy$. If $y = 0$, then $dx/dt = 0.4x(1 - 0.000005x)$, so $dx/dt = 0$ $\Leftrightarrow$ $x = 0$ or $x = 200{,}000$, which shows that the insect population increases logistically with a carrying capacity of 200,000. Since $dx/dt > 0$ for $0 < x < 200{,}000$ and $dx/dt < 0$ for $x > 200{,}000$, we expect the insect population to stabilize at 200,000.

(b) x and y are constant $\Rightarrow$ $x' = 0$ and $y' = 0$ $\Rightarrow$

$$\left.\begin{cases} 0 = 0.4x(1 - 0.000005x) - 0.002xy \\ 0 = -0.2y + 0.000008xy \end{cases}\right\} \Rightarrow \begin{cases} 0 = 0.4x[(1 - 0.000005x) - 0.005y] \\ 0 = y(-0.2 + 0.000008x) \end{cases}$$

The second equation is true if $y = 0$ or $x = \frac{0.2}{0.000008} = 25{,}000$. If $y = 0$ in the first equation, then either $x = 0$ or $x = \frac{1}{0.000005} = 200{,}000$. If $x = 25{,}000$, then $0 = 0.4(25{,}000)[(1 - 0.000005 \cdot 25{,}000) - 0.005y]$ $\Rightarrow$ $0 = 10{,}000[(1 - 0.125) - 0.005y]$ $\Rightarrow$ $0 = 8750 - 50y$ $\Rightarrow$ $y = 175$.

Case (i): $y = 0$, $x = 0$: Zero populations

Case (ii): $y = 0$, $x = 200{,}000$: In the absence of birds, the insect population is always 200,000.

Case (iii): $x = 25{,}000$, $y = 175$: The predator/prey interaction balances and the populations are stable.

(c) The populations of the birds and insects fluctuate around 175 and 25,000, respectively, and eventually stabilize at those values.

(d)

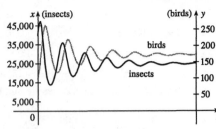

22. First note that, in this question, "weighs" is used in the informal sense, so what we really require is Barbara's mass m in kg as a function of t. Barbara's net intake of calories per day at time t (measured in days) is
$c(t) = 1600 - 850 - 15m(t) = 750 - 15m(t)$, where $m(t)$ is her mass at time t. We are given that $m(0) = 60$ kg
and $\dfrac{dm}{dt} = \dfrac{c(t)}{10,000}$, so $\dfrac{dm}{dt} = \dfrac{750 - 15m}{10,000} = \dfrac{150 - 3m}{2000} = \dfrac{-3(m - 50)}{2000}$ with $m(0) = 60$. From
$\displaystyle\int \dfrac{dm}{m - 50} = \int \dfrac{-3\,dt}{2000}$, we get $\ln|m - 50| = -\frac{3}{2000}t + C$. Since $m(0) = 60$, $C = \ln 10$. Now
$\ln \dfrac{|m - 50|}{10} = -\dfrac{3t}{2000}$, so $|m - 50| = 10e^{-3t/2000}$. The quantity $m - 50$ is continuous, initially positive, and the
right-hand side is never zero. Thus, $m - 50$ is positive for all t, and $m(t) = 50 + 10e^{-3t/2000}$ kg. As $t \to \infty$,
$m(t) \to 50$ kg. Thus, Barbara's mass gradually settles down to 50 kg.

Focus on Problem Solving

1. We use the Fundamental Theorem of Calculus to differentiate the given equation:

$[f(x)]^2 = 100 + \int_0^x \left\{ [f(t)]^2 + [f'(t)]^2 \right\} dt \quad \Rightarrow \quad 2f(x)f'(x) = [f(x)]^2 + [f'(x)]^2 \quad \Rightarrow$

$[f(x)]^2 + [f'(x)]^2 - 2f(x)f'(x) = 0 \quad \Rightarrow \quad [f(x) - f'(x)]^2 = 0 \quad \Leftrightarrow \quad f(x) = f'(x)$. We can solve this as a separable equation, or else use Theorem 7.4.2 with $k = 1$, which says that the solutions are $f(x) = Ce^x$. Now $[f(0)]^2 = 100$, so $f(0) = C = \pm 10$, and hence $f(x) = \pm 10e^x$ are the only functions satisfying the given equation.

2. $(fg)' = f'g'$, where $f(x) = e^{x^2} \quad \Rightarrow \quad \left(e^{x^2} g \right)' = 2xe^{x^2} g'$. Since the student's mistake did not affect the answer,

$\left(e^{x^2} g \right)' = e^{x^2} g' + 2xe^{x^2} g = 2xe^{x^2} g'$. So $(2x - 1)g' = 2xg$, or $\dfrac{g'}{g} = \dfrac{2x}{2x - 1} = 1 + \dfrac{1}{2x - 1} \quad \Rightarrow$

$\ln|g(x)| = x + \frac{1}{2}\ln(2x - 1) + C \quad \Rightarrow \quad g(x) = Ae^x \sqrt{2x - 1}$.

3. $f'(x) = \lim\limits_{h \to 0} \dfrac{f(x + h) - f(x)}{h} = \lim\limits_{h \to 0} \dfrac{f(x)\,[f(h) - 1]}{h} \quad$ [since $f(x + h) = f(x)f(h)$]

$\qquad = f(x) \lim\limits_{h \to 0} \dfrac{f(h) - 1}{h} = f(x) \lim\limits_{h \to 0} \dfrac{f(h) - f(0)}{h - 0} = f(x)f'(0) = f(x)$

Therefore, $f'(x) = f(x)$ for all x and from Theorem 7.4.2 we get $f(x) = Ae^x$. Now $f(0) = 1 \quad \Rightarrow \quad A = 1 \quad \Rightarrow$ $f(x) = e^x$.

4. $\left(\displaystyle\int f(x)\,dx \right) \left(\displaystyle\int \dfrac{dx}{f(x)} \right) = -1 \Rightarrow \displaystyle\int \dfrac{dx}{f(x)} = \dfrac{-1}{\int f(x)\,dx} \Rightarrow \dfrac{1}{f(x)} = \dfrac{f(x)}{\left[\int f(x)\,dx \right]^2}$ [after differentiating] $\Rightarrow$

$\int f(x)\,dx = \pm f(x)$ [after taking square roots] $\quad \Rightarrow \quad f(x) = \pm f'(x)$ [after differentiating again] $\quad \Rightarrow$

$y = Ae^x$ or $y = Ae^{-x}$ by (7.4.2). Therefore, $f(x) = Ae^x$ or $f(x) = Ae^{-x}$, for all nonzero constants A, are the functions satisfying the original equation.

5. Let $y(t)$ denote the temperature of the peach pie t minutes after 5:00 P.M. and R the temperature of the room. In Exercise 7.4.13, Newton's Law of Cooling gives us $dy/dt = k(y - R)$. Solving for y we get $\dfrac{dy}{y - R} = k\,dt \quad \Rightarrow$

$\ln|y - R| = kt + C \quad \Rightarrow \quad |y - R| = e^{kt + C} \quad \Rightarrow \quad y - R = \pm e^{kt} \cdot e^C \quad \Rightarrow \quad y = Me^{kt} + R$, where M is a nonzero constant. We are given temperatures at three times.

$$
\begin{aligned}
y(0) &= 100 \quad \Rightarrow \quad 100 = M + R \quad &\Rightarrow \quad R = 100 - M \\
y(10) &= 80 \quad \Rightarrow \quad 80 = Me^{10k} + R \quad &\textbf{(1)} \\
y(20) &= 65 \quad \Rightarrow \quad 65 = Me^{20k} + R \quad &\textbf{(2)}
\end{aligned}
$$

Substituting $100 - M$ for R in **(1)** and **(2)** gives us

$$-20 = Me^{10k} - M \quad \textbf{(3)} \quad \text{and} \quad -35 = Me^{20k} - M \quad \textbf{(4)}$$

Dividing (3) by (4) gives us $\dfrac{-20}{-35} = \dfrac{M(e^{10k}-1)}{M(e^{20k}-1)}$ $\Rightarrow$ $\dfrac{4}{7} = \dfrac{e^{10k}-1}{e^{20k}-1}$ $\Rightarrow$ $4e^{20k}-4 = 7e^{10k}-7$ $\Rightarrow$

$4e^{20k}-7e^{10k}+3 = 0$. This is a quadratic equation in e^{10k}. $(4e^{10k}-3)(e^{10k}-1) = 0$ $\Rightarrow$ $e^{10k} = \frac{3}{4}$ or 1

$\Rightarrow$ $10k = \ln\frac{3}{4}$ or $\ln 1$ $\Rightarrow$ $k = \frac{1}{10}\ln\frac{3}{4}$ since k is a nonzero constant of proportionality. Substituting $\frac{3}{4}$ for e^{10k}

in (3) gives us $-20 = M \cdot \frac{3}{4} - M$ $\Rightarrow$ $-20 = -\frac{1}{4}M$ $\Rightarrow$ $M = 80$. Now $R = 100 - M$ so $R = 20\,^{\circ}\text{C}$.

6. Let b be the number of hours before noon that it began to snow, t the time measured in hours after noon, and
$x = x(t) = $ distance traveled by the plow at time t. Then $dx/dt = $ speed of plow. Since the snow falls steadily, the
height at time t is $h(t) = k(t+b)$, where k is a constant. We are given that the rate of removal is constant, say R

(in m^3/h). If the width of the path is w, then $R = $ height $\times$ width $\times$ speed $= h(t) \times w \times \dfrac{dx}{dt} = k(t+b)w\,\dfrac{dx}{dt}$.

Thus, $\dfrac{dx}{dt} = \dfrac{C}{t+b}$, where $C = \dfrac{R}{kw}$ is a constant. This is a separable equation. $\displaystyle\int dx = C\int \dfrac{dt}{t+b}$ $\Rightarrow$

$x(t) = C\ln(t+b) + K$.
Put $t = 0$: $0 = C\ln b + K$ $\Rightarrow$ $K = -C\ln b$, so $x(t) = C\ln(t+b) - C\ln b = C\ln(1+t/b)$.
Put $t = 1$: $6000 = C\ln(1+1/b)$ $[x = 6\text{ km}]$.
Put $t = 2$: $9000 = C\ln(1+2/b)$ $[x = (6+3)\text{ km}]$.

Solve for b: $\dfrac{\ln(1+1/b)}{6000} = \dfrac{\ln(1+2/b)}{9000}$ $\Rightarrow$ $3\ln\left(1+\dfrac{1}{b}\right) = 2\ln\left(1+\dfrac{2}{b}\right)$ $\Rightarrow$ $\left(1+\dfrac{1}{b}\right)^3 = \left(1+\dfrac{2}{b}\right)^2$

$\Rightarrow$ $1+\dfrac{3}{b}+\dfrac{3}{b^2}+\dfrac{1}{b^3} = 1+\dfrac{4}{b}+\dfrac{4}{b^2}$ $\Rightarrow$ $\dfrac{1}{b}+\dfrac{1}{b^2}-\dfrac{1}{b^3} = 0$ $\Rightarrow$ $b^2+b-1 = 0$ $\Rightarrow$ $b = \dfrac{-1\pm\sqrt{5}}{2}$.

But $b > 0$, so $b = \dfrac{-1+\sqrt{5}}{2} \approx 0.618\text{ h} \approx 37\text{ min}$. The snow began to fall $\dfrac{\sqrt{5}-1}{2}$ hours before noon; that is, at
about 11:23 A.M.

7. (a) While running from $(L,0)$ to (x,y), the dog travels a distance

$$s = \int_x^L \sqrt{1+(dy/dx)^2}\,dx = -\int_L^x \sqrt{1+(dy/dx)^2}\,dx,\ \text{so}\ \dfrac{ds}{dx} = -\sqrt{1+(dy/dx)^2}.$$ The dog and rabbit

run at the same speed, so the rabbit's position when the dog has traveled a distance s is $(0,s)$. Since the dog runs

straight for the rabbit, $\dfrac{dy}{dx} = \dfrac{s-y}{0-x}$ (see the figure).

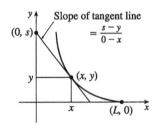

Thus, $s = y - x\,\dfrac{dy}{dx}$ $\Rightarrow$ $\dfrac{ds}{dx} = \dfrac{dy}{dx} - \left(x\,\dfrac{d^2y}{dx^2}+1\cdot\dfrac{dy}{dx}\right) = -x\,\dfrac{d^2y}{dx^2}$. Equating the two expressions for $\dfrac{ds}{dx}$

gives us $x\,\dfrac{d^2y}{dx^2} = \sqrt{1+\left(\dfrac{dy}{dx}\right)^2}$, as claimed.

(b) Letting $z = \dfrac{dy}{dx}$, we obtain the differential equation $x \dfrac{dz}{dx} = \sqrt{1 + z^2}$, or $\dfrac{dz}{\sqrt{1 + z^2}} = \dfrac{dx}{x}$. Integrating:

$\ln x = \displaystyle\int \dfrac{dz}{\sqrt{1 + z^2}} \stackrel{25}{=} \ln\!\left(z + \sqrt{1 + z^2}\right) + C$. When $x = L$, $z = dy/dx = 0$, so $\ln L = \ln 1 + C$.

Therefore, $C = \ln L$, so $\ln x = \ln\!\left(\sqrt{1 + z^2} + z\right) + \ln L = \ln\!\left[L\!\left(\sqrt{1 + z^2} + z\right)\right] \;\Rightarrow$

$x = L\!\left(\sqrt{1 + z^2} + z\right) \;\Rightarrow\; \sqrt{1 + z^2} = \dfrac{x}{L} - z \;\Rightarrow\; 1 + z^2 = \left(\dfrac{x}{L}\right)^2 - \dfrac{2xz}{L} + z^2 \;\Rightarrow$

$\left(\dfrac{x}{L}\right)^2 - 2z\!\left(\dfrac{x}{L}\right) - 1 = 0 \;\Rightarrow\; z = \dfrac{(x/L)^2 - 1}{2(x/L)} = \dfrac{x^2 - L^2}{2Lx} = \dfrac{x}{2L} - \dfrac{L}{2}\dfrac{1}{x}$ [for $x > 0$]. Since $z = \dfrac{dy}{dx}$,

$y = \dfrac{x^2}{4L} - \dfrac{L}{2}\ln x + C_1$. Since $y = 0$ when $x = L$, $0 = \dfrac{L}{4} - \dfrac{L}{2}\ln L + C_1 \;\Rightarrow\; C_1 = \dfrac{L}{2}\ln L - \dfrac{L}{4}$. Thus,

$y = \dfrac{x^2}{4L} - \dfrac{L}{2}\ln x + \dfrac{L}{2}\ln L - \dfrac{L}{4} = \dfrac{x^2 - L^2}{4L} - \dfrac{L}{2}\ln\!\left(\dfrac{x}{L}\right)$.

(c) As $x \to 0^+$, $y \to \infty$, so the dog never catches the rabbit.

8. (a) If the dog runs twice as fast as the rabbit, then the rabbit's position when the dog has traveled a distance s is $(0, s/2)$. Since the dog runs straight toward the rabbit, the tangent line to the dog's path has slope

$\dfrac{dy}{dx} = \dfrac{s/2 - y}{0 - x}$. Thus, $s = 2y - 2x\dfrac{dy}{dx} \;\Rightarrow\; \dfrac{ds}{dx} = 2\dfrac{dy}{dx} - \left(2x\dfrac{d^2y}{dx^2} + 2\dfrac{dy}{dx}\right) = -2x\dfrac{d^2y}{dx^2}$.

From Problem 7(a), $\dfrac{ds}{dx} = -\sqrt{1 + \left(\dfrac{dy}{dx}\right)^2}$, so $2x\dfrac{d^2y}{dx^2} = \sqrt{1 + \left(\dfrac{dy}{dx}\right)^2}$.

Letting $z = \dfrac{dy}{dx}$, we obtain the differential equation $2x\dfrac{dz}{dx} = \sqrt{1 + z^2}$, or $\dfrac{2\,dz}{\sqrt{1 + z^2}} = \dfrac{dx}{x}$.

Integrating, we get $\ln x = \displaystyle\int \dfrac{2\,dz}{\sqrt{1 + z^2}} = 2\ln\!\left(\sqrt{1 + z^2} + z\right) + C$. [See Problem 7(b).]

When $x = L$, $z = dy/dx = 0$, so $\ln L = 2\ln 1 + C = C$. Thus,

$\ln x = 2\ln\!\left(\sqrt{1 + z^2} + z\right) + \ln L = \ln\!\left(L\!\left(\sqrt{1 + z^2} + z\right)^2\right) \;\Rightarrow\; x = L\!\left(\sqrt{1 + z^2} + z\right)^2 \;\Rightarrow$

$\sqrt{1 + z^2} = \sqrt{\dfrac{x}{L}} - z \;\Rightarrow\; 1 + z^2 = \dfrac{x}{L} - 2\sqrt{\dfrac{x}{L}}z + z^2 \;\Rightarrow\; 2\sqrt{\dfrac{x}{L}}z = \dfrac{x}{L} - 1 \;\Rightarrow$

$\dfrac{dy}{dx} = z = \dfrac{1}{2}\sqrt{\dfrac{x}{L}} - \dfrac{1}{2\sqrt{x/L}} = \dfrac{1}{2\sqrt{L}}x^{1/2} - \dfrac{\sqrt{L}}{2}x^{-1/2} \;\Rightarrow\; y = \dfrac{1}{3\sqrt{L}}x^{3/2} - \sqrt{L}\,x^{1/2} + C_1$. When

$x = L$, $y = 0$, so $0 = \dfrac{1}{3\sqrt{L}}L^{3/2} - \sqrt{L}\,L^{1/2} + C_1 = \dfrac{L}{3} - L + C_1 = C_1 - \tfrac{2}{3}L$. Therefore, $C_1 = \tfrac{2}{3}L$ and

$y = \dfrac{x^{3/2}}{3\sqrt{L}} - \sqrt{L}\,x^{1/2} + \tfrac{2}{3}L$. As $x \to 0$, $y \to \tfrac{2}{3}L$, so the dog catches the rabbit when the rabbit is at $\left(0, \tfrac{2}{3}L\right)$.

(At that point, the dog has traveled a distance of $\tfrac{4}{3}L$, twice as far as the rabbit has run.)

(b) As in the solutions to part (a) and Problem 7, we get $z = \dfrac{dy}{dx} = \dfrac{x^2}{2L^2} - \dfrac{L^2}{2x^2}$ and hence $y = \dfrac{x^3}{6L^2} + \dfrac{L^2}{2x} - \tfrac{2}{3}L$.

We want to minimize the distance D from the dog at (x, y) to the rabbit at $(0, 2s)$. Now $s = \tfrac{1}{2}y - \tfrac{1}{2}x\dfrac{dy}{dx} \;\Rightarrow$

$$2s = y - xz = \frac{L^2}{x} - \frac{x^3}{3L^2} - \frac{2L}{3}, \text{ so}$$

$$D = \sqrt{(x-0)^2 + \left[\left(\frac{x^3}{6L^2} + \frac{L^2}{2x} - \frac{2L}{3}\right) - \left(\frac{L^2}{x} - \frac{x^3}{3L^2} - \frac{2L}{3}\right)\right]^2}$$

$$= \sqrt{x^2 + \left(\frac{L^2}{2x} - \frac{x^3}{2L^2}\right)^2} = \sqrt{\frac{x^6}{4L^4} + \frac{x^2}{2} + \frac{L^4}{4x^2}} = \sqrt{\left(\frac{x^3}{2L^2} + \frac{L^2}{2x}\right)^2} = \frac{x^3}{2L^2} + \frac{L^2}{2x}$$

$$D' = 0 \iff \frac{3x^2}{2L^2} - \frac{L^2}{2x^2} = 0 \iff \frac{3x^2}{2L^2} = \frac{L^2}{2x^2} \iff x^4 = \frac{L^4}{3} \iff x = \frac{L}{\sqrt[4]{3}}, x > 0, L > 0.$$

Since $D''(x) = \frac{3x}{L^2} + \frac{L^2}{x^3} > 0$ for all $x > 0$, we know that

$$D\left(\frac{L}{\sqrt[4]{3}}\right) = \frac{\left(L \cdot 3^{-1/4}\right)^3}{2L^2} + \frac{L^2}{2(L \cdot 3^{-1/4})} = \frac{2L}{3^{3/4}} \text{ is the minimum value of } D, \text{ that is, the closest the dog}$$

gets to the rabbit. The positions at this distance are

$$\text{Dog: } (x, y) = \left(\frac{L}{\sqrt[4]{3}}, \left(\frac{5}{3^{7/4}} - \frac{2}{3}\right)L\right) = \left(\frac{L}{\sqrt[4]{3}}, \frac{5\sqrt[4]{3} - 6}{9}L\right)$$

$$\text{Rabbit: } (0, 2s) = \left(0, \frac{8\sqrt[4]{3}L}{9} - \frac{2L}{3}\right) = \left(0, \frac{8\sqrt[4]{3} - 6}{9}L\right)$$

9. (a) We are given that $V = \frac{1}{3}\pi r^2 h$, $dV/dt = 60{,}000\pi$ ft^3/h, and $r = 1.5h = \frac{3}{2}h$. So $V = \frac{1}{3}\pi\left(\frac{3}{2}h\right)^2 h = \frac{3}{4}\pi h^3$

$$\Rightarrow \quad \frac{dV}{dt} = \frac{3}{4}\pi \cdot 3h^2 \frac{dh}{dt} = \frac{9}{4}\pi h^2 \frac{dh}{dt}. \text{ Therefore, } \frac{dh}{dt} = \frac{4(dV/dt)}{9\pi h^2} = \frac{240{,}000\pi}{9\pi h^2} = \frac{80{,}000}{3h^2} \ (\star) \Rightarrow$$

$\int 3h^2\, dh = \int 80{,}000\, dt \Rightarrow h^3 = 80{,}000t + C$. When $t = 0$, $h = 60$. Thus, $C = 60^3 = 216{,}000$, so $h^3 = 80{,}000t + 216{,}000$. Let $h = 100$. Then $100^3 = 1{,}000{,}000 = 80{,}000t + 216{,}000 \Rightarrow$ $80{,}000t = 784{,}000 \Rightarrow t = 9.8$, so the time required is 9.8 hours.

(b) The floor area of the silo is $F = \pi \cdot 200^2 = 40{,}000\pi$ ft^2, and the area of the base of the pile is $A = \pi r^2 = \pi\left(\frac{3}{2}h\right)^2 = \frac{9\pi}{4}h^2$. So the area of the floor which is not covered when $h = 60$ is $F - A = 40{,}000\pi - 8100\pi = 31{,}900\pi \approx 100{,}217$ ft^2. Now $A = \frac{9\pi}{4}h^2 \Rightarrow dA/dt = \frac{9\pi}{4} \cdot 2h\,(dh/dt)$, and from $(\star)$ in part (a) we know that when $h = 60$, $dh/dt = \frac{80{,}000}{3(60)^2} = \frac{200}{27}$ ft/h. Therefore, $dA/dt = \frac{9\pi}{4}(2)(60)\left(\frac{200}{27}\right) = 2000\pi \approx 6283$ ft^2/h.

(c) At $h = 90$ ft, $dV/dt = 60{,}000\pi - 20{,}000\pi = 40{,}000\pi$ ft^3/h. From $(\star)$ in part (a),

$$\frac{dh}{dt} = \frac{4(dV/dt)}{9\pi h^2} = \frac{4(40{,}000\pi)}{9\pi h^2} = \frac{160{,}000}{9h^2} \Rightarrow \int 9h^2\, dh = \int 160{,}000\, dt \Rightarrow 3h^3 = 160{,}000t + C.$$

When $t = 0$, $h = 90$; therefore, $C = 3 \cdot 729{,}000 = 2{,}187{,}000$. So $3h^3 = 160{,}000t + 2{,}187{,}000$. At the top, $h = 100 \Rightarrow 3(100)^3 = 160{,}000t + 2{,}187{,}000 \Rightarrow t = \frac{813{,}000}{160{,}000} \approx 5.1$. The pile reaches the top after about 5.1 h.

10. Let $P(a, b)$ be any first-quadrant point on the curve $y = f(x)$. The tangent line at P has equation $y - b = f'(a)(x - a)$, or equivalently, $y = mx + b - ma$, where $m = f'(a)$. If $Q(0, c)$ is the y-intercept, then $c = b - am$. If $R(k, 0)$ is the x-intercept, then $k = \frac{am - b}{m} = a - \frac{b}{m}$. Since the tangent line is bisected at P, we know that $|PQ| = |PR|$; that is,

$$\sqrt{(a - 0)^2 + [b - (b - am)]^2} = \sqrt{[a - (a - b/m)]^2 + (b - 0)^2}$$

Squaring and simplifying gives us $a^2 + a^2 m^2 = b^2/m^2 + b^2 \Rightarrow a^2 m^2 + a^2 m^4 = b^2 + b^2 m^2 \Rightarrow$
$a^2 m^4 + (a^2 - b^2)m^2 - b^2 = 0 \Rightarrow (a^2 m^2 - b^2)(m^2 + 1) = 0 \Rightarrow m^2 = b^2/a^2$. Since m is the slope of
the line from a positive y-intercept to a positive x-intercept, m must be negative. Since a and b are positive, we have
$m = -b/a$, so we will solve the equivalent differential equation $\dfrac{dy}{dx} = -\dfrac{y}{x} \Rightarrow \dfrac{dy}{y} = -\dfrac{dx}{x} \Rightarrow$

$\displaystyle\int \dfrac{dy}{y} = -\int \dfrac{dx}{x} \Rightarrow \ln y = -\ln x + C \ [x, y > 0] \Rightarrow y = e^{-\ln x + C} = e^{\ln x^{-1}} \cdot e^C = x^{-1} \cdot A \Rightarrow$
$y = A/x$. Since the point $(3,2)$ is on the curve, $3 = A/2 \Rightarrow A = 6$ and the curve is $y = 6/x$ with $x > 0$.

11. Let $P(a, b)$ be any point on the curve. If m is the slope of the tangent line at P, then $m = y'$ and
an equation of the normal line at P is $y - b = -\dfrac{1}{m}(x - a)$, or equivalently, $y = -\dfrac{1}{m}x + b + \dfrac{a}{m}$.
The y-intercept is always 6, so $b + \dfrac{a}{m} = 6 \Rightarrow \dfrac{a}{m} = 6 - b \Rightarrow m = \dfrac{a}{6 - b}$.
We will solve the equivalent differential equation $\dfrac{dy}{dx} = \dfrac{x}{6 - y} \Rightarrow (6 - y)\,dy = x\,dx \Rightarrow$
$\displaystyle\int (6 - y)\,dy = \int x\,dx \Rightarrow 6y - \tfrac{1}{2}y^2 = \tfrac{1}{2}x^2 + C \Rightarrow 12y - y^2 = x^2 + K$. Since $(3,2)$ is on the curve,
$12(2) - 2^2 = 3^2 + K \Rightarrow K = 11$. So the curve is given by $12y - y^2 = x^2 + 11 \Rightarrow$
$x^2 + y^2 - 12y + 36 = -11 + 36 \Rightarrow x^2 + (y - 6)^2 = 25$, a circle with center $(0, 6)$ and radius 5.

12. Suppose C is a curve with the required property and let $P = (x_0, y_0)$ be a point on C. The equation of the normal
line to C at P is $y - y_0 = -\dfrac{1}{y_0'}(x - x_0)$, where y_0' is the value of $\dfrac{dy}{dx}$ at $x = x_0$. This equation makes sense only if
$y_0' \neq 0$. If $y_0' = 0$, then the normal line at P is $x = x_0$, which does not intersect the y-axis at all unless $x_0 = 0$.
So let's assume that $y_0' \neq 0$. Then the normal line to C at P intersects the x-axis at $(x_0 + y_0 y_0', 0)$, and it
intersects the y-axis at $(0, y_0 + x_0/y_0')$. The condition on C implies that

$$[\text{distance from } P\,(x_0, y_0) \text{ to } (0, y_0 + x_0/y_0')] = [\text{distance from } (0, y_0 + x_0/y_0') \text{ to } (x_0 + y_0 y_0', 0)]$$

$$\sqrt{(0 - x_0)^2 + (y_0 + x_0/y_0' - y_0)^2} = \sqrt{(x_0 + y_0 y_0' - 0)^2 + [0 - (y_0 + x_0/y_0')]^2}$$

Squaring both sides, we get $x_0^2 + x_0^2/(y_0')^2 = (x_0 + y_0 y_0')^2 + (y_0 + x_0/y_0')^2$ or

$x_0^2 + \dfrac{x_0^2}{(y_0')^2} = x_0^2 + 2x_0 y_0 y_0' + y_0^2(y_0')^2 + y_0^2 + 2\dfrac{x_0 y_0}{y_0'} + \dfrac{x_0^2}{(y_0')^2}$. Subtracting $x_0^2 + \dfrac{x_0^2}{(y_0')^2}$ from both sides and
multiplying by y_0', we get

$$0 = y_0^2 y_0' + y_0^2 (y_0')^3 + 2x_0 y_0 \left[1 + (y_0')^2\right] = y_0 \left\{ y_0 y_0' + y_0 (y_0')^3 + 2x_0 \left[1 + (y_0')^2\right] \right\}$$

$$= y_0 \left\{ y_0 y_0' \left[1 + (y_0')^2\right] + 2x_0 \left[1 + (y_0')^2\right] \right\} = y_0 (y_0 y_0' + 2x_0) \left[1 + (y_0')^2\right]$$

Since $1 + (y_0')^2 \geq 1 > 0$, we conclude that $y_0(y_0 y_0' + 2x_0) = 0$. Now P is an arbitrary point on C for which
$y_0' \neq 0$. Thus, we have shown that $y(yy' + 2x) = 0$ for points (x, y) along C where $y' \neq 0$. One solution of this
equation is $y = 0$, but that curve (the x-axis) doesn't satisfy the condition required of C, since its normal lines at
points for $x \neq 0$ don't intersect the y-axis. Thus, we can focus our attention on points of C where $y \neq 0$, and
conclude that $yy' + 2x = 0$ at points of C where $y \neq 0$ and $y' \neq 0$. Integrating both sides of $yy' + 2x = 0$, we get
$\tfrac{1}{2}y^2 + x^2 = c$. Clearly $c > 0$ (since $y \neq 0$), so we can write $c = a^2$, where $a = \sqrt{c} > 0$. Thus, $\tfrac{1}{2}y^2 + x^2 = a^2$ and

$x^2/a^2 + y^2/(\sqrt{2}a)^2 = 1$. This shows that C is (part of) the ellipse centered at $(0,0)$ with semimajor axis $\sqrt{2}\,a$ in the y-direction and semiminor axis a in the x-direction. The points of C where $y = 0$ or $y' = 0$ are the vertices $(0, \pm\sqrt{2}\,a)$ and $(\pm a, 0)$. At these points, the condition on C is satisfied in a degenerate way. [When $P = (\pm a, 0)$, the normal line at P *is* the x-axis, so *all* the points of the normal line can be viewed as points of intersection with the x-axis. The intersection with the y-axis at $(0, 0)$ is midway between $(a, 0)$ and $(-a, 0)$; one of these points is P, and the other can be regarded as an intersection of the normal line with the x-axis. Similarly, when $P = (0, \pm\sqrt{2}\,a)$, the normal line is the y-axis, and the point $(0, \pm\sqrt{2}\,a/2)$, which can be regarded as an intersection of the normal line with the y-axis, is midway between P and $(0, 0)$, the intersection with the x-axis.]

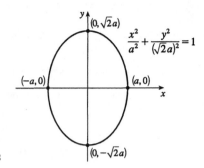

Conversely, if C is part of the ellipse $\dfrac{x^2}{a^2} + \dfrac{y^2}{2a^2} = 1$ for some $a > 0$, then the normal line at a point (x_0, y_0) of C (other than the four vertices) has equation $y - y_0 = \dfrac{y_0}{2x_0}(x - x_0)$. Its intersections with the coordinate axes are $\left(0, \dfrac{y_0}{2}\right)$ and $(-x_0, 0)$. $\left[\text{distance from } (x_0, y_0) \text{ to } \left(0, \dfrac{y_0}{2}\right)\right]^2 = x_0^2 + \dfrac{y_0^2}{4}$ and $\left[\text{distance from } \left(0, \dfrac{y_0}{2}\right) \text{ to } (-x_0, 0)\right]^2 = x_0^2 + \dfrac{y_0^2}{4}$, so the required condition is met at points other than the four vertices. As we have explained, if we are willing to interpret the condition broadly, then it can be viewed as holding even at the four vertices.

Another method: Let $P(x_0, y_0)$ be a point on the curve. Since the midpoint of the line segment determined by the normal line from (x_0, y_0) to its intersection with the x-axis has x-coordinate 0, the x-coordinate of the point of intersection with the x-axis must be $-x_0$. Hence, the normal line has slope $\dfrac{y_0 - 0}{x_0 - (-x_0)} = \dfrac{y_0}{2x_0}$. So the tangent line has slope $-\dfrac{2x_0}{y_0}$. This gives the differential equation $y' = -\dfrac{2x}{y} \ \Rightarrow \ y\,dy = -2x\,dx \ \Rightarrow \ \int y\,dy = \int(-2x)\,dx \ \Rightarrow \ \tfrac{1}{2}y^2 = -x^2 + C \ \Rightarrow \ x^2 + \tfrac{1}{2}y^2 = C \ (C > 0)$.

8 Infinite Sequences and Series

 8.1 Sequences • • • • • • • • • • • • • • • • •

1. (a) A sequence is an ordered list of numbers. It can also be defined as a function whose domain is the set of positive integers.

(b) The terms a_n approach 8 as n becomes large. In fact, we can make a_n as close to 8 as we like by taking n sufficiently large.

(c) The terms a_n become large as n becomes large.

2. (a) From Definition 1, a convergent sequence is a sequence for which $\lim\limits_{n \to \infty} a_n$ exists. Examples: $\{1/n\}$, $\{1/2^n\}$

(b) A divergent sequence is a sequence for which $\lim\limits_{n \to \infty} a_n$ *does not* exist. Examples: $\{n\}$, $\{\sin n\}$

3. The first six terms of $a_n = \dfrac{n}{2n+1}$ are: $\dfrac{1}{3}, \dfrac{2}{5}, \dfrac{3}{7}, \dfrac{4}{9}, \dfrac{5}{11}, \dfrac{6}{13}$. It appears that the sequence is approaching $\dfrac{1}{2}$.

$$\lim_{n \to \infty} \frac{n}{2n+1} = \lim_{n \to \infty} \frac{1}{2+1/n} = \frac{1}{2}$$

4. Let $n = 1$ to $n = 8$ in $\sin\left(n\frac{\pi}{2}\right)$.

$\left\{\sin\frac{\pi}{2}, \sin\pi, \sin\frac{3\pi}{2}, \sin 2\pi, \sin\frac{5\pi}{2}, \sin 3\pi, \sin\frac{7\pi}{2}, \sin 4\pi\right\} = \{1, 0, -1, 0, 1, 0, -1, 0\}$.

The sequence does not have a limit, since it repeats the pattern 1, 0, -1, 0 over and over and therefore doesn't approach any fixed number.

5. $\left\{1, -\frac{2}{3}, \frac{4}{9}, -\frac{8}{27}, \ldots\right\}$. Each term is $-\frac{2}{3}$ times the preceding one, so $a_n = \left(-\frac{2}{3}\right)^{n-1}$.

6. $\left\{-\frac{1}{4}, \frac{2}{9}, -\frac{3}{16}, \frac{4}{25}, \ldots\right\}$. The numerator of the nth term is n and its denominator is $(n+1)^2$. Including the alternating signs, we get $a_n = (-1)^n \dfrac{n}{(n+1)^2}$.

7. $\{2, 7, 12, 17, \ldots\}$. Each term is larger than the preceding one by 5, so
$a_n = a_1 + d(n-1) = 2 + 5(n-1) = 5n - 3$.

8. $\{0, 2, 0, 2, 0, 2, \ldots\}$. The number 1 is halfway between 0 and 2, so we can think of alternately subtracting and adding 1 (from 1 and to 1) to obtain the given sequence: $a_n = 1 - (-1)^{n-1}$.

9. $a_n = n(n-1)$. $a_n \to \infty$ as $n \to \infty$, so the sequence diverges.

10. $a_n = \dfrac{n+1}{3n-1} = \dfrac{1+1/n}{3-1/n}$, so $a_n \to \dfrac{1+0}{3-0} = \dfrac{1}{3}$ as $n \to \infty$. Converges

11. $a_n = \dfrac{3+5n^2}{n+n^2} = \dfrac{\left(3+5n^2\right)/n^2}{\left(n+n^2\right)/n^2} = \dfrac{5+3/n^2}{1+1/n}$, so $a_n \to \dfrac{5+0}{1+0} = 5$ as $n \to \infty$. Converges

12. $a_n = \dfrac{\sqrt{n}}{1+\sqrt{n}} = \dfrac{1}{1/\sqrt{n}+1}$, so $a_n \to \dfrac{1}{0+1} = 1$ as $n \to \infty$. Converges

13. $a_n = \dfrac{2^n}{3^{n+1}} = \dfrac{1}{3}\left(\dfrac{2}{3}\right)^n$, so $\lim\limits_{n \to \infty} a_n = \dfrac{1}{3}\lim\limits_{n \to \infty}\left(\dfrac{2}{3}\right)^n = \dfrac{1}{3} \cdot 0 = 0$ by (6) with $r = \dfrac{2}{3}$. Converges

14. $a_n = \dfrac{n}{1 + \sqrt{n}} = \dfrac{\sqrt{n}}{1/\sqrt{n} + 1}$. The numerator approaches ∞ and the denominator approaches $0 + 1 = 1$ as

$n \to \infty$, so $a_n \to \infty$ as $n \to \infty$ and the sequence diverges.

15. $a_n = \dfrac{(-1)^{n-1}\,n}{n^2 + 1} = \dfrac{(-1)^{n-1}}{n + 1/n}$, so $0 \le |a_n| = \dfrac{1}{n + 1/n} \le \dfrac{1}{n} \to 0$ as $n \to \infty$, so $a_n \to 0$ by the Squeeze

Theorem and Theorem 4. Converges

16. $2n \to \infty$ as $n \to \infty$, so since $\lim\limits_{x \to \infty} \arctan x = \frac{\pi}{2}$, we have $\lim\limits_{n \to \infty} \arctan 2n = \frac{\pi}{2}$. Convergent

17. $a_n = 2 + \cos n\pi$, so

$\{a_n\} = \{2 + \cos \pi, 2 + \cos 2\pi, 2 + \cos 3\pi, 2 + \cos 4\pi, \dots\} = \{2 - 1, 2 + 1, 2 - 1, 2 + 1, \dots\}$

$\qquad = \{1, 3, 1, 3, \dots\}$

This sequence oscillates between 1 and 3, so it diverges.

18. $0 \le |a_n| = \dfrac{n\,|\cos n|}{n^2 + 1} \le \dfrac{n}{n^2 + 1} = \dfrac{1}{n + 1/n} \to 0$ as $n \to \infty$, so by the Squeeze Theorem and Theorem 4, $\{a_n\}$

converges to 0.

19. $\lim\limits_{x \to \infty} \dfrac{\ln(x^2)}{x} = \lim\limits_{x \to \infty} \dfrac{2 \ln x}{x} \overset{\text{H}}{=} \lim\limits_{x \to \infty} \dfrac{2/x}{1} = 0$, so by Theorem 2, $\left\{ \dfrac{\ln(n^2)}{n} \right\}$ converges to 0.

20. $\lim\limits_{n \to \infty} \sin\left(\dfrac{1}{n}\right) = \sin 0 = 0$ since $\dfrac{1}{n} \to 0$ as $n \to \infty$, so by Theorem 4, $\left\{ (-1)^n \sin\left(\dfrac{1}{n}\right) \right\}$ converges to 0.

21. $b_n = \sqrt{n+2} - \sqrt{n} = \left(\sqrt{n+2} - \sqrt{n}\right) \dfrac{\sqrt{n+2} + \sqrt{n}}{\sqrt{n+2} + \sqrt{n}} = \dfrac{2}{\sqrt{n+2} + \sqrt{n}} < \dfrac{2}{\sqrt{n} + \sqrt{n}} = \dfrac{2}{2\sqrt{n}} = \dfrac{1}{\sqrt{n}} \to 0$

as $n \to \infty$. So by the Squeeze Theorem with $a_n = 0$ and $c_n = 1/\sqrt{n}$, $\left\{ \sqrt{n+2} - \sqrt{n} \right\}$ converges to 0.

22. $\lim\limits_{x \to \infty} \dfrac{\ln(2 + e^x)}{3x} \overset{\text{H}}{=} \lim\limits_{x \to \infty} \dfrac{e^x/(2 + e^x)}{3} = \dfrac{1}{3} \lim\limits_{x \to \infty} \dfrac{e^x}{2 + e^x} \overset{\text{H}}{=} \dfrac{1}{3} \lim\limits_{x \to \infty} \dfrac{e^x}{e^x} = \dfrac{1}{3}(1) = \dfrac{1}{3}$, so by Theorem 2,

$\lim\limits_{n \to \infty} \dfrac{\ln(2 + e^n)}{3n} = \dfrac{1}{3}$. Convergent

23. $\lim\limits_{x \to \infty} \dfrac{x}{2^x} \overset{\text{H}}{=} \lim\limits_{x \to \infty} \dfrac{1}{(\ln 2)2^x} = 0$, so by Theorem 2, $\{n2^{-n}\}$ converges to 0.

24. $a_n = \ln(n+1) - \ln n = \ln\left(\dfrac{n+1}{n}\right) = \ln\left(1 + \dfrac{1}{n}\right) \to \ln(1) = 0$ as $n \to \infty$. Convergent

25. $0 \le \dfrac{\cos^2 n}{2^n} \le \dfrac{1}{2^n}$ [since $0 \le \cos^2 n \le 1$], so since $\lim\limits_{n \to \infty} \dfrac{1}{2^n} = 0$, $\left\{ \dfrac{\cos^2 n}{2^n} \right\}$ converges to 0 by the Squeeze

Theorem.

26. $0 < |a_n| = \dfrac{3^n}{n!} = \dfrac{3}{1} \cdot \dfrac{3}{2} \cdot \dfrac{3}{3} \cdots \cdots \dfrac{3}{(n-1)} \cdot \dfrac{3}{n} \le \dfrac{3}{1} \cdot \dfrac{3}{2} \cdot \dfrac{3}{n} = \dfrac{27}{2n} \to 0$ as $n \to \infty$, so by the Squeeze Theorem

and Theorem 4, $\{(-3)^n / n\}$ converges to 0.

27.

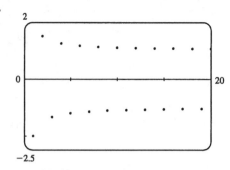

From the graph, we see that the sequence $\left\{(-1)^n \dfrac{n+1}{n}\right\}$ is divergent, since it oscillates between 1 and -1 (approximately).

28.

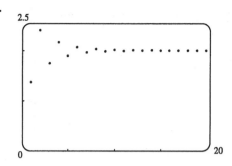

From the graph, it appears that the sequence converges to 2.

$\left\{\left(-\dfrac{2}{\pi}\right)^n\right\}$ converges to 0 by (6), and hence $\left\{2 + \left(-\dfrac{2}{\pi}\right)^n\right\}$ converges to $2 + 0 = 2$.

29.

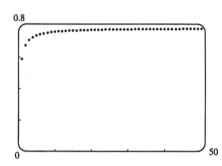

From the graph, it appears that the sequence converges to about 0.78.

$$\lim_{n\to\infty} \frac{2n}{2n+1} = \lim_{n\to\infty} \frac{2}{2+1/n} = 1, \text{ so}$$

$$\lim_{n\to\infty} \arctan\left(\frac{2n}{2n+1}\right) = \arctan 1 = \frac{\pi}{4}.$$

30.

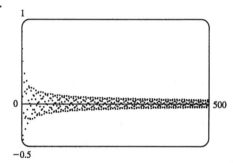

From the graph, it appears that the sequence converges (slowly) to 0.

$$0 \le \frac{|\sin n|}{\sqrt{n}} \le \frac{1}{\sqrt{n}} \to 0 \text{ as } n \to \infty, \text{ so by the}$$

Squeeze Theorem and Theorem 4, $\left\{\dfrac{\sin n}{\sqrt{n}}\right\}$ converges to 0.

31.

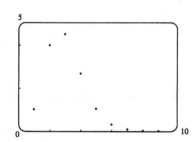

From the graph, it appears that the sequence converges to 0.

$$0 < a_n = \frac{n^3}{n!} = \frac{n}{n} \cdot \frac{n}{(n-1)} \cdot \frac{n}{(n-2)} \cdot \frac{1}{(n-3)} \cdots \cdot \frac{1}{3} \cdot \frac{1}{2} \cdot \frac{1}{1}$$

$$\le \frac{n^2}{((n-1)(n-2)(n-3)} \quad (\text{for } n \ge 4)$$

$$= \frac{1/n}{(1-1/n)(1-2/n)(1-3/n)} \to 0 \text{ as } n \to \infty$$

So by the Squeeze Theorem, $\{n^3/n!\}$ converges to 0.

32.

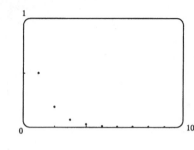

From the graph, it appears that the sequence approaches 0.

$$0 < a_n = \frac{1 \cdot 3 \cdot 5 \cdot \cdots \cdot (2n-1)}{(2n)^n} = \frac{1}{2n} \cdot \frac{3}{2n} \cdot \frac{5}{2n} \cdot \cdots \cdot \frac{2n-1}{2n}$$

$$\leq \frac{1}{2n} \cdot (1) \cdot (1) \cdot \cdots \cdot (1) = \frac{1}{2n} \to 0 \text{ as } n \to \infty$$

So by the Squeeze Theorem, $\left\{ \dfrac{1 \cdot 3 \cdot 5 \cdot \cdots \cdot (2n-1)}{(2n)^n} \right\}$ converges

to 0.

33. (a) $a_n = 1000(1.06)^n \Rightarrow a_1 = 1060, a_2 = 1123.60, a_3 = 1191.02, a_4 = 1262.48,$ and $a_5 = 1338.23$.

   (b) $\lim\limits_{n \to \infty} a_n = 1000 \lim\limits_{n \to \infty} (1.06)^n$, so the sequence diverges by (6) with $r = 1.06 > 1$.

34. $a_{n+1} = \begin{cases} \frac{1}{2}a_n & \text{if } a_n \text{ is an even number} \\ 3a_n + 1 & \text{if } a_n \text{ is an odd number} \end{cases}$ When $a_1 = 11$, the first 40 terms are 11, 34, 17, 52, 26, 13, 40,

20, 10, 5, 16, 8, 4, 2, 1, 4, 2, 1, 4, 2, 1, 4, 2, 1, 4, 2, 1, 4, 2, 1, 4, 2, 1, 4, 2, 1, 4, 2, 1, 4. When $a_1 = 25$, the first
40 terms are 25, 76, 38, 19, 58, 29, 88, 44, 22, 11, 34, 17, 52, 26, 13, 40, 20, 10, 5, 16, 8, 4, 2, 1, 4, 2, 1, 4, 2, 1, 4,
2, 1, 4, 2, 1, 4, 2, 1, 4. The famous Collatz conjecture is that this sequence always reaches 1, regardless of the
starting point a_1.

35. (a) $a_1 = 1, a_2 = 4 - a_1 = 4 - 1 = 3, a_3 = 4 - a_2 = 4 - 3 = 1, a_4 = 4 - a_3 = 4 - 1 = 3,$
   $a_5 = 4 - a_4 = 4 - 3 = 1$. Since the terms of the sequence alternate between 1 and 3, the sequence is
   divergent.

   (b) $a_1 = 2, a_2 = 4 - a_1 = 4 - 2 = 2, a_3 = 4 - a_2 = 4 - 2 = 2$. Since all of the terms are 2, $\lim\limits_{n \to \infty} a_n = 2$ and
   hence, the sequence is convergent.

36. (a) Since $\lim\limits_{n \to \infty} a_n = L$, the terms a_n approach L as n becomes large. Because we can make a_n as close to L as we
   wish, a_{n+1} will also be close, and so $\lim\limits_{n \to \infty} a_{n+1} = L$.

   (b) $a_1 = 1, a_2 = \dfrac{1}{1 + a_1} = \dfrac{1}{1+1} = \dfrac{1}{2} = 0.5, \quad a_3 = \dfrac{1}{1 + a_2} = \dfrac{1}{1 + \frac{1}{2}} = \dfrac{2}{3} \approx 0.66667,$

   $a_4 = \dfrac{1}{1 + a_3} = \dfrac{1}{1 + \frac{2}{3}} = \dfrac{3}{5} = 0.6, \quad a_5 = \dfrac{1}{1 + a_4} = \dfrac{1}{1 + \frac{3}{5}} = \dfrac{5}{8} = 0.625,$

   $a_6 = \dfrac{1}{1 + a_5} = \dfrac{1}{1 + \frac{5}{8}} = \dfrac{8}{13} \approx 0.61538, \quad a_7 = \dfrac{1}{1 + a_6} = \dfrac{1}{1 + \frac{8}{13}} = \dfrac{13}{21} \approx 0.61905,$

   $a_8 = \dfrac{1}{1 + a_7} = \dfrac{1}{1 + \frac{13}{21}} = \dfrac{21}{34} \approx 0.61765, \quad a_9 = \dfrac{1}{1 + a_8} = \dfrac{1}{1 + \frac{21}{34}} = \dfrac{34}{55} \approx 0.61818,$

   $a_{10} = \dfrac{1}{1 + a_9} = \dfrac{1}{1 + \frac{34}{55}} = \dfrac{55}{89} \approx 0.61800$. It appears that $\lim\limits_{n \to \infty} a_n \approx 0.618$; hence, the sequence is
   convergent.

   (c) If $L = \lim\limits_{n \to \infty} a_n$ then $\lim\limits_{n \to \infty} a_{n+1} = L$ also, so L must satisfy

   $L = 1/(1 + L) \Rightarrow L^2 + L - 1 = 0 \Rightarrow L = \frac{-1 + \sqrt{5}}{2} \approx 0.618$ (since L has to be non-negative if it
   exists).

37. (a) Let a_n be the number of rabbit pairs in the nth month. Clearly $a_1 = 1 = a_2$. In the nth month, each pair that is
   2 or more months old (that is, a_{n-2} pairs) will produce a new pair to add to the a_{n-1} pairs already present.
   Thus, $a_n = a_{n-1} + a_{n-2}$, so that $\{a_n\} = \{f_n\}$, the Fibonacci sequence.

(b) $a_n = \dfrac{f_{n+1}}{f_n}$ $\Rightarrow$ $a_{n-1} = \dfrac{f_n}{f_{n-1}} = \dfrac{f_{n-1} + f_{n-2}}{f_{n-1}} = 1 + \dfrac{f_{n-2}}{f_{n-1}} = 1 + \dfrac{1}{f_{n-1}/f_{n-2}} = 1 + \dfrac{1}{a_{n-2}}$. If

$L = \lim\limits_{n\to\infty} a_n$, then $L = \lim\limits_{n\to\infty} a_{n-1}$ and $L = \lim\limits_{n\to\infty} a_{n-2}$, so L must satisfy $L = 1 + \dfrac{1}{L}$ $\Rightarrow$

$L^2 - L - 1 = 0$ $\Rightarrow$ $L = \dfrac{1 \pm \sqrt{5}}{2}$ (since L must be positive).

38. $a_1 = 2^{1/2}$, $a_2 = 2^{3/4}$, $a_3 = 2^{7/8}$, $\ldots$, so $a_n = 2^{(2^n - 1)/2^n} = 2^{1-(1/2^n)}$. $\lim\limits_{n\to\infty} a_n = \lim\limits_{n\to\infty} 2^{1-(1/2^n)} = 2^1 = 2$.

Alternate solution: Let $L = \lim\limits_{n\to\infty} a_n$. (We could show the limit exists by showing that $\{a_n\}$ is bounded and

increasing.) So L must satisfy $L = \sqrt{2 \cdot L}$ $\Rightarrow$ $L^2 = 2L$ $\Rightarrow$ $L(L - 2) = 0$ ($L \neq 0$ since the sequence

increases), so $L = 2$.

39. $a_n = \dfrac{1}{2n + 3}$ is decreasing since $a_{n+1} = \dfrac{1}{2(n + 1) + 3} = \dfrac{1}{2n + 5} < \dfrac{1}{2n + 3} = a_n$ for each $n \geq 1$. The

sequence is bounded since $0 < a_n \leq \frac{1}{5}$ for all $n \geq 1$. Note that $a_1 = \frac{1}{5}$.

40. $a_n = \dfrac{2n - 3}{3n + 4}$ defines an increasing sequence since for $f(x) = \dfrac{2x - 3}{3x + 4}$,

$f'(x) = \dfrac{(3x + 4)(2) - (2x - 3)(3)}{(3x + 4)^2} = \dfrac{17}{(3x + 4)^2} > 0$. The sequence is bounded since $a_n \geq a_1 = -\frac{1}{7}$ for

$n \geq 1$, and $a_n < \dfrac{2n - 3}{3n} < \dfrac{2n}{3n} = \dfrac{2}{3}$ for $n \geq 1$.

41. $a_n = \cos(n\pi/2)$ is not monotonic. The first few terms are $0, -1, 0, 1, 0, -1, 0, 1, \ldots$. In fact, the sequence

consists of the terms $0, -1, 0, 1$ repeated over and over again in that order. The sequence is bounded since $|a_n| \leq 1$

for all $n \geq 1$.

42. $a_n = 3 + (-1)^n / n$ defines a sequence that is not monotonic. The first few terms are $2, 3.5, 2.\overline{6}, 3.25$, and 2.8,

showing that the sequence is neither increasing nor decreasing. The sequence is bounded since $2 \leq a_n \leq 3.5$ for

all $n \geq 1$.

43. Since $\{a_n\}$ is a decreasing sequence, $a_n > a_{n+1}$ for all $n \geq 1$. Because all of its terms lie between 5 and 8, $\{a_n\}$ is

a bounded sequence. By the Monotonic Sequence Theorem, $\{a_n\}$ is convergent; that is, $\{a_n\}$ has a limit L. L must

be less than 8 since $\{a_n\}$ is decreasing, so $5 \leq L < 8$.

44. (a) Let P_n be the statement that $a_{n+1} \geq a_n$ and $a_n \leq 3$. P_1 is obviously true. We will assume that P_n is true and

then show that as a consequence P_{n+1} must also be true. $a_{n+2} \geq a_{n+1}$ $\Leftrightarrow$ $\sqrt{2 + a_{n+1}} \geq \sqrt{2 + a_n}$ $\Leftrightarrow$

$2 + a_{n+1} \geq 2 + a_n$ $\Leftrightarrow$ $a_{n+1} \geq a_n$, which is the induction hypothesis. $a_{n+1} \leq 3$ $\Leftrightarrow$ $\sqrt{2 + a_n} \leq 3$ $\Leftrightarrow$

$2 + a_n \leq 9$ $\Leftrightarrow$ $a_n \leq 7$, which is certainly true because we are assuming that $a_n \leq 3$. So P_n is true for all n,

and so $a_1 \leq a_n \leq 3$ (the sequence is bounded), and hence by the Monotonic Sequence Theorem, $\lim\limits_{n\to\infty} a_n$

exists.

(b) If $L = \lim\limits_{n\to\infty} a_n$, then $\lim\limits_{n\to\infty} a_{n+1} = L$ also, so $L = \sqrt{2 + L}$ $\Rightarrow$ $L^2 = 2 + L$ $\Leftrightarrow$ $L^2 - L - 2 = 0$ $\Leftrightarrow$

$(L + 1)(L - 2) = 0$ $\Leftrightarrow$ $L = 2$ (since L can't be negative).

45. We show by induction that $\{a_n\}$ is increasing and bounded above by 3.

Let P_n be the proposition that $a_{n+1} > a_n$ and $0 < a_n < 3$. Clearly P_1 is true. Assume that P_n is true. Then

$$a_{n+1} > a_n \quad \Rightarrow \quad \frac{1}{a_{n+1}} < \frac{1}{a_n} \quad \Rightarrow \quad -\frac{1}{a_{n+1}} > -\frac{1}{a_n}.$$

Now $a_{n+2} = 3 - \dfrac{1}{a_{n+1}} > 3 - \dfrac{1}{a_n} = a_{n+1} \iff P_{n+1}$. This proves that $\{a_n\}$ is increasing and bounded above

by 3, so $1 = a_1 < a_n < 3$, that is, $\{a_n\}$ is bounded, and hence convergent by the Monotonic Sequence Theorem. If $L = \lim\limits_{n \to \infty} a_n$, then $\lim\limits_{n \to \infty} a_{n+1} = L$ also, so L must satisfy $L = 3 - 1/L \Rightarrow L^2 - 3L + 1 = 0 \Rightarrow L = \frac{3 \pm \sqrt{5}}{2}$. But $L > 1$, so $L = \frac{3 + \sqrt{5}}{2}$.

46. We use induction. Let P_n be the statement that $0 < a_{n+1} \le a_n \le 2$. Clearly P_1 is true, since $a_2 = 1/(3-2) = 1$.

Now assume that P_n is true. Then $a_{n+1} \le a_n \Rightarrow -a_{n+1} \ge -a_n \Rightarrow 3 - a_{n+1} \ge 3 - a_n \Rightarrow$

$a_{n+2} = \dfrac{1}{3 - a_{n+1}} \le \dfrac{1}{3 - a_n} = a_{n+1}$. Also $a_{n+2} > 0$ (since $3 - a_{n+1}$ is positive) and $a_{n+1} \le 2$ by the induction

hypothesis, so P_{n+1} is true.

To find the limit, we use the fact that $\lim\limits_{n \to \infty} a_n = \lim\limits_{n \to \infty} a_{n+1} \Rightarrow L = \frac{1}{3 - L} \Rightarrow L^2 - 3L + 1 = 0 \Rightarrow$

$L = \frac{3 \pm \sqrt{5}}{2}$. But $L \le 2$, so we must have $L = \frac{3 - \sqrt{5}}{2}$.

47. $(0.8)^n < 0.000001 \Rightarrow \ln(0.8)^n < \ln(0.000001) \Rightarrow n \ln(0.8) < \ln(0.000001) \Rightarrow$

$n > \dfrac{\ln(0.000001)}{\ln(0.8)} \Rightarrow n > 61.9$, so n must be at least 62 to satisfy the given inequality.

48. (a) If f is continuous, then $f(L) = f\left(\lim\limits_{n \to \infty} a_n\right) = \lim\limits_{n \to \infty} f(a_n) = \lim\limits_{n \to \infty} a_{n+1} = L$ by Exercise 36(a).

(b) By repeatedly pressing the cosine key on the calculator (that is, taking cosine of the previous answer) until the displayed value stabilizes, we see that $L \approx 0.73909$.

49. (a) First we show that $a > a_1 > b_1 > b$.

$a_1 - b_1 = \frac{a+b}{2} - \sqrt{ab} = \frac{1}{2}\left(a - 2\sqrt{ab} + b\right) = \frac{1}{2}\left(\sqrt{a} - \sqrt{b}\right)^2 > 0$ (since $a > b$) $\Rightarrow a_1 > b_1$. Also

$a - a_1 = a - \frac{1}{2}(a + b) = \frac{1}{2}(a - b) > 0$ and $b - b_1 = b - \sqrt{ab} = \sqrt{b}\left(\sqrt{b} - \sqrt{a}\right) < 0$, so $a > a_1 > b_1 > b$.

In the same way we can show that $a_1 > a_2 > b_2 > b_1$ and so the given assertion is true for $n = 1$. Suppose it is true for $n = k$, that is, $a_k > a_{k+1} > b_{k+1} > b_k$. Then

$$a_{k+2} - b_{k+2} = \frac{1}{2}(a_{k+1} + b_{k+1}) - \sqrt{a_{k+1}b_{k+1}} = \frac{1}{2}\left(a_{k+1} - 2\sqrt{a_{k+1}b_{k+1}} + b_{k+1}\right)$$

$$= \frac{1}{2}\left(\sqrt{a_{k+1}} - \sqrt{b_{k+1}}\right)^2 > 0$$

$$a_{k+1} - a_{k+2} = a_{k+1} - \frac{1}{2}(a_{k+1} + b_{k+1}) = \frac{1}{2}(a_{k+1} - b_{k+1}) > 0$$

and $b_{k+1} - b_{k+2} = b_{k+1} - \sqrt{a_{k+1}b_{k+1}} = \sqrt{b_{k+1}}\left(\sqrt{b_{k+1}} - \sqrt{a_{k+1}}\right) < 0 \Rightarrow$

$a_{k+1} > a_{k+2} > b_{k+2} > b_{k+1}$, so the assertion is true for $n = k + 1$. Thus, it is true for all n by mathematical induction.

(b) From part (a) we have $a > a_n > a_{n+1} > b_{n+1} > b_n > b$, which shows that both sequences, $\{a_n\}$ and $\{b_n\}$, are monotonic and bounded. So they are both convergent by the Monotonic Sequence Theorem.

(c) Let $\lim\limits_{n \to \infty} a_n = \alpha$ and $\lim\limits_{n \to \infty} b_n = \beta$. Then $\lim\limits_{n \to \infty} a_{n+1} = \lim\limits_{n \to \infty} \dfrac{a_n + b_n}{2} \Rightarrow \alpha = \dfrac{\alpha + \beta}{2} \Rightarrow 2\alpha = \alpha + \beta \Rightarrow \alpha = \beta$.

50. $a_1 = 1$, $a_2 = 1 + \frac{1}{1+1} = \frac{3}{2} = 1.5$, $a_3 = 1 + \frac{1}{5/2} = \frac{7}{5} = 1.4$, $a_4 = 1 + \frac{1}{12/5} = \frac{17}{12} = 1.41\overline{6}$,

$a_5 = 1 + \frac{1}{29/12} = \frac{41}{29} \approx 1.413793$, $a_6 = 1 + \frac{1}{70/29} = \frac{99}{70} \approx 1.414286$, $a_7 = 1 + \frac{1}{169/70} = \frac{239}{169} \approx 1.414201$,

$a_8 = 1 + \frac{1}{408/169} = \frac{577}{408} \approx 1.414216$. Notice that $a_1 < a_3 < a_5 < a_7$ and $a_2 > a_4 > a_6 > a_8$. It appears that the

odd terms are increasing and the even terms are decreasing. Let's prove that $a_{2n-2} > a_{2n}$ and $a_{2n-1} < a_{2n+1}$ by

mathematical induction. Suppose that $a_{2k-2} > a_{2k}$. Then $1 + a_{2k-2} > 1 + a_{2k}$ $\Rightarrow$

$\frac{1}{1 + a_{2k-2}} < \frac{1}{1 + a_{2k}}$ $\Rightarrow$ $1 + \frac{1}{1 + a_{2k-2}} < 1 + \frac{1}{1 + a_{2k}}$ $\Rightarrow$ $a_{2k-1} < a_{2k+1}$ $\Rightarrow$

$1 + a_{2k-1} < 1 + a_{2k+1}$ $\Rightarrow$ $\frac{1}{1 + a_{2k-1}} > \frac{1}{1 + a_{2k+1}}$ $\Rightarrow$ $1 + \frac{1}{1 + a_{2k-1}} > 1 + \frac{1}{1 + a_{2k+1}}$ $\Rightarrow$

$a_{2k} > a_{2k+2}$. We have thus shown, by induction, that the odd terms are increasing and the even terms are

decreasing. Also all terms lie between 1 and 2, so both $\{a_n\}$ and $\{b_n\}$ are bounded monotonic sequences and

therefore convergent by the Monotonic Sequence Theorem. Let $\lim_{n \to \infty} a_{2n} = L$. Then $\lim_{n \to \infty} a_{2n+2} = L$ also. We

have $a_{n+2} = 1 + \dfrac{1}{1 + 1 + 1/(1 + a_n)} = 1 + \dfrac{1}{(3 + 2a_n)/(1 + a_n)} = \dfrac{4 + 3a_n}{3 + 2a_n}$, so $a_{2n+2} = \dfrac{4 + 3a_{2n}}{3 + 2a_{2n}}$. Taking

limits of both sides, we get $L = \dfrac{4 + 3L}{3 + 2L}$ $\Rightarrow$ $3L + 2L^2 = 4 + 3L$ $\Rightarrow$ $L^2 = 2$ $\Rightarrow$ $L = \sqrt{2}$ (since

$L > 0$). Thus, $\lim_{n \to \infty} a_{2n} = \sqrt{2}$.

Similarly, we find that $\lim_{n \to \infty} a_{2n+1} = \sqrt{2}$. Since the even terms approach $\sqrt{2}$ and the odd terms also approach

$\sqrt{2}$, it follows that the sequence as a whole approaches $\sqrt{2}$, that is, $\lim_{n \to \infty} a_n = \sqrt{2}$.

Laboratory Project

Logistic Sequences

1. To write such a program in Maple it is best to calculate all the points first and then graph them. One possible sequence of commands [taking $p_0 = \frac{1}{2}$ and $k = 1.5$ for the difference equation] is

```
p(0):=1/2;k:=1.5;
for j from 1 to 20  do p(j):=k*p(j-1)*(1-p(j-1)) od;
plot({[t,p(t)] $t=0..20},t=0..20,p=0..0.5,style=point);
```

In Mathematica, we can use the following program:

```
p[0]=1/2
k=1.5
p[j_]:=k*p[j-1]*(1-p[j-1])
P=Table[p[t],{t,20}]
ListPlot[P]
```

With $p_0 = \frac{1}{2}$ and $k = 1.5$:

n	p_n	n	p_n	n	p_n
0	0.5	7	0.3338465076	14	0.3333373303
1	0.375	8	0.3335895255	15	0.3333353318
2	0.3515625	9	0.3334613309	16	0.3333343326
3	0.3419494629	10	0.3333973076	17	0.3333338329
4	0.3375300416	11	0.3333653143	18	0.3333335831
5	0.3354052689	12	0.3333493223	19	0.3333334582
6	0.3343628617	13	0.3333413274	20	0.3333333958

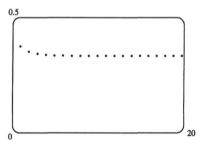

With $p_0 = \frac{1}{2}$ and $k = 2.5$:

n	p_n	n	p_n	n	p_n
0	0.5	7	0.6004164790	14	0.5999967417
1	0.625	8	0.5997913269	15	0.6000016291
2	0.5859375	9	0.6001042277	16	0.5999991854
3	0.6065368651	10	0.5999478590	17	0.6000004073
4	0.5966247409	11	0.6000260637	18	0.5999997964
5	0.6016591486	12	0.5999869664	19	0.6000001018
6	0.5991635437	13	0.6000065164	20	0.5999999491

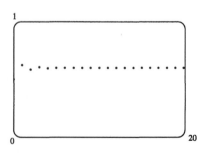

Both of these sequences seem to converge (the first to about $\frac{1}{3}$, the second to about 0.60).

With $p_0 = \frac{7}{8}$ and $k = 1.5$:

n	p_n	n	p_n	n	p_n
0	0.875	7	0.3239166554	14	0.3332554829
1	0.1640625	8	0.3284919837	15	0.3332943990
2	0.2057189941	9	0.3308775005	16	0.3333138639
3	0.2450980344	10	0.3320963702	17	0.3333235980
4	0.2775374819	11	0.3327125567	18	0.3333284655
5	0.3007656421	12	0.3330223670	19	0.3333308994
6	0.3154585059	13	0.3331777051	20	0.3333321164

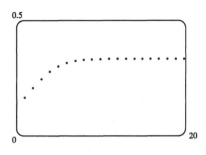

With $p_0 = \frac{7}{8}$ and $k = 2.5$:

n	p_n	n	p_n	n	p_n
0	0.875	7	0.6016572368	14	0.5999869815
1	0.2734375	8	0.5991645155	15	0.6000065088
2	0.4966735840	9	0.6004159972	16	0.5999967455
3	0.6249723374	10	0.5997915688	17	0.6000016272
4	0.5859547872	11	0.6001041070	18	0.5999991864
5	0.6065294364	12	0.5999479194	19	0.6000004068
6	0.5966286980	13	0.6000260335	20	0.5999997966

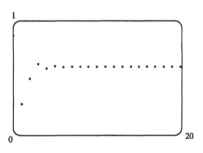

The limit of the sequence seems to depend on k, but not on p_0.

2. With $p_0 = \frac{7}{8}$ and $k = 3.2$:

n	p_n	n	p_n	n	p_n
0	0.875	7	0.5830728495	14	0.7990633827
1	0.35	8	0.7779164854	15	0.5137954979
2	0.728	9	0.5528397669	16	0.7993909896
3	0.6336512	10	0.7910654689	17	0.5131681132
4	0.7428395416	11	0.5288988570	18	0.7994451225
5	0.6112926626	12	0.7973275394	19	0.5130643795
6	0.7603646184	13	0.5171082698	20	0.7994538304

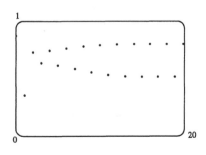

It seems that eventually the terms fluctuate between two values (about 0.5 and 0.8 in this case).

3. With $p_0 = \frac{7}{8}$ and $k = 3.42$:

n	p_n	n	p_n	n	p_n
0	0.875	7	0.4523028596	14	0.8442074951
1	0.3740625	8	0.8472194412	15	0.4498025048
2	0.8007579316	9	0.4426802161	16	0.8463823232
3	0.5456427596	10	0.8437633929	17	0.4446659586
4	0.8478752457	11	0.4508474156	18	0.8445284520
5	0.4411212220	12	0.8467373602	19	0.4490464985
6	0.8431438501	13	0.4438243545	20	0.8461207931

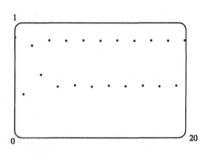

With $p_0 = \frac{7}{8}$ and $k = 3.45$:

n	p_n	n	p_n	n	p_n
0	0.875	7	0.4670259170	14	0.8403376122
1	0.37734375	8	0.8587488490	15	0.4628875685
2	0.8105962830	9	0.4184824586	16	0.8577482026
3	0.5296783241	10	0.8395743720	17	0.4209559716
4	0.8594612299	11	0.4646778983	18	0.8409445432
5	0.4167173034	12	0.8581956045	19	0.4614610237
6	0.8385707740	13	0.4198508858	20	0.8573758782

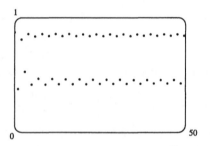

From the graphs above, it seems that for k between 3.4 and 3.5, the terms eventually fluctuate between four values. In the graph below, the pattern followed by the terms is $0.395, 0.832, 0.487, 0.869, 0.395, \ldots$. Note that even for $k = 3.42$ (as in the first graph), there are four distinct "branches; even after 1000 terms, the first and third terms in the pattern differ by about 2×10^{-9}, while the first and fifth terms differ by only 2×10^{-10}.

With $p_0 = \frac{7}{8}$ and $k = 3.48$:

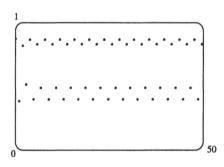

4.

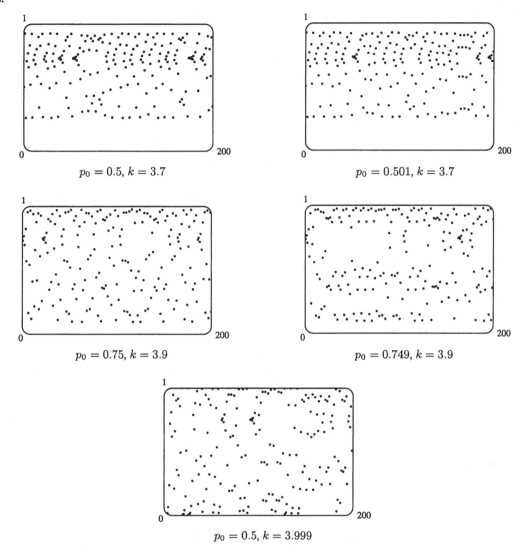

$p_0 = 0.5, k = 3.7$

$p_0 = 0.501, k = 3.7$

$p_0 = 0.75, k = 3.9$

$p_0 = 0.749, k = 3.9$

$p_0 = 0.5, k = 3.999$

From the graphs, it seems that if p_0 is changed by 0.001, the whole graph changes completely. (Note, however, that this might be partially due to accumulated round-off error in the CAS. These graphs were generated by Maple with 100-digit accuracy, and different degrees of accuracy give different graphs.) There seem to be some some fleeting patterns in these graphs, but on the whole they are certainly very chaotic. As k increases, the graph spreads out vertically, with more extreme values close to 0 or 1.

8.2 Series • • • • • • • • • • • • • • • • • • •

1. (a) A sequence is an ordered list of numbers whereas a series is the *sum* of a list of numbers.

   (b) A series is convergent if the sequence of partial sums is a convergent sequence. A series is divergent if it is not convergent.

2. $\sum_{n=1}^{\infty} a_n = 5$ means that by adding sufficiently many terms of the series we can get as close as we like to the number 5. In other words, it means that $\lim_{n \to \infty} s_n = 5$, where s_n is the nth partial sum, that is, $\sum_{i=1}^{n} a_i$.

3.

n	s_n
1	-2.40000
2	-1.92000
3	-2.01600
4	-1.99680
5	-2.00064
6	-1.99987
7	-2.00003
8	-1.99999
9	-2.00000
10	-2.00000

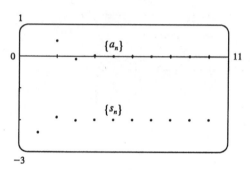

From the graph and the table, it seems that the series converges to -2. In fact, it is a geometric series with $a = -2.4$ and $r = -\frac{1}{5}$, so its sum is

$$\sum_{n=1}^{\infty} \frac{12}{(-5)^n} = \frac{-2.4}{1 - \left(-\frac{1}{5}\right)} = \frac{-2.4}{1.2} = -2.$$ Note that the dot corresponding to

$n = 1$ is part of both $\{a_n\}$ and $\{s_n\}$.

TI-86 Note: To graph $\{a_n\}$ and $\{s_n\}$, set your calculator to Param mode and DrawDot mode. (DrawDot is under GRAPH, MORE, FORMT (F3).) Now under E(t) = make the assignments: xt1=t, yt1=12/(-5)^t, xt2=t, yt2=sum seq(yt1,t,1,t,1). (sum and seq are under LIST, OPS (F5), MORE.) Under WIND use 1,10,1,0,10,1,-3,1,1 to obtain a graph similar to the one above. Then use TRACE (F4) to see the values.

4.

n	s_n
1	0.50000
2	1.90000
3	3.60000
4	5.42353
5	7.30814
6	9.22706
7	11.16706
8	13.12091
9	15.08432
10	17.05462

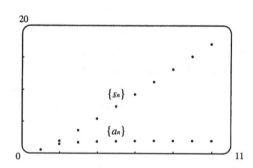

The series $\sum_{n=1}^{\infty} \frac{2n^2 - 1}{n^2 + 1}$ diverges, since its terms do not approach 0.

5.

n	s_n
1	1.55741
2	−0.62763
3	−0.77018
4	0.38764
5	−2.99287
6	−3.28388
7	−2.41243
8	−9.21214
9	−9.66446
10	−9.01610

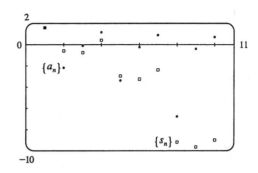

The series $\displaystyle\sum_{n=1}^{\infty} \tan n$ diverges, since its terms do not approach 0.

6.

n	s_n
1	1.00000
2	1.60000
3	1.96000
4	2.17600
5	2.30560
6	2.38336
7	2.43002
8	2.45801
9	2.47481
10	2.48488

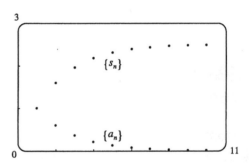

From the graph and the table, it seems that the series converges to 2.5. In fact, it is a geometric series with $a = 1$ and $r = 0.6$, so its sum is

$$\sum_{n=1}^{\infty} (0.6)^{n-1} = \frac{1}{1 - 0.6} = \frac{1}{2/5} = 2.5.$$

7.

n	s_n
1	0.64645
2	0.80755
3	0.87500
4	0.91056
5	0.93196
6	0.94601
7	0.95581
8	0.96296
9	0.96838
10	0.97259

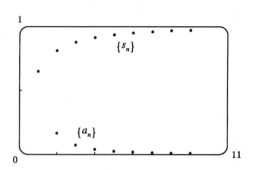

From the graph, it seems that the series converges to 1. To find the sum, we write

$$s_n = \sum_{i=1}^{n} \left(\frac{1}{i^{1.5}} - \frac{1}{(i+1)^{1.5}} \right) = \left(1 - \frac{1}{2^{1.5}} \right) + \left(\frac{1}{2^{1.5}} - \frac{1}{3^{1.5}} \right)$$

$$+ \left(\frac{1}{3^{1.5}} - \frac{1}{4^{1.5}} \right) + \cdots + \left(\frac{1}{n^{1.5}} - \frac{1}{(n+1)^{1.5}} \right) = 1 - \frac{1}{(n+1)^{1.5}}$$

So the sum is $\lim\limits_{n \to \infty} s_n = 1 - 0 = 1$.

8.

n	s_n
2	0.50000
3	0.66667
4	0.75000
5	0.80000
6	0.83333
7	0.85714
8	0.87500
9	0.88889
10	0.90000
11	0.90909
100	0.99000

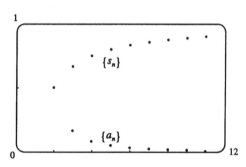

From the graph and the table, it seems that the series converges to 1. To find the sum, we write

$$s_n = \sum_{i=2}^{n} \frac{1}{i(i-1)} = \sum_{i=2}^{n} \left(\frac{1}{i-1} - \frac{1}{i} \right) \quad \text{[partial fractions]}$$

$$= \left(1 - \frac{1}{2} \right) + \left(\frac{1}{2} - \frac{1}{3} \right) + \left(\frac{1}{3} - \frac{1}{4} \right) + \cdots + \left(\frac{1}{n-1} - \frac{1}{n} \right) = 1 - \frac{1}{n},$$

and so the sum is $\lim\limits_{n \to \infty} s_n = 1 - 0 = 1$.

9. (a) $\lim\limits_{n \to \infty} a_n = \lim\limits_{n \to \infty} \dfrac{2n}{3n+1} = \dfrac{2}{3}$, so the *sequence* $\{a_n\}$ is convergent by (8.1.1).

(b) Since $\lim\limits_{n \to \infty} a_n = \frac{2}{3} \neq 0$, the *series* $\sum\limits_{n=1}^{\infty} a_n$ is divergent by the Test for Divergence (7).

10. (a) Both $\sum\limits_{i=1}^{n} a_i$ and $\sum\limits_{j=1}^{n} a_j$ represent the sum of the first n terms of the sequence $\{a_n\}$, that is, the nth partial sum.

(b) $\sum\limits_{i=1}^{n} a_j = \underbrace{a_j + a_j + \cdots + a_j}_{n \text{ terms}} = na_j$, which, in general, is not the same as $\sum\limits_{i=1}^{n} a_i = a_1 + a_2 + \cdots + a_n$.

11. $5 - \frac{10}{3} + \frac{20}{9} - \frac{40}{27} + \cdots$ is a geometric series with $a = 5$ and $r = -\frac{2}{3}$. Since $|r| = \frac{2}{3} < 1$, the series converges to $\frac{a}{1-r} = \frac{5}{1-(-2/3)} = \frac{5}{5/3} = 3$.

12. $1 + 0.4 + 0.16 + 0.064 + \cdots$ is a geometric series with ratio 0.4. The series converges to $\frac{a}{1-r} = \frac{1}{1-2/5} = \frac{5}{3}$ since $|r| = \frac{2}{5} < 1$.

13. $\sum\limits_{n=1}^{\infty} 5\left(\frac{2}{3}\right)^{n-1}$ is a geometric series with $a = 5$ and $r = \frac{2}{3}$. Since $|r| = \frac{2}{3} < 1$, the series converges to $\frac{a}{1-r} = \frac{5}{1-2/3} = \frac{5}{1/3} = 15$.

14. $\sum\limits_{n=1}^{\infty} \frac{(-6)^{n-1}}{5^{n-1}}$ is a geometric series with $a = 1$ and $r = -\frac{6}{5}$. The series diverges since $|r| = \frac{6}{5} > 1$.

15. For $\sum\limits_{n=1}^{\infty} 3^{-n} 8^{n+1} = \sum\limits_{n=1}^{\infty} \left(\frac{1}{3^n} \cdot \frac{8 \cdot 8^n}{1}\right) = \sum\limits_{n=1}^{\infty} 8\left(\frac{8}{3}\right)^n$, $a = \frac{64}{3}$ and $|r| = \frac{8}{3} > 1$, so the series diverges.

16. $\sum\limits_{n=1}^{\infty} \left(\frac{1}{e^2}\right)^n \;\Rightarrow\; a = \frac{1}{e^2} = |r| < 1$, so the series converges to $\dfrac{1/e^2}{1 - 1/e^2} = \dfrac{1}{e^2 - 1}$.

17. $\sum\limits_{n=1}^{\infty} \frac{n}{n+5}$ diverges since $\lim\limits_{n\to\infty} a_n = \lim\limits_{n\to\infty} \frac{n}{n+5} = 1 \neq 0$. [Use (7), the Test for Divergence.]

18. $\sum\limits_{n=1}^{\infty} \frac{3}{n} = 3 \sum\limits_{n=1}^{\infty} \frac{1}{n}$ diverges since each of its partial sums is 3 times the corresponding partial sum of the harmonic series $\sum\limits_{n=1}^{\infty} \frac{1}{n}$, which diverges. [If $\sum\limits_{n=1}^{\infty} \frac{3}{n}$ were to converge, then $\sum\limits_{n=1}^{\infty} \frac{1}{n}$ would also have to converge by Theorem 8(i).] In general, constant multiples of divergent series are divergent.

19. Converges. $s_n = \sum\limits_{i=1}^{n} \frac{1}{i(i+2)} = \sum\limits_{i=1}^{n} \left(\frac{1/2}{i} - \frac{1/2}{i+2}\right)$ (using partial fractions) $= \frac{1}{2} \sum\limits_{i=1}^{n} \left(\frac{1}{i} - \frac{1}{i+2}\right)$. The latter sum is a telescoping series:

$$\left(1 - \frac{1}{3}\right) + \left(\frac{1}{2} - \frac{1}{4}\right) + \left(\frac{1}{3} - \frac{1}{5}\right) + \cdots + \left(\frac{1}{n-1} - \frac{1}{n+1}\right) + \left(\frac{1}{n} - \frac{1}{n+2}\right) = 1 + \frac{1}{2} - \frac{1}{n+1} - \frac{1}{n+2}$$

Thus, $\sum\limits_{n=1}^{\infty} \frac{1}{n(n+2)} = \frac{1}{2} \lim\limits_{n\to\infty} \left(1 + \frac{1}{2} - \frac{1}{n+1} - \frac{1}{n+2}\right) = \frac{1}{2}\left(1 + \frac{1}{2}\right) = \frac{3}{4}$.

20. $\sum\limits_{n=1}^{\infty} \frac{(n+1)^2}{n(n+2)}$ diverges by (7), the Test for Divergence, since

$$\lim\limits_{n\to\infty} a_n = \lim\limits_{n\to\infty} \frac{n^2 + 2n + 1}{n^2 + 2n} = \lim\limits_{n\to\infty} \left(1 + \frac{1}{n^2 + 2n}\right) = 1 \neq 0.$$

21. $\sum\limits_{n=1}^{\infty} [2(0.1)^n + (0.2)^n] = 2 \sum\limits_{n=1}^{\infty} (0.1)^n + \sum\limits_{n=1}^{\infty} (0.2)^n$. These are convergent geometric series and so by Theorem 8, their sum is also convergent. $2\left(\frac{0.1}{1-0.1}\right) + \frac{0.2}{1-0.2} = \frac{2}{9} + \frac{1}{4} = \frac{17}{36}$

22. Converges. $s_n = \displaystyle\sum_{i=1}^{n} \frac{2}{i^2 + 4i + 3} = \sum_{i=1}^{n} \left(\frac{1}{i+1} - \frac{1}{i+3} \right)$ (using partial fractions). The latter sum is

$$\left(\tfrac{1}{2} - \tfrac{1}{4} \right) + \left(\tfrac{1}{3} - \tfrac{1}{5} \right) + \left(\tfrac{1}{4} - \tfrac{1}{6} \right) + \left(\tfrac{1}{5} - \tfrac{1}{7} \right) + \cdots + \left(\tfrac{1}{n} - \tfrac{1}{n+2} \right) + \left(\tfrac{1}{n+1} - \tfrac{1}{n+3} \right) = \tfrac{1}{2} + \tfrac{1}{3} - \tfrac{1}{n+2} - \tfrac{1}{n+3}$$

(telescoping series). Thus, $\displaystyle\sum_{n=1}^{\infty} \frac{2}{n^2 + 4n + 3} = \lim_{n \to \infty} \left(\frac{1}{2} + \frac{1}{3} - \frac{1}{n+2} - \frac{1}{n+3} \right) = \frac{1}{2} + \frac{1}{3} = \frac{5}{6}.$

23. Converges. $s_n = \left(\sin 1 - \sin \dfrac{1}{2} \right) + \left(\sin \dfrac{1}{2} - \sin \dfrac{1}{3} \right) + \cdots + \left(\sin \dfrac{1}{n} - \sin \dfrac{1}{n+1} \right) = \sin 1 - \sin \dfrac{1}{n+1}$, so

$$\displaystyle\sum_{n=1}^{\infty} \left(\sin \frac{1}{n} - \sin \frac{1}{n+1} \right) = \lim_{n \to \infty} s_n = \sin 1 - \sin 0 = \sin 1.$$

24. $\displaystyle\sum_{n=1}^{\infty} \left(\frac{1}{2^{n-1}} + \frac{2}{3^{n-1}} \right) = \sum_{n=1}^{\infty} \frac{1}{2^{n-1}} + 2 \sum_{n=1}^{\infty} \frac{1}{3^{n-1}} = \frac{1}{1 - 1/2} + 2 \left(\frac{1}{1 - 1/3} \right) = 5$

25. Converges. $\displaystyle\sum_{n=1}^{\infty} \frac{3^n + 2^n}{6^n} = \sum_{n=1}^{\infty} \left(\frac{3^n}{6^n} + \frac{2^n}{6^n} \right) = \sum_{n=1}^{\infty} \left[\left(\tfrac{1}{2} \right)^n + \left(\tfrac{1}{3} \right)^n \right] = \frac{1/2}{1 - 1/2} + \frac{1/3}{1 - 1/3} = 1 + \frac{1}{2} = \frac{3}{2}$

26. $\displaystyle\lim_{n \to \infty} a_n = \lim_{n \to \infty} \frac{1}{5 + 2^{-n}} = \frac{1}{5} \neq 0$, so the series diverges by the Test for Divergence.

27. $\displaystyle\lim_{n \to \infty} a_n = \lim_{n \to \infty} \arctan n = \frac{\pi}{2} \neq 0$, so the series diverges by the Test for Divergence.

28. $s_n = (\ln 1 - \ln 2) + (\ln 2 - \ln 3) + (\ln 3 - \ln 4) + \cdots + [\ln n - \ln(n + 1)] = \ln 1 - \ln(n + 1) = -\ln(n + 1)$ (telescoping series). Thus, $\displaystyle\lim_{n \to \infty} s_n = -\infty$, so the series is divergent.

29. $0.\overline{2} = \dfrac{2}{10} + \dfrac{2}{10^2} + \cdots$ is a geometric series with $a = \dfrac{2}{10}$ and $r = \dfrac{1}{10}$. It converges to $\dfrac{a}{1 - r} = \dfrac{2/10}{1 - 1/10} = \dfrac{2}{9}.$

30. $0.\overline{73} = \dfrac{73}{10^2} + \dfrac{73}{10^4} + \cdots = \dfrac{73/10^2}{1 - 1/10^2} = \dfrac{73/100}{99/100} = \dfrac{73}{99}$

31. $3.\overline{417} = 3 + \dfrac{417}{10^3} + \dfrac{417}{10^6} + \cdots = 3 + \dfrac{417/10^3}{1 - 1/10^3} = 3 + \dfrac{417}{999} = \dfrac{3414}{999} = \dfrac{1138}{333}$

32. $6.2\overline{54} = 6.2 + \dfrac{54}{10^3} + \dfrac{54}{10^5} + \cdots = 6.2 + \dfrac{54/10^3}{1 - 1/10^2} = \dfrac{62}{10} + \dfrac{54}{990} = \dfrac{6192}{990} = \dfrac{344}{55}$

33. $\displaystyle\sum_{n=1}^{\infty} \frac{x^n}{3^n} = \sum_{n=1}^{\infty} \left(\frac{x}{3} \right)^n$ is a geometric series with $r = \dfrac{x}{3}$, so the series converges $\Leftrightarrow |r| < 1 \Leftrightarrow \dfrac{|x|}{3} < 1 \Leftrightarrow$

$|x| < 3$; that is, $-3 < x < 3$. In that case, the sum of the series is $\dfrac{a}{1 - r} = \dfrac{x/3}{1 - x/3} = \dfrac{x/3}{1 - x/3} \cdot \dfrac{3}{3} = \dfrac{x}{3 - x}.$

34. $\displaystyle\sum_{n=0}^{\infty} 2^n (x + 1)^n = \sum_{n=0}^{\infty} [2(x + 1)]^n = \sum_{n=1}^{\infty} [2(x + 1)]^{n-1}$ is a geometric series with $r = 2(x + 1)$, so the series

converges $\Leftrightarrow |r| < 1 \Leftrightarrow |2(x + 1)| < 1 \Leftrightarrow |x + 1| < \tfrac{1}{2} \Leftrightarrow -\tfrac{1}{2} < x + 1 < \tfrac{1}{2} \Leftrightarrow$

$-\tfrac{3}{2} < x < -\tfrac{1}{2}$. In that case, the sum of the series is $\dfrac{a}{1 - r} = \dfrac{1}{1 - 2(x + 1)} = \dfrac{1}{-1 - 2x}$ or $\dfrac{-1}{2x + 1}.$

35. $\displaystyle\sum_{n=0}^{\infty}\left(\frac{1}{x}\right)^{n} = \sum_{n=1}^{\infty}\left(\frac{1}{x}\right)^{n-1}$ is geometric with $r = \dfrac{1}{x}$, so it converges whenever $\left|\dfrac{1}{x}\right| < 1 \iff$

$\dfrac{1}{|x|} < 1 \iff 1 < |x| \iff |x| > 1 \iff x > 1$ or $x < -1$, and the sum is

$\dfrac{a}{1-r} = \dfrac{1}{1 - 1/x} = \dfrac{1}{1 - 1/x} \cdot \dfrac{x}{x} = \dfrac{x}{x-1}$.

36. $\displaystyle\sum_{n=0}^{\infty} \tan^{n} x = \sum_{n=1}^{\infty} (\tan x)^{n-1}$ is geometric and converges when $|\tan x| < 1 \iff -1 < \tan x < 1 \iff$

$n\pi - \frac{\pi}{4} < x < n\pi + \frac{\pi}{4}$ (n any integer). On these intervals the sum is $\dfrac{1}{1 - \tan x}$.

37. After defining f, We use `convert(f,parfrac);` in Maple, `Apart` in Mathematica, or `Expand Rational`
and `Simplify` in Derive to find that the general term is $\dfrac{1}{(4n+1)(4n-3)} = -\dfrac{1/4}{4n+1} + \dfrac{1/4}{4n-3}$. So the nth
partial sum is

$$s_n = \sum_{k=1}^{n}\left(-\frac{1/4}{4k+1} + \frac{1/4}{4k-3}\right) = \frac{1}{4}\sum_{k=1}^{n}\left(\frac{1}{4k-3} - \frac{1}{4k+1}\right)$$

$$= \frac{1}{4}\left[\left(1 - \frac{1}{5}\right) + \left(\frac{1}{5} - \frac{1}{9}\right) + \left(\frac{1}{9} - \frac{1}{13}\right) + \cdots + \left(\frac{1}{4n-3} - \frac{1}{4n+1}\right)\right] = \frac{1}{4}\left(1 - \frac{1}{4n+1}\right)$$

The series converges to $\displaystyle\lim_{n\to\infty} s_n = \frac{1}{4}$. This can be confirmed by directly computing the sum using
`sum(f,1..infinity);` (in Maple), `Sum[f,{n,1,Infinity}]` (in Mathematica), or `Calculus Sum`
(from 1 to ∞) and `Simplify` (in Derive).

38. See Exercise 37 for specific CAS commands. $\dfrac{n^2 + 3n + 1}{(n^2 + n)^2} = \dfrac{1}{n^2} + \dfrac{1}{n} - \dfrac{1}{(n+1)^2} - \dfrac{1}{n+1}$. So the nth partial
sum is

$$s_n = \sum_{k=1}^{n}\left(\frac{1}{k^2} + \frac{1}{k} - \frac{1}{(k+1)^2} - \frac{1}{k+1}\right)$$

$$= \left(1 + 1 - \frac{1}{2^2} - \frac{1}{2}\right) + \left(\frac{1}{2^2} + \frac{1}{2} - \frac{1}{3^2} - \frac{1}{3}\right) + \cdots + \left(\frac{1}{n^2} + \frac{1}{n} - \frac{1}{(n+1)^2} - \frac{1}{n+1}\right)$$

$$= 1 + 1 - \frac{1}{(n+1)^2} - \frac{1}{n+1}$$

The series converges to $\displaystyle\lim_{n\to\infty} s_n = 2$.

39. For $n = 1$, $a_1 = 0$ since $s_1 = 0$. For $n > 1$,

$$a_n = s_n - s_{n-1} = \frac{n-1}{n+1} - \frac{(n-1)-1}{(n-1)+1} = \frac{(n-1)n - (n+1)(n-2)}{(n+1)n} = \frac{2}{n(n+1)}$$

Also, $\displaystyle\sum_{n=1}^{\infty} a_n = \lim_{n\to\infty} s_n = \lim_{n\to\infty} \frac{1 - 1/n}{1 + 1/n} = 1$.

40. $a_1 = s_1 = 3 - \frac{1}{2} = \frac{5}{2}$. For $n \neq 1$,

$$a_n = s_n - s_{n-1} = \left(3 - n2^{-n}\right) - \left[3 - (n-1)2^{-(n-1)}\right] = -\frac{n}{2^n} + \frac{n-1}{2^{n-1}} \cdot \frac{2}{2} = \frac{2(n-1)}{2^n} - \frac{n}{2^n} = \frac{n-2}{2^n}$$

Also, $\displaystyle\sum_{n=1}^{\infty} a_n = \lim_{n\to\infty} s_n = \lim_{n\to\infty}\left(3 - \frac{n}{2^n}\right) = 3$ because $\displaystyle\lim_{x\to\infty} \frac{x}{2^x} \overset{\text{H}}{=} \lim_{x\to\infty} \frac{1}{2^x \ln 2} = 0$.

41. (a) The first step in the chain occurs when the local government spends D dollars. The people who receive it spend a fraction c of those D dollars, that is, Dc dollars. Those who receive the Dc dollars spend a fraction c of it, that is, Dc^2 dollars. Continuing in this way, we see that the total spending after n transactions is

$$S_n = D + Dc + Dc^2 + \cdots + Dc^{n-1} = \frac{D(1 - c^n)}{1 - c} \text{ by (3).}$$

(b) $\displaystyle\lim_{n\to\infty} S_n = \lim_{n\to\infty} \frac{D(1 - c^n)}{1 - c} = \frac{D}{1 - c} \lim_{n\to\infty} (1 - c^n) = \frac{D}{1 - c}$ (since $0 < c < 1$ $\Rightarrow$ $\displaystyle\lim_{n\to\infty} c^n = 0$)

$\displaystyle= \frac{D}{s}$ (since $c + s = 1$) $= kD$ (since $k = 1/s$)

If $c = 0.8$, then $s = 1 - c = 0.2$ and the multiplier is $k = 1/s = 5$.

42. (a) Initially, the ball falls a distance H, then rebounds a distance rH, falls rH, rebounds r^2H, falls r^2H, etc. The total distance it travels is

$$H + 2rH + 2r^2H + 2r^3H + \cdots = H(1 + 2r + 2r^2 + 2r^3 + \cdots)$$

$$= H\left[1 + 2r(1 + r + r^2 + \cdots)\right] = H\left[1 + 2r\left(\frac{1}{1-r}\right)\right] = H\left(\frac{1+r}{1-r}\right) \text{ meters}$$

(b) From Example 3 in Section 2.1, we know that a ball falls $\frac{1}{2}gt^2$ meters in t seconds, where g is the gravitational acceleration. Thus, a ball falls h meters in $t = \sqrt{2h/g}$ seconds. The total travel time in seconds is

$$\sqrt{\frac{2H}{g}} + 2\sqrt{\frac{2H}{g}r} + 2\sqrt{\frac{2H}{g}r^2} + 2\sqrt{\frac{2H}{g}r^3} + \cdots = \sqrt{\frac{2H}{g}}\left[1 + 2\sqrt{r} + 2\sqrt{r^2} + 2\sqrt{r^3} + \cdots\right]$$

$$= \sqrt{\frac{2H}{g}}\left(1 + 2\sqrt{r}\left[1 + \sqrt{r} + \sqrt{r^2} + \cdots\right]\right) = \sqrt{\frac{2H}{g}}\left[1 + 2\sqrt{r}\left(\frac{1}{1 - \sqrt{r}}\right)\right] = \sqrt{\frac{2H}{g}}\frac{1 + \sqrt{r}}{1 - \sqrt{r}}$$

(c) It will help to make a chart of the time for each descent and each rebound of the ball, together with the velocity just before and just after each bounce. Recall that the time in seconds needed to fall h meters is $\sqrt{2h/g}$. The ball hits the ground with velocity $-g\sqrt{2h/g} = -\sqrt{2hg}$ (taking the upward direction to be positive) and rebounds with velocity $kg\sqrt{2h/g} = k\sqrt{2hg}$, taking time $k\sqrt{2h/g}$ to reach the top of its bounce, where its velocity is 0. At that point, its height is k^2h. All these results follow from the formulas for vertical motion with gravitational acceleration $-g$: $\dfrac{d^2y}{dt^2} = -g$ $\Rightarrow$ $v = \dfrac{dy}{dt} = v_0 - gt$ $\Rightarrow$ $y = y_0 + v_0 t - \frac{1}{2}gt^2$.

number of descent	time of descent	speed before bounce	speed after bounce	time of ascent	peak height
1	$\sqrt{2H/g}$	$\sqrt{2Hg}$	$k\sqrt{2Hg}$	$k\sqrt{2H/g}$	k^2H
2	$\sqrt{2k^2H/g}$	$\sqrt{2k^2Hg}$	$k\sqrt{2k^2Hg}$	$k\sqrt{2k^2H/g}$	k^4H
3	$\sqrt{2k^4H/g}$	$\sqrt{2k^4Hg}$	$k\sqrt{2k^4Hg}$	$k\sqrt{2k^4H/g}$	k^6H
$\cdots$	$\cdots$	$\cdots$	$\cdots$	$\cdots$	$\cdots$

The total travel time in seconds is

$$\sqrt{\frac{2H}{g}} + k\sqrt{\frac{2H}{g}} + k\sqrt{\frac{2H}{g}} + k^2\sqrt{\frac{2H}{g}} + k^2\sqrt{\frac{2H}{g}} + \cdots = \sqrt{\frac{2H}{g}}(1 + 2k + 2k^2 + 2k^3 + \cdots)$$

$$= \sqrt{\frac{2H}{g}}\left[1 + 2k(1 + k + k^2 + \cdots)\right] = \sqrt{\frac{2H}{g}}\left[1 + 2k\left(\frac{1}{1-k}\right)\right] = \sqrt{\frac{2H}{g}}\frac{1+k}{1-k}$$

Another method: We could use part (b). At the top of the bounce, the height is $k^2 h = rh$, so $\sqrt{r} = k$ and the result follows from part (b).

43. $\sum_{n=2}^{\infty}(1+c)^{-n}$ is a geometric series with $a = (1+c)^{-2}$ and $r = (1+c)^{-1}$, so the series converges when
$$\left|(1+c)^{-1}\right| < 1 \quad \Leftrightarrow \quad |1+c| > 1 \quad \Leftrightarrow \quad 1+c > 1 \text{ or } 1+c < -1 \quad \Leftrightarrow \quad c > 0 \text{ or } c < -2.$$ We calculate the sum

of the series and set it equal to 2: $\dfrac{(1+c)^{-2}}{1-(1+c)^{-1}} = 2 \quad \Leftrightarrow \quad \left(\dfrac{1}{1+c}\right)^2 = 2 - 2\left(\dfrac{1}{1+c}\right) \quad \Leftrightarrow$

$1 = 2(1+c)^2 - 2(1+c) = 0 \quad \Leftrightarrow \quad 2c^2 + 2c - 1 = 0 \quad \Leftrightarrow \quad c = \dfrac{-2 \pm \sqrt{12}}{4} = \dfrac{\pm\sqrt{3}-1}{2}$. However, the negative

root is inadmissible because $-2 < \dfrac{-\sqrt{3}-1}{2} < 0$. So $c = \dfrac{\sqrt{3}-1}{2}$.

44. The area between $y = x^{n-1}$ and $y = x^n$ for $0 \le x \le 1$ is

$$\int_0^1 \left(x^{n-1} - x^n\right) dx = \left[\frac{x^n}{n} - \frac{x^{n+1}}{n+1}\right]_0^1 = \frac{1}{n} - \frac{1}{n+1}$$

$$= \frac{(n+1)-n}{n(n+1)} = \frac{1}{n(n+1)}$$

We can see from the diagram that as $n \to \infty$, the sum of the areas between the successive curves approaches the area of the unit

square, that is, 1. So $\displaystyle\sum_{n=1}^{\infty} \frac{1}{n\,(n+1)} = 1$.

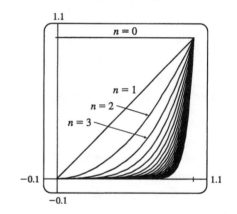

45. Let d_n be the diameter of C_n. We draw lines from the centers of the C_i to the center of D (or C), and using the Pythagorean

Theorem, we can write $1^2 + \left(1 - \frac{1}{2}d_1\right)^2 = \left(1 + \frac{1}{2}d_1\right)^2 \quad \Leftrightarrow$

$1 = \left(1 + \frac{1}{2}d_1\right)^2 - \left(1 - \frac{1}{2}d_1\right)^2 = 2d_1$ (difference of squares)

$\Rightarrow \quad d_1 = \frac{1}{2}$. Similarly,

$1 = \left(1 + \frac{1}{2}d_2\right)^2 - \left(1 - d_1 - \frac{1}{2}d_2\right)^2 = 2d_2 + 2d_1 - d_1^2 - d_1 d_2$

$= (2 - d_1)(d_1 + d_2) \quad \Leftrightarrow$

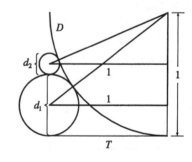

$d_2 = \dfrac{1}{2-d_1} - d_1 = \dfrac{(1-d_1)^2}{2-d_1}$, $1 = \left(1 + \frac{1}{2}d_3\right)^2 - \left(1 - d_1 - d_2 - \frac{1}{2}d_3\right)^2 \quad \Leftrightarrow \quad d_3 = \dfrac{[1-(d_1+d_2)]^2}{2-(d_1+d_2)}$, and in

general, $d_{n+1} = \dfrac{\left(1 - \sum_{i=1}^{n} d_i\right)^2}{2 - \sum_{i=1}^{n} d_i}$. If we actually calculate d_2 and d_3 from the formulas above, we find that they

are $\dfrac{1}{6} = \dfrac{1}{2 \cdot 3}$ and $\dfrac{1}{12} = \dfrac{1}{3 \cdot 4}$ respectively, so we suspect that in general, $d_n = \dfrac{1}{n\,(n+1)}$. To prove this, we

use induction: assume that for all $k \le n$, $d_k = \dfrac{1}{k(k+1)} = \dfrac{1}{k} - \dfrac{1}{k+1}$. Then

$$\sum_{i=1}^{n} d_i = 1 - \frac{1}{n+1} = \frac{n}{n+1} \quad \text{(telescoping sum)}. \text{ Substituting this into our formula for } d_{n+1}, \text{ we get}$$

$$d_{n+1} = \frac{\left[1 - \dfrac{n}{n+1}\right]^2}{2 - \left(\dfrac{n}{n+1}\right)} = \frac{\dfrac{1}{(n+1)^2}}{\dfrac{n+2}{n+1}} = \frac{1}{(n+1)(n+2)}, \text{ and the induction is complete.}$$

Now, we observe that the partial sums $\sum_{i=1}^{n} d_i$ of the diameters of the circles approach 1 as $n \to \infty$; that is,

$$\sum_{n=1}^{\infty} a_n = \sum_{n=1}^{\infty} \frac{1}{n(n+1)} = 1, \text{ which is what we wanted to prove.}$$

46. $|CD| = b\sin\theta$, $|DE| = |CD|\sin\theta = b\sin^2\theta$, $|EF| = |DE|\sin\theta = b\sin^3\theta$, ... Therefore,

$$|CD| + |DE| + |EF| + |FG| + \cdots = b\sum_{n=1}^{\infty} \sin^n\theta = b\left(\frac{\sin\theta}{1 - \sin\theta}\right) \text{ since this is a geometric series with}$$

$r = \sin\theta$ and $|\sin\theta| < 1$ (because $0 < \theta < \frac{\pi}{2}$).

47. The series $1 - 1 + 1 - 1 + 1 - 1 + \cdots$ diverges (geometric series with $r = -1$) so we cannot say that $0 = 1 - 1 + 1 - 1 + 1 - 1 + \cdots$.

48. If $\sum_{n=1}^{\infty} a_n$ is convergent, then $\lim_{n \to \infty} a_n = 0$ by Theorem 6, so $\lim_{n \to \infty} \frac{1}{a_n} \neq 0$, and so $\sum_{n=1}^{\infty} \frac{1}{a_n}$ is divergent by the Test for Divergence.

49. Suppose on the contrary that $\sum(a_n + b_n)$ converges. Then $\sum(a_n + b_n)$ and $\sum a_n$ are convergent series. So by Theorem 8, $\sum[(a_n + b_n) - a_n]$ would also be convergent. But $\sum[(a_n + b_n) - a_n] = \sum b_n$, a contradiction, since $\sum b_n$ is given to be divergent.

50. No. For example, take $\sum a_n = \sum n$ and $\sum b_n = \sum(-n)$, which both diverge, yet $\sum(a_n + b_n) = \sum 0$, which converges with sum 0.

51. The partial sums $\{s_n\}$ form an increasing sequence, since $s_n - s_{n-1} = a_n > 0$ for all n. Also, the sequence $\{s_n\}$ is bounded since $s_n \leq 1000$ for all n. So by Theorem 8.1.7, the sequence of partial sums converges, that is, the series $\sum a_n$ is convergent.

52. (a) RHS $= \dfrac{1}{f_{n-1}f_n} - \dfrac{1}{f_n f_{n+1}} = \dfrac{f_n f_{n+1} - f_n f_{n-1}}{f_n^2 f_{n-1} f_{n+1}} = \dfrac{f_{n+1} - f_{n-1}}{f_n f_{n-1} f_{n+1}} = \dfrac{(f_{n-1} + f_n) - f_{n-1}}{f_n f_{n-1} f_{n+1}}$

$= \dfrac{1}{f_{n-1} f_{n+1}} = $ LHS

(b) $\displaystyle\sum_{n=2}^{\infty} \frac{1}{f_{n-1} f_{n+1}} = \sum_{n=2}^{\infty} \left(\frac{1}{f_{n-1} f_n} - \frac{1}{f_n f_{n+1}}\right)$ [from part (a)]

$= \displaystyle\lim_{n \to \infty} \left[\left(\frac{1}{f_1 f_2} - \frac{1}{f_2 f_3}\right) + \left(\frac{1}{f_2 f_3} - \frac{1}{f_3 f_4}\right) + \left(\frac{1}{f_3 f_4} - \frac{1}{f_4 f_5}\right) + \cdots\right.$

$\left. + \left(\frac{1}{f_{n-1} f_n} - \frac{1}{f_n f_{n+1}}\right)\right]$

$= \displaystyle\lim_{n \to \infty} \left(\frac{1}{f_1 f_2} - \frac{1}{f_n f_{n+1}}\right) = \frac{1}{f_1 f_2} - 0 = \frac{1}{1 \cdot 1} = 1 \text{ because } f_n \to \infty \text{ as } n \to \infty.$

(c) $\displaystyle\sum_{n=2}^{\infty}\frac{f_n}{f_{n-1}f_{n+1}}=\sum_{n=2}^{\infty}\left(\frac{f_n}{f_{n-1}f_n}-\frac{f_n}{f_nf_{n+1}}\right)$ (as above)

$$=\sum_{n=2}^{\infty}\left(\frac{1}{f_{n-1}}-\frac{1}{f_{n+1}}\right)$$

$$=\lim_{n\to\infty}\left[\left(\frac{1}{f_1}-\frac{1}{f_3}\right)+\left(\frac{1}{f_2}-\frac{1}{f_4}\right)+\left(\frac{1}{f_3}-\frac{1}{f_5}\right)+\left(\frac{1}{f_4}-\frac{1}{f_6}\right)+\cdots\right.$$

$$\left.+\left(\frac{1}{f_{n-1}}-\frac{1}{f_{n+1}}\right)\right]$$

$$=\lim_{n\to\infty}\left(\frac{1}{f_1}+\frac{1}{f_2}-\frac{1}{f_n}-\frac{1}{f_{n+1}}\right)=1+1-0-0=2 \text{ because } f_n\to\infty \text{ as } n\to\infty.$$

53. (a) At the first step, only the interval $\left(\frac{1}{3},\frac{2}{3}\right)$ (length $\frac{1}{3}$) is removed. At the second step, we remove the intervals $\left(\frac{1}{9},\frac{2}{9}\right)$ and $\left(\frac{7}{9},\frac{8}{9}\right)$, which have a total length of $2\cdot\left(\frac{1}{3}\right)^2$. At the third step, we remove 2^2 intervals, each of length $\left(\frac{1}{3}\right)^3$. In general, at the nth step we remove 2^{n-1} intervals, each of length $\left(\frac{1}{3}\right)^n$, for a length of $2^{n-1}\cdot\left(\frac{1}{3}\right)^n=\frac{1}{3}\left(\frac{2}{3}\right)^{n-1}$. Thus, the total length of all removed intervals is $\displaystyle\sum_{n=1}^{\infty}\frac{1}{3}\left(\frac{2}{3}\right)^{n-1}=\frac{1/3}{1-2/3}=1$ (geometric series with $a=\frac{1}{3}$ and $r=\frac{2}{3}$). Notice that at the nth step, the leftmost interval that is removed is $\left(\left(\frac{1}{3}\right)^n,\left(\frac{2}{3}\right)^n\right)$, so we never remove 0, and 0 is in the Cantor set. Also, the rightmost interval removed is $\left(1-\left(\frac{2}{3}\right)^n,1-\left(\frac{1}{3}\right)^n\right)$, so 1 is never removed. Some other numbers in the Cantor set are $\frac{1}{3}$, $\frac{2}{3}$, $\frac{1}{9}$, $\frac{2}{9}$, $\frac{7}{9}$, and $\frac{8}{9}$.

(b) The area removed at the first step is $\frac{1}{9}$; at the second step, $8\cdot\left(\frac{1}{9}\right)^2$; at the third step, $(8)^2\cdot\left(\frac{1}{9}\right)^3$. In general, the area removed at the nth step is $(8)^{n-1}\left(\frac{1}{9}\right)^n=\frac{1}{9}\left(\frac{8}{9}\right)^{n-1}$, so the total area of all removed squares is

$$\sum_{n=1}^{\infty}\frac{1}{9}\left(\frac{8}{9}\right)^{n-1}=\frac{1/9}{1-8/9}=1.$$

54. (a)

a_1	1	2	4	1	1	1000
a_2	2	3	1	4	1000	1
a_3	1.5	2.5	2.5	2.5	500.5	500.5
a_4	1.75	2.75	1.75	3.25	750.25	250.75
a_5	1.625	2.625	2.125	2.875	625.375	375.625
a_6	1.6875	2.6875	1.9375	3.0625	687.813	313.188
a_7	1.65625	2.65625	2.03125	2.96875	656.594	344.406
a_8	1.67188	2.67188	1.98438	3.01563	672.203	328.797
a_9	1.66406	2.66406	2.00781	2.99219	664.398	336.602
a_{10}	1.66797	2.66797	1.99609	3.00391	668.301	332.699
a_{11}	1.66602	2.66602	2.00195	2.99805	666.350	334.650
a_{12}	1.66699	2.66699	1.99902	3.00098	667.325	333.675

The limits seem to be $\frac{5}{3}$, $\frac{8}{3}$, 2, 3, 667, and 334. Note that the limits appear to be "weighted" more toward a_2. In general, we guess that the limit is $\dfrac{a_1+2a_2}{3}$.

(b) $a_{n+1} - a_n = \frac{1}{2}(a_n + a_{n-1}) - a_n = -\frac{1}{2}(a_n - a_{n-1}) = -\frac{1}{2}\left[\frac{1}{2}(a_{n-1} + a_{n-2}) - a_{n-1}\right]$

$\qquad = -\frac{1}{2}\left[-\frac{1}{2}(a_{n-1} - a_{n-2})\right] = \cdots = \left(-\frac{1}{2}\right)^{n-1}(a_2 - a_1)$

Note that we have used the formula $a_k = \frac{1}{2}(a_{k-1} + a_{k-2})$ a total of $n-1$ times in this calculation, once for each k between 3 and $n+1$. Now we can write

$$a_n = a_1 + (a_2 - a_1) + (a_3 - a_2) + \cdots + (a_{n-1} - a_{n-2}) + (a_n - a_{n-1})$$

$$= a_1 + \sum_{k=1}^{n-1}(a_{k+1} - a_k) = a_1 + \sum_{k=1}^{n-1}\left(-\frac{1}{2}\right)^{k-1}(a_2 - a_1)$$

and so

$$\lim_{n\to\infty} a_n = a_1 + (a_2 - a_1)\sum_{k=1}^{\infty}\left(-\frac{1}{2}\right)^{k-1} = a_1 + (a_2 - a_1)\left[\frac{1}{1-(-1/2)}\right]$$

$$= a_1 + \frac{2}{3}(a_2 - a_1) = \frac{a_1 + 2a_2}{3}$$

55. (a) For $\displaystyle\sum_{n=1}^{\infty}\frac{n}{(n+1)!}$, $s_1 = \frac{1}{1\cdot 2} = \frac{1}{2}$, $s_2 = \frac{1}{2} + \frac{2}{1\cdot 2\cdot 3} = \frac{5}{6}$, $s_3 = \frac{5}{6} + \frac{3}{1\cdot 2\cdot 3\cdot 4} = \frac{23}{24}$,

$s_4 = \frac{23}{24} + \frac{4}{1\cdot 2\cdot 3\cdot 4\cdot 5} = \frac{119}{120}$. The denominators are $(n+1)!$, so a guess would be $s_n = \frac{(n+1)!-1}{(n+1)!}$.

(b) For $n=1$, $s_1 = \frac{1}{2} = \frac{2!-1}{2!}$, so the formula holds for $n=1$. Assume $s_k = \frac{(k+1)!-1}{(k+1)!}$. Then

$$s_{k+1} = \frac{(k+1)!-1}{(k+1)!} + \frac{k+1}{(k+2)!} = \frac{(k+1)!-1}{(k+1)!} + \frac{k+1}{(k+1)!(k+2)}$$

$$= \frac{(k+2)!-(k+2)+k+1}{(k+2)!} = \frac{(k+2)!-1}{(k+2)!}$$

Thus, the formula is true for $n=k+1$. So by induction, the guess is correct.

(c) $\displaystyle\lim_{n\to\infty} s_n = \lim_{n\to\infty}\frac{(n+1)!-1}{(n+1)!} = \lim_{n\to\infty}\left[1 - \frac{1}{(n+1)!}\right] = 1$ and so $\displaystyle\sum_{n=1}^{\infty}\frac{n}{(n+1)!} = 1$.

56.

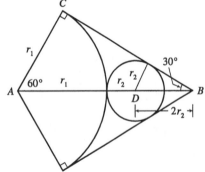

Let r_1 = radius of the large circle, r_2 = radius of next circle, and so on. From the figure we have $\angle BAC = 60°$ and $\cos 60° = r_1/|AB|$, so $|AB| = 2r_1$ and $|DB| = 2r_2$. Therefore, $2r_1 = r_1 + r_2 + 2r_2 = r_1 + 3r_2 \Rightarrow$ $r_1 = 3r_2$. In general, we have $r_{n+1} = \frac{1}{3}r_n$, so the total area is

$$A = \pi r_1^2 + 3\pi r_2^2 + 3\pi r_3^2 + \cdots$$

$$= \pi r_1^2 + 3\pi r_2^2\left(1 + \frac{1}{3^2} + \frac{1}{3^4} + \frac{1}{3^6} + \cdots\right)$$

$$= \pi r_1^2 + 3\pi r_2^2 \cdot \frac{1}{1-1/9} = \pi r_1^2 + \frac{27}{8}\pi r_2^2$$

Since the sides of the triangle have length 1, $|BC| = \frac{1}{2}$ and $\tan 30° = \dfrac{r_1}{1/2}$. Thus, $r_1 = \dfrac{\tan 30°}{2} = \dfrac{1}{2\sqrt{3}} \Rightarrow$

$r_2 = \frac{1}{6\sqrt{3}}$, so $A = \pi\left(\frac{1}{2\sqrt{3}}\right)^2 + \frac{27\pi}{8}\left(\frac{1}{6\sqrt{3}}\right)^2 = \frac{\pi}{12} + \frac{\pi}{32} = \frac{11\pi}{96}$. The area of the triangle is $\frac{\sqrt{3}}{4}$, so the circles occupy about 83.1% of the area of the triangle.

8.3 The Integral and Comparison Tests; Estimating Sums • • •

1. The picture shows that $a_2 = \dfrac{1}{2^{1.3}} < \displaystyle\int_1^2 \dfrac{1}{x^{1.3}}\,dx$,

$a_3 = \dfrac{1}{3^{1.3}} < \displaystyle\int_2^3 \dfrac{1}{x^{1.3}}\,dx$, and so on, so $\displaystyle\sum_{n=2}^{\infty} \dfrac{1}{n^{1.3}} < \int_1^{\infty} \dfrac{1}{x^{1.3}}\,dx$. The

integral converges by (5.10.2) with $p = 1.3 > 1$, so the series converges.

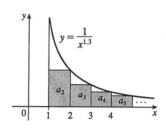

2. From the first figure, we see that

$\int_1^6 f(x)\,dx < \sum_{i=1}^5 a_i$. From the second

figure, we see that

$\sum_{i=2}^6 a_i < \int_1^6 f(x)\,dx$. Thus, we have

$\sum_{i=2}^6 a_i < \int_1^6 f(x)\,dx < \sum_{i=1}^5 a_i$.

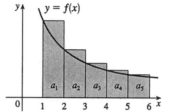

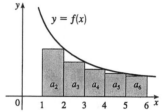

3. (a) We cannot say anything about $\sum a_n$. If $a_n > b_n$ for all n and $\sum b_n$ is convergent, then $\sum a_n$ could be convergent or divergent. (See the note on page 587.)

(b) If $a_n < b_n$ for all n, then $\sum a_n$ is convergent. [This is part (i) of the Comparison Test.]

4. (a) If $a_n > b_n$ for all n, then $\sum a_n$ is divergent. [This is part (ii) of the Comparison Test.]

(b) We cannot say anything about $\sum a_n$. If $a_n < b_n$ for all n and $\sum b_n$ is divergent, then $\sum a_n$ could be convergent or divergent.

5. $\displaystyle\sum_{n=1}^{\infty} n^b$ is a p-series with $p = -b$. $\displaystyle\sum_{n=1}^{\infty} b^n$ is a geometric series. By (1), the p-series is convergent if $p > 1$. In this

case, $\displaystyle\sum_{n=1}^{\infty} n^b = \sum_{n=1}^{\infty} (1/n^{-b})$, so $-b > 1 \iff b < -1$ are the values for which the series converge. A geometric

series $\displaystyle\sum_{n=1}^{\infty} ar^{n-1}$ converges if $|r| < 1$, so $\displaystyle\sum_{n=1}^{\infty} b^n$ converges if $|b| < 1 \iff -1 < b < 1$.

6. The function $f(x) = 1/\sqrt[4]{x} = x^{-1/4}$ is continuous, positive, and decreasing on $[1, \infty)$, so the Integral Test applies.

$\displaystyle\int_1^{\infty} x^{-1/4}\,dx = \lim_{t\to\infty} \int_1^t x^{-1/4}\,dx = \lim_{t\to\infty} \left[\tfrac{4}{3}x^{3/4}\right]_1^t = \lim_{t\to\infty} \left(\tfrac{4}{3}t^{3/4} - \tfrac{4}{3}\right) = \infty$, so $\sum_{n=1}^{\infty} 1/\sqrt[4]{n}$ diverges.

7. The function $f(x) = 1/x^4$ is continuous, positive, and decreasing on $[1, \infty)$, so the Integral Test applies.

$\displaystyle\int_1^{\infty} \frac{1}{x^4}\,dx = \lim_{t\to\infty} \int_1^t x^{-4}\,dx = \lim_{t\to\infty} \left[\frac{x^{-3}}{-3}\right]_1^t = \lim_{t\to\infty} \left(-\frac{1}{3t^3} + \frac{1}{3}\right) = \frac{1}{3}$. Since this improper integral is

convergent, the series $\displaystyle\sum_{n=1}^{\infty} \frac{1}{n^4}$ is also convergent by the Integral Test.

8. The function $f(x) = 1/(x^2 + 1)$ is continuous, positive, and decreasing on $[1, \infty)$, so the Integral Test applies.

$\displaystyle\int_1^{\infty} \frac{1}{x^2+1}\,dx = \lim_{t\to\infty} \int_1^t \frac{1}{x^2+1}\,dx = \lim_{t\to\infty} \left[\tan^{-1} x\right]_1^t = \lim_{t\to\infty} \left(\tan^{-1} t - \tan^{-1} 1\right) = \frac{\pi}{2} - \frac{\pi}{4} = \frac{\pi}{4}$, so

$\displaystyle\sum_{n=1}^{\infty} \frac{1}{n^2+1}$ converges.

9. $\dfrac{1}{n^2+n+1} < \dfrac{1}{n^2}$ for all $n \geq 1$, so $\displaystyle\sum_{n=1}^{\infty} \dfrac{1}{n^2+n+1}$ converges by comparison with $\displaystyle\sum_{n=1}^{\infty} \dfrac{1}{n^2}$, which converges

because it is a p-series with $p = 2 > 1$.

10. $\dfrac{1}{2n-1} > \dfrac{1}{2n} = \dfrac{1}{2} \cdot \dfrac{1}{n}$ for all $n \geq 1$, so $\displaystyle\sum_{n=1}^{\infty} \dfrac{1}{2n-1}$ diverges by comparison with $\displaystyle\sum_{n=1}^{\infty} \dfrac{1}{2n} = \dfrac{1}{2}\displaystyle\sum_{n=1}^{\infty}\dfrac{1}{n}$, which

diverges because it is a nonzero constant multiple of the divergent harmonic series.

11. $1 + \dfrac{1}{8} + \dfrac{1}{27} + \dfrac{1}{64} + \dfrac{1}{125} + \cdots = \displaystyle\sum_{n=1}^{\infty} \dfrac{1}{n^3}$. This is a p-series with $p = 3 > 1$, so it converges by (1).

12. $\displaystyle\sum_{n=1}^{\infty} \dfrac{1}{n^4}$ and $\displaystyle\sum_{n=1}^{\infty} \dfrac{1}{n^{3/2}}$ are convergent p-series with $p = 4 > 1$ and $p = \dfrac{3}{2} > 1$, respectively. Thus,

$\displaystyle\sum_{n=1}^{\infty} \left(\dfrac{5}{n^4} + \dfrac{4}{n\sqrt{n}} \right) = 5\displaystyle\sum_{n=1}^{\infty} \dfrac{1}{n^4} + 4\displaystyle\sum_{n=1}^{\infty} \dfrac{1}{n^{3/2}}$ is convergent by Theorems 8.2.8(i) and 8.2.8(ii).

13. $f(x) = xe^{-x^2}$ is continuous and positive on $[1, \infty)$, and since $f'(x) = e^{-x^2}\left(1 - 2x^2\right) < 0$ for

$x > 1$, f is decreasing as well. Thus, we can use the Integral Test.

$\int_1^{\infty} xe^{-x^2}\, dx = \lim_{t\to\infty}\left[-\tfrac{1}{2}e^{-x^2}\right]_1^t = 0 - \left(-\tfrac{1}{2}e^{-1}\right) = 1/(2e)$. Since the integral converges, the series converges.

14. $f(x) = \dfrac{\ln x}{x^2}$ is continuous and positive for $x \geq 2$, and $f'(x) = \dfrac{1 - 2\ln x}{x^3} < 0$ for $x \geq 2$, so f is decreasing.

$\int_2^{\infty} \dfrac{\ln x}{x^2}\, dx = \lim_{t\to\infty}\left[-\dfrac{\ln x}{x} - \dfrac{1}{x}\right]_2^t$ [by parts] $\overset{\text{H}}{=} 1$. Thus, $\displaystyle\sum_{n=1}^{\infty} \dfrac{\ln n}{n^2} = \displaystyle\sum_{n=2}^{\infty} \dfrac{\ln n}{n^2}$ converges by the Integral Test.

15. $f(x) = \dfrac{1}{x\ln x}$ is continuous and positive on $[2, \infty)$, and also decreasing since $f'(x) = -\dfrac{1+\ln x}{x^2(\ln x)^2} < 0$ for $x > 2$,

so we can use the Integral Test. $\int_2^{\infty} \dfrac{1}{x\ln x}\, dx = \lim_{t\to\infty}\left[\ln(\ln x)\right]_2^t = \lim_{t\to\infty}\left[\ln(\ln t) - \ln(\ln 2)\right] = \infty$, so the series

diverges.

16. $\dfrac{2}{n^3+4} < \dfrac{2}{n^3}$ for all $n \geq 1$, so $\displaystyle\sum_{n=1}^{\infty} \dfrac{2}{n^3+4}$ converges by comparison with $\displaystyle\sum_{n=1}^{\infty} \dfrac{2}{n^3} = 2\displaystyle\sum_{n=1}^{\infty} \dfrac{1}{n^3}$, which converges

because it is a constant multiple of a convergent p-series ($p = 3 > 1$).

17. $\dfrac{5}{2+3^n} < \dfrac{5}{3^n}$ for all $n \geq 1$, so $\displaystyle\sum_{n=1}^{\infty} \dfrac{5}{2+3^n}$ converges by comparison with $\displaystyle\sum_{n=1}^{\infty} \dfrac{5}{3^n} = 5\displaystyle\sum_{n=1}^{\infty} \dfrac{1}{3^n}$, which converges

because $\displaystyle\sum_{n=1}^{\infty} \dfrac{1}{3^n}$ is a convergent geometric series with $r = \dfrac{1}{3}$ ($|r| < 1$).

18. $\dfrac{\sin^2 n}{n\sqrt{n}} \leq \dfrac{1}{n\sqrt{n}} = \dfrac{1}{n^{3/2}}$ and $\displaystyle\sum_{n=1}^{\infty} \dfrac{1}{n^{3/2}}$ converges ($p = \dfrac{3}{2} > 1$), so $\displaystyle\sum_{n=1}^{\infty} \dfrac{\sin^2 n}{n\sqrt{n}}$ converges by the Comparison Test.

19. $\dfrac{n+1}{n^2} > \dfrac{n}{n^2} = \dfrac{1}{n}$ for all $n \geq 1$, so $\displaystyle\sum_{n=1}^{\infty} \dfrac{n+1}{n^2}$ diverges by comparison with the harmonic series $\displaystyle\sum_{n=1}^{\infty} \dfrac{1}{n}$.

20. $\dfrac{4+3^n}{2^n} > \dfrac{3^n}{2^n} = \left(\dfrac{3}{2}\right)^n$ for all $n \geq 1$, so $\displaystyle\sum_{n=1}^{\infty} \dfrac{4+3^n}{2^n}$ diverges by comparison with the divergent geometric series

$\displaystyle\sum_{n=1}^{\infty} \left(\dfrac{3}{2}\right)^n$.

21. Let $a_n = \dfrac{n^2+1}{n^4+1}$ and $b_n = \dfrac{1}{n^2}$. Then $\sum a_n$ and $\sum b_n$ are series with positive terms and

$$\lim_{n\to\infty} \frac{a_n}{b_n} = \lim_{n\to\infty}\left(\frac{n^2+1}{n^4+1}\cdot\frac{n^2}{1}\right) = \lim_{n\to\infty}\frac{n^4+n^2}{n^4+1} = 1 > 0.\ \text{Since } \sum_{n=1}^{\infty}\frac{1}{n^2}\text{ is a convergent } p\text{-series } (p = 2 > 1),$$

so is $\displaystyle\sum_{n=1}^{\infty}\frac{n^2+1}{n^4+1}$ by the Limit Comparison Test.

22. Let $a_n = \dfrac{1}{n^3-n}$ and $b_n = \dfrac{1}{n^3}$. Then $\displaystyle\sum_{n=2}^{\infty} a_n$ and $\displaystyle\sum_{n=2}^{\infty} b_n$ are series with positive terms and

$$\lim_{n\to\infty}\frac{a_n}{b_n} = \lim_{n\to\infty}\frac{n^3}{n^3-n} = 1 > 0.\ \text{Since } \sum_{n=2}^{\infty}\frac{1}{n^3}\text{ is a convergent } p\text{-series without the } n=1 \text{ term } (p = 3 > 1),$$

$\displaystyle\sum_{n=2}^{\infty}\frac{1}{n^3-n}$ is convergent by the Limit Comparison Test.

23. Use the Limit Comparison Test with $a_n = \sin\left(\dfrac{1}{n}\right)$ and $b_n = \dfrac{1}{n}$. Then $\sum a_n$ and $\sum b_n$ are series with positive

terms and $\displaystyle\lim_{n\to\infty}\frac{a_n}{b_n} = \lim_{n\to\infty}\frac{\sin(1/n)}{1/n} = \lim_{\theta\to 0}\frac{\sin\theta}{\theta} = 1 > 0.\ \text{Since } \sum_{n=1}^{\infty} b_n$ is the divergent harmonic series,

$\sum_{n=1}^{\infty}\sin\left(1/n\right)$ also diverges. (Note that we could also use l'Hospital's Rule to evaluate the limit:

$$\lim_{x\to\infty}\frac{\sin(1/x)}{1/x} \overset{\text{H}}{=} \lim_{x\to\infty}\frac{\cos(1/x)\cdot(-1/x^2)}{-1/x^2} = \lim_{x\to\infty}\cos\frac{1}{x} = \cos 0 = 1.)$$

24. If $a_n = \dfrac{n+5}{\sqrt[3]{n^7+n^2}}$ and $b_n = \dfrac{n}{\sqrt[3]{n^7}} = \dfrac{n}{n^{7/3}} = \dfrac{1}{n^{4/3}}$, then

$$\lim_{n\to\infty}\frac{a_n}{b_n} = \lim_{n\to\infty}\frac{n^{7/3}+5n^{4/3}}{(n^7+n^2)^{1/3}}\cdot\frac{n^{-7/3}}{n^{-7/3}} = \lim_{n\to\infty}\frac{1+5/n}{[(n^7+n^2)/n^7]^{1/3}}$$

$$= \lim_{n\to\infty}\frac{1+5/n}{(1+1/n^5)^{1/3}} = \frac{1+0}{(1+0)^{1/3}} = 1 > 0,$$

so $\displaystyle\sum_{n=1}^{\infty}\frac{n+5}{\sqrt[3]{n^7+n^2}}$ converges by the Limit Comparison Test with the convergent p-series $\displaystyle\sum_{n=1}^{\infty}\frac{1}{n^{4/3}}$.

25. We have already shown (in Exercise 15) that when $p = 1$ the series $\displaystyle\sum_{n=2}^{\infty}\frac{1}{n(\ln n)^p}$ diverges, so assume that $p \neq 1$.

$f(x) = \dfrac{1}{x(\ln x)^p}$ is continuous and positive on $[2, \infty)$, and $f'(x) = -\dfrac{p+\ln x}{x^2(\ln x)^{p+1}} < 0$ if $x > e^{-p}$, so that f is

eventually decreasing and we can use the Integral Test.

$$\int_2^{\infty}\frac{1}{x(\ln x)^p}\,dx = \lim_{t\to\infty}\left[\frac{(\ln x)^{1-p}}{1-p}\right]_2^t \quad(\text{for } p \neq 1) = \lim_{t\to\infty}\left[\frac{(\ln t)^{1-p}}{1-p}\right] - \frac{(\ln 2)^{1-p}}{1-p}$$

This limit exists whenever $1 - p < 0 \iff p > 1$, so the series converges for $p > 1$.

26. (a) $f(x) = 1/x^4$ is positive and continuous and $f'(x) = -4/x^5$ is negative for $x > 0$, and so the Integral

Test applies. $\displaystyle\sum_{n=1}^{\infty}\frac{1}{n^4} \approx s_{10} = \frac{1}{1^4} + \frac{1}{2^4} + \frac{1}{3^4} + \cdots + \frac{1}{10^4} \approx 1.082037.$

$$R_{10} \leq \int_{10}^{\infty}\frac{1}{x^4}\,dx = \lim_{t\to\infty}\left[\frac{1}{-3x^3}\right]_{10}^t = \lim_{t\to\infty}\left(-\frac{1}{3t^3} + \frac{1}{3(10)^3}\right) = \frac{1}{3000},\ \text{so the error is at most } 0.000\overline{3}.$$

(b) $s_{10} + \int_{11}^{\infty} \frac{1}{x^4}\, dx \le s \le s_{10} + \int_{10}^{\infty} \frac{1}{x^4}\, dx \;\Rightarrow\; s_{10} + \frac{1}{3(11)^3} \le s \le s_{10} + \frac{1}{3(10)^3} \;\Rightarrow$

$1.082037 + 0.000250 = 1.082287 \le s \le 1.082037 + 0.000333 = 1.082370$, so we get $s \approx 1.08233$ with error ≤ 0.00005.

(c) $R_n \le \int_n^{\infty} \frac{1}{x^4}\, dx = \frac{1}{3n^3}$. So $R_n < 0.00001 \;\Rightarrow\; \frac{1}{3n^3} < \frac{1}{10^5} \;\Rightarrow\; 3n^3 > 10^5 \;\Rightarrow$

$n > \sqrt[3]{(10)^5/3} \approx 32.2$, that is, for $n > 32$.

27. (a) $f(x) = \frac{1}{x^2}$ is positive and continuous and $f'(x) = -\frac{2}{x^3}$ is negative for $x > 0$, and so the Integral

Test applies. $\sum_{n=1}^{\infty} \frac{1}{n^2} \approx s_{10} = \frac{1}{1^2} + \frac{1}{2^2} + \frac{1}{3^2} + \cdots + \frac{1}{10^2} \approx 1.549768$.

$R_{10} \le \int_{10}^{\infty} \frac{1}{x^2}\, dx = \lim_{t \to \infty} \left[\frac{-1}{x}\right]_{10}^{t} = \lim_{t \to \infty}\left(-\frac{1}{t} + \frac{1}{10}\right) = \frac{1}{10}$, so the error is at most 0.1.

(b) $s_{10} + \int_{11}^{\infty} \frac{1}{x^2}\, dx \le s \le s_{10} + \int_{10}^{\infty} \frac{1}{x^2}\, dx \;\Rightarrow\; s_{10} + \frac{1}{11} \le s \le s_{10} + \frac{1}{10} \;\Rightarrow$

$1.549768 + 0.090909 = 1.640677 \le s \le 1.549768 + 0.1 = 1.649768$, so we get $s \approx 1.64522$ (the average of 1.640677 and 1.649768) with error ≤ 0.005 (the maximum of $1.649768 - 1.64522$ and $1.64522 - 1.640677$, rounded up).

(c) $R_n \le \int_n^{\infty} \frac{1}{x^2}\, dx = \frac{1}{n}$. So $R_n < 0.001$ if $\frac{1}{n} < \frac{1}{1000} \;\Leftrightarrow\; n > 1000$.

28. $f(x) = 1/x^5$ is positive and continuous and $f'(x) = -5/x^6$ is negative for $x > 0$, and so the Integral Test applies.

Using (3), $R_n \le \int_n^{\infty} x^{-5}\, dx = \lim_{t \to \infty} \left[\frac{-1}{4x^4}\right]_n^t = \frac{1}{4n^4}$. If we take $n = 5$, then $s_5 \approx 1.036662$ and $R_5 \le 0.0004$.

So $s \approx s_5 \approx 1.037$.

29. $f(x) = x^{-3/2}$ is positive and continuous and $f'(x) = -\frac{3}{2}x^{-5/2}$ is negative for $x > 0$, so the Integral Test applies. From the end of Example 7, we see that the error is at most half the length of the interval. From (4), the interval is

$\left(s_n + \int_{n+1}^{\infty} f(x)\, dx,\; s_n + \int_n^{\infty} f(x)\, dx\right)$, so its length is $\int_n^{\infty} f(x)\, dx - \int_{n+1}^{\infty} f(x)\, dx$. Thus, we need n such that

$0.01 > \frac{1}{2}\left(\int_n^{\infty} x^{-3/2}\, dx - \int_{n+1}^{\infty} x^{-3/2}\, dx\right) = \frac{1}{2}\left(\lim_{t \to \infty}\left[\frac{-2}{\sqrt{x}}\right]_n^t - \lim_{t \to \infty}\left[\frac{-2}{\sqrt{x}}\right]_{n+1}^t\right) = \frac{1}{\sqrt{n}} - \frac{1}{\sqrt{n+1}}$

$\Leftrightarrow\; n > 13.08$ (use a graphing calculator to solve $1/\sqrt{x} - 1/\sqrt{x+1} < 0.01$). Again from the end of Example 7, we approximate s by the midpoint of this interval. In general, the midpoint is

$\frac{1}{2}\left[\left(s_n + \int_{n+1}^{\infty} f(x)\, dx\right) + \left(s_n + \int_n^{\infty} f(x)\, dx\right)\right] = s_n + \frac{1}{2}\left(\int_{n+1}^{\infty} f(x)\, dx + \int_n^{\infty} f(x)\, dx\right)$. So using $n = 14$,

we have $s \approx s_{14} + \frac{1}{2}\left(\int_{14}^{\infty} x^{-3/2}\, dx + \int_{15}^{\infty} x^{-3/2}\, dx\right) \approx 2.0872 + \frac{1}{\sqrt{14}} + \frac{1}{\sqrt{15}} \approx 2.6127 \approx 2.61$. Any larger

value of n will also work. For instance, $s \approx s_{30} + \frac{1}{\sqrt{30}} + \frac{1}{\sqrt{31}} \approx 2.6124$.

30. $f(x) = \frac{1}{x(\ln x)^2}$ is positive and continuous and $f'(x) = -\frac{\ln x + 2}{x^2(\ln x)^3}$ is negative for $x > 1$, so the Integral Test

applies. Using (3), we need $0.01 > \int_n^{\infty} \frac{dx}{x(\ln x)^2} = \lim_{t \to \infty}\left[\frac{-1}{\ln x}\right]_n^t = \frac{1}{\ln n}$. This is true for $n > e^{100}$, so we would

have to take this many terms, which would be problematic because $e^{100} \approx 2.7 \times 10^{43}$.

31. $\sum\limits_{n=1}^{10} \dfrac{1}{n^4+n^2} = \dfrac{1}{2} + \dfrac{1}{20} + \dfrac{1}{90} + \cdots + \dfrac{1}{10,100} \approx 0.567975$. Now $\dfrac{1}{n^4+n^2} < \dfrac{1}{n^4}$, so using the reasoning and

notation of Example 8, the error is $R_{10} \le T_{10} = \sum\limits_{n=11}^{\infty} \dfrac{1}{n^4} \le \displaystyle\int_{10}^{\infty} \dfrac{dx}{x^4} = \lim\limits_{t\to\infty}\left[-\dfrac{x^{-3}}{3}\right]_{10}^{t} = \dfrac{1}{3000} = 0.000\overline{3}$.

32. $\sum\limits_{n=1}^{10} \dfrac{n}{(n+1)3^n} = \dfrac{1}{6} + \dfrac{2}{27} + \dfrac{3}{108} + \cdots + \dfrac{10}{649,539} \approx 0.283597$. Now $\dfrac{n}{(n+1)3^n} < \dfrac{n}{n\cdot 3^n} = \dfrac{1}{3^n}$, so the error is

$R_{10} \le T_{10} = \sum\limits_{n=11}^{\infty} \dfrac{1}{3^n} = \dfrac{1/3^{11}}{1-1/3} \approx 0.0000085$.

33. (a) From the figure, $a_2 + a_3 + \cdots + a_n \le \int_1^n f(x)\,dx$, so with

$$f(x) = \dfrac{1}{x}, \ \dfrac{1}{2} + \dfrac{1}{3} + \dfrac{1}{4} + \cdots + \dfrac{1}{n} \le \int_1^n \dfrac{1}{x}\,dx = \ln n. \text{ Thus,}$$

$$s_n = 1 + \dfrac{1}{2} + \dfrac{1}{3} + \dfrac{1}{4} + \cdots + \dfrac{1}{n} \le 1 + \ln n.$$

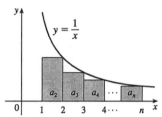

(b) By part (a), $s_{10^6} \le 1 + \ln 10^6 \approx 14.82 < 15$ and $s_{10^9} \le 1 + \ln 10^9 \approx 21.72 < 22$.

34. $\sum\limits_{n=1}^{\infty} n^{-1.001} = \sum\limits_{n=1}^{\infty} \dfrac{1}{n^{1.001}}$ is a convergent p-series with $p = 1.001 > 1$. Using (3), we get

$R_n \le \displaystyle\int_n^{\infty} x^{-1.001}\,dx = \lim\limits_{t\to\infty}\left[\dfrac{x^{-0.001}}{-0.001}\right]_n^t = -1000\lim\limits_{t\to\infty}\left[\dfrac{1}{x^{0.001}}\right]_n^t = -1000\left(-\dfrac{1}{n^{0.001}}\right) = \dfrac{1000}{n^{0.001}}$. We want

$R_n < 0.000\,000\,005 \ \Leftrightarrow \ \dfrac{1000}{n^{0.001}} < 5\times 10^{-9} \ \Leftrightarrow \ n^{0.001} > \dfrac{1000}{5\times 10^{-9}} \ \Leftrightarrow$

$n > \left(2\times 10^{11}\right)^{1000} = 2^{1000}\times 10^{11,000} \approx 1.07\times 10^{301}\times 10^{11,000} = 1.07\times 10^{11,301}$.

35. Since $\dfrac{d_n}{10^n} \le \dfrac{9}{10^n}$ for each n, and since $\sum\limits_{n=1}^{\infty} \dfrac{9}{10^n}$ is a convergent geometric series ($|r| = \tfrac{1}{10} < 1$),

$0.d_1 d_2 d_3 \ldots = \sum\limits_{n=1}^{\infty} \dfrac{d_n}{10^n}$ will always converge by the Comparison Test.

36. $b^{\ln n} = \left(e^{\ln b}\right)^{\ln n} = \left(e^{\ln n}\right)^{\ln b} = n^{\ln b} = \dfrac{1}{n^{-\ln b}}$. This is a p-series, which converges for all b such that $-\ln b > 1$

$\Leftrightarrow \ \ln b < -1 \ \Leftrightarrow \ b < e^{-1} \ \Leftrightarrow \ b < 1/e$ [with $b > 0$].

37. Yes. Since $\sum a_n$ is a convergent series with positive terms, $\lim\limits_{n\to\infty} a_n = 0$ by (8.2.6), and $\sum b_n = \sum \sin(a_n)$ is a

series with positive terms (for large enough n). The Limit Comparison Test gives us

$\lim\limits_{n\to\infty} \dfrac{b_n}{a_n} = \lim\limits_{n\to\infty} \dfrac{\sin(a_n)}{a_n} = 1 > 0$ by Theorem 3.4.2. Thus, $\sum b_n$ is also convergent.

38. First we observe that, by l'Hospital's Rule, $\lim\limits_{x\to\infty} \dfrac{\ln(1+x)}{x} = \lim\limits_{x\to\infty} \dfrac{1}{1+x} = 1$. Also, if $\sum a_n$ converges, then

$\lim\limits_{n\to\infty} a_n = 0$ by Theorem 8.2.6. Therefore, $\lim\limits_{n\to\infty} \dfrac{\ln(1+a_n)}{a_n} = 1 > 0$. We are given that $\sum a_n$ is convergent and

$a_n > 0$. Thus, $\sum \ln(1+a_n)$ is convergent by the Limit Comparison Test.

8.4 Other Convergence Tests • • • • • • • • •

1. (a) An alternating series is a series whose terms are alternately positive and negative.

(b) An alternating series $\sum_{n=1}^{\infty}(-1)^{n-1}b_n$ converges if $0 < b_{n+1} \le b_n$ for all n and $\lim_{n \to \infty} b_n = 0$. (This is the Alternating Series Test.)

(c) The error involved in using the partial sum s_n as an approximation to the total sum s is the remainder $R_n = s - s_n$ and the size of the error is smaller than b_{n+1}; that is, $|R_n| \le b_{n+1}$. (This is the Alternating Series Estimation Theorem.)

2. (a) Since $\lim_{n \to \infty}\left|\dfrac{a_{n+1}}{a_n}\right| = 8 > 1$, part (b) of the Ratio Test tells us that the series $\sum a_n$ is divergent.

(b) Since $\lim_{n \to \infty}\left|\dfrac{a_{n+1}}{a_n}\right| = 0.8 < 1$, part (a) of the Ratio Test tells us that the series $\sum a_n$ is absolutely convergent (and therefore convergent).

(c) Since $\lim_{n \to \infty}\left|\dfrac{a_{n+1}}{a_n}\right| = 1$, the Ratio Test fails and the series $\sum a_n$ might converge or it might diverge.

3. $\dfrac{4}{7} - \dfrac{4}{8} + \dfrac{4}{9} - \dfrac{4}{10} + \dfrac{4}{11} - \cdots = \sum_{n=1}^{\infty}(-1)^{n-1}\dfrac{4}{n+6}$. Now $b_n = \dfrac{4}{n+6} > 0$, $\{b_n\}$ is decreasing, and $\lim_{n \to \infty} b_n = 0$, so the series converges by the Alternating Series Test.

4. $-\dfrac{1}{3} + \dfrac{2}{4} - \dfrac{3}{5} + \dfrac{4}{6} - \dfrac{5}{7} + \cdots = \sum_{n=1}^{\infty}(-1)^{n}\dfrac{n}{n+2}$. Here $a_n = (-1)^{n}\dfrac{n}{n+2}$. Since $\lim_{n \to \infty} a_n \ne 0$ (in fact the limit does not exist), the series diverges by the Test for Divergence.

5. $b_n = \dfrac{1}{\sqrt{n}} > 0$, $\{b_n\}$ is decreasing, and $\lim_{n \to \infty} b_n = 0$, so the series $\sum_{n=1}^{\infty}\dfrac{(-1)^{n-1}}{\sqrt{n}}$ converges by the Alternating Series Test.

6. $\sum_{n=1}^{\infty} a_n = \sum_{n=1}^{\infty}(-1)^{n}\dfrac{\sqrt{n}}{1+2\sqrt{n}} = \sum_{n=1}^{\infty}(-1)^{n}b_n$. Now $\lim_{n \to \infty} b_n = \lim_{n \to \infty}\dfrac{1}{2+1/\sqrt{n}} = \dfrac{1}{2} \ne 0$. Since $\lim_{n \to \infty} a_n \ne 0$ (in fact the limit does not exist), the series diverges by the Test for Divergence.

7. $\sum_{n=1}^{\infty} a_n = \sum_{n=1}^{\infty}(-1)^{n}\dfrac{3n-1}{2n+1} = \sum_{n=1}^{\infty}(-1)^{n}b_n$. Now $\lim_{n \to \infty} b_n = \lim_{n \to \infty}\dfrac{3-1/n}{2+1/n} = \dfrac{3}{2} \ne 0$. Since $\lim_{n \to \infty} a_n \ne 0$ (in fact the limit does not exist), the series diverges by the Test for Divergence.

8. $\sum_{n=1}^{\infty}(-1)^{n-1}\left(\dfrac{\ln n}{n}\right) = 0 + \sum_{n=2}^{\infty}(-1)^{n-1}\left(\dfrac{\ln n}{n}\right)$. $b_n = \dfrac{\ln n}{n} > 0$ for $n \ge 2$, and if $f(x) = \dfrac{\ln x}{x}$, then $f'(x) = \dfrac{1-\ln x}{x^2} < 0$ for $x > e$, so $\{b_n\}$ is eventually decreasing. Also, $\lim_{n \to \infty} b_n = \lim_{n \to \infty}\dfrac{\ln n}{n} \overset{\text{H}}{=} \lim_{n \to \infty}\dfrac{1/n}{1} = 0$, so the series converges by the Alternating Series Test.

9. $\sum_{n=1}^{\infty}\dfrac{(-1)^{n-1}}{n} = 1 - \dfrac{1}{2} + \dfrac{1}{3} - \dfrac{1}{4} + \cdots + \dfrac{1}{49} - \dfrac{1}{50} + \dfrac{1}{51} - \dfrac{1}{52} + \cdots$. The 50th partial sum of this series is an underestimate, since $\sum_{n=1}^{\infty}\dfrac{(-1)^{n-1}}{n} = s_{50} + \left(\dfrac{1}{51} - \dfrac{1}{52}\right) + \left(\dfrac{1}{53} - \dfrac{1}{54}\right) + \cdots$, and the terms in parentheses are all positive. The result can be seen geometrically in Figure 1.

10.

n	a_n	s_n
1	1	1
2	−0.125	0.875
3	0.03704	0.91204
4	−0.01563	0.89641
5	0.008	0.90441
6	−0.00463	0.89978
7	0.00292	0.90270
8	−0.00195	0.90074
9	0.00137	0.90212
10	−0.001	0.90112

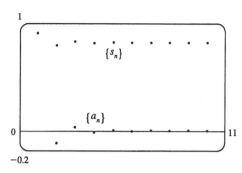

By the Alternating Series Estimation Theorem, the error in the

approximation $\displaystyle\sum_{n=1}^{\infty} \frac{(-1)^{n-1}}{n^3} \approx 0.90112$ is

$$|s - s_{10}| \le b_{11} = 1/11^3 \approx 0.0007513.$$

11. If $p > 0$, $\dfrac{1}{(n+1)^p} \le \dfrac{1}{n^p}$ ($\{1/n^p\}$ is decreasing) and $\displaystyle\lim_{n\to\infty} \frac{1}{n^p} = 0$, so the series converges by the Alternating

Series Test. If $p \le 0$, $\displaystyle\lim_{n\to\infty} \frac{(-1)^{n-1}}{n^p}$ does not exist, so the series diverges by the Test for Divergence. Thus,

$\displaystyle\sum_{n=1}^{\infty} \frac{(-1)^{n-1}}{n^p}$ converges $\Leftrightarrow$ $p > 0$.

12. The series $\displaystyle\sum_{n=1}^{\infty} (-1)^{n+1} \frac{1}{n^4}$ satisfies (a) of the Alternating Series Test because $\dfrac{1}{(n+1)^4} < \dfrac{1}{n^4}$ and

(b) $\displaystyle\lim_{n\to\infty} \frac{1}{n^4} = 0$, so the series is convergent. Now $b_5 = 1/5^4 = 0.0016 > 0.001$ and

$b_6 = 1/6^4 \approx 0.00077 < 0.001$, so by the Alternating Series Estimation Theorem, $n = 5$.

13. Using the Ratio Test with the series $\displaystyle\sum_{n=1}^{\infty} \frac{(-2)^n}{n!}$,

$$\lim_{n\to\infty} \left| \frac{a_{n+1}}{a_n} \right| = \lim_{n\to\infty} \left| a_{n+1} \cdot \frac{1}{a_n} \right| = \lim_{n\to\infty} \left| \frac{(-2)^{n+1}}{(n+1)!} \cdot \frac{n!}{(-2)^n} \right| = \lim_{n\to\infty} \left| \frac{-2}{n+1} \right|$$

$$= 2 \lim_{n\to\infty} \frac{1}{n+1} = 2(0) = 0 < 1,$$

so the series is absolutely convergent (and therefore convergent). Now $b_7 = 2^7/7! \approx 0.025 > 0.01$ and

$b_8 = 2^8/8! \approx 0.006 < 0.01$, so by the Alternating Series Estimation Theorem, $n = 7$. (That is, since the 8th term

is less than the desired error, we need to add the first 7 terms to get the sum to the desired accuracy.)

14. Using the Ratio Test with the series $\displaystyle\sum_{n=1}^{\infty} \frac{(-1)^n n}{4^n}$,

$$\lim_{n\to\infty} \left| \frac{a_{n+1}}{a_n} \right| = \lim_{n\to\infty} \left| \frac{(-1)^{n+1}(n+1)}{4^{n+1}} \cdot \frac{4^n}{(-1)^n n} \right| = \lim_{n\to\infty} \left| \frac{(-1)^1(n+1)}{4n} \right|$$

$$= \frac{1}{4} \lim_{n\to\infty} \frac{n+1}{n} = \frac{1}{4}(1) = \frac{1}{4} < 1,$$

so the series is absolutely convergent (and therefore convergent). Now $b_5 = 5/4^5 \approx 0.0049 > 0.002$ and

$b_6 = 6/4^6 \approx 0.0015 < 0.002$, so by the Alternating Series Estimation Theorem, $n = 5$.

15. The graph gives us an estimate for the sum of the series

$$\sum_{n=1}^{\infty} \frac{(-1)^{n-1}}{(2n-1)!} \text{ of } 0.84. \; b_5 = \frac{1}{(2\cdot5-1)!} = \frac{1}{362{,}880} \approx 0.000\,003,$$

so $\displaystyle\sum_{n=1}^{\infty} \frac{(-1)^{n-1}}{(2n-1)!} \approx s_4 = \sum_{n=1}^{4} \frac{(-1)^{n-1}}{(2n-1)!} = 1 - \frac{1}{6} + \frac{1}{120} - \frac{1}{5040}$

$$\approx 0.841468.$$

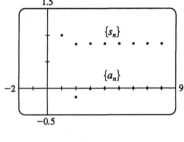

Adding b_5 to s_4 does not change the fourth decimal place of s_4, so
the sum of the series, correct to four decimal places, is 0.8415.

16. The graph gives us an estimate for the sum of the series $\displaystyle\sum_{n=0}^{\infty} \frac{(-1)^n}{(2n)!}$

of 0.54. $b_4 = \dfrac{1}{(2\cdot4)!} = \dfrac{1}{40{,}320} \approx 0.000\,025$, so

$$\sum_{n=0}^{\infty} \frac{(-1)^n}{(2n)!} \approx s_3 = \sum_{n=0}^{3} \frac{(-1)^n}{(2n)!} = 1 - \frac{1}{2} + \frac{1}{24} - \frac{1}{720} \approx 0.540278.$$

Adding b_4 to s_3 does not change the fourth decimal place of s_3, so
the sum of the series, correct to four decimal places, is 0.5403.

17. $b_6 = \dfrac{1}{2^6 6!} = \dfrac{1}{46{,}080} \approx 0.000\,022$, so

$\displaystyle\sum_{n=0}^{\infty} \frac{(-1)^n}{2^n n!} \approx s_5 = \sum_{n=0}^{5} \frac{(-1)^n}{2^n n!} = 1 - \frac{1}{2} + \frac{1}{8} - \frac{1}{48} + \frac{1}{384} - \frac{1}{3840} \approx 0.606510.$ Adding b_6 to s_5 does not change
the fourth decimal place of s_5, so the sum of the series, correct to four decimal places, is 0.6065.

18. $b_8 = \dfrac{1}{8^6} = \dfrac{1}{262{,}144} \approx 0.000\,0038$, so

$\displaystyle\sum_{n=1}^{\infty} \frac{(-1)^{n-1}}{n^6} \approx s_7 = \sum_{n=1}^{7} \frac{(-1)^{n-1}}{n^6} = 1 - \frac{1}{64} + \frac{1}{729} - \frac{1}{4096} + \frac{1}{15{,}625} - \frac{1}{46{,}656} + \frac{1}{117{,}649} \approx 0.9855537.$
Subtracting b_8 from s_7 does not change the fifth decimal place of s_7, so the sum of the series, correct to five decimal
places, is 0.98555.

19. Consider the series whose terms are the absolute values of the terms of the given series.

$\displaystyle\sum_{n=1}^{\infty} \left| \frac{(-1)^{n-1}}{\sqrt{n}} \right| = \sum_{n=1}^{\infty} \frac{1}{n^{1/2}}$, which is a divergent p-series ($p = \frac{1}{2} \le 1$). Thus, $\displaystyle\sum_{n=1}^{\infty} \frac{(-1)^{n-1}}{\sqrt{n}}$ is *not* absolutely
convergent.

20. The series $\displaystyle\sum_{n=1}^{\infty} \frac{n^2}{2^n}$ has positive terms and $\displaystyle\lim_{n\to\infty} \frac{a_{n+1}}{a_n} = \lim_{n\to\infty} \left[\frac{(n+1)^2}{2^{n+1}} \cdot \frac{2^n}{n^2} \right] = \lim_{n\to\infty} \left(1 + \frac{1}{n} \right)^2 \cdot \frac{1}{2} = \frac{1}{2} < 1,$
so the series is absolutely convergent by the Ratio Test.

21. Using the Ratio Test,

$$\lim_{n\to\infty} \left| \frac{a_{n+1}}{a_n} \right| = \lim_{n\to\infty} \left| \frac{(-3)^{n+1}/(n+1)^3}{(-3)^n/n^3} \right| = \lim_{n\to\infty} \left| \frac{(-3)n^3}{(n+1)^3} \right| = 3 \lim_{n\to\infty} \left(\frac{n}{n+1} \right)^3 = 3 > 1, \text{ so the series}$$
diverges.

22. Using the Ratio Test, $\displaystyle\lim_{n\to\infty} \left| \frac{a_{n+1}}{a_n} \right| = \lim_{n\to\infty} \left| \frac{(-3)^{n+1}/(n+1)!}{(-3)^n/n!} \right| = 3 \lim_{n\to\infty} \frac{1}{n+1} = 0 < 1$, so the series is
absolutely convergent.

23. $\left|\dfrac{\sin 2n}{n^2}\right| \le \dfrac{1}{n^2}$ and $\displaystyle\sum_{n=1}^{\infty} \dfrac{1}{n^2}$ converges (p-series, $p = 2 > 1$), so $\displaystyle\sum_{n=1}^{\infty} \dfrac{\sin 2n}{n^2}$ converges absolutely by the

Comparison Test.

24. $\displaystyle\sum_{n=1}^{\infty} \left|(-1)^n \dfrac{n}{n^2+1}\right| = \sum_{n=1}^{\infty} \dfrac{n}{n^2+1} = \sum_{n=1}^{\infty} a_n$. If $b_n = \dfrac{1}{n}$, then $\displaystyle\sum_{n=1}^{\infty} b_n$ is the divergent harmonic series. Applying

the Limit Comparison Test, $\displaystyle\lim_{n\to\infty} \dfrac{a_n}{b_n} = \lim_{n\to\infty} \dfrac{n/(n^2+1)}{1/n} = \lim_{n\to\infty} \dfrac{n^2}{n^2+1} = 1 > 0$, so both series diverge and

the given series is *not* absolutely convergent. (The Integral Test could also be used.)

25. $\displaystyle\lim_{n\to\infty} \left|\dfrac{a_{n+1}}{a_n}\right| = \lim_{n\to\infty} \left[\dfrac{10^{n+1}}{(n+2)4^{2(n+1)+1}} \cdot \dfrac{(n+1)4^{2n+1}}{10^n}\right] = \lim_{n\to\infty} \left[\dfrac{10^{n+1}}{(n+2)4^{2n+3}} \cdot \dfrac{(n+1)4^{2n+1}}{10^n}\right] =$

$\displaystyle\lim_{n\to\infty} \left(\dfrac{10}{4^2} \cdot \dfrac{n+1}{n+2}\right) = \dfrac{5}{8} < 1$, so the series is absolutely convergent by the Ratio Test. Since the terms of this

series are positive, absolute convergence is the same as convergence.

26. $\left|\cos \dfrac{n\pi}{6}\right| \le 1$, so since $\displaystyle\sum_{n=1}^{\infty} \dfrac{1}{n\sqrt{n}}$ converges ($p = \tfrac{3}{2} > 1$), the given series converges absolutely by the

Comparison Test.

27. $\displaystyle\lim_{n\to\infty} \left|\dfrac{a_{n+1}}{a_n}\right| = \lim_{n\to\infty} \dfrac{(n+1)!/[1\cdot3\cdot5\cdots\cdots(2n-1)(2n+1)]}{n!/[1\cdot3\cdot5\cdots\cdots(2n-1)]} = \lim_{n\to\infty} \dfrac{n+1}{2n+1} = \dfrac{1}{2} < 1$, so the series

converges absolutely by the Ratio Test.

28. $\displaystyle\lim_{n\to\infty} \left|\dfrac{a_{n+1}}{a_n}\right| = \lim_{n\to\infty} \dfrac{5^n/[(n+2)^2\, 4^{n+3}]}{5^{n-1}/[(n+1)^2\, 4^{n+2}]} = \dfrac{5}{4} \lim_{n\to\infty} \left(\dfrac{n+1}{n+2}\right)^2 = \dfrac{5}{4} > 1$, so the series diverges by the

Ratio Test.

29. By the recursive definition, $\displaystyle\lim_{n\to\infty} \left|\dfrac{a_{n+1}}{a_n}\right| = \lim_{n\to\infty} \left|\dfrac{5n+1}{4n+3}\right| = \dfrac{5}{4} > 1$, so the series diverges by the Ratio Test.

30. By the recursive definition, $\displaystyle\lim_{n\to\infty} \left|\dfrac{a_{n+1}}{a_n}\right| = \lim_{n\to\infty} \left|\dfrac{2+\cos n}{\sqrt{n}}\right| = 0 < 1$, so the series converges absolutely by the

Ratio Test.

31. (a) $\displaystyle\lim_{n\to\infty} \left|\dfrac{1/(n+1)^3}{1/n^3}\right| = \lim_{n\to\infty} \dfrac{n^3}{(n+1)^3} = \lim_{n\to\infty} \dfrac{1}{(1+1/n)^3} = 1$. Inconclusive.

(b) $\displaystyle\lim_{n\to\infty} \left|\dfrac{(n+1)}{2^{n+1}} \cdot \dfrac{2^n}{n}\right| = \lim_{n\to\infty} \dfrac{n+1}{2n} = \lim_{n\to\infty} \left(\dfrac{1}{2} + \dfrac{1}{2n}\right) = \dfrac{1}{2}$. Conclusive (convergent).

(c) $\displaystyle\lim_{n\to\infty} \left|\dfrac{(-3)^n}{\sqrt{n+1}} \cdot \dfrac{\sqrt{n}}{(-3)^{n-1}}\right| = 3 \lim_{n\to\infty} \sqrt{\dfrac{n}{n+1}} = 3 \lim_{n\to\infty} \sqrt{\dfrac{1}{1+1/n}} = 3$. Conclusive (divergent).

(d) $\displaystyle\lim_{n\to\infty} \left|\dfrac{\sqrt{n+1}}{1+(n+1)^2} \cdot \dfrac{1+n^2}{\sqrt{n}}\right| = \lim_{n\to\infty} \left[\sqrt{1+\dfrac{1}{n}} \cdot \dfrac{1/n^2+1}{1/n^2+(1+1/n)^2}\right] = 1$. Inconclusive.

32. We use the Ratio Test:

$$\lim_{n\to\infty} \left|\dfrac{a_{n+1}}{a_n}\right| = \lim_{n\to\infty} \left|\dfrac{[(n+1)!]^2/[k(n+1)]!}{(n!)^2/(kn)!}\right| = \lim_{n\to\infty} \left|\dfrac{(n+1)^2}{[k(n+1)]\,[k(n+1)-1]\cdots[kn+1]}\right|$$

(continued)

Now if $k = 1$, then this is equal to $\displaystyle\lim_{n\to\infty} \left|\frac{(n+1)^2}{(n+1)}\right| = \infty$, so the series diverges; if $k = 2$, the limit is

$\displaystyle\lim_{n\to\infty} \left|\frac{(n+1)^2}{(2n+2)(2n+1)}\right| = \frac{1}{4} < 1$, so the series converges, and if $k > 2$, then the highest power of n in the

denominator is larger than 2, and so the limit is 0, indicating convergence. So the series converges for $k \geq 2$.

33. (a) $\displaystyle\lim_{n\to\infty}\left|\frac{a_{n+1}}{a_n}\right| = \lim_{n\to\infty}\left|\frac{x^{n+1}}{(n+1)!}\cdot\frac{n!}{x^n}\right| = \lim_{n\to\infty}\left|\frac{x}{n+1}\right| = |x|\lim_{n\to\infty}\frac{1}{n+1} = |x|\cdot 0 = 0 < 1$, so by the Ratio

Test the series $\displaystyle\sum_{n=0}^{\infty}\frac{x^n}{n!}$ converges for all x.

(b) Since the series of part (a) always converges, we must have $\displaystyle\lim_{n\to\infty}\frac{x^n}{n!} = 0$ by Theorem 8.2.6.

34. (a) $R_n = a_{n+1} + a_{n+2} + a_{n+3} + a_{n+4} + \cdots = a_{n+1}\left(1 + \dfrac{a_{n+2}}{a_{n+1}} + \dfrac{a_{n+3}}{a_{n+1}} + \dfrac{a_{n+4}}{a_{n+1}} + \cdots\right)$

$= a_{n+1}\left(1 + \dfrac{a_{n+2}}{a_{n+1}} + \dfrac{a_{n+3}}{a_{n+2}}\dfrac{a_{n+2}}{a_{n+1}} + \dfrac{a_{n+4}}{a_{n+3}}\dfrac{a_{n+3}}{a_{n+2}}\dfrac{a_{n+2}}{a_{n+1}} + \cdots\right)$

$= a_{n+1}(1 + r_{n+1} + r_{n+2}r_{n+1} + r_{n+3}r_{n+2}r_{n+1} + \cdots)$ $(\star)$

$\leq a_{n+1}(1 + r_{n+1} + r_{n+1}^2 + r_{n+1}^3 + \cdots)$ [since $\{r_n\}$ is decreasing] $= \dfrac{a_{n+1}}{1 - r_{n+1}}$

(b) Note that since $\{r_n\}$ is increasing and $r_n \to L$ as $n \to \infty$, we have $r_n < L$ for all n. So, starting with
equation $(\star)$,

$R_n = a_{n+1}(1 + r_{n+1} + r_{n+2}r_{n+1} + r_{n+3}r_{n+2}r_{n+1} + \cdots) \leq a_{n+1}(1 + L + L^2 + L^3 + \cdots) = \dfrac{a_{n+1}}{1-L}$

35. (a) $s_5 = \displaystyle\sum_{n=1}^{5}\frac{1}{n2^n} = \frac{1}{2} + \frac{1}{8} + \frac{1}{24} + \frac{1}{64} + \frac{1}{160} = \frac{661}{960} \approx 0.68854$. Now the ratios

$r_n = \dfrac{a_{n+1}}{a_n} = \dfrac{n2^n}{(n+1)2^{n+1}} = \dfrac{n}{2(n+1)}$ form an increasing sequence, since

$r_{n+1} - r_n = \dfrac{n+1}{2(n+2)} - \dfrac{n}{2(n+1)} = \dfrac{(n+1)^2 - n(n+2)}{2(n+1)(n+2)} = \dfrac{1}{2(n+1)(n+2)} > 0$. So by Exercise 34(b),

the error in using s_5 is $R_5 \leq \dfrac{a_6}{1 - \lim\limits_{n\to\infty} r_n} = \dfrac{1/(6\cdot 2^6)}{1 - 1/2} = \dfrac{1}{192} \approx 0.00521$.

(b) The error in using s_n as an approximation to the sum is $R_n = \dfrac{a_{n+1}}{1 - \frac{1}{2}} = \dfrac{2}{(n+1)2^{n+1}}$. We want

$R_n < 0.00005 \;\Leftrightarrow\; \dfrac{1}{(n+1)2^n} < 0.00005 \;\Leftrightarrow\; (n+1)2^n > 20{,}000$. To find such an n we can use trial

and error or a graph. We calculate $(11+1)2^{11} = 24{,}576$, so $s_{11} = \displaystyle\sum_{n=1}^{11}\frac{1}{n2^n} \approx 0.693109$ is within 0.00005 of

the actual sum.

36. $s_{10} = \displaystyle\sum_{n=1}^{10}\frac{n}{2^n} = \frac{1}{2} + \frac{2}{4} + \frac{3}{8} + \cdots + \frac{10}{1024} \approx 1.988$. The ratios

$r_n = \dfrac{a_{n+1}}{a_n} = \dfrac{n+1}{2^{n+1}}\cdot\dfrac{2^n}{n} = \dfrac{n+1}{2n} = \dfrac{1}{2}\left(1 + \dfrac{1}{n}\right)$ form a decreasing sequence, so $r_{11} = \dfrac{11+1}{2(11)} = \dfrac{12}{22} = \dfrac{6}{11}$,

and by Exercise 34(a), the error in using s_{10} to approximate the sum of the series $\displaystyle\sum_{n=1}^{\infty}\frac{n}{2^n}$ is

$R_{10} \leq \dfrac{a_{11}}{1 - r_{11}} = \dfrac{\frac{11}{2048}}{1 - \frac{6}{11}} = \dfrac{121}{10{,}240} \approx 0.0118$.

8.5 Power Series • • • • • • • • • • • • • • •

1. A power series is a series of the form $\sum_{n=0}^{\infty} c_n x^n = c_0 + c_1 x + c_2 x^2 + c_3 x^3 + \cdots$, where x is a variable and the c_n's are constants called the coefficients of the series.
   More generally, a series of the form $\sum_{n=0}^{\infty} c_n (x - a)^n = c_0 + c_1 (x - a) + c_2 (x - a)^2 + \cdots$ is called a power series in $(x - a)$ or a power series centered at a or a power series about a, where a is a constant.

2. (a) Given the power series $\sum_{n=0}^{\infty} c_n (x - a)^n$, the radius of convergence is:
   (i) 0 if the series converges only when $x = a$
   (ii) ∞ if the series converges for all x, or
   (iii) a positive number R such that the series converges if $|x - a| < R$ and diverges if $|x - a| > R$.
   In most cases, R can be found by using the Ratio Test.

   (b) The interval of convergence of a power series is the interval that consists of all values of x for which the series converges. Corresponding to the cases in part (a), the interval of convergence is: (i) the single point $\{a\}$, (ii) all real numbers; that is, the real number line $(-\infty, \infty)$, or (iii) an interval with endpoints $a - R$ and $a + R$ which can contain neither, either, or both of the endpoints. In this case, we must test the series for convergence at each endpoint to determine the interval of convergence.

3. If $a_n = \dfrac{x^n}{\sqrt{n}}$, then $\displaystyle\lim_{n\to\infty} \left| \dfrac{a_{n+1}}{a_n} \right| = \lim_{n\to\infty} \left| \dfrac{x^{n+1}}{\sqrt{n+1}} \cdot \dfrac{\sqrt{n}}{x} \right| = \lim_{n\to\infty} \left| \dfrac{x}{\sqrt{n+1}/\sqrt{n}} \right| = \lim_{n\to\infty} \dfrac{|x|}{\sqrt{1+1/n}} = |x|$.

   By the Ratio Test, the series $\displaystyle\sum_{n=1}^{\infty} \dfrac{x^n}{\sqrt{n}}$ converges when $|x| < 1$, so the radius of convergence $R = 1$. When $x = 1$,

   the series $\displaystyle\sum_{n=1}^{\infty} \dfrac{1}{\sqrt{n}}$ diverges because it is a p-series with $p = \frac{1}{2} \le 1$. When $x = -1$, the series $\displaystyle\sum_{n=1}^{\infty} \dfrac{(-1)^n}{\sqrt{n}}$

   converges by the Alternating Series Test. Thus, the interval of convergence is $I = [-1, 1)$.

4. If $a_n = \dfrac{(-1)^n x^n}{n+1}$, then $\displaystyle\lim_{n\to\infty} \left| \dfrac{a_{n+1}}{a_n} \right| = \lim_{n\to\infty} \left| \dfrac{x^{n+1}}{n+2} \cdot \dfrac{n+1}{x^n} \right| = \lim_{n\to\infty} \dfrac{|x|}{1 + 1/(n+1)} = |x|$. By the Ratio Test,

   the series $\displaystyle\sum_{n=0}^{\infty} \dfrac{(-1)^n x^n}{n+1}$ converges when $|x| < 1$, so $R = 1$. When $x = -1$, the series diverges because it is the

   harmonic series; when $x = 1$, it is the alternating harmonic series, which converges by the Alternating Series Test.
   Thus, $I = (-1, 1]$.

5. If $a_n = n x^n$, then $\displaystyle\lim_{n\to\infty} \left| \dfrac{a_{n+1}}{a_n} \right| = \lim_{n\to\infty} \left| \dfrac{(n+1) x^{n+1}}{n x^n} \right| = \lim_{n\to\infty} \left| \dfrac{x(n+1)}{n} \right| = |x| \lim_{n\to\infty} \dfrac{n+1}{n} = |x| < 1$ for

   convergence (by the Ratio Test), so $R = 1$. When $x = 1$ or -1, $\displaystyle\lim_{n\to\infty} n x^n$ does not exist, so $\sum_{n=0}^{\infty} n x^n$ diverges

   for $x = \pm 1$. Thus, $I = (-1, 1)$.

6. If $a_n = \dfrac{x^n}{n^2}$, then $\displaystyle\lim_{n\to\infty} \left| \dfrac{a_{n+1}}{a_n} \right| = \lim_{n\to\infty} \left| \dfrac{x^{n+1}}{(n+1)^2} \cdot \dfrac{n^2}{x^n} \right| = |x| \lim_{n\to\infty} \left(\dfrac{n}{n+1} \right)^2 = |x| < 1$ for convergence

   (by the Ratio Test), so $R = 1$. If $x = \pm 1$, $\displaystyle\sum_{n=1}^{\infty} |a_n| = \sum_{n=1}^{\infty} \dfrac{1}{n^2}$, which is a convergent p-series ($p = 2 > 1$).
   Thus, $I = [-1, 1]$.

7. If $a_n = \dfrac{x^n}{n!}$, then $\displaystyle\lim_{n\to\infty} \left| \dfrac{a_{n+1}}{a_n} \right| = \lim_{n\to\infty} \left| \dfrac{x^{n+1}}{(n+1)!} \cdot \dfrac{n!}{x^n} \right| = \lim_{n\to\infty} \left| \dfrac{x}{n+1} \right| = |x| \lim_{n\to\infty} \dfrac{1}{n+1} = |x| \cdot 0 = 0 < 1$ for

   all x. So, by the Ratio Test, $R = \infty$, and $I = (-\infty, \infty)$.

8. If $a_n = \dfrac{x^n}{n3^n}$, then $\lim\limits_{n\to\infty}\left|\dfrac{a_{n+1}}{a_n}\right| = \lim\limits_{n\to\infty}\left|\dfrac{x^{n+1}}{(n+1)3^{n+1}}\cdot\dfrac{n3^n}{x^n}\right| = \lim\limits_{n\to\infty}\left|\dfrac{xn}{(n+1)3}\right| = \dfrac{|x|}{3}\lim\limits_{n\to\infty}\dfrac{n}{n+1} = \dfrac{|x|}{3}$.

By the Ratio Test, the series converges when $\dfrac{|x|}{3} < 1$ ⟺ $|x| < 3$, so $R = 3$. When $x = -3$, the series is the alternating harmonic series, which converges by the Alternating Series Test. When $x = 3$, it is the harmonic series, which diverges. Thus, $I = [-3, 3)$.

9. If $a_n = \dfrac{3^n x^n}{(n+1)^2}$, then

$\lim\limits_{n\to\infty}\left|\dfrac{a_{n+1}}{a_n}\right| = \lim\limits_{n\to\infty}\left|\dfrac{3^{n+1}x^{n+1}}{(n+2)^2}\cdot\dfrac{(n+1)^2}{3^n x^n}\right| = 3|x|\lim\limits_{n\to\infty}\left(\dfrac{n+1}{n+2}\right)^2 = 3|x|\cdot 1 = 3|x|$. By the Ratio Test,

the series converges when $3|x| < 1$ ⟺ $|x| < \frac{1}{3}$, so $R = \frac{1}{3}$. When $x = \frac{1}{3}$,

$\displaystyle\sum_{n=0}^{\infty}\dfrac{3^n x^n}{(n+1)^2} = \sum_{n=0}^{\infty}\dfrac{1}{(n+1)^2} = \sum_{n=1}^{\infty}\dfrac{1}{n^2}$, which is a convergent p-series ($p = 2 > 1$). When $x = -\frac{1}{3}$,

$\displaystyle\sum_{n=0}^{\infty}\dfrac{3^n x^n}{(n+1)^2} = \sum_{n=0}^{\infty}\dfrac{(-1)^n}{(n+1)^2}$, which converges by the Alternating Series Test. Thus, $I = \left[-\frac{1}{3}, \frac{1}{3}\right]$.

10. If $a_n = \dfrac{n^2 x^n}{10^n}$, then $\lim\limits_{n\to\infty}\left|\dfrac{a_{n+1}}{a_n}\right| = \lim\limits_{n\to\infty}\left|\dfrac{(n+1)^2 x^{n+1}}{10^{n+1}}\cdot\dfrac{10^n}{n^2 x^n}\right| = \dfrac{|x|}{10}\lim\limits_{n\to\infty}\left(\dfrac{n+1}{n}\right)^2 = \dfrac{|x|}{10} < 1$ for

convergence (by the Ratio Test), so $R = 10$. If $x = \pm 10$, $|a_n| = n^2 \to \infty$ as $n \to \infty$, so $\sum_{n=0}^{\infty} a_n$ diverges (Test for Divergence) and $I = (-10, 10)$.

11. If $a_n = (-1)^n\dfrac{x^n}{4^n \ln n}$, then

$\lim\limits_{n\to\infty}\left|\dfrac{a_{n+1}}{a_n}\right| = \lim\limits_{n\to\infty}\left|\dfrac{x^{n+1}}{4^{n+1}\ln(n+1)}\cdot\dfrac{4^n \ln n}{x^n}\right| = \dfrac{|x|}{4}\lim\limits_{n\to\infty}\dfrac{\ln n}{\ln(n+1)} = \dfrac{|x|}{4}\cdot 1$ (by l'Hospital's Rule) $= \dfrac{|x|}{4}$.

By the Ratio Test, the series converges when $\dfrac{|x|}{4} < 1$ ⟺ $|x| < 4$, so $R = 4$. When $x = -4$,

$\displaystyle\sum_{n=2}^{\infty}(-1)^n\dfrac{x^n}{4^n \ln n} = \sum_{n=2}^{\infty}\dfrac{(-1\cdot-4)^n}{4^n \ln n} = \sum_{n=2}^{\infty}\dfrac{1}{\ln n}$. Since $\ln n < n$ for $n \geq 2$, $\dfrac{1}{\ln n} > \dfrac{1}{n}$ and $\displaystyle\sum_{n=2}^{\infty}\dfrac{1}{n}$ is the

divergent harmonic series (without the $n = 1$ term), $\displaystyle\sum_{n=2}^{\infty}\dfrac{1}{\ln n}$ is divergent by the Comparison Test. When $x = 4$,

$\displaystyle\sum_{n=2}^{\infty}(-1)^n\dfrac{x^n}{4^n \ln n} = \sum_{n=2}^{\infty}(-1)^n\dfrac{1}{\ln n}$, which converges by the Alternating Series Test. Thus, $I = (-4, 4]$.

12. If $a_n = n^3(x - 5)^n$, $\lim\limits_{n\to\infty}\left|\dfrac{a_{n+1}}{a_n}\right| = \lim\limits_{n\to\infty}\left|\dfrac{(n+1)^3(x-5)^{n+1}}{n^3(x-5)^n}\right| = \lim\limits_{n\to\infty}\left(1 + \dfrac{1}{n}\right)^3|x - 5| = |x - 5|$. By the

Ratio Test, the series converges when $|x - 5| < 1$ ⟺ $-1 < x - 5 < 1$ ⟺ $4 < x < 6$. When $x = 4$, the series becomes $\sum_{n=0}^{\infty}(-1)^n n^3$, which diverges by the Test for Divergence. When $x = 6$, the series becomes $\sum_{n=0}^{\infty} n^3$, which also diverges by the Test for Divergence. Thus, $R = 1$ and $I = (4, 6)$.

13. If $a_n = \sqrt{n}\,(x - 1)^n$, then $\lim\limits_{n\to\infty}\left|\dfrac{a_{n+1}}{a_n}\right| = \lim\limits_{n\to\infty}\left|\dfrac{\sqrt{n+1}\,|x - 1|^{n+1}}{\sqrt{n}\,|x - 1|^n}\right| = \lim\limits_{n\to\infty}\sqrt{1 + \dfrac{1}{n}}\,|x - 1| = |x - 1|$. By

the Ratio Test, the series converges when $|x - 1| < 1$ [so $R = 1$] ⟺ $-1 < x - 1 < 1$ ⟺ $0 < x < 2$.

When $x = 0$, the series becomes $\sum_{n=0}^{\infty}(-1)^n\sqrt{n}$, which diverges by the Test for Divergence. When $x = 2$, the series becomes $\sum_{n=0}^{\infty}\sqrt{n}$, which also diverges by the Test for Divergence. Thus, $I = (0, 2)$.

14. If $a_n = \dfrac{(-1)^n x^{2n-1}}{(2n-1)!}$, then $\lim\limits_{n\to\infty} \left| \dfrac{a_{n+1}}{a_n} \right| = \lim\limits_{n\to\infty} \left| \dfrac{x^{2n+1}}{(2n+1)!} \cdot \dfrac{(2n-1)!}{x^{2n-1}} \right| = \lim\limits_{n\to\infty} \dfrac{x^2}{(2n+1)(2n)} = 0 < 1$ for

all x. By the Ratio Test the series converges for all x, so $R = \infty$ and $I = (-\infty, \infty)$.

15. If $a_n = (-1)^n \dfrac{(x+2)^n}{n2^n}$, then

$$\lim_{n\to\infty} \left| \frac{a_{n+1}}{a_n} \right| = \lim_{n\to\infty} \left[\frac{|x+2|^{n+1}}{(n+1)\,2^{n+1}} \cdot \frac{n2^n}{|x+2|^n} \right] = \lim_{n\to\infty} \frac{n}{n+1} \cdot \frac{|x+2|}{2} = \frac{|x+2|}{2}. \text{ By the Ratio Test, the}$$

series converges when $\dfrac{|x+2|}{2} < 1 \;\Leftrightarrow\; |x+2| < 2 \;[\text{so } R = 2] \;\Leftrightarrow\; -2 < x+2 < 2 \;\Leftrightarrow\; -4 < x < 0$.

When $x = -4$, the series becomes $\sum\limits_{n=1}^{\infty} (-1)^n \dfrac{(-2)^n}{n2^n} = \sum\limits_{n=1}^{\infty} \dfrac{2^n}{n2^n} = \sum\limits_{n=1}^{\infty} \dfrac{1}{n}$, which is the divergent harmonic series.

When $x = 0$, the series is $\sum\limits_{n=1}^{\infty} \dfrac{(-1)^n}{n}$, the alternating harmonic series, which converges by the Alternating Series

Test. Thus, $I = (-4, 0]$.

16. If $a_n = \dfrac{(-2)^n}{\sqrt{n}}(x+3)^n$, then

$$\lim_{n\to\infty} \left| \frac{a_{n+1}}{a_n} \right| = \lim_{n\to\infty} \left| \frac{(-2)^{n+1}(x+3)^{n+1}}{\sqrt{n+1}} \cdot \frac{\sqrt{n}}{(-2)^n(x+3)^n} \right| = \lim_{n\to\infty} \frac{2|x+3|}{\sqrt{1+1/n}} = 2|x+3| < 1 \;\Leftrightarrow$$

$|x+3| < \frac{1}{2} \;[\text{so } R = \frac{1}{2}] \;\Leftrightarrow\; -\frac{7}{2} < x < -\frac{5}{2}$. When $x = -\frac{7}{2}$, the series becomes $\sum\limits_{n=1}^{\infty} \dfrac{1}{\sqrt{n}}$, which diverges

because it is a p-series with $p = \frac{1}{2} \le 1$. When $x = -\frac{5}{2}$, the series becomes $\sum\limits_{n=1}^{\infty} \dfrac{(-1)^n}{\sqrt{n}}$, which converges by the

Alternating Series Test. Thus, $I = \left(-\frac{7}{2}, -\frac{5}{2} \right]$.

17. If $a_n = n!(2x-1)^n$, then $\lim\limits_{n\to\infty} \left| \dfrac{a_{n+1}}{a_n} \right| = \lim\limits_{n\to\infty} \left| \dfrac{(n+1)!(2x-1)^{n+1}}{n!(2x-1)^n} \right| = \lim\limits_{n\to\infty} (n+1)\,|2x-1| \to \infty$ as

$n \to \infty$ for all $x \ne \frac{1}{2}$. Since the series diverges for all $x \ne \frac{1}{2}$, $R = 0$ and $I = \left\{ \frac{1}{2} \right\}$.

18. If $a_n = \dfrac{nx^n}{1 \cdot 3 \cdot 5 \cdot \cdots \cdot (2n-1)}$, then

$$\lim_{n\to\infty} \left| \frac{a_{n+1}}{a_n} \right| = \lim_{n\to\infty} \left| \frac{(n+1)x^{n+1}}{1 \cdot 3 \cdot 5 \cdot \cdots \cdot (2n+1)} \cdot \frac{1 \cdot 3 \cdot 5 \cdot \cdots \cdot (2n-1)}{nx^n} \right| = |x| \lim_{n\to\infty} \frac{n+1}{n(2n+1)} = 0 \text{ for all } x.$$

By the Ratio Test, the series converges for all x, so $R = \infty$ and $I = (-\infty, \infty)$.

19. (a) We are given that the power series $\sum_{n=0}^{\infty} c_n x^n$ is convergent for $x = 4$. So by Theorem 3, it must converge for

at least $-4 < x \le 4$. In particular, it converges when $x = -2$; that is, $\sum_{n=0}^{\infty} c_n(-2)^n$ is convergent.

(b) It does not follow that $\sum_{n=0}^{\infty} c_n(-4)^n$ is necessarily convergent. [See the comments after Theorem 3 about

convergence at the endpoint of an interval. An example is $c_n = (-1)^n / (n4^n)$.]

20. We are given that the power series $\sum_{n=0}^{\infty} c_n x^n$ is convergent for $x = -4$ and divergent when $x = 6$. So by

Theorem 3 it converges for at least $-4 \le x < 4$ and diverges for at least $x \ge 6$ and $x < -6$. Therefore:

(a) It converges when $x = 1$; that is, $\sum c_n$ is convergent.

(b) It diverges when $x = 8$; that is, $\sum c_n 8^n$ is divergent.

(c) It converges when $x = -3$; that is, $\sum c_n (-3)^n$ is convergent.

(d) It diverges when $x = -9$; that is, $\sum c_n(-9)^n = \sum (-1)^n c_n 9^n$ is divergent.

21. If $a_n = \dfrac{(n!)^k}{(kn)!} x^n$, then

$$\lim_{n\to\infty} \left| \frac{a_{n+1}}{a_n} \right| = \lim_{n\to\infty} \frac{[(n+1)!]^k (kn)!}{(n!)^k [k(n+1)]!} |x| = \lim_{n\to\infty} \frac{(n+1)^k}{(kn+k)(kn+k-1)\cdots(kn+2)(kn+1)} |x|$$

$$= \lim_{n\to\infty} \left[\frac{(n+1)}{(kn+1)} \frac{(n+1)}{(kn+2)} \cdots \frac{(n+1)}{(kn+k)} \right] |x|$$

$$= \lim_{n\to\infty} \left[\frac{n+1}{kn+1} \right] \lim_{n\to\infty} \left[\frac{n+1}{kn+2} \right] \cdots \lim_{n\to\infty} \left[\frac{n+1}{kn+k} \right] |x| = \left(\frac{1}{k} \right)^k |x| < 1 \quad \Leftrightarrow$$

$|x| < k^k$ for convergence, and the radius of convergence is $R = k^k$.

22. The partial sums of the series $\sum_{n=0}^{\infty} x^n$ definitely do not converge to $f(x) = 1/(1-x)$ for $x \geq 1$, since f is undefined at $x = 1$ and negative on $(1, \infty)$, while all the partial sums are positive on this interval. The partial sums also fail to converge to f for $x \leq -1$, since $0 < f(x) < 1$ on this interval, while the partial sums are either larger than 1 or less than 0. The partial sums seem to converge to f on $(-1, 1)$. This graphical evidence is consistent with what we know about geometric series: convergence for $|x| < 1$, divergence for $|x| \geq 1$ (see Example 8.2.5).

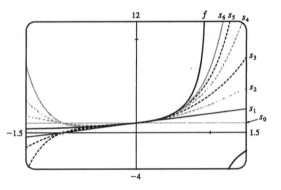

23. (a) If $a_n = \dfrac{(-1)^n x^{2n+1}}{n!(n+1)! 2^{2n+1}}$, then

$$\lim_{n\to\infty} \left| \frac{a_{n+1}}{a_n} \right| = \lim_{n\to\infty} \left| \frac{x^{2n+3}}{(n+1)!(n+2)! 2^{2n+3}} \cdot \frac{n!(n+1)! 2^{2n+1}}{x^{2n+1}} \right| = \left(\frac{x}{2} \right)^2 \lim_{n\to\infty} \frac{1}{(n+1)(n+2)} = 0 \text{ for}$$

all x. So $J_1(x)$ converges for all x and its domain is $(-\infty, \infty)$.

(b), (c) The initial terms of $J_1(x)$ up to $n = 5$ are $a_0 = \dfrac{x}{2}$,

$a_1 = -\dfrac{x^3}{16}, a_2 = \dfrac{x^5}{384}, a_3 = -\dfrac{x^7}{18,432}$,

$a_4 = \dfrac{x^9}{1,474,560}$, and $a_5 = -\dfrac{x^{11}}{176,947,200}$. The

partial sums seem to approximate $J_1(x)$ well near the origin, but as $|x|$ increases, we need to take a large number of terms to get a good approximation.

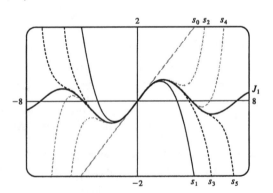

24. (a) $A(x) = 1 + \displaystyle\sum_{n=1}^{\infty} a_n$, where $a_n = \dfrac{x^{3n}}{2 \cdot 3 \cdot 5 \cdot 6 \cdot \cdots \cdot (3n-1)(3n)}$, so

$$\lim_{n\to\infty} \left| \frac{a_{n+1}}{a_n} \right| = |x|^3 \lim_{n\to\infty} \frac{1}{(3n+2)(3n+3)} = 0 \text{ for all } x, \text{ so the domain is } \mathbb{R}.$$

(b), (c)

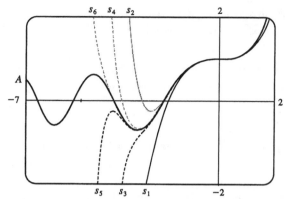

$s_0 = 1$ has been omitted from the graph. The partial sums seem to approximate $A(x)$ well near the origin, but as $|x|$ increases, we need to take a large number of terms to get a good approximation.

To plot A, we must first define $A(x)$ for the CAS. Note that for $n \geq 1$, the denominator of a_n is

$$2 \cdot 3 \cdot 5 \cdot 6 \cdots (3n-1) \cdot 3n = \frac{(3n)!}{1 \cdot 4 \cdot 7 \cdots (3n-2)} = \frac{(3n)!}{\prod_{k=1}^{n}(3k-2)}, \text{ so } a_n = 1 + \frac{\prod_{k=1}^{n}(3k-2)}{(3n)!} x^{3n}$$

and thus $A(x) = 1 + \displaystyle\sum_{n=1}^{\infty} \frac{\prod_{k=1}^{n}(3k-2)}{(3n)!} x^{3n}$. Both Maple and Mathematica are able to plot A if we define it

this way, and Derive is able to produce a similar graph using a suitable partial sum of $A(x)$.

Derive, Maple and Mathematica all have two initially known Airy functions, called AI_SERIES(z,m) and BI_SERIES(z,m) from BESSEL.MTH in Derive and AiryAi and AiryBi in Maple and Mathematica (just Ai and Bi in older versions of Maple). However, it is very difficult to solve for A in terms of the CAS's Airy

functions, although in fact $A(x) = \dfrac{\sqrt{3}\,\text{AiryAi}(x) + \text{AiryBi}(x)}{\sqrt{3}\,\text{AiryAi}(0) + \text{AiryBi}(0)}$.

25. $s_{2n-1} = 1 + 2x + x^2 + 2x^3 + x^4 + 2x^5 + \cdots + x^{2n-2} + 2x^{2n-1}$

$\qquad = 1(1+2x) + x^2(1+2x) + x^4(1+2x) + \cdots + x^{2n-2}(1+2x)$

$\qquad = (1+2x)\left(1 + x^2 + x^4 + \cdots + x^{2n-2}\right)$

$\qquad = (1+2x)\dfrac{1-x^{2n}}{1-x^2}$ [by (8.2.3) with $r = x^2$] $\to \dfrac{1+2x}{1-x^2}$ as $n \to \infty$ [by (8.2.4)],

when $|x| < 1$. Also $s_{2n} = s_{2n-1} + x^{2n} \to \dfrac{1+2x}{1-x^2}$ since $x^{2n} \to 0$ for $|x| < 1$. Therefore, $s_n \to \dfrac{1+2x}{1-x^2}$ since

s_{2n} and s_{2n-1} both approach $\dfrac{1+2x}{1-x^2}$ as $n \to \infty$. Thus, the interval of convergence is $(-1, 1)$ and

$f(x) = \dfrac{1+2x}{1-x^2}$.

26. $s_{4n-1} = c_0 + c_1 x + c_2 x^2 + c_3 x^3 + c_0 x^4 + c_1 x^5 + c_2 x^6 + c_3 x^7 + \cdots + c_3 x^{4n-1}$

$\qquad = \left(c_0 + c_1 x + c_2 x^2 + c_3 x^3\right)\left(1 + x^4 + x^8 + \cdots + x^{4n-4}\right) \to \dfrac{c_0 + c_1 x + c_2 x^2 + c_3 x^3}{1 - x^4}$ as $n \to \infty$

[by (8.2.4) with $r = x^4$] for $|x^4| < 1 \quad \Leftrightarrow \quad |x| < 1$. Also s_{4n}, s_{4n+1}, s_{4n+2} have the same limits (for example,

$s_{4n} = s_{4n-1} + c_0 x^{4n}$ and $x^{4n} \to 0$ for $|x| < 1$.) So if at least one of c_0, c_1, c_2, and c_3 is nonzero, then the interval

of convergence is $(-1, 1)$ and $f(x) = \dfrac{c_0 + c_1 x + c_2 x^2 + c_3 x^3}{1 - x^4}$.

27. For $2 < x < 3$, $\sum c_n x^n$ diverges and $\sum d_n x^n$ converges. By Exercise 8.2.49, $\sum (c_n + d_n) x^n$ diverges. Since both series converge for $|x| < 2$, the radius of convergence of $\sum (c_n + d_n) x^n$ is 2.

28. Since $\sum c_n x^n$ converges whenever $|x| < R$, $\sum c_n x^{2n} = \sum c_n (x^2)^n$ converges whenever $|x^2| < R$ $\Leftrightarrow$ $|x| < \sqrt{R}$, so the second series has radius of convergence $\sqrt{R}$.

8.6 Representations of Functions as Power Series • • • • • •

1. If $f(x) = \sum_{n=0}^{\infty} c_n x^n$ has radius of convergence 10, then $f'(x) = \sum_{n=1}^{\infty} n c_n x^{n-1}$ also has radius of convergence 10 by Theorem 2.

2. If $f(x) = \sum_{n=0}^{\infty} b_n x^n$ converges on $(-2, 2)$, then $\int f(x)dx = C + \sum_{n=0}^{\infty} \frac{b_n}{n+1} x^{n+1}$ has the same radius of convergence (by Theorem 2), but may not have the same interval of convergence—it may happen that the integrated series converges at an endpoint (or both endpoints).

3. Our goal is to write the function in the form $\dfrac{1}{1 - r}$, and then use Equation (1) to represent the function as a sum of a power series. $f(x) = \dfrac{1}{1 + x} = \dfrac{1}{1 - (-x)} = \sum_{n=0}^{\infty} (-x)^n = \sum_{n=0}^{\infty} (-1)^n x^n$ with $|-x| < 1$ $\Leftrightarrow$ $|x| < 1$, so $R = 1$ and $I = (-1, 1)$.

4. $f(x) = \dfrac{x}{1 - x} = x\left(\dfrac{1}{1 - x}\right) = x \sum_{n=0}^{\infty} x^n = \sum_{n=0}^{\infty} x^{n+1} = \sum_{n=1}^{\infty} x^n$ with $R = 1$ and $I = (-1, 1)$.

5. Replacing x with x^3 in (1) gives $f(x) = \dfrac{1}{1 - x^3} = \sum_{n=0}^{\infty} (x^3)^n = \sum_{n=0}^{\infty} x^{3n}$. The series converges when $|x^3| < 1$ $\Leftrightarrow$ $|x|^3 < 1$ $\Leftrightarrow$ $|x| < \sqrt[3]{1}$ $\Leftrightarrow$ $|x| < 1$. Thus, $R = 1$ and $I = (-1, 1)$.

6. $f(x) = \dfrac{1}{1 + 9x^2} = \dfrac{1}{1 - (-9x^2)} = \sum_{n=0}^{\infty} (-9x^2)^n = \sum_{n=0}^{\infty} (-1)^n 3^{2n} x^{2n}$. The series converges when $|-9x^2| < 1$; that is, when $|x| < \frac{1}{3}$, so $I = \left(-\frac{1}{3}, \frac{1}{3}\right)$.

7. If the constant term in the denominator is something other than 1, factor it out of the binomial to obtain a 1.

$f(x) = \dfrac{1}{4 + x^2} = \dfrac{1}{4}\left(\dfrac{1}{1 + x^2/4}\right) = \dfrac{1}{4}\left(\dfrac{1}{1 - (-x^2/4)}\right) = \dfrac{1}{4} \sum_{n=0}^{\infty} \left(-\dfrac{x^2}{4}\right)^n = \sum_{n=0}^{\infty} \dfrac{(-1)^n x^{2n}}{4^{n+1}}$. The series

converges when $\left|-\dfrac{x^2}{4}\right| < 1$ $\Leftrightarrow$ $x^2 < 4$ $\Leftrightarrow$ $|x| < 2$, so $R = 2$ and $I = (-2, 2)$.

8. $f(x) = \dfrac{1 + x^2}{1 - x^2} = \dfrac{(1 - x^2) + 2x^2}{1 - x^2} = 1 + \dfrac{2x^2}{1 - x^2} = 1 + 2x^2 \sum_{n=0}^{\infty} (x^2)^n = 1 + \sum_{n=0}^{\infty} 2x^{2n+2} = 1 + \sum_{n=1}^{\infty} 2x^{2n}$,

with $|x^2| < 1$ $\Leftrightarrow$ $|x| < 1$, so $R = 1$ and $I = (-1, 1)$.

9. $f(x) = \dfrac{1}{x-5} = -\dfrac{1}{5}\left(\dfrac{1}{1-x/5}\right) = -\dfrac{1}{5}\sum_{n=0}^{\infty}\left(\dfrac{x}{5}\right)^n$ or equivalently, $-\sum_{n=0}^{\infty}\dfrac{1}{5^{n+1}}x^n$. The series converges when

$\left|\dfrac{x}{5}\right| < 1$; that is, when $|x| < 5$, so $I = (-5,5)$.

10. $f(x) = \dfrac{x}{4x+1} = x \cdot \dfrac{1}{1-(-4x)} = x\sum_{n=0}^{\infty}(-4x)^n = \sum_{n=0}^{\infty}(-1)^n 2^{2n}x^{n+1}$. The series converges when $|-4x| < 1$;

that is, when $|x| < \frac{1}{4}$, so $I = \left(-\frac{1}{4}, \frac{1}{4}\right)$.

11. (a) $f(x) = \dfrac{1}{(1+x)^2} = \dfrac{d}{dx}\left(\dfrac{-1}{1+x}\right) = -\dfrac{d}{dx}\left[\sum_{n=0}^{\infty}(-1)^n x^n\right]$ [from Exercise 3]

$= \sum_{n=1}^{\infty}(-1)^{n+1}nx^{n-1}$ [from Theorem 2(a)] $= \sum_{n=0}^{\infty}(-1)^n(n+1)x^n$ with $R = 1$.

In the last step, note that we *decreased* the initial value of the summation variable n by 1, and then *increased* each occurrence of n in the term by 1 [also note that $(-1)^{n+2} = (-1)^n$].

(b) $f(x) = \dfrac{1}{(1+x)^3} = -\dfrac{1}{2}\dfrac{d}{dx}\left[\dfrac{1}{(1+x)^2}\right] = -\dfrac{1}{2}\dfrac{d}{dx}\left[\sum_{n=0}^{\infty}(-1)^n(n+1)x^n\right]$ [from part (a)]

$= -\dfrac{1}{2}\sum_{n=1}^{\infty}(-1)^n(n+1)nx^{n-1} = \dfrac{1}{2}\sum_{n=0}^{\infty}(-1)^n(n+2)(n+1)x^n$ with $R = 1$.

(c) $f(x) = \dfrac{x^2}{(1+x)^3} = x^2 \cdot \dfrac{1}{(1+x)^3} = x^2 \cdot \dfrac{1}{2}\sum_{n=0}^{\infty}(-1)^n(n+2)(n+1)x^n$ [from part (b)]

$= \dfrac{1}{2}\sum_{n=0}^{\infty}(-1)^n(n+2)(n+1)x^{n+2}$. To write the power series with x^n rather than x^{n+2},

we will *decrease* each occurrence of n in the term by 2 and *increase* the initial value of the summation variable

by 2. This gives us $\dfrac{1}{2}\sum_{n=2}^{\infty}(-1)^n(n)(n-1)x^n$.

12. (a) $f(x) = \dfrac{1}{1+x} = \sum_{n=0}^{\infty}(-1)^n x^n$ [geometric series with $R = 1$], so

$$f(x) = \ln(1+x) = \int \dfrac{dx}{1+x} = \int\left[\sum_{n=0}^{\infty}(-1)^n x^n\right]dx = C + \sum_{n=0}^{\infty}(-1)^n\dfrac{x^{n+1}}{n+1}$$

$$= \sum_{n=1}^{\infty}\dfrac{(-1)^{n-1}x^n}{n} \quad [C = 0 \text{ since } f(0) = 0], \text{ with } R = 1$$

(b) $f(x) = x\ln(1+x) = x\left[\sum_{n=1}^{\infty}\dfrac{(-1)^{n-1}x^n}{n}\right]$ [by part (a)] $= \sum_{n=1}^{\infty}\dfrac{(-1)^{n-1}x^{n+1}}{n} = \sum_{n=2}^{\infty}\dfrac{(-1)^n x^n}{n-1}$

with $R = 1$.

13. $f(x) = \ln(5-x) = -\int \dfrac{dx}{5-x} = -\dfrac{1}{5}\int\dfrac{dx}{1-x/5}$

$= -\dfrac{1}{5}\int\left[\sum_{n=0}^{\infty}\left(\dfrac{x}{5}\right)^n\right]dx = C - \dfrac{1}{5}\sum_{n=0}^{\infty}\dfrac{x^{n+1}}{5^n(n+1)} = C - \sum_{n=1}^{\infty}\dfrac{x^n}{n5^n}$

Putting $x = 0$, we get $C = \ln 5$. The series converges for $|x/5| < 1 \iff |x| < 5$, so $R = 5$.

14. We know that $\dfrac{1}{1-2x} = \sum\limits_{n=0}^{\infty}(2x)^n$. Differentiating, we get $\dfrac{2}{(1-2x)^2} = \sum\limits_{n=1}^{\infty}2^n n x^{n-1} = \sum\limits_{n=0}^{\infty}2^{n+1}(n+1)x^n$, so

$f(x) = \dfrac{x^2}{(1-2x)^2} = \dfrac{x^2}{2} \cdot \dfrac{2}{(1-2x)^2} = \dfrac{x^2}{2}\sum\limits_{n=0}^{\infty}2^{n+1}(n+1)x^n = \sum\limits_{n=0}^{\infty}2^n(n+1)x^{n+2}$ or $\sum\limits_{n=2}^{\infty}2^{n-2}(n-1)x^n$,

with $R = \frac{1}{2}$.

15. $\dfrac{1}{2-x} = \dfrac{1}{2(1-x/2)} = \dfrac{1}{2}\sum\limits_{n=0}^{\infty}\left(\dfrac{x}{2}\right)^n = \sum\limits_{n=0}^{\infty}\dfrac{1}{2^{n+1}}x^n$ for $\left|\dfrac{x}{2}\right| < 1 \iff |x| < 2$. Now

$\dfrac{1}{(x-2)^2} = \dfrac{d}{dx}\left(\dfrac{1}{2-x}\right) = \dfrac{d}{dx}\left(\sum\limits_{n=0}^{\infty}\dfrac{1}{2^{n+1}}x^n\right) = \sum\limits_{n=1}^{\infty}\dfrac{n}{2^{n+1}}x^{n-1} = \sum\limits_{n=0}^{\infty}\dfrac{n+1}{2^{n+2}}x^n$. So

$f(x) = \dfrac{x^3}{(x-2)^2} = x^3\sum\limits_{n=0}^{\infty}\dfrac{n+1}{2^{n+2}}x^n = \sum\limits_{n=0}^{\infty}\dfrac{n+1}{2^{n+2}}x^{n+3}$ or $\sum\limits_{n=3}^{\infty}\dfrac{n-2}{2^{n-1}}x^n$ for $|x| < 2$. Thus, $R = 2$ and

$I = (-2, 2)$.

16. From Example 7, $g(x) = \arctan x = \sum\limits_{n=0}^{\infty}(-1)^n\dfrac{x^{2n+1}}{2n+1}$. Thus,

$f(x) = \arctan(x/3) = \sum\limits_{n=0}^{\infty}(-1)^n\dfrac{(x/3)^{2n+1}}{2n+1} = \sum\limits_{n=0}^{\infty}(-1)^n\dfrac{1}{3^{2n+1}(2n+1)}x^{2n+1}$ for $\left|\dfrac{x}{3}\right| < 1 \iff |x| < 3$,

so $R = 3$.

17. $f(x) = \ln(3+x) = \displaystyle\int\dfrac{dx}{3+x} = \dfrac{1}{3}\int\dfrac{dx}{1+x/3} = \dfrac{1}{3}\int\dfrac{dx}{1-(-x/3)} = \dfrac{1}{3}\int\sum\limits_{n=0}^{\infty}\left(-\dfrac{x}{3}\right)^n dx$

$= C + \dfrac{1}{3}\sum\limits_{n=0}^{\infty}\dfrac{(-1)^n}{(n+1)3^n}x^{n+1} = \ln 3 + \dfrac{1}{3}\sum\limits_{n=1}^{\infty}\dfrac{(-1)^{n-1}}{n3^{n-1}}x^n$ $[C = f(0) = \ln 3]$

$= \ln 3 + \sum\limits_{n=1}^{\infty}\dfrac{(-1)^{n-1}}{n3^n}x^n$. The series converges when $|-x/3| < 1 \iff |x| < 3$, so $R = 3$.

The terms of the series are $a_0 = \ln 3, a_1 = \dfrac{x}{3}, a_2 = -\dfrac{x^2}{18}, a_3 = \dfrac{x^3}{81}, a_4 = -\dfrac{x^4}{324}, a_5 = \dfrac{x^5}{1215}, \ldots$.

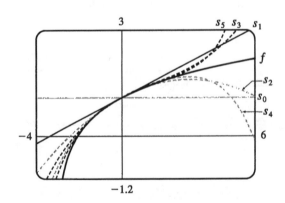

As n increases, $s_n(x)$ approximates f better on the interval of convergence, which is $(-3, 3)$.

18. $f(x) = \dfrac{1}{x^2 + 25} = \dfrac{1}{25}\left(\dfrac{1}{1 + x^2/25}\right) = \dfrac{1}{25}\left(\dfrac{1}{1 - (-x^2/25)}\right) = \dfrac{1}{25}\displaystyle\sum_{n=0}^{\infty}\left(-\dfrac{x^2}{25}\right)^n = \dfrac{1}{25}\displaystyle\sum_{n=0}^{\infty}(-1)^n\left(\dfrac{x}{5}\right)^{2n}$.

The series converges when $\left|-x^2/25\right| < 1 \iff x^2 < 25 \iff |x| < 5$, so $R = 5$. The terms of the series are

$a_0 = \dfrac{1}{25}, a_1 = -\dfrac{x^2}{625}, a_2 = \dfrac{x^4}{15{,}625}, \ldots$

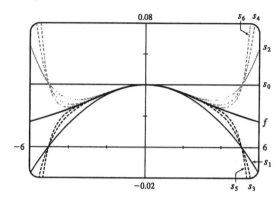

As n increases, $s_n(x)$ approximates f better on the interval of convergence, which is $(-5, 5)$.

19. $f(x) = \ln\left(\dfrac{1+x}{1-x}\right) = \ln(1+x) - \ln(1-x) = \displaystyle\int \dfrac{dx}{1+x} + \int \dfrac{dx}{1-x}$

$\qquad = \displaystyle\int \dfrac{dx}{1 - (-x)} + \int \dfrac{dx}{1 - x} = \int \left[\sum_{n=0}^{\infty}(-1)^n x^n + \sum_{n=0}^{\infty} x^n\right] dx$

$\qquad = \displaystyle\int \left[(1 - x + x^2 - x^3 + x^4 - \cdots) + (1 + x + x^2 + x^3 + x^4 + \cdots)\right] dx$

$\qquad = \displaystyle\int (2 + 2x^2 + 2x^4 + \cdots)\, dx = \int \sum_{n=0}^{\infty} 2x^{2n}\, dx = C + \sum_{n=0}^{\infty} \dfrac{2x^{2n+1}}{2n+1}$

But $f(0) = \ln\frac{1}{1} = 0$, so $C = 0$ and we have $f(x) = \displaystyle\sum_{n=0}^{\infty} \dfrac{2x^{2n+1}}{2n+1}$ with $R = 1$. If $x = \pm 1$, then

$f(x) = \pm 2 \displaystyle\sum_{n=0}^{\infty} \dfrac{1}{2n+1}$, which both diverge by the Limit Comparison Test with $b_n = \dfrac{1}{n}$.

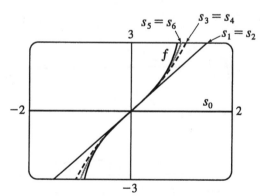

As n increases, $s_n(x)$ approximates f better on the interval of convergence, which is $(-1, 1)$.

20. $f(x) = \tan^{-1}(2x) = 2\int \dfrac{dx}{1 + 4x^2} = 2\int \sum\limits_{n=0}^{\infty} (-1)^n \left(4x^2\right)^n \, dx = 2\int \sum\limits_{n=0}^{\infty} (-1)^n 4^n x^{2n} \, dx$

$= C + 2\sum\limits_{n=0}^{\infty} \dfrac{(-1)^n 4^n x^{2n+1}}{2n+1} = \sum\limits_{n=0}^{\infty} \dfrac{(-1)^n 2^{2n+1} x^{2n+1}}{2n+1}$ $\quad [f(0) = \tan^{-1} 0 = 0, \text{ so } C = 0]$.

The series converges when $\left|4x^2\right| < 1 \Leftrightarrow |x| < \frac{1}{2}$, so $R = \frac{1}{2}$. If $x = \pm\frac{1}{2}$, then $f(x) = \sum\limits_{n=0}^{\infty} (-1)^n \dfrac{1}{2n+1}$ and

$f(x) = \sum\limits_{n=0}^{\infty} (-1)^{n+1} \dfrac{1}{2n+1}$, respectively. Both series converge by the Alternating Series Test.

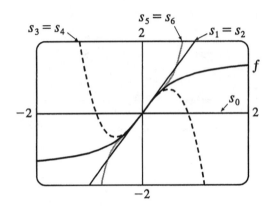

As n increases, $s_n(x)$ approximates f better on the interval of convergence, which is $\left[-\frac{1}{2}, \frac{1}{2}\right]$.

21. $\int \dfrac{dx}{1 + x^4} = \int \dfrac{dx}{1 - (-x^4)} = \int \sum\limits_{n=0}^{\infty} \left(-x^4\right)^n \, dx = \int \sum\limits_{n=0}^{\infty} (-1)^n x^{4n} \, dx = C + \sum\limits_{n=0}^{\infty} \dfrac{(-1)^n x^{4n+1}}{4n+1}$ with $R = 1$.

22. $\dfrac{1}{1 + x^5} = \sum\limits_{n=0}^{\infty} (-1)^n x^{5n} \;\Rightarrow\; \dfrac{x}{1 + x^5} = \sum\limits_{n=0}^{\infty} (-1)^n x^{5n+1} \;\Rightarrow\; \int \dfrac{x}{1 + x^5} \, dx = C + \sum\limits_{n=0}^{\infty} \dfrac{(-1)^n x^{5n+2}}{5n+2}$

with $R = 1$.

23. By Example 7, $\arctan x = \sum\limits_{n=0}^{\infty} (-1)^n \dfrac{x^{2n+1}}{2n+1}$, so

$\int \dfrac{\arctan x}{x} \, dx = \int \sum\limits_{n=0}^{\infty} (-1)^n \dfrac{x^{2n}}{2n+1} \, dx = C + \sum\limits_{n=0}^{\infty} (-1)^n \dfrac{x^{2n+1}}{(2n+1)^2}$ with $R = 1$.

24. By Example 7, $\int \tan^{-1}(x^2) \, dx = \int \sum\limits_{n=0}^{\infty} (-1)^n \dfrac{\left(x^2\right)^{2n+1}}{2n+1} \, dx = C + \sum\limits_{n=0}^{\infty} (-1)^n \dfrac{x^{4n+3}}{(2n+1)(4n+3)}$ with $R = 1$.

25. $\dfrac{1}{1 + x^5} = \dfrac{1}{1 - (-x^5)} = \sum\limits_{n=0}^{\infty} \left(-x^5\right)^n = \sum\limits_{n=0}^{\infty} (-1)^n x^{5n} \;\Rightarrow\;$

$\int \dfrac{1}{1 + x^5} \, dx = \int \sum\limits_{n=0}^{\infty} (-1)^n x^{5n} \, dx = C + \sum\limits_{n=0}^{\infty} (-1)^n \dfrac{x^{5n+1}}{5n+1}$. Thus,

$I = \displaystyle\int_0^{0.2} \dfrac{1}{1 + x^5} \, dx = \left[x - \dfrac{x^6}{6} + \dfrac{x^{11}}{11} - \cdots \right]_0^{0.2} = 0.2 - \dfrac{(0.2)^6}{6} + \dfrac{(0.2)^{11}}{11} - \cdots$. The series is alternating, so

if we use the first two terms, the error is at most $(0.2)^{11}/11 \approx 1.9 \times 10^{-9}$. So $I \approx 0.2 - (0.2)^6/6 \approx 0.199989$ to six decimal places.

26. From Example 6 we know $\ln(1-x) = -\sum\limits_{n=1}^{\infty} \dfrac{x^n}{n}$, so

$$\ln(1+x^4) = \ln[1-(-x^4)] = -\sum_{n=1}^{\infty} \frac{(-x^4)^n}{n} = \sum_{n=1}^{\infty} (-1)^{n+1} \frac{x^{4n}}{n} \quad \Rightarrow$$

$$\int \ln(1+x^4)\,dx = \int \sum_{n=1}^{\infty} (-1)^{n+1} \frac{x^{4n}}{n}\,dx = C + \sum_{n=1}^{\infty} (-1)^{n+1} \frac{x^{4n+1}}{n(4n+1)}. \text{ Thus,}$$

$$I = \int_0^{0.4} \ln(1+x^4)\,dx = \left[\frac{x^5}{5} - \frac{x^9}{18} + \frac{x^{13}}{39} - \frac{x^{17}}{68} + \cdots\right]_0^{0.4} = \frac{(0.4)^5}{5} - \frac{(0.4)^9}{18} + \frac{(0.4)^{13}}{39} - \frac{(0.4)^{17}}{68} + \cdots.$$

The series is alternating, so if we use the first three terms, the error is at most $(0.4)^{17}/68 \approx 2.5 \times 10^{-9}$. So $I \approx (0.4)^5/5 - (0.4)^9/18 + (0.9)^{13}/39 \approx 0.002034$ to six decimal places.

27. We substitute x^4 for x in Example 7, and find that

$$\int x^2 \tan^{-1}(x^4)\,dx = \int x^2 \sum_{n=0}^{\infty} (-1)^n \frac{(x^4)^{2n+1}}{2n+1}\,dx$$

$$= \int \sum_{n=0}^{\infty} (-1)^n \frac{x^{8n+6}}{2n+1}\,dx = C + \sum_{n=0}^{\infty} (-1)^n \frac{x^{8n+7}}{(2n+1)(8n+7)}$$

So $\displaystyle\int_0^{1/3} x^2 \tan^{-1}(x^4)\,dx = \left[\frac{x^7}{7} - \frac{x^{15}}{45} + \cdots\right]_0^{1/3} = \frac{1}{7\cdot 3^7} - \frac{1}{45\cdot 3^{15}} + \cdots.$ The series is alternating,

so if we use only one term, the error is at most $1/(45\cdot 3^{15}) \approx 1.5 \times 10^{-9}$. So $\int_0^{1/3} x^2 \tan^{-1}(x^4)\,dx \approx 1/(7\cdot 3^7) \approx 0.000065$ to six decimal places.

28. $\displaystyle\int_0^{0.5} \frac{dx}{1+x^6} = \int_0^{0.5} \sum_{n=0}^{\infty} (-1)^n x^{6n}\,dx = \sum_{n=0}^{\infty} \left[\frac{(-1)^n x^{6n+1}}{6n+1}\right]_0^{1/2} = \sum_{n=0}^{\infty} \frac{(-1)^n}{(6n+1)2^{6n+1}}$

$$= \frac{1}{2} - \frac{1}{7\cdot 2^7} + \frac{1}{13\cdot 2^{13}} - \frac{1}{19\cdot 2^{19}} + \cdots$$

The series is alternating, so if we use only three terms, the error is at most $\dfrac{1}{19\cdot 2^{19}} \approx 1.0 \times 10^{-7}$. So, to six

decimal places, $\displaystyle\int_0^{0.5} \frac{dx}{1+x^6} \approx \frac{1}{2} - \frac{1}{7\cdot 2^7} + \frac{1}{13\cdot 2^{13}} \approx 0.498893.$

29. Using the result of Example 6, $\ln(1-x) = -\sum\limits_{n=1}^{\infty} \dfrac{x^n}{n}$, with $x = -0.1$, we have

$$\ln 1.1 = \ln[1-(-0.1)] = 0.1 - \frac{0.01}{2} + \frac{0.001}{3} - \frac{0.0001}{4} + \frac{0.00001}{5} - \cdots. \text{ The series is alternating, so if}$$

we use only the first four terms, the error is at most $\dfrac{0.00001}{5} = 0.000002.$ So

$$\ln 1.1 \approx 0.1 - \frac{0.01}{2} + \frac{0.001}{3} - \frac{0.0001}{4} \approx 0.09531.$$

30. $f(x) = \sum\limits_{n=0}^{\infty} \dfrac{(-1)^n x^{2n}}{(2n)!} \quad \Rightarrow \quad f'(x) = \sum\limits_{n=1}^{\infty} \dfrac{(-1)^n 2n x^{2n-1}}{(2n)!}$ (the first term disappears), so

$$f''(x) = \sum_{n=1}^{\infty} \frac{(-1)^n (2n)(2n-1)x^{2n-2}}{(2n)!} = \sum_{n=1}^{\infty} \frac{(-1)^n x^{2(n-1)}}{[2(n-1)]!} = \sum_{n=0}^{\infty} \frac{(-1)^{n+1} x^{2n}}{(2n)!} \quad \text{(substituting } n+1 \text{ for } n\text{)}$$

$$= -\sum_{n=0}^{\infty} \frac{(-1)^n x^{2n}}{(2n)!} = -f(x) \quad \Rightarrow \quad f''(x) + f(x) = 0.$$

31. (a) $J_0(x) = \sum\limits_{n=0}^{\infty} \dfrac{(-1)^n\, x^{2n}}{2^{2n}(n!)^2}$, $J_0'(x) = \sum\limits_{n=1}^{\infty} \dfrac{(-1)^n\, 2nx^{2n-1}}{2^{2n}(n!)^2}$, and $J_0''(x) = \sum\limits_{n=1}^{\infty} \dfrac{(-1)^n\, 2n(2n-1)x^{2n-2}}{2^{2n}(n!)^2}$, so

$$x^2 J_0''(x) + xJ_0'(x) + x^2 J_0(x) = \sum_{n=1}^{\infty} \frac{(-1)^n\, 2n(2n-1)x^{2n}}{2^{2n}(n!)^2} + \sum_{n=1}^{\infty} \frac{(-1)^n\, 2nx^{2n}}{2^{2n}(n!)^2} + \sum_{n=0}^{\infty} \frac{(-1)^n\, x^{2n+2}}{2^{2n}(n!)^2}$$

$$= \sum_{n=1}^{\infty} \frac{(-1)^n\, 2n(2n-1)x^{2n}}{2^{2n}(n!)^2} + \sum_{n=1}^{\infty} \frac{(-1)^n\, 2nx^{2n}}{2^{2n}(n!)^2} + \sum_{n=1}^{\infty} \frac{(-1)^{n-1}\, x^{2n}}{2^{2n-2}\,[(n-1)!]^2}$$

$$= \sum_{n=1}^{\infty} \frac{(-1)^n\, 2n(2n-1)x^{2n}}{2^{2n}(n!)^2} + \sum_{n=1}^{\infty} \frac{(-1)^n\, 2nx^{2n}}{2^{2n}(n!)^2} + \sum_{n=1}^{\infty} \frac{(-1)^n(-1)^{-1}2^2 n^2 x^{2n}}{2^{2n}(n!)^2}$$

$$= \sum_{n=1}^{\infty} (-1)^n \left[\frac{2n(2n-1) + 2n - 2^2 n^2}{2^{2n}(n!)^2} \right] x^{2n} = \sum_{n=1}^{\infty} (-1)^n \left[\frac{4n^2 - 2n + 2n - 4n^2}{2^{2n}(n!)^2} \right] x^{2n} = 0$$

(b) $\displaystyle\int_0^1 J_0(x)\,dx = \int_0^1 \left[\sum_{n=0}^{\infty} \frac{(-1)^n\, x^{2n}}{2^{2n}(n!)^2} \right] dx = \int_0^1 \left(1 - \frac{x^2}{4} + \frac{x^4}{64} - \frac{x^6}{2304} + \cdots \right) dx$

$$= \left[x - \frac{x^3}{3\cdot 4} + \frac{x^5}{5\cdot 64} - \frac{x^7}{7\cdot 2304} + \cdots \right]_0^1 = 1 - \frac{1}{12} + \frac{1}{320} - \frac{1}{16{,}128} + \cdots$$

Since $\frac{1}{16{,}128} \approx 0.000062$, it follows from The Alternating Series Estimation Theorem that, correct to three decimal places, $\int_0^1 J_0(x)\,dx \approx 1 - \frac{1}{12} + \frac{1}{320} \approx 0.920$.

32. (a) $J_1(x) = \sum\limits_{n=0}^{\infty} \dfrac{(-1)^n x^{2n+1}}{n!\,(n+1)!\,2^{2n+1}}$, $J_1'(x) = \sum\limits_{n=0}^{\infty} \dfrac{(-1)^n\,(2n+1)\,x^{2n}}{n!\,(n+1)!\,2^{2n+1}}$, and

$J_1''(x) = \sum\limits_{n=1}^{\infty} \dfrac{(-1)^n\,(2n+1)\,(2n)\,x^{2n-1}}{n!\,(n+1)!\,2^{2n+1}}$.

$x^2 J_1''(x) + xJ_1'(x) + \left(x^2 - 1 \right) J_1(x)$

$$= \sum_{n=1}^{\infty} \frac{(-1)^n\,(2n+1)(2n)x^{2n+1}}{n!\,(n+1)!\,2^{2n+1}} + \sum_{n=0}^{\infty} \frac{(-1)^n\,(2n+1)x^{2n+1}}{n!\,(n+1)!\,2^{2n+1}}$$

$$+ \sum_{n=0}^{\infty} \frac{(-1)^n\, x^{2n+3}}{n!\,(n+1)!\,2^{2n+1}} - \sum_{n=0}^{\infty} \frac{(-1)^n\, x^{2n+1}}{n!\,(n+1)!\,2^{2n+1}}$$

$$= \sum_{n=1}^{\infty} \frac{(-1)^n\,(2n+1)(2n)x^{2n+1}}{n!\,(n+1)!\,2^{2n+1}} + \sum_{n=0}^{\infty} \frac{(-1)^n\,(2n+1)x^{2n+1}}{n!\,(n+1)!\,2^{2n+1}}$$

$$- \sum_{n=1}^{\infty} \frac{(-1)^n\, x^{2n+1}}{(n-1)!\,n!\,2^{2n-1}} - \sum_{n=0}^{\infty} \frac{(-1)^n\, x^{2n+1}}{n!\,(n+1)!\,2^{2n+1}} \qquad \left(\begin{array}{l} \text{Replace } n \text{ with } n-1 \\ \text{in the third term} \end{array} \right)$$

$$= \frac{x}{2} - \frac{x}{2} + \sum_{n=1}^{\infty} (-1)^n \left[\frac{(2n+1)(2n) + (2n+1) - (n)((n+1)2^2 - 1)}{n!\,(n+1)!\,2^{2n+1}} \right] x^{2n+1} = 0$$

(b) $J_0(x) = \sum_{n=0}^{\infty} \frac{(-1)^n x^{2n}}{2^{2n} (n!)^2} \quad \Rightarrow$

$$J_0'(x) = \sum_{n=1}^{\infty} \frac{(-1)^n (2n)x^{2n-1}}{2^{2n} (n!)^2} = \sum_{n=0}^{\infty} \frac{(-1)^{n+1} 2(n+1)x^{2n+1}}{2^{2n+2} [(n+1)!]^2} \quad \text{(Replace } n \text{ with } n+1\text{)}$$

$$= -\sum_{n=0}^{\infty} \frac{(-1)^n x^{2n+1}}{2^{2n+1}(n+1)! \, n!} \quad \text{(cancel 2 and } n+1\text{; take } -1 \text{ outside sum)} \quad = -J_1(x)$$

33. (a) $f(x) = \sum_{n=0}^{\infty} \frac{x^n}{n!} \quad \Rightarrow \quad f'(x) = \sum_{n=1}^{\infty} \frac{nx^{n-1}}{n!} = \sum_{n=1}^{\infty} \frac{x^{n-1}}{(n-1)!} = \sum_{n=0}^{\infty} \frac{x^n}{n!} = f(x)$

(b) By Theorem 7.4.2, the only solution to the differential equation $df(x)/dx = f(x)$ is $f(x) = Ke^x$, but $f(0) = 1$, so $K = 1$ and $f(x) = e^x$.

Or: We could solve the equation $df(x)/dx = f(x)$ as a separable differential equation.

34. $\frac{|\sin nx|}{n^2} \le \frac{1}{n^2}$, so $\sum_{n=1}^{\infty} \frac{\sin nx}{n^2}$ converges by the Comparison Test. $\frac{d}{dx}\left(\frac{\sin nx}{n^2}\right) = \frac{\cos nx}{n}$, so when $x = 2k\pi$

(k an integer), $\sum_{n=1}^{\infty} f_n'(x) = \sum_{n=1}^{\infty} \frac{\cos(2kn\pi)}{n} = \sum_{n=1}^{\infty} \frac{1}{n}$, which diverges (harmonic series). $f_n''(x) = -\sin nx$, so

$\sum_{n=1}^{\infty} f_n''(x) = -\sum_{n=1}^{\infty} \sin nx$, which converges only if $\sin nx = 0$, or $x = k\pi$ (k an integer).

35. If $a_n = \frac{x^n}{n^2}$, then by the Ratio Test, $\lim_{n\to\infty}\left|\frac{a_{n+1}}{a_n}\right| = \lim_{n\to\infty}\left|\frac{x^{n+1}}{(n+1)^2} \cdot \frac{n^2}{x^n}\right| = |x|\lim_{n\to\infty}\left(\frac{n}{n+1}\right)^2 = |x| < 1$ for

convergence, so $R = 1$. When $x = \pm1$, $\sum_{n=1}^{\infty}\left|\frac{x^n}{n^2}\right| = \sum_{n=1}^{\infty}\frac{1}{n^2}$ which is a convergent p-series ($p = 2 > 1$), so the

interval of convergence for f is $[-1, 1]$. By Theorem 2, the radii of convergence of f' and f'' are both 1, so we need

only check the endpoints. $f(x) = \sum_{n=1}^{\infty} \frac{x^n}{n^2} \quad \Rightarrow \quad f'(x) = \sum_{n=1}^{\infty} \frac{nx^{n-1}}{n^2} = \sum_{n=0}^{\infty} \frac{x^n}{n+1}$, and this series diverges for

$x = 1$ (harmonic series) and converges for $x = -1$ (Alternating Series Test), so the interval of convergence

is $[-1, 1)$. $f''(x) = \sum_{n=1}^{\infty} \frac{nx^{n-1}}{n+1}$ diverges at both 1 and -1 (Test for Divergence) since $\lim_{n\to\infty} \frac{n}{n+1} = 1 \ne 0$, so its

interval of convergence is $(-1, 1)$.

36. (a) $\sum_{n=1}^{\infty} nx^{n-1} = \sum_{n=0}^{\infty} \frac{d}{dx} x^n = \frac{d}{dx}\left[\sum_{n=0}^{\infty} x_n\right] = \frac{d}{dx}\left[\frac{1}{1-x}\right] = -\frac{1}{(1-x)^2}(-1) = \frac{1}{(1-x)^2}, |x| < 1.$

(b) (i) $\sum_{n=1}^{\infty} nx^n = x\sum_{n=1}^{\infty} nx^{n-1} = x\left[\frac{1}{(1-x)^2}\right]$ [from part (a)] $= \frac{x}{(1-x)^2}$ for $|x| < 1$.

(ii) Put $x = \frac{1}{2}$ in (i): $\sum_{n=1}^{\infty} \frac{n}{2^n} = \sum_{n=1}^{\infty} n\left(\frac{1}{2}\right)^n = \frac{1/2}{(1-1/2)^2} = 2.$

(c) (i) $\sum_{n=2}^{\infty} n(n-1)x^n = x^2 \sum_{n=2}^{\infty} n(n-1)x^{n-2} = x^2 \frac{d}{dx}\left[\sum_{n=1}^{\infty} nx^{n-1}\right] = x^2 \frac{d}{dx}\frac{1}{(1-x)^2}$

$$= x^2 \frac{2}{(1-x)^3} = \frac{2x^2}{(1-x)^3} \text{ for } |x| < 1.$$

(ii) Put $x = \frac{1}{2}$ in (i): $\sum_{n=2}^{\infty} \frac{n^2 - n}{2^n} = \sum_{n=2}^{\infty} n(n-1)\left(\frac{1}{2}\right)^n = \frac{2(1/2)^2}{(1-1/2)^3} = 4.$

(iii) From (b)(ii) and (c)(ii), we have $\sum_{n=1}^{\infty} \frac{n^2}{2^n} = \sum_{n=1}^{\infty} \frac{n^2 - n}{2^n} + \sum_{n=1}^{\infty} \frac{n}{2^n} = 4 + 2 = 6.$

8.7 **Taylor and Maclaurin Series** • • • • • • • • • •

1. Using Theorem 5 with $\sum_{n=0}^{\infty} b_n(x-5)^n$, $b_n = \dfrac{f^{(n)}(a)}{n!}$, so $b_8 = \dfrac{f^{(8)}(5)}{8!}$.

2. (a) Using Formula 6, a power series expansion of f at 1 must have the form $f(1) + f'(1)(x-1) + \cdots$. Comparing to the given series, $1.6 - 0.8(x-1) + \cdots$, we must have $f'(1) = -0.8$. But from the graph, $f'(1)$ is positive. Hence, the given series is *not* the Taylor series of f centered at 1.

(b) A power series expansion of f at 2 must have the form $f(2) + f'(2)(x-2) + \frac{1}{2}f''(2)(x-2)^2 + \cdots$. Comparing to the given series, $2.8 + 0.5(x-2) + 1.5(x-2)^2 - 0.1(x-2)^3 + \cdots$, we must have $\frac{1}{2}f''(2) = 1.5$; that is, $f''(2)$ is positive. But from the graph, f is concave downward near $x = 2$, so $f''(2)$ must be negative. Hence, the given series is *not* the Taylor series of f centered at 2.

3.

n	$f^{(n)}(x)$	$f^{(n)}(0)$
0	$\cos x$	1
1	$-\sin x$	0
2	$-\cos x$	-1
3	$\sin x$	0
4	$\cos x$	1
$\vdots$	$\vdots$	$\vdots$

We use Equation 7 with $f(x) = \cos x$.

$$\cos x = f(0) + f'(0)x + \frac{f''(0)}{2!}x^2 + \frac{f^{(3)}(0)}{3!}x^3 + \frac{f^{(4)}(0)}{4!}x^4 + \cdots$$

$$= 1 - \frac{x^2}{2!} + \frac{x^4}{4!} - \cdots = \sum_{n=0}^{\infty} \frac{(-1)^n x^{2n}}{(2n)!}$$

If $a_n = \dfrac{(-1)^n x^{2n}}{(2n)!}$, then

$$\lim_{n\to\infty}\left|\frac{a_{n+1}}{a_n}\right| = \lim_{n\to\infty}\left|\frac{x^{2n+2}}{(2n+2)!}\cdot\frac{(2n)!}{x^{2n}}\right| = x^2 \lim_{n\to\infty}\frac{1}{(2n+2)(2n+1)} = 0 < 1 \text{ for all } x.$$

So $R = \infty$ (Ratio Test).

4.

n	$f^{(n)}(x)$	$f^{(n)}(0)$
0	$\sin 2x$	0
1	$2\cos 2x$	2
2	$-2^2 \sin 2x$	0
3	$-2^3 \cos 2x$	-2^3
4	$2^4 \sin 2x$	0
$\vdots$	$\vdots$	$\vdots$

$f^{(n)}(0) = 0$ if n is even and $f^{(2n+1)}(0) = (-1)^n 2^{2n+1}$, so

$$\sin 2x = \sum_{n=0}^{\infty} \frac{f^{(n)}(0)}{n!}x^n = \sum_{n=0}^{\infty} \frac{f^{(2n+1)}(0)}{(2n+1)!}x^{2n+1}$$

$$= \sum_{n=0}^{\infty} \frac{(-1)^n 2^{2n+1} x^{2n+1}}{(2n+1)!}$$

$$\lim_{n\to\infty}\left|\frac{a_{n+1}}{a_n}\right| = \lim_{n\to\infty}\frac{2^2 |x|^2}{(2n+3)(2n+2)} = 0 < 1 \text{ for all } x,$$

so $R = \infty$ (Ratio Test).

5.

n	$f^{(n)}(x)$	$f^{(n)}(0)$
0	$(1+x)^{-3}$	1
1	$-3(1+x)^{-4}$	-3
2	$12(1+x)^{-5}$	12
3	$-60(1+x)^{-6}$	-60
4	$360(1+x)^{-7}$	360
$\vdots$	$\vdots$	$\vdots$

$$(1+x)^{-3} = f(0) + f'(0)x + \frac{f''(0)}{2!}x^2 + \frac{f'''(0)}{3!}x^3 + \frac{f^{(4)}(0)}{4!}x^4 + \cdots$$

$$= 1 - 3x + \frac{4 \cdot 3}{2!}x^2 - \frac{5 \cdot 4 \cdot 3}{3!}x^3 + \frac{6 \cdot 5 \cdot 4 \cdot 3}{4!}x^4 - \cdots$$

$$= 1 - 3x + \frac{4 \cdot 3 \cdot 2}{2 \cdot 2!}x^2 - \frac{5 \cdot 4 \cdot 3 \cdot 2}{2 \cdot 3!}x^3 + \frac{6 \cdot 5 \cdot 4 \cdot 3 \cdot 2}{2 \cdot 4!}x^4 - \cdots$$

$$= \sum_{n=0}^{\infty} \frac{(-1)^n(n+2)!\,x^n}{2(n!)} = \sum_{n=0}^{\infty} \frac{(-1)^n(n+2)(n+1)x^n}{2}$$

$$\lim_{n\to\infty}\left|\frac{a_{n+1}}{a_n}\right| = \lim_{n\to\infty}\left|\frac{(n+3)(n+2)x^{n+1}}{2} \cdot \frac{2}{(n+2)(n+1)x^n}\right| = |x|\lim_{n\to\infty}\frac{n+3}{n+1} = |x| < 1 \text{ for convergence,}$$

so $R = 1$ (Ratio Test).

6.

n	$f^{(n)}(x)$	$f^{(n)}(0)$
0	$\ln(1+x)$	0
1	$(1+x)^{-1}$	1
2	$-(1+x)^{-2}$	-1
3	$2(1+x)^{-3}$	2
4	$-6(1+x)^{-4}$	-6
5	$24(1+x)^{-5}$	24
$\vdots$	$\vdots$	$\vdots$

$$\ln(1+x) = f(0) + f'(0)x + \frac{f''(0)}{2!}x^2 + \frac{f'''(0)}{3!}x^3$$

$$+ \frac{f^{(4)}(0)}{4!}x^4 + \frac{f^{(5)}(0)}{5!}x^5 + \cdots$$

$$= x - \tfrac{1}{2}x^2 + \tfrac{2}{6}x^3 - \tfrac{6}{24}x^4 + \tfrac{24}{120}x^5 - \cdots$$

$$= x - \frac{x^2}{2} + \frac{x^3}{3} - \frac{x^4}{4} + \frac{x^5}{5} - \cdots = \sum_{n=1}^{\infty} \frac{(-1)^{n-1}}{n}x^n$$

$$\lim_{n\to\infty}\left|\frac{a_{n+1}}{a_n}\right| = \lim_{n\to\infty}\left|\frac{x^{n+1}}{n+1} \cdot \frac{n}{x^n}\right| = \lim_{n\to\infty}\frac{|x|}{1+1/n} = |x| < 1 \text{ for}$$

convergence, so $R = 1$.

7.

n	$f^{(n)}(x)$	$f^{(n)}(2)$
0	$1+x+x^2$	7
1	$1+2x$	5
2	2	2
3	0	0
4	0	0
$\vdots$	$\vdots$	$\vdots$

$$f(x) = 7 + 5(x-2) + \frac{2}{2!}(x-2)^2 + \sum_{n=3}^{\infty}\frac{0}{n!}(x-2)^n$$

$$= 7 + 5(x-2) + (x-2)^2$$

Since $a_n = 0$ for large n, $R = \infty$.

8.

n	$f^{(n)}(x)$	$f^{(n)}(-1)$
0	x^3	-1
1	$3x^2$	3
2	$6x$	-6
3	6	6
4	0	0
5	0	0
$\vdots$	$\vdots$	$\vdots$

$$f(x) = -1 + 3(x+1) - \frac{6}{2!}(x+1)^2 + \frac{6}{3!}(x+1)^3$$
$$= -1 + 3(x+1) - 3(x+1)^2 + (x+1)^3$$

Since $a_n = 0$ for large n, $R = \infty$.

9. Clearly, $f^{(n)}(x) = e^x$, so $f^{(n)}(3) = e^3$ and $e^x = \sum\limits_{n=0}^{\infty} \frac{e^3}{n!}(x-3)^n$. If $a_n = \frac{e^3}{n!}(x-3)^n$, then

$$\lim_{n\to\infty}\left|\frac{a_{n+1}}{a_n}\right| = \lim_{n\to\infty}\left|\frac{e^3(x-3)^{n+1}}{(n+1)!} \cdot \frac{n!}{e^3(x-3)^n}\right| = \lim_{n\to\infty}\frac{|x-3|}{n+1} = 0 < 1 \text{ for all } x, \text{ so } R = \infty.$$

10.

n	$f^{(n)}(x)$	$f^{(n)}(2)$
0	$\ln x$	$\ln 2$
1	x^{-1}	$\frac{1}{2}$
2	$-x^{-2}$	$-\frac{1}{4}$
3	$2x^{-3}$	$\frac{2}{8}$
4	$-3 \cdot 2x^{-4}$	$-\frac{3 \cdot 2}{16}$
$\vdots$	$\vdots$	$\vdots$

$f^{(n)}(2) = \dfrac{(-1)^{n-1}(n-1)!}{2^n}$ for $n \geq 1$, so $\ln x = \ln 2 + \sum\limits_{n=1}^{\infty} \dfrac{(-1)^{n-1}(x-2)^n}{n \cdot 2^n}$.

$$\lim_{n\to\infty}\left|\frac{a_{n+1}}{a_n}\right| = \frac{|x-2|}{2}\lim_{n\to\infty}\frac{n}{n+1} = \frac{|x-2|}{2} < 1 \text{ for convergence, so } |x-2| < 2 \quad \Rightarrow \quad R = 2.$$

11.

n	$f^{(n)}(x)$	$f^{(n)}(1)$
0	x^{-1}	1
1	$-x^{-2}$	-1
2	$2x^{-3}$	2
3	$-3 \cdot 2x^{-4}$	$-3 \cdot 2$
4	$4 \cdot 3 \cdot 2x^{-5}$	$4 \cdot 3 \cdot 2$
$\vdots$	$\vdots$	$\vdots$

So $f^{(n)}(1) = (-1)^n n!$, and $\dfrac{1}{x} = \sum\limits_{n=0}^{\infty} \dfrac{(-1)^n n!}{n!}(x-1)^n = \sum\limits_{n=0}^{\infty}(-1)^n (x-1)^n$. If $a_n = (-1)^n(x-1)^n$ then

$$\lim_{n\to\infty}\left|\frac{a_{n+1}}{a_n}\right| = |x-1| < 1 \text{ for convergence, so } R = 1.$$

12.

n	$f^{(n)}(x)$	$f^{(n)}(4)$
0	$x^{1/2}$	2
1	$\frac{1}{2}x^{-1/2}$	2^{-2}
2	$-\frac{1}{4}x^{-3/2}$	-2^{-5}
3	$\frac{3}{8}x^{-5/2}$	$3\cdot 2^{-8}$
4	$-\frac{15}{16}x^{-7/2}$	$-15\cdot 2^{-11}$
⋮	⋮	⋮

$$f^{(n)}(4) = \frac{(-1)^{n-1}1\cdot 3\cdot 5\cdot\cdots\cdot(2n-3)}{2^{3n-1}} \text{ for } n \geq 2, \text{ so}$$

$$\sqrt{x} = 2 + \frac{x-4}{4} + \sum_{n=2}^{\infty}\frac{(-1)^{n-1}1\cdot 3\cdot 5\cdot\cdots\cdot(2n-3)}{2^{3n-1}n!}(x-4)^n.$$

$$\lim_{n\to\infty}\left|\frac{a_{n+1}}{a_n}\right| = \lim_{n\to\infty}\left|\frac{1\cdot 3\cdot 5\cdot\cdots\cdot(2n-3)(2n-1)(x-4)^{n+1}}{2^{3n+2}(n+1)!}\cdot\frac{2^{3n-1}n!}{1\cdot 3\cdot 5\cdot\cdots\cdot(2n-3)(x-4)^n}\right|$$

$$= \frac{|x-4|}{8}\lim_{n\to\infty}\left(\frac{2n-1}{n+1}\right) = \frac{|x-4|}{8}\cdot 2 = \frac{|x-4|}{4} < 1 \text{ for convergence,}$$

so $|x-4| < 4 \implies R = 4$.

13.

n	$f^{(n)}(x)$	$f^{(n)}\left(\frac{\pi}{4}\right)$
0	$\sin x$	$\sqrt{2}/2$
1	$\cos x$	$\sqrt{2}/2$
2	$-\sin x$	$-\sqrt{2}/2$
3	$-\cos x$	$-\sqrt{2}/2$
4	$\sin x$	$\sqrt{2}/2$
⋮	⋮	⋮

$$\sin x = f\left(\tfrac{\pi}{4}\right) + f'\left(\tfrac{\pi}{4}\right)\left(x-\tfrac{\pi}{4}\right) + \frac{f''\left(\tfrac{\pi}{4}\right)}{2!}\left(x-\tfrac{\pi}{4}\right)^2 + \frac{f^{(3)}\left(\tfrac{\pi}{4}\right)}{3!}\left(x-\tfrac{\pi}{4}\right)^3 + \frac{f^{(4)}\left(\tfrac{\pi}{4}\right)}{4!}\left(x-\tfrac{\pi}{4}\right)^4 + \cdots$$

$$= \frac{\sqrt{2}}{2}\left[1 + \left(x-\tfrac{\pi}{4}\right) - \tfrac{1}{2!}\left(x-\tfrac{\pi}{4}\right)^2 - \tfrac{1}{3!}\left(x-\tfrac{\pi}{4}\right)^3 + \tfrac{1}{4!}\left(x-\tfrac{\pi}{4}\right)^4 + \cdots\right]$$

$$= \frac{\sqrt{2}}{2}\left[1 - \tfrac{1}{2!}\left(x-\tfrac{\pi}{4}\right)^2 + \tfrac{1}{4!}\left(x-\tfrac{\pi}{4}\right)^4 - \cdots\right] + \frac{\sqrt{2}}{2}\left[\left(x-\tfrac{\pi}{4}\right) - \tfrac{1}{3!}\left(x-\tfrac{\pi}{4}\right)^3 + \cdots\right]$$

$$= \frac{\sqrt{2}}{2}\sum_{n=0}^{\infty}(-1)^n\left[\tfrac{1}{(2n)!}\left(x-\tfrac{\pi}{4}\right)^{2n} + \tfrac{1}{(2n+1)!}\left(x-\tfrac{\pi}{4}\right)^{2n+1}\right]$$

The series can also be written in the more elegant form $\sin x = \dfrac{\sqrt{2}}{2}\sum_{n=0}^{\infty}\dfrac{(-1)^{n(n-1)/2}\left(x-\frac{\pi}{4}\right)^n}{n!}$. If

$$a_n = \frac{(-1)^{n(n-1)/2}\left(x-\frac{\pi}{4}\right)^n}{n!}, \text{ then } \lim_{n\to\infty}\left|\frac{a_{n+1}}{a_n}\right| = \lim_{n\to\infty}\frac{\left|x-\frac{\pi}{4}\right|}{n+1} = 0 < 1 \text{ for all } x, \text{ so } R = \infty.$$

14.

n	$f^{(n)}(x)$	$f^{(n)}\left(-\frac{\pi}{4}\right)$
0	$\cos x$	$\sqrt{2}/2$
1	$-\sin x$	$\sqrt{2}/2$
2	$-\cos x$	$-\sqrt{2}/2$
3	$\sin x$	$-\sqrt{2}/2$
4	$\cos x$	$\sqrt{2}/2$
⋮	⋮	⋮

$$\cos x = f\left(-\tfrac{\pi}{4}\right) + f'\left(-\tfrac{\pi}{4}\right)\left(x+\tfrac{\pi}{4}\right) + \frac{f''\left(-\tfrac{\pi}{4}\right)}{2!}\left(x+\tfrac{\pi}{4}\right)^2$$

$$+ \frac{f^{(3)}\left(-\tfrac{\pi}{4}\right)}{3!}\left(x+\tfrac{\pi}{4}\right)^3 + \frac{f^{(4)}\left(-\tfrac{\pi}{4}\right)}{4!}\left(x+\tfrac{\pi}{4}\right)^4 + \cdots$$

$$= \frac{\sqrt{2}}{2}\left[1 + \left(x+\tfrac{\pi}{4}\right) - \tfrac{1}{2!}\left(x+\tfrac{\pi}{4}\right)^2\right.$$

$$\left. - \tfrac{1}{3!}\left(x+\tfrac{\pi}{4}\right)^3 + \tfrac{1}{4!}\left(x+\tfrac{\pi}{4}\right)^4 + \cdots\right]$$

$$= \frac{\sqrt{2}}{2}\left[1 - \tfrac{1}{2!}\left(x+\tfrac{\pi}{4}\right)^2 + \tfrac{1}{4!}\left(x+\tfrac{\pi}{4}\right)^4 - \cdots\right]$$

$$+ \frac{\sqrt{2}}{2}\left[\left(x+\tfrac{\pi}{4}\right) - \tfrac{1}{3!}\left(x+\tfrac{\pi}{4}\right)^3 + \cdots\right]$$

$$= \frac{\sqrt{2}}{2}\sum_{n=0}^{\infty}(-1)^n\left[\tfrac{1}{(2n)!}\left(x+\tfrac{\pi}{4}\right)^{2n} + \tfrac{1}{(2n+1)!}\left(x+\tfrac{\pi}{4}\right)^{2n+1}\right]$$

The series can also be written in the more elegant form $\dfrac{\sqrt{2}}{2}\displaystyle\sum_{n=0}^{\infty}\dfrac{(-1)^{n(n-1)/2}\left(x+\tfrac{\pi}{4}\right)^n}{n!}$ with $R=\infty$ by the Ratio Test (as in Exercise 13).

15. If $f(x) = \cos x$, then by Formula 9 with $a = 0$, $|R_n(x)| \le \dfrac{\left|f^{(n+1)}(x)\right|}{(n+1)!}\,|x|^{n+1}$. But $f^{(n+1)}(x) = \pm\sin x$ or $\pm\cos x$. In each case, $\left|f^{(n+1)}(x)\right| \le 1$, so $|R_n(x)| \le \dfrac{1}{(n+1)!}\,|x|^{n+1} \to 0$ as $n \to \infty$ by Equation 10. So $\lim\limits_{n\to\infty} R_n(x) = 0$ and, by Theorem 8, the series in Exercise 3 represents $\cos x$ for all x.

16. If $f(x) = \sin x$, then by Formula 9 with $a = \tfrac{\pi}{4}$, $|R_n(x)| \le \dfrac{\left|f^{(n+1)}(x)\right|}{(n+1)!}\,\left|x - \tfrac{\pi}{4}\right|^{n+1}$. But $f^{(n+1)}(x) = \pm\sin x$ or $\pm\cos x$. In each case, $\left|f^{(n+1)}(x)\right| \le 1$, so $|R_n(x)| \le \dfrac{1}{(n+1)!}\,\left|x - \tfrac{\pi}{4}\right|^{n+1} \to 0$ as $n \to \infty$ by Equation 10. So $\lim\limits_{n\to\infty} R_n(x) = 0$ and, by Theorem 8, the series in Exercise 13 represents $\sin x$ for all x.

17. $\cos x = \displaystyle\sum_{n=0}^{\infty}(-1)^n\frac{x^{2n}}{(2n)!} \ \Rightarrow \ f(x) = \cos(\pi x) = \displaystyle\sum_{n=0}^{\infty}\frac{(-1)^n(\pi x)^{2n}}{(2n)!} = \displaystyle\sum_{n=0}^{\infty}\frac{(-1)^n\pi^{2n}x^{2n}}{(2n)!}, \ R = \infty$

18. $e^x = \displaystyle\sum_{n=0}^{\infty}\frac{x^n}{n!} \ \Rightarrow \ f(x) = e^{-x/2} = \displaystyle\sum_{n=0}^{\infty}\frac{(-x/2)^n}{n!} = \displaystyle\sum_{n=0}^{\infty}\frac{(-1)^n}{2^n\,n!}x^n, \ R = \infty$

19. $\tan^{-1}x = \displaystyle\sum_{n=0}^{\infty}(-1)^n\frac{x^{2n+1}}{2n+1} \ \Rightarrow \ f(x) = x\tan^{-1}x = x\displaystyle\sum_{n=0}^{\infty}(-1)^n\frac{x^{2n+1}}{2n+1} = \displaystyle\sum_{n=0}^{\infty}(-1)^n\frac{x^{2n+2}}{2n+1}, \ R = 1$

20. $\sin x = \displaystyle\sum_{n=0}^{\infty}(-1)^n\frac{x^{2n+1}}{(2n+1)!} \ \Rightarrow \ f(x) = \sin(x^4) = \displaystyle\sum_{n=0}^{\infty}(-1)^n\frac{\left(x^4\right)^{2n+1}}{(2n+1)!} = \displaystyle\sum_{n=0}^{\infty}\frac{(-1)^n}{(2n+1)!}x^{8n+4}, \ R = \infty$

21. $e^x = \displaystyle\sum_{n=0}^{\infty}\frac{x^n}{n!} \ \Rightarrow \ f(x) = x^2e^{-x} = x^2\displaystyle\sum_{n=0}^{\infty}\frac{(-x)^n}{n!} = \displaystyle\sum_{n=0}^{\infty}\frac{(-1)^n\,x^{n+2}}{n!}, \ R = \infty$

22. $\cos x = \sum\limits_{n=0}^{\infty} (-1)^n \dfrac{x^{2n}}{(2n)!} \quad \Rightarrow \quad \cos 2x = \sum\limits_{n=0}^{\infty} (-1)^n \dfrac{(2x)^{2n}}{(2n)!} = \sum\limits_{n=0}^{\infty} \dfrac{(-1)^n \, 2^{2n}}{(2n)!} x^{2n} \quad \Rightarrow$

$f(x) = x \cos 2x = \sum\limits_{n=0}^{\infty} \dfrac{(-1)^n \, 2^{2n}}{(2n)!} x^{2n+1}, \; R = \infty$

23. $\sin^2 x = \tfrac{1}{2}[1 - \cos 2x] = \dfrac{1}{2}\left[1 - \sum\limits_{n=0}^{\infty} \dfrac{(-1)^n (2x)^{2n}}{(2n)!}\right] = 2^{-1}\left[1 - 1 - \sum\limits_{n=1}^{\infty} \dfrac{(-1)^n (2x)^{2n}}{(2n)!}\right]$

$= \sum\limits_{n=1}^{\infty} \dfrac{(-1)^{n+1} 2^{2n-1} x^{2n}}{(2n)!}, \; R = \infty$

24. $\dfrac{\sin x}{x} = \dfrac{1}{x}\sum\limits_{n=0}^{\infty} \dfrac{(-1)^n x^{2n+1}}{(2n+1)!} = \sum\limits_{n=0}^{\infty} \dfrac{(-1)^n x^{2n}}{(2n+1)!}$ and this series also gives the required value at $x = 0$ (namely 1), so $R = \infty$.

25.

n	$f^{(n)}(x)$	$f^{(n)}(0)$
0	$(1+x)^{1/2}$	1
1	$\frac{1}{2}(1+x)^{-1/2}$	$\frac{1}{2}$
2	$-\frac{1}{4}(1+x)^{-3/2}$	$-\frac{1}{4}$
3	$\frac{3}{8}(1+x)^{-5/2}$	$\frac{3}{8}$
4	$-\frac{15}{16}(1+x)^{-7/2}$	$-\frac{15}{16}$
⋮	⋮	⋮

So $f^{(n)}(0) = \dfrac{(-1)^{n-1}\,1 \cdot 3 \cdot 5 \cdots (2n-3)}{2^n}$ for $n \geq 2$, and

$\sqrt{1+x} = 1 + \dfrac{x}{2} + \sum\limits_{n=2}^{\infty} \dfrac{(-1)^{n-1}\,1 \cdot 3 \cdot 5 \cdots (2n-3)}{2^n n!} x^n.$ If $a_n = \dfrac{(-1)^{n-1}\,1 \cdot 3 \cdot 5 \cdots (2n-3)}{2^n n!} x^n$,

then $\lim\limits_{n\to\infty} \left|\dfrac{a_{n+1}}{a_n}\right| = \lim\limits_{n\to\infty} \left|\dfrac{1 \cdot 3 \cdot 5 \cdots (2n-3)(2n-1)x^{n+1}}{2^{n+1}(n+1)!} \cdot \dfrac{2^n n!}{1 \cdot 3 \cdot 5 \cdots (2n-3)x^n}\right|$

$= \dfrac{|x|}{2} \lim\limits_{n\to\infty} \dfrac{2n-1}{n+1} = \dfrac{|x|}{2} \cdot 2 = |x| < 1$ for convergence, so $R = 1$.

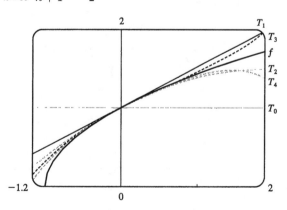

Notice that, as n increases, $T_n(x)$ becomes a better approximation to $f(x)$ for $-1 < x < 1$.

26.

n	$f^{(n)}(x)$	$f^{(n)}(0)$
0	$(1+2x)^{-1/2}$	1
1	$-\frac{1}{2}(1+2x)^{-3/2}(2)$	-1
2	$\frac{3}{2}(1+2x)^{-5/2}(2)$	3
3	$-3\cdot\frac{5}{2}(1+2x)^{-7/2}(2)$	$-3\cdot 5$
$\vdots$	$\vdots$	$\vdots$

$f^{(n)}(0) = (-1)^n\, 1\cdot 3\cdot 5\cdot 7\cdots\cdots(2n-1)$, so

$$(1+2x)^{-1/2} = \sum_{n=0}^{\infty} \frac{f^{(n)}(0)}{n!}x^n$$

$$= \sum_{n=0}^{\infty} \frac{(-1)^n\, 1\cdot 3\cdot 5\cdots\cdots(2n-1)}{n!}x^n$$

$$\lim_{n\to\infty}\left|\frac{a_{n+1}}{a_n}\right| = \lim_{n\to\infty}\frac{2n+1}{n+1}|x| = 2|x| < 1 \text{ for}$$

convergence, so $R = \frac{1}{2}$.

Another method: Use Exercise 25 and differentiate.

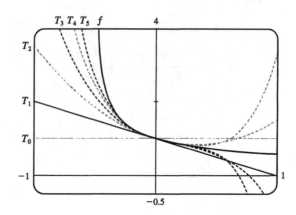

Notice that, as n increases, $T_n(x)$ becomes a better approximation to $f(x)$ for $-0.5 < x < 0.5$.

27. $\cos x = \displaystyle\sum_{n=0}^{\infty}(-1)^n\frac{x^{2n}}{(2n)!} \Rightarrow f(x) = \cos(x^2) = \displaystyle\sum_{n=0}^{\infty}\frac{(-1)^n\,(x^2)^{2n}}{(2n)!} = \displaystyle\sum_{n=0}^{\infty}\frac{(-1)^n\, x^{4n}}{(2n)!}, R = \infty$

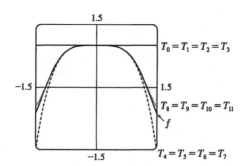

Notice that, as n increases, $T_n(x)$ becomes a better approximation to $f(x)$.

28. $2^x = \left(e^{\ln 2}\right)^x$

$\qquad = e^{x \ln 2}$

$\qquad = \displaystyle\sum_{n=0}^{\infty} \frac{(x \ln 2)^n}{n!}$

$\qquad = \displaystyle\sum_{n=0}^{\infty} \frac{(\ln 2)^n \, x^n}{n!}, \; R = \infty.$

Notice that, as n increases, $T_n(x)$ becomes a better approximation to $f(x)$.

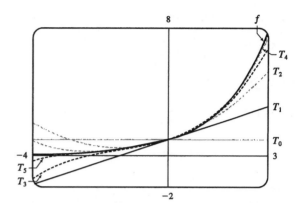

29. $e^x = \displaystyle\sum_{n=0}^{\infty} \frac{x^n}{n!}$, so $e^{-0.2} = \displaystyle\sum_{n=0}^{\infty} \frac{(-0.2)^n}{n!} = 1 - 0.2 + \frac{1}{2!}(0.2)^2 - \frac{1}{3!}(0.2)^3 + \frac{1}{4!}(0.2)^4 - \frac{1}{5!}(0.2)^5 + \frac{1}{6!}(0.2)^6 - \cdots .$

But $\dfrac{1}{6!}(0.2)^6 = 8.\overline{8} \times 10^{-8}$, so by the Alternating Series Estimation Theorem, $e^{-0.2} \approx \displaystyle\sum_{n=0}^{5} \frac{(-0.2)^n}{n!} \approx 0.81873$,

correct to five decimal places.

30. $3° = \frac{\pi}{60}$ radians and $\sin x = \displaystyle\sum_{n=0}^{\infty} \frac{(-1)^n x^{2n+1}}{(2n+1)!}$, so

$\sin \frac{\pi}{60} = \frac{\pi}{60} - \dfrac{\left(\frac{\pi}{60}\right)^3}{3!} + \dfrac{\left(\frac{\pi}{60}\right)^5}{5!} - \cdots = \frac{\pi}{60} - \dfrac{\pi^3}{1{,}296{,}000} + \dfrac{\pi^5}{93{,}312{,}000{,}000} - \cdots .$

But $\dfrac{\pi^5}{93{,}312{,}000{,}000} < 10^{-8}$, so by the Alternating Series Estimation Theorem,

$\sin \frac{\pi}{60} \approx \frac{\pi}{60} - \frac{\pi^3}{1{,}296{,}000} \approx 0.05234.$

31. $\displaystyle\int \sin(x^2) \, dx = \int \sum_{n=0}^{\infty} (-1)^n \frac{(x^2)^{2n+1}}{(2n+1)!} \, dx = \int \sum_{n=0}^{\infty} \frac{(-1)^n x^{4n+2}}{(2n+1)!} \, dx = C + \sum_{n=0}^{\infty} \frac{(-1)^n x^{4n+3}}{(4n+3)(2n+1)!}$

32. $\dfrac{\sin x}{x} = \dfrac{1}{x} \displaystyle\sum_{n=0}^{\infty} \frac{(-1)^n x^{2n+1}}{(2n+1)!} = \sum_{n=0}^{\infty} \frac{(-1)^n x^{2n}}{(2n+1)!}$, so

$\displaystyle\int \frac{\sin x}{x} \, dx = \int \sum_{n=0}^{\infty} \frac{(-1)^n x^{2n}}{(2n+1)!} \, dx = C + \sum_{n=0}^{\infty} \frac{(-1)^n x^{2n+1}}{(2n+1)(2n+1)!}$

33. Using the series from Exercise 25 and substituting x^3 for x, we get

$$\int \sqrt{x^3 + 1} \, dx = \int \left[1 + \frac{x^3}{2} + \sum_{n=2}^{\infty} \frac{(-1)^{n-1} 1 \cdot 3 \cdot 5 \cdot \cdots \cdot (2n-3)}{2^n n!} x^{3n} \right] dx$$

$$= C + x + \frac{x^4}{8} + \sum_{n=2}^{\infty} \frac{(-1)^{n-1} 1 \cdot 3 \cdot 5 \cdot \cdots \cdot (2n-3)}{2^n n! (3n+1)} x^{3n+1}$$

34. $\displaystyle\int e^{x^3} \, dx = \int \sum_{n=0}^{\infty} \frac{(x^3)^n}{n!} \, dx = C + \sum_{n=0}^{\infty} \frac{x^{3n+1}}{(3n+1)n!}$

35. Using our series from Exercise 31, we get

$$\int_0^1 \sin(x^2)\,dx = \sum_{n=0}^{\infty} \left[\frac{(-1)^n\,x^{4n+3}}{(4n+3)(2n+1)!} \right]_0^1 = \sum_{n=0}^{\infty} \frac{(-1)^n}{(4n+3)(2n+1)!} \quad \text{and}$$

$$|c_3| = \frac{1}{75,600} < 0.000014, \text{ so by the Alternating Series Estimation Theorem, we have}$$

$$\int_0^1 \sin(x^2)\,dx \approx \sum_{n=0}^{2} \frac{(-1)^n}{(4n+3)(2n+1)!} = \frac{1}{3} - \frac{1}{42} + \frac{1}{1320} \approx 0.310 \text{ (correct to three decimal places).}$$

36. $\cos(x^2) = \sum_{n=0}^{\infty} \frac{(-1)^n\,(x^2)^{2n}}{(2n)!}$, so

$$\int_0^{0.5} \cos(x^2)\,dx = \int_0^{0.5} \sum_{n=0}^{\infty} \frac{(-1)^n\,x^{4n}}{(2n)!}\,dx = \sum_{n=0}^{\infty} \left[\frac{(-1)^n\,x^{4n+1}}{(4n+1)(2n)!} \right]_0^{0.5} = 0.5 - \frac{(0.5)^5}{5 \cdot 2!} + \frac{(0.5)^9}{9 \cdot 4!} - \dots, \text{ but}$$

$$\frac{(0.5)^9}{9 \cdot 4!} \approx 0.000009, \text{ so by the Alternating Series Estimation Theorem, } \int_0^{0.5} \cos(x^2)\,dx \approx 0.5 - \frac{(0.5)^5}{5 \cdot 2!} \approx 0.497$$

(correct to three decimal places).

37. We first find a series representation for $f(x) = (1+x)^{-1/2}$, and then substitute.

n	$f^{(n)}(x)$	$f^{(n)}(0)$
0	$(1+x)^{-1/2}$	1
1	$-\frac{1}{2}(1+x)^{-3/2}$	$-\frac{1}{2}$
2	$\frac{3}{4}(1+x)^{-5/2}$	$\frac{3}{4}$
3	$-\frac{15}{8}(1+x)^{-7/2}$	$-\frac{15}{8}$
⋮	⋮	⋮

$$\frac{1}{\sqrt{1+x}} = 1 - \frac{x}{2} + \frac{3}{4}\left(\frac{x^2}{2!}\right) - \frac{15}{8}\left(\frac{x^3}{3!}\right) + \dots \quad \Rightarrow \quad \frac{1}{\sqrt{1+x^3}} = 1 - \frac{1}{2}x^3 + \frac{3}{8}x^6 - \frac{5}{16}x^9 + \dots \quad \Rightarrow$$

$$\int_0^{0.1} \frac{dx}{\sqrt{1+x^3}} = \left[x - \frac{1}{8}x^4 + \frac{3}{56}x^7 - \frac{1}{32}x^{10} + \dots \right]_0^{0.1} \approx (0.1) - \frac{1}{8}(0.1)^4, \text{ by the Alternating Series}$$

Estimation Theorem, since $\frac{3}{56}(0.1)^7 \approx 0.0000000054 < 10^{-8}$, which is the maximum desired error. Therefore,

$$\int_0^{0.1} \frac{dx}{\sqrt{1+x^3}} \approx 0.09998750.$$

38. $\int_0^{0.5} x^2 e^{-x^2}\,dx = \int_0^{0.5} \sum_{n=0}^{\infty} \frac{(-1)^n\,x^{2n+2}}{n!}\,dx = \sum_{n=0}^{\infty} \left[\frac{(-1)^n\,x^{2n+3}}{n!(2n+3)} \right]_0^{1/2} = \sum_{n=0}^{\infty} \frac{(-1)^n}{n!(2n+3)2^{2n+3}} \text{ and since}$

$$c_2 = \frac{1}{1792} < 0.001 \text{ we use } \sum_{n=0}^{1} \frac{(-1)^n}{n!(2n+3)2^{2n+3}} = \frac{1}{24} - \frac{1}{160} \approx 0.0354.$$

39. $\lim\limits_{x \to 0} \dfrac{x - \tan^{-1} x}{x^3} = \lim\limits_{x \to 0} \dfrac{x - \left(x - \frac{1}{3}x^3 + \frac{1}{5}x^5 - \frac{1}{7}x^7 + \dots\right)}{x^3} = \lim\limits_{x \to 0} \dfrac{\frac{1}{3}x^3 - \frac{1}{5}x^5 + \frac{1}{7}x^7 - \dots}{x^3}$

$$= \lim_{x \to 0} \left(\frac{1}{3} - \frac{1}{5}x^2 + \frac{1}{7}x^4 - \dots \right) = \frac{1}{3}$$

since power series are continuous functions.

40. $\displaystyle\lim_{x\to 0}\frac{1-\cos x}{1+x-e^x}=\lim_{x\to 0}\frac{1-\left(1-\frac{1}{2!}x^2+\frac{1}{4!}x^4-\frac{1}{6!}x^6+\cdots\right)}{1+x-\left(1+x+\frac{1}{2!}x^2+\frac{1}{3!}x^3+\frac{1}{4!}x^4+\frac{1}{5!}x^5+\frac{1}{6!}x^6+\cdots\right)}$

$\displaystyle=\lim_{x\to 0}\frac{\frac{1}{2!}x^2-\frac{1}{4!}x^4+\frac{1}{6!}x^6-\cdots}{-\frac{1}{2!}x^2-\frac{1}{3!}x^3-\frac{1}{4!}x^4-\frac{1}{5!}x^5-\frac{1}{6!}x^6-\cdots}$

$\displaystyle=\lim_{x\to 0}\frac{\frac{1}{2!}-\frac{1}{4!}x^2+\frac{1}{6!}x^4-\cdots}{-\frac{1}{2!}-\frac{1}{3!}x-\frac{1}{4!}x^2-\frac{1}{5!}x^3-\frac{1}{6!}x^4-\cdots}=\frac{\frac{1}{2}-0}{-\frac{1}{2}-0}=-1$

since power series are continuous functions.

41. $\displaystyle\lim_{x\to 0}\frac{\sin x-x+\frac{1}{6}x^3}{x^5}=\lim_{x\to 0}\frac{\left(x-\frac{1}{3!}x^3+\frac{1}{5!}x^5-\frac{1}{7!}x^7+\cdots\right)-x+\frac{1}{6}x^3}{x^5}$

$\displaystyle=\lim_{x\to 0}\frac{\frac{1}{5!}x^5-\frac{1}{7!}x^7+\cdots}{x^5}=\lim_{x\to 0}\left(\frac{1}{5!}-\frac{x^2}{7!}+\frac{x^4}{9!}-\cdots\right)=\frac{1}{5!}=\frac{1}{120}$

since power series are continuous functions.

42. $\displaystyle\lim_{x\to 0}\frac{\tan x-x}{x^3}=\lim_{x\to 0}\frac{\left(x+\frac{1}{3}x^3+\frac{2}{15}x^5+\cdots\right)-x}{x^3}=\lim_{x\to 0}\frac{\frac{1}{3}x^3+\frac{2}{15}x^5+\cdots}{x^3}=\lim_{x\to 0}\left(\frac{1}{3}+\frac{2}{15}x^2+\cdots\right)=\frac{1}{3}$

since power series are continuous functions.

43. As in Example 8(a), we have $e^{-x^2}=1-\dfrac{x^2}{1!}+\dfrac{x^4}{2!}-\dfrac{x^6}{3!}+\cdots$ and we know that $\cos x=1-\dfrac{x^2}{2!}+\dfrac{x^4}{4!}-\cdots$

from Equation 16. Therefore, $e^{-x^2}\cos x=\left(1-x^2+\frac{1}{2}x^4-\cdots\right)\left(1-\frac{1}{2}x^2+\frac{1}{24}x^4-\cdots\right)$. Writing only the

terms with degree ≤ 4, we get $e^{-x^2}\cos x=1-\frac{1}{2}x^2+\frac{1}{24}x^4-x^2+\frac{1}{2}x^4+\frac{1}{2}x^4+\cdots=1-\frac{3}{2}x^2+\frac{25}{24}x^4+\cdots$.

44.

$$\begin{array}{r}1+\frac{1}{2}x^2+\frac{5}{24}x^4+\cdots\\ 1-\frac{1}{2}x^2+\frac{1}{24}x^4-\cdots\;\big|\;\overline{\;1\phantom{-\frac{1}{2}x^2}}\\ \underline{1-\frac{1}{2}x^2+\frac{1}{24}x^4-\cdots}\\ \frac{1}{2}x^2-\frac{1}{24}x^4+\cdots\\ \underline{\frac{1}{2}x^2-\frac{1}{4}x^4+\cdots}\\ \frac{5}{24}x^4+\cdots\\ \underline{\frac{5}{24}x^4+\cdots}\\ \cdots\end{array}$$

$$\sec x=\frac{1}{\cos x}=\frac{1}{1-\frac{1}{2}x^2+\frac{1}{24}x^4-\cdots}.$$

From the long division above,

$$\sec x=1+\tfrac{1}{2}x^2+\tfrac{5}{24}x^4+\cdots.$$

45.

$$\begin{array}{r}-x+\frac{1}{2}x^2-\frac{1}{3}x^3+\cdots\\ 1+x+\frac{1}{2}x^2+\frac{1}{6}x^3+\cdots\;\big|\;\overline{\;-x-\frac{1}{2}x^2-\frac{1}{3}x^3-\cdots}\\ \underline{-x-\phantom{\frac{1}{2}}x^2-\frac{1}{2}x^3-\cdots}\\ \frac{1}{2}x^2+\frac{1}{6}x^3-\cdots\\ \underline{\frac{1}{2}x^2+\frac{1}{2}x^3+\cdots}\\ -\frac{1}{3}x^3+\cdots\\ \underline{-\frac{1}{3}x^3+\cdots}\\ \cdots\end{array}$$

From Example 6 in Section 8.6, we have

$\ln(1-x)=-x-\frac{1}{2}x^2-\frac{1}{3}x^3-\cdots,\;|x|<1.$

Therefore,

$$y=\frac{\ln(1-x)}{e^x}=\frac{-x-\frac{1}{2}x^2-\frac{1}{3}x^3-\cdots}{1+x+\frac{1}{2}x^2+\frac{1}{6}x^3+\cdots}.$$

So by the long division above,

$$\frac{\ln(1-x)}{e^x}=-x+\frac{x^2}{2}-\frac{x^3}{3}+\cdots,\;|x|<1.$$

46. From Example 6 in Section 8.6, we have $\ln(1-x)=-x-\frac{1}{2}x^2-\frac{1}{3}x^3-\cdots,\;|x|<1.$ Therefore,

$$e^x\ln(1-x)=\left(1+x+\tfrac{1}{2}x^2+\cdots\right)\left(-x-\tfrac{1}{2}x^2-\tfrac{1}{3}x^3-\cdots\right)$$

$$=-x-\tfrac{1}{2}x^2-\tfrac{1}{3}x^3-x^2-\tfrac{1}{2}x^3-\tfrac{1}{2}x^3-\cdots.$$

$$= -x - \tfrac{3}{2}x^2 - \tfrac{4}{3}x^3 - \cdots, \ |x| < 1$$

47. $\displaystyle\sum_{n=0}^{\infty} (-1)^n \frac{x^{4n}}{n!} = \sum_{n=0}^{\infty} \frac{(-x^4)^n}{n!} = e^{-x^4}$, by (11).

48. $\displaystyle\sum_{n=0}^{\infty} \frac{(-1)^n \pi^{2n}}{6^{2n}(2n)!} = \sum_{n=0}^{\infty} (-1)^n \frac{\left(\frac{\pi}{6}\right)^{2n}}{(2n)!} = \cos\frac{\pi}{6} = \frac{\sqrt{3}}{2}$, by (16).

49. $\displaystyle\sum_{n=0}^{\infty} \frac{(-1)^n \pi^{2n+1}}{4^{2n+1}(2n+1)!} = \sum_{n=0}^{\infty} \frac{(-1)^n \left(\frac{\pi}{4}\right)^{2n+1}}{(2n+1)!} = \sin\frac{\pi}{4} = \frac{1}{\sqrt{2}}$, by (15).

50. $\displaystyle\sum_{n=0}^{\infty} \frac{3^n}{5^n n!} = \sum_{n=0}^{\infty} \frac{(3/5)^n}{n!} = e^{3/5}$, by (11).

51. $3 + \dfrac{9}{2!} + \dfrac{27}{3!} + \dfrac{81}{4!} + \cdots = \dfrac{3^1}{1!} + \dfrac{3^2}{2!} + \dfrac{3^3}{3!} + \dfrac{3^4}{4!} + \cdots = \displaystyle\sum_{n=1}^{\infty} \frac{3^n}{n!} = \sum_{n=0}^{\infty} \frac{3^n}{n!} - 1 = e^3 - 1$, by (11).

52. $1 - \ln 2 + \dfrac{(\ln 2)^2}{2!} - \dfrac{(\ln 2)^3}{3!} + \cdots = \displaystyle\sum_{n=0}^{\infty} \frac{(-\ln 2)^n}{n!} = e^{-\ln 2} = (e^{\ln 2})^{-1} = 2^{-1} = \tfrac{1}{2}$, by (11).

53. Assume that $|f'''(x)| \leq M$, so $f'''(x) \leq M$ for $a \leq x \leq a + d$. Now $\int_a^x f'''(t)\,dt \leq \int_a^x M\,dt \Rightarrow$
$f''(x) - f''(a) \leq M(x-a) \Rightarrow f''(x) \leq f''(a) + M(x-a)$. Thus, $\int_a^x f''(t)\,dt \leq \int_a^x [f''(a) + M(t-a)]\,dt$
$\Rightarrow f'(x) - f'(a) \leq f''(a)(x-a) + \tfrac{1}{2}M(x-a)^2 \Rightarrow f'(x) \leq f'(a) + f''(a)(x-a) + \tfrac{1}{2}M(x-a)^2 \Rightarrow$
$\int_a^x f'(t)\,dt \leq \int_a^x \left[f'(a) + f''(a)(t-a) + \tfrac{1}{2}M(t-a)^2\right] dt \Rightarrow$
$f(x) - f(a) \leq f'(a)(x-a) + \tfrac{1}{2}f''(a)(x-a)^2 + \tfrac{1}{6}M(x-a)^3$. So
$f(x) - f(a) - f'(a)(x-a) - \tfrac{1}{2}f''(a)(x-a)^2 \leq \tfrac{1}{6}M(x-a)^3$. But
$R_2(x) = f(x) - T_2(x) = f(x) - f(a) - f'(a)(x-a) - \tfrac{1}{2}f''(a)(x-a)^2$, so $R_2(x) \leq \tfrac{1}{6}M(x-a)^3$. A similar
argument using $f'''(x) \geq -M$ shows that $R_2(x) \geq -\tfrac{1}{6}M(x-a)^3$. So $|R_2(x_2)| \leq \tfrac{1}{6}M\,|x-a|^3$.
Although we have assumed that $x > a$, a similar calculation shows that this inequality is also true if $x < a$.

54. (a) $f(x) = \begin{cases} e^{-1/x^2} & \text{if } x \neq 0 \\ 0 & \text{if } x = 0 \end{cases}$ so

$f'(0) = \displaystyle\lim_{x \to 0} \frac{f(x) - f(0)}{x - 0} = \lim_{x \to 0} \frac{e^{-1/x^2}}{x} = \lim_{x \to 0} \frac{1/x}{e^{1/x^2}} = \lim_{x \to 0} \frac{x}{2e^{1/x^2}} = 0$ (using l'Hospital's Rule and

simplifying in the penultimate step). Similarly, we can use the definition of the derivative and l'Hospital's Rule
to show that $f''(0) = 0$, $f^{(3)}(0) = 0$, ..., $f^{(n)}(0) = 0$, so that the Maclaurin series for f consists entirely of
zero terms. But since $f(x) \neq 0$ except for $x = 0$, we see that f cannot equal its Maclaurin series except
at $x = 0$.

(b)

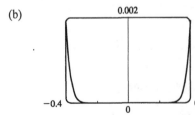

From the graph, it seems that the function is extremely flat at the
origin. In fact, it could be said to be "infinitely flat" at $x = 0$, since
all of its derivatives are 0 there.

The Binomial Series • • • • • • • • • • • • •

1. The general binomial series in (2) is

$$(1+x)^k = \sum_{n=0}^{\infty} \binom{k}{n} x^n = 1 + kx + \frac{k(k-1)}{2!}x^2 + \frac{k(k-1)(k-2)}{3!}x^3 + \cdots.$$

$$(1+x)^{1/2} = \sum_{n=0}^{\infty} \binom{\frac{1}{2}}{n} x^n = 1 + (\tfrac{1}{2})x + \frac{(\frac{1}{2})(-\frac{1}{2})}{2!}x^2 + \frac{(\frac{1}{2})(-\frac{1}{2})(-\frac{3}{2})}{3!}x^3 + \cdots$$

$$= 1 + \frac{x}{2} - \frac{x^2}{2^2 \cdot 2!} + \frac{1 \cdot 3 \cdot x^3}{2^3 \cdot 3!} - \frac{1 \cdot 3 \cdot 5 \cdot x^4}{2^4 \cdot 4!} + \cdots$$

$$= 1 + \frac{x}{2} + \sum_{n=2}^{\infty} \frac{(-1)^{n-1} 1 \cdot 3 \cdot 5 \cdot \cdots \cdot (2n-3)x^n}{2^n \cdot n!} \text{ for } |x| < 1, \text{ so } R = 1$$

2. $\dfrac{1}{(1+x)^4} = (1+x)^{-4} = \sum_{n=0}^{\infty} \binom{-4}{n} x^n$. The binomial coefficient is

$$\binom{-4}{n} = \frac{(-4)(-5)(-6) \cdot \cdots \cdot (-4-n+1)}{n!} = \frac{(-4)(-5)(-6) \cdot \cdots \cdot [-(n+3)]}{n!}$$

$$= \frac{(-1)^n \cdot 2 \cdot 3 \cdot 4 \cdot 5 \cdot 6 \cdot \cdots \cdot (n+1)(n+2)(n+3)}{2 \cdot 3 \cdot n!} = \frac{(-1)^n (n+1)(n+2)(n+3)}{6}$$

Thus, $\dfrac{1}{(1+x)^4} = \sum_{n=0}^{\infty} \dfrac{(-1)^n (n+1)(n+2)(n+3)}{6} x^n$ for $|x| < 1$, so $R = 1$.

3. $\dfrac{1}{(2+x)^3} = \dfrac{1}{[2(1+x/2)]^3} = \dfrac{1}{8}\left(1+\dfrac{x}{2}\right)^{-3} = \dfrac{1}{8}\sum_{n=0}^{\infty}\binom{-3}{n}\left(\dfrac{x}{2}\right)^n$. The binomial coefficient is

$$\binom{-3}{n} = \frac{(-3)(-4)(-5) \cdot \cdots \cdot (-3-n+1)}{n!} = \frac{(-3)(-4)(-5) \cdot \cdots \cdot [-(n+2)]}{n!}$$

$$= \frac{(-1)^n \cdot 2 \cdot 3 \cdot 4 \cdot 5 \cdot \cdots \cdot (n+1)(n+2)}{2 \cdot n!} = \frac{(-1)^n (n+1)(n+2)}{2}$$

Thus, $\dfrac{1}{(2+x)^3} = \dfrac{1}{8}\sum_{n=0}^{\infty} \dfrac{(-1)^n (n+1)(n+2)}{2} \dfrac{x^n}{2^n} = \sum_{n=0}^{\infty} \dfrac{(-1)^n (n+1)(n+2)x^n}{2^{n+4}}$ for $\left|\dfrac{x}{2}\right| < 1 \Leftrightarrow$

$|x| < 2$, so $R = 2$.

4. $(1+x^2)^{1/3} = \sum_{n=0}^{\infty} \binom{\frac{1}{3}}{n} x^{2n} = 1 + \dfrac{x^2}{3} + \dfrac{(\frac{1}{3})(-\frac{2}{3})}{2!}x^4 + \dfrac{(\frac{1}{3})(-\frac{2}{3})(-\frac{5}{3})}{3!}x^6 + \cdots$

$$= 1 + \frac{x^2}{3} + \sum_{n=2}^{\infty} \frac{(-1)^{n-1} \cdot 2 \cdot 5 \cdot 8 \cdot \cdots \cdot (3n-4)x^{2n}}{3^n n!}, \text{ with } R = 1.$$

5. We must write the binomial in the form (1+ expression), so we'll factor out a 4.

$$\frac{x}{\sqrt{4+x^2}} = \frac{x}{\sqrt{4(1+x^2/4)}} = \frac{x}{2\sqrt{1+x^2/4}} = \frac{x}{2}\left(1+\frac{x^2}{4}\right)^{-1/2} = \frac{x}{2}\sum_{n=0}^{\infty}\binom{-\frac{1}{2}}{n}\left(\frac{x^2}{4}\right)^n$$

$$= \frac{x}{2}\left[1+\left(-\frac{1}{2}\right)\frac{x^2}{4}+\frac{\left(-\frac{1}{2}\right)\left(-\frac{3}{2}\right)}{2!}\left(\frac{x^2}{4}\right)^2+\frac{\left(-\frac{1}{2}\right)\left(-\frac{3}{2}\right)\left(-\frac{5}{2}\right)}{3!}\left(\frac{x^2}{4}\right)^3+\cdots\right]$$

$$= \frac{x}{2}+\frac{x}{2}\sum_{n=1}^{\infty}(-1)^n\frac{1\cdot3\cdot5\cdot\cdots\cdot(2n-1)}{2^n\cdot4^n\cdot n!}x^{2n}$$

$$= \frac{x}{2}+\sum_{n=1}^{\infty}(-1)^n\frac{1\cdot3\cdot5\cdot\cdots\cdot(2n-1)}{n!\,2^{3n+1}}x^{2n+1}\ \text{and}\ \frac{x^2}{4}<1\ \Leftrightarrow\ \frac{|x|}{2}<1\ \Leftrightarrow$$

$|x|<2$, so $R=2$.

6.
$$\frac{x^2}{\sqrt{2+x}} = \frac{x^2}{\sqrt{2(1+x/2)}} = \frac{x^2}{\sqrt{2}}\left(1+\frac{x}{2}\right)^{-1/2} = \frac{x^2}{\sqrt{2}}\sum_{n=0}^{\infty}\binom{-\frac{1}{2}}{n}\left(\frac{x}{2}\right)^n$$

$$= \frac{x^2}{\sqrt{2}}\left[1+\left(-\frac{1}{2}\right)\left(\frac{x}{2}\right)+\frac{\left(-\frac{1}{2}\right)\left(-\frac{3}{2}\right)}{2!}\left(\frac{x}{2}\right)^2+\frac{\left(-\frac{1}{2}\right)\left(-\frac{3}{2}\right)\left(-\frac{5}{2}\right)}{3!}\left(\frac{x}{2}\right)^3+\cdots\right]$$

$$= \frac{x^2}{\sqrt{2}}+\frac{x^2}{\sqrt{2}}\sum_{n=1}^{\infty}(-1)^n\frac{1\cdot3\cdot5\cdot\cdots\cdot(2n-1)}{n!\,2^{2n}}x^n$$

$$= \frac{x^2}{\sqrt{2}}+\sum_{n=1}^{\infty}(-1)^n\frac{1\cdot3\cdot5\cdot\cdots\cdot(2n-1)}{n!\,2^{2n+1/2}}x^{n+2}\ \text{and}\ \left|\frac{x}{2}\right|<1\ \Leftrightarrow\ |x|<2,\ \text{so}\ R=2.$$

7.
$$\frac{1}{\sqrt[3]{8+x}} = \frac{1}{\sqrt[3]{8(1+x/8)}} = \frac{1}{\sqrt[3]{8}\sqrt[3]{1+x/8}} = \frac{1}{2}\left(1+\frac{x}{8}\right)^{-1/3}$$

$$= \frac{1}{2}\left[1+\left(-\frac{1}{3}\right)\left(\frac{x}{8}\right)+\frac{\left(-\frac{1}{3}\right)\left(-\frac{4}{3}\right)}{2!}\left(\frac{x}{8}\right)^2+\frac{\left(-\frac{1}{3}\right)\left(-\frac{4}{3}\right)\left(-\frac{7}{3}\right)}{3!}\left(\frac{x}{8}\right)^3+\cdots\right]$$

$$= \frac{1}{2}\left[1+\sum_{n=1}^{\infty}\frac{(-1)^n 1\cdot4\cdot7\cdot\cdots\cdot(3n-2)}{3^n\cdot n!\,8^n}x^n\right]$$

$$= \frac{1}{2}+\frac{1}{2}\sum_{n=1}^{\infty}\frac{(-1)^n 1\cdot4\cdot7\cdot\cdots\cdot(3n-2)}{24^n\,n!}x^n\ \text{and}\ \left|\frac{x}{8}\right|<1\ \Leftrightarrow\ |x|<8,\ \text{so}\ R=8.$$

The three Taylor polynomials are $T_1(x) = \frac{1}{2}-\frac{1}{48}x$, $T_2(x) = \frac{1}{2}-\frac{1}{48}x+\frac{1}{576}x^2$, and $T_3(x) = \frac{1}{2}-\frac{1}{48}x+\frac{1}{576}x^2-\frac{7}{41,472}x^3$.

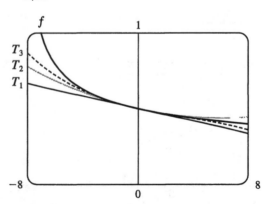

8. $(4+x)^{3/2} = \left[4\left(1+\dfrac{x}{4}\right)\right]^{3/2} = 4^{3/2}\left(1+\dfrac{x}{4}\right)^{3/2} = 8\left(1+\dfrac{x}{4}\right)^{3/2} = 8\displaystyle\sum_{n=0}^{\infty}\binom{\frac{3}{2}}{n}\left(\dfrac{x}{4}\right)^n$

$= 8\left[1 + \dfrac{3}{2}\left(\dfrac{x}{4}\right) + \dfrac{\left(\frac{3}{2}\right)\left(\frac{1}{2}\right)}{2!}\left(\dfrac{x}{4}\right)^2 + \dfrac{\left(\frac{3}{2}\right)\left(\frac{1}{2}\right)\left(-\frac{1}{2}\right)}{3!}\left(\dfrac{x}{4}\right)^3 + \cdots\right]$

$= 8 + 3x + \displaystyle\sum_{n=2}^{\infty}\dfrac{(3)(1)(-1)\cdots\cdots(5-2n)x^n}{8^{n-1}\cdot n!}$ and $\left|\dfrac{x}{4}\right| < 1 \ \Leftrightarrow\ |x| < 4$, so $R = 4$.

The three Taylor polynomials are $T_1(x) = 8 + 3x$, $T_2(x) = 8 + 3x + \frac{3}{16}x^2$, and

$T_3(x) = 8 + 3x + \frac{3}{16}x^2 - \frac{1}{128}x^3$.

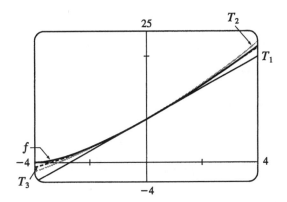

9. (a) $1/\sqrt{1-x^2} = \left[1 + (-x^2)\right]^{-1/2}$

$= 1 + \left(-\tfrac{1}{2}\right)(-x^2) + \dfrac{\left(-\frac{1}{2}\right)\left(-\frac{3}{2}\right)}{2!}(-x^2)^2 + \dfrac{\left(-\frac{1}{2}\right)\left(-\frac{3}{2}\right)\left(-\frac{5}{2}\right)}{3!}(-x^2)^3 + \cdots$

$= 1 + \displaystyle\sum_{n=1}^{\infty}\dfrac{1\cdot 3\cdot 5\cdots\cdots(2n-1)}{2^n\cdot n!}x^{2n}$

(b) $\sin^{-1}x = \displaystyle\int\dfrac{1}{\sqrt{1-x^2}}\,dx = C + x + \displaystyle\sum_{n=1}^{\infty}\dfrac{1\cdot 3\cdot 5\cdots\cdots(2n-1)}{(2n+1)2^n\cdot n!}x^{2n+1}$

$= x + \displaystyle\sum_{n=1}^{\infty}\dfrac{1\cdot 3\cdot 5\cdots\cdots(2n-1)}{(2n+1)2^n\cdot n!}x^{2n+1}$ since $0 = \sin^{-1}0 = C$.

10. (a) $\sqrt[3]{8+x} = \sqrt[3]{8(1+x/8)} = \sqrt[3]{8}\sqrt[3]{1+x/8} = 2\left(1+\dfrac{x}{8}\right)^{1/3} = 2\displaystyle\sum_{n=0}^{\infty}\binom{\frac{1}{3}}{n}\left(\dfrac{x}{8}\right)^n$

$= 2\left[1 + \dfrac{1}{3}\left(\dfrac{x}{8}\right) + \dfrac{\left(\frac{1}{3}\right)\left(-\frac{2}{3}\right)}{2!}\left(\dfrac{x}{8}\right)^2 + \dfrac{\left(\frac{1}{3}\right)\left(-\frac{2}{3}\right)\left(-\frac{5}{3}\right)}{3!}\left(\dfrac{x}{8}\right)^3 + \cdots\right]$

$= 2\left[1 + \dfrac{x}{24} + \displaystyle\sum_{n=2}^{\infty}\dfrac{(-1)^{n-1}\cdot 2\cdot 5\cdots\cdots(3n-4)\,x^n}{24^n\cdot n!}\right]$

(b) $(8+0.2)^{1/3} = 2\left[1 + \dfrac{0.2}{24} - \dfrac{(0.2)^2}{24^2} + \dfrac{2\cdot 5(0.2)^3}{24^3\cdot 3!} - \cdots\right] \approx 2\left[1 + \dfrac{0.2}{24} - \dfrac{(0.2)^2}{24^2}\right]$

since $2\cdot\dfrac{2\cdot 5(0.2)^3}{24^3\cdot 3!} \approx 0.000002$, so $\sqrt[3]{8.2} \approx 2.0165$.

11. (a) $[1 + (-x)]^{-2} = 1 + (-2)(-x) + \dfrac{(-2)(-3)}{2!}(-x)^2 + \dfrac{(-2)(-3)(-4)}{3!}(-x)^3 + \cdots$

$$= 1 + 2x + 3x^2 + 4x^3 + \cdots = \sum_{n=0}^{\infty}(n+1)x^n,$$

so $\dfrac{x}{(1-x)^2} = x\sum_{n=0}^{\infty}(n+1)x^n = \sum_{n=0}^{\infty}(n+1)x^{n+1} = \sum_{n=1}^{\infty}nx^n.$

(b) With $x = \frac{1}{2}$ in part (a), we have $\sum_{n=1}^{\infty} n\left(\frac{1}{2}\right)^n = \sum_{n=1}^{\infty}\dfrac{n}{2^n} = \dfrac{\frac{1}{2}}{\left(1-\frac{1}{2}\right)^2} = \dfrac{\frac{1}{2}}{\frac{1}{4}} = 2.$

12. (a) $[1 + (-x)]^{-3} = \sum_{n=0}^{\infty}\binom{-3}{n}(-x)^n$

$$= 1 + (-3)(-x) + \dfrac{(-3)(-4)}{2!}(-x)^2 + \dfrac{(-3)(-4)(-5)}{3!}(-x)^3 + \cdots$$

$$= 1 + \sum_{n=1}^{\infty}\dfrac{3\cdot 4\cdot 5\cdots\cdots(n+2)}{n!}x^n = \sum_{n=0}^{\infty}\dfrac{2\cdot 3\cdot 4\cdot 5\cdots\cdots(n+2)}{2\cdot n!}x^n$$

$$= \sum_{n=0}^{\infty}\dfrac{(n+1)(n+2)}{2}x^n \quad\Rightarrow$$

$$(x + x^2)[1 + (-x)]^{-3} = x\,[1 + (-x)]^{-3} + x^2\,[1 + (-x)]^{-3}$$

$$= \sum_{n=0}^{\infty}\dfrac{(n+1)(n+2)}{2}x^{n+1} + \sum_{n=0}^{\infty}\dfrac{(n+1)(n+2)}{2}x^{n+2}$$

$$= \sum_{n=1}^{\infty}\dfrac{n(n+1)}{2}x^n + \sum_{n=1}^{\infty}\dfrac{n(n+1)}{2}x^{n+1}$$

$$= x + \sum_{n=2}^{\infty}\dfrac{n(n+1)}{2}x^n + \sum_{n=2}^{\infty}\dfrac{(n-1)n}{2}x^n = x + \sum_{n=2}^{\infty}\left[\dfrac{n(n+1)}{2} + \dfrac{(n-1)n}{2}\right]x^n$$

$$= x + \sum_{n=2}^{\infty}n^2x^n = \sum_{n=1}^{\infty}n^2x^n, \quad -1 < x < 1$$

(b) Setting $x = \frac{1}{2}$ in the last series above gives the required series, so $\sum_{n=1}^{\infty}\dfrac{n^2}{2^n} = \dfrac{\frac{1}{2} + \left(\frac{1}{2}\right)^2}{\left(1 - \frac{1}{2}\right)^3} = \dfrac{\frac{3}{4}}{\frac{1}{8}} = 6.$

13. (a) $(1 + x^2)^{1/2} = 1 + \left(\frac{1}{2}\right)x^2 + \dfrac{\left(\frac{1}{2}\right)\left(-\frac{1}{2}\right)}{2!}\left(x^2\right)^2 + \dfrac{\left(\frac{1}{2}\right)\left(-\frac{1}{2}\right)\left(-\frac{3}{2}\right)}{3!}\left(x^2\right)^3 + \cdots$

$$= 1 + \dfrac{x^2}{2} + \sum_{n=2}^{\infty}\dfrac{(-1)^{n-1}\,1\cdot 3\cdot 5\cdots\cdots(2n-3)}{2^n\cdot n!}x^{2n}$$

(b) The coefficient of x^{10} (corresponding to $n = 5$) in the above Maclaurin series is $\dfrac{f^{(10)}(0)}{10!}$, so

$$\dfrac{f^{(10)}(0)}{10!} = \dfrac{(-1)^4\cdot 1\cdot 3\cdot 5\cdot 7}{2^5\cdot 5!} \quad\Rightarrow\quad f^{(10)}(0) = 10!\left(\dfrac{1\cdot 3\cdot 5\cdot 7}{2^5\cdot 5!}\right) = 99{,}225.$$

14. (a) $(1 + x^3)^{-1/2} = \sum_{n=0}^{\infty}\binom{-\frac{1}{2}}{n}\left(x^3\right)^n$

$$= 1 + \left(-\frac{1}{2}\right)\left(x^3\right) + \dfrac{\left(-\frac{1}{2}\right)\left(-\frac{3}{2}\right)}{2!}\left(x^3\right)^2 + \dfrac{\left(-\frac{1}{2}\right)\left(-\frac{3}{2}\right)\left(-\frac{5}{2}\right)}{3!}\left(x^3\right)^3 + \cdots$$

$$= 1 + \sum_{n=1}^{\infty}\dfrac{(-1)^n\,1\cdot 3\cdot 5\cdots\cdots(2n-1)\,x^{3n}}{2^n\cdot n!}$$

(b) The coefficient of x^9 (corresponding to $n = 3$) in the preceding series is

$\dfrac{f^{(9)}(0)}{9!}$, so $\dfrac{f^{(9)}(0)}{9!} = \dfrac{(-1)^3\,1 \cdot 3 \cdot 5}{2^3 \cdot 3!}$ $\Rightarrow$ $f^{(9)}(0) = -\dfrac{9! \cdot 5}{8 \cdot 2} = -113{,}400.$

15. (a) $g(x) = \displaystyle\sum_{n=0}^{\infty} \binom{k}{n} x^n$ $\Rightarrow$ $g'(x) = \displaystyle\sum_{n=1}^{\infty} \binom{k}{n} n x^{n-1}$, so

$$(1+x)g'(x) = (1+x) \sum_{n=1}^{\infty} \binom{k}{n} n x^{n-1} = \sum_{n=1}^{\infty} \binom{k}{n} n x^{n-1} + \sum_{n=1}^{\infty} \binom{k}{n} n x^{n}$$

$$= \sum_{n=0}^{\infty} \binom{k}{n+1}(n+1) x^n + \sum_{n=0}^{\infty} \binom{k}{n} n x^n \quad \begin{bmatrix} \text{Replace } n \text{ with } n+1 \\ \text{in the first series} \end{bmatrix}$$

$$= \sum_{n=0}^{\infty} (n+1) \frac{k(k-1)(k-2)\cdots(k-n+1)(k-n)}{(n+1)!} x^n$$

$$+ \sum_{n=0}^{\infty} \left[(n) \frac{k(k-1)(k-2)\cdots(k-n+1)}{n!} \right] x^n$$

$$= \sum_{n=0}^{\infty} \frac{(n+1)k(k-1)(k-2)\cdots(k-n+1)}{(n+1)!} \left[(k-n) + n \right] x^n$$

$$= k \sum_{n=0}^{\infty} \frac{k(k-1)(k-2)\cdots(k-n+1)}{n!} x^n = k \sum_{n=0}^{\infty} \binom{k}{n} x^n = kg(x)$$

Thus, $g'(x) = \dfrac{kg(x)}{1+x}$.

(b) $h(x) = (1+x)^{-k} g(x)$ $\Rightarrow$

$$h'(x) = -k(1+x)^{-k-1}g(x) + (1+x)^{-k} g'(x) \quad \text{[Product Rule]}$$

$$= -k(1+x)^{-k-1}g(x) + (1+x)^{-k} \frac{kg(x)}{1+x} \quad \text{[from part (a)]}$$

$$= -k(1+x)^{-k-1}g(x) + k(1+x)^{-k-1}g(x) = 0$$

(c) From part (b) we see that $h(x)$ must be constant for $x \in (-1,1)$, so $h(x) = h(0) = 1$ for $x \in (-1,1)$.

Thus, $h(x) = 1 = (1+x)^{-k} g(x)$ $\Leftrightarrow$ $g(x) = (1+x)^k$ for $x \in (-1,1)$.

16. (a) $4\sqrt{\dfrac{L}{g}} \displaystyle\int_0^{\pi/2} \dfrac{dx}{\sqrt{1 - k^2 \sin^2 x}} = 4\sqrt{\dfrac{L}{g}} \int_0^{\pi/2} \left[1 + (-k^2 \sin^2 x) \right]^{-1/2} dx$

$$= 4\sqrt{\frac{L}{g}} \int_0^{\pi/2} \left[1 - \frac{1}{2}(-k^2 \sin^2 x) + \frac{\frac{1}{2} \cdot \frac{3}{2}}{2!}(-k^2 \sin^2 x)^2 - \frac{\frac{1}{2} \cdot \frac{3}{2} \cdot \frac{5}{2}}{3!}(-k^2 \sin^2 x)^3 + \cdots \right] dx$$

$$= 4\sqrt{\frac{L}{g}} \int_0^{\pi/2} \left[1 + \left(\frac{1}{2}\right) k^2 \sin^2 x + \left(\frac{1 \cdot 3}{2 \cdot 4}\right) k^4 \sin^4 x + \left(\frac{1 \cdot 3 \cdot 5}{2 \cdot 4 \cdot 6}\right) k^6 \sin^6 x + \cdots \right] dx$$

[split up the integral and use the result from Exercise 5.6.36]

$$= 4\sqrt{\frac{L}{g}} \left[\frac{\pi}{2} + \left(\frac{1}{2}\right)\left(\frac{1}{2} \cdot \frac{\pi}{2}\right) k^2 + \left(\frac{1 \cdot 3}{2 \cdot 4}\right)\left(\frac{1 \cdot 3}{2 \cdot 4} \cdot \frac{\pi}{2}\right) k^4 \right.$$

$$\left. + \left(\frac{1 \cdot 3 \cdot 5}{2 \cdot 4 \cdot 6}\right)\left(\frac{1 \cdot 3 \cdot 5}{2 \cdot 4 \cdot 6} \cdot \frac{\pi}{2}\right) k^6 + \cdots \right]$$

$$= 2\pi\sqrt{\frac{L}{g}} \left[1 + \frac{1^2}{2^2} k^2 + \frac{1^2 \cdot 3^2}{2^2 \cdot 4^2} k^4 + \frac{1^2 \cdot 3^2 \cdot 5^2}{2^2 \cdot 4^2 \cdot 6^2} k^6 + \cdots \right]$$

(b) The first of the two inequalities is true because all of the terms in the series are positive. For the second,

$$T = 2\pi \sqrt{\frac{L}{g}} \left[1 + \frac{1^2}{2^2}k^2 + \frac{1^2 \cdot 3^2}{2^2 \cdot 4^2}k^4 + \frac{1^2 \cdot 3^2 \cdot 5^2}{2^2 \cdot 4^2 \cdot 6^2}k^6 + \frac{1^2 \cdot 3^2 \cdot 5^2 \cdot 7^2}{2^2 \cdot 4^2 \cdot 6^2 \cdot 8^2}k^8 + \cdots \right]$$

$$\leq 2\pi \sqrt{\frac{L}{g}} \left[1 + \frac{1}{4}k^2 + \frac{1}{4}k^4 + \frac{1}{4}k^6 + \frac{1}{4}k^8 + \cdots \right]$$

The terms in brackets (after the first) form a geometric series with $a = \frac{1}{4}k^2$ and $r = k^2 = \sin^2\left(\frac{1}{2}\theta_0\right) < 1$.

So $T \leq 2\pi \sqrt{\frac{L}{g}} \left[1 + \frac{k^2/4}{1 - k^2} \right] = 2\pi \sqrt{\frac{L}{g}} \frac{4 - 3k^2}{4 - 4k^2}$.

(c) We substitute $L = 1$, $g = 9.8$, and $k = \sin(10°/2) \approx 0.08716$, and the inequality from part (b) becomes $2.01090 \leq T \leq 2.01093$, so $T \approx 2.0109$. The estimate $T \approx 2\pi\sqrt{L/g} \approx 2.0071$ differs by about 0.2%. If $\theta_0 = 42°$, then $k \approx 0.35837$ and the inequality becomes $2.07153 \leq T \leq 2.08103$, so $T \approx 2.0763$. The one-term estimate is the same, and the discrepancy between the two estimates increases to about 3.4%.

◆8.9 Applications of Taylor Polynomials · · · · · · · ·

1. (a)

n	$f^{(n)}(x)$	$f^{(n)}(0)$	$T_n(x)$
0	$\cos x$	1	1
1	$-\sin x$	0	1
2	$-\cos x$	-1	$1 - \frac{1}{2}x^2$
3	$\sin x$	0	$1 - \frac{1}{2}x^2$
4	$\cos x$	1	$1 - \frac{1}{2}x^2 + \frac{1}{24}x^4$
5	$-\sin x$	0	$1 - \frac{1}{2}x^2 + \frac{1}{24}x^4$
6	$-\cos x$	-1	$1 - \frac{1}{2}x^2 + \frac{1}{24}x^4 - \frac{1}{720}x^6$

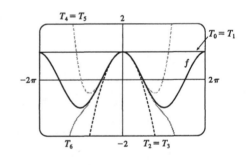

(b)

x	f	$T_0 = T_1$	$T_2 = T_3$	$T_4 = T_5$	T_6
$\frac{\pi}{4}$	0.7071	1	0.6916	0.7074	0.7071
$\frac{\pi}{2}$	0	1	-0.2337	0.0200	-0.0009
π	-1	1	-3.9348	0.1239	-1.2114

(c) As n increases, $T_n(x)$ is a good approximation to $f(x)$ on a larger and larger interval.

2. (a)

n	$f^{(n)}(x)$	$f^{(n)}(1)$	$T_n(x)$
0	x^{-1}	1	1
1	$-x^{-2}$	-1	$1-(x-1)=2-x$
2	$2x^{-3}$	2	$1-(x-1)+(x-1)^2=x^2-3x+3$
3	$-6x^{-4}$	-6	$1-(x-1)+(x-1)^2-(x-1)^3=-x^3+4x^2-6x+4$

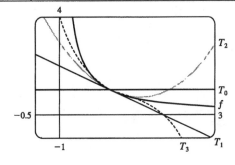

(b)

x	f	T_0	T_1	T_2	T_3
0.9	$1.\overline{1}$	1	1.1	1.11	1.111
1.3	0.7692	1	0.7	0.79	0.763

(c) As n increases, $T_n(x)$ is a good approximation to $f(x)$ on a larger and larger interval.

3.

n	$f^{(n)}(x)$	$f^{(n)}(1)$
0	$\ln x$	0
1	$1/x$	1
2	$-1/x^2$	-1
3	$2/x^3$	2
4	$-6/x^4$	-6

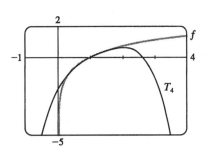

$$T_4(x)=\sum_{n=0}^{4}\frac{f^{(n)}(1)}{n!}(x-1)^n=0+(x-1)-\tfrac{1}{2}(x-1)^2+\tfrac{1}{3}(x-1)^3-\tfrac{1}{4}(x-1)^4$$

4.

n	$f^{(n)}(x)$	$f^{(n)}(2)$
0	e^x	e^2
1	e^x	e^2
2	e^x	e^2
3	e^x	e^2

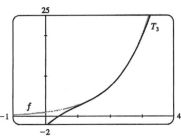

$$T_3(x)=\sum_{n=0}^{3}\frac{f^{(n)}(2)}{n!}(x-2)^n=e^2+e^2(x-2)+\frac{e^2}{2}(x-2)^2+\frac{e^2}{6}(x-2)^3$$

5.

n	$f^{(n)}(x)$	$f^{(n)}\left(\frac{\pi}{6}\right)$
0	$\sin x$	$\frac{1}{2}$
1	$\cos x$	$\frac{\sqrt{3}}{2}$
2	$-\sin x$	$-\frac{1}{2}$
3	$-\cos x$	$-\frac{\sqrt{3}}{2}$

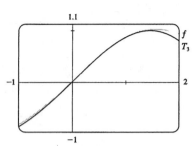

$$T_3(x) = \sum_{n=0}^{3} \frac{f^{(n)}\left(\frac{\pi}{6}\right)}{n!}\left(x - \frac{\pi}{6}\right)^n = \frac{1}{2} + \frac{\sqrt{3}}{2}\left(x - \frac{\pi}{6}\right) - \frac{1}{4}\left(x - \frac{\pi}{6}\right)^2 - \frac{\sqrt{3}}{12}\left(x - \frac{\pi}{6}\right)^3$$

6.

n	$f^{(n)}(x)$	$f^{(n)}\left(\frac{2\pi}{3}\right)$
0	$\cos x$	$-\frac{1}{2}$
1	$-\sin x$	$-\frac{\sqrt{3}}{2}$
2	$-\cos x$	$\frac{1}{2}$
3	$\sin x$	$\frac{\sqrt{3}}{2}$
4	$\cos x$	$-\frac{1}{2}$

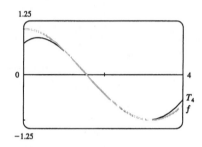

$$T_4(x) = \sum_{n=0}^{4} \frac{f^{(n)}\left(\frac{2\pi}{3}\right)}{n!}\left(x - \frac{2\pi}{3}\right)^n = -\frac{1}{2} - \frac{\sqrt{3}}{2}\left(x - \frac{2\pi}{3}\right) + \frac{1}{4}\left(x - \frac{2\pi}{3}\right)^2 + \frac{\sqrt{3}}{12}\left(x - \frac{2\pi}{3}\right)^3 - \frac{1}{48}\left(x - \frac{2\pi}{3}\right)^4$$

7.

n	$f^{(n)}(x)$	$f^{(n)}(0)$
0	$e^x \sin x$	0
1	$e^x(\sin x + \cos x)$	1
2	$2e^x \cos x$	2
3	$2e^x(\cos x - \sin x)$	2

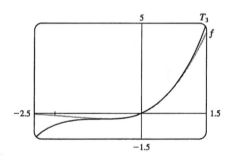

$$T_3(x) = \sum_{n=0}^{3} \frac{f^{(n)}(0)}{n!}x^n = x + x^2 + \frac{1}{3}x^3$$

8.

n	$f^{(n)}(x)$	$f^{(n)}(1)$
0	$(3 + x^2)^{1/2}$	2
1	$x(3 + x^2)^{-1/2}$	$\frac{1}{2}$
2	$3(3 + x^2)^{-3/2}$	$\frac{3}{8}$

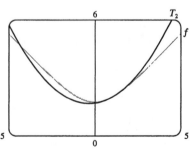

$$T_2(x) = \sum_{n=0}^{2} \frac{f^{(n)}(1)}{n!}(x - 1)^n = 2 + \frac{1}{2}(x - 1) + \frac{3/8}{2}(x - 1)^2 = 2 + \frac{1}{2}(x - 1) + \frac{3}{16}(x - 1)^2$$

9. In Maple, we can find the Taylor polynomials by the following method: first define `f:=sec(x);` and then set
`T2:=convert(taylor(f,x=0,3),polynom);`, `T4:=convert(taylor(f,x=0,5),polynom);`,
etc. (The third argument in the `taylor` function is one more than the degree of the desired polynomial). We must
convert to the type `polynom` because the output of the
`taylor` function contains an error term which we do not
want. In Mathematica, we use
`Tn:=Normal[Series[f,{x,0,n}]]`, with n=2, 4,
etc. Note that in Mathematica, the "degree" argument is the
same as the degree of the desired polynomial. In Derive,
author sec x, then enter `Calculus,Taylor,8,0`; and
then simplify the expression. The eighth Taylor polynomial is
$$T_8(x) = 1 + \tfrac{1}{2}x^2 + \tfrac{5}{24}x^4 + \tfrac{61}{720}x^6 + \tfrac{277}{8064}x^8.$$

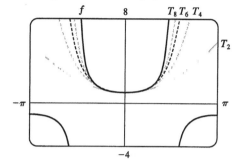

10. See Exercise 9 for the CAS commands used to generate the
Taylor polynomials. The ninth Taylor polynomial for $\tan x$ is
$$T_9(x) = x + \tfrac{1}{3}x^3 + \tfrac{2}{15}x^5 + \tfrac{17}{315}x^7 + \tfrac{62}{2835}x^9.$$

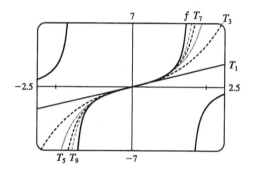

11.
$$\begin{aligned}
f(x) &= \sqrt{x} & f(4) &= 2 \\
f'(x) &= \tfrac{1}{2}x^{-1/2} & f'(4) &= \tfrac{1}{4} \\
f''(x) &= -\tfrac{1}{4}x^{-3/2} & f''(4) &= -\tfrac{1}{32} \\
f'''(x) &= \tfrac{3}{8}x^{-5/2}
\end{aligned}$$

(a) $f(x) = \sqrt{x} \approx T_2(x) = 2 + \tfrac{1}{4}(x-4) - \tfrac{1/32}{2!}(x-4)^2 = 2 + \tfrac{1}{4}(x-4) - \tfrac{1}{64}(x-4)^2$

(b) $|R_2(x)| \leq \dfrac{M}{3!}|x-4|^3$, where $|f'''(x)| \leq M$. Now $4 \leq x \leq 4.2 \Rightarrow |x-4| \leq 0.2 \Rightarrow$
$|x-4|^3 \leq 0.008$. Since $f'''(x)$ is decreasing on $[4, 4.2]$, we can take $M = |f'''(4)| = \tfrac{3}{8}4^{-5/2} = \tfrac{3}{256}$, so
$|R_2(x)| \leq \tfrac{3/256}{6}(0.008) = \tfrac{0.008}{512} = 0.000015625$.

(c) From the graph of $|R_2(x)| = |\sqrt{x} - T_2(x)|$, it seems that the error is
less than 1.52×10^{-5} on $[4, 4.2]$.

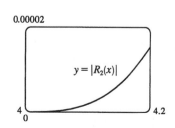

12.
$$f(x) = x^{-2} \qquad f(1) = 1$$
$$f'(x) = -2x^{-3} \qquad f'(1) = -2$$
$$f''(x) = 6x^{-4} \qquad f''(4) = 6$$
$$f'''(x) = -24x^{-5}$$

(a) $f(x) = x^{-2} \approx T_2(x)$
$$= 1 - 2(x-1) + \tfrac{6}{2!}(x-1)^2$$
$$= 1 - 2(x-1) + 3(x-1)^2$$

(b) $|R_2(x)| \leq \dfrac{M}{3!}\,|x-1|^3$, where $|f'''(x)| \leq M$. Now

$0.9 \leq x \leq 1.1 \Rightarrow |x-1| \leq 0.1 \Rightarrow$

$|x-1|^3 \leq 0.001$. Since $f'''(x)$ is decreasing on

$[0.9, 1.1]$, we can take $M = |f'''(0.9)| = \frac{24}{(0.9)^5}$, so

$|R_2(x)| \leq \frac{24/(0.9)^5}{6}(0.001) = \frac{0.004}{0.59049}$

≈ 0.00677404

(c)
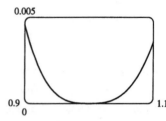

From the graph of $|R_2(x)| = \left|x^{-2} - T_2(x)\right|$,
it seems that the error is less than 0.0046
on $[0.9, 1.1]$.

13.
$$f(x) = e^{x^2} \qquad f(0) = 1 \qquad f'''(x) = e^{x^2}\left(12x + 8x^3\right) \qquad f'''(0) = 0$$
$$f'(x) = e^{x^2}(2x) \qquad f'(0) = 0 \qquad f^{(4)}(x) = e^{x^2}\left(12 + 48x^2 + 16x^4\right)$$
$$f''(x) = e^{x^2}\left(2 + 4x^2\right) \qquad f''(0) = 2$$

(a) $f(x) = e^{x^2} \approx T_3(x) = 1 + \tfrac{2}{2!}x^2 = 1 + x^2$

(b) $|R_3(x)| \leq \dfrac{M}{4!}\,|x|^4$, where $\left|f^{(4)}(x)\right| \leq M$.

Now $0 \leq x \leq 0.1 \Rightarrow x^4 \leq (0.1)^4$, and

letting $x = 0.1$ gives

$|R_3(x)| \leq \dfrac{e^{0.01}\,(12 + 0.48 + 0.0016)}{24}(0.1)^4 \approx$

0.00006.

(c)
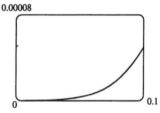

From the graph of

$|R_3(x)| = \left|e^{x^2} - (1 + x^2)\right|$, it appears that

the error is less than 0.000051 on $[0, 0.1]$.

14.
$$f(x) = \cos x \qquad f\left(\tfrac{\pi}{3}\right) = \tfrac{1}{2} \qquad f'''(x) = \sin x \qquad f'''\left(\tfrac{\pi}{3}\right) = \tfrac{\sqrt{3}}{2}$$
$$f'(x) = -\sin x \qquad f'\left(\tfrac{\pi}{3}\right) = -\tfrac{\sqrt{3}}{2} \qquad f^{(4)}(x) = \cos x \qquad f^{(4)}\left(\tfrac{\pi}{3}\right) = \tfrac{1}{2}$$
$$f''(x) = -\cos x \qquad f''\left(\tfrac{\pi}{3}\right) = -\tfrac{1}{2} \qquad f^{(5)}(x) = -\sin x$$

(a) $f(x) = \cos x \approx T_4(x)$
$$= \tfrac{1}{2} - \tfrac{\sqrt{3}}{2}\left(x - \tfrac{\pi}{3}\right) - \tfrac{1}{4}\left(x - \tfrac{\pi}{3}\right)^2 + \tfrac{\sqrt{3}}{12}\left(x - \tfrac{\pi}{3}\right)^3 + \tfrac{1}{48}\left(x - \tfrac{\pi}{3}\right)^4$$

(b) $|R_4(x)| \leq \dfrac{M}{5!}\,\left|x - \tfrac{\pi}{3}\right|^5$, where $\left|f^{(5)}(x)\right| \leq M$. Now $0 \leq x \leq \tfrac{2\pi}{3} \Rightarrow \left(x - \tfrac{\pi}{3}\right)^5 \leq \left(\tfrac{\pi}{3}\right)^5$, and letting

$x = \tfrac{\pi}{2}$ gives $M = 1$, so $|R_4(x)| \leq \tfrac{1}{5!}\left(\tfrac{\pi}{3}\right)^5 \approx 0.0105$.

(c)

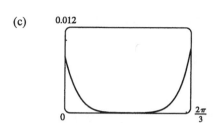

0.012

$\frac{2\pi}{3}$

0

From the graph of $|R_4(x)| = |\cos x - T_4(x)|$, it seems that the error is less than 0.01 on $\left[0, \frac{2\pi}{3}\right]$.

15.

$f(x) = \tan x$ $f(0) = 0$ $f'''(x) = 4\sec^2 x \tan^2 x + 2\sec^4 x$ $f'''(0) = 2$

$f'(x) = \sec^2 x$ $f'(0) = 1$ $f^{(4)}(x) = 8\sec^2 x \tan^3 x + 16\sec^4 x \tan x$

$f''(x) = 2\sec^2 x \tan x$ $f''(0) = 0$

(a) $f(x) = \tan x \approx T_3(x) = x + \frac{1}{3}x^3$

(c)

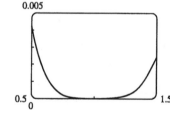

0.01

$\frac{\pi}{6}$

0

(b) $|R_3(x)| \leq \dfrac{M}{4!}\,|x|^4$, where $\left|f^{(4)}(x)\right| \leq M$. Now

$0 \leq x \leq \frac{\pi}{6} \;\Rightarrow\; x^4 \leq \left(\frac{\pi}{6}\right)^4$, and letting $x = \frac{\pi}{6}$ gives

$$|R_3(x)| \leq \dfrac{8\left(\frac{2}{\sqrt{3}}\right)^2\left(\frac{1}{\sqrt{3}}\right)^3 + 16\left(\frac{2}{\sqrt{3}}\right)^4\left(\frac{1}{\sqrt{3}}\right)}{4!}\left(\frac{\pi}{6}\right)^4$$

$$= \frac{4\sqrt{3}}{9}\left(\frac{\pi}{6}\right)^4 \approx 0.057859$$

From the graph of

$|R_3(x)| = |\tan x - T_3(3)|$, it seems that the error is less than 0.006 on $[0, \pi/6]$.

16.

$f(x) = \ln(1 + 2x)$ $f(1) = \ln 3$

$f'(x) = 2/(1 + 2x)$ $f'(1) = \frac{2}{3}$

$f''(x) = -4/(1 + 2x)^2$ $f''(1) = -\frac{4}{9}$ $f''(1)/2! = -\frac{2}{9}$

$f'''(x) = 16/(1 + 2x)^3$ $f'''(1) = \frac{16}{27}$ $f'''(1)/3! = \frac{8}{81}$

$f^{(4)}(x) = -96/(1 + 2x)^4$

(a) $f(x) = \ln(1 + 2x) \approx T_3(x)$

$= \ln 3 + \frac{2}{3}(x - 1) - \frac{2}{9}(x - 1)^2 + \frac{8}{81}(x - 1)^3$

(b) $|R_3(x)| \leq \dfrac{M}{4!}\,|x - 1|^4$, where $\left|f^{(4)}(x)\right| \leq M$.

Now $0.5 \leq x \leq 1.5 \;\Rightarrow\; -0.5 \leq x - 1 \leq 0.5$

$\Rightarrow\; |x - 1| \leq 0.5 \;\Rightarrow\; |x - 1|^4 \leq \frac{1}{16}$, and

letting $x = 0.5$ gives $M = 6$, so

$|R_3(x)| \leq \dfrac{6}{4!} \cdot \dfrac{1}{16} = \dfrac{1}{64} = 0.015625.$

(c)

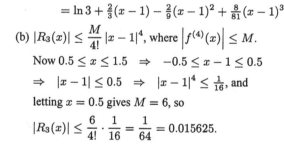

0.005

0.5   1.5

0

From the graph of

$|R_3(x)| = |\ln(1 + 2x) - T_3(x)|$, it seems that the error is less than 0.005 on $[0.5, 1.5]$.

17. From Exercise 5, $\sin x = \frac{1}{2} + \frac{\sqrt{3}}{2}\left(x - \frac{\pi}{6}\right) - \frac{1}{4}\left(x - \frac{\pi}{6}\right)^2 - \frac{\sqrt{3}}{12}\left(x - \frac{\pi}{6}\right)^3 + R_3(x)$, where $|R_3(x)| \leq \dfrac{M}{4!}\,\left|x - \frac{\pi}{6}\right|^4$

with $\left|f^{(4)}(x)\right| = |\sin x| \leq M = 1$. Now $x = 35° = (30° + 5°) = \left(\frac{\pi}{6} + \frac{\pi}{36}\right)$ radians, so the error is

$\left|R_3\left(\frac{\pi}{36}\right)\right| \leq \dfrac{\left(\frac{\pi}{36}\right)^4}{4!} < 0.000003$. Therefore, to five decimal places,

$\sin 35° \approx \frac{1}{2} + \frac{\sqrt{3}}{2}\left(\frac{\pi}{36}\right) - \frac{1}{4}\left(\frac{\pi}{36}\right)^2 - \frac{\sqrt{3}}{12}\left(\frac{\pi}{36}\right)^3 \approx 0.57358.$

18. From Exercise 14, $\cos x = \frac{1}{2} - \frac{\sqrt{3}}{2}\left(x - \frac{\pi}{3}\right) - \frac{1}{4}\left(x - \frac{\pi}{3}\right)^2 + \frac{\sqrt{3}}{12}\left(x - \frac{\pi}{3}\right)^3 + \frac{1}{48}\left(x - \frac{\pi}{3}\right)^4 + R_4(x)$. Now since

$x = 69° = (60° + 9°) = \left(\frac{\pi}{3} + \frac{\pi}{20}\right)$ radians, the error is $|R_4(x)| \leq \dfrac{\left(\frac{\pi}{20}\right)^5}{5!} < 8 \times 10^{-7}$. Therefore, to five

decimal places, $\cos 69° \approx \frac{1}{2} - \frac{\sqrt{3}}{2}\left(\frac{\pi}{20}\right) - \frac{1}{4}\left(\frac{\pi}{20}\right)^2 + \frac{\sqrt{3}}{12}\left(\frac{\pi}{20}\right)^3 + \frac{1}{48}\left(\frac{\pi}{20}\right)^4 \approx 0.35837$.

19. All derivatives of e^x are e^x, so $|R_n(x)| \leq \dfrac{e^x}{(n+1)!}\,|x|^{n+1}$, where $0 < x < 0.1$. Letting $x = 0.1$,

$R_n(0.1) \leq \dfrac{e^{0.1}}{(n+1)!}(0.1)^{n+1} < 0.00001$, and by trial and error we find that $n = 3$ satisfies this inequality since

$R_3(0.1) < 0.0000046$. Thus, by adding the four terms of the Maclaurin series for e^x corresponding to $n = 0, 1, 2,$ and 3, we can estimate $e^{0.1}$ to within 0.00001. (In fact, this sum is $1.1051\overline{6}$ and $e^{0.1} \approx 1.10517$.)

20. Example 6 in Section 8.6 gives the Maclaurin series for $\ln(1 + x)$ as $-\sum_{n=1}^{\infty} \dfrac{x^n}{n}$ for $|x| < 1$. Thus,

$\ln 1.4 = \ln[1 - (-0.4)] = -\sum_{n=1}^{\infty} \dfrac{(-0.4)^n}{n} = \sum_{n=1}^{\infty} (-1)^{n+1}\dfrac{(0.4)^n}{n}$. Since this is an alternating series, the error is

less than the first neglected term by the Alternating Series Estimation Theorem, and we find that

$|a_6| = (0.4)^6/6 \approx 0.0007 < 0.001$. So we need the first five (non-zero) terms of the Maclaurin series for the

desired accuracy. (In fact, this sum is approximately 0.33698 and $\ln 1.4 \approx 0.33647$.)

21. $\sin x = x - \frac{1}{3!}x^3 + \frac{1}{5!}x^5 - \cdots$. By the Alternating

Series Estimation Theorem, the error in the

approximation $\sin x = x - \frac{1}{3!}x^3$ is less than

$\left|\frac{1}{5!}x^5\right| < 0.01 \iff |x^5| < 120(0.01) \iff$

$|x| < (1.2)^{1/5} \approx 1.037$. The curves intersect at

$x \approx 1.043$, so the graph confirms our estimate. Since

both the sine function and the given approximation are

odd functions, we need to check the estimate only for

$x > 0$. Thus, the desired range of values for x is

$-1.037 < x < 1.037$.

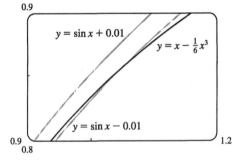

22. $\cos x = 1 - \frac{1}{2!}x^2 + \frac{1}{4!}x^4 - \frac{1}{6!}x^6 + \cdots$. By the

Alternating Series Estimation Theorem, the error is less

than $\left|-\frac{1}{6!}x^6\right| < 0.005 \iff x^6 < 720(0.005) \iff$

$|x| < (3.6)^{1/6} \approx 1.238$. The curves intersect at

$x \approx 1.244$, so the graph confirms our estimate. Since

both the cosine function and the given approximation

are even functions, we need to check the estimate only

for $x > 0$. Thus, the desired range of values for x is

$-1.238 < x < 1.238$.

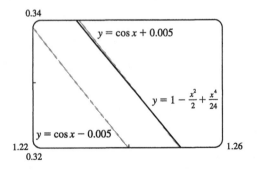

23. Let $s(t)$ be the position function of the car, and for convenience set $s(0) = 0$. The velocity of the car is $v(t) = s'(t)$ and the acceleration is $a(t) = s''(t)$, so the second degree Taylor polynomial is

$$T_2(t) = s(0) + v(0)t + \frac{a(0)}{2}t^2 = 20t + t^2.$$ We estimate the distance travelled during the next second to be

$s(1) \approx T_2(1) = 20 + 1 = 21$ m. The function $T_2(t)$ would not be accurate over a full minute, since the car could not possibly maintain an acceleration of 2 m/s^2 for that long (if it did, its final speed would be 140 m/s $\approx$ 313 mi/h!)

24. (a) $\dfrac{n_1}{\ell_o} + \dfrac{n_2}{\ell_i} = \dfrac{1}{R}\left(\dfrac{n_2 s_i}{\ell_i} - \dfrac{n_1 s_o}{\ell_o}\right)$ (Equation 1) where

$$\ell_o = \sqrt{R^2 + (s_o + R)^2 - 2R(s_o + R)\cos\phi} \quad \text{and} \quad \ell_i = \sqrt{R^2 + (s_i - R)^2 + 2R(s_i - R)\cos\phi} \quad (2)$$

Using $\cos\phi \approx 1$ gives

$$\ell_o = \sqrt{R^2 + (s_o + R)^2 - 2R(s_o + R)} = \sqrt{R^2 + s_o^2 + 2Rs_o + R^2 - 2Rs_o - 2R^2} = \sqrt{s_o^2} = s_o$$

and similarly, $\ell_i = s_i$. Thus, Equation 1 becomes

$$\frac{n_1}{s_o} + \frac{n_2}{s_i} = \frac{1}{R}\left(\frac{n_2 s_i}{s_i} - \frac{n_1 s_o}{s_o}\right) \quad \Rightarrow \quad \frac{n_1}{s_o} + \frac{n_2}{s_i} = \frac{n_2 - n_1}{R}$$

(b) Using $\cos\phi \approx 1 - \frac{1}{2}\phi^2$ in (2) gives us

$$\ell_o = \sqrt{R^2 + (s_o + R)^2 - 2R(s_o + R)\left(1 - \frac{1}{2}\phi^2\right)}$$

$$= \sqrt{R^2 + s_o^2 + 2Rs_o + R^2 - 2Rs_o + Rs_o\phi^2 - 2R^2 + R^2\phi^2} = \sqrt{s_o^2 + Rs_o\phi^2 + R^2\phi^2}$$

Anticipating that we will use the binomial series expansion $(1 + x)^k \approx 1 + kx$, we can write the last expression for ℓ_o as $s_o\sqrt{1 + \phi^2\left(\dfrac{R}{s_o} + \dfrac{R^2}{s_o^2}\right)}$ and similarly, $\ell_i = s_i\sqrt{1 - \phi^2\left(\dfrac{R}{s_i} - \dfrac{R^2}{s_i^2}\right)}$. Thus, from Equation 1,

$$\frac{n_1}{\ell_o} + \frac{n_2}{\ell_i} = \frac{1}{R}\left(\frac{n_2 s_i}{\ell_i} - \frac{n_1 s_o}{\ell_o}\right) \quad \Leftrightarrow \quad n_1\ell_o^{-1} + n_2\ell_i^{-1} = \frac{n_2}{R}\cdot\frac{s_i}{\ell_i} - \frac{n_1}{R}\cdot\frac{s_o}{\ell_o} \quad \Leftrightarrow$$

$$\frac{n_1}{s_o}\left[1 + \phi^2\left(\frac{R}{s_o} + \frac{R^2}{s_o^2}\right)\right]^{-1/2} + \frac{n_2}{s_i}\left[1 - \phi^2\left(\frac{R}{s_i} - \frac{R^2}{s_i^2}\right)\right]^{-1/2}$$

$$= \frac{n_2}{R}\left[1 - \phi^2\left(\frac{R}{s_i} - \frac{R^2}{s_i^2}\right)\right]^{-1/2} - \frac{n_1}{R}\left[1 + \phi^2\left(\frac{R}{s_o} + \frac{R^2}{s_o^2}\right)\right]^{-1/2}$$

Approximating the expressions for ℓ_o^{-1} and ℓ_i^{-1} by the first two terms in their binomial series, we get

$$\frac{n_1}{s_o}\left[1 - \frac{1}{2}\phi^2\left(\frac{R}{s_o} + \frac{R^2}{s_o^2}\right)\right] + \frac{n_2}{s_i}\left[1 + \frac{1}{2}\phi^2\left(\frac{R}{s_i} - \frac{R^2}{s_i^2}\right)\right]$$

$$= \frac{n_2}{R}\left[1 + \frac{1}{2}\phi^2\left(\frac{R}{s_i} - \frac{R^2}{s_i^2}\right)\right] - \frac{n_1}{R}\left[1 - \frac{1}{2}\phi^2\left(\frac{R}{s_o} + \frac{R^2}{s_o^2}\right)\right] \quad \Leftrightarrow$$

$$\frac{n_1}{s_o} - \frac{n_1\phi^2}{2s_o}\left(\frac{R}{s_o} + \frac{R^2}{s_o^2}\right) + \frac{n_2}{s_i} + \frac{n_2\phi^2}{2s_i}\left(\frac{R}{s_i} - \frac{R^2}{s_i^2}\right)$$

$$= \frac{n_2}{R} + \frac{n_2\phi^2}{2R}\left(\frac{R}{s_i} - \frac{R^2}{s_i^2}\right) - \frac{n_1}{R} + \frac{n_1\phi^2}{2R}\left(\frac{R}{s_o} + \frac{R^2}{s_o^2}\right) \quad \Leftrightarrow$$

$$\frac{n_1}{s_o} + \frac{n_2}{s_i} = \frac{n_2}{R} - \frac{n_1}{R} + \frac{n_1\phi^2}{2s_o}\left(\frac{R}{s_o} + \frac{R^2}{s_o^2}\right) + \frac{n_1\phi^2}{2R}\left(\frac{R}{s_o} + \frac{R^2}{s_o^2}\right) + \frac{n_2\phi^2}{2R}\left(\frac{R}{s_i} - \frac{R^2}{s_i^2}\right) - \frac{n_2\phi^2}{2s_i}\left(\frac{R}{s_i} - \frac{R^2}{s_i^2}\right)$$

$$= \frac{n_2 - n_1}{R} + \frac{n_1\phi^2}{2}\left(\frac{R}{s_o} + \frac{R^2}{s_o^2}\right)\left(\frac{1}{s_o} + \frac{1}{R}\right) + \frac{n_2\phi^2}{2}\left(\frac{R}{s_i} - \frac{R^2}{s_i^2}\right)\left(\frac{1}{R} - \frac{1}{s_i}\right)$$

$$= \frac{n_2 - n_1}{R} + \frac{n_1\phi^2 R^2}{2s_o}\left(\frac{1}{R} + \frac{1}{s_o}\right)\left(\frac{1}{R} + \frac{1}{s_o}\right) + \frac{n_2\phi^2 R^2}{2s_i}\left(\frac{1}{R} - \frac{1}{s_i}\right)\left(\frac{1}{R} - \frac{1}{s_i}\right)$$

$$= \frac{n_2 - n_1}{R} + \phi^2 R^2\left[\frac{n_1}{2s_o}\left(\frac{1}{R} + \frac{1}{s_o}\right)^2 + \frac{n_2}{2s_i}\left(\frac{1}{R} - \frac{1}{s_i}\right)^2\right]$$

From Figure 8, we see that $\sin\phi = h/R$. So if we approximate $\sin\phi$ with ϕ, we get $h = R\phi$ and $h^2 = \phi^2 R^2$ and hence, Equation 4, as desired.

25. $E = \dfrac{q}{D^2} - \dfrac{q}{(D+d)^2} = \dfrac{q}{D^2} - \dfrac{q}{D^2(1 + d/D)^2} = \dfrac{q}{D^2}\left[1 - \left(1 + \dfrac{d}{D}\right)^{-2}\right].$

We use the Binomial Series to expand $(1 + d/D)^{-2}$:

$$E = \frac{q}{D^2}\left[1 - \left(1 - 2\left(\frac{d}{D}\right) + \frac{2\cdot3}{2!}\left(\frac{d}{D}\right)^2 - \frac{2\cdot3\cdot4}{3!}\left(\frac{d}{D}\right)^3 + \cdots\right)\right]$$

$$= \frac{q}{D^2}\left[2\left(\frac{d}{D}\right) - 3\left(\frac{d}{D}\right)^2 + 4\left(\frac{d}{D}\right)^3 - \cdots\right] \approx \frac{q}{D^2}\cdot2\left(\frac{d}{D}\right) = 2qd\cdot\frac{1}{D^3}$$

when D is much larger than d; that is, when P is far away from the dipole.

26. (a)

$$\rho(t) = \rho_{20}e^{\alpha(t-20)} \qquad\qquad \rho(20) = \rho_{20}$$

$$\rho'(t) = \alpha\rho_{20}e^{\alpha(t-20)} \qquad\qquad \rho'(20) = \alpha\rho_{20}$$

$$\rho''(t) = \alpha^2\rho_{20}e^{\alpha(t-20)} \qquad\qquad \rho''(20) = \alpha^2\rho_{20}$$

The linear approximation is $T_1(t) = \rho(20) + \rho'(20)(t-20) = \rho_{20}\left[1 + \alpha(t-20)\right]$. The quadratic approximation is

$$T_2(t) = \rho(20) + \rho'(20)(t-20) + \frac{\rho''(20)}{2}(t-20)^2 = \rho_{20}\left[1 + \alpha(t-20) + \tfrac{1}{2}\alpha^2(t-20)^2\right]$$

(b)

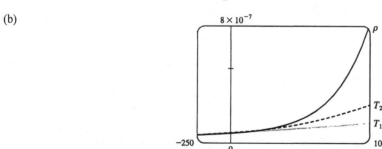

(c)

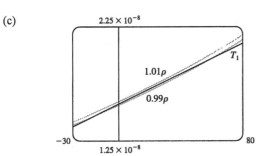

From the graph, it seems that $T_1(t)$ is within 1% of $\rho(t)$, that is, $0.99\rho(t) \le T_1(t) \le 1.01\rho(t)$, for $-14\,°\text{C} \le t \le 58\,°\text{C}$.

27. Using $f(x) = T_n(x) + R_n(x)$ with $n = 1$ and $x = r$, we have $f(r) = T_1(r) + R_1(r)$, where T_1 is the first-degree Taylor polynomial of f at a. Because $a = x_n$, $f(r) = f(x_n) + f'(x_n)(r - x_n) + R_1(r)$. But r is a root of f, so $f(r) = 0$ and we have $0 = f(x_n) + f'(x_n)(r - x_n) + R_1(r)$. Taking the first two terms to the left side and dividing by $f'(x_n)$, we have $f'(x_n)(x_n - r) - f(x_n) = R_1(r) \implies x_n - r - \dfrac{f(x_n)}{f'(x_n)} = \dfrac{R_1(r)}{f'(x_n)}$. By the formula for Newton's method, the left side of the preceding equation is $x_{n+1} - r$, so $|x_{n+1} - r| = \left| \dfrac{R_1(r)}{f'(x_n)} \right|$.

Taylor's Inequality gives us $|R_1(r)| \le \dfrac{|f''(r)|}{2!}\,|r - x_n|^2$. Combining this inequality with the facts $|f''(x)| \le M$ and $|f'(x)| \ge K$ gives us $|x_{n+1} - r| \le \dfrac{M}{2K}\,|x_n - r|^2$.

Applied Project	**Radiation from the Stars**

1. If we write $f(\lambda) = \dfrac{8\pi hc\lambda^{-5}}{e^{hc/(\lambda kT)} - 1} = \dfrac{a\lambda^{-5}}{e^{b/(\lambda T)} - 1}$, then as $\lambda \to 0^+$, it is of the form ∞/∞, and as $\lambda \to \infty$ it is of the form $0/0$, so in either case we can use l'Hospital's Rule. First of all,

$$\lim_{\lambda \to \infty} f(\lambda) \overset{\text{H}}{=} \lim_{\lambda \to \infty} \frac{a\left(-5\lambda^{-6}\right)}{-\dfrac{bT}{(\lambda T)^2}e^{b/(\lambda T)}} = 5\frac{aT}{b} \lim_{\lambda \to \infty} \frac{\lambda^2\lambda^{-6}}{e^{b/(\lambda T)}} = 5\frac{aT}{b} \lim_{\lambda \to \infty} \frac{\lambda^{-4}}{e^{b/(\lambda T)}} = 0$$

Also,

$$\lim_{\lambda \to 0^+} f(\lambda) \overset{\text{H}}{=} 5\frac{aT}{b} \lim_{\lambda \to 0^+} \frac{\lambda^{-4}}{e^{b/(\lambda T)}} \overset{\text{H}}{=} 5\frac{aT}{b} \lim_{\lambda \to 0^+} \frac{-4\lambda^{-5}}{-\dfrac{bT}{(\lambda T)^2}e^{b/(\lambda T)}} = 20\frac{aT^2}{b^2} \lim_{\lambda \to 0^+} \frac{\lambda^{-3}}{e^{b/(\lambda T)}}$$

This is still indeterminate, but note that each time we use l'Hospital's Rule, we gain a factor of λ in the numerator, as well as a constant factor, and the denominator is unchanged. So if we use l'Hospital's Rule three more times, the exponent of λ in the numerator will become 0. That is, for some $\{k_i\}$, all constant,

$$\lim_{\lambda \to 0^+} f(\lambda) \overset{\text{H}}{=} k_1 \lim_{\lambda \to 0^+} \frac{\lambda^{-3}}{e^{b/(\lambda T)}} \overset{\text{H}}{=} k_2 \lim_{\lambda \to 0^+} \frac{\lambda^{-2}}{e^{b/(\lambda T)}} \overset{\text{H}}{=} k_3 \lim_{\lambda \to 0^+} \frac{\lambda^{-1}}{e^{b/(\lambda T)}} \overset{\text{H}}{=} k_4 \lim_{\lambda \to 0^+} \frac{1}{e^{b/(\lambda T)}} = 0$$

2. We expand the denominator of Planck's Law using the Taylor series $e^x = 1 + x + \dfrac{x^2}{2!} + \dfrac{x^3}{3!} + \cdots$ with $x = \dfrac{hc}{\lambda kT}$, and use the fact that if λ is large, then all subsequent terms in the Taylor expansion are very small compared to the first one, so we can approximate using the Taylor polynomial T_1:

$$f(\lambda) = \frac{8\pi hc\lambda^{-5}}{e^{hc/(\lambda kT)} - 1}$$

$$= \frac{8\pi hc\lambda^{-5}}{\left[1 + \dfrac{hc}{\lambda kT} + \dfrac{1}{2!}\left(\dfrac{hc}{\lambda kT}\right)^2 + \dfrac{1}{3!}\left(\dfrac{hc}{\lambda kT}\right)^3 + \cdots\right] - 1}$$

$$\approx \frac{8\pi hc\lambda^{-5}}{\left(1 + \dfrac{hc}{\lambda kT}\right) - 1} = \frac{8\pi kT}{\lambda^4}$$

which is the Rayleigh-Jeans Law.

3. To convert to μm, we substitute $\lambda/10^6$ for λ in both laws. The first figure shows that the two laws are similar for large λ. The second figure shows that the two laws are very different for short wavelengths (Planck's Law gives a maximum at $\lambda \approx 0.51$ μm; the Rayleigh-Jeans Law gives no minimum or maximum.).

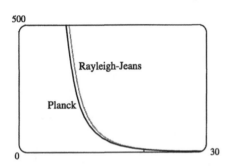

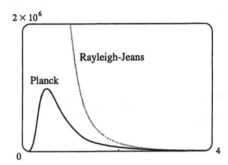

4. From the graph in Problem 3, $f(\lambda)$ has a maximum under Planck's Law at $\lambda \approx 0.51$ μm.

5.

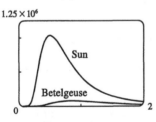

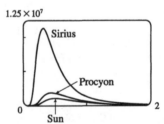

As T gets larger, the total area under the curve increases, as we would expect: the hotter the star, the more energy it emits. Also, as T increases, the λ-value of the maximum decreases, so the higher the temperature, the shorter the peak wavelength (and consequently the average wavelength) of light emitted. This is why Sirius is a blue star and Betelgeuse is a red star: most of Sirius's light is of a fairly short wavelength; that is, a higher frequency, toward the blue end of the spectrum, whereas most of Betelgeuse's light is of a lower frequency, toward the red end of the spectrum.

8.10 **Using Series to Solve Differential Equations** • • • • •

1. Let $y(x) = \sum\limits_{n=0}^{\infty} c_n x^n$. Then $y'(x) = \sum\limits_{n=1}^{\infty} nc_n x^{n-1}$ and the given equation, $y' - y = 0$, becomes

$\sum\limits_{n=1}^{\infty} nc_n x^{n-1} - \sum\limits_{n=0}^{\infty} c_n x^n = 0$. Replacing n by $n+1$ in the first sum gives $\sum\limits_{n=0}^{\infty} (n+1)c_{n+1} x^n - \sum\limits_{n=0}^{\infty} c_n x^n = 0$,

so $\sum\limits_{n=0}^{\infty} [(n+1)c_{n+1} - c_n] x^n = 0$. Equating coefficients gives $(n+1)c_{n+1} - c_n = 0$, so the recursion relation is

$c_{n+1} = \dfrac{c_n}{n+1}$, $n = 0, 1, 2, \ldots$. Then $c_1 = c_0$, $c_2 = \dfrac{1}{2}c_1 = \dfrac{c_0}{2}$, $c_3 = \dfrac{1}{3}c_2 = \dfrac{1}{3} \cdot \dfrac{1}{2}c_0 = \dfrac{c_0}{3!}$, $c_4 = \dfrac{1}{4}c_3 = \dfrac{c_0}{4!}$, and

in general, $c_n = \dfrac{c_0}{n!}$. Thus, the solution is

$$y(x) = \sum_{n=0}^{\infty} c_n x^n = \sum_{n=0}^{\infty} \frac{c_0}{n!} x^n = c_0 \sum_{n=0}^{\infty} \frac{x^n}{n!} = c_0 e^x$$

2. Let $y(x) = \sum\limits_{n=0}^{\infty} c_n x^n$. Then $y' = xy \;\Rightarrow\; y' - xy = 0 \;\Rightarrow\; \sum\limits_{n=1}^{\infty} nc_n x^{n-1} - x \sum\limits_{n=0}^{\infty} c_n x^n = 0$ or

$\sum\limits_{n=1}^{\infty} nc_n x^{n-1} - \sum\limits_{n=0}^{\infty} c_n x^{n+1} = 0$. Replacing n with $n+1$ in the first sum and n with $n-1$ in the second gives

$\sum\limits_{n=0}^{\infty} (n+1)c_{n+1} x^n - \sum\limits_{n=1}^{\infty} c_{n-1} x^n = 0$ or $c_1 + \sum\limits_{n=1}^{\infty} (n+1)c_{n+1} x^n - \sum\limits_{n=1}^{\infty} c_{n-1} x^n = 0$. Thus,

$c_1 + \sum\limits_{n=1}^{\infty} [(n+1)c_{n+1} - c_{n-1}] x^n = 0$. Equating coefficients gives $c_1 = 0$ and $(n+1)c_{n+1} - c_{n-1} = 0$. Thus,

the recursion relation is $c_{n+1} = \dfrac{c_{n-1}}{n+1}$, $n = 1, 2, \ldots$. But $c_1 = 0$, so $c_3 = 0$ and $c_5 = 0$ and in general $c_{2n+1} = 0$.

Also, $c_2 = \dfrac{c_0}{2}$, $c_4 = \dfrac{c_2}{4} = \dfrac{c_0}{4 \cdot 2} = \dfrac{c_0}{2^2 \cdot 2!}$, $c_6 = \dfrac{c_4}{6} = \dfrac{c_0}{6 \cdot 4 \cdot 2} = \dfrac{c_0}{2^3 \cdot 3!}$ and in general $c_{2n} = \dfrac{c_0}{2^n \cdot n!}$. Thus, the

solution is

$$y(x) = \sum_{n=0}^{\infty} c_n x^n = \sum_{n=0}^{\infty} c_{2n} x^{2n} = \sum_{n=0}^{\infty} \frac{c_0}{2^n \cdot n!} x^{2n} = c_0 \sum_{n=0}^{\infty} \frac{\left(x^2/2\right)^n}{n!} = c_0 e^{x^2/2}$$

3. Assuming $y(x) = \sum\limits_{n=0}^{\infty} c_n x^n$, we have $y'(x) = \sum\limits_{n=1}^{\infty} nc_n x^{n-1} = \sum\limits_{n=0}^{\infty} (n+1)c_{n+1} x^n$ and

$-x^2 y = -\sum\limits_{n=0}^{\infty} c_n x^{n+2} = -\sum\limits_{n=2}^{\infty} c_{n-2} x^n$. Hence, the equation $y' = x^2 y$ becomes

$\sum\limits_{n=0}^{\infty} (n+1)c_{n+1} x^n - \sum\limits_{n=2}^{\infty} c_{n-2} x^n = 0$ or $c_1 + 2c_2 x + \sum\limits_{n=2}^{\infty} [(n+1)c_{n+1} - c_{n-2}] x^n = 0$. Equating coefficients

gives $c_1 = c_2 = 0$ and $c_{n+1} = \dfrac{c_{n-2}}{n+1}$ for $n = 2, 3, \ldots$. But $c_1 = 0$, so $c_4 = 0$ and $c_7 = 0$ and in general

$c_{3n+1} = 0$. Similarly $c_2 = 0$ so $c_{3n+2} = 0$. Finally $c_3 = \dfrac{c_0}{3}$, $c_6 = \dfrac{c_3}{6} = \dfrac{c_0}{6 \cdot 3} = \dfrac{c_0}{3^2 \cdot 2!}$,

$c_9 = \dfrac{c_6}{9} = \dfrac{c_0}{9 \cdot 6 \cdot 3} = \dfrac{c_0}{3^3 \cdot 3!}$, $\ldots$, and $c_{3n} = \dfrac{c_0}{3^n \cdot n!}$. Thus, the solution is

$$y(x) = \sum_{n=0}^{\infty} c_n x^n = \sum_{n=0}^{\infty} c_{3n} x^{3n} = \sum_{n=0}^{\infty} \frac{c_0}{3^n \cdot n!} x^{3n} = c_0 \sum_{n=0}^{\infty} \frac{x^{3n}}{3^n n!} = c_0 \sum_{n=0}^{\infty} \frac{\left(x^3/3\right)^n}{n!} = c_0 e^{x^3/3}$$

4. Let $y(x) = \sum\limits_{n=0}^{\infty} c_n x^n$. Then $y''(x) = \sum\limits_{n=2}^{\infty} n(n-1)c_n x^{n-2} = \sum\limits_{n=0}^{\infty} (n+2)(n+1)c_{n+2}x^n$. Hence, the equation

$y'' = y$ becomes $\sum\limits_{n=0}^{\infty} (n+2)(n+1)c_{n+2}x^n - \sum\limits_{n=0}^{\infty} c_n x^n = 0$ or $\sum\limits_{n=0}^{\infty} [(n+2)(n+1)c_{n+2} - c_n]x^n = 0$. So the

recursion relation is $c_{n+2} = \dfrac{c_n}{(n+2)(n+1)}$, $n = 0, 1, \ldots$. Given c_0 and c_1, $c_2 = \dfrac{c_0}{2 \cdot 1}$, $c_4 = \dfrac{c_2}{4 \cdot 3} = \dfrac{c_0}{4!}$,

$c_6 = \dfrac{c_4}{6 \cdot 5} = \dfrac{c_0}{6!}, \ldots, c_{2n} = \dfrac{c_0}{(2n)!}$ and $c_3 = \dfrac{c_1}{3 \cdot 2}$, $c_5 = \dfrac{c_3}{5 \cdot 4} = \dfrac{c_1}{5 \cdot 4 \cdot 3 \cdot 2} = \dfrac{c_1}{5!}$, $c_7 = \dfrac{c_5}{7 \cdot 6} = \dfrac{c_1}{7!}, \ldots$,

$c_{2n+1} = \dfrac{c_1}{(2n+1)!}$. Thus, the solution is

$$y(x) = \sum_{n=0}^{\infty} c_n x^n = \sum_{n=0}^{\infty} c_{2n} x^{2n} + \sum_{n=0}^{\infty} c_{2n+1} x^{2n+1} = c_0 \sum_{n=0}^{\infty} \frac{x^{2n}}{(2n)!} + c_1 \sum_{n=0}^{\infty} \frac{x^{2n+1}}{(2n+1)!}$$

The solution can be written as $y(x) = c_0 \cosh x + c_1 \sinh x$

$$\left[\text{or } y(x) = c_0 \frac{e^x + e^{-x}}{2} + c_1 \frac{e^x - e^{-x}}{2} = \frac{c_0 + c_1}{2} e^x + \frac{c_0 - c_1}{2} e^{-x} \right].$$

5. Let $y(x) = \sum\limits_{n=0}^{\infty} c_n x^n$. Then $3xy'(x) = 3x \sum\limits_{n=1}^{\infty} nc_n x^{n-1} = \sum\limits_{n=0}^{\infty} 3nc_n x^n$,

$y''(x) = \sum\limits_{n=2}^{\infty} n(n-1)c_n x^{n-2} = \sum\limits_{n=0}^{\infty} (n+2)(n+1)c_{n+2}x^n$, and the equation

$y'' + 3xy' + 3y = 0$ becomes $\sum\limits_{n=0}^{\infty} (n+2)(n+1)c_{n+2}x^n + \sum\limits_{n=0}^{\infty} 3nc_n x^n + \sum\limits_{n=0}^{\infty} 3c_n x^n = 0 \iff$

$\sum\limits_{n=0}^{\infty} [(n+2)(n+1)c_{n+2} + 3nc_n + 3c_n]x^n = 0$. Thus, the recursion relation is

$c_{n+2} = \dfrac{-3nc_n - 3c_n}{(n+2)(n+1)} = \dfrac{-3c_n(n+1)}{(n+2)(n+1)} = -\dfrac{3c_n}{n+2}$ for $n = 0, 1, 2, \ldots$. Given c_0 and c_1, $c_2 = -\dfrac{3c_0}{2}$,

$c_4 = -\dfrac{3c_2}{4} = (-1)^2 \dfrac{3^2 c_0}{2^2 \cdot 2!}$, $c_6 = -\dfrac{3c_4}{6} = (-1)^3 \dfrac{3^3 c_0}{2^3 \cdot 3!}, \ldots, c_{2n} = (-1)^n \dfrac{3^n c_0}{2^n n!}$ or, equivalently, $c_0 \left(-\dfrac{3}{2}\right)^n \dfrac{1}{n!}$.

Also, $c_3 = -\dfrac{3c_1}{3}$, $c_5 = -\dfrac{3c_3}{5} = (-1)^2 \dfrac{3^2 c_1}{5 \cdot 3}$, $c_7 = -\dfrac{3c_5}{7} = (-1)^3 \dfrac{3^3 c_1}{7 \cdot 5 \cdot 3}, \ldots$,

$c_{2n+1} = (-1)^n \dfrac{3^n c_1}{(2n+1)(2n-1) \cdots \cdots 5 \cdot 3}$. Since $(2n+1)(2n-1) \cdots \cdots 5 \cdot 3$ can be written as

$$\frac{(2n+1) \ (2n) \ (2n-1) \ (2n-2) \ \cdots \cdots 5 \cdot \ 4 \ \cdot \ 3 \ \cdot \ 2}{(2 \cdot n) \quad \cdot \quad [2(n-1)] \quad \cdot \quad (2 \cdot 2) \ \cdot \ (2 \cdot 1)} = \frac{(2n+1)!}{2^n \cdot n!},$$

c_{2n+1} can be written as $(-1)^n \dfrac{3^n c_1 2^n n!}{(2n+1)!} = c_1 \dfrac{(-6)^n n!}{(2n+1)!}$. Thus, the solution is

$$y(x) = \sum_{n=0}^{\infty} c_{2n} x^{2n} + \sum_{n=0}^{\infty} c_{2n+1} x^{2n+1} = c_0 \sum_{n=0}^{\infty} \left(-\frac{3}{2}\right)^n \frac{1}{n!} x^{2n} + c_1 \sum_{n=0}^{\infty} \frac{(-6)^n n!}{(2n+1)!} x^{2n+1}$$

Note that the c_0-term can be written as $c_0 \sum\limits_{n=0}^{\infty} \left(-\dfrac{3x^2}{2}\right)^n \dfrac{1}{n!} = c_0 e^{-3x^2/2}$.

6. Assuming $y(x) = \sum\limits_{n=0}^{\infty} c_n x^n$, $y''(x) = \sum\limits_{n=2}^{\infty} n(n-1)c_n x^{n-2} = \sum\limits_{n=0}^{\infty} (n+2)(n+1)c_{n+2}x^n$ and

$-xy(x) = -\sum\limits_{n=0}^{\infty} c_n x^{n+1} = -\sum\limits_{n=1}^{\infty} c_{n-1}x^n$. The equation $y'' = xy$ becomes

$\sum\limits_{n=0}^{\infty} (n+2)(n+1)c_{n+2}x^n - \sum\limits_{n=1}^{\infty} c_{n-1}x^n = 0$ or $2c_2 + \sum\limits_{n=1}^{\infty} [(n+2)(n+1)c_{n+2} - c_{n-1}] x^n = 0$. Equating

coefficients gives $c_2 = 0$ and $c_{n+2} = \dfrac{c_{n-1}}{(n+2)(n+1)}$ for $n = 1, 2, \ldots$. Since $c_2 = 0$,

$c_{3n+2} = 0$ for $n = 0, 1, 2, \ldots$. Given c_0, $c_3 = \dfrac{c_0}{3 \cdot 2}$, $c_6 = \dfrac{c_3}{6 \cdot 5} = \dfrac{c_0}{6 \cdot 5 \cdot 3 \cdot 2}, \ldots$,

$c_{3n} = \dfrac{c_0}{3n(3n-1)(3n-3)(3n-4) \cdots \cdot 6 \cdot 5 \cdot 3 \cdot 2}$. Given c_1, $c_4 = \dfrac{c_1}{4 \cdot 3}$, $c_7 = \dfrac{c_4}{7 \cdot 6} = \dfrac{c_1}{7 \cdot 6 \cdot 4 \cdot 3}, \ldots$,

$c_{3n+1} = \dfrac{c_1}{(3n+1)3n(3n-2)(3n-3) \ldots 7 \cdot 6 \cdot 4 \cdot 3}$. The solution can be written as

$$y(x) = c_0 \sum\limits_{n=0}^{\infty} \frac{(3n-2)(3n-5) \cdots \cdot 7 \cdot 4 \cdot 1}{(3n)!} x^{3n} + c_1 \sum\limits_{n=0}^{\infty} \frac{(3n-1)(3n-4) \cdots \cdot 8 \cdot 5 \cdot 2}{(3n+1)!} x^{3n+1}$$

7. Let $y(x) = \sum\limits_{n=0}^{\infty} c_n x^n$. Then $-xy'(x) = -x \sum\limits_{n=1}^{\infty} nc_n x^{n-1} = -\sum\limits_{n=1}^{\infty} nc_n x^n = -\sum\limits_{n=0}^{\infty} nc_n x^n$,

$y''(x) = \sum\limits_{n=0}^{\infty} (n+2)(n+1)c_{n+2}x^n$, and the equation $y'' - xy' - y = 0$ becomes

$\sum\limits_{n=0}^{\infty} [(n+2)(n+1)c_{n+2} - nc_n - c_n]x^n = 0$. Thus, the recursion relation is

$c_{n+2} = \dfrac{nc_n + c_n}{(n+2)(n+1)} = \dfrac{c_n(n+1)}{(n+2)(n+1)} = \dfrac{c_n}{n+2}$ for $n = 0, 1, 2, \ldots$. One of the given conditions is

$y(0) = 1$. But $y(0) = \sum\limits_{n=0}^{\infty} c_n(0)^n = c_0 + 0 + 0 + \cdots = c_0$, so $c_0 = 1$. Hence, $c_2 = \dfrac{c_0}{2} = \dfrac{1}{2}$, $c_4 = \dfrac{c_2}{4} = \dfrac{1}{2 \cdot 4}$,

$c_6 = \dfrac{c_4}{6} = \dfrac{1}{2 \cdot 4 \cdot 6}, \ldots, c_{2n} = \dfrac{1}{2^n n!}$. The other given condition is $y'(0) = 0$. But

$y'(0) = \sum\limits_{n=1}^{\infty} nc_n(0)^{n-1} = c_1 + 0 + 0 + \cdots = c_1$, so $c_1 = 0$. By the recursion relation, $c_3 = \dfrac{c_1}{3} = 0$, $c_5 = 0, \ldots$,

$c_{2n+1} = 0$ for $n = 0, 1, 2, \ldots$. Thus, the solution to the initial-value problem is

$$y(x) = \sum\limits_{n=0}^{\infty} c_n x^n = \sum\limits_{n=0}^{\infty} c_{2n} x^{2n} = \sum\limits_{n=0}^{\infty} \frac{x^{2n}}{2^n n!} = \sum\limits_{n=0}^{\infty} \frac{(x^2/2)^n}{n!} = e^{x^2/2}$$

8. Assuming that $y(x) = \sum\limits_{n=0}^{\infty} c_n x^n$, we have $x^2 y = \sum\limits_{n=0}^{\infty} c_n x^{n+2}$ and

$$y''(x) = \sum\limits_{n=2}^{\infty} n(n-1)c_n x^{n-2} = \sum\limits_{n=-2}^{\infty} (n+4)(n+3)c_{n+4}x^{n+2}$$

$$= 2c_2 + 6c_3 x + \sum\limits_{n=0}^{\infty} (n+4)(n+3)c_{n+4}x^{n+2}$$

Thus, the equation $y'' + x^2 y = 0$ becomes $2c_2 + 6c_3 x + \sum\limits_{n=0}^{\infty} [(n+4)(n+3)c_{n+4} + c_n] x^{n+2} = 0$. So

$c_2 = c_3 = 0$ and the recursion relation is $c_{n+4} = -\dfrac{c_n}{(n+4)(n+3)}$, $n = 0, 1, 2, \ldots$.

But $c_1 = y'(0) = 0 = c_2 = c_3$ and by the recursion relation, $c_{4n+1} = c_{4n+2} = c_{4n+3} = 0$ for $n = 0, 1, 2, \ldots$.
Also, $c_0 = y(0) = 1$, so

$$c_4 = -\dfrac{c_0}{4 \cdot 3} = -\dfrac{1}{4 \cdot 3}, \quad c_8 = -\dfrac{c_4}{8 \cdot 7} = \dfrac{(-1)^2}{8 \cdot 7 \cdot 4 \cdot 3}, \ldots, c_{4n} = \dfrac{(-1)^n}{4n(4n-1)(4n-4)(4n-5) \cdots \cdots 4 \cdot 3}.$$

Thus, the solution to the initial-value problem is

$$y(x) = \sum_{n=0}^{\infty} c_n x^n = c_0 + \sum_{n=0}^{\infty} c_{4n} x^{4n} = 1 + \sum_{n=1}^{\infty} (-1)^n \dfrac{x^{4n}}{4n(4n-1)(4n-4)(4n-5) \cdots \cdots 4 \cdot 3}.$$

9. Assuming that $y(x) = \sum_{n=0}^{\infty} c_n x^n$, we have $xy = x \sum_{n=0}^{\infty} c_n x^n = \sum_{n=0}^{\infty} c_n x^{n+1}$,

$$x^2 y' = x^2 \sum_{n=1}^{\infty} n c_n x^{n-1} = \sum_{n=0}^{\infty} n c_n x^{n+1},$$

$$y''(x) = \sum_{n=2}^{\infty} n(n-1) c_n x^{n-2} = \sum_{n=-1}^{\infty} (n+3)(n+2) c_{n+3} x^{n+1} \quad \text{[replace n with $n+3$]}$$

$$= 2c_2 + \sum_{n=0}^{\infty} (n+3)(n+2) c_{n+3} x^{n+1},$$

and the equation $y'' + x^2 y' + xy = 0$ becomes $2c_2 + \sum_{n=0}^{\infty} [(n+3)(n+2) c_{n+3} + n c_n + c_n] x^{n+1} = 0$.

So $c_2 = 0$ and the recursion relation is $c_{n+3} = \dfrac{-n c_n - c_n}{(n+3)(n+2)} = -\dfrac{(n+1) c_n}{(n+3)(n+2)}$, $n = 0, 1, 2, \ldots$.

But $c_0 = y(0) = 0 = c_2$ and by the recursion relation, $c_{3n} = c_{3n+2} = 0$ for $n = 0, 1, 2, \ldots$.
Also, $c_1 = y'(0) = 1$, so

$$c_4 = -\dfrac{2c_1}{4 \cdot 3} = -\dfrac{2}{4 \cdot 3}, \quad c_7 = -\dfrac{5c_4}{7 \cdot 6} = (-1)^2 \dfrac{2 \cdot 5}{7 \cdot 6 \cdot 4 \cdot 3} = (-1)^2 \dfrac{2^2 5^2}{7!}, \ldots,$$

$$c_{3n+1} = (-1)^n \dfrac{2^2 5^2 \cdots \cdots (3n-1)^2}{(3n+1)!}. \text{ Thus, the solution is}$$

$$y(x) = \sum_{n=0}^{\infty} c_n x^n = x + \sum_{n=1}^{\infty} \left[(-1)^n \dfrac{2^2 5^2 \cdots \cdots (3n-1)^2 x^{3n+1}}{(3n+1)!} \right].$$

10. (a) Let $y(x) = \sum_{n=0}^{\infty} c_n x^n$. Then $x^2 y''(x) = \sum_{n=2}^{\infty} n(n-1) c_n x^n = \sum_{n=0}^{\infty} (n+2)(n+1) c_{n+2} x^{n+2}$,

$$xy'(x) = \sum_{n=1}^{\infty} n c_n x^n = \sum_{n=-1}^{\infty} (n+2) c_{n+2} x^{n+2} = c_1 x + \sum_{n=0}^{\infty} (n+2) c_{n+2} x^{n+2}, \text{ and the equation}$$

$x^2 y'' + xy' + x^2 y = 0$ becomes $c_1 x + \sum_{n=0}^{\infty} \{[(n+2)(n+1) + (n+2)] c_{n+2} + c_n\} x^{n+2} = 0$. So $c_1 = 0$

and the recursion relation is $c_{n+2} = -\dfrac{c_n}{(n+2)^2}$, $n = 0, 1, 2, \ldots$. But $c_1 = y'(0) = 0$ so $c_{2n+1} = 0$ for

$n = 0, 1, 2, \ldots$. Also, $c_0 = y(0) = 1$, so $c_2 = -\dfrac{1}{2^2}$, $c_4 = -\dfrac{c_2}{4^2} = (-1)^2 \dfrac{1}{4^2 2^2} = (-1)^2 \dfrac{1}{2^4 (2!)^2}$,

$c_6 = -\dfrac{c_4}{6^2} = (-1)^3 \dfrac{1}{2^6 (3!)^2}, \ldots, c_{2n} = (-1)^n \dfrac{1}{2^{2n} (n!)^2}$. The solution is

$$y(x) = \sum_{n=0}^{\infty} c_n x^n = \sum_{n=0}^{\infty} (-1)^n \dfrac{x^{2n}}{2^{2n} (n!)^2}$$

(b) The Taylor polynomials T_0 to T_{12} are shown in the graph. Because T_{10} and T_{12} are close together throughout the interval $[-5, 5]$, it is reasonable to assume that T_{12} is a good approximation to the Bessel function on that interval.

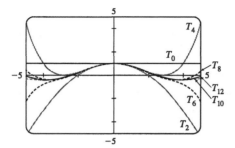

8 Review

• CONCEPT CHECK •

1. (a) See Definition 8.1.1.

(b) See Definition 8.2.2.

(c) The terms of the sequence $\{a_n\}$ approach 3 as n becomes large.

(d) By adding sufficiently many terms of the series, we can make the partial sums as close to 3 as we like.

2. (a) See the definition on page 569.

(b) A sequence is monotonic if it is either increasing or decreasing.

(c) By Theorem 8.1.7, every bounded, monotonic sequence is convergent.

3. (a) See (4) in Section 8.2.

(b) See (1) in Section 8.3.

4. If $\sum a_n = 3$, then $\lim\limits_{n \to \infty} a_n = 0$ and $\lim\limits_{n \to \infty} s_n = 3$.

5. (a) See the Test for Divergence on page 578.

(b) See the Integral Test on page 584.

(c) See the Comparison Test on page 586.

(d) See the Limit Comparison Test on page 588.

(e) See the Alternating Series Test on page 593.

(f) See the Ratio Test on page 597.

6. (a) See the definition on page 595.

(b) By (8.4.1), it is convergent.

7. (a) Use (4) in Section 8.3.

(b) See Example 8 in Section 8.4.

(c) By adding terms until you reach the desired accuracy given by the Alternating Series Estimation Theorem on page 594.

8. (a) $\sum_{n=0}^{\infty} c_n(x-a)^n$

   (b) Given the power series $\sum_{n=0}^{\infty} c_n(x-a)^n$, the radius of convergence is:

     (i) 0 if the series converges only when $x = a$

     (ii) ∞ if the series converges for all x, or

     (iii) a positive number R such that the series converges if $|x-a| < R$ and diverges if $|x-a| > R$.

   (c) The interval of convergence of a power series is the interval that consists of all values of x for which the series converges. Corresponding to the cases in part (b), the interval of convergence is: (i) the single point $\{a\}$, (ii) all real numbers, that is, the real number line $(-\infty, \infty)$, or (iii) an interval with endpoints $a - R$ and $a + R$ which can contain neither, either, or both of the endpoints. In this case, we must test the series for convergence at each endpoint to determine the interval of convergence.

9. (a), (b) See Theorem 8.6.2.

10. (a) $T_n(x) = \sum_{i=0}^{n} \dfrac{f^{(i)}(a)}{i!}(x-a)^i$

   (b) $\sum_{n=0}^{\infty} \dfrac{f^{(n)}(a)}{n!}(x-a)^n$

   (c) $\sum_{n=0}^{\infty} \dfrac{f^{(n)}(0)}{n!}x^n$ [$a = 0$ in part (b)]

   (d) See Theorem 8.7.8.

   (e) See Taylor's Inequality (8.7.9).

11. (a) – (e) See the table on page 618.

12. See the Binomial Series (8.8.2) for the expansion. The radius of convergence for the binomial series is 1.

─────────────────────────────── ▲ **TRUE–FALSE QUIZ** ▲ ───────────────────────────────

1. False.   See Note 2 after Theorem 8.2.6.

2. True by Theorem 8.5.3.

   Or: Use the Comparison Test to show that $\sum c_n(-2)^n$ converges absolutely.

3. False.   For example, take $c_n = (-1)^n / (n6^n)$.

4. True by Theorem 8.5.3.

5. False, since $\lim\limits_{n\to\infty} \left| \dfrac{a_{n+1}}{a_n} \right| = \lim\limits_{n\to\infty} \left| \dfrac{n^3}{(n+1)^3} \right| = \lim\limits_{n\to\infty} \dfrac{1}{(1+1/n)^3} = 1.$

6. True, since $\lim\limits_{n\to\infty} \left| \dfrac{a_{n+1}}{a_n} \right| = \lim\limits_{n\to\infty} \left| \dfrac{n!}{(n+1)!} \right| = \lim\limits_{n\to\infty} \dfrac{1}{n+1} = 0 < 1.$

7. False.   See the note after Example 4 in Section 8.3.

8. True, since $\dfrac{1}{e} = e^{-1}$ and $e^x = \sum\limits_{n=0}^{\infty} \dfrac{x^n}{n!}$, so $e^{-1} = \sum\limits_{n=0}^{\infty} \dfrac{(-1)^n}{n!}.$

9. True.   See (6) in Section 8.1.

10. True, because if $\sum |a_n|$ is convergent, then so is $\sum a_n$ by Theorem 8.4.1.

11. True.   By Theorem 8.7.5 the coefficient of x^3 is $\dfrac{f'''(0)}{3!} = \dfrac{1}{3} \;\Rightarrow\; f'''(0) = 2.$

     Or: Use Theorem 8.6.2 to differentiate f three times.

12. **False.** Let $a_n = n$ and $b_n = -n$. Then $\{a_n\}$ and $\{b_n\}$ are divergent, but $a_n + b_n = 0$, so $\{a_n + b_n\}$ is convergent.

13. **False.** For example, let $a_n = b_n = (-1)^n$. Then $\{a_n\}$ and $\{b_n\}$ are divergent, but $a_n b_n = 1$, so $\{a_n b_n\}$ is convergent.

14. **True** by Theorem 8.1.7 (the Monotonic Sequence Theorem), since $\{a_n\}$ is decreasing and $0 < a_n \le a_1$ for all n $\Rightarrow$ $\{a_n\}$ is bounded.

15. **True** by Theorem 8.4.1. $\left[\sum (-1)^n \, a_n \text{ is absolutely convergent and hence convergent.} \right]$

16. **True.** $\lim\limits_{n \to \infty} \dfrac{a_{n+1}}{a_n} < 1 \;\Rightarrow\; \sum a_n$ converges (Ratio Test) $\;\Rightarrow\; \lim\limits_{n \to \infty} a_n = 0$ [Theorem 8.2.6].

17. **False.** The Integral Test tells us that the series $\sum_{n=1}^{\infty} a_n$ also converges, but its value is not equal to the value of $\int_1^{\infty} f(x)\,dx$. In fact, a picture like Figure 2 on page 584 shows that the sum of the series is larger than the value of the integral.

◆ **EXERCISES** ◆

---

1. $\left\{ \dfrac{2 + n^3}{1 + 2n^3} \right\}$ converges since $\lim\limits_{n \to \infty} \dfrac{2 + n^3}{1 + 2n^3} = \lim\limits_{n \to \infty} \dfrac{2/n^3 + 1}{1/n^3 + 2} = \dfrac{1}{2}$.

2. $a_n = \dfrac{9^{n+1}}{10^n} = 9 \cdot \left(\tfrac{9}{10} \right)^n$, so $\lim\limits_{n \to \infty} a_n = 9 \lim\limits_{n \to \infty} \left(\tfrac{9}{10} \right)^n = 9 \cdot 0 = 0$ by (8.1.6).

3. $\lim\limits_{n \to \infty} a_n = \lim\limits_{n \to \infty} \dfrac{n^3}{1 + n^2} = \lim\limits_{n \to \infty} \dfrac{n}{1/n^2 + 1} = \infty$, so the sequence diverges.

4. $\left\{ \dfrac{n}{\ln n} \right\}$ diverges, since $\lim\limits_{x \to \infty} \dfrac{x}{\ln x} \overset{\text{H}}{=} \lim\limits_{x \to \infty} \dfrac{1}{1/x} = \lim\limits_{x \to \infty} x = \infty$.

5. $\{\sin n\}$ is divergent since $\lim\limits_{n \to \infty} \sin n$ does not exist.

6. $\left\{ \dfrac{\sin n}{n} \right\}$ converges, since $-\dfrac{1}{n} \le \dfrac{\sin n}{n} \le \dfrac{1}{n}$ and $\pm \dfrac{1}{n} \to 0$ as $n \to \infty$, so $\lim\limits_{n \to \infty} \dfrac{\sin n}{n} = 0$ by the Squeeze Theorem.

7. $\left\{ \left(1 + \dfrac{3}{n} \right)^{4n} \right\}$ is convergent. Let $y = \left(1 + \dfrac{3}{x} \right)^{4x}$. Then

$$\lim\limits_{x \to \infty} \ln y = \lim\limits_{x \to \infty} 4x \ln(1 + 3/x) = \lim\limits_{x \to \infty} \dfrac{\ln(1 + 3/x)}{1/(4x)} \overset{\text{H}}{=} \lim\limits_{x \to \infty} \dfrac{\dfrac{1}{1 + 3/x} \left(-\dfrac{3}{x^2} \right)}{-1/(4x^2)} = \lim\limits_{x \to \infty} \dfrac{12}{1 + 3/x} = 12$$

so $\lim\limits_{x \to \infty} y = \lim\limits_{n \to \infty} \left(1 + \dfrac{3}{n} \right)^{4n} = e^{12}$.

8. We use induction, hypothesizing that $a_{n-1} < a_n < 2$. Note first that $a_1 = 1 < a_2 = \tfrac{1}{3}(1 + 5) = \tfrac{5}{3} < 2$, so the hypothesis holds for $n = 2$. Now assume that $a_{k-1} < a_k < 2$. Then $a_k = \tfrac{1}{3}(a_{k-1} + 4) < \tfrac{1}{3}(a_k + 4) < \tfrac{1}{3}(2 + 4) = 2$. So $a_k < a_{k+1} < 2$, and the induction is complete. To find the limit of the sequence, we note that $L = \lim\limits_{n \to \infty} a_n = \lim\limits_{n \to \infty} a_{n+1} \;\Rightarrow\; L = \tfrac{1}{3}(L + 4) \;\Rightarrow$

$3L = L + 4 \;\Rightarrow\; 2L = 4 \;\Rightarrow\; L = 2$.

9. $\dfrac{n}{n^3 + 1} < \dfrac{n}{n^3} = \dfrac{1}{n^2}$, so $\sum\limits_{n=1}^{\infty} \dfrac{n}{n^3 + 1}$ converges by the Comparison Test with the convergent p-series

$\sum\limits_{n=1}^{\infty} \dfrac{1}{n^2}$ ($p = 2 > 1$).

10. Let $a_n = \dfrac{n^2+1}{n^3+1}$ and $b_n = \dfrac{1}{n}$, so $\lim\limits_{n\to\infty} \dfrac{a_n}{b_n} = \lim\limits_{n\to\infty} \dfrac{n^3+n}{n^3+1} = \lim\limits_{n\to\infty} \dfrac{1+1/n^2}{1+1/n^3} = 1 > 0$. Since $\sum_{n=1}^{\infty} b_n$ is the

divergent harmonic series, $\sum_{n=1}^{\infty} a_n$ also diverges by the Limit Comparison Test.

11. $\lim\limits_{n\to\infty} \left| \dfrac{a_{n+1}}{a_n} \right| = \lim\limits_{n\to\infty} \left[\dfrac{(n+1)^3}{5^{n+1}} \cdot \dfrac{5^n}{n^3} \right] = \lim\limits_{n\to\infty} \left(1 + \dfrac{1}{n} \right)^3 \cdot \dfrac{1}{5} = \dfrac{1}{5} < 1$, so $\sum_{n=1}^{\infty} \dfrac{n^3}{5^n}$ converges by the Ratio Test.

12. Let $b_n = \dfrac{1}{\sqrt{n+1}}$. Then b_n is positive for $n \geq 1$, the sequence $\{b_n\}$ is decreasing, and $\lim\limits_{n\to\infty} b_n = 0$, so

$\sum_{n=1}^{\infty} \dfrac{(-1)^n}{\sqrt{n+1}}$ converges by the Alternating Series Test.

13. $\left| \dfrac{\sin n}{1+n^2} \right| \leq \dfrac{1}{1+n^2} < \dfrac{1}{n^2}$ and since $\sum_{n=1}^{\infty} \dfrac{1}{n^2}$ converges (p-series with $p = 2 > 1$), so does $\sum_{n=1}^{\infty} \left| \dfrac{\sin n}{1+n^2} \right|$ by the

Comparison Test, and so does $\sum_{n=1}^{\infty} \dfrac{\sin n}{1+n^2}$ by Theorem 8.4.1.

14. $\lim\limits_{n\to\infty} \dfrac{n}{3n+1} = \dfrac{1}{3}$, so $\lim\limits_{n\to\infty} \ln\left(\dfrac{n}{3n+1} \right) = \ln\frac{1}{3} \neq 0$. Thus, $\sum_{n=1}^{\infty} \ln\left(\dfrac{n}{3n+1} \right)$ diverges by the Test for

Divergence.

15. Let $b_n = \dfrac{\sqrt{n}}{n+1} > 0$. Then $0 \leq \lim\limits_{n\to\infty} b_n = \lim\limits_{n\to\infty} \dfrac{\sqrt{n}}{n+1} \leq \lim\limits_{n\to\infty} \dfrac{\sqrt{n}}{n} = \lim\limits_{n\to\infty} \dfrac{1}{\sqrt{n}} = 0$, so $\lim\limits_{n\to\infty} b_n = 0$. If

$f(x) = \dfrac{\sqrt{x}}{x+1}$ for $x > 0$, then $f'(x) = \dfrac{(x+1)\cdot\frac{1}{2\sqrt{x}} - \sqrt{x}\cdot 1}{(x+1)^2} = \dfrac{(x+1) - 2x}{2\sqrt{x}\,(x+1)^2} = \dfrac{1-x}{2\sqrt{x}\,(x+1)^2}$, so

$f'(x) < 0$ for $x > 1$. It follows that $f(1) > f(2) > f(3) > \cdots$; that is, $b_n > b_{n+1}$ for all n. Thus,

$\sum_{n=1}^{\infty} (-1)^{n-1} \dfrac{\sqrt{n}}{n+1}$ converges by the Alternating Series Test.

16. $f(x) = \dfrac{1}{x\,(\ln x)^2}$ is continuous, positive, and decreasing on $(2, \infty)$, so we can use the Integral Test.

$\displaystyle\int_2^{\infty} \dfrac{dx}{x\,(\ln x)^2} = \lim\limits_{t\to\infty} \left[\dfrac{-1}{\ln x} \right]_2^t = \dfrac{1}{\ln 2}$, so the series $\sum_{n=2}^{\infty} \dfrac{1}{n\,(\ln n)^2}$ also converges.

17. $\lim\limits_{n\to\infty} \left| \dfrac{a_{n+1}}{a_n} \right| = \lim\limits_{n\to\infty} \dfrac{1\cdot 3\cdot 5 \cdots\cdots (2n-1)(2n+1)}{5^{n+1}(n+1)!} \cdot \dfrac{5^n n!}{1\cdot 3\cdot 5 \cdots\cdots (2n-1)} = \lim\limits_{n\to\infty} \dfrac{2n+1}{5(n+1)} = \dfrac{2}{5} < 1$, so

the series converges by the Ratio Test.

18. $\sum_{n=1}^{\infty} \dfrac{(-5)^{2n}}{n^2 9^n} = \sum_{n=1}^{\infty} \dfrac{1}{n^2} \left(\dfrac{25}{9} \right)^n$. Now $\lim\limits_{n\to\infty} \left| \dfrac{a_{n+1}}{a_n} \right| = \lim\limits_{n\to\infty} \dfrac{n^2}{(n+1)^2} \left(\dfrac{25}{9} \right)^{n+1} \left(\dfrac{9}{25} \right)^n = \dfrac{25}{9} > 1$, so the series

diverges by the Ratio Test.

19. This is a convergent geometric series with $r = \frac{4}{5}$.

$\sum_{n=1}^{\infty} \dfrac{2^{2n+1}}{5^n} = \sum_{n=1}^{\infty} \dfrac{(2^2)^n \cdot 2^1}{5^n} = 2\sum_{n=1}^{\infty} \dfrac{4^n}{5^n} = 2\sum_{n=1}^{\infty} \left(\dfrac{4}{5} \right)^n = 2\left(\dfrac{\frac{4}{5}}{1-\frac{4}{5}} \right) = 2(4) = 8$.

20. $\sum_{n=1}^{\infty} \dfrac{1}{n(n+3)} = \sum_{n=1}^{\infty} \left[\dfrac{1}{3n} - \dfrac{1}{3(n+3)} \right]$ (partial fractions).

$s_n = \sum_{i=1}^{n} \left[\dfrac{1}{3i} - \dfrac{1}{3(i+3)} \right] = \dfrac{1}{3} + \dfrac{1}{6} + \dfrac{1}{9} - \dfrac{1}{3(n+1)} - \dfrac{1}{3(n+2)} - \dfrac{1}{3(n+3)}$ (telescoping sum), so

$\sum_{n=1}^{\infty} \dfrac{1}{n(n+3)} = \lim\limits_{n\to\infty} s_n = \dfrac{1}{3} + \dfrac{1}{6} + \dfrac{1}{9} = \dfrac{11}{18}$.

21. $\sum_{n=1}^{\infty} \left[\tan^{-1}(n+1) - \tan^{-1} n\right] = \lim_{n \to \infty} \left[\left(\tan^{-1} 2 - \tan^{-1} 1\right) + \left(\tan^{-1} 3 - \tan^{-1} 2\right) + \cdots \right.$

$$\left. + \left(\tan^{-1}(n+1) - \tan^{-1} n\right)\right]$$

$$= \lim_{n \to \infty} \left[\tan^{-1}(n+1) - \tan^{-1} 1\right] = \tfrac{\pi}{2} - \tfrac{\pi}{4} = \tfrac{\pi}{4}$$

22. $\displaystyle\sum_{n=0}^{\infty} \frac{(-1)^n x^n}{2^{2n} n!} = \sum_{n=0}^{\infty} \frac{(-1)^n x^n}{4^n n!} = \sum_{n=0}^{\infty} \frac{(-x/4)^n}{n!} = e^{-x/4}$

23. $1.2345345345\ldots = 1.2 + 0.0\overline{345} = \dfrac{12}{10} + \dfrac{345/10{,}000}{1 - 1/1000} = \dfrac{12}{10} + \dfrac{345}{9990} = \dfrac{4111}{3330}$

24. This is a geometric series which converges whenever $|\ln x| < 1 \;\Rightarrow\; -1 < \ln x < 1 \;\Rightarrow\; e^{-1} < x < e.$

25. $b_8 = \dfrac{1}{8^5} = \dfrac{1}{32{,}768} \approx 0.000\,031$, so

$$\sum_{n=1}^{\infty} \frac{(-1)^{n+1}}{n^5} \approx s_7 = \sum_{n=1}^{7} \frac{(-1)^{n+1}}{n^5} = 1 - \frac{1}{32} + \frac{1}{243} - \frac{1}{1024} + \frac{1}{3125} - \frac{1}{7776} + \frac{1}{16{,}807} \approx 0.972140.$$

Subtracting b_8 from s_7 does not change the fourth decimal place of s_7, so the sum of the series, correct to four decimal places, is 0.9721.

26. (a) $s_5 = \displaystyle\sum_{n=1}^{5} \frac{1}{n^6} = 1 + \frac{1}{2^6} + \frac{1}{3^6} + \frac{1}{4^6} + \frac{1}{5^6} \approx 1.017305.$ The series $\displaystyle\sum_{n=1}^{\infty} \frac{1}{n^6}$ converges by the Integral Test, so

we estimate the remainder R_5 with (8.3.3): $R_5 \leq \displaystyle\int_5^{\infty} \frac{dx}{x^6} = \left[-\frac{x^{-5}}{5}\right]_5^{\infty} = \frac{5^{-5}}{5} = 0.000064.$ So the error is

at most 0.000064.

(b) In general, $R_n \leq \displaystyle\int_n^{\infty} \frac{dx}{x^6} = \frac{1}{5n^5}.$ If we take $n = 9$, then $s_9 \approx 1.01734$ and $R_9 \leq \dfrac{1}{5 \cdot 9^5} \approx 3.4 \times 10^{-6}.$ So to

five decimal places, $\displaystyle\sum_{n=1}^{\infty} \frac{1}{n^5} \approx \sum_{n=1}^{9} \frac{1}{n^5} \approx 1.01734.$

Another method: Use (8.3.4) instead of (8.3.3).

27. $\displaystyle\sum_{n=1}^{\infty} \frac{1}{2 + 5^n} \approx \sum_{n=1}^{8} \frac{1}{2 + 5^n} \approx 0.18976224.$ To estimate the error, note that $\dfrac{1}{2 + 5^n} < \dfrac{1}{5^n}$, so the remainder term is

$$R_8 = \sum_{n=9}^{\infty} \frac{1}{2 + 5^n} < \sum_{n=9}^{\infty} \frac{1}{5^n} = \frac{1/5^9}{1 - 1/5} = 6.4 \times 10^{-7} \quad \text{(geometric series with } a = \tfrac{1}{5^9} \text{ and } r = \tfrac{1}{5}\text{)}.$$

28. (a) $\displaystyle\lim_{n \to \infty} \left|\frac{a_{n+1}}{a_n}\right| = \lim_{n \to \infty} \frac{(n+1)^{n+1} (2n)!}{(2n+2)! \, n^n} = \lim_{n \to \infty} \frac{(n+1)^n (n+1)^1}{(2n+2)(2n+1) n^n}$

$$= \lim_{n \to \infty} \left(1 + \frac{1}{n}\right)^n \frac{1}{2(2n+1)} = e \cdot 0 = 0 < 1$$

so the series converges by the Ratio Test.

(b) The series in part (a) is convergent, so $\displaystyle\lim_{n \to \infty} a_n = 0$ by Theorem 8.2.6.

29. Use the Limit Comparison Test. $\displaystyle\lim_{n \to \infty} \left|\frac{\left(\frac{n+1}{n}\right) a_n}{a_n}\right| = \lim_{n \to \infty} \frac{n+1}{n} = \lim_{n \to \infty} \left(1 + \frac{1}{n}\right) = 1 > 0.$ Since $\sum |a_n|$ is

convergent, so is $\displaystyle\sum \left|\left(\frac{n+1}{n}\right) a_n\right|$, by the Limit Comparison Test.

30. $\lim\limits_{n\to\infty}\left|\dfrac{a_{n+1}}{a_n}\right| = \lim\limits_{n\to\infty}\left|\dfrac{x^{n+1}}{(n+1)^2\,5^{n+1}}\cdot\dfrac{n^2 5^n}{x^n}\right| = \lim\limits_{n\to\infty}\dfrac{1}{(1+1/n)^2}\dfrac{|x|}{5} = \dfrac{|x|}{5}$, so by the Ratio Test,

$\sum\limits_{n=1}^{\infty}(-1)^n\dfrac{x^n}{n^2 5^n}$ converges when $|x| < 5$. $R = 5$. When $x = -5$, the series becomes the convergent p-series

$\sum\limits_{n=1}^{\infty}\dfrac{1}{n^2}$ with $p = 2 > 1$. When $x = 5$, the series becomes $\sum\limits_{n=1}^{\infty}\dfrac{(-1)^n}{n^2}$, which converges by the Alternating Series

Test. Thus, $I = [-5, 5]$.

31. $\lim\limits_{n\to\infty}\left|\dfrac{a_{n+1}}{a_n}\right| = \lim\limits_{n\to\infty}\left[\dfrac{|x+2|^{n+1}}{(n+1)\,4^{n+1}}\cdot\dfrac{n4^n}{|x+2|^n}\right] = \lim\limits_{n\to\infty}\left[\dfrac{n}{n+1}\dfrac{|x+2|}{4}\right] = \dfrac{|x+2|}{4} < 1 \Leftrightarrow |x+2| < 4$,

so $R = 4$. $|x+2| < 4 \Leftrightarrow -4 < x+2 < 4 \Leftrightarrow -6 < x < 2$. If $x = -6$, then the series becomes

$\sum\limits_{n=1}^{\infty}\dfrac{(-4)^n}{n4^n} = \sum\limits_{n=1}^{\infty}\dfrac{(-1)^n}{n}$, the alternating harmonic series, which converges by the Alternating Series Test. When

$x = 2$, the series becomes the harmonic series $\sum\limits_{n=1}^{\infty}\dfrac{1}{n}$, which diverges. Thus, $I = [-6, 2)$.

32. $\lim\limits_{n\to\infty}\left|\dfrac{a_{n+1}}{a_n}\right| = \lim\limits_{n\to\infty}\left|\dfrac{2^{n+1}(x-2)^{n+1}}{(n+3)!}\cdot\dfrac{(n+2)!}{2^n(x-2)^n}\right| = \lim\limits_{n\to\infty}\dfrac{2}{n+3}|x-2| = 0 < 1$, so the series

$\sum\limits_{n=1}^{\infty}\dfrac{2^n(x-2)^n}{(n+2)!}$ converges for all x. $R = \infty$ and $I = \mathbb{R}$.

33. $\lim\limits_{n\to\infty}\left|\dfrac{a_{n+1}}{a_n}\right| = \lim\limits_{n\to\infty}\left|\dfrac{2^{n+1}(x-3)^{n+1}}{\sqrt{n+4}}\cdot\dfrac{\sqrt{n+3}}{2^n(x-3)^n}\right| = 2\,|x-3|\lim\limits_{n\to\infty}\sqrt{\dfrac{n+3}{n+4}} = 2\,|x-3| < 1 \Leftrightarrow$

$|x-3| < \frac{1}{2}$ [so $R = \frac{1}{2}$] $\Leftrightarrow -\frac{1}{2} < x-3 < \frac{1}{2} \Leftrightarrow \frac{5}{2} < x < \frac{7}{2}$. When $x = \frac{5}{2}$, the series becomes

$\sum\limits_{n=0}^{\infty}\dfrac{(-1)^n}{\sqrt{n+3}}$, which is a convergent alternating series. When $x = \frac{7}{2}$, the series becomes $\sum\limits_{n=0}^{\infty}\dfrac{1}{\sqrt{n+3}} = \sum\limits_{n=3}^{\infty}\dfrac{1}{n^{1/2}}$,

which diverges $(p = \frac{1}{2} \le 1)$. Thus, $I = \left[\frac{5}{2}, \frac{7}{2}\right)$.

34. If $a_n = \dfrac{(2n)!\,x^n}{(n)!^2}$, then

$\lim\limits_{n\to\infty}\left|\dfrac{a_{n+1}}{a_n}\right| = \lim\limits_{n\to\infty}\left|\dfrac{(2n+2)!\,x^{n+1}}{[(n+1)!]^2}\cdot\dfrac{(n!)^2}{(2n)!\,x^n}\right| = \lim\limits_{n\to\infty}\dfrac{(2n+2)(2n+1)}{(n+1)(n+1)}|x| = 4\,|x| < 1$ to converge,

so $R = \frac{1}{4}$.

35.
$$f(x) = \sin x \qquad f\left(\tfrac{\pi}{6}\right) = \tfrac{1}{2} \qquad\qquad f'''(x) = -\cos x \qquad f'''\left(\tfrac{\pi}{6}\right) = -\tfrac{\sqrt{3}}{2}$$
$$f'(x) = \cos x \qquad f'\left(\tfrac{\pi}{6}\right) = \tfrac{\sqrt{3}}{2} \qquad\qquad f^{(4)}(x) = \sin x \qquad f^{(4)}\left(\tfrac{\pi}{6}\right) = \tfrac{1}{2}$$
$$f''(x) = -\sin x \qquad f''\left(\tfrac{\pi}{6}\right) = -\tfrac{1}{2} \qquad\qquad\qquad\vdots \qquad\qquad\qquad \vdots$$

Note that $f^{(2n)}\left(\tfrac{\pi}{6}\right) = (-1)^n\cdot\tfrac{1}{2}$ and $f^{(2n+1)}\left(\tfrac{\pi}{6}\right) = (-1)^n\cdot\tfrac{\sqrt{3}}{2}$.

$$\sin x = \sum\limits_{n=0}^{\infty}\dfrac{f^{(n)}\left(\tfrac{\pi}{6}\right)}{n!}\left(x - \tfrac{\pi}{6}\right)^n = \sum\limits_{n=0}^{\infty}\dfrac{(-1)^n}{2(2n)!}\left(x - \tfrac{\pi}{6}\right)^{2n} + \sum\limits_{n=0}^{\infty}\dfrac{(-1)^n\sqrt{3}}{2(2n+1)!}\left(x - \tfrac{\pi}{6}\right)^{2n+1}$$

$$= \dfrac{1}{2}\sum\limits_{n=0}^{\infty}(-1)^n\left[\dfrac{1}{(2n)!}\left(x - \dfrac{\pi}{6}\right)^{2n} + \dfrac{\sqrt{3}}{(2n+1)!}\left(x - \dfrac{\pi}{6}\right)^{2n+1}\right]$$

36.

$$f(x) = \cos x \qquad f\left(\tfrac{\pi}{3}\right) = \tfrac{1}{2} \qquad f'''(x) = \sin x \qquad f'''\left(\tfrac{\pi}{3}\right) = \tfrac{\sqrt{3}}{2}$$

$$f'(x) = -\sin x \qquad f'\left(\tfrac{\pi}{3}\right) = -\tfrac{\sqrt{3}}{2} \qquad f^{(4)}(x) = \cos x \qquad f^{(4)}\left(\tfrac{\pi}{3}\right) = \tfrac{1}{2}$$

$$f''(x) = -\cos x \qquad f''\left(\tfrac{\pi}{3}\right) = -\tfrac{1}{2}$$

$$\vdots \qquad\qquad \vdots$$

Note that $f^{(2n)}\left(\tfrac{\pi}{3}\right) = (-1)^n \cdot \tfrac{1}{2}$ and $f^{(2n+1)}\left(\tfrac{\pi}{3}\right) = (-1)^{n+1} \cdot \tfrac{\sqrt{3}}{2}$.

$$\cos x = \sum_{n=0}^{\infty} \frac{f^{(n)}\left(\tfrac{\pi}{3}\right)}{n!} \left(x - \tfrac{\pi}{3}\right)^n = \sum_{n=0}^{\infty} \frac{(-1)^n}{2(2n)!}\left(x - \tfrac{\pi}{3}\right)^{2n} + \sum_{n=0}^{\infty} \frac{(-1)^{n+1}\sqrt{3}}{2(2n+1)!}\left(x - \tfrac{\pi}{3}\right)^{2n+1}$$

$$= \frac{1}{2}\sum_{n=0}^{\infty}(-1)^n\left[\frac{1}{(2n)!}\left(x - \tfrac{\pi}{3}\right)^{2n} - \frac{\sqrt{3}}{(2n+1)!}\left(x - \tfrac{\pi}{3}\right)^{2n+1}\right]$$

37. $\dfrac{1}{1+x} = \dfrac{1}{1-(-x)} = \displaystyle\sum_{n=0}^{\infty}(-x)^n = \sum_{n=0}^{\infty}(-1)^n x^n$ for $|x| < 1 \;\Rightarrow\; \dfrac{x^2}{1+x} = \sum_{n=0}^{\infty}(-1)^n x^{n+2}$ with $R = 1$.

38. $\tan^{-1} x = \displaystyle\sum_{n=0}^{\infty}(-1)^n \frac{x^{2n+1}}{2n+1}$ with interval of convergence $[-1, 1]$, so

$$\tan^{-1}\left(x^2\right) = \sum_{n=0}^{\infty}(-1)^n \frac{\left(x^2\right)^{2n+1}}{2n+1} = \sum_{n=0}^{\infty}(-1)^n \frac{x^{4n+2}}{2n+1}, \text{ which converges when } x^2 \in [-1, 1] \;\Leftrightarrow\; x \in [-1, 1].$$

Therefore, $R = 1$.

39. $\dfrac{1}{1-x} = \displaystyle\sum_{n=0}^{\infty} x^n$ for $|x| < 1 \;\Rightarrow\; \ln(1-x) = -\int \dfrac{dx}{1-x} = -\int \sum_{n=0}^{\infty} x^n\, dx = C - \sum_{n=0}^{\infty}\dfrac{x^{n+1}}{n+1}$.

$\ln(1-0) = C - 0 \;\Rightarrow\; C = 0 \;\Rightarrow\; \ln(1-x) = -\displaystyle\sum_{n=0}^{\infty}\frac{x^{n+1}}{n+1} = -\sum_{n=1}^{\infty}\frac{x^n}{n}$ with $R = 1$.

40. $e^x = \displaystyle\sum_{n=0}^{\infty} \frac{x^n}{n!} \;\Rightarrow\; xe^{2x} = x\sum_{n=0}^{\infty} \frac{(2x)^n}{n!} = \sum_{n=0}^{\infty} \frac{2^n x^{n+1}}{n!}, \; R = \infty$

41. $\sin x = \displaystyle\sum_{n=0}^{\infty} \frac{(-1)^n x^{2n+1}}{(2n+1)!} \;\Rightarrow\; \sin\left(x^4\right) = \sum_{n=0}^{\infty} \frac{(-1)^n \left(x^4\right)^{2n+1}}{(2n+1)!} = \sum_{n=0}^{\infty} \frac{(-1)^n x^{8n+4}}{(2n+1)!}$ for all x, so the radius of convergence is ∞.

42. $10^x = \left(e^{\ln 10}\right)^x = e^{x\ln 10} = \displaystyle\sum_{n=0}^{\infty} \frac{(x\ln 10)^n}{n!} = \sum_{n=0}^{\infty} \frac{(\ln 10)^n x^n}{n!}, \; R = \infty$

43. $f(x) = \dfrac{1}{\sqrt[4]{16-x}} = \dfrac{1}{\sqrt[4]{16(1-x/16)}} = \dfrac{1}{\sqrt[4]{16}\left(1-\tfrac{1}{16}x\right)^{1/4}} = \tfrac{1}{2}\left(1-\tfrac{1}{16}x\right)^{-1/4}$

$$= \frac{1}{2}\left[1 + \left(-\tfrac{1}{4}\right)\left(-\tfrac{x}{16}\right) + \frac{\left(-\tfrac{1}{4}\right)\left(-\tfrac{5}{4}\right)}{2!}\left(-\tfrac{x}{16}\right)^2 + \frac{\left(-\tfrac{1}{4}\right)\left(-\tfrac{5}{4}\right)\left(-\tfrac{9}{4}\right)}{3!}\left(-\tfrac{x}{16}\right)^3 + \cdots\right]$$

$$= \frac{1}{2} + \sum_{n=1}^{\infty} \frac{1 \cdot 5 \cdot 9 \cdots \cdots (4n-3)}{2 \cdot 4^n \cdot n! \cdot 16^n} x^n = \frac{1}{2} + \sum_{n=1}^{\infty} \frac{1 \cdot 5 \cdot 9 \cdots \cdots (4n-3)}{2^1 \cdot 2^{2n} \cdot n! \cdot 2^{4n}} x^n$$

$$= \frac{1}{2} + \sum_{n=1}^{\infty} \frac{1 \cdot 5 \cdot 9 \cdots \cdots (4n-3)}{2^{6n+1} \cdot n!} x^n$$

for $\left|-\dfrac{x}{16}\right| < 1 \;\Rightarrow\; |x| < 16 \;\Rightarrow\; R = 16$.

44. $(1 - 3x)^{-5} = \sum\limits_{n=0}^{\infty} \binom{-5}{n}(-3x)^n = 1 + (-5)(-3x) + \dfrac{(-5)(-6)}{2!}(-3x)^2 + \dfrac{(-5)(-6)(-7)}{3!}(-3x)^3 + \cdots$

$\qquad = 1 + \sum\limits_{n=1}^{\infty} \dfrac{5 \cdot 6 \cdot \cdots \cdot (n+4) \cdot 3^n x^n}{n!}, \ |-3x| < 1$ so $R = \frac{1}{3}$.

45. $e^x = \sum\limits_{n=0}^{\infty} \dfrac{x^n}{n!}$, so $\dfrac{e^x}{x} = \dfrac{1}{x}\sum\limits_{n=0}^{\infty}\dfrac{x^n}{n!} = \sum\limits_{n=0}^{\infty}\dfrac{x^{n-1}}{n!} = x^{-1} + \sum\limits_{n=1}^{\infty}\dfrac{x^{n-1}}{n!} = \dfrac{1}{x} + \sum\limits_{n=1}^{\infty}\dfrac{x^{n-1}}{n!}$ and

$\displaystyle\int \dfrac{e^x}{x}\,dx = C + \ln|x| + \sum\limits_{n=1}^{\infty}\dfrac{x^n}{n \cdot n!}$.

46. $(1 + x^4)^{1/2} = \sum\limits_{n=0}^{\infty} \binom{\frac{1}{2}}{n}(x^4)^n = 1 + (\tfrac{1}{2})x^4 + \dfrac{(\frac{1}{2})(-\frac{1}{2})}{2!}(x^4)^2 + \dfrac{(\frac{1}{2})(-\frac{1}{2})(-\frac{3}{2})}{3!}(x^4)^3 + \cdots$

$\qquad = 1 + \tfrac{1}{2}x^4 - \tfrac{1}{8}x^8 + \tfrac{1}{16}x^{12} - \cdots$

so $\int_0^1 (1 + x^4)^{1/2}\,dx = \left[x + \tfrac{1}{10}x^5 - \tfrac{1}{72}x^9 + \tfrac{1}{208}x^{13} - \cdots\right]_0^1 = 1 + \tfrac{1}{10} - \tfrac{1}{72} + \tfrac{1}{208} - \cdots$. This is an alternating

series, so by the Alternating Series Test, the error in the approximation $\int_0^1 (1 + x^4)^{1/2}\,dx \approx 1 + \tfrac{1}{10} - \tfrac{1}{72} \approx 1.086$

is less than $\tfrac{1}{208} \approx 0.0048$, sufficient for the desired accuracy. Thus, correct to two decimal places,

$\int_0^1 (1 + x^4)^{1/2}\,dx \approx 1.09$.

47. (a)

$\qquad f(x) = x^{1/2} \qquad\qquad f(1) = 1 \qquad\qquad f'''(x) = \tfrac{3}{8}x^{-5/2} \qquad\qquad f'''(1) = \tfrac{3}{8}$

$\qquad f'(x) = \tfrac{1}{2}x^{-1/2} \qquad\quad f'(1) = \tfrac{1}{2} \qquad\qquad f^{(4)}(x) = -\tfrac{15}{16}x^{-7/2}$

$\qquad f''(x) = -\tfrac{1}{4}x^{-3/2} \qquad\ f''(1) = -\tfrac{1}{4}$

$\qquad\qquad \sqrt{x} \approx T_3(x) = 1 + \dfrac{1/2}{1!}(x-1) - \dfrac{1/4}{2!}(x-1)^2 + \dfrac{3/8}{3!}(x-1)^3$

$\qquad\qquad\qquad = 1 + \tfrac{1}{2}(x-1) - \tfrac{1}{8}(x-1)^2 + \tfrac{1}{16}(x-1)^3$

(b)

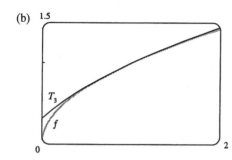

1.5

T_3

f

0

2

(c) $|R_3(x)| \leq \dfrac{M}{4!}|x-1|^4$, where $\left|f^{(4)}(x)\right| \leq M$ with

$\qquad f^{(4)}(x) = -\tfrac{15}{16}x^{-7/2}$. Now $0.9 \leq x \leq 1.1 \ \Rightarrow$

$\qquad -0.1 \leq x - 1 \leq 0.1 \quad \Rightarrow \quad |x-1| \leq 0.1 \quad \Rightarrow$

$\qquad (x-1)^4 \leq (0.1)^4$, and letting $x = 0.9$ gives

$\qquad M = \dfrac{15}{16(0.9)^{7/2}}$, so

$\qquad |R_3(x)| \leq \dfrac{15}{16(0.9)^{7/2}4!}(0.1)^4 \approx 0.000005648$

$\qquad\qquad\qquad \approx 0.000006 = 6 \times 10^{-6}$.

(d)

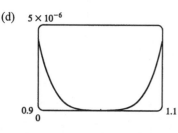

5×10^{-6}

0.9

1.1

0

From the graph of $|R_3(x)| = |\sqrt{x} - T_3(x)|$, it appears that the error

is less than 4.7×10^{-6} on $[0.9, 1.1]$.

48. (a)

$$f(x) = \sec x \qquad\qquad f(0) = 1 \qquad\qquad \sec x \approx T_2(x) = 1 + \tfrac{1}{2}x^2$$
$$f'(x) = \sec x \tan x \qquad\qquad f'(0) = 0$$
$$f''(x) = \sec x \tan^2 x + \sec^3 x \qquad f''(0) = 1$$
$$f'''(x) = \sec x \tan^3 x + 5\sec^3 x \tan x$$

(b) 1.2

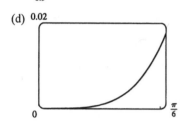

(c) $|R_2(x)| \le \dfrac{M}{3!}\,|x|^3$, where $\left|f^{(3)}(x)\right| \le M$ with

$f^{(3)}(x) = \sec x \tan^3 x + 5\sec^3 x \tan x$. Now

$0 \le x \le \tfrac{\pi}{6} \;\Rightarrow\; x^3 \le \left(\tfrac{\pi}{6}\right)^3$, and letting $x = \tfrac{\pi}{6}$

gives $M = \tfrac{14}{3}$, so

$$|R_2(x)| \le \tfrac{14}{3\cdot 6}\left(\tfrac{\pi}{6}\right)^3 \approx 0.111648.$$

(d) 0.02

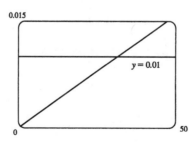

From the graph of $|R_2(x)| = |\sec x - T_2(x)|$, it appears that the error is less than 0.02 on $\left[0, \tfrac{\pi}{6}\right]$.

49. $\sin x = \displaystyle\sum_{n=0}^{\infty} (-1)^n \frac{x^{2n+1}}{(2n+1)!} = x - \frac{x^3}{3!} + \frac{x^5}{5!} - \frac{x^7}{7!} + \cdots$, so $\sin x - x = -\dfrac{x^3}{3!} + \dfrac{x^5}{5!} - \dfrac{x^7}{7!} + \cdots$ and

$\dfrac{\sin x - x}{x^3} = -\dfrac{1}{3!} + \dfrac{x^2}{5!} - \dfrac{x^4}{7!} + \cdots$ and $\displaystyle\lim_{x\to 0}\frac{\sin x - x}{x^3} = \lim_{x\to 0}\left(-\frac{1}{6} + \frac{x^2}{120} - \frac{x^4}{5040} + \cdots\right) = -\frac{1}{6}$.

50. (a) $F = \dfrac{mgR^2}{(R+h)^2} = \dfrac{mgR^2/R^2}{(R+h)^2/R^2} = \dfrac{mg}{(1+h/R)^2} = mg\left(1+\dfrac{h}{R}\right)^{-2} = mg\displaystyle\sum_{n=0}^{\infty}\binom{-2}{n}\left(\dfrac{h}{R}\right)^n$

(Binomial Series)

(b) We expand $F = mg\left[1 - 2(h/R) + 3(h/R)^2 - \cdots\right]$. This is an alternating series, so by the Alternating Series Estimation Theorem, the error in the approximation $F = mg$ is less than $2mgh/R$, so for accuracy within 1% we want $\left|\dfrac{2mgh/R}{mgR^2/(R+h)^2}\right| < 0.01 \;\Leftrightarrow\; \dfrac{2h(R+h)^2}{R^3} < 0.01$. This inequality would be difficult to solve for h, so we substitute $R = 6{,}400$ km and plot both sides of the inequality. It appears that the approximation is accurate to within 1% for $h < 31$ km.

0.015

$y = 0.01$

0   50

51. Let $y(x) = \sum\limits_{n=0}^{\infty} c_n x^n$. Then $xy' = x \sum\limits_{n=1}^{\infty} n c_n x^{n-1} = \sum\limits_{n=0}^{\infty} n c_n x^n$,

$y''(x) = \sum\limits_{n=2}^{\infty} n(n-1)c_n x^{n-2} = \sum\limits_{n=0}^{\infty} (n+2)(n+1)c_{n+2} x^n$, and the equation $y'' + xy' + y = 0$ becomes

$\sum\limits_{n=0}^{\infty} [(n+2)(n+1)c_{n+2} + n c_n + c_n]x^n = 0$. Thus, the recursion relation is

$c_{n+2} = \dfrac{-n c_n - c_n}{(n+2)(n+1)} = \dfrac{-c_n(n+1)}{(n+2)(n+1)} = -\dfrac{c_n}{n+2}$ for $n = 0, 1, 2, \ldots$. But $c_0 = y(0) = 0$, so $c_{2n} = 0$

for $n = 0, 1, 2, \ldots$. Also, $c_1 = y'(0) = 1$, so $c_3 = -\dfrac{c_1}{3} = -\dfrac{1}{3}$, $c_5 = \dfrac{(-1)^2}{3 \cdot 5} = \dfrac{(-1)^2 2^2 2!}{5!}$,

$c_7 = \dfrac{(-1)^3}{3 \cdot 5 \cdot 7} = \dfrac{(-1)^3 2^3 3!}{7!}, \ldots, c_{2n+1} = \dfrac{(-1)^n 2^n n!}{(2n+1)!} = \dfrac{(-2)^n n!}{(2n+1)!}$ for $n = 0, 1, 2, \ldots$. Note that

$2^n n! = (2 \cdot 1) \cdot (2 \cdot 2) \cdot (2 \cdot 3) \cdots\cdots (2 \cdot n)$. Thus, the solution to the initial-value problem is

$$y(x) = \sum\limits_{n=0}^{\infty} c_n x^n = \sum\limits_{n=0}^{\infty} \dfrac{(-2)^n n!}{(2n+1)!} x^{2n+1}$$

52. Let $y(x) = \sum\limits_{n=0}^{\infty} c_n x^n$. Then $xy' = x \sum\limits_{n=1}^{\infty} n c_n x^{n-1} = \sum\limits_{n=0}^{\infty} n c_n x^n$,

$y''(x) = \sum\limits_{n=2}^{\infty} n(n-1)c_n x^{n-2} = \sum\limits_{n=0}^{\infty} (n+2)(n+1)c_{n+2} x^n$, and the equation $y'' - xy' - 2y = 0$ becomes

$\sum\limits_{n=0}^{\infty} [(n+2)(n+1)c_{n+2} - n c_n - 2c_n]x^n = 0$. Thus, the recursion relation is

$c_{n+2} = \dfrac{n c_n + 2 c_n}{(n+2)(n+1)} = \dfrac{c_n(n+2)}{(n+2)(n+1)} = \dfrac{c_n}{n+1}$ for $n = 0, 1, 2, \ldots$.

Given c_0, we have $c_2 = \dfrac{c_0}{1}$, $c_4 = \dfrac{c_2}{3} = \dfrac{c_0}{1 \cdot 3}$,

$c_6 = \dfrac{c_4}{5} = \dfrac{c_0}{1 \cdot 3 \cdot 5}, \ldots, c_{2n} = \dfrac{c_0}{1 \cdot 3 \cdot 5 \cdots\cdots (2n-1)} = c_0 \dfrac{2 \cdot 4 \cdot 6 \cdots\cdots (2n-2)}{1 \cdot 2 \cdot 3 \cdot 4 \cdot 5 \cdots\cdots (2n-1)} = c_0 \dfrac{2^{n-1}(n-1)!}{(2n-1)!}$.

Given c_1, $c_3 = \dfrac{c_1}{2}$, $c_5 = \dfrac{c_3}{4} = \dfrac{c_1}{2 \cdot 4}$, $c_7 = \dfrac{c_5}{6} = \dfrac{c_1}{2 \cdot 4 \cdot 6}, \ldots, c_{2n+1} = \dfrac{c_1}{2 \cdot 4 \cdot 6 \cdots\cdots 2n} = \dfrac{c_1}{2^n n!}$.

Thus, the general solution is

$$y(x) = \sum\limits_{n=0}^{\infty} c_n x^n = c_0 + c_0 \sum\limits_{n=1}^{\infty} \dfrac{2^{n-1}(n-1)! x^{2n}}{(2n-1)!} + c_1 \sum\limits_{n=0}^{\infty} \dfrac{x^{2n+1}}{2^n n!}$$

But $\sum\limits_{n=0}^{\infty} \dfrac{x^{2n+1}}{2^n n!} = x \sum\limits_{n=0}^{\infty} \dfrac{(x^2/2)^n}{n!} = x e^{x^2/2}$, so

$$y(x) = c_1 x e^{x^2/2} + c_0 + c_0 \sum\limits_{n=1}^{\infty} \dfrac{2^{n-1}(n-1)! x^{2n}}{(2n-1)!}$$

53. (a) From Formula 14a in Appendix C, with $x = y = \theta$, we get $\tan 2\theta = \dfrac{2 \tan \theta}{1 - \tan^2 \theta}$, so $\cot 2\theta = \dfrac{1 - \tan^2 \theta}{2 \tan \theta} \Rightarrow$

$2 \cot 2\theta = \dfrac{1 - \tan^2 \theta}{\tan \theta} = \cot \theta - \tan \theta$. Replacing θ by $\frac{1}{2}x$, we get $2 \cot x = \cot \frac{1}{2}x - \tan \frac{1}{2}x$,

or $\tan \frac{1}{2}x = \cot \frac{1}{2}x - 2 \cot x$.

(b) From part (a), $\tan \dfrac{x}{2^n} = \cot \dfrac{x}{2^n} - 2\cot \dfrac{x}{2^{n-1}}$, so the nth partial sum of $\displaystyle\sum_{n=1}^{\infty} \dfrac{1}{2^n}\tan\dfrac{x}{2^n}$ is

$$s_n = \frac{\tan(x/2)}{2} + \frac{\tan(x/4)}{4} + \frac{\tan(x/8)}{8} + \cdots + \frac{\tan(x/2^n)}{2^n}$$

$$= \left[\frac{\cot(x/2)}{2} - \cot x\right] + \left[\frac{\cot(x/4)}{4} - \frac{\cot(x/2)}{2}\right] + \left[\frac{\cot(x/8)}{8} - \frac{\cot(x/4)}{4}\right] + \cdots$$

$$+ \left[\frac{\cot(x/2^n)}{2^n} - \frac{\cot\left(x/2^{n-1}\right)}{2^{n-1}}\right] = -\cot x + \frac{\cot(x/2^n)}{2^n} \quad \text{[telescoping sum]}$$

Now $\dfrac{\cot(x/2^n)}{2^n} = \dfrac{\cos(x/2^n)}{2^n\sin(x/2^n)} = \dfrac{\cos(x/2^n)}{x} \cdot \dfrac{x/2^n}{\sin(x/2^n)} \to \dfrac{1}{x} \cdot 1 = \dfrac{1}{x}$ as $n \to \infty$ since $x/2^n \to 0$

for $x \neq 0$. Therefore, if $x \neq 0$ and $x \neq n\pi$, then

$$\sum_{n=1}^{\infty} \frac{1}{2^n}\tan\frac{x}{2^n} = \lim_{n\to\infty}\left(-\cot x + \frac{1}{2^n}\cot\frac{x}{2^n}\right) = -\cot x + \frac{1}{x}.$$

If $x = 0$, then all terms in the series are 0, so the sum is 0.

54. We use the problem-solving strategy of taking cases:

Case (i): If $|x| < 1$, then $0 \le x^2 < 1$, so $\displaystyle\lim_{n\to\infty} x^{2n} = 0$ (see Example 8 in Section 8.1)

and $f(x) = \displaystyle\lim_{n\to\infty} \frac{x^{2n}-1}{x^{2n}+1} = \frac{0-1}{0+1} = -1.$

Case (ii): If $|x| = 1$, that is, $x = \pm 1$, then $x^2 = 1$, so $f(x) = \displaystyle\lim_{n\to\infty} \frac{1-1}{1+1} = 0.$

Case (iii): If $|x| > 1$, then $x^2 > 1$, so $\displaystyle\lim_{n\to\infty} x^{2n} = \infty$ and

$$f(x) = \lim_{n\to\infty} \frac{x^{2n}-1}{x^{2n}+1} = \lim_{n\to\infty} \frac{1-\left(1/x^{2n}\right)}{1+\left(1/x^{2n}\right)} = \frac{1-0}{1+0} = 1.$$

Thus, $f(x) = \begin{cases} 1 & \text{if } x < -1 \\ 0 & \text{if } x = -1 \\ -1 & \text{if } -1 < x < 1 \\ 0 & \text{if } x = 1 \\ 1 & \text{if } x > 1 \end{cases}$

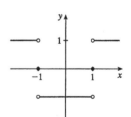

The graph shows that f is continuous everywhere except at $x = \pm 1$.

1. It would be far too much work to compute 15 derivatives of f. The key idea is to remember that $f^{(n)}(0)$ occurs in the coefficient of x^n in the Maclaurin series of f. We start with the Maclaurin series for sin:

$$\sin x = x - \frac{x^3}{3!} + \frac{x^5}{5!} - \cdots. \quad \text{Then } \sin(x^3) = x^3 - \frac{x^9}{3!} + \frac{x^{15}}{5!} - \cdots \text{ and so the coefficient of } x^{15} \text{ is}$$

$$\frac{f^{(15)}(0)}{15!} = \frac{1}{5!}. \text{ Therefore, } f^{(15)}(0) = \frac{15!}{5!} = 6 \cdot 7 \cdot 8 \cdot 9 \cdot 10 \cdot 11 \cdot 12 \cdot 13 \cdot 14 \cdot 15 = 10{,}897{,}286{,}400.$$

2. $|AP_2|^2 = 2$, $|AP_3|^2 = 2 + 2^2$, $|AP_4|^2 = 2 + 2^2 + \left(2^2\right)^2$, $|AP_5|^2 = 2 + 2^2 + \left(2^2\right)^2 + \left(2^3\right)^2$, ...,

$$|AP_n|^2 = 2 + 2^2 + \left(2^2\right)^2 + \cdots + \left(2^{n-2}\right)^2 \quad \text{(for } n \geq 3\text{)} \;\; = 2 + \left(4 + 4^2 + 4^3 + \cdots + 4^{n-2}\right)$$

$$= 2 + \frac{4\left(4^{n-2} - 1\right)}{4 - 1} \quad \text{(finite geometric sum with } a = 4,\, r = 4\text{)} \;\; = \frac{6}{3} + \frac{4^{n-1} - 4}{3} = \frac{2}{3} + \frac{4^{n-1}}{3}$$

So $\tan \angle P_n A P_{n+1} = \dfrac{|P_n P_{n+1}|}{|AP_n|} = \dfrac{2^{n-1}}{\sqrt{\dfrac{2}{3} + \dfrac{4^{n-1}}{3}}} = \dfrac{\sqrt{4^{n-1}}}{\sqrt{\dfrac{2}{3} + \dfrac{4^{n-1}}{3}}} = \dfrac{1}{\sqrt{\dfrac{2}{3 \cdot 4^{n-1}} + \dfrac{1}{3}}} \to \sqrt{3}$ as $n \to \infty$, so

$\angle P_n A P_{n+1} \to \frac{\pi}{3}$ as $n \to \infty$.

3. (a) Let $a = \arctan x$ and $b = \arctan y$. Then, from Formula 14b in Appendix C,

$$\tan(a - b) = \frac{\tan a - \tan b}{1 + \tan a \tan b} = \frac{\tan(\arctan x) - \tan(\arctan y)}{1 + \tan(\arctan x)\tan(\arctan y)} = \frac{x - y}{1 + xy} \quad \Rightarrow$$

$$\arctan x - \arctan y = a - b = \arctan \frac{x - y}{1 + xy} \quad \text{since } -\frac{\pi}{2} < \arctan x - \arctan y < \frac{\pi}{2}$$

(b) From part (a) we have

$$\arctan \tfrac{120}{119} - \arctan \tfrac{1}{239} = \arctan \frac{\tfrac{120}{119} - \tfrac{1}{239}}{1 + \tfrac{120}{119} \cdot \tfrac{1}{239}} = \arctan \frac{\tfrac{28{,}561}{28{,}441}}{\tfrac{28{,}561}{28{,}441}} = \arctan 1 = \frac{\pi}{4}$$

(c) Replacing y by $-y$ in the formula of part (a), we get $\arctan x + \arctan y = \arctan \dfrac{x + y}{1 - xy}$. So

$$4 \arctan \tfrac{1}{5} = 2\left(\arctan \tfrac{1}{5} + \arctan \tfrac{1}{5}\right) = 2 \arctan \frac{\tfrac{1}{5} + \tfrac{1}{5}}{1 - \tfrac{1}{5} \cdot \tfrac{1}{5}} = 2 \arctan \tfrac{5}{12} = \arctan \tfrac{5}{12} + \arctan \tfrac{5}{12}$$

$$= \arctan \frac{\tfrac{5}{12} + \tfrac{5}{12}}{1 - \tfrac{5}{12} \cdot \tfrac{5}{12}} = \arctan \tfrac{120}{119}$$

Thus, from part (b), we have $4 \arctan \tfrac{1}{5} - \arctan \tfrac{1}{239} = \arctan \tfrac{120}{119} - \arctan \tfrac{1}{239} = \frac{\pi}{4}$.

(d) From Example 7 in Section 8.6 we have $\arctan x = x - \dfrac{x^3}{3} + \dfrac{x^5}{5} - \dfrac{x^7}{7} + \dfrac{x^9}{9} - \dfrac{x^{11}}{11} + \cdots$, so

$$\arctan \frac{1}{5} = \frac{1}{5} - \frac{1}{3 \cdot 5^3} + \frac{1}{5 \cdot 5^5} - \frac{1}{7 \cdot 5^7} + \frac{1}{9 \cdot 5^9} - \frac{1}{11 \cdot 5^{11}} + \cdots$$

This is an alternating series and the size of the terms decreases to 0, so by the Alternating Series Estimation Theorem, the sum lies between s_5 and s_6, that is, $0.197395560 < \arctan \frac{1}{5} < 0.197395562$.

(e) From the series in part (d) we get $\arctan \dfrac{1}{239} = \dfrac{1}{239} - \dfrac{1}{3 \cdot 239^3} + \dfrac{1}{5 \cdot 239^5} - \cdots$. The third term is less than 2.6×10^{-13}, so by the Alternating Series Estimation Theorem, we have, to nine decimal places, $\arctan \frac{1}{239} \approx s_2 \approx 0.004184076$. Thus, $0.004184075 < \arctan \frac{1}{239} < 0.004184077$.

(f) From part (c) we have $\pi = 16 \arctan \frac{1}{5} - 4 \arctan \frac{1}{239}$, so from parts (d) and (e) we have

$16(0.197395560) - 4(0.004184077) < \pi < 16(0.197395562) - 4(0.004184075) \Rightarrow$
$3.141592652 < \pi < 3.141592692$. So, to 7 decimal places, $\pi \approx 3.1415927$.

4. Let's first try the case $k = 1$: $a_0 + a_1 = 0 \Rightarrow a_1 = -a_0 \Rightarrow$

$$\lim_{n \to \infty} \left(a_0 \sqrt{n} + a_1 \sqrt{n+1} \right) = \lim_{n \to \infty} \left(a_0 \sqrt{n} - a_0 \sqrt{n+1} \right) = a_0 \lim_{n \to \infty} \left(\sqrt{n} - \sqrt{n+1} \right) \frac{\sqrt{n} + \sqrt{n+1}}{\sqrt{n} + \sqrt{n+1}}$$

$$= a_0 \lim_{n \to \infty} \frac{-1}{\sqrt{n} + \sqrt{n+1}} = 0$$

In general we have $a_0 + a_1 + \cdots + a_k = 0 \Rightarrow a_k = -a_0 - a_1 - \cdots - a_{k-1} \Rightarrow$

$$\lim_{n \to \infty} \left(a_0 \sqrt{n} + a_1 \sqrt{n+1} + a_2 \sqrt{n+2} + \cdots + a_k \sqrt{n+k} \right)$$

$$= \lim_{n \to \infty} \left(a_0 \sqrt{n} + a_1 \sqrt{n+1} + \cdots + a_{k-1} \sqrt{n+k-1} - a_0 \sqrt{n+k} - a_1 \sqrt{n+k} - \cdots - a_{k-1} \sqrt{n+k} \right)$$

$$= a_0 \lim_{n \to \infty} \left(\sqrt{n} - \sqrt{n+k} \right) + a_1 \lim_{n \to \infty} \left(\sqrt{n+1} - \sqrt{n+k} \right) + \cdots + a_{k-1} \lim_{n \to \infty} \left(\sqrt{n+k-1} - \sqrt{n+k} \right)$$

Each of these limits is 0 by the same type of simplification as in the case $k = 1$. So we have

$$\lim_{n \to \infty} \left(a_0 \sqrt{n} + a_1 \sqrt{n+1} + a_2 \sqrt{n+2} + \cdots + a_k \sqrt{n+k} \right) = a_0(0) + a_1(0) + \cdots + a_{k-1}(0) = 0$$

5. (a) At each stage, each side is replaced by four shorter sides, each of length $\frac{1}{3}$ of the side length at the preceding stage. Writing s_0 and ℓ_0 for the number of sides and the length of the side of the initial triangle, we generate the table at right. In general, we have $s_n = 3 \cdot 4^n$ and $\ell_n = \left(\frac{1}{3} \right)^n$, so the length of the perimeter at the nth stage of construction is $p_n = s_n \ell_n = 3 \cdot 4^n \cdot \left(\frac{1}{3} \right)^n = 3 \cdot \left(\frac{4}{3} \right)^n$.

$s_0 = 3$	$\ell_0 = 1$
$s_1 = 3 \cdot 4$	$\ell_1 = 1/3$
$s_2 = 3 \cdot 4^2$	$\ell_2 = 1/3^2$
$s_3 = 3 \cdot 4^3$	$\ell_3 = 1/3^3$
$\vdots$	$\vdots$

(b) $p_n = \dfrac{4^n}{3^{n-1}} = 4 \left(\dfrac{4}{3} \right)^{n-1}$. Since $\frac{4}{3} > 1$, $p_n \to \infty$ as $n \to \infty$.

(c) The area of each of the small triangles added at a given stage is one-ninth of the area of the triangle added at the preceding stage. Let a be the area of the original triangle. Then the area a_n of each of the small triangles added at stage n is $a_n = a \cdot \dfrac{1}{9^n} = \dfrac{a}{9^n}$. Since a small triangle is added to each side at every stage, it follows that the total area A_n added to the figure at the nth stage is $A_n = s_{n-1} \cdot a_n = 3 \cdot 4^{n-1} \cdot \dfrac{a}{9^n} = a \cdot \dfrac{4^{n-1}}{3^{2n-1}}$.

Then the total area enclosed by the snowflake curve is

$A = a + A_1 + A_2 + A_3 + \cdots = a + a \cdot \dfrac{1}{3} + a \cdot \dfrac{4}{3^3} + a \cdot \dfrac{4^2}{3^5} + a \cdot \dfrac{4^3}{3^7} + \cdots$. After the first term, this is a

geometric series with common ratio $\frac{4}{9}$, so $A = a + \dfrac{a/3}{1 - \frac{4}{9}} = a + \dfrac{a}{3} \cdot \dfrac{9}{5} = \dfrac{8a}{5}$. But the area of the original

equilateral triangle with side 1 is $a = \frac{1}{2} \cdot 1 \cdot \sin \frac{\pi}{3} = \frac{\sqrt{3}}{4}$. So the area enclosed by the snowflake curve is

$\frac{8}{5} \cdot \frac{\sqrt{3}}{4} = \frac{2\sqrt{3}}{5}$.

6. Let the series be S. Then every term in S is of the form $\dfrac{1}{2^m 3^n}$, $m, n \geq 0$, and furthermore each term occurs only

once. So we can write

$$S = \sum_{m=0}^{\infty} \sum_{n=0}^{\infty} \frac{1}{2^m 3^n} = \sum_{m=0}^{\infty} \sum_{n=0}^{\infty} \frac{1}{2^m} \frac{1}{3^n} = \sum_{m=0}^{\infty} \frac{1}{2^m} \sum_{n=0}^{\infty} \frac{1}{3^n} = \frac{1}{1 - \frac{1}{2}} \cdot \frac{1}{1 - \frac{1}{3}} = 2 \cdot \frac{3}{2} = 3$$

7. We start with the geometric series $\displaystyle\sum_{n=0}^{\infty} x^n = \dfrac{1}{1-x}$, $|x| < 1$, and differentiate:

$\displaystyle\sum_{n=1}^{\infty} nx^{n-1} = \frac{d}{dx}\left(\sum_{n=0}^{\infty} x^n\right) = \frac{d}{dx}\left(\frac{1}{1-x}\right) = \frac{1}{(1-x)^2}$ for $|x| < 1 \Rightarrow$

$\displaystyle\sum_{n=1}^{\infty} nx^n = x \sum_{n=1}^{\infty} nx^{n-1} = \frac{x}{(1-x)^2}$ for $|x| < 1$. Differentiate again:

$\displaystyle\sum_{n=1}^{\infty} n^2 x^{n-1} = \frac{d}{dx} \frac{x}{(1-x)^2} = \frac{(1-x)^2 - x \cdot 2(1-x)(-1)}{(1-x)^4} = \frac{x+1}{(1-x)^3} \Rightarrow \sum_{n=1}^{\infty} n^2 x^n = \frac{x^2 + x}{(1-x)^3} \Rightarrow$

$\displaystyle\sum_{n=1}^{\infty} n^3 x^{n-1} = \frac{d}{dx} \frac{x^2 + x}{(1-x)^3} = \frac{(1-x)^3(2x+1) - (x^2+x)3(1-x)^2(-1)}{(1-x)^6} = \frac{x^2 + 4x + 1}{(1-x)^4} \Rightarrow$

$\displaystyle\sum_{n=1}^{\infty} n^3 x^n = \frac{x^3 + 4x^2 + x}{(1-x)^4}$, $|x| < 1$. The radius of convergence is 1 because that is the radius of convergence for

the geometric series we started with. If $x = \pm 1$, the series is $\sum n^3(\pm 1)^n$, which diverges by the Test For

Divergence, so the interval of convergence is $(-1, 1)$.

8. Place the y-axis as shown and let the length of each book be L. We want to
show that the center of mass of the system of n books lies above the table,
that is, $\bar{x} < L$. The x-coordinates of the centers of mass of the books are

$x_1 = \dfrac{L}{2}$, $x_2 = \dfrac{L}{2(n-1)} + \dfrac{L}{2}$, $x_3 = \dfrac{L}{2(n-1)} + \dfrac{L}{2(n-2)} + \dfrac{L}{2}$, and

so on. Each book has the same mass m, so if there are n books, then

$$\bar{x} = \frac{mx_1 + mx_2 + \cdots + mx_n}{mn} = \frac{x_1 + x_2 + \cdots + x_n}{n}$$

$$= \frac{1}{n}\left[\frac{L}{2} + \left(\frac{L}{2(n-1)} + \frac{L}{2}\right) + \left(\frac{L}{2(n-1)} + \frac{L}{2(n-2)} + \frac{L}{2}\right) + \cdots\right.$$

$$\left. + \left(\frac{L}{2(n-1)} + \frac{L}{2(n-2)} + \cdots + \frac{L}{4} + \frac{L}{2} + \frac{L}{2}\right)\right]$$

$$= \frac{L}{n}\left[\frac{n-1}{2(n-1)} + \frac{n-2}{2(n-2)} + \cdots + \frac{2}{4} + \frac{1}{2} + \frac{n}{2}\right] = \frac{L}{n}\left[(n-1)\frac{1}{2} + \frac{n}{2}\right] = \frac{2n-1}{2n} L < L$$

This shows that, no matter how many books are added according to the given scheme, the center of mass lies above the table. It remains to observe that the series $\frac{1}{2} + \frac{1}{4} + \frac{1}{6} + \frac{1}{8} + \cdots = \frac{1}{2}\sum(1/n)$ is divergent (harmonic series), so we can make the top book extend as far as we like beyond the edge of the table if we add enough books.

9. $u = 1 + \dfrac{x^3}{3!} + \dfrac{x^6}{6!} + \dfrac{x^9}{9!} + \cdots, v = x + \dfrac{x^4}{4!} + \dfrac{x^7}{7!} + \dfrac{x^{10}}{10!} + \cdots, w = \dfrac{x^2}{2!} + \dfrac{x^5}{5!} + \dfrac{x^8}{8!} + \cdots.$ The key idea is to

differentiate: $\dfrac{du}{dx} = \dfrac{3x^2}{3!} + \dfrac{6x^5}{6!} + \dfrac{9x^8}{9!} + \cdots = \dfrac{x^2}{2!} + \dfrac{x^5}{5!} + \dfrac{x^8}{8!} + \cdots = w.$ Similarly,

$\dfrac{dv}{dx} = 1 + \dfrac{x^3}{3!} + \dfrac{x^6}{6!} + \dfrac{x^9}{9!} + \cdots = u,$ and $\dfrac{dw}{dx} = x + \dfrac{x^4}{4!} + \dfrac{x^7}{7!} + \dfrac{x^{10}}{10!} + \cdots = v.$ So $u' = w, v' = u,$ and $w' = v.$

Now differentiate the left hand side of the desired equation:

$$\frac{d}{dx}\left(u^3 + v^3 + w^3 - 3uvw\right) = 3u^2u' + 3v^2v' + 3w^2w' - 3\left(u'vw + uv'w + uvw'\right)$$

$$= 3u^2w + 3v^2u + 3w^2v - 3\left(vw^2 + u^2w + uv^2\right) = 0 \quad \Rightarrow$$

$u^3 + v^3 + w^3 - 3uvw = C.$ To find the value of the constant C, we put $x = 0$ in the last equation and get $1^3 + 0^3 + 0^3 - 3(1 \cdot 0 \cdot 0) = C \quad \Rightarrow \quad C = 1,$ so $u^3 + v^3 + w^3 - 3uvw = 1.$

10. First notice that both series are absolutely convergent (p-series with $p > 1$.) Let the given expression be called x. Then

$$x = \frac{1 + \dfrac{1}{2^p} + \dfrac{1}{3^p} + \dfrac{1}{4^p} + \cdots}{1 - \dfrac{1}{2^p} + \dfrac{1}{3^p} - \dfrac{1}{4^p} + \cdots} = \frac{1 + \left(2 \cdot \dfrac{1}{2^p} - \dfrac{1}{2^p}\right) + \dfrac{1}{3^p} + \left(2 \cdot \dfrac{1}{4^p} - \dfrac{1}{4^p}\right) + \cdots}{1 - \dfrac{1}{2^p} + \dfrac{1}{3^p} - \dfrac{1}{4^p} + \cdots}$$

$$= \frac{\left(1 - \dfrac{1}{2^p} + \dfrac{1}{3^p} - \dfrac{1}{4^p} + \cdots\right) + \left(2 \cdot \dfrac{1}{2^p} + 2 \cdot \dfrac{1}{4^p} + 2 \cdot \dfrac{1}{6^p} + \cdots\right)}{1 - \dfrac{1}{2^p} + \dfrac{1}{3^p} - \dfrac{1}{4^p} + \cdots}$$

$$= 1 + \frac{2\left(\dfrac{1}{2^p} + \dfrac{1}{4^p} + \dfrac{1}{6^p} + \dfrac{1}{8^p} + \cdots\right)}{1 - \dfrac{1}{2^p} + \dfrac{1}{3^p} - \dfrac{1}{4^p} + \cdots} = 1 + \frac{\dfrac{1}{2^{p-1}}\left(1 + \dfrac{1}{2^p} + \dfrac{1}{3^p} + \dfrac{1}{4^p} + \cdots\right)}{1 - \dfrac{1}{2^p} + \dfrac{1}{3^p} - \dfrac{1}{4^p} + \cdots} = 1 + 2^{1-p}x$$

Therefore, $x = 1 + 2^{1-p}x \quad \Leftrightarrow \quad x - 2^{1-p}x = 1 \quad \Leftrightarrow \quad x\left(1 - 2^{1-p}\right) = 1 \quad \Leftrightarrow \quad x = \dfrac{1}{1 - 2^{1-p}}.$

11. If L is the length of a side of the equilateral triangle, then the area is $A = \frac{1}{2}L \cdot \frac{\sqrt{3}}{2}L = \frac{\sqrt{3}}{4}L^2$ and so $L^2 = \frac{4}{\sqrt{3}}A$.
Let r be the radius of one of the circles. When there are n rows of circles, the figure shows that

$$L = \sqrt{3}\,r + r + (n-2)(2r) + r + \sqrt{3}\,r = r\left(2n - 2 + 2\sqrt{3}\right), \text{ so } r = \frac{L}{2\left(n + \sqrt{3} - 1\right)}. \text{ The number of circles is}$$

$$1 + 2 + \cdots + n = \frac{n(n+1)}{2} \text{ and so the total area of the circles is}$$

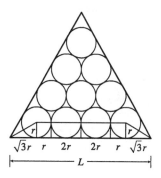

$$A_n = \frac{n(n+1)}{2}\pi r^2 = \frac{n(n+1)}{2}\pi \frac{L^2}{4\left(n + \sqrt{3} - 1\right)^2} = \frac{n(n+1)}{2}\pi \frac{4A/\sqrt{3}}{4\left(n + \sqrt{3} - 1\right)^2}$$

$$= \frac{n(n+1)}{\left(n + \sqrt{3} - 1\right)^2}\frac{\pi A}{2\sqrt{3}} \quad \Rightarrow$$

$$\frac{A_n}{A} = \frac{n(n+1)}{\left(n + \sqrt{3} - 1\right)^2}\frac{\pi}{2\sqrt{3}}$$

$$= \frac{1 + 1/n}{\left[1 + \left(\sqrt{3} - 1\right)/n\right]^2}\frac{\pi}{2\sqrt{3}} \to \frac{\pi}{2\sqrt{3}} \text{ as } n \to \infty$$

12. Given $a_0 = a_1 = 1$ and $a_n = \dfrac{(n-1)(n-2)a_{n-1} - (n-3)a_{n-2}}{n(n-1)}$, we calculate the next few terms of the

sequence: $a_2 = \dfrac{1 \cdot 0 \cdot a_1 - (-1)a_0}{2 \cdot 1} = \dfrac{1}{2}$, $a_3 = \dfrac{2 \cdot 1 \cdot a_2 - 0a_1}{3 \cdot 2} = \dfrac{1}{6}$, $a_4 = \dfrac{3 \cdot 2 \cdot a_3 - 1a_2}{4 \cdot 3} = \dfrac{1}{24}$. It seems that

$a_n = \dfrac{1}{n!}$, so we try to prove this by induction. The first step is done, so assume $a_k = \dfrac{1}{k!}$ and $a_{k-1} = \dfrac{1}{(k-1)!}$.

Then

$$a_{k+1} = \frac{k(k-1)a_k - (k-2)a_{k-1}}{(k+1)k} = \frac{\dfrac{k(k-1)}{k!} - \dfrac{k-2}{(k-1)!}}{(k+1)k} = \frac{(k-1) - (k-2)}{[(k+1)(k)](k-1)!} = \frac{1}{(k+1)!}$$

and the induction is complete. Therefore, $\sum_{n=0}^{\infty} a_n = \sum_{n=0}^{\infty} 1/n! = e$.

13. Call the series S. We group the terms according to the number of digits in their denominators:

$$S = \underbrace{\left(1 + \tfrac{1}{2} + \cdots + \tfrac{1}{8} + \tfrac{1}{9}\right)}_{g_1} + \underbrace{\left(\tfrac{1}{11} + \cdots + \tfrac{1}{99}\right)}_{g_2} + \underbrace{\left(\tfrac{1}{111} + \cdots + \tfrac{1}{999}\right)}_{g_3} + \cdots$$

Now in the group g_n, there are 9^n terms, since we have 9 choices for each of the n digits in the denominator.
Furthermore, each term in g_n is less than $\frac{1}{10^{n-1}}$. So $g_n < 9^n \cdot \frac{1}{10^{n-1}} = 9\left(\frac{9}{10}\right)^{n-1}$. Now $\sum_{n=1}^{\infty} 9\left(\frac{9}{10}\right)^{n-1}$ is a
geometric series with $a = 9$ and $r = \frac{9}{10} < 1$. Therefore, by the Comparison Test,

$$S = \sum_{n=1}^{\infty} g_n < \sum_{n=1}^{\infty} 9\left(\frac{9}{10}\right)^{n-1} = \frac{9}{1 - 9/10} = 90.$$

14. (a) Since P_n is defined as the midpoint of $P_{n-4}P_{n-3}$, $x_n = \frac{1}{2}(x_{n-4} + x_{n-3})$ for $n \geq 5$. So we prove by induction that $\frac{1}{2}x_n + x_{n+1} + x_{n+2} + x_{n+3} = 2$. The case $n = 1$ is immediate, since $\frac{1}{2}0 + 1 + 1 + 0 = 2$. Assume that the result holds for $n = k - 1$, that is, $\frac{1}{2}x_{k-1} + x_k + x_{k+1} + x_{k+2} = 2$. Then for $n = k$,

$$\frac{1}{2}x_k + x_{k+1} + x_{k+2} + x_{k+3} = \frac{1}{2}x_k + x_{k+1} + x_{k+2} + \frac{1}{2}(x_{k+3-4} + x_{k+3-3}) \quad \text{(by above)}$$

$$= \frac{1}{2}x_{k-1} + x_k + x_{k+1} + x_{k+2} = 2 \quad \text{(by the induction hypothesis)}$$

Similarly, for $n \geq 5$, $y_n = \frac{1}{2}(y_{n-4} + y_{n-3})$, so the same argument as above holds for y, with 2 replaced by $\frac{1}{2}y_1 + y_2 + y_3 + y_4 = \frac{1}{2}1 + 1 + 0 + 0 = \frac{3}{2}$. So $\frac{1}{2}y_n + y_{n+1} + y_{n+2} + y_{n+3} = \frac{3}{2}$ for all n.

(b) $\lim_{n \to \infty} \left(\frac{1}{2}x_n + x_{n+1} + x_{n+2} + x_{n+3}\right) = \frac{1}{2}\lim_{n \to \infty} x_n + \lim_{n \to \infty} x_{n+1} + \lim_{n \to \infty} x_{n+2} + \lim_{n \to \infty} x_{n+3} = 2$. Since all the limits on the left hand side are the same, we get $\frac{7}{2} \lim_{n \to \infty} x_n = 2 \Rightarrow \lim_{n \to \infty} x_n = \frac{4}{7}$. In the same way, $\lim_{n \to \infty} y_n = \frac{3}{7}$, so $P = \left(\frac{4}{7}, \frac{3}{7}\right)$.

15. Let $f(x) = \sum_{m=0}^{\infty} c_m x^m$ and $g(x) = e^{f(x)} = \sum_{n=0}^{\infty} d_n x^n$. Then $g'(x) = \sum_{n=0}^{\infty} n d_n x^{n-1}$, so $n d_n$ occurs as the coefficient of x^{n-1}. But also

$$g'(x) = e^{f(x)} f'(x) = \left(\sum_{n=0}^{\infty} d_n x^n\right) \left(\sum_{m=1}^{\infty} m c_m x^{m-1}\right)$$

$$= \left(d_0 + d_1 x + d_2 x^2 + \cdots + d_{n-1} x^{n-1} + \cdots\right)\left(c_1 + 2c_2 x + 3c_3 x^2 + \cdots + n c_n x^{n-1} + \cdots\right)$$

so the coefficient of x^{n-1} is $c_1 d_{n-1} + 2c_2 d_{n-2} + 3c_3 d_{n-3} + \cdots + n c_n d_0 = \sum_{i=1}^{n} i c_i d_{n-i}$. Therefore, $n d_n = \sum_{i=1}^{n} i c_i d_{n-i}$.

16. (a) Let $f(x) = \dfrac{x}{1 - x - x^2} = \sum_{n=0}^{\infty} c_n x^n = c_0 + c_1 x + c_2 x^2 + c_3 x^3 + \cdots$. Then

$$x = \left(1 - x - x^2\right)\left(c_0 + c_1 x + c_2 x^2 + c_3 x^3 + \cdots\right)$$

$$x = c_0 + c_1 x + c_2 x^2 + c_3 x^3 + c_4 x^4 + c_5 x^5 + \cdots$$

$$- c_0 x - c_1 x^2 - c_2 x^3 - c_3 x^4 - c_4 x^5 - \cdots$$

$$- c_0 x^2 - c_1 x^3 - c_2 x^4 - c_3 x^5 - \cdots$$

$$x = c_0 + (c_1 - c_0) x + (c_2 - c_1 - c_0) x^2 + (c_3 - c_2 - c_1) x^3 + \cdots$$

Comparing coefficients of powers of x gives us $c_0 = 0$ and

$$c_1 - c_0 = 1 \quad \Rightarrow \quad c_1 = c_0 + 1 = 1$$

$$c_2 - c_1 - c_0 = 0 \quad \Rightarrow \quad c_2 = c_1 + c_0 = 1 + 0 = 1$$

$$c_3 - c_2 - c_1 = 0 \quad \Rightarrow \quad c_3 = c_2 + c_1 = 1 + 1 = 2$$

In general, we have $c_n = c_{n-1} + c_{n-2}$ for $n \geq 3$. Each c_n is equal to the nth Fibonacci number; that is,

$$\sum_{n=0}^{\infty} c_n x^n = \sum_{n=1}^{\infty} c_n x^n = \sum_{n=1}^{\infty} f_n x^n$$

(b) Completing the square on $x^2 + x - 1$ gives us

$$\left(x^2 + x + \tfrac{1}{4}\right) - 1 - \tfrac{1}{4} = \left(x + \frac{1}{2}\right)^2 - \frac{5}{4} = \left(x + \frac{1}{2}\right)^2 - \left(\frac{\sqrt{5}}{2}\right)^2$$

$$= \left(x + \frac{1}{2} + \frac{\sqrt{5}}{2}\right)\left(x + \frac{1}{2} - \frac{\sqrt{5}}{2}\right) = \left(x + \frac{1 + \sqrt{5}}{2}\right)\left(x + \frac{1 - \sqrt{5}}{2}\right)$$

So $\dfrac{x}{1-x-x^2} = \dfrac{-x}{x^2+x-1} = \dfrac{-x}{\left(x+\frac{1+\sqrt5}{2}\right)\left(x+\frac{1-\sqrt5}{2}\right)}$. The factors in the denominator are linear, so

the partial fraction decomposition is

$$\frac{-x}{\left(x+\frac{1+\sqrt5}{2}\right)\left(x+\frac{1-\sqrt5}{2}\right)} = \frac{A}{x+\frac{1+\sqrt5}{2}} + \frac{B}{x+\frac{1-\sqrt5}{2}}$$

$$-x = A\left(x+\frac{1-\sqrt5}{2}\right) + B\left(x+\frac{1+\sqrt5}{2}\right)$$

If $x = \frac{-1+\sqrt5}{2}$, then $-\frac{-1+\sqrt5}{2} = B\sqrt5 \Rightarrow B = \frac{1-\sqrt5}{2\sqrt5}$.

If $x = \frac{-1-\sqrt5}{2}$, then $-\frac{-1-\sqrt5}{2} = A(-\sqrt5) \Rightarrow A = \frac{1+\sqrt5}{-2\sqrt5}$. Thus,

$$\frac{x}{1-x-x^2} = \frac{\frac{1+\sqrt5}{-2\sqrt5}}{x+\frac{1+\sqrt5}{2}} + \frac{\frac{1-\sqrt5}{2\sqrt5}}{x+\frac{1-\sqrt5}{2}}$$

$$= \frac{\frac{1+\sqrt5}{-2\sqrt5}}{x+\frac{1+\sqrt5}{2}} \cdot \frac{\frac{2}{1+\sqrt5}}{\frac{2}{1+\sqrt5}} + \frac{\frac{1-\sqrt5}{2\sqrt5}}{x+\frac{1-\sqrt5}{2}} \cdot \frac{\frac{2}{1-\sqrt5}}{\frac{2}{1-\sqrt5}}$$

$$= \frac{-1/\sqrt5}{1+\frac{2}{1+\sqrt5}x} + \frac{1/\sqrt5}{1+\frac{2}{1-\sqrt5}x}$$

$$= -\frac{1}{\sqrt5}\sum_{n=0}^{\infty}\left(-\frac{2}{1+\sqrt5}x\right)^n + \frac{1}{\sqrt5}\sum_{n=0}^{\infty}\left(-\frac{2}{1-\sqrt5}x\right)^n$$

$$= \frac{1}{\sqrt5}\sum_{n=0}^{\infty}\left[\left(\frac{-2}{1-\sqrt5}\right)^n - \left(\frac{-2}{1+\sqrt5}\right)^n\right]x^n$$

$$= \frac{1}{\sqrt5}\sum_{n=1}^{\infty}\left[\frac{(-2)^n(1+\sqrt5)^n - (-2)^n(1-\sqrt5)^n}{(1-\sqrt5)^n(1+\sqrt5)^n}\right]x^n \quad \text{[the } n=0 \text{ term is 0]}$$

$$= \frac{1}{\sqrt5}\sum_{n=1}^{\infty}\left[\frac{(-2)^n\left((1+\sqrt5)^n - (1-\sqrt5)^n\right)}{(1-5)^n}\right]x^n$$

$$= \frac{1}{\sqrt5}\sum_{n=1}^{\infty}\left[\frac{(1+\sqrt5)^n - (1-\sqrt5)^n}{2^n}\right]x^n \qquad [(-4)^n = (-2)^n \cdot 2^n]$$

From part (a), this series must equal $\sum_{n=1}^{\infty} f_n x^n$, so $f_n = \dfrac{(1+\sqrt5)^n - (1-\sqrt5)^n}{2^n\sqrt5}$, which is an explicit

formula for the nth Fibonacci number.

Appendixes

 A   Intervals, Inequalities, and Absolute Values · · · · · ·

1. $|5 - 23| = |-18| = 18$

2. $|\pi - 2| = \pi - 2$ because $\pi - 2 > 0$.

3. $|\sqrt{5} - 5| = -(\sqrt{5} - 5) = 5 - \sqrt{5}$ because $\sqrt{5} - 5 < 0$.

4. $\big||-2| - |-3|\big| = |2 - 3| = |-1| = 1$

5. For $x < 2$, $x - 2 < 0$, so $|x - 2| = -(x - 2) = 2 - x$.

6. For $x > 2$, $x - 2 > 0$, so $|x - 2| = x - 2$.

7. $|x + 1| = \begin{cases} x + 1 & \text{for } x + 1 \geq 0 \iff x \geq -1 \\ -(x + 1) & \text{for } x + 1 < 0 \iff x < -1 \end{cases}$

8. $|2x - 1| = \begin{cases} 2x - 1 & \text{for } 2x - 1 \geq 0 \iff x \geq \frac{1}{2} \\ 1 - 2x & \text{for } 2x - 1 < 0 \iff x < \frac{1}{2} \end{cases}$

9. $|x^2 + 1| = x^2 + 1$ (since $x^2 + 1 \geq 0$ for all x).

10. Determine when $1 - 2x^2 < 0 \iff 1 < 2x^2 \iff x^2 > \frac{1}{2} \iff \sqrt{x^2} > \sqrt{\frac{1}{2}} \iff |x| > \sqrt{\frac{1}{2}} \iff$

$x < -\frac{1}{\sqrt{2}}$ or $x > \frac{1}{\sqrt{2}}$. Thus, $|1 - 2x^2| = \begin{cases} 1 - 2x^2 & \text{if } -\frac{1}{\sqrt{2}} \leq x \leq \frac{1}{\sqrt{2}} \\ 2x^2 - 1 & \text{if } x < -\frac{1}{\sqrt{2}} \text{ or } x > \frac{1}{\sqrt{2}} \end{cases}$

11. $2x + 7 > 3 \iff 2x > -4 \iff x > -2$, so $x \in (-2, \infty)$.

12. $4 - 3x \geq 6 \iff -3x \geq 2 \iff x \leq -\frac{2}{3}$, so $x \in \left(-\infty, -\frac{2}{3}\right]$.

13. $1 - x \leq 2 \iff -x \leq 1 \iff x \geq -1$, so $x \in [-1, \infty)$.

14. $1 + 5x > 5 - 3x \iff 8x > 4 \iff x > \frac{1}{2}$, so $x \in \left(\frac{1}{2}, \infty\right)$.

15. $0 \leq 1 - x < 1 \iff -1 \leq -x < 0 \iff 1 \geq x > 0$, so $x \in (0, 1]$.

16. $1 < 3x + 4 \leq 16 \iff -3 < 3x \leq 12 \iff -1 < x \leq 4$, so $x \in (-1, 4]$.

17. $(x - 1)(x - 2) > 0.$ *Case 1:* (both factors are positive, so their product is positive)

$x - 1 > 0 \iff x > 1$, and $x - 2 > 0 \iff x > 2$, so $x \in (2, \infty)$.

Case 2: (both factors are negative, so their product is positive)

$x - 1 < 0 \iff x < 1$, and $x - 2 < 0 \iff x < 2$, so $x \in (-\infty, 1)$.

Thus, the solution set is $(-\infty, 1) \cup (2, \infty)$.

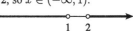

18. $x^2 < 2x + 8$ ⟺ $x^2 - 2x - 8 < 0$ ⟺ $(x-4)(x+2) < 0$. *Case 1:* $x > 4$ and $x < -2$, which is impossible. *Case 2:* $x < 4$ and $x > -2$. Thus, the solution set is $(-2, 4)$.

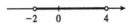

19. $x^2 < 3$ ⟺ $x^2 - 3 < 0$ ⟺ $\left(x-\sqrt{3}\right)\left(x+\sqrt{3}\right) < 0$. *Case 1:* $x > \sqrt{3}$ and $x < -\sqrt{3}$, which is impossible. *Case 2:* $x < \sqrt{3}$ and $x > -\sqrt{3}$. Thus, the solution set is $\left(-\sqrt{3}, \sqrt{3}\right)$.
Another method: $x^2 < 3$ ⟺ $|x| < \sqrt{3}$ ⟺ $-\sqrt{3} < x < \sqrt{3}$.

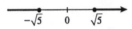

20. $x^2 \geq 5$ ⟺ $x^2 - 5 \geq 0$ ⟺ $\left(x-\sqrt{5}\right)\left(x+\sqrt{5}\right) \geq 0$. *Case 1:* $x \geq \sqrt{5}$ and $x \geq -\sqrt{5}$, so $x \in \left[\sqrt{5}, \infty\right)$. *Case 2:* $x \leq \sqrt{5}$ and $x \leq -\sqrt{5}$, so $x \in \left(-\infty, -\sqrt{5}\right]$. Thus, the solution set is $\left(-\infty, -\sqrt{5}\right] \cup \left[\sqrt{5}, \infty\right)$.
Another method: $x^2 \geq 5$ ⟺ $|x| \geq \sqrt{5}$ ⟺ $x \geq \sqrt{5}$ or $x \leq -\sqrt{5}$.

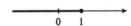

21. $x^3 - x^2 \leq 0$ ⟺ $x^2(x-1) \leq 0$. Since $x^2 \geq 0$ for all x, the inequality is satisfied when $x - 1 \leq 0$ ⟺ $x \leq 1$. Thus, the solution set is $(-\infty, 1]$.

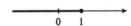

22. $(x+1)(x-2)(x+3) = 0$ ⟺ $x = -1, 2,$ or -3. Constructing a table:

Interval	$x+1$	$x-2$	$x+3$	$(x+1)(x-2)(x+3)$
$x < -3$	$-$	$-$	$-$	$-$
$-3 < x < -1$	$-$	$-$	$+$	$+$
$-1 < x < 2$	$+$	$-$	$+$	$-$
$x > 2$	$+$	$+$	$+$	$+$

Thus, $(x+1)(x-2)(x+3) \geq 0$ on $[-3, -1]$ and $[2, \infty)$, and the solution set is $[-3, -1] \cup [2, \infty)$.

23. $x^3 > x$ ⟺ $x^3 - x > 0$ ⟺ $x(x^2 - 1) > 0$ ⟺ $x(x-1)(x+1) > 0$. Constructing a table:

Interval	x	$x-1$	$x+1$	$x(x-1)(x+1)$
$x < -1$	$-$	$-$	$-$	$-$
$-1 < x < 0$	$-$	$-$	$+$	$+$
$0 < x < 1$	$+$	$-$	$+$	$-$
$x > 1$	$+$	$+$	$+$	$+$

Since $x^3 > x$ when the last column is positive, the solution set is $(-1, 0) \cup (1, \infty)$.

24. $x^3 + 3x < 4x^2$ $\Leftrightarrow$ $x^3 - 4x^2 + 3x < 0$ $\Leftrightarrow$ $x(x^2 - 4x + 3) < 0$ $\Leftrightarrow$ $x(x-1)(x-3) < 0$.

Interval	x	$x-1$	$x-3$	$x(x-1)(x-3)$
$x < 0$	$-$	$-$	$-$	$-$
$0 < x < 1$	$+$	$-$	$-$	$+$
$1 < x < 3$	$+$	$+$	$-$	$-$
$x > 3$	$+$	$+$	$+$	$+$

Thus, the solution set is $(-\infty, 0) \cup (1, 3)$.

25. $1/x < 4$. This is clearly true for $x < 0$. So suppose $x > 0$. then $1/x < 4$ $\Leftrightarrow$ $1 < 4x$ $\Leftrightarrow$ $\frac{1}{4} < x$. Thus, the solution set is $(-\infty, 0) \cup \left(\frac{1}{4}, \infty\right)$.

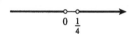

26. $-3 < 1/x \leq 1$. We solve the two inequalities separately and take the intersection of the solution sets. First, $-3 < 1/x$ is clearly true for $x > 0$. So suppose $x < 0$. Then $-3 < 1/x$ $\Leftrightarrow$ $-3x > 1$ $\Leftrightarrow$ $x < -\frac{1}{3}$, so for this inequality, the solution set is $\left(-\infty, -\frac{1}{3}\right) \cup (0, \infty)$. Now $1/x \leq 1$ is clearly true if $x < 0$. So suppose $x > 0$. Then $1/x \leq 1$ $\Leftrightarrow$ $1 \leq x$, and the solution set here is $(-\infty, 0) \cup [1, \infty)$. Taking the intersection of the two solution sets gives the final solution set: $\left(-\infty, -\frac{1}{3}\right) \cup [1, \infty)$.

27. $C = \frac{5}{9}(F - 32)$ $\Rightarrow$ $F = \frac{9}{5}C + 32$. So $50 \leq F \leq 95$ $\Rightarrow$ $50 \leq \frac{9}{5}C + 32 \leq 95$ $\Rightarrow$ $18 \leq \frac{9}{5}C \leq 63$ $\Rightarrow$ $10 \leq C \leq 35$. So the interval is $[10, 35]$.

28. Since $20 \leq C \leq 30$ and $C = \frac{5}{9}(F - 32)$, we have $20 \leq \frac{5}{9}(F - 32) \leq 30$ $\Rightarrow$ $36 \leq F - 32 \leq 54$ $\Rightarrow$ $68 \leq F \leq 86$. So the interval is $[68, 86]$.

29. (a) Let T represent the temperature in degrees Celsius and h the height in km. $T = 20$ when $h = 0$ and T decreases by $10\,°C$ for every km ($1\,°C$ for each 100-m rise). Thus, $T = 20 - 10h$ when $0 \leq h \leq 12$.

(b) From part (a), $T = 20 - 10h$ $\Rightarrow$ $10h = 20 - T$ $\Rightarrow$ $h = 2 - T/10$. So $0 \leq h \leq 5$ $\Rightarrow$ $0 \leq 2 - T/10 \leq 5$ $\Rightarrow$ $-2 \leq -T/10 \leq 3$ $\Rightarrow$ $-20 \leq -T \leq 30$ $\Rightarrow$ $20 \geq T \geq -30$ $\Rightarrow$ $-30 \leq T \leq 20$. Thus, the range of temperatures (in $°C$) to be expected is $[-30, 20]$.

30. The ball will be at least 32 ft above the ground if $h \geq 32$ $\Leftrightarrow$ $128 + 16t - 16t^2 \geq 32$ $\Leftrightarrow$ $16t^2 - 16t - 96 \leq 0$ $\Leftrightarrow$ $16(t - 3)(t + 2) \leq 0$. $t = 3$ and $t = -2$ are endpoints of the interval we're looking for, and constructing a table gives $-2 \leq t \leq 3$. But $t \geq 0$, so the ball will be at least 32 ft above the ground in the time interval $[0, 3]$.

31. $|x + 3| = |2x + 1|$ $\Leftrightarrow$ either $x + 3 = 2x + 1$ or $x + 3 = -(2x + 1)$. In the first case, $x = 2$, and in the second case, $x + 3 = -2x - 1$ $\Leftrightarrow$ $3x = -4$ $\Leftrightarrow$ $x = -\frac{4}{3}$. So the solutions are $-\frac{4}{3}$ and 2.

32. $|3x + 5| = 1$ $\Leftrightarrow$ either $3x + 5 = 1$ or -1. In the first case, $3x = -4$ $\Leftrightarrow$ $x = -\frac{4}{3}$, and in the second case, $3x = -6$ $\Leftrightarrow$ $x = -2$. So the solutions are -2 and $-\frac{4}{3}$.

33. By Property 5 of absolute values, $|x| < 3$ $\Leftrightarrow$ $-3 < x < 3$, so $x \in (-3, 3)$.

34. By Properties 4 and 6 of absolute values, $|x| \geq 3 \iff x \leq -3$ or $x \geq 3$, so $x \in (-\infty, -3] \cup [3, \infty)$.

35. $|x - 4| < 1 \iff -1 < x - 4 < 1 \iff 3 < x < 5$, so $x \in (3, 5)$.

36. $|x - 6| < 0.1 \iff -0.1 < x - 6 < 0.1 \iff 5.9 < x < 6.1$, so $x \in (5.9, 6.1)$.

37. $|x + 5| \geq 2 \iff x + 5 \geq 2$ or $x + 5 \leq -2 \iff x \geq -3$ or $x \leq -7$, so $x \in (-\infty, -7] \cup [-3, \infty)$.

38. $|x + 1| \geq 3 \iff x + 1 \geq 3$ or $x + 1 \leq -3 \iff x \geq 2$ or $x \leq -4$, so $x \in (-\infty, -4] \cup [2, \infty)$.

39. $|2x - 3| \leq 0.4 \iff -0.4 \leq 2x - 3 \leq 0.4 \iff 2.6 \leq 2x \leq 3.4 \iff 1.3 \leq x \leq 1.7$, so $x \in [1.3, 1.7]$.

40. $|5x - 2| < 6 \iff -6 < 5x - 2 < 6 \iff -4 < 5x < 8 \iff -\frac{4}{5} < x < \frac{8}{5}$, so $x \in \left(-\frac{4}{5}, \frac{8}{5}\right)$.

41. $a(bx - c) \geq bc \iff bx - c \geq \dfrac{bc}{a} \iff bx \geq \dfrac{bc}{a} + c = \dfrac{bc + ac}{a} \iff x \geq \dfrac{bc + ac}{ab}$

42. $ax + b < c \iff ax < c - b \iff x > \dfrac{c - b}{a}$ (since $a < 0$)

43. $|ab| = \sqrt{(ab)^2} = \sqrt{a^2 b^2} = \sqrt{a^2}\sqrt{b^2} = |a|\,|b|$

44. If $0 < a < b$, then $a \cdot a < a \cdot b$ and $a \cdot b < b \cdot b$ [using Rule 3 of Inequalities]. So $a^2 < ab < b^2$ and hence $a^2 < b^2$.

◆ B Coordinate Geometry · · · · · · · · · · · · ·

1. From the Distance Formula with $x_1 = 1$, $x_2 = 4$, $y_1 = 1$, $y_2 = 5$, we find the distance from $(1, 1)$ to $(4, 5)$ to be
$\sqrt{(4 - 1)^2 + (5 - 1)^2} = \sqrt{3^2 + 4^2} = \sqrt{25} = 5$.

2. The distance from $(1, -3)$ to $(5, 7)$ is $\sqrt{(5 - 1)^2 + [7 - (-3)]^2} = \sqrt{4^2 + 10^2} = \sqrt{116} = 2\sqrt{29}$.

3. With $P(-3, 3)$ and $Q(-1, -6)$, the slope m of the line through P and Q is $m = \dfrac{-6 - 3}{-1 - (-3)} = -\dfrac{9}{2}$.

4. $m = \dfrac{0 - (-4)}{6 - (-1)} = \dfrac{4}{7}$

5. Using $A(-2, 9)$, $B(4, 6)$, $C(1, 0)$, and $D(-5, 3)$, we have
$|AB| = \sqrt{[4 - (-2)]^2 + (6 - 9)^2} = \sqrt{6^2 + (-3)^2} = \sqrt{45} = \sqrt{9}\sqrt{5} = 3\sqrt{5}$,
$|BC| = \sqrt{(1 - 4)^2 + (0 - 6)^2} = \sqrt{(-3)^2 + (-6)^2} = \sqrt{45} = \sqrt{9}\sqrt{5} = 3\sqrt{5}$,
$|CD| = \sqrt{(-5 - 1)^2 + (3 - 0)^2} = \sqrt{(-6)^2 + 3^2} = \sqrt{45} = \sqrt{9}\sqrt{5} = 3\sqrt{5}$, and
$|DA| = \sqrt{[-2 - (-5)]^2 + (9 - 3)^2} = \sqrt{3^2 + 6^2} = \sqrt{45} = \sqrt{9}\sqrt{5} = 3\sqrt{5}$. So all sides are of equal length and
we have a rhombus. Moreover, $m_{AB} = \dfrac{6 - 9}{4 - (-2)} = -\dfrac{1}{2}$, $m_{BC} = \dfrac{0 - 6}{1 - 4} = 2$, $m_{CD} = \dfrac{3 - 0}{-5 - 1} = -\dfrac{1}{2}$, and
$m_{DA} = \dfrac{9 - 3}{-2 - (-5)} = 2$, so the sides are perpendicular. Thus, A, B, C, and D are vertices of a square.

6. (a) Using $A(-1, 3)$, $B(3, 11)$, and $C(5, 15)$, we have

$$|AB| = \sqrt{[3 - (-1)]^2 + (11 - 3)^2} = \sqrt{4^2 + 8^2} = \sqrt{80} = 4\sqrt{5},$$

$$|BC| = \sqrt{(5 - 3)^2 + (15 - 11)^2} = \sqrt{2^2 + 4^2} = \sqrt{20} = 2\sqrt{5}, \text{ and}$$

$$|AC| = \sqrt{[5 - (-1)]^2 + (15 - 3)^2} = \sqrt{6^2 + 12^2} = \sqrt{180} = 6\sqrt{5}. \text{ Thus, } |AC| = |AB| + |BC|.$$

(b) $m_{AB} = \dfrac{11 - 3}{3 - (-1)} = \dfrac{8}{4} = 2$ and $m_{AC} = \dfrac{15 - 3}{5 - (-1)} = \dfrac{12}{6} = 2$. Since the segments AB and AC have the

same slope, A, B and C must be collinear.

7. $x = 3$

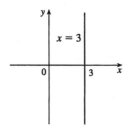

8. $y = -2$

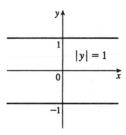

9. $xy = 0 \iff x = 0$ or $y = 0$. The graph
consists of the coordinate axes.

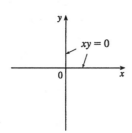

10. $|y| = 1 \iff y = 1$ or $y = -1$

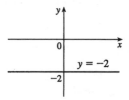

11. By the point-slope form of the equation of a line, an equation of the line through $(2, -3)$ with slope 6 is
$y - (-3) = 6(x - 2)$ or $y = 6x - 15$.

12. $y - (-5) = -\frac{7}{2}[x - (-3)]$ or $y = -\frac{7}{2}x - \frac{31}{2}$

13. The slope of the line through $(2, 1)$ and $(1, 6)$ is $m = \dfrac{6 - 1}{1 - 2} = -5$, so an equation of the line is
$y - 1 = -5(x - 2)$ or $y = -5x + 11$.

14. For $(-1, -2)$ and $(4, 3)$, $m = \dfrac{3 - (-2)}{4 - (-1)} = 1$. So $y - 3 = 1(x - 4)$ or $y = x - 1$.

15. By the slope-intercept form of the equation of a line, an equation of the line is $y = 3x - 2$.

16. By the slope-intercept form of the equation of a line, an equation of the line is $y = \frac{2}{5}x + 4$.

17. Since the line passes through $(1, 0)$ and $(0, -3)$, its slope is $m = \dfrac{-3 - 0}{0 - 1} = 3$, so an equation is $y = 3x - 3$.

Another method: From Exercise 46, $\dfrac{x}{1} + \dfrac{y}{-3} = 1 \;\Rightarrow\; -3x + y = -3 \;\Rightarrow\; y = 3x - 3$.

18. For $(-8, 0)$ and $(0, 6)$, $m = \dfrac{6 - 0}{0 - (-8)} = \dfrac{3}{4}$. So an equation is $y = \frac{3}{4}x + 6$.

Another method: From Exercise 46, $\dfrac{x}{-8} + \dfrac{y}{6} = 1 \;\Rightarrow\; -3x + 4y = 24 \;\Rightarrow\; y = \frac{3}{4}x + 6$.

19. Since $m = 0$, $y - 5 = 0(x - 4)$ or $y = 5$.

20. Since m is undefined, we have the vertical line $x = 4$.

21. Putting the line $x + 2y = 6$ into its slope-intercept form gives us $y = -\frac{1}{2}x + 3$, so we see that this line has slope $-\frac{1}{2}$. Thus, we want the line of slope $-\frac{1}{2}$ that passes through the point $(1, -6)$: $y - (-6) = -\frac{1}{2}(x - 1) \;\Leftrightarrow\; y = -\frac{1}{2}x - \frac{11}{2}$.

22. $2x + 3y + 4 = 0 \;\Leftrightarrow\; y = -\frac{2}{3}x - \frac{4}{3}$, so $m = -\frac{2}{3}$ and the required line is $y = -\frac{2}{3}x + 6$.

23. $2x + 5y + 8 = 0 \;\Leftrightarrow\; y = -\frac{2}{5}x - \frac{8}{5}$. Since this line has slope $-\frac{2}{5}$, a line perpendicular to it would have slope $\frac{5}{2}$, so the required line is $y - (-2) = \frac{5}{2}\left[x - (-1)\right] \;\Leftrightarrow\; y = \frac{5}{2}x + \frac{1}{2}$.

24. $4x - 8y = 1 \;\Leftrightarrow\; y = \frac{1}{2}x - \frac{1}{8}$. Since this line has slope $\frac{1}{2}$, a line perpendicular to it would have slope -2, so the required line is $y - \left(-\frac{2}{3}\right) = -2\left(x - \frac{1}{2}\right) \;\Leftrightarrow\; y = -2x + \frac{1}{3}$.

25. $x + 3y = 0 \;\Leftrightarrow\; y = -\frac{1}{3}x$, so the slope is $-\frac{1}{3}$ and the y-intercept is 0.

26. $2x - 3y + 6 = 0 \;\Leftrightarrow\; y = \frac{2}{3}x + 2$, so the slope is $\frac{2}{3}$ and the y-intercept is 2.

27. $3x - 4y = 12 \;\Leftrightarrow\; y = \frac{3}{4}x - 3$, so the slope is $\frac{3}{4}$ and the y-intercept is -3.

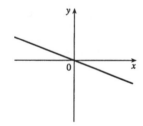

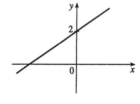

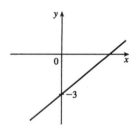

28. $4x + 5y = 10 \;\Leftrightarrow\; y = -\frac{4}{5}x + 2$, so the slope is $-\frac{4}{5}$ and the y-intercept is 2.

29. $\{(x, y) \mid x < 0\}$

30. $\{(x, y) \mid x \geq 1 \text{ and } y < 3\}$

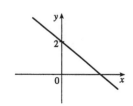

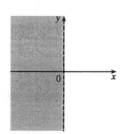

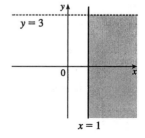

31. $\left\{(x,y)\,\big|\,|x|\leq 2\right\} =$
$\{(x,y)\mid -2\leq x\leq 2\}$

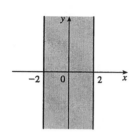

32. $\left\{(x,y)\,\big|\,|x|<3 \text{ and } |y|<2\right\}$

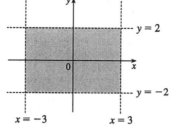

33. $\{(x,y)\mid 0\leq y\leq 4, x\leq 2\}$

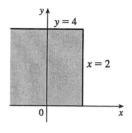

34. $\{(x,y)\mid y>2x-1\}$

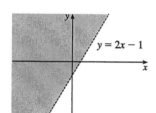

35. $\{(x,y)\mid 1+x\leq y\leq 1-2x\}$

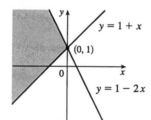

36. $\left\{(x,y)\mid -x\leq y<\dfrac{x+3}{2}\right\}$

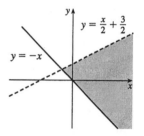

37. An equation of the circle with center $(3,-1)$ and radius 5 is $(x-3)^2+(y+1)^2=5^2=25$.

38. The equation has the form $(x+1)^2+(y-5)^2=r^2$. Since $(-4,-6)$ lies on the circle, we have $r^2=(-4+1)^2+(-6-5)^2=130$. So an equation is $(x+1)^2+(y-5)^2=130$.

39. $x^2+y^2-4x+10y+13=0 \;\Leftrightarrow\; x^2-4x+y^2+10y=-13 \;\Leftrightarrow\;$
$\left(x^2-4x+4\right)+\left(y^2+10y+25\right)=-13+4+25=16 \;\Leftrightarrow\; (x-2)^2+(y+5)^2=4^2$. Thus, we have a circle with center $(2,-5)$ and radius 4.

40. $x^2+y^2+6y+2=0 \;\Leftrightarrow\; x^2+\left(y^2+6y+9\right)=-2+9 \;\Leftrightarrow\; x^2+(y+3)^2=7$. Thus, we have a circle with center $(0,-3)$ and radius $\sqrt{7}$.

41. $2x-y=4 \;\Leftrightarrow\; y=2x-4 \;\Rightarrow\; m_1=2$ and $6x-2y=10 \;\Leftrightarrow\; 2y=6x-10 \;\Leftrightarrow\; y=3x-5 \;\Rightarrow\;$ $m_2=3$. Since $m_1\neq m_2$, the two lines are not parallel. To find the point of intersection: $2x-4=3x-5 \;\Leftrightarrow\;$ $x=1 \;\Rightarrow\; y=-2$. Thus, the point of intersection is $(1,-2)$.

42. $3x-5y+19=0 \;\Leftrightarrow\; 5y=3x+19 \;\Leftrightarrow\; y=\frac{3}{5}x+\frac{19}{5} \;\Rightarrow\; m_1=\frac{3}{5}$ and $10x+6y-50=0 \;\Leftrightarrow\;$ $6y=-10x+50 \;\Leftrightarrow\; y=-\frac{5}{3}x+\frac{25}{3} \;\Rightarrow\; m_2=-\frac{5}{3}$. Since $m_1m_2=\frac{3}{5}\left(-\frac{5}{3}\right)=-1$, the two lines are perpendicular. To find the point of intersection: $\frac{3}{5}x+\frac{19}{5}=-\frac{5}{3}x+\frac{25}{3} \;\Leftrightarrow\; 9x+57=-25x+125 \;\Leftrightarrow\;$ $34x=68 \;\Leftrightarrow\; x=2 \;\Rightarrow\; y=\frac{3}{5}\cdot 2+\frac{19}{5}=\frac{25}{5}=5$. Thus, the point of intersection is $(2,5)$.

43. Let M be the point $\left(\dfrac{x_1 + x_2}{2}, \dfrac{y_1 + y_2}{2}\right)$. Then

$$|MP_1|^2 = \left(x_1 - \dfrac{x_1 + x_2}{2}\right)^2 + \left(y_1 - \dfrac{y_1 + y_2}{2}\right)^2 = \left(\dfrac{x_1 - x_2}{2}\right)^2 + \left(\dfrac{y_1 - y_2}{2}\right)^2 \text{ and}$$

$$|MP_2|^2 = \left(x_2 - \dfrac{x_1 + x_2}{2}\right)^2 + \left(y_2 - \dfrac{y_1 + y_2}{2}\right)^2 = \left(\dfrac{x_2 - x_1}{2}\right)^2 + \left(\dfrac{y_2 - y_1}{2}\right)^2. \text{ Hence, } |MP_1| = |MP_2|; \text{ that}$$

is, M is equidistant from P_1 and P_2.

44. Using the midpoint formula from Exercise 43 with $(1, 3)$ and $(7, 15)$, we get $\left(\frac{1+7}{2}, \frac{3+15}{2}\right) = (4, 9)$.

45. With $A(1, 4)$ and $B(7, -2)$, the slope of segment AB is $\frac{-2-4}{7-1} = -1$, so its perpendicular bisector has slope 1.
The midpoint of AB is $\left(\frac{1+7}{2}, \frac{4+(-2)}{2}\right) = (4, 1)$, so an equation of the perpendicular bisector is $y - 1 = 1(x - 4)$
or $y = x - 3$.

46. (a) Since the x-intercept is a, the point $(a, 0)$ is on the line, and similarly since the y-intercept is b, $(0, b)$ is on the
line. Hence, the slope of the line is $m = \dfrac{b - 0}{0 - a} = -\dfrac{b}{a}$. Substituting into $y = mx + b$ gives $y = -\dfrac{b}{a}x + b$ $\Leftrightarrow$
$\dfrac{b}{a}x + y = b$ $\Leftrightarrow$ $\dfrac{x}{a} + \dfrac{y}{b} = 1$.

(b) Letting $a = 6$ and $b = -8$ gives $\dfrac{x}{6} + \dfrac{y}{-8} = 1$ $\Leftrightarrow$ $-8x + 6y = -48$ $\Leftrightarrow$ $6y = 8x - 48$ $\Leftrightarrow$
$y = \frac{4}{3}x - 8$.

47. If $P(x, y)$ is any point on the parabola, then the distance from P to the focus is $|PF| = \sqrt{x^2 + (y - p)^2}$ and the
distance from P to the directrix is $|y + p|$. (Figure 14 in the text illustrates the case where $p > 0$.) The defining
property of a parabola is that these distances are equal: $\sqrt{x^2 + (y - p)^2} = |y + p|$. We get an equivalent equation
by squaring and simplifying: $x^2 + (y - p)^2 = |y + p|^2 = (y + p)^2$ $\Leftrightarrow$ $x^2 + y^2 - 2py + p^2 = y^2 + 2py + p^2$
$\Leftrightarrow$ $x^2 = 4py$. Thus, an equation of a parabola with focus $(0, p)$ and directrix $y = -p$ is $x^2 = 4py$.

48. From Exercise 47, we have $x^2 = 4py$ as a general equation of a parabola.
Here, we have $x^2 = y$, so $4p = 1$ $\Leftrightarrow$ $p = \frac{1}{4}$. Thus, the focus is $\left(0, \frac{1}{4}\right)$
and the directrix has equation $y = -\frac{1}{4}$.

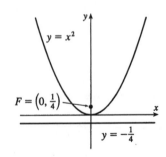

49. See Figure 20 in the text. $P(x, y)$ is a point on the ellipse when $|PF_1| + |PF_2| = 2a$; that is,

$\sqrt{(x + c)^2 + y^2} + \sqrt{(x - c)^2 + y^2} = 2a$ or $\sqrt{(x + c)^2 + y^2} = 2a - \sqrt{(x + c)^2 + y^2}$. Squaring both sides, we
have $x^2 - 2cx + c^2 + y^2 = 4a^2 - 4a\sqrt{(x + c)^2 + y^2} + x^2 + 2cx + c^2 + y^2$, which simplifies to
$a\sqrt{(x + c)^2 + y^2} = a^2 + cx$. We square again: $a^2\left(x^2 + 2cx + c^2 + y^2\right) = a^4 + 2a^2cx + c^2x^2$, which becomes
$(a^2 - c^2)x^2 + a^2y^2 = a^2(a^2 - c^2)$. From triangle F_1F_2P in Figure 20, we see that $2c < 2a$, so $c < a$ and,
therefore, $a^2 - c^2 > 0$. For convenience, let $b^2 = a^2 - c^2$. Then the equation of the ellipse becomes
$b^2x^2 + a^2y^2 = a^2b^2$ or, if both sides are divided by a^2b^2, $\dfrac{x^2}{a^2} + \dfrac{y^2}{b^2} = 1$.

50. $x^2 + 4y^2 = 4 \;\Leftrightarrow\; \frac{1}{4}x^2 + y^2 = 1 \;\Rightarrow\; a = 2,\, b = 1,$

$c = \sqrt{2^2 - 1^2} = \sqrt{3} \;\Rightarrow$

center $(0,0)$, vertices $(\pm 2, 0)$, foci $(\pm\sqrt{3}, 0)$

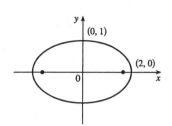

51. From Figure 23 in the text, $|PF_1| - |PF_2| = \pm 2a \;\Leftrightarrow\; \sqrt{(x+c)^2 + y^2} - \sqrt{(x-c)^2 + y^2} = \pm 2a \;\Leftrightarrow$

$\sqrt{(x+c)^2 + y^2} = \sqrt{(x-c)^2 + y^2} \pm 2a \;\Leftrightarrow$

$(x+c)^2 + y^2 = (x-c)^2 + y^2 + 4a^2 \pm 4a\sqrt{(x-c)^2 + y^2} \;\Leftrightarrow\; 4cx - 4a^2 = \pm 4a\sqrt{(x-c)^2 + y^2} \;\Leftrightarrow$

$c^2 x^2 - 2a^2 cx + a^4 = a^2\left(x^2 - 2cx + c^2 + y^2\right) \;\Leftrightarrow\; \left(c^2 - a^2\right)x^2 - a^2 y^2 = a^2\left(c^2 - a^2\right) \;\Leftrightarrow$

$b^2 x^2 - a^2 y^2 = a^2 b^2$ [where $b^2 = c^2 - a^2$] $\;\Leftrightarrow\; \dfrac{x^2}{a^2} - \dfrac{y^2}{b^2} = 1.$

52. (a) $x^2 - y^2 = 1 \;\Rightarrow\; a = b = 1,$

$c = \sqrt{1^2 + 1^2} = \sqrt{2} \;\Rightarrow\;$ center $(0,0)$,

vertices $(\pm 1, 0)$, foci $\left(\pm\sqrt{2}, 0\right)$,

asymptotes $y = \pm x$

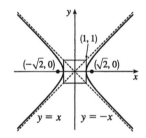

(b) $y^2 - x^2 = 1 \;\Rightarrow\; a = b = 1,$

$c = \sqrt{1^2 + 1^2} = \sqrt{2} \;\Rightarrow\;$ center $(0,0)$,

vertices $(0, \pm 1)$, foci $\left(0, \pm\sqrt{2}\right)$,

asymptotes $y = \pm x$

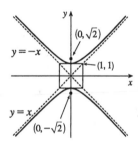

53.

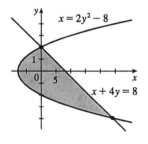

$x + 4y = 8$, $x = 2y^2 - 8$. Substitute x from the second equation into the first: $\left(2y^2 - 8\right) + 4y = 8 \;\Leftrightarrow\; 2y^2 + 4y - 16 = 0$

$\Leftrightarrow\; y^2 + 2y - 8 = 0 \;\Leftrightarrow\; (y+4)(y-2) = 0 \;\Leftrightarrow\; y = -4$ or 2. So the points of intersection are $(24, -4)$ and $(0, 2)$.

54.

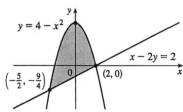

$y = 4 - x^2$, $x - 2y = 2$. Substitute y from the first equation into the second: $x - 2\left(4 - x^2\right) = 2 \;\Leftrightarrow\; 2x^2 + x - 10 = 0$

$\Leftrightarrow\; (2x + 5)(x - 2) = 0 \;\Leftrightarrow\; x = -\frac{5}{2}$ or 2. So the points of intersection are $\left(-\frac{5}{2}, -\frac{9}{4}\right)$ and $(2, 0)$.

55. Differentiating implicitly, $\dfrac{x^2}{a^2} + \dfrac{y^2}{b^2} = 1 \;\Rightarrow\; \dfrac{2x}{a^2} + \dfrac{2yy'}{b^2} = 0 \;\Rightarrow\; y' = -\dfrac{b^2x}{a^2y}\ (y \neq 0)$. Thus, the slope of

the tangent line at P is $-\dfrac{b^2x_1}{a^2y_1}$. The slope of F_1P is $\dfrac{y_1}{x_1+c}$ and of F_2P is $\dfrac{y_1}{x_1-c}$. By the formula from Focus on Problem Solving 3 (Problem 15), we have

$$
\tan\alpha = \frac{\dfrac{y_1}{x_1+c} + \dfrac{b^2x_1}{a^2y_1}}{1 - \dfrac{b^2x_1y_1}{a^2y_1(x_1+c)}} = \frac{a^2y_1^2 + b^2x_1(x_1+c)}{a^2y_1(x_1+c) - b^2x_1y_1}
$$

$$
= \frac{a^2b^2 + b^2cx_1}{c^2x_1y_1 + a^2cy_1} \qquad \begin{bmatrix} \text{using } b^2x_1^2 + a^2y_1^2 = a^2b^2 \\ \text{and } a^2 - b^2 = c^2 \end{bmatrix}
$$

$$
= \frac{b^2(cx_1 + a^2)}{cy_1(cx_1 + a^2)}
$$

$$
= \frac{b^2}{cy_1}
$$

and

$$
\tan\beta = \frac{-\dfrac{b^2x_1}{a^2y_1} - \dfrac{y_1}{x_1-c}}{1 - \dfrac{b^2x_1y_1}{a^2y_1(x_1-c)}} = \frac{-a^2y_1^2 - b^2x_1(x_1-c)}{a^2y_1(x_1-c) - b^2x_1y_1}
$$

$$
= \frac{-a^2b^2 + b^2cx_1}{c^2x_1y_1 - a^2cy_1} = \frac{b^2(cx_1 - a^2)}{cy_1(cx_1 - a^2)}
$$

$$
= \frac{b^2}{cy_1}
$$

Thus, $\alpha = \beta$.

C Trigonometry

1. (a) $210° = 210\left(\frac{\pi}{180}\right) = \frac{7\pi}{6}$ rad
(b) $9° = 9\left(\frac{\pi}{180}\right) = \frac{\pi}{20}$ rad

2. (a) $-315° = -315\left(\frac{\pi}{180}\right) = -\frac{7\pi}{4}$ rad
(b) $36° = 36\left(\frac{\pi}{180}\right) = \frac{\pi}{5}$ rad

3. (a) 4π rad $= 4\pi\left(\frac{180}{\pi}\right) = 720°$
(b) $-\frac{3\pi}{8}$ rad $= -\frac{3\pi}{8}\left(\frac{180}{\pi}\right) = -67.5°$

4. (a) $-\frac{7\pi}{2}$ rad $= -\frac{7\pi}{2}\left(\frac{180}{\pi}\right) = -630°$
(b) $\frac{8\pi}{3}$ rad $= \frac{8\pi}{3}\left(\frac{180}{\pi}\right) = 480°$

5. Using Formula 3, $a = r\theta = 36 \cdot \frac{\pi}{12} = 3\pi$ cm.

6. Using Formula 3, $a = r\theta = 10 \cdot 72\left(\frac{\pi}{180}\right) = 4\pi$ cm.

7. Using Formula 3, $\theta = a/r = \frac{1}{1.5} = \frac{2}{3}$ rad $= \frac{2}{3}\left(\frac{180}{\pi}\right) = \left(\frac{120}{\pi}\right)° \approx 38.2°$.

8. $a = r\theta \;\Rightarrow\; r = \frac{a}{\theta} = \frac{6}{3\pi/4} = \frac{8}{\pi}$ cm

9. (a)

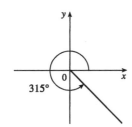

(b)

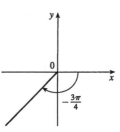

10. (a)

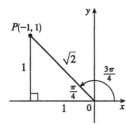

(b)

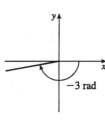

11.

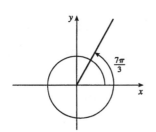

From the diagram we see that a point on the terminal side is $P(-1, 1)$. Therefore, taking $x = -1$, $y = 1$, $r = \sqrt{2}$ in the definitions of the trigonometric ratios, we have $\sin \frac{3\pi}{4} = \frac{1}{\sqrt{2}}$, $\cos \frac{3\pi}{4} = -\frac{1}{\sqrt{2}}$, $\tan \frac{3\pi}{4} = -1$, $\csc \frac{3\pi}{4} = \sqrt{2}$, $\sec \frac{3\pi}{4} = -\sqrt{2}$, and $\cot \frac{3\pi}{4} = -1$.

12.

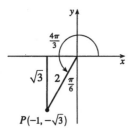

From the diagram and Figure 8, we see that a point on the terminal side is $P\left(-1, -\sqrt{3}\right)$. Therefore, taking $x = -1$, $y = -\sqrt{3}$, $r = 2$ in the definitions of the trigonometric ratios, we have $\sin \frac{4\pi}{3} = -\frac{\sqrt{3}}{2}$, $\cos \frac{4\pi}{3} = -\frac{1}{2}$, $\tan \frac{4\pi}{3} = \sqrt{3}$, $\csc \frac{4\pi}{3} = -\frac{2}{\sqrt{3}}$, $\sec \frac{4\pi}{3} = -2$, and $\cot \frac{4\pi}{3} = \frac{1}{\sqrt{3}}$.

13. $\sin \theta = y/r = \frac{3}{5} \ \Rightarrow \ y = 3$, $r = 5$, and $x = \sqrt{r^2 - y^2} = 4$ (since $0 < \theta < \frac{\pi}{2}$). Therefore taking $x = 4$, $y = 3$, $r = 5$ in the definitions of the trigonometric ratios, we have $\cos \theta = \frac{4}{5}$, $\tan \theta = \frac{3}{4}$, $\csc \theta = \frac{5}{3}$, $\sec \theta = \frac{5}{4}$, and $\cot \theta = \frac{4}{3}$.

14. Since $0 < \alpha < \frac{\pi}{2}$, α is in the first quadrant where x and y are both positive. Therefore, $\tan \alpha = y/x = \frac{2}{1} \ \Rightarrow \ y = 2$, $x = 1$, and $r = \sqrt{x^2 + y^2} = \sqrt{5}$. Taking $x = 1$, $y = 2$, $r = \sqrt{5}$ in the definitions of the trigonometric ratios, we have $\sin \alpha = \frac{2}{\sqrt{5}}$, $\cos \alpha = \frac{1}{\sqrt{5}}$, $\csc \alpha = \frac{\sqrt{5}}{2}$, $\sec \alpha = \sqrt{5}$, and $\cot \alpha = \frac{1}{2}$.

15. $\sin 35° = \dfrac{x}{10} \ \Rightarrow \ x = 10 \sin 35° \approx 5.73576$ cm

16. $\cos 40° = \dfrac{x}{25} \ \Rightarrow \ x = 25 \cos 40° \approx 19.15111$ cm

17. $\tan \frac{2\pi}{5} = \dfrac{x}{8} \ \Rightarrow \ x = 8 \tan \frac{2\pi}{5} \approx 24.62147$ cm

18. $\cos \frac{3\pi}{8} = \dfrac{22}{x} \ \Rightarrow \ x = \dfrac{22}{\cos \frac{3\pi}{8}} \approx 57.48877$ cm

19.

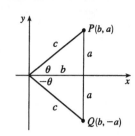

(a) From the diagram we see that $\sin \theta = \dfrac{y}{r} = \dfrac{a}{c}$, and

$$\sin(-\theta) = \frac{-a}{c} = -\frac{a}{c} = -\sin \theta.$$

(b) Again from the diagram we see that $\cos \theta = \dfrac{x}{r} = \dfrac{b}{c} = \cos(-\theta)$.

20. (a) Using (12a) and (12b), we have

$$\tan(x+y) = \frac{\sin(x+y)}{\cos(x+y)} = \frac{\sin x \cos y + \cos x \sin y}{\cos x \cos y - \sin x \sin y} = \frac{\dfrac{\sin x \cos y}{\cos x \cos y} + \dfrac{\cos x \sin y}{\cos x \cos y}}{\dfrac{\cos x \cos y}{\cos x \cos y} - \dfrac{\sin x \sin y}{\cos x \cos y}} = \frac{\tan x + \tan y}{1 - \tan x \tan y}$$

(b) From (10a) and (10b), we have $\tan(-\theta) = -\tan \theta$, so (14a) implies that

$$\tan(x-y) = \tan(x+(-y)) = \frac{\tan x + \tan(-y)}{1 - \tan x \tan(-y)} = \frac{\tan x - \tan y}{1 + \tan x \tan y}$$

21. Using (12a), we have $\sin\left(\frac{\pi}{2} + x\right) = \sin \frac{\pi}{2} \cos x + \cos \frac{\pi}{2} \sin x = 1 \cdot \cos x + 0 \cdot \sin x = \cos x$.

22. Using (13a), we have $\sin(\pi - x) = \sin \pi \cos x - \cos \pi \sin x = 0 \cdot \cos x - (-1) \sin x = \sin x$.

23. Using (6), we have $\sin \theta \cot \theta = \sin \theta \cdot \dfrac{\cos \theta}{\sin \theta} = \cos \theta$.

24. $(\sin x + \cos x)^2 = \sin^2 x + 2 \sin x \cos x + \cos^2 x = (\sin^2 x + \cos^2 x) + \sin 2x$ [by (15a)]

$$= 1 + \sin 2x \quad \text{[by (7)]}$$

25. Using (14a), we have $\tan 2\theta = \tan(\theta + \theta) = \dfrac{\tan \theta + \tan \theta}{1 - \tan \theta \tan \theta} = \dfrac{2 \tan \theta}{1 - \tan^2 \theta}$.

26. We use (12b) with $x = 2\theta$, $y = \theta$ to get

$$\cos 3\theta = \cos(2\theta + \theta) = \cos 2\theta \cos \theta - \sin 2\theta \sin \theta$$

$$= (2 \cos^2 \theta - 1) \cos \theta - 2 \sin^2 \theta \cos \theta \quad \text{[by (16a) and (15a)]}$$

$$= (2 \cos^2 \theta - 1) \cos \theta - 2(1 - \cos^2 \theta) \cos \theta \quad \text{[by (7)]}$$

$$= 2 \cos^3 \theta - \cos \theta - 2 \cos \theta + 2 \cos^3 \theta = 4 \cos^3 \theta - 3 \cos \theta$$

27. Since $\sin x = \frac{1}{3}$ we can label the opposite side as having length 1, the hypotenuse as having length 3, and use the Pythagorean Theorem to get that the adjacent side has length $\sqrt{8}$. Then, from the diagram, $\cos x = \frac{\sqrt{8}}{3}$. Similarly we have that $\sin y = \frac{3}{5}$. Now use (12a):

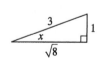

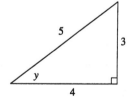

$$\sin(x+y) = \sin x \cos y + \cos x \sin y = \frac{1}{3} \cdot \frac{4}{5} + \frac{\sqrt{8}}{3} \cdot \frac{3}{5} = \frac{4}{15} + \frac{3\sqrt{8}}{15} = \frac{4 + 6\sqrt{2}}{15}.$$

28. Using (16a) with $\cos y = \frac{4}{5}$, we have $\cos 2y = 2 \cos^2 y - 1 = 2\left(\frac{4}{5}\right)^2 - 1 = \frac{32}{25} - 1 = \frac{7}{25}$.

29. $2 \cos x - 1 = 0 \Leftrightarrow \cos x = \frac{1}{2} \Rightarrow x = \frac{\pi}{3}, \frac{5\pi}{3}$ for $x \in [0, 2\pi]$.

30. $2 \sin^2 x = 1 \Leftrightarrow \sin^2 x = \frac{1}{2} \Leftrightarrow \sin x = \pm\frac{1}{\sqrt{2}} \Rightarrow x = \frac{\pi}{4}, \frac{3\pi}{4}, \frac{5\pi}{4}, \frac{7\pi}{4}$.

31. Using (15a), we have $\sin 2x = \cos x \quad \Leftrightarrow \quad 2\sin x \cos x - \cos x = 0 \quad \Leftrightarrow \quad \cos x(2\sin x - 1) = 0 \quad \Leftrightarrow$
$\cos x = 0$ or $2\sin x - 1 = 0 \quad \Rightarrow \quad x = \frac{\pi}{2}, \frac{3\pi}{2}$ or $\sin x = \frac{1}{2} \quad \Rightarrow \quad x = \frac{\pi}{6}$ or $\frac{5\pi}{6}$. Therefore, the solutions are
$x = \frac{\pi}{6}, \frac{\pi}{2}, \frac{5\pi}{6}, \frac{3\pi}{2}$.

32. $|\tan x| = 1 \quad \Leftrightarrow \quad \tan x = -1$ or $\tan x = 1 \quad \Leftrightarrow \quad x = \frac{3\pi}{4}, \frac{7\pi}{4}$ or $x = \frac{\pi}{4}, \frac{5\pi}{4}$.

33. We know that $\sin x = \frac{1}{2}$ when $x = \frac{\pi}{6}$ or $\frac{5\pi}{6}$, and from Figure 13(a), we see that $\sin x \leq \frac{1}{2} \quad \Rightarrow \quad 0 \leq x \leq \frac{\pi}{6}$ or
$\frac{5\pi}{6} \leq x \leq 2\pi$ for $x \in [0, 2\pi]$.

34. $2\cos x + 1 > 0 \quad \Rightarrow \quad 2\cos x > -1 \quad \Rightarrow \quad \cos x > -\frac{1}{2}$. $\cos x = -\frac{1}{2}$ when $x = \frac{2\pi}{3}, \frac{4\pi}{3}$ and from Figure 13(b),
we see that $\cos x > -\frac{1}{2}$ when $0 \leq x < \frac{2\pi}{3}, \frac{4\pi}{3} < x \leq 2\pi$.

35. $\tan x = -1$ when $x = \frac{3\pi}{4}, \frac{7\pi}{4}$, and $\tan x = 1$ when $x = \frac{\pi}{4}$ or $\frac{5\pi}{4}$. From Figure 14 we see that $-1 < \tan x < 1$
$\Rightarrow \quad 0 \leq x < \frac{\pi}{4}, \frac{3\pi}{4} < x < \frac{5\pi}{4}$, and $\frac{7\pi}{4} < x \leq 2\pi$.

36. We know that $\sin x = \cos x$ when $x = \frac{\pi}{4}, \frac{5\pi}{4}$, and from the diagram we see that $\sin x > \cos x$ when $\frac{\pi}{4} < x < \frac{5\pi}{4}$.

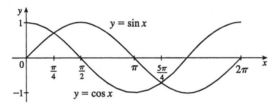

37. $y = \cos\left(x - \frac{\pi}{3}\right)$. We start with the graph of
$y = \cos x$ and shift it $\frac{\pi}{3}$ units to the right.

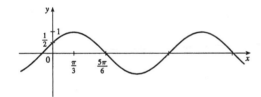

38. $y = \tan 2x$. Start with the graph of $y = \tan x$
with period π and compress it to a period of $\frac{\pi}{2}$.

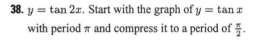
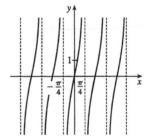

39. $y = \frac{1}{3}\tan\left(x - \frac{\pi}{2}\right)$. We start with the graph of
$y = \tan x$, shift it $\frac{\pi}{2}$ units to the right and
compress it to $\frac{1}{3}$ of its original vertical size.

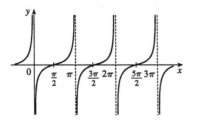

40. $y = |\sin x|$. We start with the graph of $y = \sin x$
and reflect the parts below the x-axis about the
x-axis.

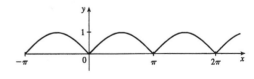

41. (a) $\sin^{-1}(0.5) = \frac{\pi}{6}$ since $\sin \frac{\pi}{6} = 0.5$ and $-\frac{\pi}{2} \le \frac{\pi}{6} \le \frac{\pi}{2}$.

(b) $\arctan(-1) = -\frac{\pi}{4}$ since $\tan\left(-\frac{\pi}{4}\right) = -1$ and $-\frac{\pi}{4}$ is in $\left(-\frac{\pi}{2}, \frac{\pi}{2}\right)$.

42. (a) $\tan^{-1} \sqrt{3} = \frac{\pi}{3}$ since $\tan \frac{\pi}{3} = \sqrt{3}$ and $\frac{\pi}{3}$ is in $\left(-\frac{\pi}{2}, \frac{\pi}{2}\right)$.

(b) $\arcsin 1 = \frac{\pi}{2}$ since $\sin \frac{\pi}{2} = 1$ and $\frac{\pi}{2}$ is in $\left[-\frac{\pi}{2}, \frac{\pi}{2}\right]$.

43. (a) $\sin\left(\sin^{-1} 0.7\right) = 0.7$ since 0.7 is in $[-1, 1]$.

(b) $\arcsin\left(\sin \frac{5\pi}{4}\right) = \arcsin\left(-\frac{1}{\sqrt{2}}\right) = -\frac{\pi}{4}$

44. (a) Let $\theta = \arctan 2$, so $\tan \theta = 2$. Now $\sec^2 \theta = 1 + \tan^2 \theta = 1 + 2^2 = 5 \Rightarrow \sec \theta = \sqrt{5}$ ($\sec \theta > 0$ since $0 < \theta < \pi/2$). Thus, $\sec(\arctan 2) = \sec \theta = \sqrt{5}$.

(b) Let $\theta = \sin^{-1} \frac{3}{5}$. Then $\sin \theta = \frac{3}{5} \Rightarrow \cos \theta = \sqrt{1 - \left(\frac{3}{5}\right)^2} = \frac{4}{5}$, so

$\sin\left(2 \sin^{-1} \frac{3}{5}\right) = \sin 2\theta = 2 \sin \theta \cos \theta = 2 \cdot \frac{3}{5} \cdot \frac{4}{5} = \frac{24}{25}$.

45. Let $y = \sin^{-1} x$. Then $-\frac{\pi}{2} \le y \le \frac{\pi}{2} \Rightarrow \cos y \ge 0$, so $\cos\left(\sin^{-1} x\right) = \cos y = \sqrt{1 - \sin^2 y} = \sqrt{1 - x^2}$.

46. (a) For the restricted cosine function, we have domain $= [0, \pi]$ and range $= [-1, 1]$. So for the inverse cosine function, domain $= [-1, 1]$ and range $= [0, \pi]$.

(b)

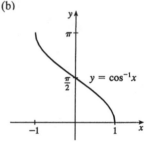

47. $g(x) = \sin^{-1}(3x + 1)$.

Domain $(g) = \{x \mid -1 \le 3x + 1 \le 1\} = \{x \mid -2 \le 3x \le 0\} = \{x \mid -\frac{2}{3} \le x \le 0\} = \left[-\frac{2}{3}, 0\right]$.

Range $(g) = \left\{y \mid -\frac{\pi}{2} \le y \le \frac{\pi}{2}\right\} = \left[-\frac{\pi}{2}, \frac{\pi}{2}\right]$.

48. (a) $f(x) = \sin\left(\sin^{-1} x\right)$ (b) $g(x) = \sin^{-1}(\sin x)$

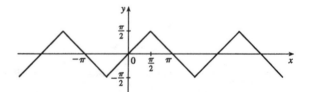

Since one function undoes what the other one does, we get the identity function, $y = x$, on the restricted domain $-1 \le x \le 1$.

This is similar to part (a), but with domain $\mathbb{R}$. Equations for g on intervals of the form $\left(-\frac{\pi}{2} + \pi n, \frac{\pi}{2} + \pi n\right)$, for any integer n, can be found using $g(x) = (-1)^n x + (-1)^{n+1} n\pi$. The sine function is monotonic on each of these intervals, and hence, so is g (but in a linear fashion).

49. From the figure in the text, we see that $x = b \cos \theta$, $y = b \sin \theta$, and from the distance formula we have that the distance c from (x, y) to $(a, 0)$ is $c = \sqrt{(x - a)^2 + (y - 0)^2} \Rightarrow$

$$c^2 = (b \cos \theta - a)^2 + (b \sin \theta)^2 = b^2 \cos^2 \theta - 2ab \cos \theta + a^2 + b^2 \sin^2 \theta$$

$$= a^2 + b^2 \left(\cos^2\theta + \sin^2\theta\right) - 2ab\cos\theta = a^2 + b^2 - 2ab\cos\theta \quad \text{[by (7)]}$$

50. $|AB|^2 = |AC|^2 + |BC|^2 - 2|AC||BC|\cos\angle C = (820)^2 + (910)^2 - 2(820)(910)\cos 103°$
$$\approx 1{,}836{,}217 \quad\Rightarrow\quad |AB| \approx 1355 \text{ m}$$

51. Using the Law of Cosines, we have $c^2 = 1^2 + 1^2 - 2(1)(1)\cos(\alpha - \beta) = 2\left[1 - \cos(\alpha - \beta)\right]$. Now, using the distance formula, $c^2 = |AB|^2 = (\cos\alpha - \cos\beta)^2 + (\sin\alpha - \sin\beta)^2$. Equating these two expressions for c^2, we get $2\left[1 - \cos(\alpha - \beta)\right] = \cos^2\alpha + \sin^2\alpha + \cos^2\beta + \sin^2\beta - 2\cos\alpha\cos\beta - 2\sin\alpha\sin\beta \Rightarrow$ $1 - \cos(\alpha - \beta) = 1 - \cos\alpha\cos\beta - \sin\alpha\sin\beta \Rightarrow \cos(\alpha - \beta) = \cos\alpha\cos\beta + \sin\alpha\sin\beta$.

52. $\cos(x + y) = \cos(x - (-y)) = \cos x\cos(-y) + \sin x\sin(-y)$
$$= \cos x\cos y - \sin x\sin y \quad \text{[using Equations 10a and 10b]}$$

53. In Exercise 52 we used the subtraction formula for cosine to prove the addition formula for cosine. Using that formula with $x = \frac{\pi}{2} - \alpha$, $y = \beta$, we get $\cos\left[\left(\frac{\pi}{2} - \alpha\right) + \beta\right] = \cos\left(\frac{\pi}{2} - \alpha\right)\cos\beta - \sin\left(\frac{\pi}{2} - \alpha\right)\sin\beta \Rightarrow$ $\cos\left[\frac{\pi}{2} - (\alpha - \beta)\right] = \cos\left(\frac{\pi}{2} - \alpha\right)\cos\beta - \sin\left(\frac{\pi}{2} - \alpha\right)\sin\beta$. Now we use the identities given in the problem, $\cos\left(\frac{\pi}{2} - \theta\right) = \sin\theta$ and $\sin\left(\frac{\pi}{2} - \theta\right) = \cos\theta$, to get $\sin(\alpha - \beta) = \sin\alpha\cos\beta - \cos\alpha\sin\beta$.

54. (a) If $0 < \theta < \frac{\pi}{2}$, we have the case depicted in the first diagram. In this case, we see that the height of the triangle is $h = a\sin\theta$. If $\frac{\pi}{2} \le \theta < \pi$, we have the case depicted in the second diagram. In this case, the height of the triangle is $h = a\sin(\pi - \theta) = a\sin\theta$ (by the identity proved in Exercise 22). So in either case, the area of the triangle is $\frac{1}{2}bh = \frac{1}{2}ab\sin\theta$.

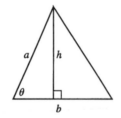 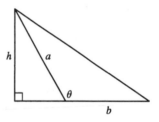

(b) Using the formula from part (a), the area of the triangle is $\frac{1}{2}(10)(3)\sin 107° \approx 14.34457 \text{ cm}^2$.

D ◆ Precise Definitions of Limits   • • • • • • • • • •

1. On the left side of $x = 2$, we need $|x - 2| < \left|\frac{10}{7} - 2\right| = \frac{4}{7}$. On the right side, we need $|x - 2| < \left|\frac{10}{3} - 2\right| = \frac{4}{3}$. For both of these conditions to be satisfied at once, we need the more restrictive of the two to hold, that is, $|x - 2| < \frac{4}{7}$. So we can choose $\delta = \frac{4}{7}$, or any smaller positive number.

2. The left-hand question mark is the positive solution of $x^2 = \frac{1}{2}$, that is, $x = \frac{1}{\sqrt{2}}$, and the right-hand question mark is the positive solution of $x^2 = \frac{3}{2}$, that is, $x = \sqrt{\frac{3}{2}}$. On the left side, we need $|x - 1| < \left|\frac{1}{\sqrt{2}} - 1\right| \approx 0.292$ (rounding down to be safe). On the right side, we need $|x - 1| < \left|\sqrt{\frac{3}{2}} - 1\right| \approx 0.224$. The more restrictive of these two conditions must apply, so we choose $\delta = 0.224$ (or any smaller positive number).

3. $\left|\sqrt{4x + 1} - 3\right| < 0.5$ ⟺ $2.5 < \sqrt{4x + 1} < 3.5$. We plot the three parts of this inequality on the same screen and identify the x-coordinates of the points of intersection using the cursor. It appears

that the inequality holds for $1.3125 \leq x \leq 2.8125$. Since

$|2 - 1.3125| = 0.6875$ and $|2 - 2.8125| = 0.8125$, we choose

$0 < \delta < \min\{0.6875, 0.8125\} = 0.6875$.

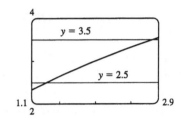

4. $\left|\sin x - \frac{1}{2}\right| < 0.1$ ⟺ $0.4 < \sin x < 0.6$. From the graph, we see that for this inequality to hold, we need $A \leq x \leq B$ with $A \approx 0.412$ and $B \approx 0.644$. So since $\left|\frac{\pi}{6} - A\right| \approx 0.112$ and

$\left|\frac{\pi}{6} - B\right| \approx 0.120$, we choose

$0 < \delta \leq \min\{0.112, 0.120\} = 0.112$.

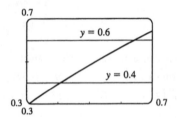

5. For $\varepsilon = 1$, the definition of a limit requires that we find δ such that $\left|(4 + x - 3x^3) - 2\right| < 1$ ⟺ $1 < 4 + x - 3x^3 < 3$ whenever $0 < |x - 1| < \delta$. If we plot the graphs of $y = 1$, $y = 4 + x - 3x^3$ and $y = 3$ on the same screen, we see that we need $0.86 \leq x \leq 1.11$. So since $|1 - 0.86| = 0.14$ and $|1 - 1.11| = 0.11$, we choose $\delta = 0.11$ (or any smaller positive number). For $\varepsilon = 0.1$, we must find δ such that $\left|(4 + x - 3x^3) - 2\right| < 0.1$ ⟺ $1.9 < 4 + x - 3x^3 < 2.1$ whenever $0 < |x - 1| < \delta$. From the graph, we see that we need $0.988 \leq x \leq 1.012$. So since $|1 - 0.988| = 0.012$ and $|1 - 1.012| = 0.012$, we choose $\delta = 0.012$ (or any smaller positive number) for the inequality to hold.

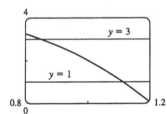 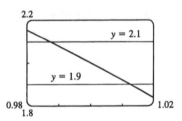

6. For $\varepsilon = 0.5$, the definition of a limit requires that we find δ such that $\left|\frac{e^x - 1}{x} - 1\right| < 0.5$ ⟺

$0.5 < \frac{e^x - 1}{x} < 1.5$ whenever $0 < |x - 0| < \delta$. If we plot the graphs of $y = 0.5$, $y = \frac{e^x - 1}{x}$, and $y = 1.5$ on the same screen, we see that we need $-1.59 \leq x \leq 0.76$. So since $|0 - (-1.59)| = 1.59$ and $|0 - 0.76| = 0.76$, we choose $\delta = 0.76$ (or any smaller positive number). For $\varepsilon = 0.1$, we must find δ such that

$\left|\frac{e^x - 1}{x} - 1\right| < 0.1$ ⟺ $0.9 < \frac{e^x - 1}{x} < 1.1$ whenever $0 < |x - 0| < \delta$. From the graph, we see that we need

$-0.21 \leq x \leq 0.18$. So since $|0 - (-0.21)| = 0.21$ and $|0 - 0.18| = 0.18$, we choose $\delta = 0.18$ (or any smaller positive number) for the inequality to hold.

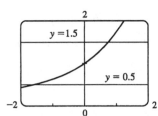

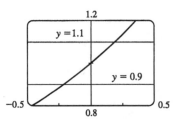

7. Given $\varepsilon > 0$, we need $\delta > 0$ such that if $|x| < \delta$ then $|x^3 - 0| < \varepsilon$ $\Leftrightarrow$ $|x|^3 < \varepsilon$ $\Leftrightarrow$ $|x| < \sqrt[3]{\varepsilon}$. Take $\delta = \sqrt[3]{\varepsilon}$. Then $|x - 0| < \delta$ $\Rightarrow$ $|x^3 - 0| < \delta^3 = \varepsilon$. Thus, $\lim_{x \to 0} x^3 = 0$ by the definition of a limit.

8. (a) We must restrict the open interval $(a - \delta, a + \delta)$ in Definition 1 to the right half of the interval, $(a, a + \delta)$. Hence, $\lim_{x \to a^+} f(x) = L$ if for every number $\varepsilon > 0$ there is a corresponding number $\delta > 0$ such that $|f(x) - L| < \varepsilon$ whenever $a < x < a + \delta$.

(b) 1. *Guessing a value for* δ. Let ε be a given positive number. Here $a = 0$ and $L = 0$, so we want to find a number δ such that $|\sqrt{x} - 0| < \varepsilon$ whenever $0 < x < \delta$, that is, $\sqrt{x} < \varepsilon$ whenever $0 < x < \delta$ or, squaring both sides of the inequality $\sqrt{x} < \varepsilon$, we get $x < \varepsilon^2$ whenever $0 < x < \delta$. This suggests that we should choose $\delta = \varepsilon^2$.

2. *Showing that this* δ *works.* Given $\varepsilon > 0$, let $\delta = \varepsilon^2$. If $0 < x < \delta$, then $\sqrt{x} < \sqrt{\delta} = \sqrt{\varepsilon^2} = \varepsilon$, so $|\sqrt{x} - 0| < \varepsilon$. According to the definition in part (a), this shows that $\lim_{x \to 0^+} \sqrt{x} = 0$.

9. Given $\varepsilon > 0$, we need $\delta > 0$ such that if $|x - 2| < \delta$, then

$|(3x - 2) - 4| < \varepsilon$ $\Leftrightarrow$ $|3x - 6| < \varepsilon \Leftrightarrow 3|x - 2| < \varepsilon \Leftrightarrow$

$|x - 2| < \varepsilon/3$. So if we choose $\delta = \varepsilon/3$, then

$|x - 2| < \delta$ $\Rightarrow$ $|(3x - 2) - 4| < \varepsilon$. Thus, $\lim_{x \to 2} (3x - 2) = 4$ by

the definition of a limit.

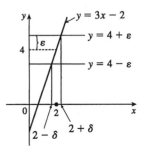

10. Given $\varepsilon > 0$, we need $\delta > 0$ such that if $|x - 4| < \delta$, then

$|(5 - 2x) - (-3)| < \varepsilon$ $\Leftrightarrow$ $|-2x + 8| < \varepsilon$ $\Leftrightarrow$ $2|x - 4| <$

ε $\Leftrightarrow$ $|x - 4| < \varepsilon/2$. So if we choose $\delta = \varepsilon/2$, then

$|x - 4| < \delta$ $\Rightarrow$ $|(5 - 2x) - (-3)| < \varepsilon$. Thus,

$\lim_{x \to 4} (5 - 2x) = -3$ by the definition of a limit.

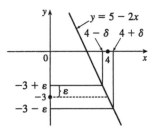

11. (a) $A = \pi r^2$ and $A = 1000 \text{ cm}^2 \Rightarrow \pi r^2 = 1000 \Rightarrow r^2 = \frac{1000}{\pi} \Rightarrow$

$r = \sqrt{\frac{1000}{\pi}} \quad (r > 0) \quad \approx 17.8412 \text{ cm}.$

(b) $|A - 1000| \le 5 \Rightarrow -5 \le \pi r^2 - 1000 \le 5 \Rightarrow 1000 - 5 \le \pi r^2 \le 1000 + 5 \Rightarrow$

$\sqrt{\frac{995}{\pi}} \le r \le \sqrt{\frac{1005}{\pi}} \Rightarrow 17.7966 \le r \le 17.8858.$ $\sqrt{\frac{1000}{\pi}} - \sqrt{\frac{995}{\pi}} \approx 0.04466$ and

$\sqrt{\frac{1005}{\pi}} - \sqrt{\frac{1000}{\pi}} \approx 0.04455.$ So if the machinist gets the radius within 0.0445 cm of 17.8412, the area will be

within 5 cm^2 of 1000.

(c) x is the radius, $f(x)$ is the area, a is the target radius given in part (a), L is the target area (1000), ε is the tolerance in the area (5), and δ is the tolerance in the radius given in part (b).

12. (a) $T = 0.1w^2 + 2.155w + 20$ and $T = 200 \Rightarrow$

$0.1w^2 + 2.155w + 20 = 200 \Rightarrow$ (by the quadratic formula or

from the graph) $w \approx 33.0$ watts $(w > 0)$

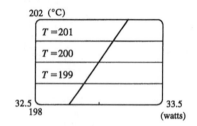

(b) From the graph, $199 \le T \le 201 \Rightarrow 32.89 < w < 33.11.$

(c) x is the input power, $f(x)$ is the temperature, a is the target input power given in part (a), L is the target temperature (200), ε is the tolerance in the temperature (1), and δ is the tolerance in the power input in watts indicated in part (b) (0.11 watts).

13. $\left| \dfrac{6x^2 + 5x - 3}{2x^2 - 1} - 3 \right| < 0.2 \Leftrightarrow 2.8 < \dfrac{6x^2 + 5x - 3}{2x^2 - 1} < 3.2.$ So

we graph the three parts of this inequality on the same screen, and

find that the curve $y = \dfrac{6x^2 + 5x - 3}{2x^2 - 1}$ seems to lie between the

lines $y = 2.8$ and $y = 3.2$ whenever $x > 12.5.$ So we can choose

$N = 13$ (or any larger number), so that the inequality holds

whenever $x \ge N.$

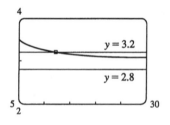

14. For $\varepsilon = 0.5$, we must find N such that whenever $x \ge N$, we have

$\left| \dfrac{\sqrt{4x^2 + 1}}{x + 1} - 2 \right| < 0.5 \Leftrightarrow 1.5 < \dfrac{\sqrt{4x^2 + 1}}{x + 1} < 2.5.$ We graph the three parts of this inequality on the same

screen, and find that it holds whenever $x > 2.82.$ So we choose $N = 3$ (or any larger number). For $\varepsilon = 0.1$, we

must have $1.9 < \dfrac{\sqrt{4x^2 + 1}}{x + 1} < 2.1$, and the graphs show that this holds whenever $x > 18.9.$ So we choose $N = 19$

(or any larger number).

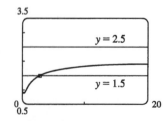

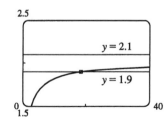

15. (a) $1/x^2 < 0.0001 \quad \Leftrightarrow \quad x^2 > 1/0.0001 = 10{,}000 \quad \Leftrightarrow \quad x > 100 \quad (x > 0)$

(b) If $\varepsilon > 0$ is given, then $1/x^2 < \varepsilon \quad \Leftrightarrow \quad x^2 > 1/\varepsilon \quad \Leftrightarrow \quad x > 1/\sqrt{\varepsilon}$. Let $N = 1/\sqrt{\varepsilon}$. Then $x > N \quad \Rightarrow$

$$x > \frac{1}{\sqrt{\varepsilon}} \quad \Rightarrow \quad \left| \frac{1}{x^2} - 0 \right| = \frac{1}{x^2} < \varepsilon, \text{ so } \lim_{x \to \infty} \frac{1}{x^2} = 0.$$

16. (a) $1/x^2 < 0.0001 \quad \Leftrightarrow \quad x^2 > 1/0.0001 = 10{,}000 \quad \Leftrightarrow \quad x > 100 \quad (x > 0)$

(b) If $\varepsilon > 0$ is given, then $1/x^2 < \varepsilon \quad \Leftrightarrow \quad x^2 > 1/\varepsilon \quad \Leftrightarrow \quad x > 1/\sqrt{\varepsilon}$. Let $N = 1/\sqrt{\varepsilon}$. Then $x > N \quad \Rightarrow$

$$x > \frac{1}{\sqrt{\varepsilon}} \quad \Rightarrow \quad \left| \frac{1}{x^2} - 0 \right| = \frac{1}{x^2} < \varepsilon, \text{ so } \lim_{x \to \infty} \frac{1}{x^2} = 0.$$

17. (a)

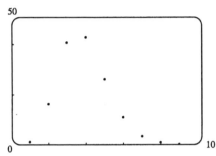

From the graph, it appears that the sequence $\left\{ \dfrac{n^5}{n!} \right\}$ converges to 0, that is, $\lim_{n \to \infty} \dfrac{n^5}{n!} = 0$.

(b)

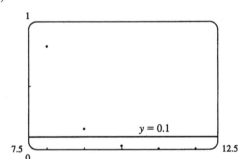 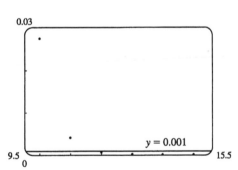

From the first graph, it seems that the smallest possible value of N corresponding to $\varepsilon = 0.1$ is 9, since $n^5/n! < 0.1$ whenever $n \geq 10$, but $9^5/9! > 0.1$. From the second graph, it seems that for $\varepsilon = 0.001$, the smallest possible value for N is 11 since $n^5/n! < 0.001$ whenever $n \geq 12$.

18. Let $\varepsilon > 0$ and let N be any positive integer larger than $\ln(\varepsilon)/\ln|r|$. If $n > N$, then $n > \ln(\varepsilon)/\ln|r| \quad \Rightarrow$
$n \ln|r| < \ln \varepsilon \quad [\text{since } |r| < 1 \quad \Rightarrow \quad \ln|r| < 0] \quad \Rightarrow \quad \ln(|r|^n) < \ln \varepsilon \quad \Rightarrow \quad |r|^n < \varepsilon \quad \Rightarrow \quad |r^n - 0| < \varepsilon$,
and so by Definition 3, $\lim_{n \to \infty} r^n = 0$.

19. If $\lim_{n \to \infty} |a_n| = 0$, then $\lim_{n \to \infty} (-|a_n|) = 0$, and since $-|a_n| \leq a_n \leq |a_n|$, we have that $\lim_{n \to \infty} a_n = 0$ by the

Squeeze Theorem.

20. Let M be any positive number. Then $n^3 > M \quad \Leftrightarrow \quad n > \sqrt[3]{M}$. So if we take $N = \sqrt[3]{M}$, then $n^3 > M$
whenever $n > N$. By Definition 4, $\lim_{n \to \infty} n^3 = \infty$.

Sigma Notation • • • • • • • • • • • • • • • • •

1. $\displaystyle\sum_{i=1}^{5} \sqrt{i} = \sqrt{1} + \sqrt{2} + \sqrt{3} + \sqrt{4} + \sqrt{5}$

2. $\displaystyle\sum_{i=1}^{6} \frac{1}{i+1} = \frac{1}{2} + \frac{1}{3} + \frac{1}{4} + \frac{1}{5} + \frac{1}{6} + \frac{1}{7}$

3. $\displaystyle\sum_{i=4}^{6} 3^i = 3^4 + 3^5 + 3^6$

4. $\displaystyle\sum_{i=4}^{6} i^3 = 4^3 + 5^3 + 6^3$

5. $\displaystyle\sum_{k=0}^{4} \frac{2k-1}{2k+1} = -1 + \frac{1}{3} + \frac{3}{5} + \frac{5}{7} + \frac{7}{9}$

6. $\displaystyle\sum_{k=5}^{8} x^k = x^5 + x^6 + x^7 + x^8$

7. $\displaystyle\sum_{i=1}^{n} i^{10} = 1^{10} + 2^{10} + 3^{10} + \cdots + n^{10}$

8. $\displaystyle\sum_{j=n}^{n+3} j^2 = n^2 + (n+1)^2 + (n+2)^2 + (n+3)^2$

9. $\displaystyle\sum_{j=0}^{n-1} (-1)^j = 1 - 1 + 1 - 1 + \cdots + (-1)^{n-1}$

10. $\displaystyle\sum_{i=1}^{n} f(x_i)\,\Delta x_i = f(x_1)\,\Delta x_1 + f(x_2)\,\Delta x_2$
$$+ f(x_3)\,\Delta x_3 + \cdots + f(x_n)\,\Delta x_n$$

11. $1 + 2 + 3 + 4 + \cdots + 10 = \displaystyle\sum_{i=1}^{10} i$

12. $\sqrt{3} + \sqrt{4} + \sqrt{5} + \sqrt{6} + \sqrt{7} = \displaystyle\sum_{i=3}^{7} \sqrt{i}$

13. $\dfrac{1}{2} + \dfrac{2}{3} + \dfrac{3}{4} + \dfrac{4}{5} + \cdots + \dfrac{19}{20} = \displaystyle\sum_{i=1}^{19} \frac{i}{i+1}$

14. $\dfrac{3}{7} + \dfrac{4}{8} + \dfrac{5}{9} + \dfrac{6}{10} + \cdots + \dfrac{23}{27} = \displaystyle\sum_{i=3}^{23} \frac{i}{i+4}$

15. $2 + 4 + 6 + 8 + \cdots + 2n = \displaystyle\sum_{i=1}^{n} 2i$

16. $1 + 3 + 5 + 7 + \cdots + (2n-1) = \displaystyle\sum_{i=1}^{n} (2i-1)$

17. $1 + 2 + 4 + 8 + 16 + 32 = \displaystyle\sum_{i=0}^{5} 2^i$

18. $\dfrac{1}{1} + \dfrac{1}{4} + \dfrac{1}{9} + \dfrac{1}{16} + \dfrac{1}{25} + \dfrac{1}{36} = \displaystyle\sum_{i=1}^{6} \frac{1}{i^2}$

19. $x + x^2 + x^3 + \cdots + x^n = \displaystyle\sum_{i=1}^{n} x^i$

20. $1 - x + x^2 - x^3 + \cdots + (-1)^n x^n = \displaystyle\sum_{i=0}^{n} (-1)^i x^i$

21. $\displaystyle\sum_{i=4}^{8} (3i-2) = [3(4)-2] + [3(5)-2] + [3(6)-2] + [3(7)-2] + [3(8)-2] = 10 + 13 + 16 + 19 + 22 = 80$

22. $\displaystyle\sum_{i=3}^{6} i(i+2) = 3\cdot 5 + 4\cdot 6 + 5\cdot 7 + 6\cdot 8 = 15 + 24 + 35 + 48 = 122$

23. $\displaystyle\sum_{j=1}^{6} 3^{j+1} = 3^2 + 3^3 + 3^4 + 3^5 + 3^6 + 3^7 = 9 + 27 + 81 + 243 + 729 + 2187 = 3276$

(For a more general method, see Exercise 47.)

24. $\displaystyle\sum_{k=0}^{8} \cos k\pi = \cos 0 + \cos \pi + \cos 2\pi + \cos 3\pi + \cos 4\pi + \cos 5\pi + \cos 6\pi + \cos 7\pi + \cos 8\pi$
$$= 1 - 1 + 1 - 1 + 1 - 1 + 1 - 1 + 1 = 1$$

25. $\displaystyle\sum_{n=1}^{20} (-1)^n = -1 + 1 - 1 + 1 - 1 + 1 - 1 + 1 - 1 + 1 - 1 + 1 - 1 + 1 - 1 + 1 - 1 + 1 - 1 + 1 = 0$

26. $\displaystyle\sum_{i=1}^{100} 4 = \underbrace{4+4+4+\cdots+4}_{(100 \text{ summands})} = 100 \cdot 4 = 400$

27. $\displaystyle\sum_{i=0}^{4}\left(2^i + i^2\right) = (1+0)+(2+1)+(4+4)+(8+9)+(16+16) = 61$

28. $\displaystyle\sum_{i=-2}^{4} 2^{3-i} = 2^5 + 2^4 + 2^3 + 2^2 + 2^1 + 2^0 + 2^{-1} = 63.5$

29. $\displaystyle\sum_{i=1}^{n} 2i = 2\sum_{i=1}^{n} i = 2 \cdot \frac{n(n+1)}{2}$ [by Theorem 3(c)] $= n(n+1)$

30. $\displaystyle\sum_{i=1}^{n}(2-5i) = \sum_{i=1}^{n} 2 - \sum_{i=1}^{n} 5i = 2n - 5\sum_{i=1}^{n} i = 2n - \frac{5n(n+1)}{2} = \frac{4n}{2} - \frac{5n^2 + 5n}{2} = -\frac{n(5n+1)}{2}$

31. $\displaystyle\sum_{i=1}^{n}\left(i^2 + 3i + 4\right) = \sum_{i=1}^{n} i^2 + 3\sum_{i=1}^{n} i + \sum_{i=1}^{n} 4 = \frac{n(n+1)(2n+1)}{6} + \frac{3n(n+1)}{2} + 4n$

$\qquad = \frac{1}{6}\left[\left(2n^3 + 3n^2 + n\right) + \left(9n^2 + 9n\right) + 24n\right] = \frac{1}{6}\left(2n^3 + 12n^2 + 34n\right)$

$\qquad = \frac{1}{3}n\left(n^2 + 6n + 17\right)$

32. $\displaystyle\sum_{i=1}^{n}(3 + 2i)^2 = \sum_{i=1}^{n}\left(9 + 12i + 4i^2\right) = \sum_{i=1}^{n} 9 + 12\sum_{i=1}^{n} i + 4\sum_{i=1}^{n} i^2$

$\qquad = 9n + 6n(n+1) + \frac{2n(n+1)(2n+1)}{3} = \frac{27n + 18n^2 + 18n + 4n^3 + 6n^2 + 2n}{3}$

$\qquad = \frac{1}{3}\left(4n^3 + 24n^2 + 47n\right) = \frac{1}{3}n\left(4n^2 + 24n + 47\right)$

33. $\displaystyle\sum_{i=1}^{n}(i+1)(i+2) = \sum_{i=1}^{n}\left(i^2 + 3i + 2\right) = \sum_{i=1}^{n} i^2 + 3\sum_{i=1}^{n} i + \sum_{i=1}^{n} 2$

$\qquad = \frac{n(n+1)(2n+1)}{6} + \frac{3n(n+1)}{2} + 2n = \frac{n(n+1)}{6}\left[(2n+1)+9\right] + 2n$

$\qquad = \frac{n(n+1)}{3}(n+5) + 2n = \frac{n}{3}\left[(n+1)(n+5)+6\right] = \frac{n}{3}\left(n^2 + 6n + 11\right)$

34. $\displaystyle\sum_{i=1}^{n} i(i+1)(i+2) = \sum_{i=1}^{n}\left(i^3 + 3i^2 + 2i\right) = \sum_{i=1}^{n} i^3 + 3\sum_{i=1}^{n} i^2 + 2\sum_{i=1}^{n} i$

$\qquad = \left[\frac{n(n+1)}{2}\right]^2 + \frac{3n(n+1)(2n+1)}{6} + \frac{2n(n+1)}{2}$

$\qquad = n(n+1)\left[\frac{n(n+1)}{4} + \frac{2n+1}{2} + 1\right] = \frac{n(n+1)}{4}\left(n^2 + n + 4n + 2 + 4\right)$

$\qquad = \frac{n(n+1)}{4}\left(n^2 + 5n + 6\right) = \frac{n(n+1)(n+2)(n+3)}{4}$

35. $\displaystyle\sum_{i=1}^{n}\left(i^3 - i - 2\right) = \sum_{i=1}^{n} i^3 - \sum_{i=1}^{n} i - \sum_{i=1}^{n} 2 = \left[\frac{n(n+1)}{2}\right]^2 - \frac{n(n+1)}{2} - 2n$

$\qquad = \frac{1}{4}n(n+1)\left[n(n+1) - 2\right] - 2n = \frac{1}{4}n(n+1)(n+2)((n-1)) - 2n$

$\qquad = \frac{1}{4}n\left[(n+1)((n-1)(n+2)) - 8\right] = \frac{1}{4}n\left[\left(n^2 - 1\right)(n+2) - 8\right] = \frac{1}{4}n\left(n^3 + 2n^2 - n - 10\right)$

36. By Theorem 3(c) we have that $\sum\limits_{i=1}^{n} i = \dfrac{n(n+1)}{2} = 78 \iff n(n+1) = 156 \iff n^2 + n - 156 = 0 \iff$

$(n+13)(n-12) = 0 \iff n = 12$ or -13. But $n = -13$ produces a negative answer for the sum, so $n = 12$.

37. By Theorem 2(a) and Example 3, $\sum\limits_{i=1}^{n} c = c \sum\limits_{i=1}^{n} 1 = cn.$

38. Let S_n be the statement that $\sum\limits_{i=1}^{n} i^3 = \left[\dfrac{n(n+1)}{2}\right]^2$.

1. S_1 is true because $1^3 = \left(\dfrac{1 \cdot 2}{2}\right)^2$.

2. Assume S_k is true. Then $\sum\limits_{i=1}^{k} i^3 = \left[\dfrac{k(k+1)}{2}\right]^2$, so

$$\sum_{i=1}^{k+1} i^3 = \left[\frac{k(k+1)}{2}\right]^2 + (k+1)^3 = \frac{(k+1)^2}{4}\left[k^2 + 4(k+1)\right] = \frac{(k+1)^2}{4}(k+2)^2$$

$$= \left(\frac{(k+1)\left[(k+1)+1\right]}{2}\right)^2$$

showing that S_{k+1} is true.

Therefore, S_n is true for all n by mathematical induction.

39. $\sum\limits_{i=1}^{n} \left[(i+1)^4 - i^4\right] = (2^4 - 1^4) + (3^4 - 2^4) + (4^4 - 3^4) + \cdots + \left[(n+1)^4 - n^4\right]$

$$= (n+1)^4 - 1^4 = n^4 + 4n^3 + 6n^2 + 4n$$

On the other hand,

$$\sum_{i=1}^{n} \left[(i+1)^4 - i^4\right] = \sum_{i=1}^{n} (4i^3 + 6i^2 + 4i + 1) = 4\sum_{i=1}^{n} i^3 + 6\sum_{i=1}^{n} i^2 + 4\sum_{i=1}^{n} i + \sum_{i=1}^{n} 1$$

$$= 4S + n(n+1)(2n+1) + 2n(n+1) + n \quad \left[\text{where } S = \sum_{i=1}^{n} i^3\right]$$

$$= 4S + 2n^3 + 3n^2 + n + 2n^2 + 2n + n = 4S + 2n^3 + 5n^2 + 4n$$

Thus, $n^4 + 4n^3 + 6n^2 + 4n = 4S + 2n^3 + 5n^2 + 4n$, from which it follows that

$4S = n^4 + 2n^3 + n^2 = n^2(n^2 + 2n + 1) = n^2(n+1)^2$ and $S = \left[\dfrac{n(n+1)}{2}\right]^2$.

40. The area of G_i is

$$\left(\sum_{k=1}^{i} k\right)^2 - \left(\sum_{k=1}^{i-1} k\right)^2 = \left[\frac{i(i+1)}{2}\right]^2 - \left[\frac{(i-1)i}{2}\right]^2 = \frac{i^2}{4}\left[(i+1)^2 - (i-1)^2\right]$$

$$= \frac{i^2}{4}\left[(i^2 + 2i + 1) - (i^2 - 2i + 1)\right] = \frac{i^2}{4}(4i) = i^3$$

Thus, the area of $ABCD$ is $\sum\limits_{i=1}^{n} i^3 = \left[\dfrac{n(n+1)}{2}\right]^2$.

41. (a) $\sum\limits_{i=1}^{n} \left[i^4 - (i-1)^4\right] = (1^4 - 0^4) + (2^4 - 1^4) + (3^4 - 2^4) + \cdots + \left[n^4 - (n-1)^4\right] = n^4 - 0 = n^4$

(b) $\displaystyle\sum_{i=1}^{100}\left(5^i - 5^{i-1}\right) = (5^1 - 5^0) + (5^2 - 5^1) + (5^3 - 5^2) + \cdots + \left(5^{100} - 5^{99}\right) = 5^{100} - 5^0 = 5^{100} - 1$

(c) $\displaystyle\sum_{i=3}^{99}\left(\frac{1}{i} - \frac{1}{i+1}\right) = \left(\frac{1}{3} - \frac{1}{4}\right) + \left(\frac{1}{4} - \frac{1}{5}\right) + \left(\frac{1}{5} - \frac{1}{6}\right) + \cdots + \left(\frac{1}{99} - \frac{1}{100}\right) = \frac{1}{3} - \frac{1}{100} = \frac{97}{300}$

(d) $\displaystyle\sum_{i=1}^{n}(a_i - a_{i-1}) = (a_1 - a_0) + (a_2 - a_1) + (a_3 - a_2) + \cdots + (a_n - a_{n-1}) = a_n - a_0$

42. Summing the inequalities $-|a_i| \le a_i \le |a_i|$ for $i = 1, 2, \ldots, n$, we get $-\displaystyle\sum_{i=1}^{n}|a_i| \le \sum_{i=1}^{n} a_i \le \sum_{i=1}^{n}|a_i|$. Since

$|x| \le c \iff -c \le x \le c$, we have $\left|\displaystyle\sum_{i=1}^{n} a_i\right| \le \sum_{i=1}^{n}|a_i|$. *Another method:* Use mathematical induction.

43. $\displaystyle\lim_{n\to\infty}\sum_{i=1}^{n}\frac{1}{n}\left(\frac{i}{n}\right)^2 = \lim_{n\to\infty}\frac{1}{n^3}\sum_{i=1}^{n}i^2 = \lim_{n\to\infty}\frac{1}{n^3}\frac{n(n+1)(2n+1)}{6} = \lim_{n\to\infty}\frac{1}{6}\left(1+\frac{1}{n}\right)\left(2+\frac{1}{n}\right)$

$\qquad = \frac{1}{6}(1)(2) = \frac{1}{3}$

44. $\displaystyle\lim_{n\to\infty}\sum_{i=1}^{n}\frac{1}{n}\left[\left(\frac{i}{n}\right)^3 + 1\right] = \lim_{n\to\infty}\sum_{i=1}^{n}\left[\frac{i^3}{n^4} + \frac{1}{n}\right] = \lim_{n\to\infty}\left[\frac{1}{n^4}\sum_{i=1}^{n}i^3 + \frac{1}{n}\sum_{i=1}^{n}1\right]$

$\qquad = \displaystyle\lim_{n\to\infty}\left[\frac{1}{n^4}\left(\frac{n(n+1)}{2}\right)^2 + \frac{1}{n}(n)\right] = \lim_{n\to\infty}\frac{1}{4}\left(1+\frac{1}{n}\right)^2 + 1 = \frac{1}{4} + 1 = \frac{5}{4}$

45. $\displaystyle\lim_{n\to\infty}\sum_{i=1}^{n}\frac{2}{n}\left[\left(\frac{2i}{n}\right)^3 + 5\left(\frac{2i}{n}\right)\right] = \lim_{n\to\infty}\sum_{i=1}^{n}\left[\frac{16}{n^4}i^3 + \frac{20}{n^2}i\right] = \lim_{n\to\infty}\left[\frac{16}{n^4}\sum_{i=1}^{n}i^3 + \frac{20}{n^2}\sum_{i=1}^{n}i\right]$

$\qquad = \displaystyle\lim_{n\to\infty}\left[\frac{16}{n^4}\frac{n^2(n+1)^2}{4} + \frac{20}{n^2}\frac{n(n+1)}{2}\right] = \lim_{n\to\infty}\left[\frac{4(n+1)^2}{n^2} + \frac{10n(n+1)}{n^2}\right]$

$\qquad = \displaystyle\lim_{n\to\infty}\left[4\left(1+\frac{1}{n}\right)^2 + 10\left(1+\frac{1}{n}\right)\right] = 4\cdot 1 + 10\cdot 1 = 14$

46. $\displaystyle\lim_{n\to\infty}\sum_{i=1}^{n}\frac{3}{n}\left[\left(1+\frac{3i}{n}\right)^3 - 2\left(1+\frac{3i}{n}\right)\right] = \lim_{n\to\infty}\sum_{i=1}^{n}\frac{3}{n}\left[1 + \frac{9i}{n} + \frac{27i^2}{n^2} + \frac{27i^3}{n^3} - 2 - \frac{6i}{n}\right]$

$\qquad = \displaystyle\lim_{n\to\infty}\sum_{i=1}^{n}\left[\frac{81}{n^4}i^3 + \frac{81}{n^3}i^2 + \frac{9}{n^2}i - \frac{3}{n}\right]$

$\qquad = \displaystyle\lim_{n\to\infty}\left[\frac{81}{n^4}\frac{n^2(n+1)^2}{4} + \frac{81}{n^3}\frac{n(n+1)(2n+1)}{6} + \frac{9}{n^2}\frac{n(n+1)}{2} - \frac{3}{n}n\right]$

$\qquad = \displaystyle\lim_{n\to\infty}\left[\frac{81}{4}\left(1+\frac{1}{n}\right)^2 + \frac{27}{2}\left(1+\frac{1}{n}\right)\left(2+\frac{1}{n}\right) + \frac{9}{2}\left(1+\frac{1}{n}\right) - 3\right] = \frac{81}{4} + \frac{54}{2} + \frac{9}{2} - 3 = \frac{195}{4}$

47. Let $S = \displaystyle\sum_{i=1}^{n} ar^{i-1} = a + ar + ar^2 + \cdots + ar^{n-1}$. Multiplying both sides by r gives us

$rS = ar + ar^2 + \cdots + ar^{n-1} + ar^n$. Subtracting the first equation from the second, we find

$(r-1)S = ar^n - a = a(r^n - 1)$, so $S = \dfrac{a(r^n - 1)}{r - 1}$ (since $r \ne 1$).

48. $\displaystyle\sum_{i=1}^{n} \frac{3}{2^{i-1}} = 3\sum_{i=1}^{n}\left(\frac{1}{2}\right)^{i-1} = \frac{3\left[\left(\frac{1}{2}\right)^n - 1\right]}{\frac{1}{2} - 1}$ [using Exercise 47 with $a = 3$ and $r = \frac{1}{2}$] $= 6\left[1 - \left(\frac{1}{2}\right)^n\right]$

49. $\displaystyle\sum_{i=1}^{n}\left(2i + 2^i\right) = 2\sum_{i=1}^{n} i + \sum_{i=1}^{n} 2 \cdot 2^{i-1} = 2\frac{n(n+1)}{2} + \frac{2(2^n - 1)}{2-1} = 2^{n+1} + n^2 + n - 2.$

For the first sum we have used Theorem 3(c), and for the second, Exercise 47 with $a = r = 2$.

50. $\displaystyle\sum_{i=1}^{m}\left[\sum_{j=1}^{n}(i+j)\right] = \sum_{i=1}^{m}\left[\sum_{j=1}^{n} i + \sum_{j=1}^{n} j\right]$ [Theorem 2(b)] $= \sum_{i=1}^{m}\left[ni + \frac{n(n+1)}{2}\right]$ [Theorem 3(b) and (c)]

$$= \sum_{i=1}^{m} ni + \sum_{i=1}^{m} \frac{n(n+1)}{2} = \frac{nm(m+1)}{2} + \frac{nm(n+1)}{2} = \frac{nm}{2}(m+n+2)$$

 G **Integration of Rational Functions by Partial Fractions** · · ·

1. $\dfrac{5}{2x^2 - 3x - 2} = \dfrac{5}{(2x+1)(x-2)} = \dfrac{A}{2x+1} + \dfrac{B}{x-2}$

2. $\dfrac{z^2 - 4z}{(3z+5)^3(z+2)} = \dfrac{A}{3z+5} + \dfrac{B}{(3z+5)^2} + \dfrac{C}{(3z+5)^3} + \dfrac{D}{z+2}$

3. $\dfrac{1}{x^4 - x^3} = \dfrac{1}{x^3(x-1)} = \dfrac{A}{x} + \dfrac{B}{x^2} + \dfrac{C}{x^3} + \dfrac{D}{x-1}$

4. $\dfrac{x^4 + x^3 - x^2 - x + 1}{x^3 - x} = x + 1 + \dfrac{1}{x(x+1)(x-1)} = x + 1 + \dfrac{A}{x} + \dfrac{B}{x+1} + \dfrac{C}{x-1}$

5. Since the degree of the numerator is greater than or equal to the degree of the denominator, we first perform long

division. $\dfrac{x^2 + 1}{x^2 - 1} = 1 + \dfrac{2}{x^2 - 1} = 1 + \dfrac{2}{(x-1)(x+1)} = 1 + \dfrac{A}{x-1} + \dfrac{B}{x+1}$

6. $\dfrac{x^3 - 4x^2 + 2}{(x^2+1)(x^2+2)} = \dfrac{Ax+B}{x^2+1} + \dfrac{Cx+D}{x^2+2}$

7. $\dfrac{x^2 - 2}{x(x^2+2)} = \dfrac{A}{x} + \dfrac{Bx+C}{x^2+2}$

8. $\dfrac{x^4 + x^2 + 1}{(x^2+1)(x^2+4)^2} = \dfrac{Ax+B}{x^2+1} + \dfrac{Cx+D}{x^2+4} + \dfrac{Ex+F}{(x^2+4)^2}$

9. $\dfrac{x^3 + x^2 + 1}{x^4 + x^3 + 2x^2} = \dfrac{x^3 + x^2 + 1}{x^2(x^2 + x + 2)} = \dfrac{A}{x} + \dfrac{B}{x^2} + \dfrac{Cx+D}{x^2 + x + 2}$

10. $\dfrac{1}{x^6 - x^3} = \dfrac{1}{x^3(x^3 - 1)} = \dfrac{1}{x^3(x-1)(x^2 + x + 1)} = \dfrac{A}{x} + \dfrac{B}{x^2} + \dfrac{C}{x^3} + \dfrac{D}{x-1} + \dfrac{Ex+F}{x^2 + x + 1}$

11. $\displaystyle\int \frac{x^2 + 2}{x + 2}\,dx = \int\left(x - 2 + \frac{6}{x+2}\right)dx$ [division] $= \frac{1}{2}x^2 - 2x + 6\ln|x+2| + C$

12. $\displaystyle\int \frac{x}{x-5}\,dx = \int \frac{(x-5)+5}{x-5}\,dx = \int\left(1 + \frac{5}{x-5}\right)dx = x + 5\ln|x-5| + C$

13. $\dfrac{4x-1}{(x-1)(x+2)} = \dfrac{A}{x-1} + \dfrac{B}{x+2} \quad\Rightarrow\quad 4x-1 = A(x+2) + B(x-1).$ Take $x = 1$ to get $3 = 3A$, then $x = -2$ to get $-9 = -3B \quad\Rightarrow\quad A = 1, B = 3.$ Now

$$\int_2^4 \frac{4x-1}{(x-1)(x+2)}\,dx = \int_2^4 \left(\frac{1}{x-1} + \frac{3}{x+2}\right)\,dx = \left[\ln(x-1) + 3\ln(x+2)\right]_2^4$$

$$= \ln 3 + 3\ln 6 - \ln 1 - 3\ln 4 = \ln\left(3\cdot 6^3\right) - \ln 4^3 = \ln \tfrac{81}{8}.$$

14. $\dfrac{1}{(t+4)(t-1)} = \dfrac{A}{t+4} + \dfrac{B}{t-1} \quad\Rightarrow\quad 1 = A(t-1) + B(t+4).\ t = 1 \ \Rightarrow\ 1 = 5B \ \Rightarrow\ B = \tfrac{1}{5}.$ $t = -4 \ \Rightarrow\ 1 = -5A \ \Rightarrow\ A = -\tfrac{1}{5}.$ Thus,

$$\int \frac{1}{(t+4)(t-1)}\,dt = \int \left(\frac{-1/5}{t+4} + \frac{1/5}{t-1}\right)\,dt = -\tfrac{1}{5}\ln|t+4| + \tfrac{1}{5}\ln|t-1| + C \text{ or } \frac{1}{5}\ln\left|\frac{t-1}{t+4}\right| + C$$

15. $\dfrac{2x+3}{(x+1)^2} = \dfrac{A}{x+1} + \dfrac{B}{(x+1)^2} \quad\Rightarrow\quad 2x+3 = A(x+1) + B.$ Take $x = -1$ to get $B = 1$, and equate coefficients of x to get $A = 2$. Now

$$\int_0^1 \frac{2x+3}{(x+1)^2}\,dx = \int_0^1 \left[\frac{2}{x+1} + \frac{1}{(x+1)^2}\right]\,dx = \left[2\ln(x+1) - \frac{1}{x+1}\right]_0^1$$

$$= 2\ln 2 - \tfrac{1}{2} - (2\ln 1 - 1) = 2\ln 2 + \tfrac{1}{2}$$

16. $\dfrac{x^3 + x^2 - 12x + 1}{x^2 + x - 12} = x + \dfrac{1}{x^2 + x - 12} = x + \dfrac{1}{(x-3)(x+4)} = x + \dfrac{1}{7}\left(\dfrac{1}{x-3} - \dfrac{1}{x+4}\right).$

So $\displaystyle\int_0^2 \frac{x^3 + x^2 - 12x + 1}{x^2 + x - 12}\,dx = \left[\frac{1}{2}x^2 + \frac{1}{7}\left(\ln|x-3| - \ln|x+4|\right)\right]_0^2 = 2 + \tfrac{1}{7}\ln\tfrac{2}{9}.$

17. $\dfrac{4y^2 - 7y - 12}{y(y+2)(y-3)} = \dfrac{A}{y} + \dfrac{B}{y+2} + \dfrac{C}{y-3} \quad\Rightarrow\quad 4y^2 - 7y - 12 = A(y+2)(y-3) + By(y-3) + Cy(y+2).$ Setting $y = 0$ gives $-12 = -6A$, so $A = 2$. Setting $y = -2$ gives $18 = 10B$, so $B = \tfrac{9}{5}$. Setting $y = 3$ gives $3 = 15C$, so $C = \tfrac{1}{5}$. Now

$$\int_1^2 \frac{4y^2 - 7y - 12}{y(y+2)(y-3)}\,dy = \int_1^2 \left(\frac{2}{y} + \frac{9/5}{y+2} + \frac{1/5}{y-3}\right)\,dy = \left[2\ln|y| + \tfrac{9}{5}\ln|y+2| + \tfrac{1}{5}\ln|y-3|\right]_1^2$$

$$= 2\ln 2 + \tfrac{9}{5}\ln 4 + \tfrac{1}{5}\ln 1 - 2\ln 1 - \tfrac{9}{5}\ln 3 - \tfrac{1}{5}\ln 2$$

$$= 2\ln 2 + \tfrac{18}{5}\ln 2 - \tfrac{1}{5}\ln 2 - \tfrac{9}{5}\ln 3 = \tfrac{27}{5}\ln 2 - \tfrac{9}{5}\ln 3 = \tfrac{9}{5}(3\ln 2 - \ln 3) = \tfrac{9}{5}\ln\tfrac{8}{3}$$

18. $\dfrac{1}{x^3 + x^2 - 2x} = \dfrac{1}{x(x+2)(x-1)} = \dfrac{A}{x} + \dfrac{B}{x+2} + \dfrac{C}{x-1} \quad\Rightarrow$
$1 = A(x+2)(x-1) + Bx(x-1) + Cx(x+2).$ Setting $x = 0$ gives $1 = -2A$, so $A = -\tfrac{1}{2}$. Setting $x = -2$ gives $1 = 6B$, so $B = \tfrac{1}{6}$. Setting $x = 1$ gives $1 = 3C$, so $C = \tfrac{1}{3}$. Now

$$\int_2^3 \frac{1}{x^3 + x^2 - 2x}\,dx = \int_2^3 \left(\frac{-1/2}{x} + \frac{1/6}{x+2} + \frac{1/3}{x-1}\right)\,dx = \left[-\tfrac{1}{2}\ln|x| + \tfrac{1}{6}\ln|x+2| + \tfrac{1}{3}\ln|x-1|\right]_2^3$$

$$= -\tfrac{1}{2}\ln 3 + \tfrac{1}{6}\ln 5 + \tfrac{1}{3}\ln 2 + \tfrac{1}{2}\ln 2 - \tfrac{1}{6}\ln 4 - \tfrac{1}{3}\ln 1 = \tfrac{1}{2}\ln 2 - \tfrac{1}{2}\ln 3 + \tfrac{1}{6}\ln 5$$

19. $\dfrac{1}{(x+5)^2(x-1)} = \dfrac{A}{x+5} + \dfrac{B}{(x+5)^2} + \dfrac{C}{x-1}$ $\Rightarrow$ $1 = A(x+5)(x-1) + B(x-1) + C(x+5)^2$. Setting

$x = -5$ gives $1 = -6B$, so $B = -\frac{1}{6}$. Setting $x = 1$ gives $1 = 36C$, so $C = \frac{1}{36}$. Setting $x = -2$ gives

$1 = A(3)(-3) + B(-3) + C(3^2) = -9A - 3B + 9C = -9A + \frac{1}{2} + \frac{1}{4} = -9A + \frac{3}{4}$, so $9A = -\frac{1}{4}$ and

$A = -\frac{1}{36}$. Now

$$\int \frac{1}{(x+5)^2(x-1)}\, dx = \int \left[\frac{-1/36}{x+5} - \frac{1/6}{(x+5)^2} + \frac{1/36}{x-1} \right] dx$$

$$= -\tfrac{1}{36}\ln|x+5| + \frac{1}{6(x+5)} + \tfrac{1}{36}\ln|x-1| + C$$

20. $\dfrac{x^2}{(x-3)(x+2)^2} = \dfrac{A}{x-3} + \dfrac{B}{x+2} + \dfrac{C}{(x+2)^2}$ $\Rightarrow$ $x^2 = A(x+2)^2 + B(x-3)(x+2) + C(x-3)$. Setting

$x = 3$ gives $A = \frac{9}{25}$. Take $x = -2$ to get $C = -\frac{4}{5}$, and equate the coefficients of x^2 to get $1 = A + B$ $\Rightarrow$

$B = \frac{16}{25}$. Then

$$\int \frac{x^2}{(x-3)(x+2)^2}\, dx = \int \left[\frac{9/25}{x-3} + \frac{16/25}{x+2} - \frac{4/5}{(x+2)^2} \right] dx$$

$$= \tfrac{9}{25}\ln|x-3| + \tfrac{16}{25}\ln|x+2| + \frac{4}{5(x+2)} + C$$

21. Complete the square: $x^2 + x + 1 = \left(x + \tfrac{1}{2}\right)^2 + \tfrac{3}{4}$ and let $u = x + \tfrac{1}{2}$. Then

$$\int_0^1 \frac{x}{x^2+x+1}\, dx = \int_{1/2}^{3/2} \frac{u - 1/2}{u^2 + 3/4}\, du = \int_{1/2}^{3/2} \frac{u}{u^2+3/4}\, du - \frac{1}{2}\int_{1/2}^{3/2} \frac{1}{u^2+3/4}\, du$$

$$= \left[\tfrac{1}{2}\ln\left(u^2 + \tfrac{3}{4}\right) - \tfrac{1}{2}\tfrac{1}{\sqrt{3}/2}\tan^{-1}\left(\tfrac{2}{\sqrt{3}}u\right) \right]_{1/2}^{3/2}$$

$$= \tfrac{1}{2}\ln 3 - \tfrac{1}{\sqrt{3}}\left(\tfrac{\pi}{3} - \tfrac{\pi}{6}\right) = \ln\sqrt{3} - \tfrac{\pi}{6\sqrt{3}}.$$

22. $\displaystyle\int_0^1 \frac{x-1}{x^2+2x+2}\, dx = \int_0^1 \frac{x+1}{x^2+2x+2}\, dx - \int_0^1 \frac{2}{x^2+2x+2}\, dx$

$$= \left[\tfrac{1}{2}\ln\left(x^2 + 2x + 2\right) \right]_0^1 - 2\int_0^1 \frac{dx}{(x+1)^2 + 1} \qquad \begin{bmatrix} \text{set } u = x^2 + 2x + 2, \\ du = 2(x+1)dx \text{ in} \\ \text{the first integral} \end{bmatrix}$$

$$= \tfrac{1}{2}(\ln 5 - \ln 2) - 2\left[\tan^{-1}(x+1) \right]_0^1 = \tfrac{1}{2}\ln\tfrac{5}{2} - 2\tan^{-1}2 + \tfrac{\pi}{2}.$$

Or: Complete the square and let $u = x + 1$.

23. $\dfrac{3x^2 - 4x + 5}{(x-1)(x^2+1)} = \dfrac{A}{x-1} + \dfrac{Bx+C}{x^2+1}$ $\Rightarrow$ $3x^2 - 4x + 5 = A(x^2+1) + (Bx+C)(x-1)$. Take $x = 1$ to

get $4 = 2A$ or $A = 2$. Now $(Bx+C)(x-1) = 3x^2 - 4x + 5 - 2(x^2+1) = x^2 - 4x + 3$. Equating coefficients

of x^2 and then comparing the constant terms, we get $B = 1$ and $C = -3$. Hence,

$$\int \frac{3x^2 - 4x + 5}{(x-1)(x^2+1)}\, dx = \int \left[\frac{2}{x-1} + \frac{x-3}{x^2+1} \right] dx = 2\ln|x-1| + \int \frac{x\,dx}{x^2+1} - 3\int \frac{dx}{x^2+1}$$

$$= 2\ln|x-1| + \tfrac{1}{2}\ln\left(x^2+1\right) - 3\tan^{-1}x + C$$

$$= \ln(x-1)^2 + \ln\sqrt{x^2+1} - 3\tan^{-1}x + C$$

24. $\dfrac{x^2+3}{x^3+2x} = \dfrac{x^2+3}{x(x^2+2)} = \dfrac{A}{x} + \dfrac{Bx+C}{x^2+2}$ $\Rightarrow$ $x^2+3 = A(x^2+2) + (Bx+C)x = (A+B)x^2 + Cx + 2A$

$\Rightarrow$ $A+B=1, C=0,$ and $2A=3$ $\Rightarrow$ $A = \frac{3}{2}, B = -\frac{1}{2},$ and $C=0.$ Now

$$\int_1^2 \frac{x^2+3}{x^3+2x}\,dx = \int_1^2 \left(\frac{3/2}{x} - \frac{x/2}{x^2+2} \right) dx = \left[\tfrac{3}{2}\ln x - \tfrac{1}{4}\ln(x^2+2) \right]_1^2 = \tfrac{3}{2}\ln 2 - \tfrac{1}{4}\ln 6 - \tfrac{3}{2}\ln 1 + \tfrac{1}{4}\ln 3$$

$$= \tfrac{3}{2}\ln 2 - \tfrac{1}{4}\ln 2 - \tfrac{1}{4}\ln 3 - 0 + \tfrac{1}{4}\ln 3 = \left(\tfrac{3}{2} - \tfrac{1}{4}\right)\ln 2 = \tfrac{5}{4}\ln 2$$

25. $\dfrac{1}{x^3-1} = \dfrac{1}{(x-1)(x^2+x+1)} = \dfrac{A}{x-1} + \dfrac{Bx+C}{x^2+x+1}$ $\Rightarrow$ $1 = A(x^2+x+1) + (Bx+C)(x-1).$ Take

$x=1$ to get $A = \frac{1}{3}.$ Equating coefficients of x^2 and then comparing the constant terms, we get $0 = \frac{1}{3} + B,$

$1 = \frac{1}{3} - C,$ so $B = -\frac{1}{3}, C = -\frac{2}{3}$ $\Rightarrow$

$$\int \frac{1}{x^3-1}\,dx = \int \frac{\frac{1}{3}}{x-1}\,dx + \int \frac{-\frac{1}{3}x - \frac{2}{3}}{x^2+x+1}\,dx = \tfrac{1}{3}\ln|x-1| - \frac{1}{3}\int \frac{x+2}{x^2+x+1}\,dx$$

$$= \tfrac{1}{3}\ln|x-1| - \frac{1}{3}\int \frac{x+1/2}{x^2+x+1}\,dx - \frac{1}{3}\int \frac{(3/2)\,dx}{(x+1/2)^2 + 3/4}$$

$$= \tfrac{1}{3}\ln|x-1| - \tfrac{1}{6}\ln(x^2+x+1) - \tfrac{1}{2}\left(\tfrac{2}{\sqrt{3}}\right)\tan^{-1}\left(\frac{x+\frac{1}{2}}{\sqrt{3}/2}\right) + K$$

$$= \tfrac{1}{3}\ln|x-1| - \tfrac{1}{6}\ln(x^2+x+1) - \tfrac{1}{\sqrt{3}}\tan^{-1}\left(\tfrac{1}{\sqrt{3}}(2x+1)\right) + K$$

26. $\dfrac{x^4}{x^4-1} = 1 + \dfrac{1}{x^4-1}$ and $\dfrac{1}{x^4-1} = \dfrac{1}{(x-1)(x+1)(x^2+1)} = \dfrac{A}{x-1} + \dfrac{B}{x+1} + \dfrac{Cx+D}{x^2+1}$ $\Rightarrow$

$1 = A(x+1)(x^2+1) + B(x-1)(x^2+1) + (Cx+D)(x-1)(x+1).$ Set

$x=1$ to get $A = \frac{1}{4},$ and set $x=-1$ to get $B = -\frac{1}{4}.$ Now take $x=0$ to get

$1 = A - B - D = -D + \frac{1}{2},$ so that $D = -\frac{1}{2}.$ Finally, equate the coefficients of x^3 to get $C=0.$ Now

$$\int \frac{x^4}{x^4-1}\,dx = \int \left[1 + \frac{1/4}{x-1} - \frac{1/4}{x+1} - \frac{1/2}{x^2+1} \right] dx = x + \tfrac{1}{4}\ln\left|\frac{x-1}{x+1}\right| - \tfrac{1}{2}\tan^{-1}x + C.$$

27. $\dfrac{2t^3 - t^2 + 3t - 1}{(t^2+1)(t^2+2)} = \dfrac{At+B}{t^2+1} + \dfrac{Ct+D}{t^2+2}$ $\Rightarrow$

$$2t^3 - t^2 + 3t - 1 = (At+B)(t^2+2) + (Ct+D)(t^2+1)$$

$$= (A+C)t^3 + (B+D)t^2 + (2A+C)t + (2B+D) \quad\Rightarrow$$

$A+C=2, B+D=-1, 2A+C=3,$ and $2B+D=-1$ $\Rightarrow$ $A=1, C=1, B=0,$ and $D=-1.$ Now

$$\int \frac{2t^3 - t^2 + 3t - 1}{(t^2+1)(t^2+2)}\,dt = \int \left(\frac{t}{t^2+1} + \frac{t-1}{t^2+2} \right) dt = \frac{1}{2}\int \frac{2t\,dt}{t^2+1} + \frac{1}{2}\int \frac{2t\,dt}{t^2+2} - \int \frac{dt}{t^2+2}$$

$$= \tfrac{1}{2}\ln(t^2+1) + \tfrac{1}{2}\ln(t^2+2) - \tfrac{1}{\sqrt{2}}\tan^{-1}\left(\tfrac{1}{\sqrt{2}}t\right) + C$$

$$\text{or } \tfrac{1}{2}\ln\big((t^2+1)(t^2+2)\big) - \tfrac{\sqrt{2}}{2}\tan^{-1}\left(\tfrac{1}{\sqrt{2}}t\right) + C$$

28. $\dfrac{x^4+1}{x(x^2+1)^2} = \dfrac{A}{x} + \dfrac{Bx+C}{x^2+1} + \dfrac{Dx+E}{(x^2+1)^2}$ ⇒ $x^4+1 = A(x^2+1)^2 + (Bx+C)x(x^2+1) + (Dx+E)x$.

Setting $x=0$ gives $A=1$, and equating the coefficients of x^4 gives $1 = A+B$, so $B=0$. Now

$\dfrac{C}{x^2+1} + \dfrac{Dx+E}{(x^2+1)^2} = \dfrac{x^4+1}{x(x^2+1)^2} - \dfrac{1}{x} = \dfrac{1}{x}\left[\dfrac{x^4+1-(x^4+2x^2+1)}{(x^2+1)^2}\right] = \dfrac{-2x}{(x^2+1)^2}$, so we can take

$C=0$, $D=-2$, and $E=0$. Hence, $\displaystyle\int \dfrac{x^4+1}{x(x^2+1)^2}\,dx = \int\left[\dfrac{1}{x} - \dfrac{2x}{(x^2+1)^2}\right]dx = \ln|x| + \dfrac{1}{x^2+1} + C.$

29.

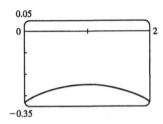

From the graph, we see that the integral will be negative, and we guess
that the area is about the same as that of a rectangle with width 2 and
height 0.3, so we estimate the integral to be $-(2\cdot 0.3) = -0.6$. Now

$\dfrac{1}{x^2-2x-3} = \dfrac{1}{(x-3)(x+1)} = \dfrac{A}{x-3} + \dfrac{B}{x+1}$ ⇔

$1 = (A+B)x + A - 3B$, so $A=-B$ and $A-3B=1$ ⇔ $A=\frac{1}{4}$

and $B=-\frac{1}{4}$, so the integral becomes

$$\int_0^2 \dfrac{dx}{x^2-2x-3} = \dfrac{1}{4}\int_0^2\dfrac{dx}{x-3} - \dfrac{1}{4}\int_0^2\dfrac{dx}{x+1} = \tfrac{1}{4}\left[\ln|x-3| - \ln|x+1|\right]_0^2$$

$$= \dfrac{1}{4}\left[\ln\left|\dfrac{x-3}{x+1}\right|\right]_0^2 = \tfrac{1}{4}\left(\ln\tfrac{1}{3} - \ln 3\right) = -\tfrac{1}{2}\ln 3 \approx -0.55$$

30. $\dfrac{1}{x^3-2x^2} = \dfrac{1}{x^2(x-2)} = \dfrac{A}{x} + \dfrac{B}{x^2} + \dfrac{C}{x-2}$ ⟹ $1 = (A+C)x^2 + (B-2A)x - 2B$, so

$A+C = B-2A = 0$ and $-2B=1$ ⇒ $B=-\frac{1}{2}$, $A=-\frac{1}{4}$, and $C=\frac{1}{4}$. So the general antiderivative of

$\dfrac{1}{x^3-2x^2}$ is

$$\int\dfrac{dx}{x^3-2x^2} = -\dfrac{1}{4}\int\dfrac{dx}{x} - \dfrac{1}{2}\int\dfrac{dx}{x^2} + \dfrac{1}{4}\int\dfrac{dx}{x-2} = -\tfrac{1}{4}\ln|x| - \tfrac{1}{2}(-1/x) + \tfrac{1}{4}\ln|x-2| + C$$

$$= \dfrac{1}{4}\ln\left|\dfrac{x-2}{x}\right| + \dfrac{1}{2x} + C$$

We plot this function with $C=0$ on the same screen as $y = \dfrac{1}{x^3-2x^2}$.

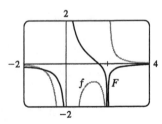

31. $\dfrac{P+S}{P\left[(r-1)P-S\right]} = \dfrac{A}{P} + \dfrac{B}{(r-1)P-S}$ ⇒ $P+S = A\left[(r-1)P-S\right] + BP = \left[(r-1)A+B\right]P - AS$

⇒ $(r-1)A+B=1, -A=1$ ⇒ $A=-1, B=r$. Now

$$t = \int\dfrac{P+S}{P\left[(r-1)P-S\right]}\,dP = \int\left[\dfrac{-1}{P} + \dfrac{r}{(r-1)P-S}\right]dP = -\int\dfrac{dP}{P} + \dfrac{r}{r-1}\int\dfrac{r-1}{(r-1)P-S}\,dP$$

so $t = -\ln P + \dfrac{r}{r-1}\ln|(r-1)P - S| + C$. Here $r = 0.10$ and $S = 900$, so

$$t = -\ln P + \tfrac{0.1}{-0.9}\ln|-0.9P - 900| + C = -\ln P - \tfrac{1}{9}\ln(|-1||0.9P + 900|)$$

$$= -\ln P - \tfrac{1}{9}\ln(0.9P + 900) + C$$

When $t = 0$, $P = 10{,}000$, so $0 = -\ln 10{,}000 - \tfrac{1}{9}\ln(9900) + C$. Thus, $C = \ln 10{,}000 + \tfrac{1}{9}\ln 9900$ [≈ 10.2326], so our equation becomes

$$t = \ln 10{,}000 - \ln P + \tfrac{1}{9}\ln 9900 - \tfrac{1}{9}\ln(0.9P + 900) = \ln \frac{10{,}000}{P} + \frac{1}{9}\ln \frac{9900}{0.9P + 900}$$

$$= \ln \frac{10{,}000}{P} + \frac{1}{9}\ln \frac{1100}{0.1P + 100} = \ln \frac{10{,}000}{P} + \frac{1}{9}\ln \frac{11{,}000}{P + 1000}$$

32. The area of a cross-section is a disk with radius $\dfrac{1}{x^2 + 3x + 2}$, so the volume is

$$V = \pi \int_0^1 \left[\frac{1}{x^2 + 3x + 2}\right]^2 dx = \pi \int_0^1 \frac{dx}{(x+1)^2(x+2)^2}.$$ To evaluate the integral, we use partial

fractions: $\dfrac{1}{(x+1)^2(x+2)^2} = \dfrac{A}{x+1} + \dfrac{B}{(x+1)^2} + \dfrac{C}{x+2} + \dfrac{D}{(x+2)^2}$ $\Rightarrow$

$1 = A(x+1)(x+2)^2 + B(x+2)^2 + C(x+1)^2(x+2) + D(x+1)^2$. We set $x = -1$, giving $B = 1$, then set $x = -2$, giving $D = 1$. Now equating coefficients of x^3 gives $A = -C$, and then equating constants gives $1 = 4A + 4 + 2(-A) + 1$ $\Rightarrow$ $A = -2$ $\Rightarrow$ $C = 2$. So the expression becomes

$$V = \pi \int_0^1 \left[\frac{-2}{x+1} + \frac{1}{(x+1)^2} + \frac{2}{(x+2)} + \frac{1}{(x+2)^2}\right] dx = \pi\left[2\ln\left|\frac{x+2}{x+1}\right| - \frac{1}{x+1} - \frac{1}{x+2}\right]_0^1$$

$$= \pi\left[\left(2\ln\tfrac{3}{2} - \tfrac{1}{2} - \tfrac{1}{3}\right) - \left(2\ln 2 - 1 - \tfrac{1}{2}\right)\right] = \pi\left(2\ln\tfrac{3/2}{2} + \tfrac{2}{3}\right) = \pi\left(\tfrac{2}{3} + \ln\tfrac{9}{16}\right).$$

33. (a) In Maple, we define $f(x)$, and then use `convert(f,parfrac,x);` to obtain

$$f(x) = \frac{24{,}110/4879}{5x+2} - \frac{668/323}{2x+1} - \frac{9438/80{,}155}{3x-7} + \frac{((22{,}098x + 48{,}935)/260{,}015)}{x^2 + x + 5}.$$

In Mathematica, we use the command `Apart`, and in Derive, we use `Expand`.

(b) $\displaystyle \int f(x)\, dx = \tfrac{24{,}110}{4879} \cdot \tfrac{1}{5}\ln|5x + 2| - \tfrac{668}{323} \cdot \tfrac{1}{2}\ln|2x + 1| - \tfrac{9438}{80{,}155} \cdot \tfrac{1}{3}\ln|3x - 7|$

$$+ \frac{1}{260{,}015}\int \frac{22{,}098\left(x + \tfrac{1}{2}\right) + 37{,}886}{\left(x + \tfrac{1}{2}\right)^2 + \tfrac{19}{4}}\, dx + C$$

$$= \tfrac{24{,}110}{4879} \cdot \tfrac{1}{5}\ln|5x + 2| - \tfrac{668}{323} \cdot \tfrac{1}{2}\ln|2x + 1| - \tfrac{9438}{80{,}155} \cdot \tfrac{1}{3}\ln|3x - 7|$$

$$+ \frac{1}{260{,}015}\left[22{,}098 \cdot \tfrac{1}{2}\ln\left(x^2 + x + 5\right) + 37{,}886 \cdot \sqrt{\tfrac{4}{19}}\tan^{-1}\left(\frac{1}{\sqrt{19/4}}\left(x + \tfrac{1}{2}\right)\right)\right] + C$$

$$= \tfrac{4822}{4879}\ln|5x + 2| - \tfrac{334}{323}\ln|2x + 1| - \tfrac{3146}{80{,}155}\ln|3x - 7| + \tfrac{11{,}049}{260{,}015}\ln\left(x^2 + x + 5\right)$$

$$+ \frac{75{,}772}{260{,}015\sqrt{19}}\tan^{-1}\left[\tfrac{1}{\sqrt{19}}(2x + 1)\right] + C$$

Using a CAS, we get

$$\frac{4822\ln(5x + 2)}{4879} - \frac{334\ln(2x + 1)}{323} - \frac{3146\ln(3x - 7)}{80{,}155}$$

$$+ \frac{11{,}049\ln\left(x^2 + x + 5\right)}{260{,}015} + \frac{3988\sqrt{19}}{260{,}115}\tan^{-1}\left[\frac{\sqrt{19}}{19}(2x + 1)\right]$$

(continued)

The main difference in this answer is that the absolute value signs and the constant of integration have been omitted. Also, the fractions have been reduced and the denominators rationalized.

34. (a) In Maple, we define $f(x)$, and then use convert(f,parfrac,x); to get

$$f(x) = \frac{5828/1815}{(5x-2)^2} - \frac{59{,}096/19{,}965}{5x-2} + \frac{2(2843x+816)/3993}{2x^2+1} + \frac{(313x-251)/363}{(2x^2+1)^2}.$$

In Mathematica, we use the command Apart, and in Derive, we use Expand.

(b) As we saw in Exercise 33, computer algebra systems omit the absolute value signs in $\int (1/y)\,dy = \ln|y|$. So we use the CAS to integrate the expression in part (a) and add the necessary absolute value signs and constant of integration to get

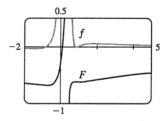

$$\int f(x)\,dx = -\frac{5828}{9075(5x-2)} - \frac{59{,}096\ln|5x-2|}{99{,}825} + \frac{2843\ln(2x^2+1)}{7986}$$

$$+\frac{503}{15{,}972}\sqrt{2}\tan^{-1}\left(\sqrt{2}\,x\right) - \frac{1}{2904}\frac{1004x+626}{2x^2+1} + C$$

(c) From the graph, we see that f goes from negative to positive at $x \approx -0.78$, then back to negative at $x \approx 0.8$, and finally back to positive at $x = 1$. Also, $\lim_{x\to 0.4} f(x) = \infty$. So we see (by the First Derivative Test) that $\int f(x)\,dx$ has minima at $x \approx -0.78$ and $x = 1$, and a maximum at $x \approx 0.80$, and that $\int f(x)\,dx$ is unbounded as $x \to 0.4$. Note also that just to the right of $x = 0.4$, f has large values, so $\int f(x)\,dx$ increases rapidly, but slows down as f drops toward 0. $\int f(x)\,dx$ decreases from about 0.8 to 1, then increases slowly since f stays small and positive.

35. There are only finitely many values of x where $Q(x) = 0$ (assuming that Q is not the zero polynomial). At all other values of x, $F(x)/Q(x) = G(x)/Q(x)$, so $F(x) = G(x)$. In other words, the values of F and G agree at all except perhaps finitely many values of x. By continuity of F and G, the polynomials F and G must agree at those values of x too.

More explicitly: if a is a value of x such that $Q(a) = 0$, then $Q(x) \neq 0$ for all x sufficiently close to a. Thus,

$$F(a) = \lim_{x\to a} F(x) \ \ (\text{by continuity of } F) \ = \lim_{x\to a} G(x) \ \ [\text{whenever } Q(x) \neq 0]$$

$$= G(a) \ \ (\text{by continuity of } G).$$

36. Let $f(x) = ax^2 + bx + c$. We calculate the partial fraction decomposition of $\dfrac{f(x)}{x^2(x+1)^3}$. Since $f(0) = 1$, we

must have $c = 1$, so $\dfrac{f(x)}{x^2(x+1)^3} = \dfrac{ax^2+bx+1}{x^2(x+1)^3} = \dfrac{A}{x} + \dfrac{B}{x^2} + \dfrac{C}{x+1} + \dfrac{D}{(x+1)^2} + \dfrac{E}{(x+1)^3}$. Now in order for the integral not to contain any logarithms (that is, in order for it to be a rational function), we must have $A = C = 0$, so $ax^2 + bx + 1 = B(x+1)^3 + Dx^2(x+1) + Ex^2$. Equating constant terms gives $B = 1$, then equating coefficients of x gives $3B = b \ \Rightarrow \ b = 3$. This is the quantity we are looking for, since $f'(0) = b$.

H   Polar Coordinates • • • • • • • • • • • • • •

H.1   Curves in Polar Coordinates • • • • • • • • • • • • •

1. (a) By adding 2π to $\frac{\pi}{2}$, we obtain the point $\left(1, \frac{5\pi}{2}\right)$. The direction opposite $\frac{\pi}{2}$ is $\frac{3\pi}{2}$, so $\left(-1, \frac{3\pi}{2}\right)$ is a point that satisfies the $r < 0$ requirement.

(b) $\left(-2, \frac{\pi}{4}\right)$

(c) $(3, 2)$

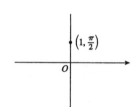

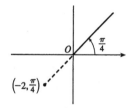

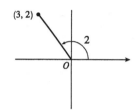

$\left(2, \frac{5\pi}{4}\right), \left(-2, \frac{9\pi}{4}\right)$

$(3, 2 + 2\pi), (-3, 2 + \pi)$

2. (a) $(3, 0)$

(b) $\left(2, -\frac{\pi}{7}\right)$

(c) $\left(-1, -\frac{\pi}{2}\right)$

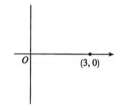

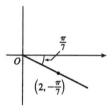

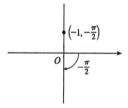

$(3, 2\pi), (-3, \pi)$

$\left(2, \frac{13\pi}{7}\right), \left(-2, \frac{6\pi}{7}\right)$

$\left(1, \frac{\pi}{2}\right), \left(-1, \frac{3\pi}{2}\right)$

3. (a)

(b)

(c)

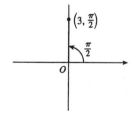

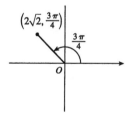

$x = 3\cos\frac{\pi}{2} = 3(0) = 0$ and $y = 3\sin\frac{\pi}{2} = 3(1) = 3$ give us the Cartesian coordinates $(0, 3)$.

$x = 2\sqrt{2}\cos\frac{3\pi}{4}$
$= 2\sqrt{2}\left(-\frac{1}{\sqrt{2}}\right) = -2$ and
$y = 2\sqrt{2}\sin\frac{3\pi}{4} = 2\sqrt{2}\left(\frac{1}{\sqrt{2}}\right) = 2$
give us $(-2, 2)$.

$x = -1\cos\frac{\pi}{3} = -\frac{1}{2}$ and
$y = -1\sin\frac{\pi}{3} = -\frac{\sqrt{3}}{2}$ give
us $\left(-\frac{1}{2}, -\frac{\sqrt{3}}{2}\right)$.

4. (a)

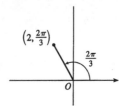

$x = 2\cos\frac{2\pi}{3} = -1,$

$y = 2\sin\frac{2\pi}{3} = \sqrt{3}$

(b)

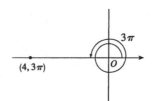

$x = 4\cos 3\pi = -4,$

$y = 4\sin 3\pi = 0$

(c)

$x = -2\cos\left(-\frac{5\pi}{6}\right) = \sqrt{3},$

$y = -2\sin\left(-\frac{5\pi}{6}\right) = 1$

5. (a) $x = 1$ and $y = 1$ $\Rightarrow$ $r = \sqrt{1^2 + 1^2} = \sqrt{2}$ and $\theta = \tan^{-1}\left(\frac{1}{1}\right) = \frac{\pi}{4}$. Since $(1, 1)$ is in the first quadrant, the polar coordinates are (i) $\left(\sqrt{2}, \frac{\pi}{4}\right)$ and (ii) $\left(-\sqrt{2}, \frac{5\pi}{4}\right)$.

(b) $x = 2\sqrt{3}$ and $y = -2$ $\Rightarrow$ $r = \sqrt{\left(2\sqrt{3}\right)^2 + (-2)^2} = \sqrt{12 + 4} = \sqrt{16} = 4$ and $\theta = \tan^{-1}\left(-\frac{2}{2\sqrt{3}}\right) = \tan^{-1}\left(-\frac{1}{\sqrt{3}}\right) = -\frac{\pi}{6}$. Since $(2\sqrt{3}, -2)$ is in the fourth quadrant and $0 \le \theta \le 2\pi$, the polar coordinates are (i) $\left(4, \frac{11\pi}{6}\right)$ and (ii) $\left(-4, \frac{5\pi}{6}\right)$.

6. (a) $(x, y) = (-1, -\sqrt{3})$, $r = \sqrt{1 + 3} = 2$, $\tan\theta = y/x = \sqrt{3}$ and (x, y) is in the third quadrant, so $\theta = \frac{4\pi}{3}$. The polar coordinates are (i) $\left(2, \frac{4\pi}{3}\right)$ and (ii) $\left(-2, \frac{\pi}{3}\right)$.

(b) $(x, y) = (-2, 3)$, $r = \sqrt{4 + 9} = \sqrt{13}$, $\tan\theta = y/x = -\frac{3}{2}$ and (x, y) is in the second quadrant, so $\theta = \tan^{-1}\left(-\frac{3}{2}\right) + \pi$. The polar coordinates are (i) $\left(\sqrt{13}, \theta\right)$ and (ii) $\left(-\sqrt{13}, \theta + \pi\right)$.

7. $r > 1$

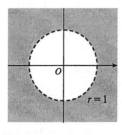

8. $0 \le \theta < \frac{\pi}{4}$

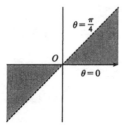

9. $0 \le r \le 2$, $\frac{\pi}{2} \le \theta \le \pi$

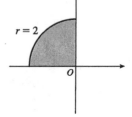

10. $1 \le r < 3$, $-\frac{\pi}{4} \le \theta \le \frac{\pi}{4}$

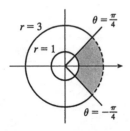

11. $2 < r < 3$, $\frac{5\pi}{3} \le \theta \le \frac{7\pi}{3}$

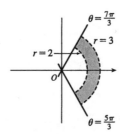

12. $-1 \le r \le 1$, $\frac{\pi}{4} \le \theta \le \frac{3\pi}{4}$

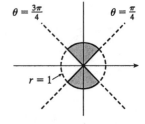

13. $r = 3\sin\theta \;\Rightarrow\; r^2 = 3r\sin\theta \;\Leftrightarrow\; x^2 + y^2 = 3y \;\Leftrightarrow\; x^2 + y^2 - 3y = 0 \;\Leftrightarrow\; x^2 + y^2 - 3y + \frac{9}{4} = \frac{9}{4}$

$\Leftrightarrow\; x^2 + \left(y - \frac{3}{2}\right)^2 = \left(\frac{3}{2}\right)^2$, a circle of radius $\frac{3}{2}$ centered at $\left(0, \frac{3}{2}\right)$. The first two equations are actually equivalent

since $r^2 = 3r\sin\theta \;\Rightarrow\; r(r - 3\sin\theta) = 0 \;\Rightarrow\; r = 0$ or $r = 3\sin\theta$. But $r = 3\sin\theta$ gives the point $r = 0$

(the pole) when $\theta = 0$. Thus, the single equation $r = 3\sin\theta$ is equivalent to the compound condition ($r = 0$

or $r = 3\sin\theta$).

14. $r\cos\theta = 1 \;\Leftrightarrow\; x = 1$, a vertical line.

15. $r^2 = \sin 2\theta = 2\sin\theta\cos\theta \;\Leftrightarrow\; r^2 \cdot r^2 = r^2 \cdot 2\sin\theta\cos\theta \;\Leftrightarrow\; r^4 = 2r\sin\theta\, r\cos\theta \;\Leftrightarrow\;$
$\left(r^2\right)^2 = 2(r\sin\theta)(r\cos\theta) \;\Leftrightarrow\; \left(x^2 + y^2\right)^2 = 2yx$

16. $r = \dfrac{1}{1 + 2\sin\theta} \;\Rightarrow\; r + 2r\sin\theta = 1 \;\Leftrightarrow\; r = 1 - 2r\sin\theta \;\Leftrightarrow\; \sqrt{x^2 + y^2} = 1 - 2y \;\Rightarrow\;$

$x^2 + y^2 = 1 - 4y + 4y^2 \;\Leftrightarrow\; 3y^2 - 4y - x^2 = -1 \;\Leftrightarrow\; 3\left(y^2 - \frac{4}{3}y + \frac{4}{9}\right) - x^2 = \frac{4}{3} - 1 \;\Leftrightarrow\;$

$3\left(y - \frac{2}{3}\right)^2 - x^2 = \frac{1}{3} \;\Leftrightarrow\; 9\left(y - \frac{2}{3}\right)^2 - 3x^2 = 1 \;\Leftrightarrow\; \dfrac{\left(y - \frac{2}{3}\right)^2}{\left(\frac{1}{3}\right)^2} - \dfrac{x^2}{\left(\frac{1}{\sqrt{3}}\right)^2} = 1$. This is a hyperbola opening

up and down and centered at $\left(0, \frac{2}{3}\right)$.

17. $y = 5 \;\Leftrightarrow\; r\sin\theta = 5$ (or $r = 5\csc\theta$)

18. $y = 2x - 1 \;\Leftrightarrow\; r\sin\theta = 2r\cos\theta - 1 \;\Leftrightarrow\; r(2\cos\theta - \sin\theta) = 1 \;\Leftrightarrow\; r = \dfrac{1}{2\cos\theta - \sin\theta}$. (We can divide

by $2\cos\theta - \sin\theta$ because it must be nonzero in order that its product with r equal 1.)

19. $x^2 + y^2 = 25 \;\Leftrightarrow\; r^2 = 25 \;\Rightarrow\; r = 5$

20. $x^2 = 4y \;\Leftrightarrow\; r^2\cos^2\theta = 4r\sin\theta \;\Leftrightarrow\; r\cos^2\theta = 4\sin\theta \;\Leftrightarrow\; r = 4\tan\theta\sec\theta$

21. (a) The description leads immediately to the polar equation $\theta = \frac{\pi}{6}$, and the Cartesian equation

$y = \tan\left(\frac{\pi}{6}\right) x = \frac{1}{\sqrt{3}} x$ is slightly more difficult to derive.

(b) The easier description here is the Cartesian equation $x = 3$.

22. (a) Because its center is not at the origin, it is more easily described by its Cartesian equation,

$(x - 2)^2 + (y - 3)^2 = 5^2$.

(b) This circle is more easily given in polar coordinates: $r = 4$. The Cartesian equation is also simple:

$x^2 + y^2 = 16$.

23. As in Example 4, $r = 5$ represents the circle with center O and radius 5.

24. $\theta = \frac{3\pi}{4}$ is a line through the origin.

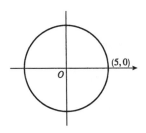

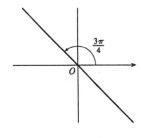

25. $r = \sin\theta \iff r^2 = r\sin\theta \iff x^2 + y^2 = y \iff$
$x^2 + \left(y - \frac{1}{2}\right)^2 = \left(\frac{1}{2}\right)^2$. The reasoning here is the same as in
Exercise 13. This is a circle of radius $\frac{1}{2}$ centered at $\left(0, \frac{1}{2}\right)$.

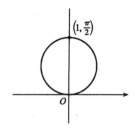

26. $r = 1 - 3\cos\theta$. This is a limaçon.

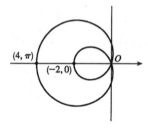

27. $r = \theta$, $\theta \geq 0$

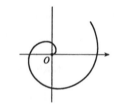

28. $r = \sqrt{\theta}$. This curve is a spiral.

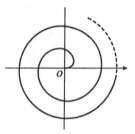

29. $r = 1 - 2\cos\theta$

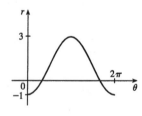

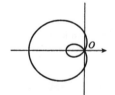

30. $r = 2 + \cos\theta$

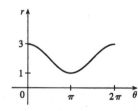

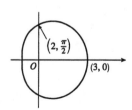

31. $r = 2\cos 4\theta$

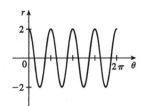

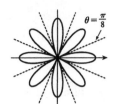

32. $r = \sin 5\theta$

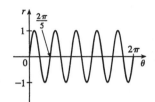

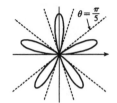

33. $r^2 = 4\cos 2\theta$

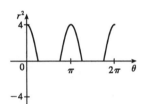

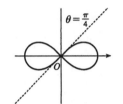

34. $r = 2\cos\left(\frac{3}{2}\theta\right)$

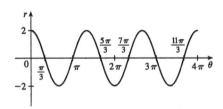

35. For $\theta = 0$, π, and 2π, r has its minimum value of about 0.5. For $\theta = \frac{\pi}{2}$ and $\frac{3\pi}{2}$, r attains its maximum value of 2. We see that the graph has a similar shape for $0 \le \theta \le \pi$ and $\pi \le \theta \le 2\pi$.

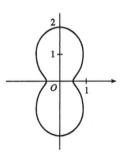

36.

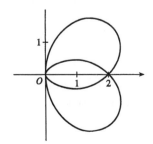

37. $x = (r)\cos\theta = (4 + 2\sec\theta)\cos\theta = 4\cos\theta + 2$. Now, $r \to \infty$ $\Rightarrow$ $(4 + 2\sec\theta) \to \infty$ $\Rightarrow$ $\theta \to \left(\frac{\pi}{2}\right)^-$ or

$\theta \to \left(\frac{3\pi}{2}\right)^+$ (since we need only consider $0 \le \theta < 2\pi$), so $\lim\limits_{r\to\infty} x = \lim\limits_{\theta\to\pi/2^-} (4\cos\theta + 2) = 2$. Also, $r \to -\infty$

$\Rightarrow$ $(4 + 2\sec\theta) \to -\infty$ $\Rightarrow$ $\theta \to \left(\frac{\pi}{2}\right)^+$ or $\theta \to \left(\frac{3\pi}{2}\right)^-$, so $\lim\limits_{r\to-\infty} x = \lim\limits_{\theta\to\pi/2^+} (4\cos\theta + 2) = 2$. Therefore,

$\lim\limits_{r\to\pm\infty} x = 2$ $\Rightarrow$ $x = 2$ is a vertical asymptote.

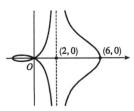

38. To show that $x = 1$ is an asymptote we must prove $\lim\limits_{r\to\pm\infty} x = 1$.

$x = (r)\cos\theta = (\sin\theta\tan\theta)\cos\theta = \sin^2\theta$. Now, $r \to \infty$ $\Rightarrow$ $\sin\theta\tan\theta \to \infty$

$\Rightarrow$ $\theta \to \left(\frac{\pi}{2}\right)^-$, so $\lim\limits_{r\to\infty} x = \lim\limits_{\theta\to\pi/2^-} \sin^2\theta = 1$. Also, $r \to -\infty$ $\Rightarrow$

$\sin\theta\tan\theta \to -\infty$ $\Rightarrow$ $\theta \to \left(\frac{\pi}{2}\right)^+$, so $\lim\limits_{r\to-\infty} x = \lim\limits_{\theta\to\pi/2^+} \sin^2\theta = 1$.

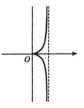

Therefore, $\lim\limits_{r\to\pm\infty} x = 1$ $\Rightarrow$ $x = 1$ is a vertical asymptote. Also notice that $x = \sin^2\theta \ge 0$ for all θ, and

$x = \sin^2\theta \le 1$ for all θ. And $x \ne 1$, since the curve is not defined at odd multiples of $\frac{\pi}{2}$. Therefore, the curve lies

entirely within the vertical strip $0 \le x < 1$.

39. (a) We see that the curve crosses itself at the origin, where $r = 0$ (in fact the inner loop corresponds to negative

r-values,) so we solve the equation of the limaçon for $r = 0$ $\Leftrightarrow$ $c\sin\theta = -1$ $\Leftrightarrow$ $\sin\theta = -1/c$. Now if

$|c| < 1$, then this equation has no solution and hence there is no inner loop. But if $c < -1$, then on the interval

$(0, 2\pi)$ the equation has the two solutions $\theta = \sin^{-1}(-1/c)$ and $\theta = \pi - \sin^{-1}(-1/c)$, and if $c > 1$, the

solutions are $\theta = \pi + \sin^{-1}(1/c)$ and $\theta = 2\pi - \sin^{-1}(1/c)$. In each case, $r < 0$ for θ between the two

solutions, indicating a loop.

(b) For $0 < c < 1$, the dimple (if it exists) is characterized by the fact that y has a local maximum at $\theta = \frac{3\pi}{2}$. So we

determine for what c-values $\dfrac{d^2y}{d\theta^2}$ is negative at $\theta = \frac{3\pi}{2}$, since by the Second Derivative Test this indicates a

maximum: $y = r\sin\theta = \sin\theta + c\sin^2\theta$ $\Rightarrow$ $\dfrac{dy}{d\theta} = \cos\theta + 2c\sin\theta\cos\theta = \cos\theta + c\sin 2\theta$ $\Rightarrow$

$\dfrac{d^2y}{d\theta^2} = -\sin\theta + 2c\cos 2\theta$. At $\theta = \frac{3\pi}{2}$, this is equal to $-(-1) + 2c(-1) = 1 - 2c$, which is negative only for

$c > \frac{1}{2}$. A similar argument shows that for $-1 < c < 0$, y only has a local minimum at $\theta = \frac{\pi}{2}$ (indicating a

dimple) for $c < -\frac{1}{2}$.

40. (a) $r = \sin(\theta/2)$. This equation must correspond to one of II, III or VI, since these are the only graphs which are

bounded. In fact it must be VI, since this is the only graph which is completed after a rotation of exactly 4π.

(b) $r = \sin(\theta/4)$. This equation must correspond to III, since this is the only graph which is completed after a rotation of exactly 8π.

(c) $r = \sec(3\theta)$. This must correspond to IV, since the graph is unbounded at $\theta = \frac{\pi}{6}, \frac{\pi}{2}, \frac{2\pi}{3}$, and so on.

(d) $r = \theta \sin \theta$. This must correspond to V. Note that $r = 0$ whenever θ is a multiple of π. This graph is unbounded, and each time θ moves through an interval of 2π, the same basic shape is repeated (because of the periodic $\sin \theta$ factor) but it gets larger each time (since θ increases each time we go around.)

(e) $r = 1 + 4 \cos 5\theta$. This corresponds to II, since it is bounded, has fivefold rotational symmetry, and takes only one takes only one rotation through 2π to be complete.

(f) $r = 1/\sqrt{\theta}$. This corresponds to I, since it is unbounded at $\theta = 0$, and r decreases as θ increases; in fact $r \to 0$ as $\theta \to \infty$.

41. Using Equation 3 with $r = 3\cos\theta$ and $dr/d\theta = -3\sin\theta$, we have

$$\frac{dy}{dx} = \frac{dy/d\theta}{dx/d\theta} = \frac{(dr/d\theta)(\sin\theta) + r\cos\theta}{(dr/d\theta)(\cos\theta) - r\sin\theta} = \frac{-3\sin\theta\sin\theta + 3\cos\theta\cos\theta}{-3\sin\theta\cos\theta - 3\cos\theta\sin\theta} = \frac{3(\cos^2\theta - \sin^2\theta)}{-3(2\sin\theta\cos\theta)}$$

$$= -\frac{\cos 2\theta}{\sin 2\theta} = -\cot 2\theta = \frac{1}{\sqrt{3}} \quad \text{when } \theta = \frac{\pi}{3}$$

Another solution: $r = 3\cos\theta \Rightarrow x = r\cos\theta = 3\cos^2\theta, y = r\sin\theta = 3\sin\theta\cos\theta \Rightarrow$

$$\frac{dy}{dx} = \frac{dy/d\theta}{dx/d\theta} = \frac{-3\sin^2\theta + 3\cos^2\theta}{-6\cos\theta\sin\theta} = \frac{\cos 2\theta}{-\sin 2\theta} = -\cot 2\theta = \frac{1}{\sqrt{3}} \quad \text{when } \theta = \frac{\pi}{3}$$

42. Using Equation 3 with $r = \cos\theta + \sin\theta$, we have

$$\frac{dy}{dx} = \frac{(dr/d\theta)\sin\theta + r\cos\theta}{(dr/d\theta)\cos\theta - r\sin\theta} = \frac{(-\sin\theta + \cos\theta)\sin\theta + (\cos\theta + \sin\theta)\cos\theta}{(-\sin\theta + \cos\theta)\cos\theta - (\cos\theta + \sin\theta)\sin\theta} = -1 \quad \text{when } \theta = \frac{\pi}{4}$$

Another solution: $r = \cos\theta + \sin\theta \Rightarrow$
$x = r\cos\theta = (\cos\theta + \sin\theta)\cos\theta, y = r\sin\theta = (\cos\theta + \sin\theta)\sin\theta \Rightarrow$

$$\frac{dy}{dx} = \frac{dy/d\theta}{dx/d\theta} = \frac{\sin\theta(-\sin\theta + \cos\theta) + (\cos\theta + \sin\theta)\cos\theta}{\cos\theta(-\sin\theta + \cos\theta) - (\cos\theta + \sin\theta)\sin\theta} = -1 \quad \text{when } \theta = \frac{\pi}{4}$$

43. $r = 1 + \cos\theta \Rightarrow x = r\cos\theta = \cos\theta + \cos^2\theta, y = r\sin\theta = \sin\theta + \sin\theta\cos\theta \Rightarrow$

$$\frac{dy}{dx} = \frac{dy/d\theta}{dx/d\theta} = \frac{\cos\theta + \cos^2\theta - \sin^2\theta}{-\sin\theta - 2\cos\theta\sin\theta} = \frac{\cos\theta + \cos 2\theta}{-\sin\theta - \sin 2\theta}$$

When $\theta = \frac{\pi}{6}$, $\dfrac{dy}{dx} = \dfrac{\frac{\sqrt{3}}{2} + \frac{1}{2}}{-\frac{1}{2} - \frac{\sqrt{3}}{2}} = \dfrac{\frac{\sqrt{3}}{2} + \frac{1}{2}}{-\left(\frac{1}{2} + \frac{\sqrt{3}}{2}\right)} = -1.$

44. $r = \ln\theta \Rightarrow x = r\cos\theta = \ln\theta\cos\theta, y = r\sin\theta = \ln\theta\sin\theta \Rightarrow$

$$\frac{dy}{dx} = \frac{dy/d\theta}{dx/d\theta} = \frac{\sin\theta(1/\theta) + \ln\theta\cos\theta}{\cos\theta(1/\theta) - \ln\theta\sin\theta} = \frac{\sin e + e\cos e}{\cos e - e\sin e} \quad \text{when } \theta = e$$

45. $r = 3\cos\theta \;\Rightarrow\; x = r\cos\theta = 3\cos\theta\cos\theta,\; y = r\sin\theta = 3\cos\theta\sin\theta \;\Rightarrow\;$
$dy/d\theta = -3\sin^2\theta + 3\cos^2\theta = 3\cos 2\theta = 0 \;\Rightarrow\; 2\theta = \frac{\pi}{2} \text{ or } \frac{3\pi}{2} \;\Leftrightarrow\; \theta = \frac{\pi}{4} \text{ or } \frac{3\pi}{4}$. So the tangent is
horizontal at $\left(\frac{3}{\sqrt{2}}, \frac{\pi}{4}\right)$ and $\left(-\frac{3}{\sqrt{2}}, \frac{3\pi}{4}\right)$ $\left[\text{same as }\left(\frac{3}{\sqrt{2}}, -\frac{\pi}{4}\right)\right]$. $dx/d\theta = -6\sin\theta\cos\theta = -3\sin 2\theta = 0 \;\Rightarrow\;$
$2\theta = 0 \text{ or } \pi \;\Leftrightarrow\; \theta = 0 \text{ or } \frac{\pi}{2}$. So the tangent is vertical at $(3, 0)$ and $\left(0, \frac{\pi}{2}\right)$.

46. $\dfrac{dy}{d\theta} = e^\theta\sin\theta + e^\theta\cos\theta = e^\theta(\sin\theta + \cos\theta) = 0 \;\Rightarrow\; \sin\theta = -\cos\theta \;\Rightarrow\; \tan\theta = -1 \;\Rightarrow\;$
$\theta = -\frac{1}{4}\pi + n\pi$ (n any integer) $\;\Rightarrow\;$ horizontal tangents at $\left(e^{\pi(n-1/4)}, \pi\left(n - \frac{1}{4}\right)\right)$.
$\dfrac{dx}{d\theta} = e^\theta\cos\theta - e^\theta\sin\theta = e^\theta(\cos\theta - \sin\theta) = 0 \;\Rightarrow\; \sin\theta = \cos\theta \;\Rightarrow\; \tan\theta = 1 \;\Rightarrow\;$
$\theta = \frac{1}{4}\pi + n\pi$ (n any integer) $\;\Rightarrow\;$ vertical tangents at $\left(e^{\pi(n+1/4)}, \pi\left(n + \frac{1}{4}\right)\right)$.

47. $r = 1 + \cos\theta \;\Rightarrow\; x = r\cos\theta = \cos\theta(1 + \cos\theta),\; y = r\sin\theta = \sin\theta(1 + \cos\theta) \;\Rightarrow\;$
$dy/d\theta = (1 + \cos\theta)\cos\theta - \sin^2\theta = 2\cos^2\theta + \cos\theta - 1 = (2\cos\theta - 1)(\cos\theta + 1) = 0 \;\Rightarrow\; \cos\theta = \frac{1}{2}$ or
$-1 \;\Rightarrow\; \theta = \frac{\pi}{3}, \pi, \text{ or } \frac{5\pi}{3} \;\Rightarrow\;$ horizontal tangent at $\left(\frac{3}{2}, \frac{\pi}{3}\right), (0, \pi)$, and $\left(\frac{3}{2}, \frac{5\pi}{3}\right)$.
$dx/d\theta = -(1 + \cos\theta)\sin\theta - \cos\theta\sin\theta = -\sin\theta(1 + 2\cos\theta) = 0 \;\Rightarrow\; \sin\theta = 0 \text{ or } \cos\theta = -\frac{1}{2} \;\Rightarrow\;$
$\theta = 0, \pi, \frac{2\pi}{3}, \text{ or } \frac{4\pi}{3} \;\Rightarrow\;$ vertical tangent at $(2, 0), \left(\frac{1}{2}, \frac{2\pi}{3}\right)$, and $\left(\frac{1}{2}, \frac{4\pi}{3}\right)$. Note that the tangent is horizontal, not
vertical when $\theta = \pi$, since $\displaystyle\lim_{\theta \to \pi} \frac{dy/d\theta}{dx/d\theta} = 0$.

48. By differentiating implicitly, $r^2 = \sin 2\theta \;\Rightarrow\; 2r\,(dr/d\theta) = 2\cos 2\theta \;\Rightarrow\;$
$dr/d\theta = (1/r)\cos 2\theta$, so

$$\frac{dy}{d\theta} = \frac{1}{r}\cos 2\theta\sin\theta + r\cos\theta = \frac{1}{r}\left(\cos 2\theta\sin\theta + r^2\cos\theta\right)$$

$$= \frac{1}{r}\left(\cos 2\theta\sin\theta + \sin 2\theta\cos\theta\right) = \frac{1}{r}\sin 3\theta$$

This is 0 when $\sin 3\theta = 0 \;\Rightarrow\; \theta = 0, \frac{\pi}{3} \text{ or } \frac{4\pi}{3}$ (restricting θ to the domain of the lemniscate), so there are
horizontal tangents at $\left(\sqrt[4]{\frac{3}{4}}, \frac{\pi}{3}\right), \left(\sqrt[4]{\frac{3}{4}}, \frac{4\pi}{3}\right)$ and $(0, 0)$. Similarly, $dx/d\theta = (1/r)\cos 3\theta = 0$ when $\theta = \frac{\pi}{6} \text{ or } \frac{7\pi}{6}$,
so there are vertical tangents at $\left(\sqrt[4]{\frac{3}{4}}, \frac{\pi}{6}\right)$ and $\left(\sqrt[4]{\frac{3}{4}}, \frac{7\pi}{6}\right)$ [and $(0, 0)$].

49. $r = a\sin\theta + b\cos\theta \;\Rightarrow\; r^2 = ar\sin\theta + br\cos\theta \;\Rightarrow\; x^2 + y^2 = ay + bx \;\Rightarrow\;$
$x^2 - bx + \left(\frac{1}{2}b\right)^2 + y^2 - ay + \left(\frac{1}{2}a\right)^2 = \left(\frac{1}{2}b\right)^2 + \left(\frac{1}{2}a\right)^2 \;\Rightarrow\; \left(x - \frac{1}{2}b\right)^2 + \left(y - \frac{1}{2}a\right)^2 = \frac{1}{4}\left(a^2 + b^2\right)$, and this
is a circle with center $\left(\frac{1}{2}b, \frac{1}{2}a\right)$ and radius $\frac{1}{2}\sqrt{a^2 + b^2}$.

50. These curves are circles which intersect at the origin and at $\left(\frac{1}{\sqrt{2}}a, \frac{\pi}{4}\right)$. At the origin, the first circle has a horizontal
tangent and the second a vertical one, so the tangents are perpendicular here. For the first circle ($r = a\sin\theta$),
$dy/d\theta = a\cos\theta\sin\theta + a\sin\theta\cos\theta = a\sin 2\theta = a$ at $\theta = \frac{\pi}{4}$ and $dx/d\theta = a\cos^2\theta - a\sin^2\theta = a\cos 2\theta = 0$ at
$\theta = \frac{\pi}{4}$, so the tangent here is vertical. Similarly, for the second circle ($r = a\cos\theta$), $dy/d\theta = a\cos 2\theta = 0$ and
$dx/d\theta = -a\sin 2\theta = -a$ at $\theta = \frac{\pi}{4}$, so the tangent is horizontal, and again the tangents are perpendicular.

Note for Exercises 51–54: Maple is able to plot polar curves using the `polarplot` command, or using the `coords=polar` option in a regular `plot` command. In Mathematica, use `PolarPlot`. In Derive, change to `Polar` under `Options State`. If your graphing device cannot plot polar equations, you must convert to parametric equations. For example, in Exercise 51,
$x = r\cos\theta = [1 + 2\sin(\theta/2)]\cos\theta, y = r\sin\theta = [1 + 2\sin(\theta/2)]\sin\theta.$

51. $r = 1 + 2\sin(\theta/2)$. The parameter interval is $[0, 4\pi]$.

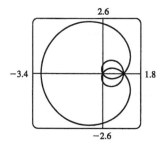

52. $r = \sqrt{1 - 0.8\sin^2\theta}$. The parameter interval is $[0, 2\pi]$.

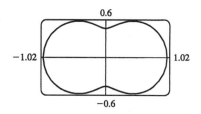

53. $r = e^{\sin\theta} - 2\cos(4\theta)$. The parameter interval is $[0, 2\pi]$.

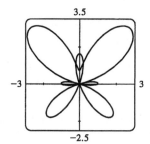

54. $r = \sin^2(4\theta) + \cos(4\theta)$. The parameter interval is $[0, 2\pi]$.

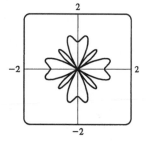

55.

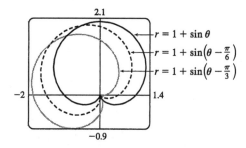

It appears that the graph of $r = 1 + \sin\left(\theta - \frac{\pi}{6}\right)$ is the same shape as the graph of $r = 1 + \sin\theta$, but rotated counterclockwise about the origin by $\frac{\pi}{6}$. Similarly, the graph of $r = 1 + \sin\left(\theta - \frac{\pi}{3}\right)$ is rotated by $\frac{\pi}{3}$. In general, the graph of $r = f(\theta - \alpha)$ is the same shape as that of $r = f(\theta)$, but rotated counterclockwise through α about the origin. That is, for any point (r_0, θ_0) on the curve $r = f(\theta)$, the point $(r_0, \theta_0 + \alpha)$ is on the curve $r = f(\theta - \alpha)$, since $r_0 = f(\theta_0) = f((\theta_0 + \alpha) - \alpha)$.

56.

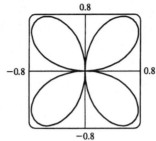

From the graph, the highest points seem to have $y \approx 0.77$. To find the exact value, we solve $dy/d\theta = 0$.
$y = r \sin\theta = \sin\theta \sin 2\theta \quad \Rightarrow$

$$dy/d\theta = 2\sin\theta \cos 2\theta + \cos\theta \sin 2\theta$$

$$= 2\sin\theta \left(2\cos^2\theta - 1\right) + \cos\theta \left(2\sin\theta\, \cos\theta\right)$$

$$= 2\sin\theta \left(3\cos^2\theta - 1\right)$$

In the first quadrant, this is 0 when $\cos\theta = \frac{1}{\sqrt{3}} \quad \Leftrightarrow \quad \sin\theta = \sqrt{\frac{2}{3}} \quad \Leftrightarrow$

$y = 2\sin^2\theta \cos\theta = 2 \cdot \frac{2}{3} \cdot \frac{1}{\sqrt{3}} = \frac{4\sqrt{3}}{9} \approx 0.77$.

57. (a) $r = \sin n\theta$. From the graphs, it seems that when n is even, the number of loops in the curve (called a rose) is
$2n$, and when n is odd, the number of loops is simply n.

This is because in the case of n odd, every point on the graph is traversed twice, due to the fact that

$$r(\theta + \pi) = \sin\left[n(\theta + \pi)\right] = \sin n\theta\, \cos n\pi + \cos n\theta\, \sin n\pi = \begin{cases} \sin n\theta & \text{if } n \text{ is even} \\ -\sin n\theta & \text{if } n \text{ is odd} \end{cases}$$

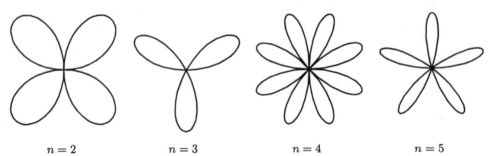

$n = 2$ $n = 3$ $n = 4$ $n = 5$

(b) The graph of $r = |\sin n\theta|$ has $2n$ loops whether n is odd or even, since $r(\theta + \pi) = r(\theta)$.

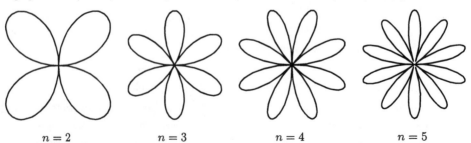

$n = 2$ $n = 3$ $n = 4$ $n = 5$

58. $r = 1 + c \sin n\theta$. We vary n while keeping c constant at 2. As n changes, the curves change in the same way as those in Exercise 57: the number of loops increases. Note that if n is even, the smaller loops are outside the larger ones; if n is odd, they are inside.

$c = 2$

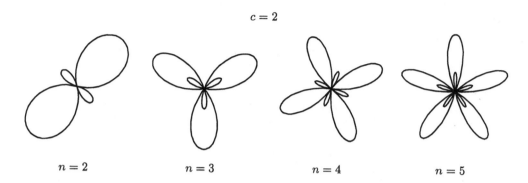

$n = 2$ $\qquad$ $n = 3$ $\qquad$ $n = 4$ $\qquad$ $n = 5$

Now we vary c while keeping $n = 3$. As c increases toward 0, the entire graph gets smaller (the graphs below are not to scale) and the smaller loops shrink in relation to the large ones. At $c = -1$, the small loops disappear entirely, and for $-1 < c < 1$, the graph is a simple, closed curve (at $c = 0$ it is a circle). As c continues to increase, the same changes are seen, but in reverse order, since $1 + (-c) \sin n\theta = 1 + c \sin n(\theta + \pi)$, so the graph for $c = c_0$ is the same as that for $c = -c_0$, with a rotation through π. As $c \to \infty$, the smaller loops get relatively closer in size to the large ones. Note that the distance between the outermost points of corresponding inner and outer loops is always 2. Maple's `animate` command (or Mathematica's `Animate`) is very useful for seeing the changes that occur as c varies.

$n = 3$

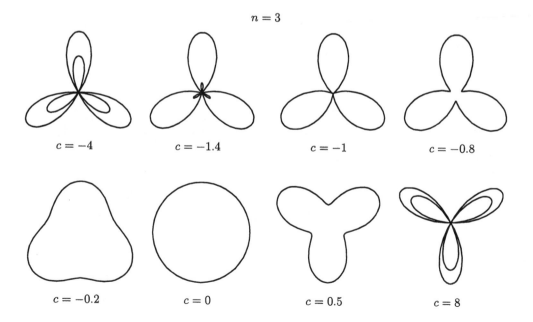

$c = -4$ $\qquad$ $c = -1.4$ $\qquad$ $c = -1$ $\qquad$ $c = -0.8$

$c = -0.2$ $\qquad$ $c = 0$ $\qquad$ $c = 0.5$ $\qquad$ $c = 8$

59. $r = \dfrac{1 - a\cos\theta}{1 + a\cos\theta}$. We start with $a = 0$, since in this case the curve is simply the circle $r = 1$.

As a increases, the graph moves to the left, and its right side becomes flattened. As a increases through about 0.4, the right side seems to grow a dimple, which upon closer investigation (with narrower θ-ranges) seems to appear at $a \approx 0.42$ (the actual value is $\sqrt{2} - 1$). As $a \to 1$, this dimple becomes more pronounced, and the curve begins to stretch out horizontally, until at $a = 1$ the denominator vanishes at $\theta = \pi$, and the dimple becomes an actual cusp. For $a > 1$ we must choose our parameter interval carefully, since $r \to \infty$ as $1 + a\cos\theta \to 0$ $\Leftrightarrow$ $\theta \to \pm\cos^{-1}(-1/a)$. As a increases from 1, the curve splits into two parts. The left part has a loop, which grows larger as a increases, and the right part grows broader vertically, and its left tip develops a dimple when $a \approx 2.42$ (actually, $\sqrt{2} + 1$). As a increases, the dimple grows more and more pronounced. If $a < 0$, we get the same graph as we do for the corresponding positive a-value, but with a rotation through π about the pole, as happened when c was replaced with $-c$ in Exercise 58.

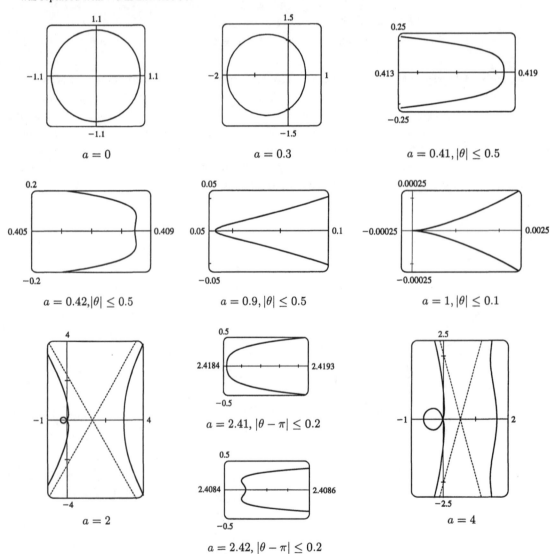

60. Most graphing devices cannot plot implicit polar equations, so we must first find an explicit expression (or expressions) for r in terms of θ, a, and c. We note that the given equation is a quadratic in r^2, so we use the quadratic formula and find that

$$r^2 = \frac{2c^2 \cos 2\theta \pm \sqrt{4c^4 \cos^2 2\theta - 4\left(c^4 - a^4\right)}}{2}$$

$$= c^2 \cos 2\theta \pm \sqrt{a^4 - c^4 \sin^2 2\theta}$$

so $r = \pm\sqrt{c^2 \cos 2\theta \pm \sqrt{a^4 - c^4 \sin^2 2\theta}}$. So for each graph, we must plot four curves to be sure of plotting all the points which satisfy the given equation. Note that all four functions have period π.

We start with the case $a = c = 1$, and the resulting curve resembles the symbol for infinity. If we let a decrease, the curve splits into two symmetric parts, and as a decreases further, the parts become smaller, further apart, and rounder. If instead we let a increase from 1, the two lobes of the curve join together, and as a increases further they continue to merge, until at $a \approx 1.4$, the graph no longer has dimples, and has an oval shape. As $a \to \infty$, the oval becomes larger and rounder, since the c^2 and c^4 terms lose their significance. Note that the shape of the graph seems to depend only on the ratio c/a, while the size of the graph varies as c and a jointly increase.

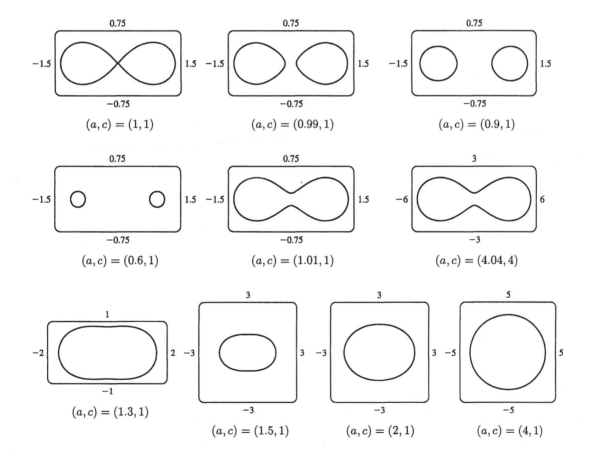

61.
$$\tan\psi = \tan(\phi - \theta) = \frac{\tan\phi - \tan\theta}{1 + \tan\phi\,\tan\theta} = \frac{\dfrac{dy}{dx} - \tan\theta}{1 + \dfrac{dy}{dx}\tan\theta} = \frac{\dfrac{dy/d\theta}{dx/d\theta} - \tan\theta}{1 + \dfrac{dy/d\theta}{dx/d\theta}\tan\theta}$$

$$= \frac{\dfrac{dy}{d\theta} - \dfrac{dx}{d\theta}\tan\theta}{\dfrac{dx}{d\theta} + \dfrac{dy}{d\theta}\tan\theta} = \frac{\left(\dfrac{dr}{d\theta}\sin\theta + r\cos\theta\right) - \tan\theta\left(\dfrac{dr}{d\theta}\cos\theta - r\sin\theta\right)}{\left(\dfrac{dr}{d\theta}\cos\theta - r\sin\theta\right) + \tan\theta\left(\dfrac{dr}{d\theta}\sin\theta + r\cos\theta\right)}$$

$$= \frac{r\cos\theta + r\cdot\dfrac{\sin^2\theta}{\cos\theta}}{\dfrac{dr}{d\theta}\cos\theta + \dfrac{dr}{d\theta}\cdot\dfrac{\sin^2\theta}{\cos\theta}} = \frac{r\cos^2\theta + r\sin^2\theta}{\dfrac{dr}{d\theta}\cos^2\theta + \dfrac{dr}{d\theta}\sin^2\theta} = \frac{r}{dr/d\theta}$$

62. (a) $r = e^\theta \implies dr/d\theta = e^\theta$, so by

Exercise 61, $\tan\psi = r/e^\theta = 1 \implies$

$\psi = \arctan 1 = \frac{\pi}{4}$.

(b) The Cartesian equation of the tangent line at $(1, 0)$ is

$y = x - 1$, and that of the tangent line at $\left(0, e^{\pi/2}\right)$

is $y = e^{\pi/2} - x$.

(c) Let a be the tangent of the angle between

the tangent and radial lines, that is,

$a = \tan\psi$. Then, by Exercise 61,

$$a = \frac{r}{dr/d\theta} \implies \frac{dr}{d\theta} = \frac{1}{a}r \implies$$

$r = Ce^{\theta/a}$ (by Theorem 7.4.2).

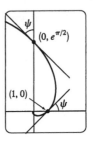

H.2 Areas and Lengths in Polar Coordinates • • • • • • • • • • •

1. $r = \sqrt{\theta}, 0 \le \theta \le \frac{\pi}{4}$. $A = \int_0^{\pi/4} \frac{1}{2}r^2\,d\theta = \int_0^{\pi/4} \frac{1}{2}\left(\sqrt{\theta}\right)^2 d\theta = \int_0^{\pi/4} \frac{1}{2}\theta\,d\theta = \left[\frac{1}{4}\theta^2\right]_0^{\pi/4} = \frac{1}{64}\pi^2$

2. $r = e^{\theta/2}, \pi \le \theta \le 2\pi$. $A = \int_\pi^{2\pi} \frac{1}{2}\left(e^{\theta/2}\right)^2 d\theta = \int_\pi^{2\pi} \frac{1}{2}e^\theta\,d\theta = \frac{1}{2}\left[e^\theta\right]_\pi^{2\pi} = \frac{1}{2}\left(e^{2\pi} - e^\pi\right)$

3. $r = \sin\theta, \frac{\pi}{3} \le \theta \le \frac{2\pi}{3}$.

$$A = \int_{\pi/3}^{2\pi/3} \frac{1}{2}\sin^2\theta\,d\theta = \frac{1}{4}\int_{\pi/3}^{2\pi/3}(1 - \cos 2\theta)\,d\theta = \frac{1}{4}\left[\theta - \frac{1}{2}\sin 2\theta\right]_{\pi/3}^{2\pi/3}$$

$$= \frac{1}{4}\left[\frac{2\pi}{3} - \frac{1}{2}\sin\frac{4\pi}{3} - \frac{\pi}{3} + \frac{1}{2}\sin\frac{2\pi}{3}\right] = \frac{1}{4}\left[\frac{2\pi}{3} - \frac{1}{2}\left(-\frac{\sqrt{3}}{2}\right) - \frac{\pi}{3} + \frac{1}{2}\left(\frac{\sqrt{3}}{2}\right)\right] = \frac{1}{4}\left(\frac{\pi}{3} + \frac{\sqrt{3}}{2}\right) = \frac{\pi}{12} + \frac{\sqrt{3}}{8}$$

4. $r = \sqrt{\sin\theta}, 0 \le \theta \le \pi$. $A = \int_0^\pi \frac{1}{2}\left(\sqrt{\sin\theta}\right)^2 d\theta = \int_0^\pi \frac{1}{2}\sin\theta\,d\theta = \left[-\frac{1}{2}\cos\theta\right]_0^\pi = \frac{1}{2} + \frac{1}{2} = 1$

5. $r = \theta, 0 \le \theta \le \pi$. $A = \int_0^\pi \frac{1}{2}\theta^2 d\theta = \left[\frac{1}{6}\theta^3\right]_0^\pi = \frac{1}{6}\pi^3$

6. $r = 1 + \sin\theta, \frac{\pi}{2} \le \theta \le \pi$.

$$A = \int_{\pi/2}^\pi \frac{1}{2}(1 + \sin\theta)^2 d\theta = \frac{1}{2}\int_{\pi/2}^\pi (1 + 2\sin\theta + \sin^2\theta)\,d\theta = \frac{1}{2}\int_{\pi/2}^\pi \left[1 + 2\sin\theta + \frac{1}{2}(1 - \cos 2\theta)\right]d\theta$$

$$= \frac{1}{2}\left[\theta - 2\cos\theta + \frac{1}{2}\theta - \frac{1}{4}\sin 2\theta\right]_{\pi/2}^\pi = \frac{1}{2}\left[\pi + 2 + \frac{\pi}{2} - 0 - \left(\frac{\pi}{2} - 0 + \frac{\pi}{4} - 0\right)\right] = \frac{1}{2}\left(\frac{3\pi}{4} + 2\right) = \frac{3\pi}{8} + 1$$

7. $r = 4 + 3\sin\theta$, $-\frac{\pi}{2} \le \theta \le \frac{\pi}{2}$.

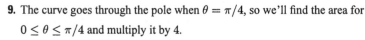

$$A = \int_{-\pi/2}^{\pi/2} \tfrac{1}{2}(4 + 3\sin\theta)^2 d\theta = \tfrac{1}{2}\int_{-\pi/2}^{\pi/2}(16 + 24\sin\theta + 9\sin^2\theta)\,d\theta$$

$$= \tfrac{1}{2}\int_{-\pi/2}^{\pi/2}(16 + 9\sin^2\theta)\,d\theta \quad \text{[by Theorem 5.5.6(b)]}$$

$$= \tfrac{1}{2}\cdot 2\int_0^{\pi/2}\left[16 + 9\cdot\tfrac{1}{2}(1 - \cos 2\theta)\right]d\theta \quad \text{[by Theorem 5.5.6(a)]}$$

$$= \int_0^{\pi/2}\left(\tfrac{41}{2} - \tfrac{9}{2}\cos 2\theta\right)d\theta = \left[\tfrac{41}{2}\theta - \tfrac{9}{4}\sin 2\theta\right]_0^{\pi/2} = \left(\tfrac{41\pi}{4} - 0\right) - (0 - 0) = \tfrac{41\pi}{4}$$

8. $r = \sin 4\theta$, $0 \le \theta \le \frac{\pi}{4}$. $A = \int_0^{\pi/4}\tfrac{1}{2}\sin^2 4\theta\,d\theta = \int_0^{\pi/4}\tfrac{1}{4}(1 - \cos 8\theta)\,d\theta = \left[\tfrac{1}{4}\theta - \tfrac{1}{32}\sin 8\theta\right]_0^{\pi/4} = \tfrac{\pi}{16}$

9. The curve goes through the pole when $\theta = \pi/4$, so we'll find the area for
$0 \le \theta \le \pi/4$ and multiply it by 4.

$$A = 4\int_0^{\pi/4}\tfrac{1}{2}r^2\,d\theta = 2\int_0^{\pi/4}(4\cos 2\theta)\,d\theta$$

$$= 8\int_0^{\pi/4}\cos 2\theta\,d\theta = 4\left[\sin 2\theta\right]_0^{\pi/4} = 4$$

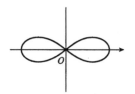

10. $A = \int_0^{2\pi}\tfrac{1}{2}r^2\,d\theta = \int_0^{2\pi}\tfrac{1}{2}\left[3(1 + \cos\theta)\right]^2 d\theta$

$$= \tfrac{9}{2}\int_0^{2\pi}(1 + 2\cos\theta + \cos^2\theta)\,d\theta$$

$$= \tfrac{9}{2}\int_0^{2\pi}\left[1 + 2\cos\theta + \tfrac{1}{2}(1 + \cos 2\theta)\right]d\theta$$

$$= \tfrac{9}{2}\left[\tfrac{3}{2}\theta + 2\sin\theta + \tfrac{1}{4}\sin 2\theta\right]_0^{2\pi} = \tfrac{27}{2}\pi$$

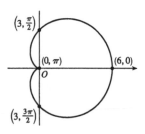

$(3, \frac{\pi}{2})$

$(0, \pi)$ $(6, 0)$

$(3, \frac{3\pi}{2})$

11. The curve is symmetric about the vertical line $\theta = \pi/2$, so we'll find the area of the right side and double it.

$$A = 2\int_{-\pi/2}^{\pi/2}\tfrac{1}{2}(4 - \sin\theta)^2\,d\theta = \int_{-\pi/2}^{\pi/2}(16 - 8\sin\theta + \sin^2\theta)\,d\theta$$

$$= \int_{-\pi/2}^{\pi/2}(16 + \sin^2\theta)\,d\theta \quad \text{[by Theorem 5.5.6(b)]}$$

$$= 2\int_0^{\pi/2}(16 + \sin^2\theta)\,d\theta \quad \text{[by Theorem 5.5.6(a)]}$$

$$= 2\int_0^{\pi/2}\left[16 + \tfrac{1}{2}(1 - \cos 2\theta)\right]d\theta = 2\left[\tfrac{33}{2}\theta - \tfrac{1}{4}\sin 2\theta\right]_0^{\pi/2}$$

$$= \tfrac{33\pi}{2}$$

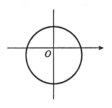

12. $A = 3\int_0^{\pi/3}\tfrac{1}{2}r^2\,d\theta = \tfrac{3}{2}\int_0^{\pi/3}\sin^2 3\theta\,d\theta$

$$= \tfrac{3}{2}\int_0^{\pi/3}\tfrac{1}{2}(1 - \cos 6\theta)\,d\theta = \tfrac{3}{4}\left[\theta - \tfrac{1}{6}\sin 6\theta\right]_0^{\pi/3}$$

$$= \tfrac{3}{4}\left(\tfrac{\pi}{3}\right) = \tfrac{\pi}{4}$$

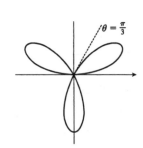

$\theta = \frac{\pi}{3}$

13. By symmetry, the total area is twice the area enclosed above the polar axis, so

$$A = 2\int_0^\pi \tfrac{1}{2}r^2\,d\theta = \int_0^\pi (2 + \cos 6\theta)^2\,d\theta = \int_0^\pi (4 + 4\cos 6\theta + \cos^2 6\theta)\,d\theta$$

$$= \int_0^\pi \left[4 + 4\cos 6\theta + \tfrac{1}{2}(1 + \cos 12\theta)\right] d\theta$$

$$= \left[4\theta + 4\left(\tfrac{1}{6}\sin 6\theta\right) + \left(\tfrac{1}{24}\sin 12\theta + \tfrac{1}{2}\theta\right)\right]_0^\pi = 4\pi + \tfrac{\pi}{2} = \tfrac{9\pi}{2}$$

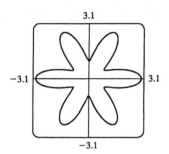

14. Note that the entire curve $r = 2\sin\theta\,\cos^2\theta$ is generated by $\theta \in [0, \pi]$. The radius is positive on this interval, so the area enclosed is

$$A = \int_0^\pi \tfrac{1}{2}r^2\,d\theta = \int_0^\pi \tfrac{1}{2}\left(2\sin\theta\,\cos^2\theta\right)^2 d\theta = 2\int_0^\pi \sin^2\theta\,\cos^4\theta\,d\theta$$

$$= 2\int_0^\pi (\sin\theta\,\cos\theta)^2\cos^2\theta\,d\theta = 2\int_0^\pi \left(\tfrac{1}{2}\sin 2\theta\right)^2\cos^2\theta\,d\theta$$

$$= \tfrac{1}{4}\int_0^\pi \sin^2 2\theta\,(\cos 2\theta + 1)\,d\theta = \tfrac{1}{4}\left[\int_0^\pi \sin^2 2\theta\,\cos 2\theta\,d\theta + \int_0^\pi \sin^2 2\theta\,d\theta\right]$$

$$= \tfrac{1}{4}\left[\tfrac{1}{2}\theta - \tfrac{1}{4}\sin 4\theta\right]_0^\pi \quad \text{[the first integral vanishes]} \quad = \tfrac{\pi}{8}$$

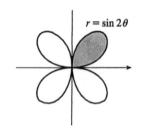

15. The shaded loop is traced out from $\theta = 0$ to $\theta = \pi/2$.

$$A = \int_0^{\pi/2} \tfrac{1}{2}r^2\,d\theta = \tfrac{1}{2}\int_0^{\pi/2}\sin^2 2\theta\,d\theta$$

$$= \tfrac{1}{2}\int_0^{\pi/2}\tfrac{1}{2}(1 - \cos 4\theta)\,d\theta = \tfrac{1}{4}\left[\theta - \tfrac{1}{4}\sin 4\theta\right]_0^{\pi/2}$$

$$= \tfrac{1}{4}\left(\tfrac{\pi}{2}\right) = \tfrac{\pi}{8}$$

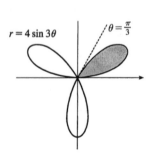

$r = \sin 2\theta$

16. $A = \int_0^{\pi/3}\tfrac{1}{2}(4\sin 3\theta)^2\,d\theta = 8\int_0^{\pi/3}\sin^2 3\theta\,d\theta$

$$= 4\int_0^{\pi/3}(1 - \cos 6\theta)\,d\theta = 4\left[\theta - \tfrac{1}{6}\sin 6\theta\right]_0^{\pi/3} = \tfrac{4\pi}{3}$$

$r = 4\sin 3\theta$

$\theta = \tfrac{\pi}{3}$

17.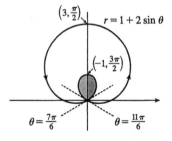

$r = 1 + 2\sin\theta$ (rect.)

$\left(3, \tfrac{\pi}{2}\right)$

$r = 1 + 2\sin\theta$

$\left(-1, \tfrac{3\pi}{2}\right)$

$\theta = \tfrac{7\pi}{6}$

$\theta = \tfrac{11\pi}{6}$

This is a limaçon, with inner loop traced out between $\theta = \tfrac{7\pi}{6}$ and $\tfrac{11\pi}{6}$ [found by solving $r = 0$].

$A = 2\int_{7\pi/6}^{3\pi/2} \frac{1}{2}(1 + 2\sin\theta)^2 \, d\theta = \int_{7\pi/6}^{3\pi/2} \left(1 + 4\sin\theta + 4\sin^2\theta\right) d\theta = \int_{7\pi/6}^{3\pi/2} \left[1 + 4\sin\theta + 4 \cdot \frac{1}{2}(1 - \cos 2\theta)\right] d\theta$

$= [\theta - 4\cos\theta + 2\theta - \sin 2\theta]_{7\pi/6}^{3\pi/2} = \left(\frac{9\pi}{2}\right) - \left(\frac{7\pi}{2} + 2\sqrt{3} - \frac{\sqrt{3}}{2}\right) = \pi - \frac{3\sqrt{3}}{2}$

18. $2 + 3\cos\theta = 0 \;\Rightarrow\; \cos\theta = -\frac{2}{3} \;\Rightarrow\; \theta = \cos^{-1}\left(-\frac{2}{3}\right) \; [= \alpha] \text{ or } 2\pi - \cos^{-1}\left(-\frac{2}{3}\right) \;\Rightarrow$

$A = 2\int_{\alpha}^{\pi} \frac{1}{2}(2 + 3\cos\theta)^2 \, d\theta = \int_{\alpha}^{\pi} \left(4 + 12\cos\theta + 9\cos^2\theta\right) d\theta = \int_{\alpha}^{\pi}\left(\frac{17}{2} + 12\cos\theta + \frac{9}{2}\cos 2\theta\right) d\theta$

$= \left[\frac{17}{2}\theta + 12\sin\theta + \frac{9}{4}\sin 2\theta\right]_{\alpha}^{\pi} = \frac{17}{2}(\pi - \alpha) - 12\sin\alpha - \frac{9}{2}\sin\alpha\cos\alpha$

$= \frac{17}{2}\left[\pi - \cos^{-1}\left(-\frac{2}{3}\right)\right] - 12\left(\frac{\sqrt{5}}{3}\right) - \frac{9}{2}\left(\frac{\sqrt{5}}{3}\right)\left(-\frac{2}{3}\right) = \frac{17}{2}\cos^{-1}\left(\frac{2}{3}\right) - 3\sqrt{5}$

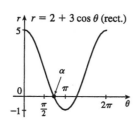

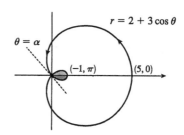

19. $4\sin\theta = 2 \;\Leftrightarrow\; \sin\theta = \frac{1}{2} \;\Leftrightarrow\; \theta = \frac{\pi}{6} \text{ or } \frac{5\pi}{6}$ (for $0 \le \theta \le 2\pi$). We'll subtract the unshaded area from the shaded area for $\pi/6 \le \theta \le \pi/2$ and double that value.

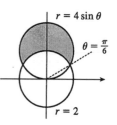

$A = 2\int_{\pi/6}^{\pi/2} \frac{1}{2}(4\sin\theta)^2 \, d\theta - 2\int_{\pi/6}^{\pi/2} \frac{1}{2}(2)^2 \, d\theta = 2\int_{\pi/6}^{\pi/2} \frac{1}{2}\left[(4\sin\theta)^2 - 2^2\right] d\theta$

$= \int_{\pi/6}^{\pi/2} \left(16\sin^2\theta - 4\right) d\theta = \int_{\pi/6}^{\pi/2} [8(1 - \cos 2\theta) - 4] \, d\theta$

$= \int_{\pi/6}^{\pi/2}(4 - 8\cos 2\theta) \, d\theta = [4\theta - 4\sin 2\theta]_{\pi/6}^{\pi/2}$

$= (2\pi - 0) - \left(\frac{2\pi}{3} - 4 \cdot \frac{\sqrt{3}}{2}\right) = \frac{4}{3}\pi + 2\sqrt{3}$

20. $3\cos\theta = 2 - \cos\theta \;\Rightarrow\; \cos\theta = \frac{1}{2} \;\Rightarrow\; \theta = \pm\frac{\pi}{3} \;\Rightarrow$

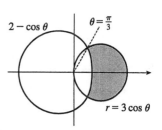

$A = 2\int_{0}^{\pi/3} \frac{1}{2}\left[(3\cos\theta)^2 - (2 - \cos\theta)^2\right] d\theta$

$= \int_{0}^{\pi/3}\left(8\cos^2\theta + 4\cos\theta - 4\right) d\theta = \int_{0}^{\pi/3}\left[4(2\cos^2\theta - 1) + 4\cos\theta\right] d\theta$

$= \int_{0}^{\pi/3}\left(4\cos 2\theta + 4\cos\theta\right) d\theta = [2\sin 2\theta + 4\sin\theta]_{0}^{\pi/3}$

$= 2 \cdot \frac{\sqrt{3}}{2} + 4 \cdot \frac{\sqrt{3}}{2} = 3\sqrt{3}$

21. $3\cos\theta = 1 + \cos\theta \ \Leftrightarrow \ \cos\theta = \frac{1}{2} \ \Rightarrow \ \theta = \frac{\pi}{3} \text{ or } -\frac{\pi}{3}.$

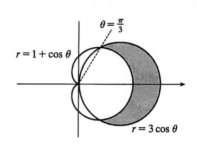

$r = 1 + \cos\theta$

$r = 3\cos\theta$

$\theta = \frac{\pi}{3}$

$$A = 2\int_0^{\pi/3} \frac{1}{2}\left[(3\cos\theta)^2 - (1+\cos\theta)^2\right]d\theta$$

$$= \int_0^{\pi/3}\left(8\cos^2\theta - 2\cos\theta - 1\right)d\theta$$

$$= \int_0^{\pi/3}\left[4(1 + \cos 2\theta) - 2\cos\theta - 1\right]d\theta$$

$$= \int_0^{\pi/3}\left(3 + 4\cos 2\theta - 2\cos\theta\right)d\theta = \left[3\theta + 2\sin 2\theta - 2\sin\theta\right]_0^{\pi/3}$$

$$= \pi + \sqrt{3} - \sqrt{3} = \pi$$

22. Note that $r = 1 + \cos\theta$ goes through the pole when $\theta = \pi$, but $r = 3\cos\theta$ goes through the pole when $\theta = \pi/2$.

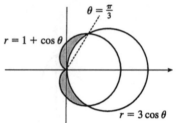

$r = 1 + \cos\theta$

$r = 3\cos\theta$

$\theta = \frac{\pi}{3}$

$$A = 2\int_{\pi/3}^{\pi}\frac{1}{2}(1+\cos\theta)^2\,d\theta - 2\int_{\pi/3}^{\pi/2}\frac{1}{2}(3\cos\theta)^2\,d\theta$$

$$= \int_{\pi/3}^{\pi}\left[1 + 2\cos\theta + \frac{1}{2}(1+\cos 2\theta)\right]d\theta - \frac{9}{2}\int_{\pi/3}^{\pi/2}(1+\cos 2\theta)\,d\theta$$

$$= \left[\theta + 2\sin\theta + \frac{1}{2}\left(\theta + \frac{1}{2}\sin 2\theta\right)\right]_{\pi/3}^{\pi} - \frac{9}{2}\left[\theta + \frac{1}{2}\sin 2\theta\right]_{\pi/3}^{\pi/2}$$

$$= \left(\pi - \frac{9}{8}\sqrt{3}\right) - \frac{9}{2}\left(\frac{\pi}{6} - \frac{1}{4}\sqrt{3}\right) = \frac{\pi}{4}$$

23. $A = 2\int_0^{\pi/4}\frac{1}{2}\sin^2\theta\,d\theta = \int_0^{\pi/4}\frac{1}{2}(1-\cos 2\theta)\,d\theta$

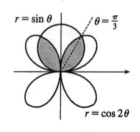

$r = \sin\theta$ $\theta = \frac{\pi}{4}$

$r = \cos\theta$

O

$$= \frac{1}{2}\left[\theta - \frac{1}{2}\sin 2\theta\right]_0^{\pi/4} = \frac{1}{2}\left[\left(\frac{\pi}{4} - \frac{1}{2}\cdot 1\right) - (0 - 0)\right]$$

$$= \frac{1}{8}\pi - \frac{1}{4}$$

24. $r = \sin 2\theta$ takes on both positive and negative values.

$\sin\theta = \pm\sin 2\theta = \pm 2\sin\theta\cos\theta \ \Rightarrow \ \sin\theta\,(1 \pm 2\cos\theta) = 0.$ From the figure we can see that the intersections occur where $\cos\theta = \pm\frac{1}{2}$, or $\theta = \frac{\pi}{3}$ and $\frac{2\pi}{3}$.

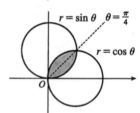

$r = \sin\theta$ $\theta = \frac{\pi}{3}$

$r = \cos 2\theta$

$$A = 2\left[\int_0^{\pi/3}\frac{1}{2}\sin^2\theta\,d\theta + \int_{\pi/3}^{\pi/2}\frac{1}{2}\sin^2 2\theta\,d\theta\right]$$

$$= \int_0^{\pi/3}\frac{1}{2}(1-\cos 2\theta)\,d\theta + \int_{\pi/3}^{\pi/2}\frac{1}{2}(1-\cos 4\theta)\,d\theta$$

$$= \frac{1}{2}\left[\theta - \frac{1}{2}\sin 2\theta\right]_0^{\pi/3} + \frac{1}{2}\left[\theta - \frac{1}{4}\sin 4\theta\right]_{\pi/3}^{\pi/2} = \frac{4\pi - 3\sqrt{3}}{16}$$

25. $\sin 2\theta = \cos 2\theta \ \Rightarrow \ \dfrac{\sin 2\theta}{\cos 2\theta} = 1 \ \Rightarrow \ \tan 2\theta = 1 \ \Rightarrow \ 2\theta = \frac{\pi}{4} \ \Rightarrow$

$\theta = \frac{\pi}{8} \ \Rightarrow$

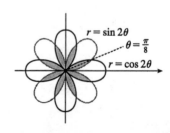

$r = \sin 2\theta$

$\theta = \frac{\pi}{8}$

$r = \cos 2\theta$

$$A = 8\cdot 2\int_0^{\pi/8}\frac{1}{2}\sin^2 2\theta\,d\theta = 8\int_0^{\pi/8}\frac{1}{2}(1-\cos 4\theta)\,d\theta$$

$$= 4\left[\theta - \frac{1}{4}\sin 4\theta\right]_0^{\pi/8} = 4\left(\frac{\pi}{8} - \frac{1}{4}\cdot 1\right) = \frac{1}{2}\pi - 1$$

26. $2 \sin 2\theta = 1^2 \Rightarrow \sin 2\theta = \frac{1}{2} \Rightarrow 2\theta = \frac{\pi}{6}$ or $\frac{5\pi}{6} \Rightarrow \theta = \frac{\pi}{12}$ or $\frac{5\pi}{12}$.

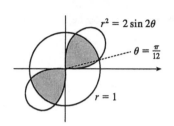

$$A = 4 \left[\int_0^{\pi/12} \frac{1}{2} \cdot 2 \sin 2\theta \, d\theta + \int_{\pi/12}^{\pi/4} \frac{1}{2} (1^2) \, d\theta \right]$$

$$= [-2 \cos 2\theta]_0^{\pi/12} + [2\theta]_{\pi/12}^{\pi/4} = -2 \left(\frac{\sqrt{3}}{2} - 1 \right) + 2 \left(\frac{1}{4}\pi - \frac{1}{12}\pi \right)$$

$$= 2 - \sqrt{3} + \frac{\pi}{3}$$

27. The darker shaded region (from $\theta = 0$ to $\theta = 2\pi/3$) represents $\frac{1}{2}$ of the desired area plus $\frac{1}{2}$ of the area of the inner loop. From this area, we'll subtract $\frac{1}{2}$ of the area of the inner loop (the lighter shaded region from $\theta = 2\pi/3$ to $\theta = \pi$), and then double that difference to obtain the desired area.

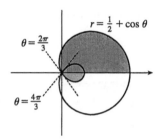

$$A = 2 \left[\int_0^{2\pi/3} \frac{1}{2} \left(\frac{1}{2} + \cos \theta \right)^2 d\theta - \int_{2\pi/3}^{\pi} \frac{1}{2} \left(\frac{1}{2} + \cos \theta \right)^2 d\theta \right]$$

$$= \int_0^{2\pi/3} \left(\frac{1}{4} + \cos \theta + \cos^2 \theta \right) d\theta - \int_{2\pi/3}^{\pi} \left(\frac{1}{4} + \cos \theta + \cos^2 \theta \right) d\theta$$

$$= \int_0^{2\pi/3} \left[\frac{1}{4} + \cos \theta + \frac{1}{2}(1 + \cos 2\theta) \right] d\theta$$

$$\qquad - \int_{2\pi/3}^{\pi} \left[\frac{1}{4} + \cos \theta + \frac{1}{2}(1 + \cos 2\theta) \right] d\theta$$

$$= \left[\frac{\theta}{4} + \sin \theta + \frac{\theta}{2} + \frac{\sin 2\theta}{4} \right]_0^{2\pi/3} - \left[\frac{\theta}{4} + \sin \theta + \frac{\theta}{2} + \frac{\sin 2\theta}{4} \right]_{2\pi/3}^{\pi}$$

$$= \left(\frac{\pi}{6} + \frac{\sqrt{3}}{2} + \frac{\pi}{3} - \frac{\sqrt{3}}{8} \right) - \left(\frac{\pi}{4} + \frac{\pi}{2} \right) + \left(\frac{\pi}{6} + \frac{\sqrt{3}}{2} + \frac{\pi}{3} - \frac{\sqrt{3}}{8} \right)$$

$$= \frac{\pi}{4} + \frac{3}{4}\sqrt{3} = \frac{1}{4} \left(\pi + 3\sqrt{3} \right)$$

28. The points of intersection occur where $\sqrt{1 - 0.8 \sin^2 \theta} = \sin \theta \Leftrightarrow 1.8 \sin^2 \theta = 1 \Leftrightarrow$

$\theta = \arcsin \sqrt{\frac{5}{9}}$ [$= \alpha$, so $\cos \alpha = \frac{2}{3}$]. So the area is

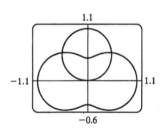

$$A = 2 \int_0^{\alpha} \frac{1}{2} \sin^2 \theta \, d\theta + 2 \int_{\alpha}^{\pi/2} \frac{1}{2} \left(\sqrt{1 - 0.8 \sin^2 \theta} \right)^2 d\theta$$

$$= \left[\frac{1}{2}\theta - \frac{1}{4} \sin 2\theta \right]_0^{\alpha} + \left[\theta - 0.8 \left(\frac{1}{2}\theta - \frac{1}{4} \sin 2\theta \right) \right]_{\alpha}^{\pi/2}$$

$$= \frac{1}{2}\alpha - \frac{1}{4}(2 \sin \alpha \cos \alpha) + 0.6 \cdot \frac{\pi}{2} - [0.6\alpha + 0.2(2 \sin \alpha \cos \alpha)]$$

$$= \frac{1}{2} \arcsin \frac{\sqrt{5}}{3} - \frac{1}{2} \frac{\sqrt{5}}{3} \frac{2}{3} + 0.3\pi - 0.6 \arcsin \frac{\sqrt{5}}{3} - 0.4 \cdot \frac{\sqrt{5}}{3} \frac{2}{3}$$

$$= \frac{3}{10}\pi - \frac{1}{10} \arcsin \frac{\sqrt{5}}{3} - \frac{1}{5}\sqrt{5} \approx 0.411$$

29. The curves intersect at the pole since $\left(0, \frac{\pi}{2} \right)$ satisfies $r = \cos \theta$ and

$(0, 0)$ satisfies $r = 1 - \cos \theta$. Now $\cos \theta = 1 - \cos \theta \Rightarrow$

$2 \cos \theta = 1 \Rightarrow \cos \theta = \frac{1}{2} \Rightarrow \theta = \frac{\pi}{3}$ or $\frac{5\pi}{3} \Rightarrow$

the other intersection points are $\left(\frac{1}{2}, \frac{\pi}{3} \right)$ and $\left(\frac{1}{2}, \frac{5\pi}{3} \right)$.

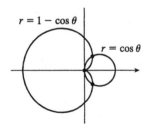

30. Clearly the pole lies on both curves. $\sin 3\theta = \cos 3\theta \implies$
$\tan 3\theta = 1 \implies 3\theta = \frac{\pi}{4} + n\pi$ (n any integer) $\implies$
$\theta = \frac{\pi}{12} + \frac{\pi}{3}n \implies \theta = \frac{\pi}{12}, \frac{5\pi}{12},$ or $\frac{3\pi}{4}$, so the three remaining
intersection points are $\left(\frac{1}{\sqrt{2}}, \frac{\pi}{12}\right), \left(-\frac{1}{\sqrt{2}}, \frac{5\pi}{12}\right),$ and $\left(\frac{1}{\sqrt{2}}, \frac{3\pi}{4}\right).$

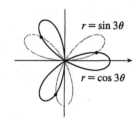

31. The pole is a point of intersection. $\sin \theta = \sin 2\theta = 2\sin\theta \cos\theta$
$\Leftrightarrow \sin\theta (1 - 2\cos\theta) = 0 \Leftrightarrow \sin\theta = 0$ or $\cos\theta = \frac{1}{2} \implies$
$\theta = 0, \pi, \frac{\pi}{3}, -\frac{\pi}{3} \implies \left(\frac{\sqrt{3}}{2}, \frac{\pi}{3}\right)$ and $\left(\frac{\sqrt{3}}{2}, \frac{2\pi}{3}\right)$ (by symmetry) are
the other intersection points.

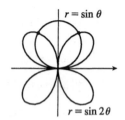

32. Clearly the pole is a point of intersection. $\sin 2\theta = \cos 2\theta \implies$
$\tan 2\theta = 1 \implies 2\theta = \frac{\pi}{4} + 2n\pi$ (since $\sin 2\theta$ and $\cos 2\theta$ must be
positive in the equations) $\implies \theta = \frac{\pi}{8} + n\pi \implies \theta = \frac{\pi}{8}$ or $\frac{9\pi}{8}$.
So the curves also intersect at $\left(\frac{1}{\sqrt[4]{2}}, \frac{\pi}{8}\right)$ and $\left(\frac{1}{\sqrt[4]{2}}, \frac{9\pi}{8}\right).$

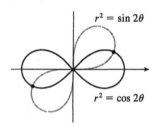

33.

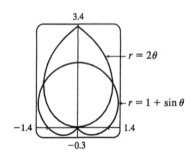

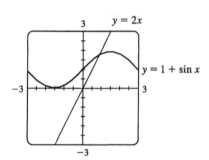

From the first graph, we see that the pole is one point of intersection. By zooming in or using the cursor, we find the
θ-values of the intersection points to be $\alpha \approx 0.88786 \approx 0.89$ and $\pi - \alpha \approx 2.25$. (The first of these values may be
more easily estimated by plotting $y = 1 + \sin x$ and $y = 2x$ in rectangular coordinates; see the second graph.)
By symmetry, the total area contained is twice the area contained in the first quadrant, that is,

$$A = 2\int_0^\alpha \frac{1}{2}(2\theta)^2 \, d\theta + 2\int_\alpha^{\pi/2} \frac{1}{2}(1+\sin\theta)^2 \, d\theta = \int_0^\alpha 4\theta^2 \, d\theta + \int_\alpha^{\pi/2}\left[1 + 2\sin\theta + \frac{1}{2}(1-\cos 2\theta)\right] d\theta$$

$$= \left[\frac{4}{3}\theta^3\right]_0^\alpha + \left[\theta - 2\cos\theta + \left(\frac{1}{2}\theta - \frac{1}{4}\sin 2\theta\right)\right]_\alpha^{\pi/2}$$

$$= \frac{4}{3}\alpha^3 + \left[\left(\frac{\pi}{2} + \frac{\pi}{4}\right) - \left(\alpha - 2\cos\alpha + \frac{1}{2}\alpha - \frac{1}{4}\sin 2\alpha\right)\right] \approx 3.4645$$

34.

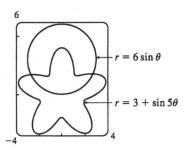   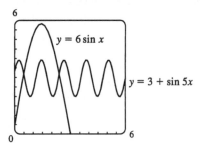

From the first graph, it appears that the θ-values of the points of intersection are $\alpha \approx 0.57504 \approx 0.58$ and $\pi - \alpha \approx 2.57$. (These values may be more easily estimated by plotting $y = 3 + \sin 5x$ and $y = 6 \sin x$ in rectangular coordinates; see the second graph.) By symmetry, the total area enclosed in both curves is

$$A = 2 \int_0^\alpha \tfrac{1}{2}(6\sin\theta)^2 \, d\theta + 2 \int_\alpha^{\pi/2} \tfrac{1}{2}(3 + \sin 5\theta)^2 \, d\theta = \int_0^\alpha 36 \sin^2\theta \, d\theta + \int_\alpha^{\pi/2} (9 + 6\sin 5\theta + \sin^2 5\theta) \, d\theta$$

$$= \int_0^\alpha 36 \cdot \tfrac{1}{2}(1 - \cos 2\theta) \, d\theta + \int_\alpha^{\pi/2} \left[9 + 6\sin 5\theta + \tfrac{1}{2}(1 - \cos 10\theta)\right] d\theta$$

$$= \left[36\left(\tfrac{1}{2}\theta - \tfrac{1}{4}\sin 2\theta\right)\right]_0^\alpha + \left[9\theta - \tfrac{6}{5}\cos 5\theta + \left(\tfrac{1}{2}\theta - \tfrac{1}{20}\sin 10\theta\right)\right]_\alpha^{\pi/2} \approx 10.41$$

35. $L = \int_a^b \sqrt{r^2 + (dr/d\theta)^2} \, d\theta = \int_0^{3\pi/4} \sqrt{(5\cos\theta)^2 + (-5\sin\theta)^2} \, d\theta = \int_0^{3\pi/4} \sqrt{25\cos^2\theta + 25\sin^2\theta} \, d\theta$

$= 5\int_0^{3\pi/4} \sqrt{\cos^2\theta + \sin^2\theta} \, d\theta = 5\int_0^{3\pi/4} d\theta = 5[\theta]_0^{3\pi/4} = 5\left(\tfrac{3\pi}{4}\right) = \tfrac{15}{4}\pi$

36. $L = \int_a^b \sqrt{r^2 + (dr/d\theta)^2} \, d\theta = \int_0^{2\pi} \sqrt{(e^{2\theta})^2 + (2e^{2\theta})^2} \, d\theta = \int_0^{2\pi} \sqrt{e^{4\theta} + 4e^{4\theta}} \, d\theta = \int_0^{2\pi} \sqrt{5e^{4\theta}} \, d\theta$

$= \sqrt{5}\int_0^{2\pi} e^{2\theta} \, d\theta = \tfrac{\sqrt{5}}{2}\left[e^{2\theta}\right]_0^{2\pi} = \tfrac{\sqrt{5}}{2}\left(e^{4\pi} - 1\right)$

37. $L = \int_a^b \sqrt{r^2 + (dr/d\theta)^2} \, d\theta = \int_0^{2\pi} \sqrt{(\theta^2)^2 + (2\theta)^2} \, d\theta = \int_0^{2\pi} \sqrt{\theta^4 + 4\theta^2} \, d\theta$

$= \int_0^{2\pi} \sqrt{\theta^2(\theta^2 + 4)} \, d\theta = \int_0^{2\pi} \theta\sqrt{\theta^2 + 4} \, d\theta$

Now let $u = \theta^2 + 4$, so that $du = 2\theta \, d\theta \; \left[\theta \, d\theta = \tfrac{1}{2} \, du\right]$ and

$$\int_0^{2\pi} \theta\sqrt{\theta^2 + 4} \, d\theta = \int_4^{4\pi^2 + 4} \tfrac{1}{2}\sqrt{u} \, du = \tfrac{1}{2} \cdot \tfrac{2}{3}\left[u^{3/2}\right]_4^{4(\pi^2 + 1)} = \tfrac{1}{3}\left[4^{3/2}(\pi^2 + 1)^{3/2} - 4^{3/2}\right]$$

$$= \tfrac{8}{3}\left[(\pi^2 + 1)^{3/2} - 1\right]$$

38. $L = \int_a^b \sqrt{r^2 + (dr/d\theta)^2} \, d\theta = \int_0^{2\pi} \sqrt{\theta^2 + 1} \, d\theta \overset{21}{=} \left[\tfrac{\theta}{2}\sqrt{\theta^2 + 1} + \tfrac{1}{2}\ln\left(\theta + \sqrt{\theta^2 + 1}\right)\right]_0^{2\pi}$

$= \pi\sqrt{4\pi^2 + 1} + \tfrac{1}{2}\ln\left(2\pi + \sqrt{4\pi^2 + 1}\right)$

39. From Figure 4 in Example 1 with $r = \cos 2\theta$ and $r' = -2\sin 2\theta$,

$$L = \int_{-\pi/4}^{\pi/4} \sqrt{r^2 + (r')^2} \, d\theta = 2\int_0^{\pi/4} \sqrt{\cos^2 2\theta + 4\sin^2 2\theta} \, d\theta \approx 2(1.211056) \approx 2.4221$$

40. We first determine the values of θ for which $r = 4 + 2\sec\theta$ goes

through the pole. $4 + 2\sec\theta = 0 \;\Rightarrow\; \sec\theta = -2 \;\Rightarrow\;$

$\cos\theta = -\frac{1}{2} \;\Rightarrow\; \theta = \frac{2\pi}{3}, \frac{4\pi}{3}$.

$L = \int_{2\pi/3}^{4\pi/3} \sqrt{r^2 + (r')^2}\, d\theta$

$\quad = \int_{2\pi/3}^{4\pi/3} \sqrt{(4 + 2\sec\theta)^2 + (2\sec\theta\tan\theta)^2}\, d\theta \approx 5.8128$

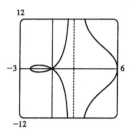

| **Discovery Project** | **Conic Sections in Polar Coordinates** |

---

1. We see from Figure 1 that $|PF| = r$ and $|Pl| = d - r\cos\theta$. Thus, the condition $|PF|/|Pl| = e$, or $|PF| = e\,|Pl|$, becomes $r = e(d - r\cos\theta)$.

2. If we square both sides of $r = e(d - r\cos\theta)$ and convert to rectangular coordinates, we get
$$x^2 + y^2 = e^2(d - x)^2 = e^2(d^2 - 2dx + x^2) \text{ or } (1 - e^2)x^2 + 2de^2x + y^2 = e^2d^2.$$ After completing the square,

we have $\left(x + \dfrac{e^2d}{1 - e^2}\right)^2 + \dfrac{y^2}{1 - e^2} = \dfrac{e^2d^2}{(1 - e^2)^2}$ **(1)**. If $e < 1$, we recognize Equation 1 as the equation of an

ellipse. In fact, it is of the form $\dfrac{(x - h)^2}{a^2} + \dfrac{y^2}{b^2} = 1$, where $h = -\dfrac{e^2d}{1 - e^2}$, $a^2 = \dfrac{e^2d^2}{(1 - e^2)^2}$ **(⋆)**, and

$b^2 = \dfrac{e^2d^2}{1 - e^2}$.

3. If $e > 1$, then $1 - e^2 < 0$ and we see that Equation 1 represents a hyperbola. Just as we did in Problem 2, we could

rewrite Equation 1 in the form $\dfrac{(x - h)^2}{a^2} - \dfrac{y^2}{b^2} = 1$ and see that $e = \dfrac{c}{a}$, where $c^2 = a^2 + b^2$.

4. By solving $r = e(d - r\cos\theta)$ for r, we see that the polar equation of the conic shown in Figure 1 can be written as

$r = \dfrac{ed}{1 + e\cos\theta}$.

5. (a) $r = \dfrac{4}{1 + 3\cos\theta} \;\Rightarrow\; e = 3 > 1 \;\Rightarrow\;$ hyperbola;

$ed = 4 \;\Rightarrow\; d = \frac{4}{3} \;\Rightarrow\;$ directrix $x = \frac{4}{3}$; vertices $(1, 0)$ and

$(-2, \pi) = (2, 0)$; center $\left(\frac{3}{2}, 0\right)$; asymptotes parallel to

$\theta = \pm\cos^{-1}\left(-\frac{1}{3}\right)$

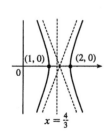

(b) $r = \dfrac{8}{3 + 3\cos\theta} = \dfrac{\frac{8}{3}}{1 + \cos\theta} \Rightarrow e = 1$

$\Rightarrow$ parabola; $ed = \frac{8}{3} \Rightarrow d = \frac{8}{3} \Rightarrow$

directrix $x = \frac{8}{3}$; vertex $\left(\frac{4}{3}, 0\right)$

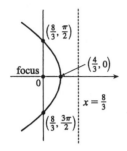

(c) $r = \dfrac{2}{2 + \cos\theta} = \dfrac{1}{1 + \frac{1}{2}\cos\theta} \Rightarrow$

$e = \frac{1}{2} < 1 \Rightarrow$ ellipse;

$ed = 1 \Rightarrow d = 2 \Rightarrow$ directrix $x = 2$;

vertices $\left(\frac{2}{3}, 0\right)$ and $(2, \pi) = (-2, 0)$.

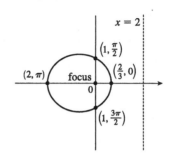

6. For $e < 1$ the curve is an ellipse. It is nearly circular when e is close to 0. As e increases, the graph is stretched out to the right, and grows larger (that is, its right-hand focus moves to the right while its left-hand focus remains at the origin.) At $e = 1$, the curve becomes a parabola with focus at the origin.

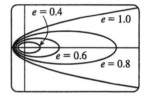

7. (a) If the directrix is $x = d$, then $r = \dfrac{ed}{1 + e\cos\theta}$ and, from (⋆) in Problem 2,

$a^2 = \dfrac{e^2 d^2}{(1 - e^2)^2} \Rightarrow ed = a(1 - e^2)$. Therefore, $r = \dfrac{a(1 - e^2)}{1 + e\cos\theta}$.

(b) $e = 0.017$ and the length of the major axis $= 2a = 2.99 \times 10^8 \Rightarrow a = 1.495 \times 10^8$. Therefore,

$r = \dfrac{1.495 \times 10^8 \left[1 - (0.017)^2\right]}{1 + 0.017\cos\theta} \approx \dfrac{1.495 \times 10^8}{1 + 0.017\cos\theta}$.

8. (a) The Sun is at point F in Figure 1 so that perihelion is in the positive x-direction and aphelion is in the negative x-direction. At perihelion, $\theta = 0$, so $r = \dfrac{a(1 - e^2)}{1 + e\cos 0} = \dfrac{a(1 - e)(1 + e)}{1 + e} = a(1 - e)$.

At aphelion, $\theta = \pi$, so $r = \dfrac{a(1 - e^2)}{1 + e\cos\pi} = \dfrac{a(1 - e)(1 + e)}{1 - e} = a(1 + e)$.

(b) At perihelion, $r = a(1 - e) \approx \left(1.495 \times 10^8\right)(1 - 0.017) \approx 1.47 \times 10^8$ km.

At aphelion, $r = a(1 + e) \approx \left(1.495 \times 10^8\right)(1 + 0.017) \approx 1.52 \times 10^8$ km.

9. (a) The minimum distance is at perihelion, where

$4.6 \times 10^7 = r = a(1 - e) = a(1 - 0.206) = a(0.794) \Rightarrow a = 4.6 \times 10^7/0.794$. So the maximum distance, which is at aphelion, is $r = a(1 + e) = \left(4.6 \times 10^7/0.794\right)(1.206) \approx 7.0 \times 10^7$ km.

(b) From part (a), we have $e = 0.206$ and $a(1 - e) = 4.6 \times 10^7$ km. Thus, $a = 4.6 \times 10^7/0.794$. From Problem 7, we can write the equation of Mercury's orbit as $r = a\dfrac{1 - e^2}{1 + e \cos\theta}$. So since $\dfrac{dr}{d\theta} = \dfrac{a(1 - e^2)\,e\sin\theta}{(1 - e\cos\theta)^2}$ $\Rightarrow$

$$r^2 + \left(\frac{dr}{d\theta}\right)^2 = \frac{a^2(1 - e^2)^2}{(1 + e\cos\theta)^2} + \frac{a^2(1 - e^2)^2 e^2 \sin^2\theta}{(1 + e\cos\theta)^4} = \frac{a^2(1 - e^2)^2}{(1 + e\cos\theta)^4}(1 + 2e\cos\theta + e^2),$$ the length of

the orbit is $L = \displaystyle\int_0^{2\pi} \sqrt{r^2 + (dr/d\theta)^2}\, d\theta = a(1 - e^2) \int_0^{2\pi} \frac{\sqrt{1 + e^2 + 2e\cos\theta}}{(1 + e\cos\theta)^2}\, d\theta \approx 3.6 \times 10^8$ km.

This seems reasonable, since Mercury's orbit is nearly circular, and the circumference of a circle of radius a is $2\pi a \approx 3.6 \times 10^8$ km.

 Complex Numbers • • • • • • • • • • • • •

1. $(3 + 2i) + (7 - 3i) = (3 + 7) + (2 - 3)i = 10 - i$

2. $(1 + i) - (2 - 3i) = (1 - 2) + (1 + 3)i = -1 + 4i$

3. $(3 - i)(4 + i) = 12 + 3i - 4i - (-1)\ [i^2 = -1] = 13 - i$

4. $(4 - 7i)(1 + 3i) = 4 + 12i - 7i - 21(-1) = 25 + 5i$

5. $\overline{12 + 7i} = 12 - 7i$

6. $2i\left(\frac{1}{2} - i\right) = i - 2(-1) = 2 + i \ \Rightarrow\ \overline{2i\left(\frac{1}{2} - i\right)} = \overline{2 + i} = 2 - i$

7. $\dfrac{2 + 3i}{1 - 5i} = \dfrac{2 + 3i}{1 - 5i} \cdot \dfrac{1 + 5i}{1 + 5i} = \dfrac{2 + 10i + 3i + 15(-1)}{1 - 25(-1)} = \dfrac{-13 + 13i}{26} = -\dfrac{1}{2} + \dfrac{1}{2}i$

8. $\dfrac{5 - i}{3 + 4i} = \dfrac{5 - i}{3 + 4i} \cdot \dfrac{3 - 4i}{3 - 4i} = \dfrac{15 - 20i - 3i + 4(-1)}{9 - 16(-1)} = \dfrac{11 - 23i}{25} = \dfrac{11}{25} - \dfrac{23}{25}i$

9. $\dfrac{1}{1 + i} = \dfrac{1}{1 + i} \cdot \dfrac{1 - i}{1 - i} = \dfrac{1 - i}{1 - (-1)} = \dfrac{1 - i}{2} = \dfrac{1}{2} - \dfrac{1}{2}i$

10. $\dfrac{3}{4 - 3i} = \dfrac{3}{4 - 3i} \cdot \dfrac{4 + 3i}{4 + 3i} = \dfrac{12 + 9i}{16 - 9(-1)} = \dfrac{12}{25} + \dfrac{9}{25}i$

11. $i^3 = i^2 \cdot i = (-1)i = -i$

12. $i^{100} = \left(i^2\right)^{50} = (-1)^{50} = 1$

13. $\sqrt{-25} = \sqrt{25}\, i = 5i$

14. $\sqrt{-3}\,\sqrt{-12} = \sqrt{3}\, i\, \sqrt{12}\, i = \sqrt{3 \cdot 12}\, i^2 = \sqrt{36}\,(-1) = -6$

15. $\overline{3 + 4i} = 3 - 4i$, $|3 + 4i| = \sqrt{3^2 + 4^2} = \sqrt{25} = 5$

16. $\overline{\sqrt{3} - i} = \sqrt{3} + i$, $\left|\sqrt{3} - i\right| = \sqrt{\left(\sqrt{3}\right)^2 + (-1)^2} = \sqrt{4} = 2$

17. $\overline{-4i} = \overline{0 - 4i} = 0 + 4i = 4i$, $|-4i| = \sqrt{0^2 + (-4)^2} = \sqrt{16} = 4$

18. Let $z = a + bi$, $w = c + di$.

(a) $\overline{z + w} = \overline{(a + bi) + (c + di)} = \overline{(a + c) + (b + d)i}$
$= (a + c) - (b + d)i = (a - bi) + (c - di) = \bar{z} + \bar{w}$

(b) $\overline{zw} = \overline{(a + bi)(c + di)} = \overline{(ac - bd) + (ad + bc)i} = (ac - bd) - (ad + bc)i.$
On the other hand, $\bar{z}\,\bar{w} = (a - bi)(c - di) = (ac - bd) - (ad + bc)i = \overline{zw}.$

(c) Use mathematical induction and part (b): Let S_n be the statement that $\overline{z^n} = \overline{z}^n$.

S_1 is true because $\overline{z^1} = \overline{z} = \overline{z}^1$. Assume S_k is true, that is $\overline{z^k} = \overline{z}^k$. Then $\overline{z^{k+1}} = \overline{z^{1+k}} = \overline{z z^k} = \overline{z}\,\overline{z^k}$ [part (b) with $w = z^k$] $= \overline{z}^1\overline{z}^k = \overline{z}^{1+k} = \overline{z}^{k+1}$, which shows that S_{k+1} is true. Therefore, by mathematical induction, $\overline{z^n} = \overline{z}^n$ for every positive integer n.

Another proof: Use part (b) with $w = z$, and mathematical induction.

19. $4x^2 + 9 = 0 \iff 4x^2 = -9 \iff x^2 = -\frac{9}{4} \iff x = \pm\sqrt{-\frac{9}{4}} = \pm\sqrt{\frac{9}{4}}\,i = \pm\frac{3}{2}i.$

20. $x^4 = 1 \iff x^4 - 1 = 0 \iff (x^2 - 1)(x^2 + 1) = 0 \iff x^2 - 1 = 0$ or $x^2 + 1 = 0 \iff$ $x = \pm 1$ or $x = \pm i$.

21. By the quadratic formula, $x^2 - 8x + 17 = 0 \iff x = \frac{-(-8) \pm \sqrt{(-8)^2 - 4(1)(17)}}{2(1)} = \frac{8 \pm \sqrt{-4}}{2} = \frac{8 \pm 2i}{2} = 4 \pm i.$

22. $x^2 - 4x + 5 = 0 \iff x = \frac{-(-4) \pm \sqrt{(-4)^2 - 4(1)(5)}}{2(1)} = \frac{4 \pm \sqrt{-4}}{2} = \frac{4 \pm 2i}{2} = 2 \pm i$

23. By the quadratic formula, $z^2 + z + 2 = 0 \iff z = \frac{-1 \pm \sqrt{1^2 - 4(1)(2)}}{2(1)} = \frac{-1 \pm \sqrt{-7}}{2} = -\frac{1}{2} \pm \frac{\sqrt{7}}{2}i.$

24. $z^2 + \frac{1}{2}z + \frac{1}{4} = 0 \iff 4z^2 + 2z + 1 = 0 \iff$

$z = \frac{-2 \pm \sqrt{2^2 - 4(4)(1)}}{2(4)} = \frac{-2 \pm \sqrt{-12}}{8} = \frac{-2 \pm 2\sqrt{3}\,i}{8} = -\frac{1}{4} \pm \frac{\sqrt{3}}{4}i$

25. For $z = -3 + 3i$, $r = \sqrt{(-3)^2 + 3^2} = 3\sqrt{2}$ and $\tan\theta = \frac{3}{-3} = -1 \implies \theta = \frac{3\pi}{4}$ (since z lies in the second quadrant). Therefore, $-3 + 3i = 3\sqrt{2}\left(\cos\frac{3\pi}{4} + i\sin\frac{3\pi}{4}\right).$

26. For $z = 1 - \sqrt{3}\,i$, $r = \sqrt{1^2 + \left(-\sqrt{3}\right)^2} = 2$ and $\tan\theta = \frac{-\sqrt{3}}{1} = -\sqrt{3} \implies \theta = \frac{5\pi}{3}$ (since z lies in the fourth quadrant). Therefore, $1 - \sqrt{3}\,i = 2\left(\cos\frac{5\pi}{3} + i\sin\frac{5\pi}{3}\right).$

27. For $z = 3 + 4i$, $r = \sqrt{3^2 + 4^2} = 5$ and $\tan\theta = \frac{4}{3} \implies \theta = \tan^{-1}\left(\frac{4}{3}\right)$ (since z lies in the first quadrant). Therefore, $3 + 4i = 5\left[\cos\left(\tan^{-1}\frac{4}{3}\right) + i\sin\left(\tan^{-1}\frac{4}{3}\right)\right].$

28. For $z = 8i$, $r = \sqrt{0^2 + 8^2} = 8$ and $\tan\theta = \frac{8}{0}$ is undefined, so $\theta = \frac{\pi}{2}$ (since z lies on the positive imaginary axis). Therefore, $8i = 8\left(\cos\frac{\pi}{2} + i\sin\frac{\pi}{2}\right).$

29. For $z = \sqrt{3} + i$, $r = \sqrt{\left(\sqrt{3}\right)^2 + 1^2} = 2$ and $\tan\theta = \frac{1}{\sqrt{3}} \implies \theta = \frac{\pi}{6} \implies z = 2\left(\cos\frac{\pi}{6} + i\sin\frac{\pi}{6}\right).$

For $w = 1 + \sqrt{3}\,i$, $r = 2$ and $\tan\theta = \sqrt{3} \implies \theta = \frac{\pi}{3} \implies w = 2\left(\cos\frac{\pi}{3} + i\sin\frac{\pi}{3}\right).$

Therefore, $zw = 2 \cdot 2\left[\cos\left(\frac{\pi}{6} + \frac{\pi}{3}\right) + i\sin\left(\frac{\pi}{6} + \frac{\pi}{3}\right)\right] = 4\left(\cos\frac{\pi}{2} + i\sin\frac{\pi}{2}\right),$

$z/w = \frac{2}{2}\left[\cos\left(\frac{\pi}{6} - \frac{\pi}{3}\right) + i\sin\left(\frac{\pi}{6} - \frac{\pi}{3}\right)\right] = \cos\left(-\frac{\pi}{6}\right) + i\sin\left(-\frac{\pi}{6}\right),$ and $1 = 1 + 0i = 1(\cos 0 + i\sin 0) \implies$

$1/z = \frac{1}{2}\left[\cos\left(0 - \frac{\pi}{6}\right) + i\sin\left(0 - \frac{\pi}{6}\right)\right] = \frac{1}{2}\left[\cos\left(-\frac{\pi}{6}\right) + i\sin\left(-\frac{\pi}{6}\right)\right].$ For $1/z$, we could also use the formula that precedes Example 5 to obtain $1/z = \frac{1}{8}\left(\cos\frac{\pi}{6} - i\sin\frac{\pi}{6}\right).$

30. For $z = 4\sqrt{3} - 4i$, $r = \sqrt{\left(4\sqrt{3}\right)^2 + (-4)^2} = \sqrt{64} = 8$ and $\tan\theta = \frac{-4}{4\sqrt{3}} = -\frac{1}{\sqrt{3}} \implies \theta = \frac{11\pi}{6} \implies$

$z = 8\left(\cos\frac{11\pi}{6} + i\sin\frac{11\pi}{6}\right).$ For $w = 8i$, $r = \sqrt{0^2 + 8^2} = 8$ and $\tan\theta = \frac{8}{0}$ is undefined, so $\theta = \frac{\pi}{2} \implies$

$w = 8\left(\cos\frac{\pi}{2} + i\sin\frac{\pi}{2}\right).$ Therefore, $zw = 8 \cdot 8\left[\cos\left(\frac{11\pi}{6} + \frac{\pi}{2}\right) + i\sin\left(\frac{11\pi}{6} + \frac{\pi}{2}\right)\right] = 64\left(\cos\frac{\pi}{3} + i\sin\frac{\pi}{3}\right),$

$z/w = \frac{8}{8}\left[\cos\left(\frac{11\pi}{6} - \frac{\pi}{2}\right) + i\sin\left(\frac{11\pi}{6} - \frac{\pi}{2}\right)\right] = \cos\frac{4\pi}{3} + i\sin\frac{4\pi}{3},$ and

$1 = 1 + 0i = 1(\cos 0 + i\sin 0) \implies 1/z = \frac{1}{8}\left[\cos\left(0 - \frac{11\pi}{6}\right) + i\sin\left(0 - \frac{11\pi}{6}\right)\right] = \frac{1}{8}\left[\cos\left(\frac{\pi}{6}\right) + i\sin\left(\frac{\pi}{6}\right)\right].$

For $1/z$, we could also use the formula that precedes Example 5 to obtain $1/z = \frac{1}{8}\left(\cos\frac{11\pi}{6} - i\sin\frac{11\pi}{6}\right).$

31. For $z = 2\sqrt{3} - 2i$, $r = \sqrt{\left(2\sqrt{3}\right)^2 + (-2)^2} = 4$ and $\tan\theta = \frac{-2}{2\sqrt{3}} = -\frac{1}{\sqrt{3}}$

$\Rightarrow \quad \theta = -\frac{\pi}{6} \quad \Rightarrow \quad z = 4\left[\cos\left(-\frac{\pi}{6}\right) + i\sin\left(-\frac{\pi}{6}\right)\right]$. For $w = -1 + i$, $r = \sqrt{2}$,

$\tan\theta = \frac{1}{-1} = -1 \quad \Rightarrow \quad \theta = \frac{3\pi}{4} \quad \Rightarrow \quad z = \sqrt{2}\left(\cos\frac{3\pi}{4} + i\sin\frac{3\pi}{4}\right)$. Therefore,

$zw = 4\sqrt{2}\left[\cos\left(-\frac{\pi}{6} + \frac{3\pi}{4}\right) + i\sin\left(-\frac{\pi}{6} + \frac{3\pi}{4}\right)\right] = 4\sqrt{2}\left(\cos\frac{7\pi}{12} + i\sin\frac{7\pi}{12}\right)$,

$z/w = \frac{4}{\sqrt{2}}\left[\cos\left(-\frac{\pi}{6} - \frac{3\pi}{4}\right) + i\sin\left(-\frac{\pi}{6} - \frac{3\pi}{4}\right)\right] = \frac{4}{\sqrt{2}}\left[\cos\left(-\frac{11\pi}{12}\right) + i\sin\left(-\frac{11\pi}{12}\right)\right]$

$\qquad = 2\sqrt{2}\left(\cos\frac{13\pi}{12} + i\sin\frac{13\pi}{12}\right)$, and

$1/z = \frac{1}{4}\left[\cos\left(-\frac{\pi}{6}\right) - i\sin\left(-\frac{\pi}{6}\right)\right] = \frac{1}{4}\left(\cos\frac{\pi}{6} + i\sin\frac{\pi}{6}\right)$.

32. For $z = 4(\sqrt{3} + i) = 4\sqrt{3} + 4i$, $r = \sqrt{\left(4\sqrt{3}\right)^2 + 4^2} = \sqrt{64} = 8$ and $\tan\theta = \frac{4}{4\sqrt{3}} = \frac{1}{\sqrt{3}} \quad \Rightarrow \quad \theta = \frac{\pi}{6} \quad \Rightarrow$

$z = 8\left(\cos\frac{\pi}{6} + i\sin\frac{\pi}{6}\right)$. For $w = -3 - 3i$, $r = \sqrt{(-3)^2 + (-3)^2} = \sqrt{18} = 3\sqrt{2}$ and

$\tan\theta = \frac{-3}{-3} = 1 \quad \Rightarrow \quad \theta = \frac{5\pi}{4} \quad \Rightarrow \quad w = 3\sqrt{2}\left(\cos\frac{5\pi}{4} + i\sin\frac{5\pi}{4}\right)$. Therefore,

$zw = 8 \cdot 3\sqrt{2}\left[\cos\left(\frac{\pi}{6} + \frac{5\pi}{4}\right) + i\sin\left(\frac{\pi}{6} + \frac{5\pi}{4}\right)\right] = 24\sqrt{2}\left(\cos\frac{17\pi}{12} + i\sin\frac{17\pi}{12}\right)$,

$z/w = \frac{8}{3\sqrt{2}}\left[\cos\left(\frac{\pi}{6} - \frac{5\pi}{4}\right) + i\sin\left(\frac{\pi}{6} - \frac{5\pi}{4}\right)\right] = \frac{4\sqrt{2}}{3}\left[\cos\left(-\frac{13\pi}{12}\right) + i\sin\left(-\frac{13\pi}{12}\right)\right]$, and

$1/z = \frac{1}{8}\left(\cos\frac{\pi}{6} - i\sin\frac{\pi}{6}\right)$.

33. For $z = 1 + i$, $r = \sqrt{2}$ and $\tan\theta = \frac{1}{1} = 1 \quad \Rightarrow \quad \theta = \frac{\pi}{4} \quad \Rightarrow \quad z = \sqrt{2}\left(\cos\frac{\pi}{4} + i\sin\frac{\pi}{4}\right)$. So by

De Moivre's Theorem,

$$(1+i)^{20} = \left[\sqrt{2}\left(\cos\frac{\pi}{4} + i\sin\frac{\pi}{4}\right)\right]^{20} = \left(2^{1/2}\right)^{20}\left(\cos\frac{20\cdot\pi}{4} + i\sin\frac{20\cdot\pi}{4}\right)$$

$$= 2^{10}(\cos 5\pi + i\sin 5\pi) = 2^{10}[-1 + i(0)] = -2^{10} = -1024$$

34. For $z = 1 - \sqrt{3}\,i$, $r = \sqrt{1^2 + \left(-\sqrt{3}\right)^2} = 2$ and $\tan\theta = \frac{-\sqrt{3}}{1} = -\sqrt{3} \quad \Rightarrow \quad \theta = \frac{5\pi}{3} \quad \Rightarrow$

$z = 2\left(\cos\frac{5\pi}{3} + i\sin\frac{5\pi}{3}\right)$. So by De Moivre's Theorem,

$$\left(1 - \sqrt{3}\,i\right)^5 = \left[2\left(\cos\frac{5\pi}{3} + i\sin\frac{5\pi}{3}\right)\right]^5 = 2^5\left(\cos\frac{5\cdot 5\pi}{3} + i\sin\frac{5\cdot 5\pi}{3}\right)$$

$$= 2^5\left(\cos\frac{\pi}{3} + i\sin\frac{\pi}{3}\right) = 32\left(\frac{1}{2} + \frac{\sqrt{3}}{2}i\right) = 16 + 16\sqrt{3}\,i$$

35. For $z = 2\sqrt{3} + 2i$, $r = \sqrt{\left(2\sqrt{3}\right)^2 + 2^2} = \sqrt{16} = 4$ and $\tan\theta = \frac{2}{2\sqrt{3}} = \frac{1}{\sqrt{3}} \quad \Rightarrow \quad \theta = \frac{\pi}{6} \quad \Rightarrow$

$z = 4\left(\cos\frac{\pi}{6} + i\sin\frac{\pi}{6}\right)$. So by De Moivre's Theorem,

$$\left(2\sqrt{3} + 2i\right)^5 = \left[4\left(\cos\frac{\pi}{6} + i\sin\frac{\pi}{6}\right)\right]^5 = 4^5\left(\cos\frac{5\pi}{6} + i\sin\frac{5\pi}{6}\right) = 1024\left[-\frac{\sqrt{3}}{2} + \frac{1}{2}i\right] = -512\sqrt{3} + 512i$$

36. For $z = 1 - i$, $r = \sqrt{2}$ and $\tan\theta = \frac{-1}{1} = -1 \quad \Rightarrow \quad \theta = \frac{7\pi}{4} \quad \Rightarrow \quad z = \sqrt{2}\left(\cos\frac{7\pi}{4} + i\sin\frac{7\pi}{4}\right) \quad \Rightarrow$

$$(1-i)^8 = \left[\sqrt{2}\left(\cos\frac{7\pi}{4} + i\sin\frac{7\pi}{4}\right)\right]^8 = 2^4\left(\cos\frac{8\cdot 7\pi}{4} + i\sin\frac{8\cdot 7\pi}{4}\right)$$

$$= 16(\cos 14\pi + i\sin 14\pi) = 16(1 + 0i) = 16$$

37. $1 = 1 + 0i = 1(\cos 0 + i\sin 0)$. Using Equation 3 with $r = 1$, $n = 8$, and $\theta = 0$, we have

$$w_k = 1^{1/8}\left[\cos\left(\frac{0 + 2k\pi}{8}\right) + i\sin\left(\frac{0 + 2k\pi}{8}\right)\right] = \cos\frac{k\pi}{4} + i\sin\frac{k\pi}{4}, \text{ where } k = 0, 1, 2, \ldots, 7.$$

$w_0 = 1(\cos 0 + i \sin 0) = 1$, $w_1 = 1\left(\cos \frac{\pi}{4} + i \sin \frac{\pi}{4}\right) = \frac{1}{\sqrt{2}} + \frac{1}{\sqrt{2}}i$,

$w_2 = 1\left(\cos \frac{\pi}{2} + i \sin \frac{\pi}{2}\right) = i$, $w_3 = 1\left(\cos \frac{3\pi}{4} + i \sin \frac{3\pi}{4}\right) = -\frac{1}{\sqrt{2}} + \frac{1}{\sqrt{2}}i$,

$w_4 = 1(\cos \pi + i \sin \pi) = -1$, $w_5 = 1\left(\cos \frac{5\pi}{4} + i \sin \frac{5\pi}{4}\right) = -\frac{1}{\sqrt{2}} - \frac{1}{\sqrt{2}}i$,

$w_6 = 1\left(\cos \frac{3\pi}{2} + i \sin \frac{3\pi}{2}\right) = -i$, $w_7 = 1\left(\cos \frac{7\pi}{4} + i \sin \frac{7\pi}{4}\right) = \frac{1}{\sqrt{2}} - \frac{1}{\sqrt{2}}i$

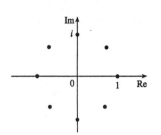

38. $32 = 32 + 0i = 32\,(\cos 0 + i \sin 0)$. Using Equation 3 with $r = 32$, $n = 5$, and $\theta = 0$, we have

$w_k = 32^{1/5}\left[\cos\left(\dfrac{0 + 2k\pi}{5}\right) + i \sin\left(\dfrac{0 + 2k\pi}{5}\right)\right] = 2\left(\cos \frac{2}{5}\pi k + i \sin \frac{2}{5}\pi k\right)$, where $k = 0, 1, 2, 3, 4$.

$w_0 = 2(\cos 0 + i \sin 0) = 2$

$w_1 = 2\left(\cos \frac{2\pi}{5} + i \sin \frac{2\pi}{5}\right)$

$w_2 = 2\left(\cos \frac{4\pi}{5} + i \sin \frac{4\pi}{5}\right)$

$w_3 = 2\left(\cos \frac{6\pi}{5} + i \sin \frac{6\pi}{5}\right)$

$w_4 = 2\left(\cos \frac{8\pi}{5} + i \sin \frac{8\pi}{5}\right)$

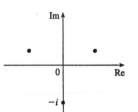

39. $i = 0 + i = 1\left(\cos \frac{\pi}{2} + i \sin \frac{\pi}{2}\right)$. Using Equation 3 with $r = 1$, $n = 3$, and $\theta = \frac{\pi}{2}$, we have

$w_k = 1^{1/3}\left[\cos\left(\dfrac{\frac{\pi}{2} + 2k\pi}{3}\right) + i \sin\left(\dfrac{\frac{\pi}{2} + 2k\pi}{3}\right)\right]$, where $k = 0, 1, 2$.

$w_0 = \left(\cos \frac{\pi}{6} + i \sin \frac{\pi}{6}\right) = \frac{\sqrt{3}}{2} + \frac{1}{2}i$

$w_1 = \left(\cos \frac{5\pi}{6} + i \sin \frac{5\pi}{6}\right) = -\frac{\sqrt{3}}{2} + \frac{1}{2}i$

$w_2 = \left(\cos \frac{9\pi}{6} + i \sin \frac{9\pi}{6}\right) = -i$

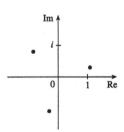

40. $1 + i = \sqrt{2}\left(\cos \frac{\pi}{4} + i \sin \frac{\pi}{4}\right)$. Using Equation 3 with $r = \sqrt{2}$, $n = 3$, and $\theta = \frac{\pi}{4}$, we have

$w_k = \left(\sqrt{2}\right)^{1/3}\left[\cos\left(\dfrac{\frac{\pi}{4} + 2k\pi}{3}\right) + i \sin\left(\dfrac{\frac{\pi}{4} + 2k\pi}{3}\right)\right]$, where $k = 0, 1, 2$.

$w_0 = 2^{1/6}\left(\cos \frac{\pi}{12} + i \sin \frac{\pi}{12}\right)$

$w_1 = 2^{1/6}\left(\cos \frac{3\pi}{4} + i \sin \frac{3\pi}{4}\right) = 2^{1/6}\left(-\frac{1}{\sqrt{2}} + \frac{1}{\sqrt{2}}i\right) = -2^{-1/3} + 2^{-1/3}i$

$w_2 = 2^{1/6}\left(\cos \frac{17\pi}{12} + i \sin \frac{17\pi}{12}\right)$

41. Using Euler's formula (6) with $y = \frac{\pi}{2}$, we have $e^{i\pi/2} = \cos \frac{\pi}{2} + i \sin \frac{\pi}{2} = 0 + 1i = i$.

42. Using Euler's formula (6) with $y = 2\pi$, we have $e^{2\pi i} = \cos 2\pi + i \sin 2\pi = 1$.

43. Using Euler's formula (6) with $y = \frac{3\pi}{4}$, we have $e^{i3\pi/4} = \cos \frac{3\pi}{4} + i \sin \frac{3\pi}{4} = -\frac{1}{\sqrt{2}} + \frac{1}{\sqrt{2}}i$.

44. Using Euler's formula (6) with $y = -\pi$, we have $e^{-i\pi} = \cos(-\pi) + i \sin(-\pi) = -1$.

45. Using Equation 7 with $x = 2$ and $y = \pi$, we have $e^{2+i\pi} = e^2 e^{i\pi} = e^2(\cos \pi + i \sin \pi) = e^2(-1 + 0) = -e^2$.

46. Using Equation 7 with $x = 1$ and $y = 2$, we have $e^{1+2i} = e^1 e^{2i} = e(\cos 2 + i \sin 2) = e \cos 2 + (e \sin 2)i$.

47. Take $r = 1$ and $n = 3$ in De Moivre's Theorem to get

$$[1(\cos\theta + i\sin\theta)]^3 = 1^3(\cos 3\theta + i\sin 3\theta)$$

$$(\cos\theta + i\sin\theta)^3 = \cos 3\theta + i\sin 3\theta$$

$$\cos^3\theta + 3(\cos^2\theta)(i\sin\theta) + 3(\cos\theta)(i\sin\theta)^2 + (i\sin\theta)^3 = \cos 3\theta + i\sin 3\theta$$

$$\cos^3\theta + (3\cos^2\theta\sin\theta)i - 3\cos\theta\sin^2\theta - (\sin^3\theta)i = \cos 3\theta + i\sin 3\theta$$

$$(\cos^3\theta - 3\sin^2\theta\cos\theta) + (3\sin\theta\cos^2\theta - \sin^3\theta)i = \cos 3\theta + i\sin 3\theta$$

Equating real and imaginary parts gives

$$\cos 3\theta = \cos^3\theta - 3\sin^2\theta\cos\theta \quad\text{and}\quad \sin 3\theta = 3\sin\theta\cos^2\theta - \sin^3\theta$$

48. Using Formula 6,

$$e^{ix} + e^{-ix} = (\cos x + i\sin x) + [\cos(-x) + i\sin(-x)]$$

$$= \cos x + i\sin x + \cos x - i\sin x = 2\cos x$$

Thus, $\cos x = \dfrac{e^{ix} + e^{-ix}}{2}$.

Similarly,

$$e^{ix} - e^{-ix} = (\cos x + i\sin x) - [\cos(-x) + i\sin(-x)]$$

$$= \cos x + i\sin x - \cos x - (-i\sin x) = 2i\sin x$$

Therefore, $\sin x = \dfrac{e^{ix} - e^{-ix}}{2i}$.

49. $F(x) = e^{rx} = e^{(a+bi)x} = e^{ax+bxi} = e^{ax}(\cos bx + i\sin bx) = e^{ax}\cos bx + i(e^{ax}\sin bx) \Rightarrow$

$F'(x) = (e^{ax}\cos bx)' + i(e^{ax}\sin bx)' = (ae^{ax}\cos bx - be^{ax}\sin bx) + i(ae^{ax}\sin bx + be^{ax}\cos bx)$

$= a\left[e^{ax}(\cos bx + i\sin bx)\right] + b\left[e^{ax}(-\sin bx + i\cos bx)\right] = ae^{rx} + b\left[e^{ax}(i^2\sin bx + i\cos bx)\right]$

$= ae^{rx} + bi\left[e^{ax}(\cos bx + i\sin bx)\right] = ae^{rx} + bie^{rx} = (a + bi)e^{rx} = re^{rx}$

50. (a) From Exercise 49, $F(x) = e^{(1+i)x} \Rightarrow F'(x) = (1+i)e^{(1+i)x}$. So

$$\int e^{(1+i)x}\,dx = \frac{1}{1+i}\int F'(x)\,dx = \frac{1}{1+i}F(x) + C = \frac{1-i}{2}F(x) + C = \frac{1-i}{2}e^{(1+i)x} + C$$

(b) $\int e^{(1+i)x}\,dx = \int e^x e^{ix}\,dx = \int e^x(\cos x + i\sin x)\,dx = \int e^x\cos x\,dx + i\int e^x\sin x\,dx$ **(1)**.

Using the above result for $e^{(1+i)x}$ (without the $\int dx$), we have

$$\frac{1-i}{2}e^{(1+i)x} = \frac{1}{2}e^{(1+i)x} - \frac{1}{2}ie^{(1+i)x} = \frac{1}{2}e^{x+ix} - \frac{1}{2}ie^{x+ix}$$

$$= \frac{1}{2}e^x(\cos x + i\sin x) - \frac{1}{2}ie^x(\cos x + i\sin x)$$

$$= \frac{1}{2}e^x\cos x + \frac{1}{2}e^x\sin x + \frac{1}{2}ie^x\sin x - \frac{1}{2}ie^x\cos x$$

$$= \frac{1}{2}e^x(\cos x + \sin x) + i\left[\frac{1}{2}e^x(\sin x - \cos x)\right] \quad\textbf{(2)}$$

Equating the real and imaginary parts in **(1)** and **(2)**, we see that $\int e^x\cos x\,dx = \frac{1}{2}e^x(\cos x + \sin x) + C$ and $\int e^x\sin x\,dx = \frac{1}{2}e^x(\sin x - \cos x) + C$.